DEVELOPMENTAL DISABILITIES IN ONTARIO, THIRD EDITION

DEVELOPMENTAL DISABILITIES

IN ONTARIO

3rd Edition

Edited by

Ivan BROWN

Faculty of Social Work, University of Toronto; and
Centre for Applied Disability Studies, Brock University

Maire PERCY

Departments of Physiology and Obstetrics and Gynaecology,
University of Toronto; and
Surrey Place Centre

ONTARIO ASSOCIATION on
DEVELOPMENTAL DISABILITIES

Reprint and Terms of Use

Developmental Disabilities in Ontario, Third Edition may not be reproduced or copied, in whole or in part, without the express permission from the copyright holders or their agent(s), except as provided by Canadian and international copyright laws. For permission to copy and use specific chapters, or parts of chapters from the book, or for permission to purchase PDFs of chapters for use in academic courses and professional training, contact *oadd@oadd.org*

Disclaimers

The points of view in this book are those of the authors and do not necessarily represent the official policy or opinion of the Ontario Association on Developmental Disabilities or any of the authors' employers. Publication does not imply endorsement by the Editors, the Ontario Association on Developmental Disabilities, or its individual members. The publisher and editors have made every reasonable effort to ensure that the information in this book is accurate and safe, and that identifying information for people has been altered or deleted. The publisher and editors cannot accept liability for any injury, damage, or loss to persons or property that may result from any information or instructions in this book. Every reasonable effort to trace the copyright holders of materials appearing in this book has been made. Information that will enable the publisher and editors to rectify any error or omission is welcome.

Canadian Cataloguing-in-Publication Data

Main entry under title:
Developmental Disabilities in Ontario, Third edition
Includes bibliographical references and index.
ISBN 978-0-9731573-1-4
1. Developmentally disabled - Ontario. 2. Developmentally disabled - Services for - Ontario.
I. Brown, Ivan, 1947-   . II. Percy, Maire, Ede, 1939-   .

Citation (APA)

Brown, I., & Percy M. (2011). *Developmental disabilities in Ontario* (3rd ed.). Toronto, ON: Ontario Association on Developmental Disabilities.

Cover and book design, layout, and production: Tom Dearie, Threesixty Creative
Associate editors: Barry Isaacs and Lynn Martin
Assistant to the editors: Juanito Anga-angan
Student research assistants: Annie Cheung, Melody Guan, Valerie Ho, Amy Jiang, Andrea Leung, Alyssia Parpia, Michael Wong
Proofreaders: Sarah Brown, Shirley Brown, Stewart Brown, Patricia Crockford.

Availability

Ontario Association on Developmental Disabilities
http://www.oadd.org/
First impression 2011
Printed and bound in Toronto, Canada.

*To all those who have inspired and enabled us over the years:
the many people with developmental disabilities and their families,
our colleagues, and our students.*

Contents

Foreword   v

Acknowledgements   vii

Special Acknowledgement   viii

About the Editors   ix

About OADD   xi

Chapter Authors   xii

Introduction   xxi

I. The Context for Developmental Disabilities in Ontario

1. What is Meant by Developmental Disability   5
   Ivan Brown

2. Towards a Post-Asylum Society: A Brief History of   25
   Developmental Disability Policy in Ontario
   John P. Radford

3. Changing Perspectives on Developmental Disabilities   41
   Michael Bach

4. Current Trends and Issues in Developmental Disabilities in Ontario   53
   Philip Burge, Ivan Brown, and Maire Percy

5. The Rights of People with Intellectual Disabilities in Ontario   65
   Marcia H. Rioux, Catherine L. Frazee, and Lora M. Patton

6. Select Rights, Benefits, and Entitlements for Individuals with   75
   Developmental Disabilities
   Rivka Birkan and Orna Raubfogel

7. Self-Advocacy   105
   Ann Fudge Schormans, Carol Krause, Kelly MacDougall, and Kerr Wattie

8. Making Services More Effective Through Research and Evaluation: 129
   An Introductory Guide
   Barry J. Isaacs

II.   Etiology and Conditions

9. Introduction to Human Genetics   145
    Maire Percy, Melissa Carter, Sheldon Z. Lewkis, Miles Thompson, and Ivan Brown

10. Introduction to Early Development: A Multidisciplinary Perspective   169
    Maire Percy and Ivan Brown

11. Introduction to the Nervous Systems   185
    William MacKay and Maire Percy

12. Factors that Cause or Contribute to Developmental Disabilities   207
    Maire Percy and Ivan Brown

13. Other Syndromes and Disorders Associated with Developmental Disabilities   227
    Miles Thompson and Maire Percy

14. Down Syndrome: Characteristics and Health Issues   267
    Maire Percy, Jane Summers, and John S. Lovering

15. Cerebral Palsy   293
    Darcy Fehlings and Carolyn I. Hunt

16. Autism and Related Disabilities   305
    Adrienne Perry, Alvin Loh, Melissa Carter, Glen Dunlap, Anne Black, and Kerry Wells

17. Individuals with Asperger Syndrome: A Lifespan Perspective   329
    Kevin P. Stoddart and Barbara Muskat

18. Fragile X Syndrome   341
    Cynthia J. Forster-Gibson and Jeanette Jeltje Anne Holden

19. Fetal Alcohol Spectrum Disorder. Part I: Triumphs and Challenges   357
    Irena Nulman and Ariel Pulver

    Fetal Alcohol Syndrome, Part II: Challenges in Adulthood   379
    Valerie Temple, Leeping Tao, and Trudy Clifford

20. Children with HIV and Their Families   387
    Rebecca Renwick, Robyn Salter, Susan King, and Stanley Read

21. Intractable Epilepsy: The Invisible Disability   405
    W. McIntyre Burnham

III.   Support and Intervention

22. An Introduction to Assessment, Diagnosis, Interventions and Services   419
    Ivan Brown and Maire Percy

23. Introduction to Services and to Ontario's Developmental Disability Service System   433
    Ivan Brown and Diane Galambos

24. Behavioural Intervention and Developmental Disabilities   445
    Rosemary A. Condillac

25. Challenging Families: Mending Broken Spirits through Support and Therapy   459
    J. Dale Munro

26. Augmentative and Alternative Communication   475
    Nora Rothschild and Ralf Schlosser

27. Communication Considerations Associated with Developmental Disabilities   495
    Jill Taylor, Maureen Burke, and Leora Palace

28. Role of Diversity in Psychological Assessment and Intervention   509
    Farrokh Sedighdeilami and Shahar Gindi

29. Roles, Education, Training, and Professional Values of Disability Personnel   525
    Roy I. Brown

IV. Health and Developmental Disabilities

30. Ethical Issues Relating to Consent in Providing Treatment and Care   551
    John Heng and William F. Sullivan

31. Physical Health and People with Developmental Disabilities   561
    Tom Cheetham and Shirley McMillan

32. Nutritional Considerations in Children with Developmental Disabilities   575
    Diana Mager and Paul Pencharz

33. Safe Medication Practice and Front Line Professional Practice   593
    Andrea Rutherford

34. Psychopharmacology of People with Developmental Disabilities   599
    Kenneth Boss

35. Introduction to Abnormal Behaviour and Associated Conditions   619
    Wai Lun Alan Fung, Maire Percy, and Ivan Brown

36. Developmental Disabilities and Mental Ill-Health   641
    Jane Summers, Elspeth Bradley, and John Flannery

37. Alzheimer Disease: Implications in Down Syndrome and Other   673
    Developmental Disabilities
    Vee Prasher, Maire Percy, Emoke Jozsvai, and Joseph Berg

V. Developmental Disabilities Through the Lifespan

38. Prenatal and Early Life   697
    Karolina Machalek, Maire Percy, Melissa Carter, and Ivan Brown

39. Early Intervention for Young Children   719
    Elaine B. Frankel and Kathryn Underwood

40. Developmental Disabilities and Child Maltreatment   739
    Ann Fudge Schormans

41. Developmental Disabilities and Ontario's Schools   771
    Eileen C. Winter and Ester Cole

42. The Transition from School to Adult Life   789
    Ivan Brown and Lynn Martin

43. Work and Employment for People with Developmental Disabilities in Ontario   809
    Judith Sandys

44. Lifestyles of Adults with Developmental Disabilities in Ontario   831
    M. Katherine Buell, Jonathan Weiss, and Ivan Brown

45. Family life and developmental disability   851
    Patricia Minnes and Julie Burbidge

46. Sexuality and Developmental Disability: From Myth to Emerging Practices   873
    Dorothy Griffiths

47. Developmental Disabilities and Women's Issues: Roles and Relationships   885
    Lillian Burke

48. Parenting by Persons with Intellectual Disabilities   909
    Marjorie Aunos and Maurice Feldman

49. Aging in People with Developmental Disabilities   925
    Lilian Thorpe and Nancy Jokinen

Index   941

Foreword

Editor's note:

Marion Fields Wyllie, a long-time resident of Owen Sound and the nearby village of Kilsyth, is one of the many pioneering parents who established the first schools and workshops for people with disabilities in Ontario. Marion was born near Collingwood, Ontario, in 1906 but spent her early life in Toronto near High Park. Her family moved back to the Collingwood area when she was 8 years old, although she returned to Toronto as a young woman to work as a copyholder for the Evening Telegram before moving to Owen Sound at age 21 to work as a proofreader for the Daily Sun-Times. She met her husband Victor, and they had three sons. Douglas, their middle son, had a developmental disability.

In Marion's foreword below, she recounts some of her early experiences at a time when there were no schools or services, other than institutions, for children with disabilities in Ontario, and sketches some of the journey toward acceptance and success. We owe a great debt to Marion, and to the dozens more like her across Ontario, who faced considerable odds in setting in place the beginnings of the schools, services, and supports we have for people with developmental disabilities today.

It has been my pleasure to know Marion all my life, as I was also raised near the village of Kilsyth where I attended school, church, and the many activities of rural communities in those days. My own childhood recollections of Marion were of a creative, positive, spiritual, and fun-loving woman, who integrated Douglas seamlessly into all the activities of the community. At the time of this book's publication, Marion is 104 years old. She has written stories and poems, and has published her work, for several decades. She published her autobiography *My Nine Lives* in 2006 to help celebrate her 100th birthday, and a book of short stories *The Tree and Other Stories* in 2010 on her 104th birthday. Marion continues to write and inspire all those around her.

Ivan Brown

Douglas was five years old, but hardly saying a word and stubbornly refusing most foods, except Pablum. Yet he was a sturdy, rosy-cheeked, bright-eyed boy. Some thought him to be deaf. Running up and down our long, upstairs hallway, he gave no response when called — unless I asked, "Do you want some pudding?" Then he would come running down at breakneck speed. He did not join his brothers playing with cars and trucks in the sandpile, but lined up clothes-pegs or jar rubbers on a ledge, or pulled twigs from low-hanging evergreens. Naturally, we felt worried.

Douglas spent some time in the Ontario Hospital School in Orillia (renamed Huronia Regional Centre in 1974), because it was all we had in those days. I felt guilty all the time he was there. I kept asking myself, "Why is a member of our family living among strangers a hundred miles away?"

In 1954, the late Melba Croft, after intensive research, called together a group of parents and friends. She organized an Association, of which she asked me to be president. Melba and I were so closely associated from then on that people often credit me with being the founder of what is now Community Living Owen Sound and District. But it was Melba who found us a hall for a classroom, and procured a teacher who had taught children with developmental disabilities in Scotland. With seven children, we started a half-day school in September. Soon we had four more.

Crofthaven School was a blessing both for Douglas and for us. Back home now, Douglas went to Crofthaven daily, and later to the workshop we also started. Eventually, he lived away from our family home, among caring friends.

Melba always stressed the importance of viewing these children not through their disabilities, but through their abilities — especially their potential. What Douglas can be, she said in effect, we must help him to become. Years later, when visiting a workshop, I realized just how much this had come to be. When I asked to speak with Douglas, the response was, "Oh! He is over at the Crèche, reading to the little tots!"

A popular misconception is that "they never grow up." Not so! They grow and change physically, emotionally, and socially. So do we all.

Over the years, there are many people whom I recall fondly. There were Sam and Ivan, now retired, each in his apartment, living independently. I remember Patsy, who used to offer me a coffee as soon as I entered the shop. Nancy, Benita and others work in our store on the main street. Much of their merchandise consists of useful or decorative items made from recycled parts of discarded electronic things. Many others have part time jobs with printing or publishing firms. People who once signed petitions against having a shop nearby, now tell me they couldn't have quieter or better-behaved neighbours.

The special school that was Crofthaven is now integrated into the elementary school system. The students are learning to live in a world of mainly "normal" people, and their fellow students are learning to accept and appreciate them.

Who is "normal" anyway? I know one of the reasons I used to exasperate my mother. I would ask her to repeat something, and then realize I had heard her the first time. I now understand that it takes my brain a second or more to process sounds into words. I still have a problem with fast talkers! In four years of high school, I could not pass my Junior Matriculation (grade 12), yet I consistently topped the class in English Composition, and am now a published author and poet.

Every human being should be helped to reach his or her highest potential. Some can climb higher than others, but all are needed for a properly functioning society. It is therefore important that this book be written, published, and used as scientists, inventors, teachers, support workers, and caring people everywhere keep finding new ways to help people with disabilities grow and learn.

As a life member of Community Living Owen Sound and District, I feel a personal sense of gratitude to Ivan Brown and Maire Percy for providing a splendid learning tool for all those of us who care to help.

Marion Fields Wyllie
Owen Sound, Ontario
January 21, 2011

Acknowledgements

As editors, we must begin by acknowledging the outstanding contributions of the chapter authors. Without their expertise and wisdom, this book would not have been possible. We thank all those who assisted them, and the organizations with which they are affiliated for supporting their participation. This has truly been a large-team undertaking that has drawn broadly from the considerable expertise in developmental disabilities in Ontario. A spirit of co-operation from all the authors and production staff was evident throughout the writing and editing of this book.

We would particularly like to thank Barry Isaacs and Lynn Martin for their work as Associate Editors reviewing and editing the content of some of the chapters; Juanito Anga-angan for his organizational and communication work; Tom Dearie and his team from Threesixty Creative for strong cooperation and expert design, layout, and production management; our team of University of Toronto High School Mentorship students who provided critical feedback about chapters in their draft form; and to our volunteer proofreaders whose diligence contributed greatly to chapter quality and appearance. We are thankful to the Board of Directors of the Ontario Association on Developmental Disabilities for their ongoing support and dedication to this book. We especially thank Liz Froese and Joe Persaud who so ably represented the Board throughout the production of the book and facilitated its timely production; Geoff McMullen, past Chair, and Michelle Palmer, current Chair, for their unwavering faith in the editors; and Jennifer Shaw, Executive Officer, whose organizational ability, careful note-taking, helpful insights, practical suggestions, and common sense, contributed enormously to the creation and completion of the third edition. Their efforts and goodwill have been very much appreciated.

On behalf of the other authors and the publisher, we offer fond remembrance of Dr. John Lovering and Dr. Susan King, who passed away before the completion of this book. Both authors made strong and important contributions to all three editions, and they will be sincerely missed both as professionals in our field and as vibrant individuals.

We would like to recognize our institutions, particularly Surrey Place Centre and the Factor-Inwentash Faculty of Social Work, University of Toronto, for providing the editors and publisher with in-kind support, encouragement, and office space to complete some of the work of this book. A number of authors have included case examples in their chapters to illustrate their material more clearly for the reader. Although some of these are composite examples drawn from the broad experiences of the authors, others are stories of specific individuals, and we would like to thank those people who have given the authors permission to include their stories. Finally, on behalf of all the members of the editorial team, the editors thank all those with whom we have lived and worked during the book production for their patience and understanding.

Special Acknowledgement: Paul H. Brookes Publishing Co., Inc.

The editors and publisher of *Developmental Disabilities in Ontario*, third edition, are particularly grateful to Paul H. Brookes Publishing Co., Inc. in Baltimore, Maryland for their ongoing strong cooperation. Material from the second edition of *Developmental Disabilities in Ontario*, published by the Ontario Association on Developmental Disabilities in 2003, was updated, expanded, and adapted for an international and broader readership by Ivan Brown and Maire Percy (editors) to create Brookes Publishing's 2007 book *A Comprehensive Guide to Intellectual & Developmental Disabilities*.

In turn, Brookes Publishing has kindly provided permission for material from *A Comprehensive Guide to Intellectual & Developmental Disabilities* to be updated and adapted for use throughout this third edition of our Ontario-specific book. This special relationship is highly beneficial to both publishers, and we very much appreciate Brookes Publishing's helpfulness and strong spirit of collaboration.

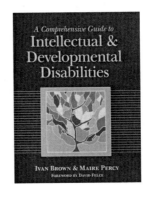

A Comprehensive Guide to Intellectual & Developmental Disabilities is, as its name suggests, the most comprehensive general textbook on intellectual and developmental disabilities anywhere in the world. Development of a second edition is underway at the time of this book's printing.

www.brookespublishing.com/

About the Editors

Ivan Brown, B.A., B.A. (Hons.), B. Ed., M. Ed., Ph.D., FIASSID

Ivan has worked in, and contributed to, the field of disabilities for the past 30 years. He began his career as an elementary school teacher for 8 years before taking a position with what is now Community Living Toronto, where he worked as a vocational counsellor, a community support worker, and an APSW while completing his graduate studies in counselling psychology (M.Ed.) and special education (Ph.D.). In 1991, he took a position as Research Associate with the Centre for Health Promotion, Department of Public Health Sciences, University of Toronto, where he managed a number of large research projects. Several of these addressed quality of life of children with disabilities, adults with developmental disabilities, seniors, and adolescents. He held appointments during the 1990s as Assistant Professor in the Departments of Occupational Therapy and Public Health Sciences, both at the University of Toronto, and taught both in the graduate health promotion program in the Department of Public Health Sciences and in the School of Early Childhood Education at Ryerson University in Toronto, which has a special focus on young children with special needs. From 2001-2010, Ivan held the position of Manager of the Centre of Excellence for Child Welfare, a national body for research and policy development in child welfare, to which he brought the essential disability focus. The Centre was housed within the graduate Faculty of Social Work at the University of Toronto, which continues to be Ivan's home department. Research in disability has been, and continues to be, a critical part of his ongoing work, with a strong recent focus on international family quality of life. Since 2009, Ivan has taught Toronto-based masters level students as an Adjunct Professor for Brock University's Centre for Applied Disability Studies.

Ivan has a strong history of community involvement in disability, serving on numerous government and community agency committees and boards, participating in research projects, and acting in leadership roles with several professional organizations. In particular, he was a longstanding member of the Board of Directors of the Ontario Association on Developmental Disabilities and served as the Board's Chair for a 2-year period. In 2001, he was awarded this association's Directors' Award of Excellence. He was the founding editor of the *Journal on Developmental Disabilities* in 1992, served as Editor-in-Chief for many years, and is still a member of the Chief Editorial Board. In addition, he is on the Editorial Boards of several Canadian and international journals. Ivan is a fellow of the International Association for the Scientific Study of Intellectual Disability (IASSID), a member of IASSID Council, chair of IASSID's Quality of Life Special Interest Group, and an active international speaker and workshop leader of IASSID's Academy on Education, Teaching, and Research. He is also a long-standing member of the American Association on Intellectual and Developmental Disabilities.

Ivan has contributed substantially to the Canadian and international literature, particularly in the areas of quality of life and intellectual disabilities. He has 11 books to his credit (including the two previous editions of *Developmental Disabilities in Ontario*), and more than 100 peer-reviewed journal articles and book chapters, as well as numerous other articles, editorials, reviews, booklets, scales, and manuals. He has made 118 presentations at academic conferences in the past 20 years, and several keynote speeches.

Ivan continues to be personally involved in disability issues, through active community work and consultation, sharing the lives of many friends with disabilities, and sharing his household with a man who has visual and cognitive impairments. He holds a strong belief that including disability as part of our daily life activities is an enriching experience for us all.

Maire Percy, B.Sc. (Hons.), M.A., A.R.C.T., Ph.D.

Maire is Professor Emeritus of Physiology and Obstetrics & Gynaecology, Faculty of Medicine, at the University of Toronto. From 1989-2011, she directed the Neurogenetics Laboratory at Surrey Place Centre. She holds a bachelor's degree in physiology and biochemistry, a master's degree in medical biophysics, and a doctoral degree in biochemistry all from the University of Toronto; in addition, she is an Associate of the Royal Conservatory of Music of Toronto (A.R.C.T.). She did postdoctoral training as a Medical Research Council Fellow in immunology at the Agricultural Research Council Institute of Animal Physiology, Babraham, United Kingdom, and in immunology and genetics at the Hospital for Sick Children in Toronto. As a National Health Research Scholar (Health Canada), Maire entered the field of intellectual and developmental disabilities by serendipity after a chance meeting with Dr. Arthur Dalton, then Director of Behaviour Research at Surrey Place Centre. He recognized the potential of her multidisciplinary background and enthusiasm for research in intellectual disabilities and suggested a collaborative project, for which he found the funding, to study the involvement of oxidative stress in the development of dementia in older persons with Down syndrome. The rest is history.

Research in this field soon took precedence for her. In 1989, she was invited to join the Department of Biomedical Services and Research at Surrey Place Centre, under the direction of Joseph M. Berg, eminent clinical geneticist and psychiatrist. Maire's knowledge and expertise in the field of intellectual and developmental disabilities continued to expand as the result of her research, and also by osmosis as the result of interacting with colleagues at Surrey Place Centre (especially Dr. Vera Markovic and Marika Korossy) and other activities that included: chairing/co-chairing the Research Ethics Board at Surrey Place Centre; cofounding the Research Special Interest Group of the OADD and the Fragile X Research Foundation of Canada; chairing the Publication Committee of the OADD; and being a member of the Chief Editorial Committee of the Journal on Developmental Disabilities. A dedicated teacher, Maire developed a graduate course entitled Neuroscience of the Developmental Disabilities, providing her with the inspiration and background material for the first edition of Developmental Disabilities in Ontario that came to life with Ivan Brown. Author of more than 250 published papers, book chapters, and presentations, and reviewer of publications and grants for numerous scientific journals and granting agencies, Maire is internationally known for her work on risk factors in serious human disorders and diseases and as an exemplary mentor of students at all levels.

In 2004, in recognition for her lifetime contributions to the field of intellectual and developmental disabilities, she received the OADD's Award for Excellence in Research. In 2011, she received the OADD Award of Excellence in recognition for many years of contributions to the field of developmental disabilities above and beyond the call of duty. The asteroid mairepercy is named in honour of her scientific and research contributions. Maire currently is involved in collaborative studies of the roles of iron, aluminum, and B vitamins in dementia, and recently conducted later life learning courses in the community and at Glendon College (York University). She shares her home with her husband John (Professor of Astronomy), a cat, and is the mother of Carol (Professor of English).

About OADD

The Ontario Association on Developmental Disabilities, known less formally as OADD, was formed in 1989 by professionals in the field of development disabilities who saw a need to come together in Ontario as a profession. OADD is, according to its website (*www.oadd.org*), "a professional organization of people working and studying in the field of developmental disabilities, throughout Ontario." Since its inception, OADD has hosted an annual conference that features new ideas, policies, and practices stemming from research, best practice, and recent policy decisions. One of the conference days features OADD's Research Special Interest Group and focuses on research begin carried out in Ontario; a pre-conference day, co-sponsored by the Great Lakes Society for Developmental Services in Ontario, provides training in new approaches to support for front-line workers. Throughout the year, OADD engages in activities, and works with other organizations, to ensure ongoing training and professional education in a variety of ways.

OADD also has another strong role. It supports Ontario professionals in the field of developmental disabilities by giving out awards for excellence in research and practice, and for outstanding contributions made to the field of developmental disabilities. It provides scholarships to students who are studying in developmental disabilities, and an award for a student publication in its journal. OADD first published the Journal on Developmental Disabilities in 1992, and has demonstrated an ongoing commitment to support Ontario and other researchers by provided an important venue for publishing their work.

In 1998, OADD entered into an agreement with the editors of *Developmental Disabilities in Ontario*, Ivan Brown and Maire Percy, to produce a comprehensive text in developmental disabilities that would be of particular interest to professionals, students, and families living and working in Ontario. The first edition of this text was published in 1999, and a second edition followed in 2003. This third edition, published in 2011, demonstrates OADD's ongoing and strong commitment to the advancement of knowledge in our field.

Chapter Authors

Chapter 1: What is Meant by Developmental Disability

Ivan Brown, *Ph.D., (Special Education),* is a Senior Research Associate in the Factor-Inwentash Faculty of Social Work, University of Toronto, and a Professor (adjunct) in the Centre for Applied Disabilities Studies, Brock University.

Chapter 2: Towards a Post-Asylum Society: A Brief History of Developmental Disability Policy in Ontario

John P. Radford, *Ph.D.,* is Professor Emeritus in the Faculty of Liberal Arts and Professional Studies at York University. He also teaches and supervises students in the Critical Disability Studies Program. He is interested in the political economy of disability and has written extensively on the history of intellectual disability and disabling environments.

Chapter 3 Changing Perspectives on Developmental Disabilities

Michael Bach, *Ph.D.,* is Executive Vice-President, Canadian Association for Community Living in Toronto, Ontario.

Chapter 4: Current Trends and Issues in Developmental Disabilities in Ontario

Philip Burge, *Ph.D., RSW,* is a Registered Social Worker working clinically with individuals who have a developmental disability and mental health concerns for over 15 years. He is also an Adjunct Associate Professor of Psychiatry at Queen's University involved in teaching and research and has advocated for a range of services and policy changes alongside persons with developmental disabilities and their families.

Ivan Brown, see Chapter 1.

Maire Percy, *B.Sc., M.A., Ph.D.,* is a neurogeneticist whose research is focussed on the identification of genetic and environmental factors resulting in cognitive impairment and dementia, both in the general population and in persons with developmental disabilities. She is Professor Emeritus, Departments of Physiology and Obstetrics & Gynaecology, University of Toronto, former Director of the Neurogenetics Laboratory at Surrey Place Centre, and member of the Chief Editorial Board of the Journal on Developmental Disabilities.

Chapter 5: The Rights of People with Intellectual Disabilities in Ontario

Marcia H. Rioux, *Ph.D.,* Jurisprudence and Social Policy (U. California, Berkeley), teaches and does research in human rights and disability. She teaches in the graduate program in Critical Disability Studies in the Faculty of Health at York University and is also a Graduate Program Director in the graduate program in Health and Equity. She is a Director and PI for Disability Rights Promotion International.

Catherine L. Frazee, *D.Litt., LLD. (Hon.),* is Professor Emerita in the School of Disability Studies at Ryerson University. A former Chief Commissioner of the Ontario Human Rights Commission, she draws from her own experience of disablement in entering ethical and cultural dialogues about human rights, precarious citizenship and disability resistance.

Lora M. Patton is a Toronto lawyer working in the area of disability law with a focus on mental health issues. She is a lawyer member of the Ontario Consent and Capacity Board, adjudicating issues under the Mental Health Act, Health Care Consent Act, Substitute Decisions Act, and other legislation. Ms Patton also conducts research related to disability and social justice matters and has written on topics that include mental health law, employment equity and disability and low income.

Chapter 6: Select Rights, Benefits, and Entitlements for Individuals with Developmental Disabilities

Rivka Birkan, *B. Arts & Sc.,* is a lawyer. She is an Associate at Lerners LLP in Toronto, practising in Health Law and Insurance Defence.

Orna Raubfogel, *B.A., J.D.,* works as in-house legal counsel for Toronto Community Housing Corporation.

Chapter 7: Self-Advocacy

Ann Fudge Schormans, *Ph.D., RSW,* is an Assistant Professor in the School of Social Work at McMaster University. Her teaching, research, and university-service activities focus on disability. Ann has an extensive social work practice history with children and adults with intellectual and developmental disabilities, and is on the Chief Editorial Board of the Journal on Developmental Disabilities.

Carol Krause, a graduate of Osgoode Hall Law School, enjoys working, living, and sharing relationships with people who have intellectual disabilities in her personal and professional life. She has been involved in the disability community as an advocate and community organizer and currently facilitates self-advocacy in Developmental Services Toronto. Carol has edited and created the book Between Myself and Them: Stories of Disability and Difference, is currently working on her second book, and speaks publicly about her own experiences with mental health disability and the importance of welcoming difference.

Kelly MacDougall. I am thirty-six years old, and I'm a "self-advocate" from Family Services Toronto, a volunteer at the Developmental Services Toronto Council, the Relationships Work Group and the Relationships Advisory Group.

Kerr Wattie is an educator, activist and artist dedicated to social justice and inclusion. He has given over 20 presentations at venues such as York University, the International Society for Augmentative and Alternative Communication, and Ryerson University. His advocacy was the subject of a Toronto Star article called, "Battling Bureaucracy Without Speaking a Word." Kerr is a co-founder of Kilometres for Communication, a public education and fundraising campaign about empowering the voices and lives of people who speak in alternative ways.

Chapter 8: Making Services More Effective Through Research and Evaluation: An Introductory Guide

Barry J. Isaacs, *Ph.D.,* received his doctorate from York University in 2004. He is currently Director of Research and Evaluation at Surrey Place Centre and holds adjunct appointments at Brock University and York University.

Chapter 9: Introduction to Human Genetics

Maire Percy, see Chapter 4.

Melissa Carter, *M.Sc., M.D., FRCPC* is a Clinical Geneticist specializing in Developmental Disabilities. She is an Assistant Professor in the Department of Pediatrics at the University of Toronto, and her clinical practice is based at The Hospital for Sick Children in Toronto, in the Division of Clinical and Metabolic Genetics. She is cross-appointed in the Division of Developmental Pediatrics at Holland-

Bloorview Kids Rehabilitation Hospital, also in Toronto.

Sheldon Z. Lewkis, *B.Sc. (Hon), M.A., Ph.D., RPsych,* is a registered psychologist in private practice in Vancouver, British Columbia.

Miles Thompson, holds a Ph.D. in pharmacology from the University of Toronto (2003) and is doing advanced training in the Department of Laboratory Medicine, Hospital for Sick Children, Toronto.

Ivan Brown, see Chapter 1.

Chapter 10: Introduction to Early Development: A Multidisciplinary Perspective

Maire Percy, see Chapter 4.

Ivan Brown, see Chapter 1.

Chapter 11: Introduction to the Nervous Systems

William MacKay, *Ph.D.,* is a neurophysiologist specializing in motor control. He is an Associate Professor in the Department of Physiology at the University of Toronto.

Maire Percy, see Chapter 1.

Chapter 12: Factors that Cause of Contribute to Developmental Disabilities

Maire Percy, see Chapter 4.

Ivan Brown, see Chapter 1.

Chapter 13: Other Syndromes and Disorders Associated with Developmental Disabilities

Miles Thompson, see Chapter 9.

Maire Percy, see Chapter 4.

Chapter 14: Down Syndrome: Characteristics and Health Issues

Maire Percy, see Chapter 4.

Jane Summers, *Ph.D., C.Psych.,* is a registered psychologist. She is an Assistant Professor in the Department of Psychiatry and Behavioural Neurosciences in the Faculty of Health Sciences at McMaster University. She is also the co-director of the Specialized Developmental and Behavioural Service and a clinical supervisor with the Hamilton-Niagara Regional Autism Intervention Program, both at McMaster Children's Hospital.

Chapter 15: Cerebral Palsy

Darcy Fehlings, *M.D., M.Sc., FRCP(C)* is a Developmental Paediatrician. She is an Associate Professor in the Faculty of Medicine, Deparment of Paediatrics at the University of Toronto and is head of the Division of Developmental Paediatrics. She is physician director of the cerebral palsy program at the Holland Bloorview Kids Rehabilitation Hospital and is a senior scientist in the Bloorview Research Institute.

Carolyn I. Hunt, *B.Sc., M.D., FRCP(C)* is a Developmental Pediatrician. She is the Medical Director of Grandview Children's Centre. She is an adjunct Associate Professor at the University of Toronto in the Community Section of Developmental Pediatricians and is an adjunct Associate Professor at the University of Ontario Institute of Technology, Department of Health Sciences.

Chapter 16: Autism and Related Disabilities

Adrienne Perry, *Ph.D., C. Psych., BCBA,* is a Clinical Psychologist and Board Certified Behavior Analyst. She is an Associate Professor in the Clinical-Developmental Psychology program at York University, and is a Consulting Psychologist to TRE-ADD (Treatment, Research, and Education for Autism and Developmental Disorders) Thistletown Regional Centre in Toronto.

Alvin Loh, *M.D., FRCPC,* is a Developmental Paediatrician at Surrey Place Centre. He is a leader in the

Autism Treatment Network – Toronto, which is striving to improve the standard of medical care for children with autism. He is an Assistant Professor in the Division of Developmental Pediatrics at the University of Toronto.

Melissa Carter, see Chapter 9.

Glen Dunlap, *Ph.D.,* is a research professor with the University of South Florida and the University of Nevada at Reno. He works on several research, training, and demonstration projects in the areas of positive behaviour support, early intervention, autism, and family support. Glen was a founding editor of the Journal of Positive Behavior Interventions and is currently the editor of Topics in Early Childhood Special Education.

Anne Black, *B.A., M.Ed.,* is a Professor in the Community Services Division at George Brown College and also teaches Child and Youth Studies at Ryerson Polytechnic University, both in Toronto.

Kerry Wells, *M.A. is a Ph.D.* Candidate at York University, and Behaviour Consultant at TRE-ADD (Treatment, Research, and Education for Autism and Developmental Disorders) Thistletown Regional Centre in Toronto.

Chapter 17: Individuals with Asperger Syndrome: A Lifespan Perspective

Kevin P. Stoddart, *Ph.D., RSW,* is Founding Director at The Redpath Centre (Toronto, ON) and Assistant Professor (Status-only) at the Factor-Inwentash Faculty of Social Work, University of Toronto.

Barbara Muskat, *Ph.D., RSW* is Academic and Clinical Specialist/Manager in the Department of Social Work at the Hospital for Sick Children, Child and Adolescent Therapist at The Redpath Centre (Toronto, ON), and Assistant Professor (Status-only) at the Factor-Inwentash Faculty of Social Work, University of Toronto.

Chapter 18: Fragile X Syndrome

Cynthia J. Forster-Gibson, *M.D., Ph.D.,* is Associate Professor, Department of Family Medicine, Queen's University, Kingston and GP, practicing in Clinical Genetics, Genetics Program, Credit Valley Hospital, Mississauga, ON. She is Past Chair, Canadian Association for Research and Education in Developmental Disabilities (CARE-ID/ACREDI)

Jeanette Jeltje Anne Holden, *B.Sc., Ph.D., FCCMG,* is a Professor in the Departments of Psychiatry and Physiology at Queen's University, and the Director, Autism Research Program and DNA Research Laboratory at Ongwanada in Kingston.

Chapter 19: Fetal Alcohol Spectrum disorder. Part I: Triumphs and Challenges

Irena Nulman, *M.D., FRCPC Neurology, Ph.D.(c),* is an Associate Professor at the University of Toronto and staff pharmacologist in the Department of Pediatrics, at the Hospital for Sick Children in Toronto.

Ariel Pulver, *B.A. (Psychology, McGill University),* is a Clinical Research Project Assistant at the Hospital for Sick Children in Toronto.

Chapter 19: Fetal Alcohol Spectrum disorder. Part II: Challenges in Adulthood

Valerie Temple, *Ph.D., C.Psych.,* is a Clinical Psychologist and the Professional Practice Leader for Psychology at Surrey Place Centre. She is also Clinical Lead for the Surrey Place Centre FASD Adult Diagnostic Clinic and Co-Chair of the Diagnostic Working Group of FASD-ONE, a provincial network aimed at increasing FASD diagnostic capacity across Ontario.

Leeping Tao, *R.N.(EC), M.N., Nurse Practitioner - Adult,* is a nurse practitioner with Surrey Place Centre in Toronto. She provides services to clients in the adult program / FASD adult diagnostic clinic / Fragile X clinic.

Trudy Clifford, *R.N., PHN,* is currently employed at Surrey Place Centre, where she has had extensive experience as an Intake Coordinator. She also serves as the Clinic Coordinator for the FASD Adult Diagnostic Clinic, which she helped develop. She is an adoptive parent of a son with FASD.

Chapter 20: Children with HIV and Their Families

Rebecca Renwick, *Ph.D., B.A., Dip PT & OT, OT(C), OT Reg (Ont)* is a Professor in the Department of Occupational Science and Occupational Therapy and the Graduate Department of Rehabilitation Science, and Director of the Quality of Life Research Unit at the University of Toronto.

Robyn Salter, *M.S.W., RSW,* is the social worker with the HIV Program and the Infectious Diseases Program at Sick Kids Hospital in Toronto. She provides clinical social work and conducts research on psychosocial issues for families with HIV.

Stanley Read, *M.D., Ph.D., FRCPC,* is Infectious Diseases Consultant and Director, HIV/AIDS Program, Division of Infectious Diseases, Sickkids Senior Associate Scientist, Physiology and Experimental Medicine Program, Sickkids Research Institute, Hospital for Sick Children in Toronto.

Chapter 21: Intractable Epilepsy: The Invisible Disability

W. McIntyre Burnham, *Ph.D.,* is a Professor Emeritus in the Department of Pharmacology and Toxicology at the University of Toronto. He is the Director of the University of Toronto Epilepsy Research Program and a Past President of Epilepsy Ontario.

Chapter 22: An Introduction to Assessment, Diagnosis, Interventions, and Services

Ivan Brown, see Chapter 1.

Maire Percy, see Chapter 4.

Chapter 23: Introduction to Services and to Ontario's Developmental Disability Service System

Ivan Brown, see Chapter 1.

Diane Galambos, *Ed.D.,* is Professor and Program Coordinator, Sheridan College Institute of Technology and Advanced Learning in Oakville, Ontario.

Chapter 24: Behavioural Intervention and Developmental Disabilities

Rosemary A. Condillac, *Ph.D., C.Psych.,* is a Registered Psychologist and Assistant Professor in the Centre for Applied Disability Studies at Brock University, in St. Catharines, Ontario. Dr. Condillac is a consulting psychologist to Surrey Place Centre and Behaviour Management Services of York and Simcoe.

Chapter 25: Challenging Families: Mending Broken Spirits through Support and Therapy

J. Dale Munro, *M.S.W., RSW, FAAIDD,* has worked in the field of developmental disabilities for 40 years. For many years, he was a clinical supervisor, and individual, couple and family therapist with Regional Support Associates in London, Ontario. He recently went into full time private practice and is affiliated with The Redpath Centre, which specializes in Asperger syndrome, in Toronto.

Chapter 26: Augmentative and Alternative Communication

Nora Rothschild, *B.A., D.S.P., Reg CASLPO,* is a Speech-Language Pathologist with Holland Bloorview Kids Rehabilitation Hospital, and Team Facilitator of the York Region Augmentative Communication Consultation Service with the Children's Treatment Network of Simcoe York.

Ralf Schlosser, *B.S., B.S.W., M.A., Ph.D.,* is a Professor in Speech-Language Pathology with a joint appointment in the School Psychology Program at Northeastern University and Director of Clinical Research at the Center for Communication Enhancement of Children's Hospital Boston.

Chapter 27: Communication Considerations Associated with Developmental Disabilities

Jill Taylor, *Au.D.,* is a pediatric, clinical audiologist at Surrey Place Centre in Toronto.

Maureen Burke, *M.Sc.,* is an educational audiologist at The Toronto Catholic District School Board in Toronto.

Leora Palace, *B.A. (Hons.),* is a speech-language pathologist in private practice in Thornhill, ON.

Chapter 28: Role of Diversity in Psychological Assessment and Intervention

Farrokh Sedighdeilami, *Ph.D., C.Psych,* is a clinical psychologist. He is a psychologist and coordinator of internship program at Surrey Place Centre in Toronto, and in private practice in Thornhill, Ontario.

Shahar Gindi, received a Ph. D. at the University of Toronto in 2005. He is a lecturer in the Beit Berl Academic College in Israel and consultant for the school psychological services in Tel Aviv. His areas of research include inclusion of students with autism spectrum disorder in educational setting and multicultural practice. Dr. Gindi is a school and clinical psychologist.

Chapter 29: Roles, Education, Training, and Professional Values of Disability Personnel

Roy I. Brown, *Ph.D., FIASSID,* a Psychologist and Professor Emeritus of Educational Psychology, University of Calgary, and Emeritus Professor at Flinders University, Australia with adjunct professorial appoints at the Universities of Victoria, Canada and New England, Australia. He is currently Director of the IASSID Academy on Education, Teaching, and Research.

Chapter 30: Ethical Issues Relating to Consent in Providing Treatment and Care

John Heng, *B.Sc., M.A., Ph.D.,* teaches Philosophy and Ethics in the Department of Philosophy and Religious Studies and Program in Thanatology of King's University College, University of Western Ontario in London, ON.

William F. Sullivan, *B.A., B.Sc., M.A., M. D., CCFP, Ph.D. (Ethics),* is a family doctor at Surrey Place Centre and the Department of Family and Community Medicine at St. Michael's Hospital, Toronto, where he focusses on care of people with developmental disabilities. He leads the Developmental Disabilities Primary Care Initiative which has produced Canadian guidelines and tools for the primary care of adults with developmental disabilities. He is Chair of the Ethics Committee of the College of Family Physicians of Canada.

Chapter 31: Physical Health and People with Developmental Disabilities

Tom Cheetham, *B.A., M.D., CCFP,* has more than 35 years of experience supporting people with intellectual disabilities, starting as a live-in house parent and then his career as a family physician. After spending his career in Ontario in 2011 he moved to Tennessee USA where he is the State Medical Director for the Department of Intellectual and Developmental Disabilities.

Shirley McMillan, *R.N., B.Sc.N., M.N., CDDN,* has spent most of her nursing career in the field of developmental disabilities. Currently, she is Advanced Practice Nurse in the Mental Health Program at Surrey Place Centre in Toronto. She is a Ph.D. candidate in learning disability at the University of Glamorgan, Wales.

Chapter 32: Nutritional Considerations in Children with Developmental Disabilities

Diana Mager, *Ph.D., M.Sc., RD,* is a Registered Dietitian and Assistant Professor of Clinical Nutrition in the Departments of Agriculture, Food and Nutritional Science and Paediatrics at the University of Alberta. Her area of research expertise is in the area of clinical nutrition support in infants, children and adolescents with chronic gastrointestinal and liver disease.

Paul Pencharz, *M.D., Ch.B., Ph.D., FRCPC,* is a Professor of Pediatrics and Nutritional Sciences,

University of Toronto; The Hospital for Sick Children, Toronto, ON.

Chapter 33: Safe Medication Practice and Front Line Professional Practice

Andrea Rutherford, *R.N., CPRP, M.Sc.N.,* is a Registered Nurse and Certified Psychiatric Rehabilitation Practitioner. She is a Professor in the Developmental Services Worker (DSW) Program, School of Social & Community Services, Humber Institute of Technology & Advanced Learning in Toronto, and provides community agency consultation and training in safe medication administration and pharmacology.

Chapter 34: Psychopharmacology of People with Developmental Disabilities

Kenneth Boss, *M.D., FRCP(C)* is a psychiatrist working in the Developmental Disabilities Service of the North Bay Regional Health Centre. He is currently working towards a Master's in Disability Studies and Board Certification in Behaviour Analysis through Brock University.

Chapter 35: Introduction to Abnormal Behaviour and Associated Conditions

Wai Lun Alan Fung, *M.D., M.Phil., S.M., FRCP(C), D.A.B.P.N.,* is a medical specialist in psychiatry, focusing on neuropsychiatry and genetics, cross-cultural medicine, and medical psychotherapy. He is an Assistant Professor at the Department of Psychiatry of the University of Toronto, Faculty of Medicine, and a Faculty Member of the University of Toronto Neuroscience Program. He is also an Attending Staff Physician of the Departments of Psychiatry and Clinical Genetics at North York General Hospital in Toronto.

Maire Percy, see Chapter 4.

Ivan Brown, see Chapter 1.

Chapter 36: Developmental Disabilities and Mental Ill-Health

Jane Summers, see Chapter 14.

Elspeth Bradley, *B.Sc., Ph.D., MBBS, FRCPsych, FRCPC Intellectual Disabilities Psychiatrist (Specialist Register, Learning Disabilities, U.K.),* is Psychiatrist-in-Chief, Surrey Place Centre in Toronto, and Associate Professor, Department of Psychiatry, University of Toronto.

John Flannery, *R.N., B.Sc.N., M.Sc.N.,* is Chief Executive Officer at Surrey Place Centre in Toronto, and Clinical-Appointee in the Faculty of Nursing at the University of Toronto.

Chapter 37: Alzheimer's Disease: Implications in Down Syndrome and Other Developmental Disabilities

Vee Prasher, *MBChB, MedSc, MRCPsych, M.D., Ph.D., FIASSID,* is Professor of Neuro-Developmental Psychiatry, The Greenfields, Kings Norton, Birmingham, UK.

Maire Percy, see Chapter 4.

Emoke Jozsvai, *B.A. (Hons.), M.A., Ph.D., C.Psych.,* is a psychologist at Surrey Place Centre in Toronto.

Joseph Berg, *M.B., B.Ch., B.Sc., M.Sc., FRCPsych, FCCMG,* is Professor Emeritus, Faculty of Medicine, University of Toronto.

Chapter 38: Prenatal and Early Life

Karolina Machalek, *B.Sc.(Hons.), M.P.H.,* currently works as a Public Health Officer, Epidemiologist for the Canadian Public Health Service, Public Health Agency of Canada and is stationed at the Department of Health and Social Services, Government of Yukon in Whitehorse, Yukon.

Maire Percy, see Chapter 4.

Melissa Carter, see Chapter 9.

Ivan Brown, see Chapter 1.

Chapter 39: Early Intervention for Young Children

Elaine B. Frankel, *Ed.D.,* is a Professor in the School of Early Childhood Education, Ryerson University in Toronto, and is the Teaching Chair within the Faculty of Community Services.

Kathryn Underwood, *Ph.D.,* is an Assistant Professor in the School of Early Childhood Education at Ryerson University in Toronto.

Chapter 40: Developmental Disabilities and Child Maltreatment

Ann Fudge Schormans, see Chapter 7.

Chapter 41: Developmental Disabilities and Ontario's Schools

Eileen C. Winter, *Ph.D.,* is Lecturer, School of Education, Queen's University, Belfast, Ireland.

Ester Cole, *Ph.D., C.Psych.,* is a psychologist in private practice. She was a supervising psychologist at the Toronto Board of Education, and taught courses at OISE for two decades. She was also the President of the Ontario Psychological Association, and the Chair of the Psychology Foundation of Canada.

Chapter 42: The Transition from School to Adult Life

Ivan Brown, see Chapter 1.

Lynn Martin, *Ph.D.,* is an Associate Professor in the Department of Health Sciences at Lakehead University in Thunder Bay, ON, and a Ministry of Health and Long-term Care Career Scientist. She is also a member of the Chief Editorial Board for the Journal on Developmental Disabilities.

Chapter 43: Work and Employment for People with Developmental Disabilities in Ontario

Judith Sandys, *M.S.W., Ph.D.,* is an Associate Professor in the School of Social Work at Ryerson University and an active member of many disability organizations. Currently she is a member of the Social Policy Committee of Community Living Ontario, Co-chair of the Board of Directors of ERDCO (Ethno-Racial People with Disabilities Coalition of Ontario), and a founding member of the Southern Ontario Training Group.

Chapter 44: Lifestyles of Adults with Developmental Disabilities in Ontario

M. Katherine Buell, *Ph.D., C.Psych.,* is a Psychologist and Coordinator, Psychological and Community Behavioural Services at Ongwanada (Kingston, Ontario), Director of Clinical Training (Kingston Internship Consortium), and an Adjunct Assistant Professor, Departments of Psychology and Psychiatry, at Queen's University, Kingston, Ontario, Canada.

Jonathan Weiss, *Ph.D., C.Psych.,* is an Assistant Professor at York University, and a Clinical Psychologist, who works with people with developmental disabilities. He completed a post-doctoral fellowship in the Dual Diagnosis Program at the Centre for Addiction and Mental Health, and was a research fellow in the Department of Psychiatry at the University of Toronto.

Ivan Brown, see Chapter 1.

Chapter 45: Family Life and Developmental Disability

Patricia Minnes, *Ph.D., C.Psych.,* is a professor in the Departments of Psychology and Psychiatry and the School of Rehabilitation Therapy at Queen's University in Kingston Ontario. She is also a clinical psychologist and member of the Queen's University Developmental Disabilities Consulting Program: an inter-professional team serving individuals with developmental disabilities and mental health/behavioural challenges and their families.

Julie Burbidge, *M.Sc.,* is a Ph.D. candidate in clinical psychology in the Department of Psychology at Queens University.

Chapter 46: Sexuality and Developmental Disability: From Myth to Emerging Practices

Dorothy Griffiths, *Ph.D., O. Ont.,* is a Professor in the Child and Youth Studies Department and the Centre for Applied Disabilities Studies at Brock University, and Co-Director of the International Dual Diagnosis Certificate Programme.

Chapter 47: Developmental Disabilities and Women's Issues: Roles and Relationships

Lillian Burke, *Ph.D., C.Psych.,* is a Psychologist in Private Practice, and the Assistant Director of The Redpath Centre, Toronto.

Chapter 48: Parenting by Persons with Intellectual Disabilities

Marjorie Aunos, *Ph.D.,* is a clinical psychologist and manager of a parenting program for persons with intellectual disabilities at the West Montreal Readaptation Centre. She is also an Associate Professor at the University of Québec in Montreal (UQAM) and at Brock University.

Maurice Feldman, *Ph.D., C.Psych., BCBA-D,* is Professor and Director of the Centre for Applied Disability Studies at Brock University. He is a Clinical Psychologist and Board Certified Behavior Analyst (Doctoral). Professor Feldman is a Fellow of the Canadian Psychological Association and a Brock University Chancellor's Research Chair and Distinguished Researcher. He conducts life span research in developmental disabilities and consults to governmental and nongovernmental organizations.

Chapter 49: Aging in People with Developmental Disabilities

Lilian Thorpe, *M.D., Ph.D., FRCP(Psychiatry),* is a geriatric psychiatrist with special interest in aging in people with intellectual disabilities (ID). She has academic appointments in Psychiatry and Community Health and Epidemiology, University of Saskatchewan, and sees patients with and without ID in various clinical settings.

Nancy Jokinen, *M.S.W., Ph.D.,* is an Assistant Professor at the School of Social Work, University of Northern British Columbia in Prince George, British Columbia. She was previously a Post Doctoral Fellow at the Centre for Education and Research on Aging and Health, at Lakehead University in Thunder Bay, Ontario, and recipient of the Early Researcher Award sponsored by the Ontario Research Coalition of Research Institutes / Centres on Health & Aging.

Introduction

We are very pleased to bring you *Developmental Disabilities in Ontario*, Third Edition. Our first edition, published in 1999, was the first text that provided broad and multi-disciplinary information about developmental disabilities and, at the same time, was specifically for people who live and work in Ontario. The second edition, published in 2003, updated the information in the first edition, and added several new chapters. This third edition updates and reorganizes that information, and adds five new chapters to provide additional information that was not previously included.

Developmental Disabilities in Ontario, Third Edition, is intended to appeal to a broad range of people in Ontario. Students in Ontario colleges and universities use it as a comprehensive text with specific reference to Ontario to guide their learning. We consider this to be particularly important, since these students are the future professionals and community leaders in the field of developmental disabilities. This book is also intended for use by people who directly support people with developmental disabilities, educators, health care workers, social workers, academics, policy makers, government leaders, those concerned with legal and ethical issues, and many others. Perhaps most important, the book provides one way for family members to learn about a broad range of issues in the field of developmental disabilities. At a time when many families want to have a stronger voice in determining support for their family members with disabilities, such information is needed. Finally, it is our hope that the material contained between these covers will help the general public to understand developmental disability better, and to include people with developmental disabilities of all ages in Ontario society.

This book has attempted to capture core research and practical knowledge in the developmental disabilities field and to present it in a format for learning and for day-to-day use. The main goal of the book is to promote sharing of information, experience, solutions, and insights in order to help people with developmental disabilities, their families, and their other supporters improve their quality of life.

We have assembled *Developmental Disabilities in Ontario*, Third Edition, for three additional reasons. First, interest in the book arose from our collective experiences as researchers and teachers, and from networking through our activities with the Ontario Association on Developmental Disabilities (OADD) — an organization whose mandate is to promote the education of professionals in the field — and OADD's Research Special Interest Group. We realized that service providers of all disciplines, service recipients, students, educators, researchers, policy makers, and others would benefit from a book that presented core and practical information from a multi-disciplinary perspective. There is a tremendous amount of information in the developmental disabilities field. Because the field is changing so quickly, and because most people do not have a broad understanding of all the issues in the field, much valuable information is not readily accessible to people who need it when they need it. Second, there is a large body of informal knowledge based on the extensive experiences of clinicians, educators, and researchers that has not been brought together before. Finally, new philosophical and policy directions in developmental services have emerged in recent years, and good responses to these require solid knowledge of the field.

The term developmental disabilities requires elaboration (see also Chapter 1). In its broad sense, the term refers to disabilities that are related to development. To a great extent, though, the term developmental disabilities as it is commonly used in Ontario and elsewhere grew out of, and replaced, the terms mental retardation, mental handicap, and developmental handicap, which had become outdated by the mid 1980s. The term intellectual disability is used in many countries of the world, and is increasingly being used in Ontario as an equivalent term to developmental disability. In this book, we have continued to use the term developmental disability, because that is the term used in the major policy documents that influence the field in Ontario. It is also in keeping with the current name of the book's publisher, the Ontario Association on Developmental Disabilities.

The field of developmental disabilities in Ontario is, in many ways, not substantially different from that of other parts of Canada or other countries. Thus, much of the information in this book will be very useful indeed to people in other jurisdictions. Still, people live within cultural and political environments that often have considerable influence upon their lives. People with developmental disabilities who live in Ontario are influenced by the customs, the values, the laws, the natural and human resources, and the many other characteristics that comprise the Ontario environment.

One of the primary intents of this book is to capture as much as possible of the Ontario environment that influences the lives of people with developmental disabilities. In doing so, our aim is to place the lives of such people — and the field of developmental disabilities itself — within its environment, and to explore, as much as we can, the interrelationship among people, the field, and the environment. Every chapter contains references to resources that are available in Ontario — a list of "where to start" when confronted with a question about developmental disabilities. This provides a way for new parents, family members, students, adults supporting people with disabilities, professionals in education and health care, and many others to connect with other people and supports right here in Ontario.

We have tried to capture a great deal of the complexity in the broad field of developmental disabilities in the 49 chapters that comprise Developmental Disabilities in Ontario. In doing so, we have not been able to include every aspect of life of people with developmental disabilities, nor have we been able to raise every issue or perspective that is of importance to people with developmental disabilities, their families, and those who support them in the many ways they do. We have brought to you, though, a comprehensive set of chapters under one cover about developmental disabilities. We have endeavoured to place the material of each of these chapters within the Ontario context, and it is this unique feature of which we are most proud.

One of the interesting by-products of producing this book has been the opportunity for interaction among a wide variety of people whose lives are affected by developmental disabilities, including family members, professionals, policy makers, researchers, and those who provide numerous types of supports. A team of 86 experts, almost all of whom live and work in Ontario, contributed to this book. This represents a vast amount of knowledge from professionals whose life work includes sharing and connecting with others.

In producing *Developmental Disabilities in Ontario*, Third Edition, we are very pleased to continue to collaborate with the Ontario Association on Developmental Disabilities. OADD, an organization of people who pursue careers in the field of developmental disabilities in Ontario, was formed in 1989. Both of us have been strong supporters of OADD for many years, and have acted in leadership roles on its Board of Directors and its Research Special Interest Group. Since one of the principal goals of OADD is to promote learning opportunities for people who work in the field of developmental disabilities, this book very much supports its mandate.

In presenting to you the 49 chapters of *Developmental Disabilities in Ontario*, Third Edition, it is our hope that they will be informative and helpful to you in your understanding of developmental disabilities in Ontario, and that the contents of this book will encourage you to network with others in the developmental disabilities field.

Ivan Brown

Maire Percy

Editors

Part I

The Context for Developmental Disabilities in Ontario

1

What is Meant by Developmental Disability

Ivan Brown

What you will learn:

- Why we need to exercise care in using the term developmental disability
- Personal, literal, social, critical disability, and definitional meanings of developmental disability
- Terms used in other countries
- Advantages and disadvantages of disability terms
- Current usage of the term developmental disability

The term *developmental disability* is widely used in Ontario, and thus is used throughout this text. Other terms that are also used in Ontario mean essentially the same thing, especially *intellectual disability*, which is used internationally (see Box 1 for other terms). Thus, when we refer to people with developmental disability here, we are also referring to people who might also be described by synonymous terms.

The use of terms has been controversial for several decades. There are a number of reasons that general and specialized terms are useful (see section below), but misuse has no doubt also occurred (Foreman, 2005). Moreover, people whom we might describe as having disabilities themselves often eschew the use of any term that sets them apart, marginalizing them. For this reason, those of us who are practitioners, students, and teachers must use terms with caution, and always be aware — even in writing and reading this book — that the term developmental disability and its many related terms are considered by some to be demeaning and inappropriate.

In one sense, the term developmental disability need not be used. People with developmental disabilities have existed throughout history in every part of the globe, and they make up part of all cultures. They are part of the wide variety of people that exists in the human population at any one time.

Box 1: Some Other Terms Used to Describe Developmental Disability

Currently in use:
- *Intellectual disability*

Sometimes used, but not preferred:
- *Mental disability*
- *Mental handicap*
- *Developmental handicap*
- *Challenged*

Used in some countries, but not in Ontario:
(see also Table 1)
- *Mental retardation*
- *Learning disabilities*

Obsolete Terms:
(see also Chapter 2)
- *Mental deficiency*
- *Feebleminded*
- *Moron*
- *Imbecile*
- *Idiot*
- *Natural fool*

Although it is sometimes useful for us to describe them as groups for various positive purposes, they are not distinct groups of people at all; rather, they are individuals who each add one piece to the mosaic that illustrates the rich, interesting diversity that is characteristic of the human condition.

Still, the term developmental disability, like the numerous other terms that describe aspects of it, is widely used. It is important to know why this continues to be so and to understand the meanings that are ascribed to them. In spite of the view that disabilities are part of the human condition, people with and without disabilities have been categorized in response to the strong trend in recent centuries to conceive the world around us in "scientific" ways. The word "normal" emerged to describe some people and the word "abnormal" then described those

who were not considered to be normal (Davis, 2010). Within the field that is now known as developmental disability, sub-categories have been described and refined over the past 150 years. For example, John Langdon Down, best known for first describing what we call Down syndrome today, described what he called his "ethnic classification of idiots" in 1866 (Health Alert, 2002). Since the early 1900s people with disabilities have been described and classified in increasing complex ways (see Chapters 2 and 3). The rationale for doing this was to identify those individuals who need special learning and lifestyle support and to capture the ever-expanding knowledge of disability. There were other, more sinister, reasons as well, such as controlling propagation of "feebleminded" people through sterilization, isolation, and other means so that society could be improved over time (the eugenics movement; see Chapters 2 and 44). Over the past few decades, numerous new categories have emerged to describe people with disabilities that reflect new knowledge of environmental, genetic, and other biological causes of disability (see especially Chapters 9, 11, 12, and 13). Our use of categorization within more general terms such as developmental disability is at an historic high.

The question of who should create and use terms and categories — if they should be used at all — is also controversial. Historically, individuals have been ascribed terms and are placed into categories based on physical or behavioural characteristics that can be described by "other" people, usually disability or medical professionals and not people with disabilities themselves. This is a matter of some concern today among those who advocate for self-determination and those who promote a critical disability perspective (see below and Chapter 2 for a fuller explanation).

In this chapter and indeed in this book, our purpose is not to "take sides" on the question of use of the term developmental disability and its many categories. Instead, the focus is on understanding what we mean by the term developmental disability, and on learning what similar terms are used in various parts of the world. Such knowledge should help us to make wise judgements about their use.

Five Meanings of Developmental Disability

In this section, five inter-related perspectives on the meaning of developmental disability are described: personal meaning, literal meaning, social meaning, critical disability meaning, and definitional meaning. As noted in other chapters of this book, definitional meanings very often are taken as the only meaning, especially when children or adults are being considered for diagnosis or eligibility for services. But, as we will see here, developmental disability means much more than meeting the criteria set out in a definition. The contention of this chapter is that it is necessary to understand developmental disability as a blend of all five meanings for effective work in our field today.

PERSONAL MEANING

Developmental disability has, first and foremost, a personal meaning for an individual because it is a part of his or her whole life over the entire lifespan. At the personal level, there is no disability, developmental or otherwise. There is not something that can be described as a condition, or a limitation, or a challenge. Nor is there something that can be defined as abnormal or unfortunate. It is not anything other than just an aspect of life, just part of who he or she is as a person. Each person simply uses what abilities are available to live in a way that is personal and that serves his or her individual needs.

Developmental disability is a term devised by "others" to describe people who function and behave in ways that seem less abled than most people. There are personal consequences to the fact that we label people as having a developmental disability, or, less formally, as being "different" from the general population. This very labelling or being considered as different can create within people a sense that "something is wrong with me" and "I am different" and it can create in other people a sense that they can view and treat people with developmental disabilities as different. Knowledge that they regard themselves, and other people regard them, as "disabled" can result in a personal meaning attached to developmental disability that can affect self-percep-

tion and self-confidence, often in negative ways.

There are many excellent accounts available that help professionals, family members, and members of the general community to understand the personal meaning of developmental disability better. The Internet contains numerous personal stories about what it is like to lead the life of a person with a developmental disability (e.g., Regional Oral History Office, 2010) from the perspective of the people themselves or from the perspective of a family member. Baggs (n.d.) and autistics.org each list books written by people with Austism Spectrum Disorder. Nasatir (2002) provides an excellent list of children's books about disability, and Articlebase (2009) lists books that depict characters with disabilities in a positive light. There are also lists of movies that depict developmental disability (e.g., VideoHound, 2011). The best understanding about the personal meaning of developmental disabilities, though, probably comes from direct conversation and interaction with individuals and with members of their families. Listening to and learning about the full scope of their everyday lives can help us know better what development disability means to them personally.

LITERAL MEANING

The literal meaning of developmental disability is relevant after "others" have designated specific people or populations to it. The literal meaning of a term refers to its semantics, or our understanding of the words that make up a term. It represents the simplest and broadest understanding of a term, because it goes no farther than an understanding of what the term's words mean. This literal meaning is the basic foundation for how a term is conceptualized and, for this reason, it is a good place to begin to understand what others mean by it.

Literal meanings vary slightly from one source to another. According to Webster's College Dictionary (2001), ability means the "power or capacity to do or act physically, mentally, legally, morally, or financially," and dis-, as a prefix, has a "privative, negative, or reversing force relative to [a word]." The prefix dis- is used with ability in this way to mean not able, except that there is an implication that one

Box 2: Growing Expectations of Ability and Acceptance of Disability

Growing Acceptance of Ability

Many of the expectations associated with carrying out the practical and social activities of everyday life are becoming increasingly complex. A large majority of the world's population now lives in urban areas, where it is typically necessary to use complicated transportation systems; shop in a large choice of venues; take specific action to maintain personal relationships; and deal with everchanging technology (e.g., banking, public telephones, elevators, computers, social networking), crowds, and many other challenges. Although many accommodations have been made in most cities to make daily life activities easier for people with disabilities, the very nature of urban life increases the expectations that people should be able to perform numerous everyday activities that are rather complex.

Whether or not people live in urban areas, daily life is becoming more complex. Technology used in the home — involving such things as telephones, televisions, equipment to play music and movies, and many adaptive devices — has been extremely helpful to many people with disabilities. At the same time, however, it changes at a rather rapid pace — a pace that is often bewildering even to those who eagerly embrace it. Literacy is a required skill in today's urban world. Computer literacy (the ability to use computer equipment to communicate with others and gather information) is very helpful to some people with disabilities and is quickly becoming a required skill; the "e-divide" is a term to describe those who are and are not computer literate. It is still too early to describe how much of an asset computer literacy will be to people with various types of disabilities (Davies, Stock, & Wehmeyer, 2004), but it is quite possible that it will be another way that they are separated from others in their environments (i.e., they are on the "wrong" side of the "e-divide").

Growing Acceptance of Disability

Paradoxically, in Ontario and elsewhere there is a trend toward altering the social view of developmental disabilities so that people are more tolerant of them. It is increasingly recognized that people have a broad range of skills and lifestyles, and there is growing acceptance of people of varying skill levels and lifestyle choices. This view holds that not only should all people be free to live their lives in general accordance with the rules of society, but also they must be supported in doing so if help is required.

Considerable effort has been made especially since approximately 1980 to remove some of the social and environmental barriers to inclusion so that all people — regardless of ability level, age, cultural background, and so forth — can live more ably in the general society. As a result, the social meaning of developmental disability has narrowed somewhat. Increasing numbers of people with these disabilities are included in society and are carrying out many socially expected life functions quite ably and independently.

is not able due to a specific reason or cause. Thus, disability means more than simply not able; it means not able because of something that deprives a person of performing or accomplishing something. The word developmental, as an adjective on its own, refers to "a state of developing or being developed" over time (Oxford Advanced Learner's Dictionary, 2000). When developmental is put together with disability and the two words are used as one term, developmental disability refers to something in the way a person develops over time that deprives him or her of being able to perform or accomplish

specific things. Thus, developmental disability refers to some restriction or lack of ability having to do with human development.

The literal meaning of a term that a person uses is the basic way that person, and others, understand it. An interesting question is whether the literal meaning of developmental disability, as it is used today, adequately describes the area or field of inquiry that this book addresses. A related question is whether the meaning of the term used adequately encompasses and reflects the values a person wants to promote about his or her area or field of inquiry.

SOCIAL MEANING

The personal and literal meanings of developmental disability contribute to how that term is understood in the larger social group, but they are also shaped by broader social perceptions and meanings (Foreman, 2005). In real-life social situations, developmental disability is thought of, spoken about, and responded to differently by different groups of people. This is because its social meaning is subject, over time and place, to a wide variety of changing social values and attitudes, and by cultural, political, and economic trends. Such differences in attitude and use reflect the sometimes fluid social meaning of a term, or the particular and sometimes unique way the term is understood and used by people within their own social contexts.

For these reasons, the interpretation of the word abilities varies. Perceptions of what abilities people "should" have, and thus the things that they "should" be able to perform and accomplish, differ considerably from one group of people to another and from one time period to another. Tolerance of people who have "too few" or "too many" abilities also differs among cultures and over time periods. Many interweaving factors are part of the emergence of such perceptions and levels of tolerance — social and political structures, economic conditions, cultural values and attitudes, and environmental demands — but somehow, in all social orders, a general understanding emerges about what constitutes typical development, and what things almost all people "should" be able to do. This general understanding forms the basis of what a person is expected to do in his or her social environment. Thus, the word ability takes on a particular meaning that is derived from social expectations.

People who do not have sufficient ability and cannot do the things that are socially expected of most people in their living environments are viewed as having disabilities. There are many reasons why people do not have ability or meet socially derived expectations in their particular environments. These include, among other things, genetic inheritance, chance occurrences both before and after conception, injury, lack of learning opportunities, languages understood and used, poor family and social support, physical barriers (e.g., steps rather than ramps), systems that are too complex (e.g., electronic banking, complicated application procedures for services, use of written words rather than icons on signs), practices that are inappropriately difficult (e.g., sending letters to people who are visually impaired or who cannot read), unavailability of resources (e.g., money, housing, support personnel) in the immediate and broader environments, and very often a combination of several things.

People who, during their childhood and adolescence, develop limited ability to do the things that are socially expected of most people in their particular living environments are those considered to have developmental disabilities. Thus, the term developmental disability, when socially applied, builds on personal and literal meanings to take on social meanings that may vary somewhat from one jurisdiction to another — meanings that are shaped by the perceptions and expectations of each of the social environments in which individuals live. (See Box 2 for an interesting paradox about current perceptions and expectations.)

THE CRITICAL DISABILITY MEANING

Since about 1990, there has emerged world-wide a strong voice from within the disability community declaring itself to be a valid and necessary part of the human social order (Oliver, 1990). This movement, sometimes referred to as the critical disability movement, is influenced by race, feminist, and oppression theories (Asch, 2001), and regards disability terminology and the enormous number of systems and social conventions that have emerged from terminology as the wrongly focussed, somewhat unnecessary, and sometimes illegitimate constructed ideas of "other" people. It views the discourse of disability (the formal ideas, discussions, and writings about disability) as the domain mainly of people with disabilities themselves, and considers that it is primarily people with disabilities who can move the field forward in ways that are truly helpful and valid. It examines power in its various forms — intellectual, political, economic, moral — and considers recognition of all difference as a social necessity (Davis, 2010).

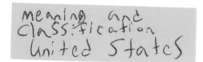
Meaning and Classification United States

Box 3: Unique Meaning of Developmental Disability in the United States

In Canada and many other countries of the world, the term developmental disability is used as a synonym for intellectual disability. In the United States, however, developmental disability was defined separately from mental retardation (which was replaced beginning in 2006 by intellectual disability). There are a number of definitions of developmental disability in the United States, but the most influential is that of the Developmental Disabilities Assistance and Bill of Rights Act Amendments of 2000 (PL 106-402):

The term 'developmental disability' means a severe, chronic disability of an individual 5 years of age or older that:

A. *is attributable to a mental or physical impairment or a combination of mental and physical impairments;*

B. *is manifested before the individual attains age 22;*

C. *is likely to continue indefinitely;*

D. *results in substantial functional limitations in three or more of the following areas of major life activity: (i) self-care, (ii) receptive and expressive language, (iii) learning, (iv) mobility, (v) self-direction, (vi) capacity for independent learning, and (vii) economic self-sufficiency; and*

E. *reflects the individual's need for a combination and sequence of special, interdisciplinary, or generic services, individualized supports, or other forms of assistance that are of lifelong or extended duration and are individually planned and coordinated.*

Thus, developmental disability in the United States can mean blindness, deafness, mobility impairments, severe elilepsy, and other conditions that are expected to be ongoing. They may or may not involve intellectual disability (lower intelligence levels and adaptive functioning, and their associated need for support).

The critical disability movement emerges from the philosophy of equal human rights for people with disabilities, a "sister" movement that has championed disability rights worldwide. Human rights emphasizes that all people, no matter what their abilities or disabilities may be, are members of the human family and as such are equally entitled to the same rights. Gaining such equality involves putting laws in place, but also it is a matter of people with disabilities claiming their equal rights and being seen by others as being fully entitled to them. A closely-related philosophical underpinning is social responsibility, which emerges out of the social model (Shakespeare, 2010), where disability is considered to exist not because of impairment (which is a part of all social orders in any case), but because of a society's inability to accept its responsibility to provide the necessary means to include and accommodate all of its members. The critical disability movement also includes what is referred to as political necessity, or the need to speak out about past oppression, to make the experience of disability explicitly known to both those who are disabled and

those who are not, to advocate, and to act in a political way to bring about needed change. As such, its main thrust is empowerment, equality, and emancipation (Pothier & Devlin, 2006).

For people with developmental disabilities, involvement in the critical disability movement has been limited. Closest, perhaps, People First is an international organization with chapters in many countries, including Canada, that advocates for the voice of people with developmental disabilities to be heard and for their human rights to be respected. In addition, there are in every community individuals with developmental disabilities and family members who may well never have heard of the critical disability movement but understand from their own experiences the need to express similar views. Still, the critical disability movement has had an impact on the meaning of disability, including developmental disability, that adds to other meanings we hold. It is leading us to understand that the way we have conceptualized and treated people with disabilities in the past — the meanings we have ascribed to disability — may have been well-intended but have also been harmful, and that there is a need to have people with disabilities define the experience and discourse of disability in the future. In short, the critical disability meaning of developmental disabilities is oppression of individuals by others in power, the need for self-expression and self-determination and, eventually, emancipation.

DEFINITIONAL MEANING

There is often a perceived need to define the above meanings of a term more specifically (and more narrowly) for specific purposes, such as establishing entitlement to educational, medical, or social services. For this reason, many professional organizations, government bodies, and other groups have set out their own formal definitions of developmental disability (or similar terms), in which they specify the essential aspects of their definition. From this view, developmental disability means having the characteristics that are specified in the definition. Definitions of developmental disability largely ignore its personal, social, and critical disability meanings and, instead, emphasize the results of sound scientific assessment as the best way to show adherence to their definition's criteria.

One of the criticisms of definitional meanings is that, although they are specific and usually rely on scientific assessment for evidence, their "specifics" can differ among particular groups or organizations that create and use them for their own purposes. The meaning of something then becomes whatever you have defined it to be at a particular point in time (and almost all definitions change over time). Thus, definitions of the same thing can differ somewhat, and each can represent the interest or bias of whoever created it and put it into practice. This is especially problematic if a definitional meaning for something is the only meaning used, as is often the case for the definition of developmental disability in Ontario and elsewhere in Canada and the world.

On the other hand, definitions of developmental disability and related terms in Ontario and around the world have relied quite strongly on the definitional meaning of intellectual disability, developmental disability, and mental retardation of one or more of the following organizations: the American Association on Intellectual & Developmental Disabilities (AAIDD), the American Psychiatric Association (APA), and the World Health Organization (WHO). For this reason, it is essential to understand such definitions.

AAIDD definition

AAIDD's definition of intellectual disability, and its predecessor term mental retardation, have probably had the most international impact. This includes impact on how developmental disability is defined in Ontario (see below).

The definition of intellectual disability (AAIDD, 2010, p.1) is:

Intellectual disability is characterized by significant limitations both in intellectual functioning and in adaptive behavior as expressed in conceptual, social, and practical adaptive skills. This disability originates before age 18. The following five assumptions are essential to the application of this definition:

1. *Limitations in present functioning must be considered within the context of community environments typical of the individual's age peers and culture.*
2. *Valid assessment considers cultural and linguistic diversity as well as differences in communication, sensory, motor, and behavioral factors.*
3. *Within an individual, limitations often coexist with strengths.*
4. *An important purpose of describing limitations is to develop a profile of needed supports.*
5. *With appropriate personalized supports over a sustained period, the life functioning of the person with intellectual disability generally will improve.*

AAIDD's definition contains three clearly articulated criteria for ascribing the term intellectual disability to an individual: intellectual functioning approximately two standard deviations below the norm (keeping in mind margin or error on tests), limitations in adaptive functioning, and onset before age 18. It goes beyond adherence to the three criteria, however, in clearly specifying that level of support required, cultural and environmental factors, and clinical judgement are all essential ingredients of an informed and clinically useful diagnosis of intellectual disability.

APA definition

At the time of this book's publication (spring 2011), the American Psychiatric Association was involved in multi-year planning for its *Diagnostic and Statistical Manual of Mental Disorders, Fifth Edition* (DSM-5), expected to be in publication by May 2013. It is expected that the the DSM-5 will contain a new definition of intellectual disabilities and criteria for diagnosing it, as well as new definitions and diagnostic criteria for several sub-categories of intellectual disability such as Autism. The DSN-5 website can be checked for ongoing updates (American Psychiatric Association, 2010).

Still in use is APA's *Diagnostic and Statistical Manual of Mental Disorders, Fourth Edition, Text Revision* (DSM-IV-TR, 2000), which features a definition of mental retardation that is similar to the 1992 definition of mental retardation (Luckasson et al., 1992) provided by the American Association on Mental Retardation (which became AAIDD in 2006). The DSM-IV-TR describes three characteristics of individuals with mental retardation (APA, 2000, p. 41):

1. *sub-average intellectual functioning, IQ of 70 or below measured by an individually administered intelligence test;*
2. *concurrent limitations or alterations in adaptive functioning, lowered ability to cope with common life demands and to meet the standards of personal independence expected of them in at least two of the following domains: communication, self-care, domestic skills, social skills, self-direction, community, academic skills, work, leisure, and health and safety; and*
3. *onset before age 18.*

APA's definition is considerably more limited than that offered by AAIDD. But this definition is still in use, partly because it is only recently that the term mental retardation has been replaced by intellectual disability in the United States, and because

the considerable scholarly literature in the fields of intellectual disability and developmental disability produced in the United States still reflects some usage of the term mental retardation. Moreover, definitions of intellectual disability and developmental disability throughout the world are highly influenced by definitions of mental retardation that have emerged in the United States. For example, the three characteristics of mental retardation set out in the DSM-IV-TR above are similar to the main components of the definition of developmental disability of the Ontario Ministry of Community and Social Services in its *Services and Supports to Promote the Social Inclusion of Persons with Developmental Disabilities Act, 2008* (see below).

WHO definition

The WHO published a classification system in 2001 called the *International Classification of Functioning, Disability, and Health* (ICF). The ICF replaced two versions of the *International Classification of Impairments, Disabilities, and Handicaps* (ICIDH, 1980, and ICIDH-2, 1997). The ICF is one of several classification systems developed by the WHO, and is considered to be complementary to that organization's *International Statistical Classification of Diseases and Related Health Problems* (ICD-10) (2003). Many disability critics believe that the ICD has too strong a "medical model" focus, because it conceptualizes disability as an impairment that is influenced by personal and environmental factors but does not encompass disability arising out of social factors such as marginalization, discrimination, and oppression. The ICF view of disability is broader than simply impairment, however, encompassing an impairment of body structure or function, a limitation in activities, or a restriction in participation, all of which are influenced by personal and environmental factors in a dynamic way (WHO, 2011).

Although the ICF is used to describe disability populations in general — not just developmental disability — it serves two main functions for our field:

1. It provides a way to understand disability in a more general way, avoiding the problems associated with specific terms taking on different

meanings in different countries or the same condition being described by different terms in different countries.

2. It provides a framework for disabilities in general, within which developmental disability has a legitimate place.

Definitions used in Ontario

The term developmental disability is not officially defined by any major disability organization in Ontario or elsewhere in Canda (e.g., Community Living Ontario, Ontario Association on Developmental Disabilities, Canadian Association for Community Living). It is more usual for professional and service organizations to describe, rather than to define, developmental disability.

The website of Ontario's Ministry of Community and Social Service's Developmental Services Branch provides a description of developmental disability that contains aspects of a formal definition (MCSS, 2011):

A developmental disability:
- *is a disability that a person is born with or that begins before he or she turns 18*
- *permanently limits a person's ability to learn*
- *can be mild or severe.*

People with a developmental disability may learn, understand or remember things at a slower pace than others. This can affect their personal care, language skills and their ability to live without support.

Ontario's Ministry of Children and Youth Services (2010) uses the definition of developmental disability from the 1990 Child and Family Services Act: "A condition of mental impairment, present or occurring during a person's formative years that is associated with limitations in adaptive behaviour." Its website explains the definition this way: "In other words, it's an impairment in cognitive function that arises before adulthood and usually lasts throughout life."

The Ministry of Community and Social Services follows the definition of developmental disabilities set out in its *Services and Supports to Promote the Social Inclusion of Persons with Developmental Disabilities Act, 2008*. Developmental disability is defined as (Service Ontario, 2011):

A person has a developmental disability for the purposes of this Act if the person has the prescribed significant limitations in cognitive functioning and adaptive functioning and those limitations,

a. *originated before the person reached 18 years of age;*
b. *are likely to be life-long in nature; and*
c. *affect areas of major life activity, such as personal care, language skills, learning abilities, the capacity to live independently as an adult or any other prescribed activity.*

The use of definitions in establishing eligibility for services (including education; see Chapter 41 for more details) is controversial because of measurement difficulties when standardized tests are used, and because not everyone agrees that definitions alone are a good way to describe what we mean by developmental disability. Still, many services offered in Ontario do require "proof" that applicants have developmental disabilities and, when this is the case, that "proof" is usually adherence to formal definitions and the results of formal testing. For example, the application processes for Passport and for Special Services At Home each require supporting documentation confirming developmental disability from a physician or a psychologist (the two professions in Ontario that can communicate a diagnosis of developmental disability). Community agencies, and sometimes specific services within community agencies, have their own eligibility criteria for services. Some of these rely on definitions of developmental disability while others rely more on meanings. In Ontario, there is no standard practice at the present time, but the trend is toward requiring confirmation of developmental disability as measured by formal definitions alone in order to be eligible for services.

Terms Used in Other Countries

Various terms are used to describe people around the world with approximately the same levels of cognition and other functioning as people in Ontario who have developmental disabilities. These terms

Table 1: Terms in Use for Developmental Disability in Sample Canadian Provinces

	Terms in Use	Source for Official Definition (if any)	Other Terms Used	Explanation of Term Usage
Ontario	*Developmental Disability; Intellectual disability*	*http://www.mcss. gov.on.ca/en/mcss/ programs/developmental/understanding_ds.aspx*	*Mental handicap is sometimes used in the media. Exceptional student and special needs student are used in schools.*	*Developmental disability is the term used by the Ontario government and is widely used in social services, in the media, and by the general public. Intellectual disability is increasingly being used as well, and its meaning is virtually the same as developmental disability.*
Alberta	*Developmental Disability; Cognitive disability*	*http://www.seniors. gov.ab.ca/pdd/policies/CISF.pdf* *http://education. alberta.ca/admin/ special/programming/ access.aspx*	*Intellectual disability is sometimes used*	*Developmental disability is used by the Alberta government Persons with Developmental Disabilities (PDD) program that supports adults. The Alberta Education Ministry uses the term cognitive disability.*
British Columbia	*Developmental Disability*	*Community Living British Columbia*	*Intellectual disability is used more in the academic world*	*Developmental disability is the term used in the Community Living Authority Act, and defined very narrowly using DSM-IV. Initially, it had a more open definition, but after a court case regarding IQ as criteria the definition was tightened.*
Manitoba	*Mental Disability and Intellectual Disability are both used, but mainly Mental Disability*	*http://www.gov. mb.ca/fs/pwd/supported_living.html* *The Vulnerable Persons Living with a Mental Disability Act*	*Manitoba's legislation uses the term vulnerable person, with a definition of mental disability.*	*Our legislation uses the term vulnerable person with a definition of mental disability (significantly impaired intellectual functioning existing concurrently with impaired adaptive behaviour and manifested prior to the age of 18 years), and much of our historical and on-line material uses the term mental disability as well. Increasingly, though, in our internal documents and reports, we are using the term intellectual disability. It seems more respectful.*

Table 1b: Terms in Use for Developmental Disability in Other Countries

	Terms in Use	Source for Official Definition (if any)	Other Terms Used	Explanation of Term Usage
Australia and New Zealand	*Intellectual disability*	*Australian Institute of Health and Welfare http://www.aihw. gov.au/publications/ hwi/109/11794.pdf*	*Developmental disabilities; developmental delay*	*In Australia and New Zealand, the term most widely used in legislation, service policy, and statutory data collection is Intellectual Disability. Sometimes, developmental disability is also used to denote a much wider group of people, many of whom do not necessarily have a cognitive impairment (e.g., Cerebral Palsy, Spinabifida, etc.). Developmental delay is applicable to children aged 0-5 only, and is used to identify conditions appearing in the early developmental period, but with no specific diagnosis.*
Austria	*Geistige Behinderung; Intellektuelle Behinderung, intellektuelle Beeinträchtigung; Lernschwierigkeiten*	*www.lebenshilfe.at*	*Mental retardation; Intellectual disability, Intellectual impairment* *Learning difficulties*	*Geistige Behinderung is still in use in the legal context and public-administration, but not in services. Since 2005, Lebenshilfe Austria, Austria's major advocacy oganization, does not make use of the term geistige Behinderung and now uses the terms intellectual disability and intellectual impairment. These terms are now also used by public officers and officials from other disability organizations. Self-advocates refer to themselves as people with learning difficulties.*
Belgium	*Flanders: Personen met een verstandelijke beperking (persons with an intellectual disability)*		*Flanders: Personen met een verstandelijke handicap (persons with an intellectual handicap)*	*In keeping with international trends (e.g., AAIDD, IASSID), the term intellectual disability ("verstandelijke beperking") is increasingly used.*

Table 1b: Terms in Use for Developmental Disability in Other Countries (cont'd)

	Terms in Use	Source for Official Definition (if any)	Other Terms Used	Explanation of Term Usage
Bosnia & Herzegovina	*Mental retardation; Developmental and Intellectual disability*	*American Association on Developmental and Intellectual Disabilities (AAIDD)*	*Special needs is the term used in a UNICEF Project in B&H; Persons with invalidity*	*Persons with invalidity is the term used in the Canton of Sarajevo (legislation term) and in B&H.* *Special need is the term used in schools and some Associations followed by the UNICEF Project in B&H.* *Intellectual and Developmental Disabilities are the terms used by professionals and in scientific research in B&H.*
Islamic Republic of Iran	*Ekhtelal-e-Roshd Malouliiat-e- Zehni*	*None*	*Aghab mandeie Zehni*	*Malouliiat-e-Zehni is used in official services and Aghab mandeie Zehni is used widely by community people and media.* *Malouliiat-e-Zehni means mental disability or intellectual disability and therefore Maloul-e-Zehni means mentally disabled person or intellectual disabled person.* *Aghab mandegi-e-Zahni means mental retardation and therefore Aghab mandei-e-Zehni means mentally retarded person.* *These words are usually used by community people. In the Persian language -e- is used for connection between two words , zehn = mental , Maloul = disabled person , Aghab madegi = retardation.*

Table 1b: Terms in Use for Developmental Disability in Other Countries (cont'd)

	Terms in Use	Source for Official Definition (if any)	Other Terms Used	Explanation of Term Usage
Israel	*The Ministry of Social Affairs has a department that is responsible for Ha"Adam Ha' Mfager, literally translated "Retarded Persons." It services persons with pigur sichli (mental retardation)*	*Ministry of Social Affaires* *http://www.molsa.gov.il/MisradHarevacha/Disabilities/MentalRetardation/Community-Services/* *The Ministry of Social Affaires cites AAIDD 11th ed. as its source for nomenclature. In spite of this, it does not use their term — Intellectual disability.*	*The Ministry of Social Affaires has a Division for "mental retardation" and separate departments for: Autism, Physical Disability, Vision impairment, and Learning disabilities.*	*There is no general term for developmental disabilities in the government system, but that is the preferred term generally used by professionals. The Hebrew word for "mental retardation" sticks in many throats, and is considered derogatory.*
Italy	*Mental Retardation (Ritardo Mentale); Intellectual Disability (Disabilità Intellettiva)*	*International Classification of Diseases; SIRM (Italian Association for the study of Mental Retardation)*	*Oligofrenia, minus cognitivo, diversa abilità cognitiva.*	*Ritardo Mentale is the official term for clinical documentation. Professionals and practitioners now commonly use Disabilità Intellettiva.*
Japan	*Developmental*	*No official definition in law http://www.rehab.go.jp/ddis/index.php?action=pages_view_main (Japanese only)*	*Mental retardation (Seishinchitai) is rarely used*	*Developmental disability is used for a wide rage of mental-related conditions and disabilities, including intellectual disability.*

Table 1b: Terms in Use for Developmental Disability in Other Countries (cont'd)

	Terms in Use	Source for Official Definition (if any)	Other Terms Used	Explanation of Term Usage
Mexico	*Mexico City and more advanced areas: Personas con discapacidad (Persons with disabilities).* *Some rural and remote areas, and Indigenous populations: Personas con discapacidad, discapacitados (people with disabilities, sick little people)*	*U.N. Convention for the rights of people with disabilities; WHO ICF (International classification of functioning, disability and health)* *www.who.int/classifications/icf/en/* *Traditional meanings and reference points.*	*Little sick people, blind people, deaf people, mad people, retarded people.*	*Influence comes from several organizations and movements such as the social movement of organizations of people with disabilities, The Consultive Council from people with disabilities, The National Council for people with disabilities, The United Nations in México, The National Mexican Confederation of Organizations on behalf people with intellectual disabilities, and Inclusion International.* *Terms and meanings are traditional in remote communities.*
Nigeria	*Mental retardation*	*Federal Republic of Nigeria: National Policy on Education. (2004). Section 10: Special Education, pp. 47-50. Lagos, Nigeria: NERDCE Press.*		*Mental retardation is the official term used in Nigeria's National Policy on Education, the official document of the government. Although some professionals who are current in special education and disability trends would like to adopt the term intellectual disability, it will require widespread education and consistent effort to bring about change in the term used.*
Poland	*Intellectual disability (pełnosprawnoś ć intelektualna); Mental handicap (upośledzenie umysłowe)*		*Special education needs (dzieci ze specjalnymi potzrebami edukacyjnymi) is the general term used in pedagogical sciences, and sometimes in the media; developmental disorders (zaburzenia rozwojowe) is used in the medical and psychological sciences.*	*Intellectual disability and mental handicap are the terms used by the Polish goverment, by social services, in the general public and in the media. The meaning of the two terms is the same.*

Table 1b: Terms in Use for Developmental Disability in Other Countries (cont'd)

	Terms in Use	Source for Official Definition (if any)	Other Terms Used	Explanation of Term Usage
Singapore	*Intellectual Disability;* *Developmental Disability;* *Mental retardation*	*http://www.ncss. org.sg/social_ser- vice/rightwords.asp*		*The term most commonly used in Singapore, especially in the Educational & Disability sector, is Intellectual Disability. In the Medical sector, there is a tendency to use the wider term Developmental Disability. In the Legal sector, for pur- poses of definition, the term Mental Retardation is often used.*
Slovenia	*Developmental disability /razvojna motnja/ Intellectual dis- ability /motnja v duševnem razvoju/*	*MKB-10 klasifi- kacija duševnih in vedenjskih mo- tenj pri otrocih in adolescentih / ICD -10 classification of mental and behav- ioural disorders in children and ado- lescents/*	*Mental retarda- tion /zaostajanje v duševnem razvoju/ is sometimes used in the media and health services.*	*Developmental disability is the term generally used by the professional teams in health and social services. Intellec- tual disability is increasingly being used as well, and its meaning is virtually the same as developmental disability.*
Spain	*Students with special education needs;* *Students with disabilities (mental, motor, visual, hear- ing, etc.);* *Persons with disabilities*	*Ministerio de Edu- cación (Ministry of Education)* *http://www.educa- cion.es/educacion/ sistema-educativo/ educacion-inclu- siva/necesidad- apoyo-educativo. html* *Ministerio de Sani- dad y Política Social* *http://www.msps. es/politicaSocial/ discapacidad/infor- macion/III_PAPCD. pdf*	*Developmental dis- abilities is used by some organizations, and autism and pervasive develop- mental disorders in some cases of autism.*	

Table 1b: Terms in Use for Developmental Disability in Other Countries (cont'd)

	Terms in Use	Source for Official Definition (if any)	Other Terms Used	Explanation of Term Usage
Taiwan	*Intellectual Disability; Developmental disabilities; Developmental delay.*	*Ministry of Education Ministry of Health Bureau of Social Welfare*	*Developmental Delay Developmental Disability*	*In Taiwan, we have early intervention programs for children with developmental delay or disability. Parent groups in this county prefer to use the term developmental delay instead of developmental disabilities, since they are hopeful that their children will be cured by various EI programs. However, in our official usage and all relevant services for people with intellectual disabilities, we are using intellectual disabilities.*
United Arab Emirates	*Developmental Disability; Intellectual disability; Mental Retardation*		*Mental Handicap is also widely used, as the Arabic word for disability is handicap.*	*Very little work in intellectual disability is occurring in the UAE. Thus, the terms developmental disability or intellectual disability are used by the English language users with the same meaning as in the rest of the world.*
United Kingdom	*Learning Disability; Learning Difficulties*	*There are various definitions given in different legislation – some of which are now outdated. The Valuing People Review (2001) contains the most accepted definition with the UK. http://www.dh.gov.uk/en/PublicationsandstatisticsPublications/PublicationsPolicyAndGuidance/DH_4009153*	*Intellectual Disability*	*The education system uses the term learning difficulties and qualifies it into moderate and severe learning difficulties. This term refers to the whole range – not just those with intellectual disabilities – so it would include children with ADHD, Dyslexia, Dyspraxia etc. Health and Social Services uses the term learning disability with people requiring specialist services generally having "severe" learning disabilities. The term learning disability is equivalent to the AAIDD definition of intellectual disability. In academic circles the term intellectual disability is used more and more.*

have their own meanings related to the personal experiences and specific words and language used, are influenced in a wide variety of ways by social meanings ascribed to them, and may or may not be shaped both by formal definitions included in legislation or described by large organizations. Thus, similar terms can take on quite different meanings in different countries, even when they generally refer to the same populations.

There are also various degrees of acceptance of terms, even when they are used by people of the same language. For example, the term mental retardation fell into disrepute more than two decades go in Australia, Canada, Sweden, the United Kingdom and other countries, but has only recently been changed to intellectual disabilities in the United States. For example, in 2010, Rosa's Law, named for a girl with Down syndrome, amended the language in all federal health, education, and labour laws to refer to Americans living with an intellectual disability. The term mental retardation is still used in some countries of the world, although less frequently than was formerly the case. The tendency to move away from terms that have taken on negative connotations and have become offensive creates a situation where international usage of terms can be somewhat fluid and confusing.

Table 1 lists terms similar to developmental disabilities that are used in sample Canadian provinces and countries around the world. Overall, with some notable exceptions, there is considerable overlap among the terms that are used around the world. (Note the terms used in Bosnia and Herzegovina and in Mexico for some interesting exceptions.) Still, although people may be addressed in similar ways, the actual meanings of the words used to describe them across various languages may differ in many, often subtle ways. The social contexts within which these terms are used vary considerably from region to region, and even the same word in the same language may be accompanied by values, attitudes, or connotations that render quite distinct meanings.

Should We Use Disability Terms?

Throughout history, people who have disabilities have often been referred to through the use of special terminology. An interesting question is whether other people today, such as this book's editors and contributors and its readers, need to use such terms at all.

Dangers of using disability terms

Terms that are related to developmental disability have been misused, both directly and indirectly, in numerous well-documented ways. These include isolating people from their families, friends, and communities; segregating people in schools, residences, and workplaces; denying personal freedoms and human rights; and preventing procreation (Roeher Institute, 1997; Zola, 1993). These misuses have had a significant negative impact on individuals' lives, and many of them continue in some form today. Misuse of terminology has caused some terms to become obsolete, a situation about which many disability advocacy groups have spoken (e.g., self-advocacy groups in some countries objected to individuals being called "retarded" after the term took on derogatory connotations). Some groups of people, such as those who have low hearing or vision, sometimes avoid the term disability altogether and instead describe their lifestyle as a subculture (e.g., Freebody & Power, 2001).

For reasons such as these, the cautions about mis-

Sources and Acknowledgement for Table 1: *The author would like to thank the following for their contributions to Table 1: Paul Ajuwon (Nigeria), Marco Bertelli (Italy), Linda Burnside (Manitoba), Mitch Clark (Alberta), Gare Fabila (Mexico), Majda Schmidt Krajnc (Slovenia), Roy McConkey and Julie Beadle-Brown (United Kingdom), Keith McVilly (Australia and New Zealand), Hossein Nahvinejad (Islamic Republic of Iran), Shimshon Neikrug (Israel), Balbir Singh and Moses Lee (Singapore), Tim Stainton (British Columbia), Stijn Vandevelde and Riet Steel (Belgium), Emira Svraka (Bosnia & Herzegovina), Ryo Takahashi (Japan), Saroj Thapa (United Arab Emirates), Miguel Ángel Verdugo (Spain), Lisa Wang (Taiwan), Germain Weber (Austria), and Ewa Zasepa (Poland).*

use of terms that are found throughout the literature on developmental disabilities need to be clearly understood and assiduously applied. Another danger more closely related to the meaning of terms is that terms used to describe those on the margins of society have a nasty habit of taking on negative connotations because of stereotyping (Blaska, 1993), even resulting at times in people with disabilities themselves not always wanting to be associated with the terms (Kaplan, 2005). It is almost impossible for individuals in the 21st century to believe that those with lower intellectual functioning were once referred to as idiots, morons, feeble-minded, and mentally deficient by well-meaning and caring people. Throughout the last half of the 20th century, the term mentally retarded was quite respectable in most parts of the world, whereas most people now feel thoroughly insulted if they are called mentally retarded. What are the chances of developmental disability or intellectual disability remaining respectable terms? Probably not good! In time, other more "appropriate" terms will replace them because the social meanings of the terms will change.

Why is there such a turnover of terms? Because of our lack of value placed on disability, using special terms to refer to people whose lower abilities lead others to believe they are on the margins of society leads to a cycle of devaluation and degradation. The terms classify people, either formally or informally, as different. Classifying others as different carries with it perceptions that they are "not worthy" and "outsiders." Such perceptions lead others to treat those classified as different as if they really are different. Finally, treating people differently leads them to act differently. The irony is that because they act differently, those who classified them in the first place feel assured that their classification has been correct all along and that it was therefore justified. Thus, the cycle may continue. This situation suggests that terms such as developmental disability are harmful and perhaps best abandoned wherever possible.

Reasons for using disability terms

The term developmental disability and related terms are useful for several purposes. Six of the most important are highlighted in this section.

1. The principal argument that is used to support the use of terms such as developmental disability is that they help to identify, and thus to assist, people who have special needs. Within the present context, it is often useful to classify people as having such disabilities so that they may receive the help they need to carry out the activities of daily living. This help may occur at any age and in many places, such as in family homes, in health services, in schools, in vocational and life skills development programs, or in the homes of adults with disabilities. Those who fund special assistance programs and those who provide them often want to be assured that their efforts are going to the intended recipients. Thus, classifying people as having developmental disabilities can often lead to much-needed supports from those who fund programs. In practice, either formal or informal definitions may be used for such purposes, although there is often considerably more flexibility to respond to the needs of individuals when informal definitions influenced by the social meaning of developmental disability are used.

2. People who are somewhat marginalized in society, such as those with developmental disabilities, often need specific legal protection to express themselves personally and to participate fully in their communities. Terms that are identified with such groups can be used in legislation and legal documents to set out such protections. At the same time, including terms in legal documents demonstrates a commitment by the broader society to include identified marginalized groups. The material presented in Chapters 5, 6 and 7 outlines rights and entitlements and illustrates the importance of such terms as physical or mental handicap for providing protection for people with disabilities.

3. Professionals who work in the developmental disabilities field, parents, and others sometimes need to use these terms to clarify to others what might be expected of a person with a disability. At times, people find it helpful to use other terms that have similar meanings to help others understand the nature of a disability. For example, a

professional who is explaining, for the first time, the nature of delayed development in a young child to parents who have had no experience with disabilities might say something like, "Your child appears to have a developmental delay. Some people call this a developmental handicap, or developmentally challenged, or mental retardation, or mental handicap, but these all basically mean the same thing — that your child will be able to do many of the things that other children her age can typically do, but it will take her more time and effort to learn to do them. Some of those things she may not learn to do at all. However, she will learn other things that are important to her" (A. Perry, personal communication, Sep 17, 2002).

4. The term developmental disability, and its numerous subterms, are useful to classify various categories of disabilities. By allowing for precision, such classification helps to broaden knowledge of specific disabilities through research and practice and to understand better what services and treatments are required for people to live in the best possible ways.

5. Individual self-advocates and groups of self-advocates, such as People First and numerous others (see Chapter 7), take advantage of terms such as developmental disability to make their cause known to others in ways that can be clearly understood. Parent and family groups, some of which play a strong advocacy role in various jurisdictions, often find it very helpful to draw attention to what it means to have a child or family member with a developmental disability and to show that this experience is different from that of having a child or family member without a disability.

6. Leaders in the field of developmental disabilities — such as academics, researchers, policy makers, and heads of organizations — need a term that describes their area of interest and that focusses attention on a specific set of issues. Having a field that is identified by the name of the disability adds legitimacy to this area of interest and its set of issues, and sets it apart as something that is worthwhile. In the same line

of thinking, national and international organizations find it helpful to use these terms to describe their focus of interest. Some examples include the International Association for the Scientific Study of Intellectual Disabilities, the Ontario Association on Developmental Disabilities, the American Association on Intellectual & Developmental Disabilities, and the Australasian Society for the Study of Intellectual Disability.

Current Usage of the Term Developmental Disability(ies)

For children, the term developmental delay is commonly used instead of developmental disability. The reasoning is that all aspects of development are still in progress. It is possible that the delay is caused by a condition that will not persist over time and that there will not be an ongoing disability.

As of the date of publication of this book, it is quite acceptable to talk about developmental disabilities as a group of disabilities, about the field of developmental disabilities, or about people with developmental disabilities as a whole population. (For a summary of acceptable terms, see Table 2.) When referring to a specific individual, however, the practice is to simply use the person's name. The reason for this was set out clearly by the Canadian Association for Community Living (2004), which noted that:

> Intellectual disability, or mental handicap, was at one time called mental retardation. We have been informed by people who have an intellectual disability that they resent being labeled by this term. For this reason, we always refer to people for who they are, rather than by what they are (i.e., the "disabled").

Sometimes, for purposes of clarification, a term such as developmental disability is added in people-first format, as in the following example: "Sarah, a woman with a developmental disability." Alternatively, professionals who work in services for people with developmental disabilities very often use the verb support when clarification is needed. Thus, they would say, "Sarah, a woman we

Table 2: Acceptable Use of the Term Developmental Disabilities

Term (applicable group)	Generally acceptable use	Example
Developmental disabilities (adults or children)	*A group of disabilities*	"Genetically-caused development disabilities"
	A field of study or service	"Support for research in developmental disabilities"
	Descriptor for group of people	"Individuals with developmental disabilities"
Developmental disability (adults or children)	*The term in general*	"A definition of developmental disability"
	Descriptor for an individual	"Jose, a man with a developmental disability"
Developmental delay (children only)	*The field of study or service*	"Study in developmental delay"
	Descriptor for a group of children	"Education for children with developmental delay"
	Descriptor for an individual child	"Kareem, a boy with developmental delay"

support." This is thought to be more respectful of the person and to promote current thinking that the principal purpose of services is to support individuals in ways that will maximize their potential and their enjoyment of life.

People First, a large international organization that represents people with intellectual and developmental disabilities, suggests that people-first language should always be used. It is interesting to note that people with disabilities seldom refer to themselves by terminology at all in the course of carrying out their daily lives (Finlay & Lyons, 2005). The principal reason for this has been documented in many personal stories — it is simply that people with developmental disabilities see themselves primarily as human beings, living in a world with other human beings. Like most of us, though, they recognize that they have more things in common with some people than others, and thus they often associate naturally with other people who have similar abilities and interests.

Summary *Summary Important*

The term developmental disability is widely used in Ontario, and is used to mean the same thing as intellectual disability. Five meanings of the term developmental disabilities — personal, literal, social, critical disability, and definitional meanings — illustrate different aspects of how it is understood, and it is useful for practitioners to understand it as a blend of all five. There is danger in over-relying on the definitioinal meaning of developmental disability alone. Specific meanings vary somewhat among populations and geographical areas. Populations similar to people with developmental disabilities in Ontario are described by various terms in other countries, but there is more similarity than difference worldwide. The question of whether or not disability terms should be used at all is an interesting one, as there are several advantages and disadvantages of doing so. In Ontario, people-first language is typically used today to describe people with disabilities or, where it is not necessary to identify disability for clarification, use of the person's name is most acceptable.

For Further Thought and Discussion

1. Examine your own personal ideas and values around the term developmental disability, and describe the social meaning you attach to the term.

2. To what degree should there be internationally understood meanings of the terms intellectual disability and developmental disability? What are the advantages and disadvantages to having such internationally understood meanings?

3. Does the term developmental disability encompass and reflect the values you hold for your field?

4. Compare the literal meaning of the term developmental disability to the common definitional meanings for this term used in Ontario. What are some of the factors in Ontario that contribute to the social meaning and the critical disability meaning of developmental disability? How do these factors alter how you think of the term's meaning?

5. The term developmental delay is often used for children, because they are still in their developmental years. Should different terms be used for children and adults? What are the advantages and disadvantages of using different terms for children and adults? When shaping your response, consider adolescents. If different terms are used for children and adults, at what age or stage of life is it best to change from using one term to using the other?

6. Discuss the meaning and use of the word "retarded" in popular culture, and compare it to the use of the words "idiot" and "moron."

References

American Association on Intellectual and Developmental Disabilities (AAIDD). (2010). *Intellectual disability: Definition, classification, and systems of supports* (11th ed.). Washington, DC: Author.

American Psychiatric Association. (2000). *Diagnostic and statistical manual of mental disorders* (4th ed., text rev.). Washington, DC: Author.

American Pschiatric Association. (2010). *DSM-5: The future of psychiatric diagnosis.* Retrieved from http://www.dsm5.org/Pages/Default.aspx

Articlebase. (2009). *List of books where people with disabilities are shown in a positive light.* Retrieved from http://www.articlesbase.com/book-reviews-articles/list-of-books-where-people-with-disabilities-are-shown-in-a-positive-light-1530258.html

Asch, A. (2001). Critical race theory, feminism, and disability: Reflections on social justice and personal identity. *Ohio State Law Journal, 62,* 1-17.

autistics.org. (2006). *Autistic authors booklist and facts.* Retrieved from http://www.autistics.org/library/booklist.html

Blaska, J. (1993). The power of language: Speak and write using "person first." In M. Nager (Ed.), *Perspectives on disability* (2nd ed.) (pp. 25–32). Palo Alto, CA: Health Markets Research.

Baggs, A. M. (n. d.). *Books by people with Autism Spectrum Disorders.* Retrieved from http://www.ont-autism.uoguelph.ca/books-by-ASD-authors.html

Canadian Association for Community Living. (2004). *Some definitions.* Retrieved from http://www.cacl.ca/english/aboutus/definitions.html

Davies, D. K., Stock, S. E., & Wehmeyer, M. L. (2004). Computer mediated, self-directed computer training and skill assessment for individuals with mental retardation. *Journal of Developmental and Physical Disabilities, 16,* 95–105.

Davis, L. J. (2010). *The disability studies reader* (3rd ed.). New York: Routledge.

Developmental Disabilities Assistance and Bill of

Rights Act Amendments of 2000, PL 106-402, 42 U.S.C. §§ 6000 et seq.

Finlay, W. M. L., & Lyons, E. (2005). Rejecting the label: A social constructionist analysis. *Mental Retardation, 43*, 120–134.

Foreman, P. (2005). Language and disability. *Journal of Intellectual & Developmental Disability, 30*, 57–59.

Freebody, P., & Power, D. (2001). Interviewing deaf adults in postsecondary educational settings: Stories, cultures, and life histories. *Journal of Deaf Studies and Deaf Education, 6*, 130–142.

Health Alert. (2002). *History of Down's syndrome.* Retrieved from http://www.intellectualdisability.info/changing-values/history-of-downs-syndrome

Kaplan, D. (2005). *The definition of disability.* Retrieved from http://www.accessiblesociety.org/topics/demographics-identity/dkaplanpaper.htm

Luckasson, R., Coulter, D. L., Polloway, E. A., Reiss, S., Schalock, R. L., Snell, M. E., et al. (1992). *Mental retardation: Definition, classification, and systems of supports* (9th ed.). Washington, DC: Author.

MCSS. (2011). *Understanding developmental disabilities.* Retrieved from http://www.mcss.gov.on.ca/en/mcss/programs/developmental/understanding_ds.aspx

Nasatir, D. (2002). *Guide for reviewing children's literature that include people with disabilities.* Retrieved from http://www.circleofinclusion.org/english/books/

Oliver, M. J. (1990). *The politics of disablement: Critical texts in social work and the welfare state.* Basingstoke, UK: Macmillan.

Ontario Ministry of Children and Youth Services. (2010). *Developmental disabilities.* Retrieved from http://www.children.gov.on.ca/htdocs/English/topics/specialneeds/developmental/index.aspx

Oxford Advanced Learner's Dictionary of Current English (6th ed.). (2000). Oxford, United Kingdom: Oxford University Press.

Pothier, D., & Devlin, R. (2006). *Critical disability theory: Essays in philosophy, politics, policy, and law.* Vancouver, BC: UBC Press.

Regional Oral History Office. (2010). *Leaders with developmental disabilities in the self-advocacy movement.* Retrieved from http://bancroft.berkeley.edu/ROHO/collections/subjectarea/ics_movements/self_advocacy.html

Roeher Institute. (1997). *Disability, community and society: Exploring the links.* Toronto, ON: Author.

Service Ontario. (2011). *Services and Supports to Promote the Social Inclusion of Persons with Developmental Disabilities Act, 2008.* Retrieved from http://www.e-laws.gov.on.ca/html/statutes/english/elaws_statutes_08s14_e.htm

Shakespeare, T. (2010). The social model of disability. In L. J. Davis (Ed.), *The disability studies reader* (3rd ed.) (pp. 266-273). New York: Routledge.

VideoHound. (2011). *Mental retardation.* Retrieved from http://www.movieretriever.com/videohound_lists/23700/Mental-Retardation

Webster's College Dictionary. (2001). London: Random House.

World Health Organization. (1980). *International Classification of Impairments, Disabilities, and Handicaps.* Retrieved from http://www.alternatives.com/wow/who-old.htm

World Health Organization. (1997). *ICIDH-2: International Classification of Impairments, Activities, and Participation: A manual of dimensions of disablement and functioning.* Geneva: Author.

World Health Organization. (2001). *International Classification of Functioning, Disability and Health (ICF).* Geneva: Author.

World Health Organization. (2003). *International Statistical Classification of Diseases and Related Health Problems* (10th Rev.) (ICD-10). Geneva: Author.

World Health Organization. (2011). *Classifications: International Classification of Functioning, Disability, and Health (ICF).* Retrieved from http://www.who.int/classifications/icf/en/

Zola, I. K. (1993). Self, identity and the naming question: Reflections on the language of disability. In M. Nager (Ed.), *Perspectives on disability* (2nd ed.) (pp. 15–23). Palo Alto, CA: Health Markets Research.

Towards a Post-Asylum Society: A Brief History of Developmental Disability Policy in Ontario

John P. Radford

What you will learn:

- Changing conceptions of developmental disability and labelling
- Changing political and social context in Ontario and other jurisdictions
- Founding and growth of Ontario's main specialized asylum at Orillia
- Post-World War II regionalization and the creation of a provincial asylum system
- Normalization, deinstitutionalization, and the focus on community living

Some of the terms used in this chapter reflect histori-cal conceptions of developmental disability. Labels in particular were integral to the social construction of developmental disability in the past and, however demeaning they seem to us today, it is impossible to understand past policies without referring to them.

On March 31, 2009 the government of Ontario announced it had "end(ed) the era of institution-alization" in the province. After more than three decades of postponed deadlines by Liberal, New Democratic and Conservative administrations, clo-sure of the three remaining institutions established to house significant numbers of people diagnosed with some sort of developmental disability finally closed ahead of the most recent target date of 2012. This was a significant event. Among the final three institutions to be closed was Huronia Regional Centre, formerly the Ontario Asylum for Idiots, established in 1876. The Asylum was a prototype for other similar facilities subsequently established throughout Ontario. More than 130 years of institu-tional confinement had ended.

The asylum was a state of mind as well as a place. It was a physical representation of the view that people with a developmental disability, variously labelled and stigmatized, "belonged in an asylum." This *asy-lum mentalité* predated the creation of asylums and is likely to outlive them. Closing the institutions is one thing, escaping from the state of mind that enveloped them is quite another. Here too, however, there is promise. The *Services and Supports to Promote the Social Inclusion of Persons with Developmental Disabilities Act, 2008* (Government of Ontario, 2009) talks of social inclusion, new services and supports, new methods of assessment, new "person-directed planning," direct funding and greater government accountability. The president of Community Living Ontario, Dianne Garrels-Munro, greeted passage of the Act with enthusiasm: "We are past the era of institutionalization" (Community Living Ontario, 2008). Certainly, the language of the Act is a world away from that of its 35 year old predecessor, which was directed almost entirely to the inhabitants of Ontario's institutions.

Yet before we can assess the degree to which Ontario has fully embraced a post-asylum era, we will need evidence that the resources that were pumped into institutions have been fully re-directed into the community to facilitate acceptable levels of "independent living." Essential to this assessment is an awareness of the past. The notion of a post-asylum era presupposes a time when public discourses and policies were infused with an *asylum mentalité.* This *asylum era* is well documented in Ontario. It mirrors developments in most other jurisdictions in Western Europe and North America, especially England and the Northeastern and Midwestern states of the United States.

Trends over the past few centuries can be thought of in terms of three eras: pre-asylum, asylum and post-asylum. Before the last quarter of the 1800s, no systematic provision was made for people with developmental disabilities in Ontario. Some were cared for at home, others depended on charity, either on their own or in places such as houses of refuge or insane asylums, and still others undoubtedly ended up in prison. There was poor access to medical help, and, partly because of this, infant mortality was high and life expectancy short.

Then, beginning in 1876, Ontario adopted a "solution" — one that had begun to take shape in parts of England and the United States a few years earlier: the specialized institution designed specifically to accommodate people considered to be "idiots" and later as "mentally deficient" and to cater to their needs. This was the beginning of the asylum era in Ontario.

This era was characterized by the setting up of numerous institutions, and reached its peak in Ontario in the years after World War II. By the 1960s, though, it was apparent that attitudes were changing and new policies were required. Thus began the *post-asylum era,* an era that saw gradual acceptance of the closure of institutions. Today, with all of Ontario's institutions closed, we are now fully entering into this era.

These three eras will be dealt with in more detail below. For the moment, it is sufficient to appreciate that, looking back over the past 150 years, we see a dominant middle phase over which looms the spectre of the asylum. This *asylum era* defined the other two phases — one preceding it, the other involving its demise. Indeed, in some ways the whole process is circular: the opening and expansion of the asylums, their establishment as a "norm" for people diagnosed with what we would now call developmental disabilities, and the retreat from the asylum model that is still continuing.

The attitude and policy shifts that accompanied these changes were clearly part of much broader social and political forces that affected society in general. But they also reflected specific changes in conceptualizations of developmental disability as a phenomenon. This is strikingly indicated by shifts in language, especially labelling. Historically, the most durable term was *idiot,* a word that was well-established in medieval England. Although it continued to be used until recently, the term idiot reflected the prevailing pre-1930 view of a "condition" with a single etiology. Precisely what "caused" this condition, however, remained a mystery, and the attention of medical and educational professionals tended to focus on quantifying degrees of "idiocy." This focus on degree of idiocy gave rise to the identification of the *imbecile,* a person not severely affected but still lacking the ability to lead an independent life. In the early years of the twentieth century, a preoccupation among the middle class with *mental deficiency* and *feeblemindedness* led researchers to identify the "moron" as a hidden group with "subnormal" intelligence apparently lurking within society's "prob-

Table 1: Historical Roles Imposed on People with Developmental Disabilities

A Subhuman Organism	*Animal-like or a "vegetable"*
A Menace	*An "alien" or a genetic threat to civilization*
An Object of Dread	*Sent as God's punishment; possibly a "changeling"*
An Object of Pity	*An unfortunate person, deserving charity*
A Holy Innocent	*Sent by God for some special purpose and incapable of sin*
A Diseased Organism	*Sick and probably incurable*
An Object of Ridicule	*The "village idiot" or "court fool" or "jester"*
An Eternal Child	*Persistently "subnormal," the victim of "arrested development"*

Source: Wolfensberger (1972).

lem populations." Closer to our own time, the term "mental retardation" was standard for many decades, and is still used in some parts of the United States and elsewhere even today, though much in dispute. In Canada, mental retardation was replaced for a time by *mental handicap* or *developmental handicap*, but today the preferred terms are *developmental* or *intellectual disability*.

It is impossible to understand the way society thought about developmental disability in the past without referring to the terms that were in common use at particular times. These terms are cultural phenomena (inventions or constructions of reality) that tell us more about the societies that used them than about the nature of developmental disability itself. The fact that most of them seem to us highly derogatory and discriminatory is just one indication of how our attitudes have changed.

Before the Asylum

Our simple three-stage chronology serves to structure this discussion, but we should avoid thinking of the pre-asylum era as a time of steady progression toward an era that would be characterized by large asylums for people with developmental disabilities. The pre-asylum era was, in fact, characterized by numerous social undercurrents and a wide variety of attitudes. Wolfensberger (1972) has rendered this complexity into eight stereotypes — eight ways that disability was commonly viewed (see Table 1). His

argument is grounded in the sociological literature on deviancy, and he suggested that people with developmental disabilities, like other groups regarded as deviant, have had certain role-perceptions thrust upon them with little objective verification.

Some people would now object to describing a person with a developmental disability as in any way "deviant," but Wolfensberger's contribution was an important one. It recognized that not all of the characteristics of "mental retardation" were medical or genetic, but that many were constructed and imposed on people with disabilities by society. Social expectations were seen as playing a key role in moulding individual behaviour and personal expectations. It also recognized that many of the role-expectations that society held for people with developmental disabilities were also held for other minority or disadvantaged groups. Thus, it broke through some of the barriers that had isolated the study of disability, keeping it an academic and social backwater unworthy of the attention of serious researchers. This, in turn, paved the way for Wolfensberger's own presentation of *normalization*, referred to later in this chapter, out of which the human rights perspective was later to emerge.

It is important to note that the eight stereotypes in Table 1 are not listed in any progression. The role-expectations are often contradictory, yet they have often co-existed in the same society. Some are benevolent — if patronizing — while others are embedded in hostility. What they all share is the

Figure 1. The Orillia Asylum (1914).

idea of the person with a developmental disability as "the other," as "different," and not as one of "us." Even before the asylum, the dominant social traditions were characterized by exclusion.

The Asylum Era

The asylum was conceived by its instigators as an instrument of reform. Without abandoning the idea of "difference," the early asylum advocates saw a need for specialized training facilities that would prepare people with severe developmental disabilities for a life in the world outside. The outworn stereotypes were to be abandoned in favour of a "modern" approach. The pioneers of this thinking in the 1850s had the decades of experience with the mental illness asylums to guide them, and undoubtedly their professional ambitions played a part in fostering enthusiasm for new facilities in which they could develop their expertise. Also, the managers of the mental illness asylums were complaining that people with developmental disabilities with whom they were burdened were not responsive to their treatment programs, seemed largely "incurable" and were therefore wasting the energies of their staffs. Wherever possible, *mental defectives* — as opposed to those diagnosed as mentally ill — were placed in separate annexes or wings of the "insane asylums," where they often received nothing more than custodial care. Specialized institutions for people diagnosed as "mentally deficient" seemed to be the answer.

The initial focus was on highly disabled children, so-called *idiots*. These people, it was quite suddenly claimed in the middle of the 19th century, could be intensively trained and educated within a controlled environment and prepared for a greatly enhanced future life in the community.

This movement gave rise to a small profession of sorts (a handful of physicians) and to the construction of several asylums in England and the United States. But the optimism of the pioneers was short-lived. The old stereotypes proved durable, and the reformers were unable to demonstrate many successes. The need to justify their existence as therapeutic facilities led, in some cases, to setting up demonstration projects where education programs were applied only to the least disabled children. Gradually, the ideal of habilitation faded, and the managers resigned themselves to a custodial, rather than an educational, role. The asylums became places in which people grew old, and this was a powerful social symbol that *mental deficiency* was both permanent and incurable.

It has already been noted that the asylum era was marked as much by attitudes as by buildings. Only a small proportion of people diagnosed as *mentally deficient* were actually institutionalized, but this was due mainly to lack of space and resistance to the level of public spending that would have been required. It was widely agreed that, in a perfect society, all such people would be "put away," and it was often said of those who remained in the community that they "belonged in an asylum." The asylums created a place for mental deficiency within the social order, and it was widely believed that this place was both proper and beneficial, not only for society but also for those who were "mentally deficient."

By the time Ontario opened its first specialized mental deficiency asylum in 1876, the early era of optimism in England and the northern United States was largely over. The Ontario Asylum for Idiots initially occupied a building that had functioned earlier as a branch of the Toronto Lunatic Asylum on a plot of land on Lake Couchiching near the centre of Orillia. Its capacity of 150 "patients" was soon exceeded, and in 1885 the government purchased 150 acres of land a mile south of the town for development as a large custodial institution. Frequent expansion of the site and construction of new buildings brought the "patient" capacity to 1,916 by 1934. By the time it reached its peak population of 2,800 in 1961, thousands of people diagnosed as *mentally deficient* had lived out their entire lives in these

segregated facilities. "Patients," separated according to gender and diagnosis, were allocated beds in one of more than a dozen buildings, some of which contained several wings and corridors. The staff numbered 1,120 and, in addition to the 120 acres occupied by buildings, the facility had 318 acres that "patients" used for growing crops, and a further 220 acres of bush (see Figure 1).

The facility at Orillia remained the only large asylum in Ontario until the 1950s, although smaller institutions had opened in Woodstock in 1905 and Cobourg in 1920. Plans to develop a large asylum at Smiths Falls date back at least to 1934; however, the asylum did not open until 1951, one year after another small institution had opened in Aurora. The Smiths Falls institution, later called Rideau Regional Centre, quickly became the second largest facility in Ontario with a capacity of over two thousand. Many other facilities were opened over the next 20 years, reflecting a concerted effort by the Ontario government to effect a program of regionalization (see Table 2 and Figure 2). At the height of the asylum era, about 1970, Ontario had 20 institutions, almost half the number that existed in Canada (see Table 3).

The reasons for continued demand for increased space at Orillia in the first half of the 20th century were partly demographic. Not only was Ontario's population increasing, but also medical improvements extended life expectancy for vulnerable people. However, political and social changes were more important. Beginning around the turn of the century, some of the earlier stereotypes were newly reinforced by "scientific" research. Social Darwinists suggested that too many of the "unfit" were surviving beyond infancy, resulting in larger numbers of disabled people requiring care. An influential body of opinion argued for limiting the birth rate of people with low intelligence. The rise of intelligence testing, applied to recent immigrants as well as schoolchildren, and the medical testing of military recruits, suggested that the overall level of intelligence of the population was at stake. This line of thinking was common in Britain, the United States, Canada, and elsewhere. It placed the so-called *feebleminded* at the centre of the eugenic movement.

Table 2: Ontario Institutions

Huronia Regional Centre[1], Orillia
   Opened: 1876
   1971 resident population: 1857

   Designated as a Hospital School. Originally known as the Orillia Asylum for Idiots, this facility served all of Ontario for most of its history. By 1970, the catchment admission area was narrowed to accommodate individuals from Halton, Peel, York, Simcoe, Muskoka and Parry Sound. Classified as a residential facility providing medical intervention, education and training to people with mild, moderate, severe and profound disabilities of all ages.

Oxford Regional Centre[2], Woodstock
   Opened: 1905
   1971 resident population: 317

   Designated as a Mental Retardation Unit in a Psychiatric Hospital. Originally designed to accommodate epileptics and TB patients from the Orillia facility, care was also provided to residents classed as "ambulatory epileptics." Residents came from all parts of Ontario and ranged in age from 45 to 55 years.

D'Arcy Place[2], Cobourg
   Opened: 1920
   1971 resident population: 281

   Designated an Ontario Hospital (Mental Retardation Services Branch). Constructed in 1900 as a school and turned into a hospital in 1915. Became a mental hospital in 1920. Was appropriated to serve the southeastern planning area of Ontario and to provide training and rehabilitation for women over 16 years of age. A population with social and behavioural problems and some psychoses came to dominate this facility.

Pine Ridge Centre[2], Aurora
   Opened: 1950
   1971 resident population: 190

   Designated an Ontario Hospital (Mental Retardation Services Branch). Constructed in 1915 as a school for boys, the facility was taken over in 1950 to ease overcrowding at Orillia. Accommodation was for males from 16 years of age. Ambulatory care was provided for those with serious disabilities. Referrals came from all of Ontario.

Rideau Regional Centre[1], Smiths Falls
   Opened: 1951
   1971 resident population: 2070

   Designated as a Hospital School. Intended to serve the southeastern and northeastern region of Ontario. Designed as a residential facility for people of all ages and all degrees of disability.

Durham Regional Centre[2], Whitby
   Opened: 1950s

   Provided diagnostic and counselling services for Victoria and Durham counties,as well as institutional placement.

Northwestern Regional Centre[2], Lakehead
   Opened: 1960s
   1971 resident population: 300

   Designated as a Mental Retardation Unit in a Psychiatric Hospital. Located in the northwestern planning region of Ontario, accommodation provided for children classified as ambulatory, educable and trainable. The adult unit had a capacity of 160 for the purpose of rehabilitation.

Surrey Place Centre[5], Toronto
   Opened: 1960s

   Designated as a Diagnostic Centre. It remains open as an assessment, service, and research centre.

Children's Psychiatric Research Institution[6] London
   Opened: 1960

   Designated as a Diagnostic Centre. This was the first community-centred psychiatric hospital designed for the treatment of "mentally retarded" children. This research institute provides primarily an out-patient service, but has accommodation for in-patient services.

Cedar Springs (Southwestern Regional Centre)[1], Blenheim
   Opened: 1960
   1971 resident population: 937

   Designated as a Hospital School. Catchment area included the southwestern portion of Ontario but experienced difficulty in procuring community contact owing to its isolated location. Care was provided for all degrees of mental and physical disability as well as out-patient services for Kent County.

Muskoka Centre[2], Gravenhurst

Opened: 1963

1971 resident population: 358

Established and administered as an extension to Orillia to relieve overcrowding. Care was provided to infants, adolescents, adults and geriatrics with varying degrees of disability. Residents were predominantly female. A travelling clinical team serviced Simcoe, Muskoka, Parry Sound and the northern portions of Ontario.

Midwestern Regional Centre[2], Palmerston

Opened: 1965

1971 resident population: 216

Designated as a Hospital School. Intended as a residential facility for children over six years of age, it was outmoded by 1971 owing to the influx of an adult population. Designated to service the southwestern region of Ontario.

Adult Occupational Centre[2], Edgar

Opened: 1966

1971 resident population: 250

Designated an Adult Occupational Centre. While originally a radar station, it became co-educational and a community preparation facility for young adults diagnosed with mild intellectual disabilities. Its goal was community placement.

Prince Edward Heights[2], Picton

Opened: 1970

1971 resident population: 60

Designated an Adult Occupational Centre. Designed to serve the Lake Ontario planning region,accommodation was made for people at all levels of disability. Facility was designed to house 600.

Penrose Division of the Ongwananda Hospital[2], Kingston

Opened: 1970

1971 resident population: 140

Designated as a Mental Retardation Unit in a Psychiatric Hospital. Located in the southeastern planning region of Ontario; accommodation was provided for young adults with any degree of disability, but individuals were required to be ambulatory. Also known as Ongwanada Sanatorium.

Other centres 1950 to 1980

Bethesda Home, Vineland[3]

Blue Water Centre, Goderich[3]

Brantwood Resident Development Centre, Brantford[3]

Centre for the Developmentally Challenged, Thunder Bay

Chistopher Robin Home, Ajax[3]

Dr. Mackinnin Philips Hospital, Fort William Sanatorium, Thunder Bay

Nippissing Regional Centre, North Bay

Oaklands Regional Centre, Oakville[3]

Ontario Homes for Mentally Retarded Infants, Plainfield/Plainfield Children's Home, Belleville[3]

Rygiel Home, Hamilton[3]

St. Lawrence Regional Centre, Brockville[2]

St. Thomas Adult Rehabilitation and Training Centre, St. Thomas[2]

Sunbeam Residential Development Centre, Kitchener[3]

Thistletown Regional Centre for Children and Adolescents, Toronto[6]

Cochrane Temiskaming Resource Centre, South Porcupine[5]

[1] *MCSS Schedule I facility, closed in 2009*

[2] *MCSS Schedule I facility, closed prior to 2009*

[3] *MCSS Schedule II facility, closed*

[4] *Formerly an MCSS Schedule I facility, now under MCSS's Child and Family Services Act, still in operation*

[5] *Formerly an MCSS operated centre, still in operation as community agencies*

[6] *Now operated by the Ontario Ministry of Children and Youth Services*

* *MCSS: Ontario Ministry of Community and Social Services*

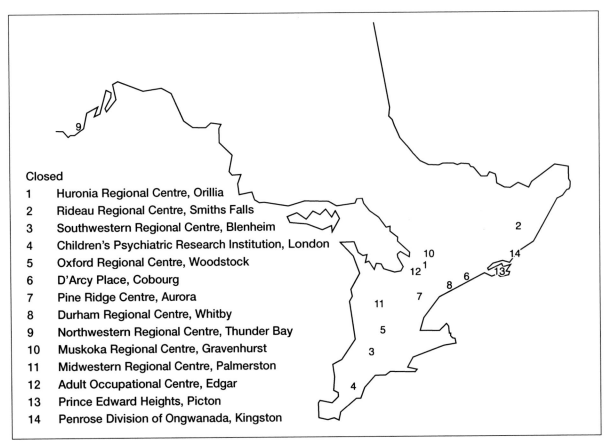

Figure 2. Ontario Schedule 1 Facilities.
Note: Schedule 1 facilities were operated by the Ontario Ministry of Community and Social Services (MCSS)

Table 3: Canadian Institutions (1970)

Province	Institutional Population	No. Reporting Institutions
Prince Edward Island	19	1
Nova Scotia	421	5
New Brunswick	165	1
Quebec	3736	6
Ontario	7256	20
Manitoba	1417	2
Saskatchewan	1463	2
Alberta	2342	2
British Columbia	2270	2

Source: Dominion Bureau of Statistics (Health and Welfare Division) (1970).

Box 1: Eugenics

The word "eugenics" was first used by Sir Francis Galton in the late 19th century to designate a policy, based as he claimed on "scientific principles" of intervening in the rate of reproduction of particular social groups. Charles Darwin had already pointed out that modern medicine and charity interfered with traditional Malthusian checks on the reproduction of the poor. Galton argued that unless this was remedied by assisting nature in weeding out the "unfit," society would continue to be plagued by poverty, prostitution, slums and other problems. Prominent among the "problem populations" were people with low intelligence, especially those marginally "subnormal" and lacking physical stigmata — a group newly identified as the "feebleminded."

Eugenic ideas in their various forms permeated British society up to World War II. Both of the most commonly proposed solutions to the "problem of the menace of the feebleminded" — birth control and forced sterilization — met with technical, legal and moral barriers. One alternative was to establish criteria whereby obvious "offenders" could be detained in asylums during their reproductive years on grounds of low intelligence. The Mental Deficiency Act of 1913, although less draconian than what eugenic activists wanted, laid the legal groundwork for this and in the 1920s, a huge expansion took place in the number and size of custodial institutions in response to demands created by referrals from social workers, physicians and magistrates.

Eugenic ideology was adopted in the United States, where implementation was much more rapid. Some states established institutions that were explicitly eugenic in inspiration. One example of this is the Asylum for Feebleminded Women at Newark, NY, set up to restrict women "of childbearing age." In addition, programs of involuntary sterilization of both males and females were instituted in 30 states by 1940. These programs rested on dubious legal grounds until 1927 when the US Supreme Court sanctioned involuntary sterilization of "imbeciles," especially if their condition could be shown to have been "passed down" beyond two generations. Sterilization and custodial segregation were jointly implemented as eugenic control measures.

Canada experienced the same trends, but generally later and less intensively. Sterilization programs were established in Alberta in 1928 and British Columbia in 1933. More than two thousand people were sterilized under the Alberta law before it was repealed in 1971, a large proportion of them after 1955. A similar law was recommended by a commission in Ontario in 1929, but was never passed and the province relied instead on segregation. Yet, given the position of numerous officials in Ontario (including professional bodies such as the Ontario Medical Association, and key figures like H. A. Bruce, Lieutenant Governor from 1932 to 1937), it seems unlikely that the province remained free of eugenic sterilization procedures.

In 1906, Ontario was sufficiently concerned about the problem of feeblemindedness to appoint an Inspector of the Feebleminded, Dr. Helen MacMurchy, who held the post until 1919. MacMurchy believed strongly in the necessity of "care and control" of the feebleminded. For her, the keys to care and control were intelligence testing and providing adequate facilities. In her annual reports, she claimed that Ontario lagged behind Britain, Germany and several jurisdictions in the United States in these areas. She believed that the two main foci of concern should be children and "feebleminded women of childbearing age." A classification of *mentally defective individuals* from 1914 illustrates the deterministic view of the time: once a person was placed into a "scientifi-cally" assigned category he or she remained there, doomed by some kind of arrested development to occupy for life a particular rung on the hierarchical ladder of intelligence (see Figure 3). By the 1920s, some of the cruder assumptions of the early eugenicists had been abandoned, but the basic ideas lived on through movements such as the campaign for mental hygiene.

The large asylum at Orillia was not the only institution to feel the impact of the increasing tendency in the early years of the 20th century to label people as feebleminded and thereby to indicate the desirability of removing them from the mainstream. An example was The Haven, a residential program for the Toronto Prison Gate Mission. The Haven was established in 1878 to serve women labelled as

Table 4: Chatham Chamber of Commerce (1956)

The following advantages of Chatham as a location for a new "hospital for the retarded" were presented in a letter from the Chatham Junior Chamber of Commerce to the Hon. Leslie Frost (Fall 1956).

- *Kent County is the hub of four surrounding counties*
- *Chatham is central to the area with a population of nearly one million people*
- *Chatham has a fine railway and bus service of benefit to people visiting the facility and staff*
- *Chatham is situated in an ideal land area with good land elevation and close to an abundant supply of water*
- *Chatham has extensive hotel, motel and tourist accommodation*
- *Chatham is near the best agricultural land in Canada*
- *Chatham is from every aspect and consideration as to location, for patient, staff member of visiting parent, the ideal place*

Source: Ontario Archives, RG 10-107-0-986, Container 156 "Retarded Children's Hospital Requests, 1955-56, Proposed Hospital for Retarded Children, Southwestern Ontario"

"friendless" and "fallen," but some of its residents would probably have been recognized as *mentally deficient* in some way. In 1909, its superintendent reported in a letter:

> The branch of our work which has increased greatly…is the care of the feeble-minded… In recognition of what we are trying to do for them in the way of mental and industrial training, the Ontario Government has given us a special grant. (Gunn, 1962)

This function was given official recognition in a 1918 amendment that added the "custodial care of the feeble-minded" to its mission statement. The purpose of The Haven was revised in 1925 to admit "retarded" children under six years of age from other Toronto care-giving institutions pending their admission to Orillia.

Not all of the impetus to institutional expansion stemmed from fear or a sense of threat to society. There was genuine professional and social concern over the burden placed on families by having to care for a son or daughter with a disability. Surely, it was thought, it was better that the individual have access to constant professional care and that the heavy responsibility be lifted from the family. Also, with an increasing tendency to look upon developmental disability primarily as a medical condition,

placement in specialized facilities seemed entirely appropriate. Many of the asylums were re-named "hospitals," and their division into wards and the enumeration of their capacity in terms of "beds" indicated a medical model of care. In most jurisdictions, including Ontario, asylums were run by the health authorities and staffed by medical doctors and nurses along with an army of psychologists, dietary nutritionists, and dentists.

Although their budgets paled in comparison to those of some other health units, the amount of government investment and staffing required to operate one of these facilities was sufficient to generate competition among Ontario communities whenever expansion of the system was under consideration (see Table 4). Even so, the facilities never kept up with the demand for placement and, as a result, they became places of last resort. Conditions within them precipitated a series of scandals that contributed to the demise of the asylum era.

Post Asylum Era

No single event marked the end of the asylum era. Instead, the transition has extended over many decades. The pressure for change came from outside the asylum system, and largely from outside the professions that had delivered services both

Box 2: Pierre Berton's Visit to Orillia

On January 7, 1960 Pierre Berton, the well-known journalist and historian, published a column in the Toronto Star reporting on a visit he had made to the asylum at Orillia. The article precipitated a series of attacks on the provincial government's policy of relying on huge, out-of-date and overcrowded institutions rather than committing resources to community facilities. It also gave great encouragement to members of voluntary associations such as the Ontario Association for Retarded Children, which had long advocated for policy changes.

In 1982, Harvey Simmons, a professor of political science at York University, recognized the pivotal role that Berton's article had played in reinforcing calls for changes in policy by featuring it in the prelude to his book From Asylum to Welfare (Simmons, 1982). Here is an edited version of Simmons' description of Berton's visit and his summary of the Toronto Star article:

On the last day of 1959, Pierre Berton, a well-known columnist with the Toronto Star, Jerry Anglin, institutions chairman of the Ontario Association for Retarded Children (later the Ontario Association for the Mentally Retarded) and Anglin's twelve-year-old retarded son Mark drove from Toronto to return Mark to the Ontario Hospital at Orillia. Berton had heard some disturbing rumours about poor conditions at Orillia and had decided to visit the institution, but fearing the staff there might not be completely frank, he invited Anglin to go along. While Berton and Anglin were chatting in the front seat of the car, Mark became sick and vomited in the back seat. This was his reaction to returning to Orillia. Upon their arrival, Berton was shown around the institution and given a tour of some of the oldest and worst buildings. Six days later, under the heading: "What's Wrong at Orillia: Out of Sight, Out of Mind," Berton wrote about what he had seen. There were, he claimed, 2,807 people in facilities for 1,000 while 900 of the residents were housed in seventy-year-old buildings. "It is distressing to visit these older buildings ... The thought of fire makes the hair rise on your neck ... the paint peels in great curly patches from wooden ceilings and enormous, gaping holes in the plaster show the lathes behind. The roofs leak, the floors are pitted with holes and patched with plywood ... The beds are crowded together head to head, sometimes less than a foot apart. I counted 90 in a room designed for 70. There are beds on the veranda. There are beds in the classroom ... The stench is appalling even in winter. There are 4,000 names on file at Orillia and an active waiting list of 1,500 people who have written in the last year. Political considerations have made Orillia's situation more acute. The hospital was originally designed for children six years and older. It is now heavily crowded with children under that age ... Orillia's real problem is political neglect" (Simmons, 1982, p. xv).

within the asylums and in the wider community. Professionals and their associations and unions were often resistant to change. The main impetus to end the asylum era came from the voluntary sector, especially from parent and other advocacy groups that strongly criticized living conditions in the "hospitals for the retarded." Sometimes they called for increased funding and improved asylum programs. Increasingly, though, they argued for resources to provide care in community settings as an alternative to large institutions.

In Ontario, the most effective group was the Ontario Association for Retarded Children (OARC), formed in 1953 from a number of regional parental groups. Constant rumours about the poor conditions at the Orillia institution were brought into focus in 1959-1960, when Pierre Berton accompanied the chair of

the OARC and his son to the Orillia Hospital and wrote about his impressions (see Box 2). The fact that living conditions in this institution were experienced in a negative way by many "patients" became particularly evident in 2010 when a class action suit was initiated by former residents who claimed to have experienced ongoing abuses while they lived there.

The 1960s saw important initiatives at the federal level that affected all provinces. The Federal-Provincial Conference on Mental Retardation in 1964 stimulated research, and proved a catalyst in identifying needs and effecting better co-ordination of provincial services (Mooney, 1971). A significant milestone was the creation of the National Institute on Mental Retardation (NIMR) in 1967 under the authority of the Canadian Association for the Mentally Retarded (CAMR). Following the appoint-

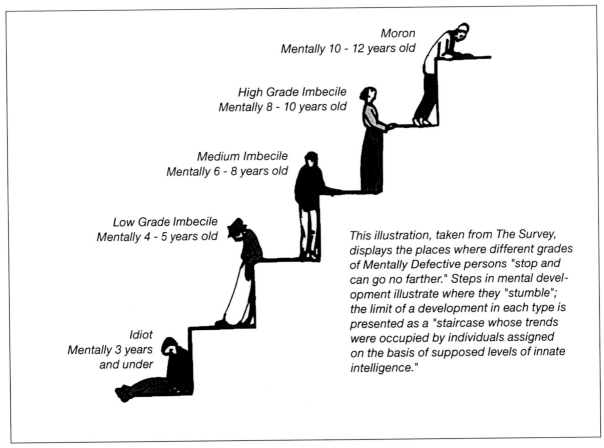

Moron
Mentally 10 - 12 years old

High Grade Imbecile
Mentally 8 - 10 years old

Medium Imbecile
Mentally 6 - 8 years old

Low Grade Imbecile
Mentally 4 - 5 years old

This illustration, taken from The Survey, displays the places where different grades of Mentally Defective persons "stop and can go no farther." Steps in mental development illustrate where they "stumble"; the limit of a development in each type is presented as a "staircase whose trends were occupied by individuals assigned on the basis of supposed levels of innate intelligence."

Idiot
Mentally 3 years and under

Figure 3. 1914 Classification of Mentally Defective Individuals. *Source: Ontario Sessional Papers (1914) 23:72*

ment of G. Allan Roeher as its first full time director (coinciding with the move to a new building on the York University campus in 1970), NIMR quickly became an unrivalled information and resource centre, library, and research organization devoted entirely to developmental disability issues.

An emerging body of theory, developed in close association with advocacy groups, lent authority to the movement away from closed institutions. Known as *normalization*, it set forth principles that endeavoured to demolish the restricting constructs of disability by altering the disabled individual's environment. In the view of Bengt Nirje, one of the pioneers in the movement, disability consists of three components. First, there is the primary medical or physical condition that is usually the most visible, but that is increasingly open to medical and other scientific advances. Second, there is

the broader environment — the living conditions, daily routines, economic status, and prevailing social attitudes. The third component is the identity of the disabled person, himself or herself, affected by the physical condition certainly, but not in the deterministic way often presented, and comprising self-images that are reflections of the broader environment (Nirje, 1969). Herein lay some of the key ideas at the root of the social model of disability that exploded onto the scene 20 years later.

In Nirje's view, the key to reform was to intervene in this complex inter-relationship by altering the physical and social environments. But what kinds of environments are most suitable? The answer, quite simply, was the same rich variety of social niches within which everyone else creates their life-worlds — in other words, a set of "normal" environments.

People with developmental disabilities, Nirje argued, should be afforded normal daily, weekly and yearly routines, ordinary housing, ordinary economic circumstances, and the usual life-chances. Similar ideas were advanced by other researchers, notably Wolf Wolfensberger, whose 1972 book *The Principle of Normalization in Human Services* (one of NIMR's first major publications and, arguably, its most influential) is the classic and most comprehensive statement of the concept and its application. Normalization, it was claimed, was all about abandoning the stereotypes and ideologies of difference, and substituting in their place the principle of inclusion.

The implications were enormous. Clearly, they would involve the closing of institutions where rhythms of daily life, the life-worlds, and life-chances were antithetical to any conception of normal living. But, as Wolfensberger claimed, the effect would be felt on every aspect of "human management services," requiring the total integration of people with a disability into the community.

From our perspective in the early twenty-first century, it is difficult to appreciate why these proposals were so controversial. In the society of the early 1970s, though, people were still attuned to the "difference" of developmental disability, and normalization was widely misunderstood, or at least misrepresented. Some charged that to portray the person with a developmental disability as "normal" was to deny "reality." Here, it seemed to the critics, was another instance of unfounded optimism. Some of the opposition stemmed from a sense of protectiveness. "Normal" environments can be hazardous, and it was considered by many that some people had needs that could only be met in the safety of the asylum. Family members who had placed their relatives in closed institutions were often worried by the prospect of having to provide unaccustomed care in their homes. Many others were concerned — with some justification as it turned out — that the savings from institutional closures would not be fully re-invested in community services. The advocates of normalization responded to this by claiming that all individuals benefit from a degree of uncertainty. They grow through problem-solving and should be

allowed to experience the *dignity of risk* (see especially Perske, 1972).

Despite all the reservations, the principles of normalization, consolidated first in Scandinavia, permeated almost every jurisdiction in Western Europe and North America during the 1970s and 1980s. A combination of circumstances made Ontario one of the first to incorporate them into official policy. In 1971, Walter Williston, a prominent Toronto lawyer was appointed to investigate several incidents, including a suicide that had occurred at the Smiths Falls institution. Not only did Williston undertake to visit all major mental retardation facilities in the province, as well as smaller residences and sheltered workshops, but he also heard presentations from national, provincial, and local organizations. Williston recommended the phased-in closure of all provincial hospitals for the retarded, and in doing so he was guided both by his personal observations and by the views of organizations such as the Ontario Association for the Mentally Retarded (OMAR), formerly the Association for Retarded Children. The result was to cast normalization ideas into the arena of public policy.

The commitment to community services was strengthened by the Welch report of 1973, which recommended substantial expansion of community programs and, in addition, proposed a consolidation of services by transferring responsibility for large institutions from the Ministry of Health to the Ministry of Community and Social Services. The latter objective was accomplished within a year, largely because it made the Ontario government eligible for federal cost-sharing funds under the Canada Assistance Plan. At the same time, Ontario Premier William Davis committed his government to a steady reduction in "hospital" spaces, and the development of community-based facilities in partnership with private and voluntary sectors. By 1974, then, a new direction had been firmly established in Ontario.

Yet the institutions proved to be more durable, and community places much harder to open up than expected. Staffing problems, funding limitations, resistance by labour unions who feared lower standards of care as well as loss of jobs, municipal zoning by-laws excluding group homes from residential neighbourhoods — these and other obstacles had to be overcome. In 1983, the Ontario government set out a Five Year Plan that attempted to increase the pace of change by setting target dates for the closure of St Lawrence Centre, Brockville; Bluewater Centre, Goderich; Pine Ridge Centre, Aurora; S.T.A.R.T. Centre, St. Thomas; D'Arcy Place, Coburg; and Durham Centre, Whitby. It also projected 800 new community-based "beds" and 750 new foster care placements, in addition to 1800 vocational and pre-vocational employment training places. The trend toward community integration for people with developmental disabilities made a further gain when the Ontario government enacted Bill 82 in 1980, bringing education for children with disabilities within the domain of the public school system.

An OAMR follow-up investigation of the former residents of Pine Ridge, Aurora, offers a valuable case study of the short term effects of institutional closure under the Five Year Plan. One year after closure, 63 of the 145 former residents lived in group homes run by Associations for the Mentally Retarded, 66 were with other community based agencies, and 16 had been transferred to other provincial institutions. Surveys of former residents, their families, and the agencies caring for them found a high degree of satisfaction among all three groups. The report concluded that the process had been conducted in a satisfactory manner, in line with the goals and philosophy of OAMR (OAMR, 1985).

Successive governments in Ontario continued the direction established in the early 1970s. Ontario's residents who have developmental disabilities have clearly benefited from deinstitutionalization. Whether community living, in all its anticipated richness, was readily achieved is another question. For example, Laws and Radford (1998) examined narratives of a group of people with developmental disabilities in Toronto and found that they revealed little real participation in the wider community, and a high degree of marginalization. Still today, developmental disability is too closely associated with poverty, affordable housing seems elusive for many, and real inclusion in communities across Ontario is questionable for a great many people with developmental disabilities. Yet today, the voluntary sec-

tor remains strong. There is encouraging idealism in many sectors of Ontario society and, in contrast with too much of our past history, overt hostility towards people with disabilities is the exception rather than the rule. The principles of normalization that underlay the shift of the 1970s are today questioned not so much by people who think them too radical, as by those who consider that they do not go far enough.

The 2008 Social Inclusion Act (Government of Ontario, 2009) provides a coherent policy basis on which a truly post-asylum society could be created. People with developmental disabilities are increasingly becoming empowered, asserting their rights, and working to create social networks. The struggle continues, but delving into our recent history demonstrates that significant progress has been made and indicates that there is hope for the future.

Summary

Provincial policy in Ontario has historically included a mandate to provide care and treatment to people with a *mental handicap*. A custodial model of care was expanded in the asylum era, a period that extended from the 1870s to the 1960s when a great many people labelled idiots, morons, feeble-minded, mentally deficient, and mentally retarded were placed in a network of institutions throughout Ontario. After the 1960s — particularly after the publication of the Williston Report — developmental services in Ontario became gradually more based on policies of normalization and community living.

For Further Thought and Discussion

1. What role did stereotypes, labels, constructs, attitudes and changing conceptions play in the institutionalization and deinstitutionalization of people with developmental disabilities in Ontario?

2. Place yourself in the early 1900s in Ontario and ask: Was the asylum a good "solution"? If so, for what specific problem?

3. Was a program of regionalization necessary in light of population growth and new patterns

of distribution in Ontario? Would it have been more efficient to have one central institution?

4. What lessons can we learn from the past?
5. Despite deinstitutionalization and a community care approach, to what degree do we still use the asylum model of care, albeit on a different scale?

Acknowledgement

The author wishes to acknowledge the contribution of Deborah Carter Park to earlier versions of the chapter.

More Resources

Printed materials:

Brown, I., & Radford, J. P. (2007). Historical overview of intellectual and developmental disabilities. In I. Brown, & M. Percy (Eds.), *A comprehensive guide to intellectual & developmental disabilities* (pp. 17-33). Baltimore: Paul H. Brookes Publishing.

McLaren, A. (1990). *Our own master race: Eugenics in Canada.* Toronto, ON: McClelland and Stewart.

Park, D. C. (1995). *An imprisoned text: Reading the Canadian Mental Handicap Asylum.* Unpublished Ph.D. Dissertation, York University, Toronto, ON.

Radford, J. P., & Park, D. C. (1993). 'A convenient means of riddance': Institutionalization of people diagnosed as 'mentally deficient' in Ontario, 1876-1934. *Health and Canadian Society, 1,* 369-392.

Radford, J. P., & Park, D. C. (1993). The asylum as place: An historical geography of the Huronia Regional Centre. In J. R. Gibson (Ed.), *Canada: Geographical interpretations: Essays in honour of John Warkentin* (pp. 103-130). North York, ON: Geographical Monograph Series, York University, Atkinson College.

Simmons, H. G. (1982). *From asylum to welfare.* Toronto, ON: National Institute on Mental Retardation (now The Roeher Institute).

The Ontario Sessional Papers provides historical detail and interesting commentary on the development of care in Ontario for the "mentally retarded" and can be located in any provincial government repository such as the Government Documents Library at York University.

Electronic materials:

Bibliography of the Histories of Idiocy
www.personal.dundee.ac.uk/~mksimpso/histories.htm

Disability History Museum
www.disabilitymuseum.org

Historic Asylums
www.rootsweb.com/~asylums/index.html#il

Parallels in Time: A History of Developmental Disabilities
http://www.mncdd.org/parallels/menu.html

Audiovisual materials:

Henry and Verlin (1994). Malo Film Distribution Ltd and Sussex Productions (416-368-4039) lends itself to an analysis of the social practice of institutionalization, community acceptance, and institutional life in rural Ontario during the Great Depression.

National Film Board of Canada (type disability into search option) *www.onf-nfb.gc.ca*

References

Community Living Ontario. (2008). *Community Living Ontario: Inspiring stories.* Retrieved from http://www.communitylivingontario.ca/

Dominion Bureau of Statistics (Health and Welfare Division). (1970). Mental Health Statistics: Patient Movement.

Government of Ontario. (2009). *Services and Supports to Promote the Social Inclusion of Persons with Developmental Disabilities Act,* 2008. Retrieved from http://www.e-laws.gov.on.ca/html/statutes/english/elaws_statutes_08s14_e.htm

Gunn, G. B. (1962). Letter to Cyril Greenland, Social Work Advisor, Mental Health Branch, Ontario Department of Health, Queen's Park, Toronto, 2 April 1962. Queen Street Mental Health Archives. (Gunn was Executive Director, Lorimer Lodge, The Haven).

40 Towards a Post-Asylum Society: A Brief History of Developmental Disability Policy in Ontario

Laws, G., & Radford, J. (1998). Place, identity and disability: Narratives of intellectually disabled people in Toronto. In R. A. Kearns, & W. M. Gesler (Eds.), *Putting health into place: Landscape, identity and well-being* (pp. 77-101). Syracuse, NY: Syracuse University Press.

Mooney, C. M. (1971). *Mental retardation developments in Canada: 1964-1970*. Ottawa, ON: Health and Welfare Canada.

Nirje, B. (1969). The normalization principle and its human management implications. In R. Kugel, & W. Wolfensberger (Eds.), *Changing patterns in residential services for the mentally retarded* (179-195). Washington, DC: President's Committee on Mental Retardation.

OAMR. (1985). *Pine Ridge: A follow up study: One year later*. Toronto, ON: Ontario Association for the Mentally Retarded (now the Ontario Association for Community Living).

Ontario Archives, RG 10-107-0-986, Container 156. *Retarded children's hospital requests, 1955-56, Proposed Hospital for Retarded Children, Southwestern Ontario.*

Ontario Sessional Papers, 1907. *Report upon the care of the feebleminded in Ontario.*

Perske, R. (1972). The dignity of risk and the mentally retarded. *Mental Retardation, 10*, 24-27. Retrieved from http://www.robertperske.com/Articles.html

Simmons, H. G. (1982). *From asylum to welfare*. Toronto, ON: National Institute on Mental Retardation (now The Roeher Institute).

Welch, R. (1973). *Community living for the mentally retarded: A new policy focus*. Toronto, ON: Queen's Printer.

Williston, W. B. (1971). *Present arrangement for the care and supervision of mentally retarded persons in Ontario*. Report to the Ontario Minister of Health. Toronto, ON: Ontario Department of Health.

Wolfensberger, W. (1972). *The principle of normalization in human services*. Toronto, ON: National Institute on Mental Retardation (now The Roeher Institute).

Changing Perspectives on Developmental Disabilities

Michael Bach

What you will learn:

- How we understand the term "developmental disability" today
- Three perspectives on disability: legal, bio-medical, and social/human rights models
- The historical roots in law of these perspectives
- Limitations of perspectives that focus only on "deficits" and "impairments"
- How the claims to human rights are changing predominant perspectives on disability

This chapter looks at three different perspectives on developmental disability, and how these have influenced supports to people with disabilities. Perspectives have shifted over time as the limitations of certain concepts of disability became apparent and alternatives were put forth. Underlying the shifting perspectives are different responses to the questions: What is developmental disability? How should we identify and come to know the needs of persons labelled this way? and What are family, community, and state obligations to this group?

Understanding Developmental Disabilities

Developmental disability is often understood to be one of a cluster of categories we use to refer to people whose intellectual capacities, communication skills, and/or behaviour are determined to be developing, or to have developed, at a slower rate or to a lesser extent than what is deemed to be normal. In defining developmental disability this way, the focus is on what scientific, legal, and service communities have determined to be "normal" paths of human development. These terms suggest that there is a "normal" path to human development and to human intellectual activity and that people who are deemed to have disabilities in these areas are somehow different because they do not fit within the "normal" path. The notion that normalcy can be reliably defined in these areas — as well as the advisability of even doing so — have increasingly come into question over the past 20 years (Amundson, 2000; Davis, 2010).

Today, there is a growing view that what is considered to be normal or abnormal, competent or incompetent, or abled or disabled is a matter of perspective — where one is "coming from" in life at a particular time. This view, referred to as postmodernism, claims that, for everything, there can be several or multiple "truths" and that these "truths" about the same thing sometimes compete with one another. The word "truth" is placed in quotation marks on purpose, because truth is recognized to be an idea or an understanding constructed at a particular time by particular people (called a social construction), and this changes over time.

Applying this to the term developmental disability, normal-abnormal is only one of many perspectives. For example, McIntosh (2002), Peters (2000), and Danforth and Virginia (1998) claimed in separate analyses that people with disabilities are actively socially constructed by others as passive and in need of control and management by others. Another perspective is that those humans with the power to generate and control the use of knowledge and language pathologize other humans because of their particular intellectual, physical, and genetic characteristics (Fawcett, 2000). Yet another perspective is that most legitimate knowledge about disabilities emerges from the diverse voices of people with disabilities themselves, rather than from others talking about them. These and other views may seem to compete with one another, and indeed many do, but each represents its own "truth" about how we understand disabilities. Together, these views help us to understand that developmental disability is not a fixed and absolute fact or feature of a person. It is a human-made lens through which a person can be seen, but other lenses can also be used.

If different lenses are used to view people with disabilities, language (the words we generate and use, and the meanings we attach to them) drive how we look through the lenses. The creation and use of language shapes our understandings about who assigns the label of disability to others and about who gets assigned that label, about the kinds of things we say about disability, about values we attach to disability, and about the connotations, emotions, and nuances that surround it. As Cocks and Allen (1996) wrote,

intellectual disability is more about language and the value assigned to those who are different from a norm, than about a particular form of impairment:

> *A history of intellectual disability is, to a great degree, a history of language, knowledge, and power. It recalls the languages used to describe, classify and thus constitute certain members of society as "disabled." (p. 283)*

In the postmodern period, scientific knowledge that assumes it can describe actual things or people by creating linguistic categories such as developmental disability is seen by many as no longer legitimate (Lyotard, 1984). The discussion below illustrates that this is certainly true in the case of disability, which we now understand to have multiple and competing meanings. Three of the most important in our history — legal, bio-medical, and social and human rights perspectives — are discussed in this chapter.

Developmental Disability as a Legal Status

There are many legal and social histories to the term developmental disability (and similar terms that predate it). They evolve in tandem with the institution of legal personhood, which expresses what defines persons to whom rights and responsibilities apply in any particular legal context. Early Roman law established the legal category of *personne,* and thus provided a legal norm from which those we now think of as having developmental disabilities begin to be marked as different. Carrithers and colleagues (1985) reviewed the development of notions of personhood in different cultures over the centuries preceding and succeeding this early Roman innovation, and showed how the category of person, just like the category of developmental disability, is subject to shifting perspectives and conflicts over what counts as personhood.

In this section, I pick up the threads of the legal history of personhood in English law in the 14th century where the roots of the term "developmental disability" can be found in legal distinctions that still influence public policy and services today. The 14th century English statute under Edward II, titled *De Prerogativa Regis*, or the Royal prerogative, now referred to as the *parens patriae* jurisdiction, imposed an obligation on the state to provide for those deemed incompetent to manage their personal or financial affairs. Chapter IX of the law states:

The King shall have the Custody of the Lands of natural Fools, taking the Profits of them without Waste or Destruction, and shall find them their necessaries.

Determinations of incompetency to manage one's estate or person were made by jury trials at inquisitions called for the purpose. These determinations were the purview of the courts and juries exclusively, but they acted on the Royal prerogative — the *parens patriae* power (Neugebauer, 1996). As Foucault (1965) argued, it was from the 14th century on that reason and rationality became the defining feature of what it meant to be a person, and culture, science, and public policy since that time rests largely on this assumption. Development of statutory law during this period suggests that what reason comes to mean is constructed in tandem with the legal articulation of lunacy and idiocy.

State obligations to people with a developmental disability were consolidated in England with the passage of the Poor Law in 1601 (Hirst & Michael 2003; King, 2000; Rushton, 1988). This statute established a distinction between the "worthy" and the "unworthy" poor, and was later adopted in many of England's colonies. Adults with disabilities considered unable to work were, by this law, deemed worthy and entitled to state provision. The law contributed to both a marginalized economic and social status for people with disabilities that is still felt today. By linking disability and inability to work, the law institutionalized the idea that people with disabilities did not fit into the labour market, an assumption that still drives much employment-related policy. As well, by considering people with disabilities as "worthy poor," the state promised slightly better provision than for the "unworthy" poor — those who were deemed able-minded and able-bodied but unwilling to work. However, the cost of obtaining richer provision was the adoption of disability as a legally sanctioned charity status, one that people with disabilities are still trying to shake in favour of recognition as full citizens.

As contracts between persons more and more came to define both economic and social relationships, especially with industrialization beginning in the 18th century, a figure of "market man," a freely contracting agent, began to emerge. To protect the sanctity of contracts, parties had to be seen to fully understand their nature and consequences. Thus, industrialization and the infrastructure of contract law that supported it, established requirements for what it meant to be a person at law, and to be recognized as such in social and economic relationships (Cossman, 1990; Poole, 1985, 1991). People with developmental disabilities thus came to be seen as a threat to the upholding of contract law — they were not seen as having the necessary reason and rationality to exercise responsibility in entering and fulfilling contracts. So a means other than providing them a right to enter contracts had to be found to ensure their basic needs were met.

The 1890 English *Lunacy Act* was a successor to *De Prerogative Regis* and consolidated legal provisions related to lunacy and the *parens patriae* jurisdiction of the courts. The legislation was made effective under colonial law in many other countries under colonial rule. By conferring a differential legal status on people with a developmental disability, the parens patriae power helped to institutionalize the idea that what made a human being a person was the ability to meet certain tests of reason. Institutional care for people labelled as "idiots" or "fools" or "lunatics" grew in succeeding years for those who were not considered to have the requisite "reason" to be recognized as a person, and thus to enter contracts or take on other rights and responsibilities. Consequently, they were shut more and more away from the mainstream of society.

The Bio-Medical View

By the 18th century, a legal perspective on disability was being supplanted by a bio-medical one.

With the rise of institutional care, the need grew for regulation, licensing, and due process in committal to institutions. The growing medical profession was called upon to play this regulatory role and, over the 18th and 19th centuries, the powers to determine competence shifted from juries of inquisition under the courts, to physicians. By the end of the 18th century, the Royal College of Physicians in England was responsible for the licensing of "madhouses." By mid-19th century, resident physicians were required in madhouses of more than 100 persons. In the same period, the Association of Medical Officers of Hospitals for the Insane was established, and the organization published a diagnostic manual that included such categories as "mania," "melancholy," "monomania," "dementia," "moral insanity," "idiocy," "imbecility," "general paralysis," and "epilepsy" (Weistubb, 1990). The manual is one of the precursors of the *Diagnostic and Statistical Manual of Mental Disorders* (American Psychiatric Association, 2000), widely used to "diagnose" developmental and other disabilities.

The idea that disability was not a status that was conferred, but was in fact an individual deficit gained strength in the late 19th century when Binet and Simon developed the first intelligence tests to identify children in France who were not progressing in school. The test was adapted and, in the early 20th century, became one of the common instruments for diagnosing "mental deficiency" and "feeblemindedness." Standardized intelligence tests were later developed for different age ranges, and normal deviations constructed as a means of identifying as subnormal those who fell below what was considered to be the normal range. Developmental tests were later designed to measure how closely individuals met "developmental" targets at each age. The discrepancy in measures on language, motor, and behavioural development assisted in defining various categories of what is now called developmental disability.

These various strands in the evolution of the law and science of developmental disability converged with research and public policy in disability generally. Many definitions were generated over the 20th century and, in 1980, the World Health Organization (WHO) suggested three elements of a definition within what came to be known as the International Classification of Impairments, Disabilities and Handicaps:

- *Impairment.* In the context of health experience, an impairment is any loss or abnormality of psychological, physiological, or anatomical structure or function.
- *Disability.* In the context of health experience, a disability is any restriction or lack (resulting from an impairment) of ability to perform an activity in the manner or within the range considered normal for a human being.
- *Handicap.* In the context of health experience, a handicap is a disadvantage for a given individual, resulting from an impairment or disability, that limits or prevents the fulfilment of a role that is normal (depending on age, sex, social and cultural factors) for that individual (Wood, 1980, pp. 27-29).

This definition, with its focus on abnormality and lack of ability in relation to a norm and on placing pathology within the individual's body (Siebers, 2008; Straus, 2010), is consistent with the language of developmental disability since its inception in law over 600 years ago. It is also consistent with the many other definitions where developmental or intellectual disability is related to "deficits" or "impairments" in conceptual, practical, and social intelligence (Greenspan & Driscoll, 1997), or lower than "normal" functioning in intellectual abilities (e.g., reasoning, acculturation knowledge, short and long-term memory, visual and auditory processing, processing speed, quantitative knowledge) (Horn & Noll, 1997).

But this bio-medical view is not without problems. Above all, it categorizes individuals as abnormal. Measurement and statistical analysis of a population can be conducted in ways to define certain "norms" of development, but these norms remain just that — statistical constructions. Deviations from the norms do not signify "abnormal" development, they merely represent statistical deviations. But such deviations have been used to describe and define normalcy. In this view, if children, youth, or adults do not proceed developmentally through a set of common functions, developmental stages, or critical developmental periods, then they are to be considered abnormal or to have deviations in physical, emotional, or skill development. This assumption, which has served to frame much of our practice in education, developmental psychology, and social science research, is increasingly being called into question (Amundson, 2000; Skrtic, 1991). It has been suggested that rather than being scientific and objective, the concept of functional normality reflects the beliefs, preferences, and cultural expectations of a majority of the members of society. As Amundson (2000) suggested, if what it means to be normal is indeed a product of our culture, then the yardsticks for measuring normalcy lack universal and scientific validity, and "disadvantages experienced by people assessed as abnormal derive not from biology, but from implicit social judgments about the acceptability of certain kinds of biological variation" (p.33). The definition of normal becomes arbitrary, relative, and specific to the limited context in which it occurs.

A critique of normalcy does not suggest that particular individuals do not have real limitations and difficulties or face barriers as a result, or that they do not require early intervention to help remediate limitations or address diseases and ill-health. It simply means that each person must be considered as a unique person. Their developmental progress will proceed like no other person's, even though at a population level we can look at trends in development across children and sub-groups of children.

Mackelprang and Salsgiver (1999) pointed to some of the intellectual foundations of a broader view of developmental theory that begin to address the cultural biases of predominant approaches based on normalcy. This work stresses that we need to shift our focus in developmental theory. We need to move from measuring the gap between age and expected developmental achievements and measuring the standard deviations of that gap, to focusing on the conditions that enable children and adults with disabilities to carry out "developmental tasks" that are culturally shared and defined. To be able to communicate with others, for instance, is a developmental task whose achievement need not be measured by verbal language skills in the dominant language. Moving into adulthood need not be defined by the capacity for independence, which would exclude from successful adult achievement those who require ongoing personal supports. It can also be defined by the control one is given over one's supports, development of mutually supportive, interdependent relationships, and the opportunity to develop and pursue a wider range of goals.

The WHO definition, its antecedents and its contemporaries, all placed disability firmly within the individual, while recognizing that it often brings needs for support from others, and social stigma for not measuring up to the norm. A bio-medical view of disability is not inherently harming to people with intellectual disabilities. It can provide an understanding of a person's genetic differences and possible consequences. It can provide information (e.g., through a diagnosis) at an early stage of a person's life about the particular challenges to be faced in communication, motor, and behavioural development, and thus it can encourage access to early intervention programs and other developmental supports. Such information is vital to a child and to his or her family seeking to nurture as many life chances as possible.

The "harm" in a bio-medical perspective comes from using it as the only way of viewing a person. This often leads to the assumption that all the challenges to be faced arise from genetic or other differences. In order to address the challenges that arise from a de-valued legal and social status, a broader perspective for viewing a person is needed — one that sheds light on how the legal system and economic, social, educational and other environments in which a person lives can determine their life chances. A social and human rights perspective on developmental disability can help to shed this light.

A Social and Human Rights Model

An alternative social and human rights model of disability — often referred to simply as the social model — has been advanced by those who find in the WHO and other definitions a "reductionist" tendency — reducing the disability to individual characteristics (Barnes, 1991; Oliver, 1996; Rioux, 1996). In a social model, disability arises from the discrimination and disadvantage individuals experience in relation to others because of their particular differences and characteristics. This shift in thinking finds a primary source in feminist theories of "difference" where the challenge is to recognize such differences as gender, race, sexual orientation, and disability without assigning social or economic value on the basis of these differences (Minow, 1990). A parallel body of theory in disability, critical disability theory, contends that past and current conceptualizations of disability and their accompanying policies and practices have been both discriminatory and oppressive, and that redress is necessary through overt action that seeks to situate disability in a full and value-neutral way within the human condition. It is from critical disability theory that the social model emerges (see, for example, Davis, 2010; Pothier & Devlin, 2006).

In a social model of disability, the "pathology," to use Rioux's terminology, is not individual, but rather social in nature. The unit of analysis shifts from the individual to the legal, social, economic, and political structures that calculate value and status on the basis of difference. Informed by principles of human rights, and an equality of outcomes that takes account of differences, the social model does not reject bio-medical knowledge of impairments and research on individual rehabilitation. Rather, it suggests that such a perspective should not exhaust the understanding of disability in society. As well, the model suggests a reconstruction of the legal, social, and economic status of people with disabilities, starting with a recognition that first and foremost people are full, rights-bearing citizens. Their equality and citizenship rights bring into question the status that was first carved out for them under statutes such as *De Prerogativas Regis*, and the forms of institutional and community care that have taken away their basic rights to self-determination, citizenship, and freedom from discrimination in employment.

There remains some question about the place of "impairment" within the social and human rights model of disability. In the response of Disabled Persons International (DPI) to the WHO definition, the term handicap was dropped, but "impairment" and "functional limitation" were kept as the foundation of the definition (DPI, 1982). Oliver (1996) suggested that this emphasis reinforces normalizing tendencies within the definition that need to be questioned. In keeping with Oliver's view, Shakespeare (1996) suggested that only by turning to the stories and experience of people with disabilities themselves can a legitimate place be given to their lived realities of impairment, as the meaning they give to their physical and intellectual differences. This approach acknowledges the reality of impairment while, at the same time, challenging the assumption that one person is given the status to define another as "impaired" from some so-called "objective" criteria of "normal" functioning. It is argued that, by their very nature, such assessments reinforce a norm at the same time as they define someone as deficient in relation to the norm. Rather, impairment is a lived and subjective reality, given meaning within the individual and collective narratives expressed by people with disabilities themselves, and those who are in personal relationship to them. Frazee (1997) has stressed the importance of creating a "culture" of disability where people's differences, or impairments if they define them as such, can be named, given meaning, celebrated, and thereby transformed into a cultural and personal resource, even while people may experience limitations and needs for support.

The notions of a "social model of disability," "personal experience of impairment," and a "culture of disability" may not at first glance provide much hope to all individuals with a disability. Many who are labelled with a developmental disability have very challenging needs, are unable to communicate in ways that most others understand, sometimes act in ways that bring alarm to some, and sometimes demand attention from family and support workers. Those who advocate a social rather than bio-medical perspective for understanding developmental disability argue that it is most important to bring this perspective to individuals who are in such a situation. It is they whose voices about their own lives and life conditions are least likely to be heard, but need to be for an understanding of disability (see Charlton, 1998, 2010; Couser, 1997, 2010). It is they who are most at risk of being devalued in society for their differences, who are defined as farthest from the norm, and who are perceived to be lacking a personal story or narrative that others value.

Challenges in Moving a Social Model into Reality

If the social, cultural, and political landscapes of our times are shaped by competing perspectives on disability, how can we best move a social and human rights model forward? Through the 1980s and 1990s, much was accomplished in codifying in law human rights protections for people with disabilities and prohibitions against discrimination on this basis. In 2006 the United Nations Convention on the Rights of Persons with Disabilities (United Nations, 2006) established a comprehensive human rights standard to guide states (countries) in developing their own human rights, and to provide a basis for global monitoring of human rights and disability. The dilemma now is to put those commitments into reality.

Although human rights laws have advanced, not as much has changed in the lives of people with disabilities in terms of poverty rates, unemployment, exclusion from regular education, exclusion from community activities, exclusion from housing, and rates of physical, psychological, and sexual abuse. Moreover, the inequities affecting people with disabilities within countries and between countries grow. The World Health Organization, for example, estimated that, in 2000, 98% of children with disabilities in developing countries did not attend school (United Nations, 2011). In the more affluent countries of the world, including Canada where children with disabilities are required to go to school, it is still challenging moving from a segregated to an inclusive approach as the social model would suggest.

So, if we have accomplished legal change that significantly addresses the centuries of differential legal status imposed on people with disabilities, what are the next steps? A defining feature of today's global society is that it is knowledge-driven. Innovation in policies, systems, and practices comes with creating, managing, and disseminating knowledge through processes that bring actors together in new ways

(Homer-Dixon, 2001). As Fullen (2001) argued, innovation in social institutions such as education, or in grappling with growing diversity like disability, requires leaders who build "relationships, relationships, relationships" and manage and broker knowledge for system change.

This perspective can help to guide next steps in advancing the full inclusion of people with developmental disabilities. In sectors across society — education, recreation, employment, public sector services, health care, and others — there is a growing commitment to, and belief in, the equality of persons with disabilities. But the leadership, relationships, and knowledge required in these sectors to make full inclusion a reality is often missing. Closing the gap between exclusion and inclusion will require new roles and partnerships for actors who for many years advocated for legal change. With that now increasingly accomplished, advocacy groups, professionals, and governments must also engage in new ways to create, broker, and network the knowledge needed for teachers, health care professionals, government leaders, and others to change systems and practices to make them more inclusive of people with developmental and other disabilities. This will also require a new place for people with disabilities, their families, and advocates in the process of knowledge creation about disability.

Just as Lyotard (1984) challenged the "metanarratives" that make scientific knowledge paramount in shaping society, so too it is time to challenge the metanarratives of disability. People with developmental disabilities are not simply deficits, needing fixing by others. They bring voices and knowledge about what it means to create a more inclusive society. Their place in negotiating a new social order of inclusion should be central if knowledge is to be developed that shows the way to inclusive schools, workplaces, and communities.

Conclusion

This brief overview of both the term developmental disability and public policy, and their historical roots, makes clear that there are different ways of making sense of the term developmental disability.

In the past 25 years, a broad perspective has begun to take shape that goes significantly beyond delineating norms to guide the assessment of developmental disability (e.g., intelligence, adaptive behaviours, social competencies, genetic structure), focusing instead on what needs to be done so that people, whatever their personal challenges and social and economic disadvantage, can exercise their human rights and full citizenship.

The discourse of human rights has not yet influenced thinking in the area of developmental disability as much as it has in other areas, such as gender, race, and religion. Nonetheless, with the recognition that the label has brought with it a devalued legal, social, and economic status, a human rights framework now has a hold on understanding developmental disability that is irrevocable. Since 1948, when the Universal Declaration of Human Rights was adopted, human rights provisions have been successively passed by national and state/provincial governments. The implications of these changes are being witnessed in the reform of federal and regional statutes — for the right to vote, to participate on juries, for access to health care, for the right to education, and for other rights.

The adoption of a human rights perspective for understanding state obligations to its citizens is arguably the most profound conceptual advance for understanding developmental disability since the terminology was first born in law hundreds of years ago. Human rights provisions have become the infrastructure for a social model of disability, and indeed have made a social perspective on disability possible. They introduce a distinction into previous debates about the bio-medical and behavioural nature of developmental disability, between an understanding of a person's competencies and what those competencies should mean for a person's legal, social, and economic status.

By stressing the value of human rights in understanding developmental disability, a social model needs not reject bio-medical information. There is much to be learned and valued from an understanding of people's particular differences and the bio-medical consequences and challenges they bring. A social model recognizes a bio-medical view as one

source of information for understanding developmental disability. But it changes the vision and purpose of intervention from "fixing," "impairments," and "abnormalities" to supporting people to exercise their human rights and thereby become full and valued members of society.

Although the implications of human rights obligations are still to be fully worked out, the vantage point they allow helps to reveal the inequalities in status between people with disabilities and the rest of the population, and among people with disabilities themselves. They provide a legitimate ground on which to restructure the institutions and policies that have brought inequality in the past, and to consider what entitlements people require in order to fully exercise their citizenship and equality rights. As understandings of these inequalities in status inch farther and farther into public consciousness, we can hope that genetic, behavioural, communicational, and intellectual differences will be seen for what they are — signs of diversity, horizons of human possibility, and a place to nurture support and foster reciprocity.

Summary

Developmental disability is usually thought of as an intellectual deficit or developmental delay arising from a genetic "deficiency" or other condition, which becomes visible in the early years of life. Stepping back from this assumed definition, we can see that "developmental disability" is, first and foremost, a term applied by some people to others. The term is rooted in legal distinctions that go back hundreds of years to a time when the state first became concerned with distinguishing those considered to have the requisite "reason" to manage property and financial affairs.

The bio-medical view, in which developmental disability tends to be seen primarily as a delay in normal human development, arose as the medical profession was increasingly called upon to determine to whom the category would be applied. A social and human rights model of disability has more recently emerged to question the exclusive focus in a bio-medical perspective on "deficits" and "delays." It aims to shed light on the social, economic, and political barriers to full citizenship that come when a person is labelled as intellectually delayed or disabled.

The legal, bio-medical, and human rights perspectives on disability all underlie public policies for people with developmental disabilities. There has been a gradual shift in public policy from "care" for people with developmental disabilities to policies that enable greater social and economic inclusion of such people. However, concerns are growing that there is a "re-medicalization" of disability underway that will be used to distinguish between those who are deemed worthy of public support and those who are not. With human rights commitments now in place, the next step is to develop the knowledge needed for all sectors of society to build inclusive policies and practices that enable people with developmental disabilities to take their rightful place.

Acknowledgement

The author is grateful to Maureen Connolly and Ivan Brown for their helpful suggestions for additions to the chapter.

For Further Thought and Discussion

1. Why do you think it is that a person with a disability has a right to health care and medical interventions in many countries (even if this right is not always fulfilled), but can only obtain disability-related supports as a matter of charity?
2. What arguments would you use to encourage a potential employer who would like to hire a person with a disability, but who is concerned about the functional and behavioural assessments provided by a vocational counsellor?
3. You are supporting a young person with a developmental disability and her parents. The mother is three months pregnant and finds out that her second child will have Down syndrome. The mother turns to you for advice on whether she should abort her fetus. How do you counsel her?
4. Children have a right to education. But some are excluded from attending their neighbourhood school because they do not have the communication capacities or the needed augmentative communication systems are considered too expensive or cumbersome in the classroom. Should education be a matter of right or of capacity? Can functional and other bio-medical assessments be used to help a child and a school to more fully exercise the right to education? In what ways might they undermine the possibility of full inclusion?
5. What is the difference between a physician's knowledge about the human rights of a person with a disability, knowledge about how to provide medical care to a person with a developmental disability, and knowledge about how to ensure that a person with a developmental disability can access the physician's office and be supported to make health care decisions?

More Resources

Inclusion International. (1994). *Just technology? From principles to practice in bio-ethical issues.* Toronto, ON, Canada: The Roeher Institute.

Ingstad, B., & Whyte, S. R. (Eds.). (2001). *Disability and culture.* Berkeley, CA: University of California Press.

Renwick, R., Brown, I., & Nagler, M. (1996). *Quality of life in health promotion and rehabilitation: Conceptual approaches, issues, and applications.* Thousand Oaks, CA: Sage Publications.

Rioux, M., & Bach, M. (1994). *Disability is not measles: New research paradigms in disability.* Toronto, ON: The Roeher Institute.

Shakespeare, T. (2010). The social model of disability. In L. J. Davis (Ed.), *The disability studies reader* (3rd ed.) (pp. 266-273). New York: Routledge.

Taylor, S. J., Bogdan, R., & Lutfiyya, Z. (Eds.). (1995). *The variety of community experience: Qualitative studies of family and community experience.* Baltimore: Paul H. Brookes Publishing.

The Roeher Institute. (1997). *Disability, community and society: Exploring the links.* Toronto, ON: Author.

The Roeher Institute. (1993). *Social well-being: A*

paradigm for reform. Toronto, ON: Author.

The Roeher Institute. (1992). *On target? Canada's employment-related programs for persons with disabilities.* Toronto, ON: Author.

The Roeher Institute. (1991). *Changing Canadian schools: Perspectives on disability and inclusion.* Toronto, ON: Author.

United Nations. (1988). *Human rights: A compilation of international instruments.* New York: Author.

References

American Psychiatric Association. (2000). *Diagnostic and statistical manual of mental disorders* (4th ed., text rev.). Washington, DC: Author.

Amundson, R. (2000). Against normal function. *Studies in History and Philosophy of Biomedical Science, 31*, 33-53.

Barnes, C. (1991). *Disabled people in Britain and discrimination.* London, UK: Hurst & Co.

Carrithers, M., Collins, S., & Lukes, S. (1985). *The category of the person: Anthropology, philosophy, history.* New York: Cambridge University Press.

Charlton, J. (1998). *Nothing about us without us: Disability, oppression and empowerment.* Berkeley, CA: University of California Press.

Charlton, J. (2010). The dimensions of disability oppression. In L. J. Davis (Ed.), *The disability studies reader* (3rd ed.) (pp. 52-62). New York: Routledge.

Cocks, E., & Allen, M. (1996). Discourses of disability. In E. Cocks, C. Fox, M. Brogan & M. Lee (Eds.), *Under blue skies: The social construction of intellectual disability in Western Australia.* Perth, Australia: Centre for Disability Research and Development.

Cossman, B. (1990). A matter of difference: Domestic contracts and gender equality. *Osgoode Hall Law Journal, 28*(2), 303-377.

Couser, G. T. (1997). *Recovering bodies: Illness, disability and life writing.* Madison, WI: University of Wisconsin Press.

Couser, G. T. (2010). Disability, life narrative and representation. In L. J. Davis (Ed.), *The disability studies reader* (3rd ed.) (pp. 531-534). New York:

Routledge.

Danforth, S., & Virginia, N. (1998). Speech acts: Sampling the social construction of mental retardation in everyday life. *Mental Retardation, 36*, 31-43.

Davis, L. J. (2010). *The disability studies reader* (3rd ed.). New York: Routledge.

Disabled Persons International. (1982). *Proceedings of the First World Congress.* Singapore: Author.

Fawcett, B. (2000). *Feminist perspectives on disability.* London: Prentice-Hall.

Foucault, M. (1965). *Madness and civilization* (R. Howard, Trans.). New York: Random House.

Frazee, C. (1997). Prideful culture. *Entourage, 10*, 87-94.

Fullen, M. (2001). *Leading in a culture of change.* San Fransisco: Jossey-Bass.

Greenspan, S., & Driscoll, J. (1997). The Role of intelligence in a broad model of personal competence. In D. Flanagan, J. Genshaft, & P. Harrison (Eds.), *Contemporary intellectual assessment: Theories, tests, and issues.* New York: The Guilford Press.

Hirst, D., & Michael, P. (2003). Family, community and the 'Idiot' in mid-nineteenth century North Wales. *Disability and Society, 18*, 145-163.

Horn, J., & Noll, J. (1997). Human Cognitive Capabilities: Gf-Gc Theory. In D. Flanagan, J. Genshaft & P. Harrison (Eds.), *Contemporary intellectual assessment: Theories, tests, and issues.* New York: The Guilford Press.

Homer-Dixon, T. (2001). *The ingenuity gap.* Toronto, ON: Vintage.

King, S. (2000). *Poverty and welfare in England, 1700–1850.* Manchester: Manchester University Press.

Lyotard, J. F. (1984). *The postmodern condition.* Minneapolis: University of Minnesota Press.

Mackelprang, R., & Salsgiver, R. (1999). *Disability: A diversity model approach in human services practice.* Baltimore: Paul H. Brooks Publishing/Cole Publishing Company.

McIntosh, P. (2002). An archi-texture of learning disability services: The use of Michel Foucault. *Disability & Society, 17*, 65-79.

Minow, M. (1990). *Making all the difference: Inclusion, exclusion, and American law.* Ithaca, NY:

Cornell University Press.

Neugebauer, R. (1996). Mental handicap in medieval and early modern England: Criteria, measurement and care. In D. Wright and A. Digby (Eds.), *From idiocy to mental deficiency: Historical perspectives on people with learning disabilities.* London: Routledge.

Oliver, M. (1996). Defining impairment and disability: Issues at stake. In C. Barnes & G. Mercer (Eds.), *Exploring the divide: Illness and disability.* Leeds, UK: University of Leeds, The Disability Press.

Peters, S. (2000). Is there a disability culture? A syncretisation of three possible world views. *Disability and Society, 15*(4), 583-601.

Poole, R. (1985). Morality, masculinity and the market. *Radical Philosophy, 39,* 16-23.

Poole, R. (1991). *Morality and modernity.* London: Routledge.

Pothier, D., & Devlin, R. (2006). *Critical disability theory: Essays in philosophy, politics, policy, and law.* Vancouver, BC: UBC Press.

Rioux, M. (1996). Ethical and socio-political considerations on the development and use of classification. *Canadian Journal of Rehabilitation, 9*(2), 61-67.

Rushton, P. (1988). Lunatics and idiots: Mental disability, the community and poor law in north east England, 1600-1800. *Medical History, 32,* 34-50.

Shakespeare, T. (1996). Disability, identity, difference. In C. Barnes & G. Mercer (Eds.), *Exploring the divide: Illness and disability.* Leeds, UK: University of Leeds, The Disability Press.

Siebers, T. (2008). *Disability theory.* Ann Arbor, MI: University of Michigan Press

Skrtic, T. M. (1991). *Behind special sducation: A critical analysis of professional culture and school organization.* Denver, CO: Love Publishing Co.

Straus, J. N. (2010). Autism as culture. In L. J. Davis (Ed.), *The disability studies reader* (3rd ed.) (pp. 535-559). New York: Routledge.

United Nations. (2006). *Convention on the rights of persons with disabilities.* Retrieved from http://www.un.org/disabilities/convention/convention-full.shtml

United Nations. (2011). *Chapter one: Overview: The relationship between disability and development.* Retrieved from http://www.un.org/disabilities/default.asp?id=219

Weistubb, D. (1990). *Enquiry on mental competency: Final report.* Toronto, ON: Osgoode Hall Law School.

Wood, P. (1980). *International classification of impairments, disabilities, and handicaps.* Geneva, Switzerland: World Health Organization.

Current Trends and Issues in Developmental Disabilities in Ontario

Philip Burge, Ivan Brown, and Maire Percy

What you will learn:

- Factors that impact current trends and issues
- A "snapshot" of developmental disabilities in Ontario today
- Challenges for the field of developmental disabilities in Ontario

The field of developmental disabilities has a set of issues that do not change substantially over time because they are core to our field. Such issues include promoting the dignity of persons with developmental disabilities as fully participating members of our society, providing needed support to individuals and families, and ensuring that services are available and accessible.

But our field has by no means remained static in time. The past 50 years has been a time of tremendous change and growth in Ontario. On the whole, these changes have resulted in many improvements in the lives of persons with developmental disabilities and their families, but they have drawn attention to many other changes that could further improve life in the future.

Such changes have not occurred in isolation. Changes in the developmental disabilities field have occurred in response to numerous economic, social, and environmental factors, both national and international in origin. Issues that have been considered to be of utmost importance in one decade have been seen as not quite so important the following decade, and replaced by others that were seen as more timely and urgent.

In this chapter, some of the main trends and issues that are currently important to the field of developmental disabilities in Ontario are highlighted. Such trends and issues may become more important or less important over time. For the present and the near future, however, they are important for two reasons: 1) they guide how we think about our field and how we approach support for persons with developmental disabilities, and 2) they provide the "top layer" for an ever-changing groundwork, out of which future trends and issues will emerge.

Current Trends

National and international socio-political trends

Changes in the field of developmental disabilities in Ontario are often strongly influenced by much broader trends. Two of the most important and inter-related trends are briefly described below.

Emphasis on economic prosperity, rather than social justice: Beginning in the 1980s, governments and other policy makers in the most developed countries of the world began to demonstrate that they were re-thinking how money was being generated, taxed, and re-distributed. Factors that caused this shift were: a worry that the degree to which governments had been funding social and many other programs was not sustainable in the long term, and that over-spending in these areas was depleting resources that were needed to provide core programs for the whole population in the future and to re-stock the economy. The result was a stronger emphasis on economic investment and prosperity. The theory that developed to support such action was that a stronger economy would create a better environment within which even disadvantaged persons could prosper. The degree to which this view was justified or accurate will be evaluated over time, but, in the short term, it has resulted in most developed countries of the world placing more emphasis on economic prosperity and less emphasis on ensuring social justice.

In Canada, this trend began in earnest in the early 1990s in a few provinces and with the federal government. The strong emphasis on first eliminating the federal budget deficit, which then created an annual budget surplus, was accomplished at the cost of losing numerous formerly-funded federal programs, and the stagnation of many others. Most provinces moved in similar directions, although at different rates and to different degrees. The global economic recession that began in 2008 added to this emphasis when most countries sanctioned large budget deficits to stimulate their economies and to create jobs, thereby seriously tightening funding sources for social programs.

What has this meant for social justice and, in particular, developmental disabilities? There have been some advances since the early 1990s in public acceptance of disability, and efforts to include persons with disabilities in society have progressed somewhat. On the whole, however, there have been no landmark advances for persons with developmental disabilities in Canada during this time.

Perceived need to contain public spending and limit public responsibility for costs: During the 1990s there was a perceived need in the higher-income nations of the world, including Canada, to contain public spending and to limit or even reduce the financial contribution of taxpayers. This perceived need emerged from ideas that were advanced and adopted by governments, other policy makers, and a variety of organizations that worked to reduce public taxes and to share public responsibility for many aspects of life with private and community interests. This trend appears to have originally arisen from some discontent, first, from governments, which considered the public unrealistically over-reliant on them to resolve all social and economic problems, and, second, from the public, who considered that it was increasingly being asked to pay for more and more programs that were not necessarily useful or fully justified. As a result of this perceived need, funds for services in developmental disabilities were frozen, reduced, or increased only slightly in most countries. The perceived need to contain public spending appears to have been strengthened in the aftermath of the global economic recession of 2008-2009 when significant economic austerity measures were adopted by governments.

National and international trends in disability

Three strong international trends in recent decades that have occurred in Canada have influenced our current thinking about disability to a very great extent: community living, inclusion, and our increasing knowledge about disabilities.

Community living: Closing institutions and moving persons who lived there to communities have had a tremendous impact on how we view developmental disability. The significance of this trend is that all persons should be valued in society and that all persons should have a place within society.

In Ontario, the provincial government expressed a commitment in 1987 and in successive policy documents (e.g., Ministry of Community and Social Services, 2006) to close these institutional residential facilities within 25 years. Over the last two decades the number of persons who lived in large, government-run facilities was gradually reduced. Between 2003 and 2009, the final one thousand persons living in the remaining three institutions in Ontario gradually moved to community living settings; all three of these institutions officially closed in April 2009.

Inclusion: Inclusion has become the overall term for a strong international movement that seeks to improve the life circumstances of persons with developmental disabilities. As the name implies, inclusion strives to ensure that persons with developmental disabilities should not only live physically in communities, but also be valued, accepted, respected, and involved, and have the same life opportunities that non-disabled persons have. The goal of enhancing quality of life is a companion to the goal of inclusion. There has been considerable emphasis in various parts of Ontario in recent years to promote both inclusion and an enhanced quality of life for children and adults with developmental disabilities (see Chapters 23 and 44 for details).

Increasing knowledge about disabilities: Finally, an important trend is the continually increasing knowledge base about factors that cause or contribute to the occurrence of developmental disabilities — for example, the roles of environmental hazards such as alcohol abuse, brain injury (e.g., caused by accidents involving impaired driving, child battering, illness), low socio-economic status, and genetic factors (see Chapters 9 and 12 for details). The emphasis on genetics has emerged from a burst of important medical and scientific advances that have occurred as the result of the Human Genome Project, advances that, in all likelihood, will escalate in coming years.

Such advances are positive in that they have added considerably to our knowledge of the factors that cause or contribute to disabilities, and to effective interventions. In a number of cases, they are beginning to have important implications for preventing and treating developmental disabilities. At the same time, genetic advances have raised concerns. An emphasis on the genetics of disability, and especially on genetics as the key to preventing disabilities, raises new and troubling questions, including the value we place on the lives of persons with developmental disabilities. Such concerns have created a need to re-examine our core values in the field of developmental disabilities, as well as a need to expand the role of ethical considerations in testing and carrying out interventions that will almost certainly result from our rapidly growing knowledge of genetic disabilities.

Trends in Ontario

Recent trends in the field of developmental disability in Ontario have been strongly influenced by national and international trends. The impact of these and other provincial influences have resulted in a number of trends that can be described for Ontario.

The changing role of the Ontario government: A trend that grew out of the larger trends described above was a re-evaluation of the role of governments, including the Ontario government, in virtually all areas of public life. In 2004, the Ontario Ministry of Community and Social Services (MCSS), the key ministry with historical responsibility for policy and funding supports for adults with developmental disabilities, signaled its intention to embark on a grand policy overhaul. This and other factors are currently resulting in a significant repositioning of priorities, which are most clearly articulated in the passage of the *Services and Supports to Promote the Social Inclusion of Persons with Developmental Disabilities Act, 2008* (hereafter the Social Inclusion Act). With this Act, MCSS set out three key goals: to promote a new persons-centred common application process, to ensure community-based decisions for funding to address individuals' needs, and to introduce significant individualized funding opportunities for individuals to allow them flexibility in purchasing many of the services required to meet their support needs. The closures of residential institutions signified both a move by government away from directly providing services to people with developmental disabilities and were part of a larger social inclusion agenda. The social inclusion agenda must be viewed within the lens of a government trying to delineate what services it will fund and a trend toward reducing expectations that it will provide all manners of services for people with developmental disabilities.

The Social Inclusion Act aimed to formalize and standardize across Ontario the manner in which individuals with developmental disabilities are considered to be eligible for MCSS funded services. For the first time, the emphasis was on each applicant's adaptive strengths and support needs and not on intellectual functioning. One of the most significant changes was the widening of the definition of "developmental disability." For example, for the first time some individuals with a diagnosis of Asperger syndrome (often likened to a mild form of Autism; see Chapter 16) or Fetal Alcohol Spectrum Disorder (FASD; see Chapter 19), but with no significant intellectual limitations, qualified for services if there was evidence of need. At the same time, MCSS signaled its intention to limit the range of services it funds to relate more strictly to social services and to eliminate funding transfers for services that have traditionally been provided by other government ministries (e.g., health or educational services). MCSS's aim to create more opportunities for individualized funding to persons with developmental disabilities, rather than directly to service agencies, may also have a significant effect on individuals' experiences of personal choice and flexibility in acquiring supports. However, the funding "pause" noted earlier may slow the implementation, and therefore limit the impact, of this goal.

In Ontario, services for children (under 18) — other than those in education and health — are administered by the Ministry of Children and Youth Services (MCYS). This includes children with developmental delay. Besides early intervention programs (see Chapter 39), one of the interesting intersections for children with developmental delay is with the child welfare system. Over the past 15 years, Ontario's child welfare budget has more than doubled as the number of children in care has doubled. Many children with developmental delays are in care and end up as permanent wards of the state. Seldom are these children adopted out of care (Burge, 2007).

How seamless lifespan planning can be achieved in this dual ministry climate continues to cause concern for interested parties. As well, other key ministries, such as the Ministry of Health and Long-Term Care (MHLTC), are expected to perform pivotal roles for funding services and planning for many individuals with developmental disabilities. Following the work of the provincial Health Services Restructuring Commission in the late 1990s, MHLTC has adopted goals of re-investing in community-based mental health services and downsizing regional psychiatric hospitals' inpatient bed counts. Adults diagnosed with serious and persistent mental disorders are expected to be more frequently diverted from psychiatric units by accessing enhanced community services (Ministry of Health and Long-Term Care, 2001). As well, it is expected that community mental health services will assist those who are in hospital to transition more quickly back to the community. Much work is still needed to support a much higher than expected number of psychiatry inpatients who have developmental disabilities return to community settings from long stay psychiatric hospitals (Lunsky et al., 2006). Furthermore, as part of the transformation of developmental services, MCSS has established four networks of specialized care across Ontario. The purpose of the networks is to enhance service to adults with a developmental disability who need specialized care for co-existing mental health and/or behavioural issues (Community Networks of Specialized Care, 2009).

Finally, the Ontario government passed the *Accessibility for Ontarians with Disabilities Act* in 2005. This Act will not be fully implemented until 2025, but is expected to have beneficial impacts with the mandatory removal of many accessibility obstacles in a wide range of areas, starting with customer services and later transportation services, information and communications services, employment, and built environments.

Given the range of policy changes that have been

or are being implemented, it will be crucial to evaluate the effects of any practical changes on the lives of persons with developmental disabilities. Some aspects of it may work very well, and other aspects may prove not to be useful and will need to be discarded or altered in some way.

Person-centred approaches and the changing role of community agencies: A changing role of the Ontario government has meant a changing role for the community agencies that are principally funded by it. The Ontario government has placed considerable emphasis on expanding opportunities for persons with developmental disabilities to receive person-centred approaches and individualized funding. Person-centred approaches refer to methods of providing support to individuals with developmental disabilities and their families that place their wants and needs at the centre of the supports they receive. Person-centred approaches imply that service organizations should not predetermine what services they believe are important to persons with developmental disabilities, nor predetermine the best ways to implement those services. Rather, they should respond in individual ways to whatever the needs and wishes of the persons they support happen to be. If these approaches are to be realized, service organizations will need to be flexible in their organizational structure, and have the capacity to respond to a wide variety of needs and wishes.

These policy changes have resulted in a great deal of rethinking about what community agencies "should" do, and what their priorities are. This has led to some creative and innovative thinking, but it has also led to a degree of insecurity by agency managers (and likely front line workers) as they struggle to ensure staffing levels are adequate and flexible. Over time, the role of community agencies is gradually being redefined, and there seems little doubt that their role in the future will differ from what it has been in the past.

Emphasis on idealism in policy and pragmatism in practice: In recent years in Ontario, while there has been more emphasis on providing support that is based on principles of social inclusion and ideology, there has been more emphasis on encouraging support that is responsive to such ideas as efficiency, financial accountability, and family and community involvement. Ontario's role as an ideological leader in the field of developmental disabilities has improved somewhat with the closure of institutions, the adoption of some guiding social inclusion principles, and revised legislation as described above. At the same time, the key ministry for most persons with developmental disabilities, MCSS, is providing fewer but more targeted services, and it has no plans to promote current or future services as entitlements for persons with developmental disabilities.

Direct funding: A trend that is influencing services to persons with developmental disabilities in Ontario is the growth of direct funding to individuals with developmental disabilities, especially through Ontario's Special Services At Home Program. About one-quarter of all persons with developmental disabilities in Ontario who receive funding for services do so through direct funding. This has important implications for both persons with developmental disabilities and their families. For adults with developmental disabilities, it means that they are able to spend more years with their families; however, it also often reduces or removes altogether the possibility of leading lives that are more independent from their families. For families, it offers a degree of financial support, but it is often only a portion of what they need. Further, it places on them the ultimate responsibility for support of family members with disabilities. Unfortunately, many persons with developmental disabilities and families who should be receiving such support are not. The trend toward providing funding directly to individuals and families has not yet been critically examined in any depth. It needs to be evaluated to determine the degree to which it supports current trends and values in the field of developmental disabilities.

Where We Are Now: A Snapshot View

Given these trends, it is helpful to take a "snapshot" look at the field of developmental disabilities in Ontario at the present time. This snapshot looks much brighter than it might have in previous decades, on the whole, although there are some aspects of it that do not look as clear.

Philosophical base

Persons with disabilities are probably more accepted in society now than at any time during the past 100 years. A number of inter-related philosophical concepts have contributed to this. The principles of *normalization* (later re-named Social Role Valorization) and *community living* have been strongly embraced within the field, and to some degree within the general population. The concept of *quality of life*, which emerged during the 1990s was designed to bring maximum enjoyment of life for each individual. Inclusion and other concepts it encompasses, continues to guide our overall approach to persons with developmental disabilities, including the ways services and supports are developed and put into practice.

Range of Services and Supports Available

A comprehensive set of services and supports, available to individuals with developmental disabilities and their families throughout Ontario, are described throughout this book. These are generally accessible by persons who have demonstrated need and are considered to have developmental disabilities. Issues that arise in accessing and using the services include: unequal access to services and sources of funding, gaps in services (e.g., between school and adult community living), lack of continuity within and among services, services that do not respond to the specific needs of individuals, and difficulties accessing needed services.

Recent emphasis on developmental disabilities

Following some funding cuts and subsequent funding stagnation beginning in the mid-1990s, new funding was added to Developmental Services in the early part of the twenty-first century. Compared with other areas of government, this new money was substantial. Political leaders, especially in MCSS, have articulated their support for this sector, and have shown this support by funding some much-needed programs. The implementation of the new Social Inclusion Act will increase the size of the population of persons with developmental disabili-ties who are eligible for developmental services and may draw even more attention to the sector.

Restructured service administration

As already explained, in recent years, MCSS has been restructured, and services for children with developmental disabilities are within MCYS's more general children's services (the concept here is that children are children). This may be beneficial to children, but leaves adults with developmental disabilities in a separate group, creating a gap or lack of integration between children's and adults' services.

Sense of inadequacy of developmental services

There is a sense that the services we offer to people with developmental disabilities and their families is not adequate to address their needs. Yet, Ontario has one of the most comprehensive and progressive services systems in the world. An ongoing debate in our field is how to continue to improve services within the framework of available resources.

Loss of advocates for disability

In recent decades, there is a growing sense that there is a loss of passionate spokespersons for developmental disabilities. Perhaps the main factor that affects this is that, as an increasing range of community-based services and special education services have been funded by government, many community agencies have lost their activist base — primarily parents — advocating for previously non-existent publicly funded services.

As well, there is an increasing dependence upon "generic" community services available to anyone in the general public. Although this trend is welcome as an indicator of social acceptance of disability, it also increases the probability that children and adults with disabilities are seeing professionals who do not have specialized knowledge of disability issues. This is a particular problem in some sectors, such as children's mental health. In some cases, staff at generic agencies may be reluctant to accept people with disabilities for services from their agency, or even attempt to dissuade them. Champions, and effective and organized political associations are greatly needed to help bring about much needed policy changes and training enhancements, to ensure that persons with developmental disabilities obtain support when this is needed.

Need for specialized training of professionals

Professional groups have not yet taken all the necessary steps to ensure that there will be enough professionals with specialized training in developmental disabilities. For example, there is a dramatic shortage in Ontario of health care professionals trained in developmental disabilities (psychiatrists, family physicians, nurses, home care staff, etc.), and Ontario is only beginning to address the need for specialized educators whose skill would benefit many children with autism and other exceptionalities. Incentives to develop an interest in undertaking this work, which is often not initially glamorous or easy, need to be developed and put into place. For example, one incentive might be providing new bursaries and scholarships to encourage students to train as professionals and researchers in the developmental disabilities field. Except for community colleges, developmental disabilities do not have a strong presence in the programs of Ontario's education system, where professional interest might be expected to be generated. Even here, some Ontario community college programs in developmental services have closed in recent years.

Challenges in Our Field

The field of developmental disabilities has faced challenges for many decades, and will continue to do so in the future. Ten important challenges that face us at the present time are presented here:

1. What do we mean by developmental disabilities? The terms we use, and the meanings we attach to those terms, change over time (see Chapter 1 for details). At times, it is helpful to know specifically what we mean by developmental disabilities, especially if it affects access to educational, health, employment, and community living supports. Two interesting questions are the degree to which we need to understand the meaning of the term devel-

opmental disabilities, and whether or not this need differs according to the purpose for which we are using the term.

2. What are the demographics of developmental disability? Up to the present time, there has been no systematic mechanism put in place in Ontario to track such questions as: how many persons within the population of Ontario can be said to have developmental disabilities; how many persons are known to be receiving or awaiting provision of services; what kinds of services these persons need and use; where they live, what their age ranges are; what their levels of need are; what their sources of financial support are; the degree to which they have family and other social supports; and what their living conditions are.

In addition, there has never been any mechanism in Ontario to track two particular groups of persons who are important to developmental services. The first group consists of those who will probably require support in the future; these persons are not being clearly identified for purposes of future planning. For example, the school system does not typically plan in advance for students who will probably require special needs support, and adult developmental services do not typically plan in advance for those who leave school and will probably need support as adults in their communities. The second group includes many persons who have been assisted by the service system in the past but no longer require it because they have learned independent living skills, or are supported by family or others. For the most part, these persons simply become unknown, or lost, to the service system. It would be helpful to track these persons because they may need support in the future, and because valuable indicators of the success of the service system include successful independent living and the degree to which family and community support can be put in place.

Following these types of information over time, and analyzing trends are especially important for at least four reasons: 1) to help plan services and resources needed for what persons will require in the future; 2) to identify those who are not receiving any support, but need to, because they are not known to the service system; 3) to develop a better understanding of how persons with developmental disabilities can be supported by other sectors outside the education and social service systems; and 4) to provide a better measure of evaluation and accountability for public funds used in developmental services.

3. How do we ensure that high quality services for many different needs are equitably available to citizens with developmental disabilities and their families? While governments fund various services for citizens with developmental disabilities these are not always equitably available across the various regions in the province. Indeed, in significantly large rural portions of Ontario, a complete range of services is either not available or cannot be accessed due to transportation challenges.

4. What are the implications for services of people living longer than they used to? There is a growing trend for persons with developmental disabilities to live much longer than was previously the case. It is also increasingly possible, because of recent medical advances, for persons who are seniors or medically fragile to participate in community life much more than was possible even a few years ago. Sometimes, ensuring this participation requires availability of assistive devices or additional personnel. A challenge for us is to find ways to provide support to persons who are living longer, and to identify ways to balance the need for this support with the needs of others.

5. What are the implications of new genetic and clinical knowledge? Until recently, infectious diseases and malnutrition were major causes of sickness and death in the world. Because of advances in treatment of such problems, genetic disorders are now major health problems in industrialized countries (Buyrse, 1990). Any changes in the range and demographics of specific types of developmental disabilities affect the types and range of medical and social services required. Thus, it is important for us to understand such changes.

New genetic knowledge is increasing exponentially. It is anticipated that such new knowledge will have a particularly profound impact on the profession of nursing, and that nurses will become more and more involved in referring persons for genetic testing and for managing the genetic health aspects

of individuals (Lushley, 2010). Health care systems will need to provide resources for meeting professional training needs related to genetics, for educating the public as well as professionals about genetic disorders, for meeting the demands for diagnosing new disorders, and for supporting individuals and families with newly diagnosed genetic disorders.

An increasing number of developmental disabilities have been found to have a genetic basis (e.g., Rett syndrome). In addition, HIV infection in children, frequently associated with developmental disability, continues to rise in many countries of the world. Both genetic disorders and infectious disease present new challenges to professionals to develop effective interventions. As well, different developmental disabilities compete with one another for professional attention, available services, and funding.

6. How effective can individualized funding be? Although no comprehensive program has been put into place in Ontario for individualized funding, the practice of individualized funding has been expanding over the years. A number of programs are based on needs of the individual (see Chapter 23 for details), and community agencies are required to complete Individual Support Agreements (ISAs) that identify needed supports and associated costs. Although MCSS policy has indicated that the shift toward individualized funding will continue in the future, major challenges will need to be faced if it is to be equitable (to respond fairly to the needs of individuals with developmental disabilities and their families across Ontario). As a starting point, a method will have to be developed to assess needs and services in a standard way. This will involve determining what such services will cost, who should receive them, and the extent to which public money should be used to fund them.

7. Should citizens with developmental disabilities be entitled to certain guaranteed minimum levels of service? There is a growing sense, especially among parents in Ontario, that services for their children with developmental disabilities, and services for families that support children with such disabilities, should be an entitlement. Parents are often surprised to discover that they are not "entitled" by law or policy to many services, but rather that they are free to access those that are provided if they meet the eligibility criteria. Increasingly, families are continuing to assume the primary responsibility for young adults and older adults with developmental disabilities as well, and the degree to which families are willing or able to do this needs to be carefully monitored.

A lack of entitlement to community-based services can negatively impact persons with developmental disabilities by curtailing their ability to experience social inclusion and valued societal roles. For instance, when few supports are available for children with some disabilities (e.g., FASD), they end up in foster care supported by the child welfare system (Fuchs, Burnside, Marchese, & Audy, 2009). Children with developmental disabilities are also more frequently put into the care of the state than children without developmental disabilities. When this occurs they are more likely to become permanent wards and less likely to be adopted than are children without these disabilities (Burge, 2007). Similarly, some research has found that adults with developmental disabilities are far more likely to have longer stays in psychiatric hospitals than are other adults without such disabilities (Saeed et al., 2003). This is in large part due to the lack of supportive housing and other services in the community which can make transitions out of hospital difficult. A discussion of entitlement to services is particularly timely.

8. Can we initiate lifespan planning? It appears at the present time that it would be very helpful to develop a system of lifespan (long range) planning for persons with developmental disabilities. The emphasis now is more on providing services than on identifying children with developmental disabilities and planning for their needs over their lifespan. Making the shift to lifespan planning may require considerable re-structuring of our services and current ways of thinking.

A shift toward lifespan planning should spark considerable creativity in both policy and practice. For example, it should encourage creative and individualized solutions to planning for future financial needs (e.g., savings accounts, trust funds, property), and other personal support needs (e.g., designating family members who will assume responsibility at

various stages of life; connecting individuals with needed community supports). Policy will need to set the environment for such activities, and the practical work will need to be done by community agencies, other professionals and support personnel, and by individual families.

9. How can society balance the need to provide supports to persons with developmental disabilities in respectful and dignified ways while following ethical and legal accountable measures on capacity? When support workers believe individuals with developmental disabilities they support are not capable of making certain decisions, they face having to act in accordance with what they believe the person wants, balanced by their own professional ethics, or ensuring that a substitute decision maker is designated and consulted. In cases where support workers cannot endorse a decision for a variety of reasons, they face an interesting dilemma of whether to support the wishes of the person with disabilities or to adhere to their ethical standards. A decision may be considered to be "wrong" because it will almost certainly have negative effects, or because it is immoral or illegal. This is not a challenge unique to the field of developmental disabilities. Many Ontarians address this by designating familiar individuals as their Powers of Attorney when they create their personal wills. People with developmental disabilities often need help managing their money, self-care, and health care. When serious circumstances are anticipated or need to be acted upon, it is a real challenge for support workers to act responsibly from a professional and ethical point of view while showing respect for those they support.

10. What are the best models of support? At one time in Ontario, it was assumed that a good model of support was for persons with disabilities to live in large state-run institutions. This view diminished over several decades and, after 2009, no such institutions have remained open in Ontario. The current "best" model of support in Ontario is to provide a range of opportunities from which adults with developmental disabilities can choose to live: community-based group homes, boarding with other families, residing in supported independent living settings, supporting families who have children or adults with developmental disabilities living in the family home, or virtually any other viable option. More specialized models may suit the needs of some individuals (e.g., people with special medical needs, elderly persons with disabilities, or elderly parents or caregivers of persons with developmental disabilities). It is imperative that our field remain open to new and alternative practice models that best enhance the lives of those we support.

In the meantime, it is important to assess our current models in an ongoing way. For example, we need to examine whether or not four-bedroom group homes are better than institutions at improving the lives of residents, and whether or not adults are best served by living with their families. In doing this, a challenge — but one that must be addressed — is how to take into account the views of persons with developmental disabilities themselves. An additional challenge, for service providers and families in particular, is how to react if their views differ from the principles of current best models of support or if they contradict the wishes and values of family members they support.

New and alternative models of support extend beyond those traditionally or currently supported by MCSS. When considering them, some interesting questions and challenges arise for our field. Four examples are provided below:

- Persons with developmental disabilities may have numerous health problems and needs associated with growing older (see Chapter 49). For example, should older persons with developmental disabilities who need ongoing support for physical complications live in group homes, nursing homes, or other settings? Should their needs be addressed by MHLTC or by MCSS?
- Some types of disabilities are not typically suited for generic long term care supports. For example, what is the best type of residence for adults with developmental disabilities and dementia and/or other mental health problems? Should their needs be addressed by MHLTC or by MCSS?
- Various parts of government and non-government bodies, both private and public, have infrastructures for similar types of supports. An ongoing challenge for financial and human resources departments is how to enable these different bodies to work together to provide needed supports for persons with developmental disabilities.
- What changes need to be made in generic community agencies to enable them to work in partnership with government, other community services and resources, and serve persons with developmental disabilities and their families in a variety of effective ways?

Summary

The field of developmental disabilities has a set of issues that are relatively stable over time, but others are influenced by current trends. Within Canada and other developed countries, there has been an emphasis in recent years on economic prosperity and economic accountability, at the cost of ensuring social justice. These and other trends have led, within Ontario, to a re-thinking of the role of government and a policy shift toward providing for those most in need and sharing responsibility with communities and families. Overall, the field of developmental disabilities in Ontario looks better at the present time than it has in past decades. Still, there are a number of long-standing challenges, and a number of new challenges that have arisen due to recent trends.

Acknowledgement

The authors wish to thank Gordon Kyle and several others who wished to remain anonymous who gave of their time to contribute valuable ideas for the content of this chapter.

For Further Thought and Discussion

1. To what degree should trends within the field of developmental disabilities change in response to broader national and international trends?
2. How important is it for services for persons with developmental disabilities to be based on strong philosophical principles?

3. Should members of our society with developmental disabilities be entitled to a base level of guaranteed services, recognizing that some will need much more than the base level?

4. Putting current models of support aside, create a fictional system of support that addresses the problems and challenges identified in this chapter. In doing so, be sure to develop ideas that are: 1) practical, and 2) work in the best interests of persons with developmental disabilities.

More Resources

Ontario Government sources of information:

Community Networks of Specialized Care
http://www.community-networks.ca/

Ontario Ministry of Community and Social Services
http://www.mcss.gov.on.ca/index.aspx

Ontario Ministry of Children and Youth Services
www.children.gov.on.ca/

Ontario Ministry of Education
http://www.edu.gov.on.ca/

Ontario Ministry of Health and Long-Term Care
http://www.health.gov.on.ca/

Ontario Ministry of Training, Colleges, and Universities
http://www.edu.gov.on.ca/eng/tcu/

Disability organizations in Ontario:

Active Living Alliance for Canadians with a Disability
http://www.ala.ca/content/home.asp

Autism Ontario
http://www.autismontario.com/

Community Living Ontario
http://www.communitylivingontario.ca/

Family Alliance Ontario
http://www.family-alliance.com/

Ontario Association on Developmental Disabilities
http://www.oadd.org/

Persons First of Ontario
http://www.personsfirstontario.com/

United Families of Eastern Ontario
http://ufeo.ca/?p=673

Other Resources:

Links to developmental disability resources
http://www.independentliving.org/links/links-developmental-disabilities.html

Worldwide disability research sources
http://www.oasisonline.ca/service-network/service-partners

Aging and developmental disabilities
http://www.opadd.on.ca/

References

Burge, P. (2007). Prevalence of mental disorders and associated service variables among Ontario children who are permanent wards. *Canadian Journal of Psychiatry, 52*, 305-314.

Buyrse, M. L. (Ed.). (1990). *Birth defect encyclopedia.* Dover, Center for Birth Defects Information Services Incorporated. Cambridge, MA: Blackwell Scientific Publications.

Community Networks of Specialized Care. (2009). *Welcome to the Community Networks of Specialized Care.* Retrieved from http://www.community-networks.ca

Fuchs, D., Burnside, L., Marchenski, S., & Mudry, A. (2009). Children with FASD involved with the Manitoba Child Welfare System: The need for passionate action. In S. McKay, D. Fuchs, & I. Brown (Eds.), *Passion for action in child and family services: Voices from the Prairies* (pp.185–205). Regina, SK: Canadian Plains Research Centre Press.

Lunsky, Y., Bradley, E., Durbin, J., Koegl, C., Canrinus, M., & Goering, P. (2006). The clinical profile and service needs of hospitalized adults with mental retardation and a psychiatric diagnosis. *Psychiatric Services, 57*, 77-83.

Lushley, F. R. (2010). Genetics. In C. L. Betz, & W. M. Nehring (Eds.), *Nursing care for individuals with intellectual and developmental disabilities* (pp. 173–191). Baltimore: Paul H. Brookes Publishing.

Ministry of Community and Social Services. (2006). *Opportunities and action: Transforming supports in Ontario for people who have a developmental disability.* Toronto, ON: Author.

Ministry of Community and Social Services. (2008). *The Services and Supports to Promote the Social Inclusion of Persons with Developmental Disabilities Act, 2008.* Toronto, ON: Author.

Ministry of Health and Long-Term Care. (2001). *Making it happen: operational framework for the delivery of mental health services and supports.* Toronto, ON: Author.

Saeed, H., Ouellette-Kuntz, H., Stuart, H., & Burge, P. (2003). Length of stay for psychiatric inpatient services: A comparison of admissions of people with and without developmental disabilities. *Journal of Behavioral Health Services & Research, 30,* 406-417.

The Rights of People with Intellectual Disabilities in Ontario

Marcia H. Rioux, Catherine L. Frazee and Lora M. Patton

What you will learn:

- What human rights are and where they come from
- How the rights of people with intellectual disabilities are protected by our Canadian constitution, our *Canadian Human Rights Act*, the *Ontario Human Rights Code* and the *Accessibility for Ontarians with Disabilities Act*
- How international laws like the *Convention on the Rights of Persons with Disabilities* affect Canada's responsibilities to protect and promote human rights
- How some people with intellectual disabilities and their families have challenged unfair and unequal treatment by asserting their human rights
- How decisions that are made in Canadian courts can have major impact upon the lives of many people with intellectual disabilities and their families — not just the individuals involved in a particular case

Note: The terms Act, Charter, Code, Law, and Right are explained in Special Terms section following the Summary.

What are Human Rights?

When a rock climber faces the challenge of coming up out of a canyon, she or he begins by looking for a solid ledge — to grab or step onto. Ideally, several ledges, each strong enough to bear the weight of the climber, will be found in order to allow the climber to gradually access the top of the cliff.

When we speak about a person's human rights, or use a phrase such as "fundamental rights and free-doms," we are referring to laws that help people in a way that is very similar to how the ledges on the cliffside help the climber. These laws protect us from discrimination, whether we are working, studying, or looking for work, whether we are customers in a store, or tenants in a housing development. They are available for everyone to use, and just as climbers secure ropes to the canyon to help others who are coming behind them, people who achieve some human rights victory, whether large or small, make it easier for others to follow.

Many people and events have contributed to the idea we now call human rights. Throughout history, wise and courageous women and men have raised

Box 1: The Canadian Constitution

Section 15 of the Constitution Act of Canada (1982) provides that:

(1) Every individual is equal before and under the law and has the right to equal protection and equal benefit of the law without discrimination and in particular, without discrimination based on race, national or ethnic origin, colour, religion, sex, age, mental or physical disability.

(2) Subsection (1) does not preclude any law, program or activity that has as its object the amelioration of conditions of disadvantaged individuals or groups including those that are disadvantaged because of race, national or ethnic origin, colour, religion, sex, age, mental or physical disability.

The part of our constitution that is most important in terms of human rights is section number 15.

Section 15 says that our government must not discriminate. All of the laws of Canada must provide each of us with equal protection and equal benefit whether we have a disability or not.

It also says that there can be special laws or programs set up to help people cope with barriers. In other words, it would be okay to provide money to help people with disabilities buy special equipment that they need — it would not be discrimination to withhold such funds from people without disabilities.

their voices to demand freedom and dignity for themselves and others. Our system of human rights laws began to take its current shape shortly after World War II when people everywhere were deeply horrified by what had happened and wanted to make sure that human beings would never suffer like that again. The *Universal Declaration of Human Rights*, which was proclaimed by the General Assembly of the United Nations on December 10, 1948, set out in writing for the first time the basic rights of all humans. Some of the most important features of this Declaration are:

- The idea that it does not matter what country people live in — everyone, everywhere has basic human rights
- The idea that every government in the world has some responsibility to ensure that people's human rights are internationally respected
- The idea that every person has the right to live free from fear and free from want (or, in other words, to have a safe and healthy place to live and enough food to eat)

On December 13, 2006, the General Assembly of the United Nations adopted the *Convention on the Rights of Persons with Disabilities*. The members of the United Nations believed that the Convention was necessary to better promote and protect the human rights and dignity of people with disabilities. The Convention does not create new rights but it requires countries to focus their attention on disability issues and to create laws that allow everyone to enjoy their human rights, regardless of ability or disability. In other words, the rights of people with disabilities must be seen to be as important as the rights of all people.

The Convention is based on a number of general principles that are the building blocks for the rights of people with disabilities, including respect for dignity of people and full inclusion and participation in society. These key values create the foundation for laws and policies that affect people with disabilities. The Convention also talks about specific rights for people with disabilities, rights that are taken for granted by other people. One example is the right for students with disabilities to go to school in a regular classroom, instead of being separated from their fellow students and placed in a special class. Where it is possible and beneficial to the student, he or she should remain in general education systems with appropriate supports in place.

Canada signed the Convention in 2010 and agreed to follow its principles. To meet our obligations under the Convention, Canada continues to change laws and practices to move forward in our goal to protect and promote the rights of people with disabilities in all aspects of life. These build on a number of other laws that Canada already has in place to protect the human rights of all people who live in, work in, or visit this country. These laws include:

- The *Canadian Charter of Rights and Freedoms*
- The *Canadian Human Rights Act*
- Human Rights Codes in every Canadian province and territory
- The *Accessibility for Ontarians with Disabilities Act*

For people with intellectual disabilities in Ontario, these different laws provide complementary legal protection. This chapter will outline in a general way how each of these protections operates, or might operate, to protect people with intellectual disabilities from discrimination or harassment.

Even in countries with traditions of human rights protection much longer than Canada's, it is rare to find a Constitutional provision that guarantees that persons with mental or physical disabilities shall have the "equal protection and equal benefit of the law." In 1985, when the *Canadian Charter of Rights and Freedoms* came into force, Canada was the only nation in the world to extend the recognition of equality "before and under the law" to persons with mental and physical disabilities.

A constitution is a set of "rules" that apply to all levels of government in a country. In Canada, therefore, our Charter is the "supreme law," which our federal, provincial, municipal and local governments must obey. Further, since all of our laws — including laws about education, health care, immigration, taxation, and others — are made by governments at some level, all of these laws must comply with the Charter. Even our human rights laws, which will be discussed later in this chapter, must meet the standard set out in our Charter.

As you may have noticed in Box 1, which quotes a section of the Charter, this law is written in rather broad language, without much detail about what it means to be "equal before and under the law." In our Canadian justice system, it is the job of the courts to interpret how a law is to apply in any particular situation.

The first Charter case to be decided by the Supreme Court of Canada was the Andrews case. In that case, the Court reached an important conclusion about the Charter. This conclusion, or ruling, by the Court is very much like one of those important ledges on the cliffside described in the introduction to this chapter. The Court ruled that discrimination is still discrimination, even when it is unintentional. In other words, how we decide whether or not something is discrimination does not depend on whether any person or government body knew that what they were doing was unfair. We will know there has been discrimination if a person or group of persons can show that she, he or they have not been treated equally. This is why we say in human rights law that it is the effect rather than the intent that matters.

A number of other cases followed Andrews. One such case, called Eldridge, was about the government's responsibility to "accommodate" or provide supports for people with disabilities. In that case, people who were deaf were not able to communicate with their doctors because the hospitals did not have sign language interpreters. The court said that the government has to provide these types of interpreters in hospitals. The general principle that we learn from this case is that government has a duty to remove barriers that prevent people from fully participating in society. Government programs must be accessible to everyone. In other words, the government must treat people differently sometimes to be sure that they get the same benefits from the law. Equality is not treating people the same, but providing the same opportunities for them to participate fully.

The court has also made some general statements that re-enforce the importance of dignity for people with disabilities. In a case called Eaton, the court considered the appropriate accommodations for a student with a disability and said that the types of accommodations provided must consider the individual needs and characteristics of a person and cannot be based on stereotypes (this case is discussed more in Box 2). The court has also said in the recent cases of Law and Granovsky that Charter cases about equality are about how the government, by passing laws and providing programs, protects or hurts the dignity and worth of people, including people with disabilities. Every person has the right

Box 2: Two Interesting Charter Cases

The parents of Luke Elwood were the first Canadians to use the Charter of Rights and Freedoms to challenge a school board about the way it treated children with disabilities. In 1987, in their home province of Nova Scotia, the Elwoods requested that the Court stop the school board from removing Luke from his neighbourhood school and placing him instead in a segregated classroom for children with disabilities. They argued that it was Luke's right, under Section 15 of the Charter, not to be discriminated against on the basis of his mental disability. The Court ordered the School Board to wait until a full trial on this issue had been completed. A year later, before the case went to trial, a settlement was reached. Luke was allowed to be in the same school as his friends and peers.

For three years, Emily Eaton regularly attended elementary school in Brant County, Ontario with a full-time educational assistant — until an Identification, Placement and Review Committee (IPRC) found that her needs were not being met in the regular classroom. Accordingly, a Special Educational Tribunal decided that Emily should be placed in a special class for students with disabilities. The Tribunal reasoned that because of her intellectual and physical disabilities Emily would not learn in a regular classroom. Wanting her to stay in her neighbourhood school, Emily's parents argued that Emily had the right to inclusive education under s. 15 of the Charter of Rights and Freedoms. They challenged the way the School Board treated children with disabilities. The case went through several levels of appeal. At first, the Court agreed with the Tribunal, concluding that Emily needed to be in a special school to be able to learn. Next, the Appeal Court agreed with Emily's parents that placement in a segregated class without her parents' consent was a form of discrimination that violated Emily's rights under the Charter. Finally, the case went to the Supreme Court of Canada, the highest Court in the country. The Judges of the Supreme Court concluded that a segregated school was in Emily's best interests. They decided that Emily's school could treat her differently because of her inability to learn in the same way as other children.

Although many people with disabilities and their family members were disappointed with how the Judges interpreted what the Charter's promise of equality would mean for someone like Emily Eaton, there were some positive messages in this decision. The Court did say clearly that integrated education is preferable for students with disabilities because of the benefits it provides. While the Court made a particular decision in Emily's case, the Court said that, wherever possible, regular schools should accommodate students with different learning needs because of s. 15 of the Charter.

to be valued, to fully participate in his or her community and to achieve self-fulfillment without interference by the government.

The Canadian Human Rights Act

Another one of those ledges on our cliffside is the *Canadian Human Rights Act*. This law was adopted by Parliament in 1977. The Act prohibits employers and service providers from discriminating on the basis of any of the following personal characteristics, or any combination of these characteristics:

- Physical or mental disability
- Race
- Colour
- Country or place of origin
- Religion

- Age
- Sex
- Marital status
- Family status
- Sexual orientation
- In some cases, a personal history of some criminal act that has since been pardoned

The *Canadian Human Rights Act* applies to all federal government offices and employees as well as to a few companies that are federally regulated, like banks and airlines.

This act created the Canadian Human Rights Commission, which opened its doors in 1978. It is the job of the Commission to promote and enforce this important law. There are three main aspects to this work:

- Restoring the rights of people who have been discriminated against
- Preventing discrimination before it occurs by educating people about their rights and responsibilities
- Promoting greater understanding of human rights and how such rights are protected

Much of the Commission's work consists of investigating and trying to resolve complaints. A customer or employee of any organization covered by the Act who thinks that he or she has been discriminated against can file a complaint with the Commission. If it appears that the complaint can be settled between the parties at an early stage, the Commission will assist the parties to resolve their differences without a formal process. If the complaint is more serious or complicated, or the parties cannot come to an agreement, the Commission may need to conduct an investigation. In this case, an investigator will be given the task of gathering the necessary information and making a full report to the Commissioners, a group of eight or ten respected citizens who make decisions about human rights complaints.

After the investigation, if the Commissioners feel that there is evidence to support the complaint, they may decide to appoint someone with special training in conflict resolution to try to help the parties come to some agreement about a fair way to resolve the matter. Alternatively, they may decide to send the case to a Human Rights Tribunal, which is a kind of specialized court that deals only with human rights cases.

If a Human Rights Tribunal is appointed, there will be a hearing where the parties and other possible witnesses will testify (answer questions about what they know about the matter). The Commission will provide the person or persons who complained of discrimination with a lawyer to help present their case. If the Tribunal decides that the complaint is valid, it will assess the harm that was done and make an order to correct the problem. The order may be specific, like an award of money or a direction to re-hire someone who has lost a job, or it may be more general, like changing discriminatory policies or requiring human rights education. The Tribunal has

the ability to provide both a solution to the specific problem (the individual who filed a complaint) and to provide a more general solution to prevent future discrimination for people who may find themselves in the same situation.

The decision of a Human Rights Tribunal is not necessarily final. If one of the parties is unsatisfied with the decision, it can be appealed to the Canadian Federal Court and all the way to the Supreme Court of Canada.

All of the services that the Commission provides are considered to be a public service. Therefore, the Commission pays all the costs of investigating and reviewing a complaint, as well as any costs arising from the Tribunal process.

The Ontario Human Rights Code

Every province and territory in Canada has a Human Rights Code that works in a similar way as described above for the *Canadian Human Rights Act*. The *Ontario Human Rights Code* protects every person who lives in, works in, or visits Ontario. It applies to all:

- Employers (large and small — except those covered by the Canadian Human Rights Act)
- Service providers (including government, hospitals, schools, stores, newspapers, insurance companies, etc.)
- Housing providers (including apartments, condominiums, boarding houses, homes for rent or sale, etc.)
- Organizations and associations (including unions, clubs, special societies, etc.)

Persons with physical, mental and intellectual disabilities are all protected from discrimination in Ontario. The following are some examples of what this means:

- It is against the law to refuse to hire a person for a job that he or she is qualified for, simply because that person has a disability.
- It is against the law to operate a store, restaurant, theatre or other public place that is not accessible to persons who have disabilities.
- It is against the law to refuse to provide a

Box 3: Three Interesting Cases Under the Ontario Human Rights Code

Karen is a person with cerebral palsy and an intellectual disability. She was living independently in the community and renting an apartment in the basement of a woman's house. When she first moved in, the woman was nice to Karen, but then she started making comments about Karen's make-up and her boyfriends. Before too long, she started making cruel comments about Karen's mental abilities. She also criticized Karen for using too much electricity by leaving the light on in the stairway and using a heater in warm weather, although she knew that Karen needed these things because of her disability.

In 1990, a Human Rights Board of Inquiry in Ontario decided that Karen's landlady had treated her unfairly and did not respect Karen's rights and dignity as a person with an intellectual disability. This behaviour was found to amount to a kind of discrimination called harassment. Harassment consists of unwelcome comments or actions that have the effect of making a person feel embarrassed or insulted.

In 1990, an Ontario Human Rights Board of Inquiry decided that a condominium corporation did not have the right to make a rule that would discriminate against people with psychiatric and intellectual disabilities.

In 1982, a non-profit organization had signed a lease with the condominium, agreeing to pay rent for a townhouse. They planned to use the townhouse as a group home, where people could stay after they were discharged from psychiatric hospitals, but before they were ready to live independently in the community. The condominium found out that the people living there would be people with mental disabilities and tried to break the lease. They said that their rules allowed only single families to live in their buildings.

The Board of Inquiry decided that, no matter what their rules said, they would have to be interpreted in a way that did not discriminate against people with intellectual or psychiatric disabilities.

In 2005 and 2008 the Toronto Transit Commission was ordered by the Ontario Human Rights Tribunal to make changes in the way it operated public transportation services. In the first case, the applicant, Mr. Lepofsky made an application about the TTC's failure to announce subway stops. He noted that the failure to make announcements made it more difficult for people with visual impairments to travel on the public subway system. In 2008, Mr. Lepofsky brought a second complaint as the TTC had failed to make similar accommodations on bus and streetcar routes. In both cases, the TTC was ordered to take necessary steps to make the public transit systems accessible to visually impaired riders. In addition, the TTC was ordered to hold public forums to receive information about how the TTC could better accommodate all people with disabilities.

---

reasonable amount of support or accommodation to make it possible for a person with a disability to carry out his or her life activities in a manner that is similar to the way a non-disabled person does.

- It is against the law to refuse to rent an apartment to someone because he or she has a disability.
- It is against the law for co-workers to tease or insult a person about his or her disability in a way that that person finds annoying or hurtful.
- It is against the law to punish someone just because he or she has objected to being treated in a discriminatory manner or has made some effort to assert his or her human rights.

The *Ontario Human Rights Code* is enforced by the Ontario Human Rights Tribunal. A person who believes that he or she has been discriminated against may ask the Tribunal to have a hearing. First, an application must be made. The Tribunal will provide a mediator to help the different sides reach an agreement. If the different sides cannot agree, there is a hearing. The Human Rights Tribunal has authority to make the same kinds of remedial orders as the Canadian Human Rights Tribunal described above, and its decisions can also be appealed all the way to the Supreme Court of Canada.

Apart from the Tribunal, the Ontario Human Rights Commission is a government organization that monitors human rights in Ontario. The Commission plays a key role in providing public education, developing guidelines to help people and organizations meet their obligations under the *Ontario Human Rights Code* and bringing complaints to the Tribunal if there is an issue of importance to the public.

The *Accessibility for Ontarians with Disabilities Act* (AODA) is a new type of law in Ontario. Instead of being focused on fixing problems after they happen, the AODA tries to create environments that are accessible to all people, including those with various types of disabilities. The goal of the AODA is to provide fully accessible environment for goods, services, facilities, accommodation, employment, buildings, structures and premises over a number of years. One aspect of the AODA is the creation of mandatory standards for accessibility, like a standard for customer service. To make sure that the AODA is being followed, there are requirements for reporting and monitoring. Ontario is the first province to develop legislation that requires accessible environments and the AODA is an exciting step forward in promoting and protecting the rights of people with disabilities.

Challenges for Today and Tomorrow

This chapter has described some of the ways in which our basic human rights play an important role in determining whether and how people with intellectual disabilities participate in community life. Because our human rights are protected by law in Ontario, we can use the law to challenge barriers that come between us and the equal opportunities we desire at school, at work, and at play.

In addition to these barriers, however, there are other larger social forces that threaten to undermine the human rights of all people with disabilities. For example, as developments in genetic science enable doctors to predict, before a baby is born, if she or he will likely have an intellectual disability, more and more parents choose to prevent the birth of such a child, often on the basis of information provided by genetic or medical counsellors. Many self-advocates and their colleagues and supporters are deeply concerned about this trend, especially since it appears to suggest that persons with intellectual disabilities are unwelcome in the human family.

Injustice of this nature is in some ways too big a problem to be dealt with by filing a human rights complaint. Who would the complaint be filed against? The parents who refuse to give birth to a disabled child? The genetic counsellor who gives advice that emphasizes only the bad things about having a disability? The media that again and again describes people with disabilities in unflattering and disrespectful terms? The scientists, who believe that preventing the birth of disabled babies is a worthy goal? The companies that provide funding for this kind of genetic research?

As we think about the greatest challenges that lie ahead for the community of people with intellectual disabilities, it is important to remember that human rights laws are not the only tools we have in our efforts to climb out from the canyon of inequality and discrimination. Equally important to winning cases in court are the ways in which we actively teach others about the ideas that are at the heart of our human rights laws. The *Convention on the Rights of Persons with Disabilities* is a new and exciting tool for education and discussion about the principles that are important to us as a community. Compliance with this law is proactive and Canada's progress toward improving the inclusion of people with disabilities in social, economic, cultural, political, and civil areas will be monitored by international, national, and provincial organizations. Already there is a project going on to monitor this law in Canada and around the world. You can read more about Disability Rights Promotion International (*http://www.yorku.ca/drpi*) to learn about the ways people with disabilities themselves and governments can do comprehensive monitoring. Human rights education and approaches to policy decisions made in government, industry and community organizations are critical in our efforts to achieve dignity, respect and equality for persons with intellectual disabilities in Ontario, in Canada, and throughout the world.

Summary

All persons with intellectual and other disabilities have the right to be treated with respect and to participate fully in Canadian society. This right is clearly set out in the Canadian Constitution — the highest law in the land. The *Canadian Charter of Rights and Freedoms* obliges governments at all levels to ensure that they do not violate these rights, either intentionally or unintentionally. Our federal and provincial Human Rights laws extend these fundamental rights into all areas of social activity including employment, education, health care, recreation, housing, transportation and countless other sectors, while the *Accessibility for Ontarians with Disabilities Act* requires us to think ahead and develop environments that are accessible to all.

This legal framework for our human rights protections is where the story begins. The laws described in this chapter provide an important foundation, but the task of interpreting what these rights mean in any person's day-to-day life involves intensive work, critical thinking and commitment on the part of lawyers, advocates and disability rights activists, working together to make the best possible arguments before the Tribunals and the Courts.

It is important to remember that the human rights described in this chapter exist primarily as words on paper. Unless and until these rights are claimed and enforced, they are empty promises. As citizens, we must be vigilant in ensuring that our own rights and those of our fellow citizens, especially those who are unable to speak for themselves, are respected. The process can be time-consuming and requires a good deal of care and skill, much like the effort of climbing up out of a canyon. For this reason, it is vitally important that we encourage each other in working together to build a society that respects and values all of its citizens.

For Further Thought and Discussion

1. The *Convention on the Rights of Persons with Disabilities* requires Canada and other member states to promote the rights and dignity of people with disabilities. That responsibility will be monitored internationally and nationally. How can individuals and organizations raise awareness about the Convention? How can we be sure that the rights in the Convention are being respected in Canada?

2. There have been very few cases heard by courts or tribunals in Canada dealing with complaints of discrimination against persons with intellectual disabilities. Is this because there is very little discrimination against persons with intellectual disabilities? If not, what are some other reasons that might explain this?

3. What are some ways to assert our human rights without going through a formal human rights process? Beyond knowing that a person has the right, what further knowledge or actions may be required?

4. Sometimes, issues involving intellectual disability are decided by the courts without any consideration for principles of human rights. Consider, for example, the following — Krangle v. Brisco. To what extent do you think the ideas at the heart of our human rights laws are relevant to this case? To what extent are these ideas reflected in this decision? Would your approach to this case be different from the approach taken by the Court? Justify your response.

In Krangle v. Brisco, the Supreme Court of Canada was asked to determine an appropriate payment to be made by a doctor to the family of a child born with Down syndrome. In this case, Mr. and Mrs. Krangle sued their doctor after the birth of their son, Mervyn. The Krangles claimed that their doctor should have advised them that it was possible to test for Down syndrome; if Mrs. Krangle had known that her child was likely to have this condition, she said that she would have chosen to have an abortion. At the trial, everyone agreed that the doctor was at fault, not for having caused Mervyn's Down syndrome, but for having denied his parents the medical information or advice they needed to prevent Mervyn's birth. The British Columbia court that originally heard this case awarded the Krangles a sum of almost $490,000 as damages for the cost of raising Mervyn as well as for what the Supreme Court later described as the "pain, suffering and anguish associated with his birth and development."

The Supreme Court dealt only with the very specific question of whether additional money should be awarded for costs that might arise in the future, related to Mervyn's adult needs. The Court decided not to increase the amount awarded to the Krangles, concluding that the cost of Mervyn's care in an adult group home would most likely be met by the provincial government's social security program.

Special Terms

Act: refers to the means by which laws are made. Generally, Acts begin in draft form as "bills." When an Act has been approved by specified processes, it then becomes a law.

Charter: has come to be synonymous with the document that lays out the granting of rights or privileges.

Code: a collection of written laws gathered together, usually covering specific subject matter.

Law: refers to a rule or set of rules that are usually enforced through a set of institutions.

Right: an abstract idea of that which is due to a person or governmental body by law or tradition or nature. The term "right" differs from "entitlement" in the sense that the latter term usually refers to a specific right granted by law or contract (especially a right to benefits).

More Resources

Convention on the Rights of People with Disabilities
http://www.un.org/disabilities.
This UN site contains information about the Convention and other international information about disabilities.

Disability Rights Promotion International
http://www.yorku.ca/drpi
Additional information about the Convention, international disability rights monitoring, and related issues.

Charter of Rights and Freedoms
http://lois.justice.gc.ca/en/charter/

Canadian government website about disability issues
http://www.pch.gc.ca/pgm/pdp-hrp/canada/abl-eng.cfm
The site discusses the various pieces of legislation that impact rights in Canada, including those discussed in this chapter, and provides links to other interesting sites.

The Canadian Human Rights Commission
http://www.chrc-ccdp.ca/
At this site, you can access the Commission's publications, annual report, case highlights, and a copy of the *Canadian Human Rights Act.* Canadian Human Rights Tribunal decisions are also found on this site.

The Ontario Human Rights Tribunal
http://www.hrto.ca/hrto
Here, you will find guides with information about the Tribunal and the *Ontario Human Rights Code.*

The Ontario Human Rights Commission
http://www.ohrc.on.ca
The Ontario Human Rights Commission continues to provide information about its role in protecting human rights. On its site you can access a number of online publications, including an excellent educational package entitled "Teaching Human Rights in Ontario." This latter resource introduces students at the secondary school level the provisions for the *Ontario Human Rights Code.*

References

Accessibility for Ontarians with Disabilities Act, 2005, S.O. 2005, c.11. Retrieved from http://www.e-laws.gov.on.ca/html/statutes/english/elaws_statutes_05a11_e.htm

Andrews v. Law Society of British Columbia, [1989] 1 S.C.R. 143. Canadian Human Rights Act, RS, 1985, c. H-6 July 1996.

Constitution Act 1982, Part 1 - Canadian Charter of Rights and Freedoms, section 15 (1). Retrieved from http://www.efc.ca/pages/law/charter/charter.text.html

Disability Rights Promotion International. (2010). Retrieved from http://www.yorku.ca/drpi/

Eaton v. Brant County Board of Education, [1997] 1 S.C.R. 241.

Eldridge v. British Columbia (Attorney General), [1997] 3 S.C.R. 624.

Granovsky v. Canada (Minister of Employment and Immigration), [2000] 1 S.C.R. 703, 2000 SCC 28.

Law v. Canada (Minister of Employment and

Immigration), [1999] 1 S.C.R. 497.

Ontario Human Rights Code, RSO 1990. Retrieved from http://www.e-laws.gov.on.ca/html/statutes/english/elaws_statutes_90h19_e.htm

United Nations General Assembly, Convention on the Rights of Persons with Disabilities: resolution/ adopted by the General Assembly, 24 January 2007, A/RES/61/106. Retrieved from http://www.un.org/disabilities/default.asp?id=61

Select Rights, Benefits, and Entitlements for Individuals with Developmental Disabilities

Rivka Birkan and Orna Raubfogel[1]

What you will learn:

- Freedom from discrimination
- Ontario's new accessibility platform
- Capacity and substitute decision makers
- Income and disability supports
- Housing laws and regulations

*Note: Acronyms in **bold italics** are explained in the the Glossary of Acronyms following the Summary. Endnotes (superscript numbers) are explained in the section following the Glossary.*

This chapter is an introduction to ways that different areas of the law in Ontario affect, or potentially affect, the lives of people with developmental disabilities. It outlines certain rights of individuals with disabilities, and the corresponding duties upon others. Two simple examples are: the right to be free from discrimination and the corresponding prohibition against discrimination and duty to accommodate; or the right to make decisions for oneself about one's property, personal care, medical treatment, and procedures that must be followed for that right to be lawfully withdrawn. Additionally, the chapter includes an overview of some of the financial benefits available to individuals with disabilities, if they are found to qualify for such benefits. The chapter

then surveys laws related to housing and support services across different types of residential settings. As you will learn, in order to benefit from most of the services and programs discussed, individuals must apply and be found eligible for such services.

Freedom from Discrimination

Charter of Rights and Freedoms

The Canadian Charter of Rights and Freedoms (the "Charter") is part of the Constitution of Canada. The Constitution, and hence the Charter, is the supreme law that is paramount over all other laws in Canada. Any Canadian laws that are inconsistent with the Charter cannot be enforced. The Charter is binding upon the federal and provincial governments. Actions of the federal government, provincial governments, or agents acting on behalf of or with delegated authority from these governments that are inconsistent with the Charter can be challenged as illegal.[2] Section 15 of the Charter affirms Canada's commitment to ensuring the right to equality before the law — including the right to the equal protection and benefit of the law without discrimination on the basis of mental or physical disability.

Ontario Human Rights Code

In a similar fashion to the Charter, Ontario's Human Rights Code (the "Code") occupies a special place within the legal framework of Ontario. The Code has quasi-constitutional status, and, as such, is paramount over other laws of Ontario. This means that, generally speaking, any provincial laws that are inconsistent with the Code cannot be enforced.

The Code grants each person in Ontario the right to be free from discrimination on the basis of any disability he or she may have. It uses a broad and inclusive definition of disability, which expressly includes:

- mental impairment or a developmental disability,
- a learning disability, or a dysfunction in one or more of the processes involved in understanding or using symbols or spoken language, and
- a mental disorder (s. 10).

The Code prohibits discrimination against persons with disabilities in a number of contexts, including: in the provision of services (s. 1); in the provision of housing or accommodation (s. 2); in the context of employment (s. 5); in the membership or participation in vocational associations, like unions (s. 6); and in contractual relationships — where persons with disabilities are guaranteed the right to contract freely, so long as they have legal capacity (s. 3).

A person, business, or organization who is a provider in relation to any of the above-referenced contexts (hereinafter referred to as a "Provider") that discriminates against a person on the basis of his or her disability may be brought before the Human Rights Tribunal by the individual who it has discriminated against. The Human Rights Tribunal of Ontario's website provides internet hyperlinks to all of the forms used by the Tribunal, including a link to the initial application form. Legal advice is also available from the Human Rights Legal Support Centre for persons who believe their Code rights have been infringed. If the Provider is a government body, or government agent, its rules or conduct may also be the subject of a Charter challenge.

Identifying discrimination on the basis of disability

Discrimination can occur in a number of ways. An individual may be discriminated against directly or indirectly, or an individual may experience the effects of systemic discrimination. Box 1 provides examples of each type of discrimination.

Direct discrimination: Where a law, policy, or practice expressly treats people with a disability differently from those who do not have a disability.

Indirect or constructive discrimination: Where a law, policy, or practice appears to be neutral in that everyone receives the same treatment, but the effect of the policy has a disproportionately harsher consequence to persons with disabilities, or has the effect of excluding persons with disabilities from accessing a benefit or opportunity that is available to others (Code, s. 11(1)).

Systemic discrimination: Where a pattern of indirect or direct discrimination is entrenched in the day-to-day operations of an organization so that it appears normal and is propagated either intentionally or without thought.

Accommodation pursuant to the code

The purpose of the Code is to ensure that all persons are guaranteed the same rights and are able to access the same services, benefits, and opportunities, regardless of their identification with a Code-protected ground, like disability (Code, preamble).

Sometimes, to access services, benefits, or opportunities, individuals with disabilities require accommodation. The duration and type of accommodation needed will depend on the needs of the particular individual and the particular context in which a request for accommodation is being made. Each request for accommodation should be assessed on its own merits.

Accommodation often means that rules are modified or practices are adapted in order to take a person's disability into account. Examples of accom-

Box 1: Case Examples of Discrimination

Direct discrimination: Darla has spastic hemiplegic cerebral palsy. As a result of her disability, she has difficulty walking, the movement of her limbs on the left side of her body appears stiff and uncoordinated, and her speech is slightly affected. Darla applied for a job cataloguing artworks at a large art dealership in Ottawa. Within the first few minutes of arriving at the office for her interview, she is told that she is ineligible for the position because of her disability. The art dealership has no evidence that Darla's disability would prevent her from performing the job requirements adequately; the dealership is refusing to give Darla the job on the basis of her disability.

Indirect or constructive discrimination: All students at a particular university are given three hours to write their end-of-term examination without any exceptions. Jose is a political science student, and examinations in this field typically include questions that are several paragraphs in length. Jose has dyslexia. As a result, he is unable to read at the same pace as most of his class-mates. The three-hour policy appears to be neutral in that it applies equally to everyone in Jose's class; however, it has a disproportionately negative effect on Jose, because of his disability.

Systemic discrimination: Ivan has worked for a company called Biases Incorporated for five years. Ivan has a developmental disability. Ivan has applied for a promotion to shift-supervisor for the last three years without success. Frustrated, Ivan begins raising his concerns with other employees and discovers that, while thirty percent of Biases Incorporated employees have some form of developmental disability, no one with such a disability has ever been promoted above the basic entry-level position. He finds that this is true even though many have applied for a promotion. This may indicate that Ivan and his co-workers are being overlooked for promotions as a result of a perpetuation of systemic bias against persons with developmental disabilities.

---

modation might include: modifying work hours or schedules; modifying work equipment or work duties; adapting examinations or training materials at school; or offering to read notices, bills, or other documents to customers. Under the Code, the duty to accommodate is applied either when a request has been made, or when the need for accommodation is obvious without a request being made. Providers who have a duty to accommodate must identify and remove those barriers that are blocking a person with a disability from gaining equal access to the benefits and/or opportunities that they offer.

Disabilities must be accommodated unless to do so would cause undue hardship to the Provider (Code, s. 11(2)). The threshold for proving undue hardship is strict and can be quite difficult to meet. The factors to be considered are:

- the cost of accommodating: the cost must be so extreme that it would affect the viability of the Provider seeking to accommodate;
- the availability of outside sources of funding;
- whether the modifications would have health and safety consequences (s. 17(2)).

The determination that effecting an accommodation would cause undue hardship often cannot be made without clear and concrete documentation, such as cost estimates and budget calculations.

Accessibility and accommodation constitute a participatory endeavour, requiring both the person who is requesting the accommodation and the Provider to work together. The most efficient way to figure out what a person requires in order to be able to access services or benefits is to ask that person what he or she needs and have him or her participate in the process of accommodation.

An accommodation may not ultimately be what the requester initially envisioned. Discussions may result in creative problem solving and may ultimately reveal that a lesser modification, or a relatively simple change, is sufficient to meet the requester's needs. If perfect accommodation cannot be achieved because to do so would cause undue hardship, the possibility of effecting a lesser change or modification as a temporary measure should be discussed. The goal of the lesser measure would be to enable better access, if not perfect access, in the interim until the Provider is able to make the complete modifications. Without the participation of the requester, accommodation is difficult, if not impossible to achieve.

Inability to perform essential duties

An individual's Code rights are not infringed if the person is excluded from a benefit or opportunity because he or she is truly incapable of fulfilling the essential duties required of him or her by reason of a disability (s. 17(1)). If, for example, someone wanted to be a neurosurgeon but had a condition that made his or her hands shake uncontrollably, that person may be denied the position on the grounds that he or she is incapable of fulfilling the essential duties required to be a neurosurgeon. So long as the requirement for steady hands is indeed a reasonable and bona fide requirement of the job, refusing the position to an individual on that basis will not be a breach of the Code.[3]

Ameliorative programs

Code-protected groups can lawfully be treated differently when the differential treatment is part of an ameliorative program. Ameliorative programs are aimed at identifying, and then improving the positions of, Code-identified groups that have been the target of pre-existing socio-historical discrimination. Preferential treatment for persons over the age of 65 is an example of one such provision for ameliorative programs, which is specifically addressed in the Code (s. 15). Other examples of ameliorative programs that are not expressly written in the Code might include programs dedicated to assisting women who have survived domestic abuse, or programs geared at helping persons living with HIV/AIDS find supportive housing.

Ontario's Accessibility Platform

Accessibility for Ontarians with Disabilities Act

Generally, pursuant to the Code, a Provider is not required to accommodate unless a particular need for accommodation is known to it. Usually this means that someone will request accommodation in order to access the services of the Provider or a need

for accommodation will be obvious from the interactions the Provider has with the individual. Once a need for accommodation is known, any adjustments or alterations made are geared to the particular needs of that individual. Although the steps taken may ultimately benefit others who require similar modifications or assistance, the focus is on the particular case before the Provider.

The Accessibility for Ontarians with Disabilities Act, 2005 (*AODA*) came into force on June 13, 2005, and makes Ontario the first jurisdiction in Canada to develop, implement, and enforce mandatory accessibility standards applicable to both the private and public sectors.[4] The AODA requires Ontario businesses to take proactive steps to accommodate the public before any request for accommodation is made, and before any needs of particular individuals are known.

The AODA and its regulations will prescribe standards for how businesses and services in Ontario are to make their respective organizations accessible and how they will accommodate persons with disabilities. The standards will be established by five regulations that cover accessibility and accommodation in the contexts of Customer Service; Communications; Employment; Transportation; and Built Environments. The Province aims to make Ontario accessible to all persons by 2025 through the implementation of the AODA and its corresponding regulations. The first AODA standards to come into force relate to customer service ("Customer Service Standards") (O. Reg. 429/07). The final step in Ontario's accessibility overhaul will be the standards related to built environments. It is expected that the built environment standards will make significant changes to the current building codes in order to ensure accessibility. Since the Customer Service Standards have already been finalized and called into force by regulation, they are discussed in some detail below.

The AODA and the standards created pursuant to the AODA do not in any way detract from the rights enshrined in the Charter or the Code. The AODA complements the Charter and the Code. A Provider who fails to accommodate persons with disabilities will likely breach the AODA and be in breach of the

Code at the same time. If the particular Provider is a government body, it will likely have breached the Charter as well.

Customer service standards

All persons, businesses, and organizations in Ontario that provide goods or services to the public or third parties, and have one or more employees (hereinafter referred to as "providers"), are required to comply with the Customer Service Standards. All designated public sector organizations, as defined by the Customer Service Standards, were required to comply with the standards by January 1, 2010. All other providers are required to comply by January 1, 2012 (O. Reg. 429/07, s. 2).

The Customer Service Standards require all providers to draft and implement policies, practices, and procedures governing how they will provide goods or services to persons with disabilities. These must include a commitment to communicating with persons with disabilities in a manner that takes each person's disability into account (O. Reg. 429/07, s. 3). Four key principles must inform these policies, practices, and procedures. These principles are:

- respect for the *independence* of persons with disabilities,
- respect for the *dignity* of persons with disabilities,
- integration of the goods or services provided to persons with disabilities with those provided to others, and
- *equality* of opportunity for persons with disabilities and others, to obtain, use, or benefit from goods or services (O. Reg. 429/07, s. 3(2)).

General policies, practices, and procedures must also cover how providers will offer goods or services to persons who use assistive devices (O. Reg. 429/07, s. 3(3)).

Service animals: Persons with disabilities have the right to access goods and services with a service animal, provided that the service animal is not excluded from the particular premises by law. The Customer Service Standards require all providers who offer goods or services to the public out of premises that they own or operate to allow persons with service animals to enter their premises with the service animals. If the service animal is excluded by law, the provider must ensure that other measures are in place to enable those who rely on service animals to obtain, use, or benefit from the goods or services they offer (O. Reg. 429/07, s. 4).

Support persons: Persons with disabilities have the right to access goods and services with a support person. If a person with a disability is accompanied by a support person whom he or she depends on in order to access goods or services, the Customer Service Standards require each provider to ensure that the person with a disability has access to his or her support person while accessing the goods or services it provides. If an admission price is chargeable for support persons, every provider must give advanced notice of the admission charges that would apply to support persons (O. Reg. 429/07, s. 4).

Temporary interruption of services: Persons with disabilities have the right to know if services that they depend on in order to access goods or services will be discontinued temporarily. Each provider must give notice of interruptions to the services it offers that are used by persons with disabilities to access the provider's goods or services. The notice must include: the reason for the disruption; the expected duration of the disruption; and a description of alternative facilities or services, if any, that are available. These notices may be posted in a conspicuous place at the premises of the provider or on its website, or it may be provided in any other manner that is reasonable in the circumstances (O. Reg. 429/07, s. 5).

Feedback: The Customer Service Standards mandate the creation of a process for each provider to receive and respond to feedback about how it provides goods or services to persons with disabilities. Comments must be capable of being received by telephone, in writing, or electronically. The process must also specify what actions the provider will take when a complaint is received (O. Reg. 429/07, s. 7). Information about a provider's feedback process must be made readily available to members of public.

Written policies, practices, and procedures: For public sector organizations and all other providers with 20 or more employees, the general policies, practices, and procedures created to implement the Customer Service Standards must be readily available as written documents and must be produced upon request to anyone asking for them. In addition to this, the policies, practices, and procedures relating to service animals, support persons, temporary interruptions of services, and feedback must also be readily available as written documents and must be produced upon request to anyone asking for them (O. Reg. 429/07, ss. 3(5), 4(7), 5(4) and 7(4)). If any of these documents are being provided to a person with a disability, they must be provided in a format that takes into account that person's disability (O. Reg. 429/07, s. 9).

Training: All providers are required to train every person who deals with members of the public or third parties on its behalf. The training must include:

- how to interact with persons with various types of disability;
- how to deal with personal assistive devices, service animals, support persons, equipment or devices available at the provider's premises or otherwise made available by the provider; and
- what to do when a customer is having difficulty accessing goods or services (O. Reg. 429/07, s. 6).

The Customer Service Standards, and the large-scale accessibility and accommodation training that is associated with the implementation of the standards, will undoubtedly change the attitudes of Ontarians for the better. As the level of education and training increases, there should be a corresponding improvement in the understanding of disability and accommodation issues on the part of people across Ontario.

Capacity and Substitute Decision Makers

Ontarians benefit from the legal presumption that a person is capable of managing his or her own personal, medical, and financial affairs (*Health Care Consent Act, 1996*, s. 4 and *Substitute Decisions Act, 1992*, s. 2). This presumption results in a person's right to make choices for herself or himself with respect to personal care, medical treatment, and finances. With respect to healthcare, for example, a person has the right to refuse medical treatment regardless of the potential negative consequences of that decision (*Starson v. Swayze*, 2003, p. 412; Picard & Robertson, 2007, pp. 44-49). However, there are circumstances in which individuals may be found incapable of making certain decisions for themselves. In such cases, a person may either involuntarily lose the right to make decisions about personal care, health care treatment, or property, or may choose to transfer these rights to another person or entity. In Ontario, through the various processes described below, this right of decision-making may be transferred to another person or to a public guardian (i.e., the Office of the Public Guardian and Trustee). The laws surrounding incapacity are relevant to our discussion of disability rights because a finding of incapacity to manage property or personal care often results from a disability.

SUBSTITUTE DECISIONS ACT

Incapacity to manage personal property

A person may be found incapable of managing her or his personal property pursuant to either the *Substitute Decisions Act* (**SDA**) or the *Mental Health Act* (**MHA**).[5] Pursuant to the SDA, a person is incapable of managing property if that person is not able to:

1. understand information that is relevant to making a decision in the management of his or her property, or
2. appreciate the reasonably foreseeable consequences of a decision or lack thereof (s. 6).[6]

Public guardian and trustee: With a few exceptions, a finding of incapacity to manage property results in the Public Guardian and Trustee becoming the statutory guardian of the person's property (Hiltz & Szigeti, 2010). The Public Guardian and Trustee (**PGT**) becomes a statutory guardian of property if:

1. the person is already in a psychiatric facility, is found to be incapable of managing property, and a certificate of incapacity for property management is issued under the MHA (s. 15); or
2. the person receives a capacity assessment and

is determined to be unable to manage property, and an assessor issues a certificate of incapacity (s. 16).

The PGT becomes the statutory guardian from the moment it receives the certificate of incapacity (s. 16(5)). Immediately afterward, the PGT has the power to do anything in respect of the person's property that the person could have done, if capable, except make a will (s. 31). Once the PGT becomes statutory guardian, the PGT must inform the person that the PGT has become the statutory guardian of his or her property, and that the person is entitled to challenge this decision at the Consent and Capacity Board (CCB) (s. 16(6)). The PGT's statutory guardianship is terminated if, prior to the finding of incapacity, the person gave a continuing power of attorney for property that extended to all of the person's property, and the PGT receives the appropriate documentation confirming this, including a copy of the continuing power of attorney for property (s. 16.1).

A spouse, partner, relative, trust corporation, or attorney under a pre-existing continuing power of attorney for property can apply to replace the PGT as statutory guardian. The application to replace the PGT must include a management plan for the person's property (s. 17).

Continuing power of attorney for property: By establishing a valid continuing power of attorney for property prior to becoming incapable, a person can avoid having either a statutory guardian or court appointed guardian of property. The continuing power of attorney for property is a written document, executed before two witnesses (s. 10) that authorizes a named attorney or attorneys to make decisions with respect to property on behalf of the person who grants the authority (the "grantor"). As an example, a grantor who anticipates becoming incapable of making financial decisions because of illness or disability can authorize a trusted person or persons to act as attorney and look after the grantor's financial affairs. The attorney can then do almost anything in respect of the grantor's property that the grantor could do if capable (e. g., banking, or buying and selling property). The exception is that the attor-

ney cannot make a will on behalf of the grantor (s. 7).

Qualifications: To grant a continuing power of attorney for property, or act as an attorney under such a grant, a person must be at least 18 years old (ss. 4 and 5). At the time the continuing power of attorney for property is granted, the grantor must have the capacity to give such a power. The test for capacity to grant a continuing power of attorney for property and to revoke the power of attorney requires the grantor to know and understand:

- that he or she can revoke this power if he or she is capable;
- the approximate value of his or her property;
- that the attorney could misuse the authority given to him or her by the grantor (s. 8(1)).

The test for capacity to grant a continuing power of attorney for property under the SDA is not the same as the test for capacity to manage one's property. A person can grant a valid continuing power of attorney for property even if, at the time that he or she grants it, the grantor is incapable of managing his or her property (s. 9(1)).

Effective date: There are three ways that a continuing power of attorney for property can come into force.

1. *Effective upon a condition precedent:* The continuing power of attorney for property can specify that it comes into effect on a specified date, or when a specified contingency occurs (s. 7(7)). The document might, for example, indicate that it will only become effective once the grantor becomes incapable of managing his or her property. If this particular contingency is used, the document must spell out a method to determine that the person has become incapable. If a specified method of determining incapacity in the document itself is absent, the grantor's capacity must be formally assessed. There must then be a finding that the grantor is incapable before the power can become effective (s. 9(3)).

2. *Effective immediately:* The grantor may make the continuing power of attorney for property effective as of the date the document is signed. This avoids the need for a capacity assessment as it is immediately effective. The grantor must,

however, trust that the attorney will not abuse such a power.

3. *Effective upon release:* The document is kept in the custody of a third party and is made effective on its release.

Capacity assessment: Any person can request a capacity assessment to determine whether someone living outside a psychiatric institution is incapable of managing his or her property and requires the involvement of the PGT (s. 16(1)). There are certain procedures in place for capacity assessments to ensure a fair process (Hiltz & Szigeti, 2010, p. 44). These include requiring that:

- the person making the assessment (i.e. the assessor), is a member of a designated class of persons who are qualified to assess capacity (s. 1(1))[7], and
- the request for a capacity assessment, and the assessment itself, are in a prescribed form (ss. 16(2) and 16(3)).[8]

Before an assessment, the assessor must inform the person being assessed of his or her right to refuse an assessment, as well as the purpose of the assessment and the significance of a finding of capacity or incapacity (s. 78(2)). Generally, an assessor is not allowed to assess the person's capacity if the person refuses assessment (s. 78(1)). There are two exceptions to this rule:

1. A court, on a motion or on its own initiative, can make an order requiring a person to submit to an assessment if a person's capacity is at issue in a proceeding under the SDA and the court is satisfied that there are reasonable grounds to believe that the person is incapable (s. 79); and
2. An assessment can proceed despite the person's refusal if there is an effective power of attorney for personal care that authorizes the use of force for an assessment (s. 50).

If the assessor makes a finding of incapacity for the purpose of determining whether a person requires a statutory guardian, the assessor must provide a certificate of incapacity, in the appropriate form (s. 16(3)), to both the PGT and the person found inca-

pable of managing property (s. 16(4)). For any capacity assessment made under the SDA, the assessor must provide the person assessed with written notice of the assessor's findings (s. 78(5)). An assessor's finding of incapacity made pursuant to the SDA can be nullified if the assessor failed to advise a person of the consequences of a capacity assessment or of that person's right to refuse an interview (*Re Koch*, 1997).

Court appointed guardian of property

Whether or not a person already has a statutory guardian of property, any person can apply to the court to have the court appoint a guardian of property (s. 22(1)). If the court appoints a guardian, any existing statutory guardianship is terminated (s. 20). Like an attorney under a continuing power of attorney for property and like a statutory guardian of property, a court appointed guardian of property has the power to do anything in respect of the person's property that the person could do if capable, except make a will (s. 31).

The SDA prevents the court from appointing a guardian of property if it is satisfied that there is an alternative course of action that does not require a finding of incapacity and that is less restrictive of the person's decision-making rights (s. 22(3)). In order for an appointment to be made, the court must find that the person is incapable of managing property and requires that decisions to be made on his or her behalf by a person who is authorized to do so (s. 25).

There are limitations on who the court can appoint as guardian of property. Generally, the court can only appoint an Ontario resident, unless the guardian provides security for the value of the property, or the court orders otherwise (ss. 24(3) and 24(4)). A court may not appoint as guardian a person who provides health care or residential, social, training, or support services to an incapable person for compensation, unless that person is the individual's spouse, partner, relative, attorney for property, or attorney under a continuing power of attorney for property (ss. 24(1) and 24(2)). The court can appoint joint guardians or appoint one person to look after certain property and another to look after other property (s. 24(6)).

In deciding to appoint a guardian for property, the court must be guided by the over-arching principle that the arrangement it selects be in the best interests of the incapable person (*Bennet v. Gotlibowicz*, 2009, para. 19). In making its decision, the court must consider the following:

1. whether the proposed guardian is the attorney under a continuing power of attorney for property;
2. the incapable person's current wishes, if they can be ascertained; and
3. the closeness of the relationship between the proposed guardian to the incapable person (s. 24(5)).

Although the PGT is the default statutory guardian, in the case of a court appointed guardianship, the court will only appoint the PGT as the guardian if the application to the court specifies that appointment and if there is no other suitable person who is available and willing to be appointed (s. 24(2.1)).

Temporary guardian of property

The court may also order the PGT to act as a temporary guardian of property, for a period of 90 days or less. The PGT must apply to the court for such an order and must have reasonable grounds to believe that: the person is incapable of managing property; and an appointment of a temporary guardian is required to prevent either the loss of a significant part of the person's property, or to prevent that person from failing to provide the necessities of life for himself or herself or his or her dependants (s. 27).

Duties of a guardian and continuing power of attorney for property

A guardian of property, whether statutory or court appointed, has certain duties prescribed by law, including the duties to: exercise his or her duties with honesty and integrity and in good faith for the incapable person's benefit; manage the person's property in a manner consistent with decisions concerning the person's personal care, unless to do so would result in severe adverse consequences to the property; encourage the incapable person to participate in the guardian's decisions about the property; seek to foster regular personal contact between the incapable person and supportive family members and friends

of the incapable person; and make reasonable efforts to determine if the incapable person has a will, and what the provisions of the will include (ss. 32 and 38(1)).

Reviewing findings of incapacity to manage property

The Consent and Capacity Board (*CCB*) is a tribunal that is created under, and given power by, the *Health Care Consent Act*. The tribunal reviews the capacity of individuals with respect to consent to treatment, personal assistance services, admission to care facilities, and admission to hospitals, psychiatric facilities, nursing homes, or homes for the aged for the purpose of treatment. The CCB conducts reviews under the MHA, the *Health Care Consent Act*, and the SDA.

A person who has been found incapable of managing his or her property and who therefore has a statutory guardian of property has a right to apply to the CCB to review the finding of incapacity (s. 20.2).[9] This right of review does not apply if the person has a continuing power attorney for property, or a court-appointed guardian of property. If the CCB upholds the finding of incapacity to manage property, the person must wait 6 months before reapplying to the CCB for a review of the incapacity finding (s. 20.1(1)). The CCB has the power to either confirm the finding of incapacity, or, it may substitute its own decision for that of the physician or capacity assessor and decide that the person is capable of managing his or her own property (s. 20.2(5)).

Incapacity to manage personal care

Power of attorney for personal care: In addition to powers of attorney for property, the SDA also governs powers of attorney for personal care. The provisions related to powers of attorney for personal care apply in the event that a person is or becomes incapable of personal care. The SDA deems a person incapable of personal care personal care if he or she:

- cannot understand relevant information in making a decision concerning his or her health care, nutrition, shelter, clothing, hygiene, or safety, or
- cannot appreciate reasonably foreseeable consequences of his or her decisions or lack of

decision (s. 45).

A person who is incapable of personal care may still be capable of granting a valid, written power of attorney for personal care (s. 47(2)). Similar to the continuing power of attorney for property, the power of attorney for personal care is a document signed by the person granting authority (the "**grantor**") to another individual (the "**attorney**"), which authorizes the attorney to make decisions with respect to the personal care of the grantor.

Granting power of attorney: To grant power of attorney for personal care, a person must be:

- 16 years old (s. 43);
- able to understand whether the proposed attorney has a genuine concern for his or her welfare; and
- able appreciate that he or she may need to have the proposed attorney make decisions on his or her behalf (s. 47(1)).

For the document to be effective, it must be executed in the presence of two signing witnesses (s. 48). A person with the capacity to give a power of attorney is also capable of revoking the power of attorney (s. 47(3)).

The power of attorney for personal care allows capable individuals to choose who they want to act as their substitute decision maker in the event that they become incapable to make decisions for which the *Health Care Consent Act* applies. These include: decisions about psychiatric or medical treatment; admission to a long-term care facility; or personal assistance services. The power of attorney for personal care also allows individuals to give certain directions to their attorney about their wishes. Without this document, if a person becomes incapable of personal care, the substitute decision maker will be chosen on that person's behalf, in accordance with the *Health Care Consent Act* (Hiltz & Szigeti, 2010, p. 39).

The power of attorney for personal care can specify that the attorney or another person under the attorney's direction can use force that is reasonable and necessary in the circumstances to: determine the person's capacity; submit the person to any place for care; or detain/restrain the person. The document may also contain a provision that waives the grantor's right to have his or her capacity reviewed by the CCB. For such provisions to be enforceable, the grantor must make a statement in a prescribed form indicating that he or she is aware of the effects of the provisions and his or her ability to revoke them. An assessor must also make a prescribed statement to support that the grantor was capable of understanding the effects of the provisions at the time they were written (s. 50).

Qualifications

To act as an attorney for personal care, a person must be at least 16 years old (s. 44). A person cannot act as the attorney under the power of attorney if he or she is paid or otherwise compensated to provide health, residential, social training, or support services to the grantor. There is an exception to this rule for the grantor's spouse, partner, or relative (s. 46(3)).

Effective date

Unlike the power of attorney for property that can specify an effective date, the power of attorney for personal care is only effective when the person becomes incapable of making personal care decisions (s. 49). Another person cannot make personal care decisions on behalf of an individual who is capable of personal care (Hiltz & Szigeti, 2010, p. 39).

Court appointed guardian of the person

If a person is incapable of personal care, the court, on any person's application to the court, may appoint a guardian of the person (s. 55). The court can order a guardian for some but not all aspects of care (i.e. a partial guardian) (s. 60(1)). The court may also appoint a full guardian who has broad powers including the power to make decisions about the persons living arrangements, health care, nutrition, hygiene, employment, education, treatment, and legal proceedings unrelated to the person's property or to the guardian's status or powers (s. 59).

Like the restrictions for a court appointed guardian of property, the court cannot appoint as a guardian of the person a person who provides health care, or residential, social, training, or support services to an incapable person for compensation, unless:

- that person is the spouse, partner, relative, attorney for personal care, or attorney under a continuing power of attorney for property of the incapable person; or
- the court is satisfied that there is no other person who is available and willing to be appointed (s. 57).

The court will only appoint the PGT as the guardian of the person if the PGT is the proposed guardian and there is no other suitable person available and willing to be appointed (s. 57(2.2)). As in the appointment of a guardian for property, when considering the appointment of a guardian of the person, the court must be guided by the over-arching principle that the arrangement it selects be in the best interests of the incapable person (*Bennet v. Gotlibowicz*, 2009, para. 19). The court must bear in mind three considerations, which are:

1. whether the proposed guardian is the attorney under a continuing power of attorney for property;
2. the incapable person's current wishes, if they can be ascertained; and
3. the closeness of the relationship between the proposed guardian to the incapable person (s. 57(3)).

The court can appoint two or more persons as joint guardians of the person, or may appoint each of them as guardian for a specified period of time (s. 57(4)).

Temporary guardian of the person

The court may also order the PGT to act as a temporary guardian of the person for a period of, at most, 90 days. The PGT must apply to the court for such an order, and must have reasonable grounds to believe that: the person is incapable of personal care; and an appointment of a temporary guardian is required to prevent serious illness or injury, or deprivation of liberty or personal security (s. 62).

Duties of power of attorney for personal care and guardian of the person

The duties of guardians of the person and attorneys for personal care are twofold. First, the guardian must make decisions in accordance with the prior wishes of the incapable person. These "prior wishes" are those wishes that the now incapable person expressed while he or she was capable. Second, if the guardian is not aware of any applicable prior wishes, then the guardian must take into consideration the best interests of the incapable person. The person's best interests should be ascertained in accordance with the person's values and beliefs, current wishes, and whether the decision being considered is likely to do more good than harm (ss. 66 and 67).

THE HEALTH CARE CONSENT ACT
Capacity to consent to treatment

The *Health Care Consent Act* (**HCCA**) grants Ontarians the right to be informed about a proposed treatment and the right to voluntarily consent to such treatment before being treated for any medical or therapeutic purpose (HCCA, ss. 10 and 11). A person is presumed to be capable and entitled to make his or her own decisions with respect to treatment (i.e. anything that is done for a therapeutic, preventive, palliative, diagnostic, cosmetic, or other health-related purpose) (HCCA, ss. 2(1) and 4(2)).[10]

While the SDA specifies a minimum age of 16 for capacity for personal care, including treatment (SDA, s. 2(2)), the HCCA does not specify a minimum age for capacity to consent to treatment (Hiltz & Szigeti, 2010, p. 169). Like the SDA, the test for capacity under the HCCA consists of two-parts. A person is capable of consenting to treatment if the person is able to:

- understand the information that is relevant to making a decision about the treatment, admission or personal assistance service, as the case may be; and
- appreciate the reasonably foreseeable consequences of a decision or lack of decision (HCCA, s. 4(2)).

Capacity to consent to treatment is not all or nothing; a person may be capable of consenting to one treatment but not another treatment, or capable of consenting at one time but not another time (HCCA, s. 15).

The Supreme Court of Canada has clarified that the wisdom of the person's decision with respect to treatment does not determine his or capacity to make that decision. If a person meets the two-part statutory test, above, then that person has the right to make treatment decisions, and the right to refuse treatment that a physician (or the CCB) believes is beneficial (*Starson v. Swayze*, 2003).

Informed consent

A health care practitioner proposing treatment assumes a patient is capable, and therefore must get the informed consent of the patient, rather than a Substitute Decision Maker, unless the practitioner has reasonable grounds to believe that the patient is incapable with respect to the treatment (HCCA, s. 4(3)). For consent to be informed, the patient or substitute decision maker must receive information on: the nature of the treatment; the expected benefits of the treatment; the material risks of the treatment; the material side effects of the treatment; alternative courses of action; and the likely consequences of not having the treatment. Additionally, the person must receive answers to questions that he or she may have about the treatment (HCCA, s. 11).

Selecting a substitute decision maker

When a person is found to be incapable of making a decision with respect to treatment for himself or herself, another person, known as a Substitute Decision Maker (**SDM**), may be granted authority to make decisions on the incapable person's behalf (HCCA, s. 20(1)). Section 20 of the HCCA lists possible substitute decision makers for purposes of consent to treatment. The list is hierarchical, with priority in descending order. A person cannot be an SDM if a higher ranked individual is able and willing to be the SDM (HCCA, s. 20(3)). The list of possible SDMs for an incapable person is as follows:

- a guardian of the person, if the guardian has authority to give or refuse consent to treatment;
- the person's power of attorney for personal care, if the power of attorney confers the authority to make treatment decisions;
- a representative appointed by the CCB pursu-

ant to the person's application to the CCB for a representative;
- the person's spouse or partner — partner includes any person with whom the incapable person has lived for at least one year and includes same-sex partners. Partners must have a close personal relationship, that is of primary importance in both their lives;
- the person's child or parent; or a Children's Aid Society; or other person who is lawfully entitled to give or refuse consent to treatment in place of a parent. This does not include a parent who only has a right of access;
- the person's parent who only has a right of access;
- the person's siblings; and
- any other relative of the person

An individual from the above list can only act as an SDM if he or she is at least 16 years old, capable with respect to the treatment, available, willing to assume the responsibility, and not prohibited by court order or separation agreement from making such a decision (HCCA, s. 20(2)). If no one from the above list is available, or where more than one SDM is available but they cannot agree on a treatment decision, then the PGT will make the decision with respect to treatment (HCCA, ss. 20(5) and 20(6)).

Limitations and guiding principles

The HCCA does not authorize an SDM to give substitute consent to non-therapeutic sterilization, transplant, or experimental research (HCCA, s. 6). The HCCA provides guiding principles for SDMs when making a decision to accept or refuse treatment on another person's behalf. First, if the SDM is aware of the incapable person's prior wishes with respect to treatment that the person expressed or held after the age of 16 and while capable, the SDM must give or refuse treatment in accordance with these wishes. For example, the currently incapable person may have told the SDM that he or she did not wish to be resuscitated in the event that resuscitation became necessary. The SDM should make treatment decisions that align with those wishes. If the SDM does not know of a wish that applies in the given circumstances, the HCCA requires that the SDM act in the person's best interests (HCCA, s. 21).

If a health care practitioner thinks that in consenting or not consenting to treatment the SDM is not acting in the incapable person's best interests or in accordance with the person's wishes, the practitioner can apply to the CCB to determine whether the SDM is in compliance with his or her obligations (HCCA, s. 37). Similarly, both the SDM and the practitioner can apply to the CCB for direction if an incapable person's wish with respect to treatment is unclear (HCCA, s. 35), or for permission to override a wish (HCCA, s. 36).

Challenging a finding of incapacity

The finding of incapacity to consent to treatment must be communicated to the subject of the proposed treatment. The communication requirements and form thereof vary, depending on whether the patient is inside or outside a psychiatric facility (Hiltz & Szigeti, 2010, p. 173; MHA; HCCA). A person is entitled to challenge the health care practitioner's finding that he or she is incapable of consenting to treatment by applying to the CCB for a review of the decision. Absent an emergency, the practitioner cannot begin treatment if the practitioner is informed that the person has applied or intends to apply to the CCB for a review of the finding of incapacity (HCCA, s. 25). This is also true when the patient or another person has applied to have the CCB appoint a representative to give or refuse consent to the treatment on the patient's behalf (HCCA, s. 18). Hiltz & Szigeti (2010, p. 180) note that historically, when a finding of incapacity is challenged, the CCB has upheld the treating physician's finding of incapacity. The CCB has found less than ten per cent of applicants capable on the issue of treatment.

Appeals: Any party to a proceeding before the CCB (such as an appeal from a finding of incapacity to consent to treatment or manage property) can appeal the CCB's decision to the Ontario Superior Court of Justice (HCCA, s. 80(1)). On appeals, the court is to review capacity findings of the CCB with deference, and determine whether the CCB arrived at a reasonable decision in applying the facts to the

law (*Starson v. Swayze*, 2003, para. 5). The court, sitting in this appellate jurisdiction, has all the powers of CCB. The court can substitute its opinion for that of a health practitioner, an evaluator, a substitute decision-maker, or the CCB. Alternatively, the court might refer the matter back to the CCB for another hearing (HCCA, s. 80(10)).

Effect of an appeal: The effect of an appeal from the CCB differs according to the type of decision being appealed. With respect to appeals from a finding of incapacity to manage property, the resulting statutory guardianship is not terminated until the appeal is disposed of (SDA, s. 20; *Hillier v. Milojevic*, 2009). The result is that the PGT retains control over the person's property while the person awaits his or her appeal from the CCB. On the other hand, where a decision with respect to treatment is challenged, the practitioner cannot administer the treatment until the appeal is disposed of (HCCA, s. 10(2)). By comparison, under the *Mental Health Act*, where a person appeals the CCB's confirmation of a certificate of involuntary admission to a psychiatric facility, the certificate remains effective until it is withdrawn or the appeal is disposed of (MHA, s. 48(11)).

Legal representation for incapable persons versus parties under a disability: If the capacity of a person who does not have legal representation is at issue in a proceeding under the SDA or an appeal from a decision of the CCB, a court may direct the PGT to arrange for legal representation for that person (SDA, s. 3(1)(a); *Hillier v. Milojevic*, 2010, para. 13). If the appeal is with respect to incapacity to consent to treatment under the HCCA, the CCB may direct Legal Aid Ontario to arrange for legal representation to be provided for the person (HCCA, s. 81(1)(a)). If the person does not qualify for a Legal Aid certificate to fund counsel he or she will be personally responsible to pay the legal fees (SDA, s. 3(2); HCCA, s. 81(2)).[11]

Although the person's capacity may be at issue in proceedings before the CCB or the court, for purposes of the SDA and the HCCA, the person is presumed to have the capacity to retain and instruct legal counsel for proceedings under the Acts (SDA, s. 3(1)(b); HCCA, s. 81(1)(b)). This presumption of capacity to retain legal counsel for SDA and HCCA proceedings is inconsistent with other civil proceedings. In civil proceedings other than proceedings initiated pursuant to the SDA, a person found incapable of managing his property or his personal affairs is referred to as "a party under disability." A party under a disability is presumed to lack capacity to instruct legal counsel, and, unless the court orders otherwise, can only litigate with the assistance of a litigation guardian to protect the person's interests. With the exception of the PGT or Children's Lawyer, a litigation guardian must in turn be represented by a lawyer (*Rules of Civil Procedure*, rr. 1.03(1), 7.01, and 7.05(3)).

Financial Entitlements and Supports

A person with disabilities may be eligible for certain publicly administered financial and employment supports. Such supports can be beneficial or critical to individuals who are unable to work — or whose job opportunities are limited — because of their disabilities. They are also beneficial to people who financially support dependants with disabilities. The following paragraphs canvas a few of these programs and some financial resources that may be available.

ONTARIO DISABILITY SUPPORT PROGRAM

The Ontario Disability Support Program (*ODSP*) offers both Income Support and Employment Support to eligible individuals. The support programs are administered by the Ministry of Community and Social Services under the *Ontario Disability Support Program Act*, 1997 (*ODSPA*), and regulations that interpret the ODSPA (Ministry of Community and Social Services (n.d.a)).

Income support

A person may qualify for ODSP Income Support if she or he is:

- 18 years or older;
- an Ontario resident;
- is in financial need; and
- either has a substantial physical or mental disability such that he or she qualifies as "a person with a disability" under the ODSPA, or is a member of a prescribed class of eligible individuals.

For the Ministry to determine an applicant's financial need and income eligibility for Income Support, the applicant must provide a significant amount of personal information and documentation. Where applicable, this information typically includes copies of an applicant's: birth certificate; immigration papers; Social Insurance Number (SIN); Ontario Health Insurance Plan (OHIP) card; and documents about housing costs, the applicant's income, and the applicant's assets.

If a spouse or partner of an applicant is part of the applicant's "benefit unit" (i.e., a person and all of his or her dependants on behalf of whom the person receives or applies for Income Support) that partner's assets and income will also be considered in determining financial eligibility. Although dependent children are part of the applicant's benefit unit, their earnings are exempt in the calculation of the applicant's income (Wintermute, 2003b).

As of June 30, 2010, the ODSP allows maximum liquid asset (savings) levels of $5,000 for a single person; an additional $2,500 for a couple ($7,500); and an additional $500 for each dependant who is not a spouse or partner (ODSPA, s. 5(1); O. Reg. 222/98, s. 27).

Income received or earned by an ODSP recipient is generally deducted from the Income Support he or she receives through ODSP (O. Reg. 222/98, s.37). Despite income deductions and prescribed asset maximums, the ODSPA exempts certain assets and income. These exemptions allow ODSP recipients to own and benefit from additional resources. Exempted assets include:

- an interest in the home where one lives (principal residence);
- an interest in a second home if the property is found necessary for the health or well-being of one or more members of the benefit unit;
- a motor vehicle of any value;
- a second motor vehicle valued up to $15,000, if it is required to allow a dependant to maintain employment outside the home;
- business assets and "tools of the trade" up to $20, 000;
- a prepaid funeral; and
- a student loan (O. Reg. 222/98, s. 28).[12]

Prescribed persons: There are certain prescribed persons who do not have to meet the disability criteria to be eligible for Income Support under the ODSP. They include persons who:

- on May 31, 1998, were recipients of benefits under the then *Family Benefits Act* under the categories of "disabled," "permanently unemployable," or "blind";
- receive federal Canada Pension Plan Disability (CPP-D) benefits;
- receive Quebec Pension Plan Disability benefits;
- are 65 or older but do not qualify for Old Age Security; or
- live in a mental health facility or a home for people with developmental disabilities (O. Reg. 222/98, s. 4(1)).

Eligibility: In addition to income eligibility, an applicant who is not a prescribed person must meet the qualifications of being a "person with a disability" as defined by the ODSPA. "Person with a disability" is defined by the ODSPA as a person with substantial physical or mental impairment, where the impairment: is continuous or recurrent; will last at least one year; and substantially restricts the person's activities of daily living, i.e. ability to take personal care of himself or herself, function in the community, and function in the workplace. The effects and duration of the impairment must be verified by a qualified health professional (ODSPA, s. 4).

Eligibility as a person with a disability is determined by the Disability Adjudication Unit (**DAU**) of the Ministry of Community and Social Services. Eligibility is determined based on forms filled in by health professionals. The applicant must provide a consent form for the release of medical information. Additionally, the applicant has the option to fill out a "Self-Report," in which the applicant can describe his or her experience of living with the disability and its impact.

Self-reporting and investigating eligibility: It is important for Income Support recipients to inform the Director of the ODSP about changes in their financial situation or other conditions of eligibility. Misreporting income might result in the province seeking reimbursement of any funds paid pursuant

to the ODSPA. Non-compliance with the requirements of the ODSPA and regulations can also result in support being cancelled or suspended (ODSPA, s. 9). Eligibility Review Officers under the ODSPA have broad powers of investigation to determine a person's past or present eligibility for ODSP benefits, including obtaining and executing a Provincial Offences Act search warrant, and requiring applicants, recipients, and others to provide information. An ODSP applicant or recipient may be subject to home visits, with or without notice, to determine initial or ongoing eligibility for Income Support (O. Reg. 222/98, s. 10).

Appeals: An applicant who disagrees with a decision about his or her eligibility for Income Support can request an internal review of the decision to ensure that the rules governing the program were applied correctly (i.e. that the provisions within the applicable statute and regulations were applied correctly). An applicant can request a further appeal from the internal review decision to the Social Benefits Tribunal (**SBT**). However, certain decisions cannot be appealed to the SBT (ODSPA, s. 21; O. Reg. 222/98, s. 57). If a person appeals and is unsatisfied with the decision of the SBT, he or she has a further right to appeal on questions of law to the Ontario Divisional Court, which is a branch of the Superior Court of Justice (ODSPA, s. 31).

Benefits: If a person qualifies for ODSP Income Support, the amount will be based on factors such as the size of the person's family; the age of the person's dependent children; and the person's shelter costs (O. Reg. 222/98, ss. 29 to 43.1). As of June 30, 2010, the maximum allowance for one person with no dependants (which includes an allowance for basic needs and shelter) was $1,042/month (O. Reg. 222/98, ss. 30 to 33).

If a person meets the criteria for Income Support under the ODSPA, the successful applicant and his or her benefit unit are eligible (with specified restrictions) for health benefits including:

- prescription drug coverage;
- required transportation;
- diabetic and surgical supplies; and
- the consumer contribution portion for an assistive device under the Assistive Device Program, administered by the Ministry of Health.

Additionally, ODSP recipients, other than dependent children who are over 18, are eligible for: dental coverage; vision care; and hearing aids (O. Reg. 222/98, s. 44).

Employment support

A person with a disability may also be entitled to Employment Support (*ES*) under the ODSPA (ODSPA, ss. 32 to 36; O. Reg. 223/98; Wintermute, 2003a). ES provides employment and training related goods and services to help individuals with disabilities find a job or start their own business. These prescribed ES goods and services are as follows:

- employment consultation and planning;
- employment preparation and training;
- job placement services;
- the cost of transportation required by a person in order to participate in employment consultation, training, and job placement;
- job coaching;
- tools and equipment necessary for a person's employment preparation and training or necessary for a person to begin employment;
- services of an interpreter, reader or note-taker;
- mobility devices; and
- prosthetic devices or devices to assist with mobility, speech, vision, hearing, and reading.

To qualify for ES, the applicant must: be an Ontario resident; be at least 16 years old; intend to and be able to maintain "competitive employment" (defined as earning at least minimum wage or equivalent if self-employed); and enter into a funding agreement that sets out how much the applicant and the program will each contribute to employment supports. Applicants with a taxable income over $51,000 must contribute up to 30 per cent to the costs of their supports.

A person eligible for Income Support may also be eligible for ES. A person receiving Income Support is, however, only eligible for ES if he or she has exhausted other benefits intended for rehabilitation and employment support and training. Alternatively, a person who is not an Income Support recipient may be eligible for ES if he or she has a verified physical or mental impairment that is continuous or recurrent; is expected to last one year; and presents a substantial barrier to competitive employment (ODSPA, s. 32).

A person does not have to verify his or her disability if: he or she is an ODSP Income Support recipient; is registered as legally blind with the Canadian National Institute for the Blind; or has attended a provincial school for students with disabilities. Otherwise, to qualify for ES, an applicant's disability must be verified by an audiologist, chiropractor, nurse, occupational therapist, optometrist, physician, physiotherapist, or psychologist (ODSPA, s. 32(2); O. Reg. 223/98, s. 3).

An individual is not eligible for ES if he or she is eligible for or receiving disability or rehabilitation benefits from other public or private sources, or is receiving financial assistance from Ontario Works (O. Reg. 223/98, s. 2). An applicant for ES has the right to request a review of the decision that he or she is ineligible. To request a review, the individual must send a letter to his or her local ES office outlining the reasons he or she disagrees with the decision. Unlike decisions pertaining to Income Support under the ODSPA, an individual who is denied ES under the ODSPA is not eligible to appeal the decision to the SBT (O. Reg. 223/98, s. 21(3)).

Assistance for children with severe disabilities

The ODSPA also provides for financial assistance, on an income-tested basis, for parents or other eligible persons caring for child with a significant disability. This program is called Assistance for Children with Severe Disabilities (*ACSD*) (O. Reg. 224/98). In order to be eligible the child must:

- be under 18;
- have been found to have severe disabilities; and
- be living with the person applying for the financial assistance (O. Reg. 224/98, s. 2).

Factors that determine the quantum of financial assistance include: the child's age; the household income; the expenses that the parent or person is incurring or might incur solely because of the child's disability; and the extent to which the child is severely limited in activities of "normal living" such as walking, communicating, feeding himself or herself, and bathing himself or herself (O. Reg.

224/98, s. 3). As of July 2010, the financial assistance available under ACSD was between $25/month and $440/month, to help with such costs as travel to doctors and hospitals, and special shoes and clothing (O. Reg. 224/98, s. 2(1)).

If eligible for ACSD, the applicant may be eligible for other ODSP benefits, provided these benefits are "necessary for the welfare of the child" and the expense of the benefit is not otherwise reimbursed (O. Reg. 224/98, s. 6; O. Reg. 222/98, s. 44(1)(1.1)). These benefits include the following: drug card; dental services; vision and hearing services and similar items — including an amount for a periodic oculo-visual assessment for every member of the benefit unit once every 24 months; the consumer contribution portion for an assistive device under the Assistive Devices Program, and the cost of eligibility assessment for such devices; and batteries and repair for mobility devices. Like decisions about Income Support, decisions about ACSD can be appealed to the SBT.

SPECIAL SERVICES AT HOME

The Special Services at Home (**SSAH**) Program is another program administered and funded through the Ministry of Community and Social Services that provides funding to parents of children and adults with developmental and physical disabilities. To be eligible, applicants must live in Ontario; require more support than their families can provide; and either be living at home with their family or, if not living with family, then they must not be in receipt of ministry funded residential services (Ministry of Community and Social Services, n.d.c).

ONTARIO WORKS

A person in need of immediate financial assistance, with or without a disability, can apply for support from Ontario Works (**OW**), pursuant to the *Ontario Works Act, 1997*. To be eligible for OW, an individual must:

- live in Ontario;
- require immediate financial assistance to help pay for food and shelter; and
- be willing to search for employment.

If eligible, the amount a person receives from OW will depend upon family size, income, assets, and housing costs. For persons who qualify for ODSP Income Support, the benefits available under ODSP exceed those available under OW. Further, OW allows for fewer income and asset exemptions than ODSP (Wintermute, 2003b; O. Reg. 134/98, ss. 38(1) and 40 to 44).[13]

INCOME TAX ACT

The Canadian income tax system can provide certain deductions, and exemptions to individuals with disabilities. An example of a benefit available from Canada's income tax system is the Disability Credit under the *Income Tax Act* (**ITA**), s. 118.3(2). This credit can be claimed by a person with disabilities, the person's spouse or common law partner, or by a person on whom a person with disabilities is dependant. This is, however, a non-refundable tax credit. This means that it is only deductible from taxable income and is therefore only valuable to those who would otherwise owe taxes. To be eligible for the Disability Credit, a qualified person (such as a physician) must certify that the individual with a claimed disability has a severe and prolonged mental or physical impairment that either markedly restricts his or her ability to perform an activity of daily living, or significantly restricts the ability to perform more than one basic activity of daily living.

A person under 60 and eligible for the Disability Credit is also eligible for the Registered Disability Savings Plan (**RDSP**) (ITA, s. 246.4(1)). The RDSP is a savings account in which earnings can accumulate free of tax.

Pursuant to the ITA's provisions for "disability related employment benefits" (ITA, s. 6(16)), employment benefits relating to the following are exempt from taxation:

- commuting between home and work, if the person is blind or has a severe and prolonged mobility impairment (ss. 118.3(1) and 118.4(1)); and
- an attendant to assist a person with his or performance duties if the person receiving assistance has a severe and prolonged mental or physical impairment.

A tax-payer can also deduct certain disability supports. The "disability supports deduction" allows a tax-payer to fully deduct eligible expenses up to the amount of income earned.

These deductions include the costs of medically prescribed services such as sign-language interpretation; real time captioning; an electronic speech synthesizer; voice recognition software; supplementary tutoring services; reading services; and a Braille note-taker (ITA, s. 64). These deductions cannot be claimed if they have already been claimed under a medical expenses tax credit (ITA, ss. 118.2 and 64(a)(iv)).

CANADA PENSION PLAN

The *Canada Pension Plan* (*CPP*) is federally administered by Social Development Canada. The CPP is a retirement program, but also provides a disability pension (the *CPP-D*) for individuals who have contributed sufficiently to the CPP through employment or self-employment, and whose disability prevents them from continuing regular employment. In addition, it provides survivor benefits to dependent children of CPP contributors who have died.

In 2009, to qualify for a disability benefit based on CPP contribution, an individual must have earned more than $4,600 in 2009 and made CPP contributions in 4 of the last 6 years, or, in 3 of the last 6 years if the applicant had contributed for at least 25 years (Service Canada (n.d.)).

Furthermore, a person must have a medical condition, and that condition must result in a disability that is "severe and prolonged." "Severe" means that the applicant has a mental or physical disability that regularly prevents him or her from doing any type of work (full-time, part-time or seasonal). "Prolonged" means that the disability is likely to be long-term and of infinite duration, or is likely to result in death (CPP, s. 42(2)).

In 2009, the CPP-D benefit included a fixed amount of $424.43 a month, plus an amount based on how much the individual had contributed, to a maximum of $1,105.99 per month. If a person is approved and receiving a CPP-D pension, a dependent child of the recipient can receive up to $213.99 per month. A dependent child is defined as being under the age of 18 or between 18 and 25 if attending school full time (Service Canada (n.d.)).

STUDENT FINANCIAL SUPPORT
Bursaries

Post-secondary students with disabilities may be eligible for provincial and federal bursaries and grants to cover their education related expenses. For example, the Bursary for Students with Disabilities provides a maximum of $2,000 per academic year to cover disability-related education costs. To be eligible for the bursary, a student must: be enrolled on either a full-time or part-time basis; have either permanent or temporary disabilities; have disability-related educational costs for equipment or services that are not covered by another agency or service; and be eligible for either the Ontario Student Assistance Program, if full time study, or the Ontario Special Bursary, if part time study (Ministry of Training, Colleges and Universities, n.d.).

Grant for services and equipment

Pursuant to the *Canada Student Financial Assistance Act, 1994*, and regulations under the Act, Students with permanent disabilities may also be eligible for a Canada Student Grant for Services and Equipment for Persons with Permanent Disabilities (formerly, the Canada Study Grant for the Accommodation of Students with Permanent Disabilities), which provides up to $8,000. To be eligible, the student must:

- have a permanent disability, defined as a functional limitation caused by a physical or mental impairment that restricts the ability of a person to perform the daily activities necessary to participate fully in post-secondary studies or in the labour force and is expected to remain with the person for the person's expected life;
- apply for and meet the eligibility criteria for assistance under the Canada Student Loans Program for full-time or part-time study; and
- require exceptional education-related services to perform the daily activities necessary to participate in studies at a post-secondary level. Such services may include tutors, oral or sign

interpreters, attendant care for studies, specialized transportation (to and from school only), note takers, readers, and braillers.

The student must provide: proof of the disability in the form of a medical certificate, a psychoeducational assessment, or documentation proving receipt of federal or provincial disability assistance; written confirmation that he or she requires exceptional education-related services or equipment from a person qualified to determine such needs; and documentation of the exact cost of the equipment and services.

Housing and Residential Support Services

Individuals with developmental disabilities in Ontario live in different types of residential settings, for which different laws may apply. This section reviews some of the different laws and regulations applicable to different residential settings. Some of these rules are specific to residences for individuals with disabilities, whereas others apply to the population in Ontario at large.

Developmental Services Act

The Developmental Services Act (**DSA**) and regulations pursuant to the DSA are administered by the Ministry of Community, Family and Children's Services and regulate facilities directly operated by the Ministry as well as certain group homes operated by community service providers.

The DSA authorizes the Minister to operate facilities that provide assistance or services to individuals with developmental disabilities, and provides a framework for securing funding for the facilities; inspecting the facilities; maintaining the facilities and equipment therein; maintaining safety and sanitary standards; ensuring the residents have access to medical care; and auditing and keeping financial records of facilities.

Rules for physical restraint of residents, including mandatory reporting of such restraint, are included in O. Reg. 272.

Services and supports to promote the Social Inclusion of Persons with Developmental Disabilities Act, 2008

On July 1, 2011, the DSA was replaced by *Services and Supports to Promote the Social Inclusion of Persons with Developmental Disabilities Act, 2008* ("*Social Inclusion Act*"),[14] which is also administered by the Ministry of Community, Family and Children's Services. To be eligible for services under the *Social Inclusion Act*, a person must be:

- an Ontario resident;
- over 18;
- a person with a disability, which, for the purpose of the Act, is defined as a person with significant limitations in cognitive functioning and adaptive functioning that:
  a. originated before the person reached 18 years of age;
  b. are likely to be life-long in nature; and
  c. affect areas of major life activity, such aspersonal care, language skills, learning abilities, the capacity to live independently as an adult or any other prescribed activity (*Social Inclusion Act*, ss. 3, 5, and 14).

The *Social Inclusion Act* governs how "service agencies" administer different types of services and supports for persons with disabilities, as well as how these services are funded, and how a person applies and is determined to be eligible for such services. A "service agency" is a corporation or prescribed entity that enters into a written funding agreement with the Minister of Community and Social Services to provide services for individuals with disabilities. The services provided by service agencies that are governed under the *Social Inclusion Act* include:

- services and supports related to activities of daily living (such as hygiene, dressing, grooming, meal preparation, etc.);
- services and supports related to community participation;
- services and supports related to caregiver respite;
- professional and specialized services;
- services and supports related to person-directed planning; and

- residential services and supports.

The residential services governed by the new act include the following:

- *Intensive Support Residence*: a staff-supported residence operated by a service agency in which: (a) one or two persons with developmental disabilities reside, and (b) each resident requires and receives intensive support that meets the prescribed requirements;
- *Supported Group Living Residence*: a staff-supported residence operated by a service agency, in which three or more persons with developmental disabilities reside and receive services and supports from the agency;
- *Host Family Residence*: the residence of a family, composed of one or more persons, in which a person with a developmental disability who is not a family member is placed by a service agency to reside and receive care, support, and supervision from the host family, in exchange for remuneration provided to the host family by the service agency; and
- *Supportive Independent Living Residence*: a residence operated by a service agency that is not supported by staff and in which one or more persons with developmental disabilities resides independently and receives support from an agency (*Social Inclusion Act*, s. 4).

Long-term Care Act & Community Care Access Centres

In Ontario, a person who requires in-home professional services, personal support services, or homemaking services is advised to contact a local Community Care Access Centre (**CCAC**). CCACs do the following:

- provide care in people's own homes;
- coordinate care in the community;
- provide information about community based services, including adult day programs;
- provide information about long-term care options;
- assess and authorize eligibility for admission to long-term care facilities; and

- maintain waiting lists for facilities in a particular geographic area ("Community Based Services in Ontario," 2004; "Entering a Long-Term Care Facility," 2004; Community Care Access Centres (n.d.)).

CCACs in Ontario are funded through the Ministry of Health and Long-term Care, and governed under the *Long-term Care Act, 1994*, the *Community Care Access Corporations Act, 2001*, and the regulations under both Acts. CCAC coordinators determine who is eligible for publicly funded in-home services, and they are responsible to arrange for the delivery of these services. CCAC coordinators also monitor a person's changing needs. For individuals found eligible for services, coordinators may be able to arrange for the following types of services: homemaking (e.g., laundry, shopping, finances, meal preparation, child care), personal support (e.g., personal hygiene, dressing, eating, bathing), and professional services (e.g., nursing, occupational therapy, physiotherapy, social work, speech-language pathology). Note that help within each of these areas may include training a person to do or assist with these activities, and providing prescribed equipment and supplies (*Long-term Care Act*, s. 2).

To be eligible for these above services, the person must:

- consent to an assessment for eligibility (*Long-term Care Act*, s. 24), or have a substitute decision maker who consents on her or his behalf pursuant to the provisions of the SDA and the HCCA;
- be insured under the *Health Insurance Act*; and
- have the proper features for the services in the home in which the services are provided, and the home must not pose a significant risk to the person delivering the services (O. Reg. 386/99, ss. 2, 2.1, and 3.4).

Additionally, to be eligible for homemaking services, a person must require homemaking services, or their caregiver must require such services in order to continue to provide the person with care (O. Reg. 386/99, s. 2). To be eligible for professional services, the services must be necessary to enable the person to remain in his or her home or enable him or her to return home from a hospital or other health care facility (O. Reg. 386/99, s. 3.4).

Further, school health support services may be available for children covered under OHIP who have health needs that impact their ability to attend at participate at school or to receive satisfactory instruction at home. As with other services, the school or home in which the services are provided has to have the proper features for the services, and must not pose a significant risk to the person delivering the services (O. Reg. 386/99, s. 5).

Long-Term Care Homes Act

A person with disabilities may be eligible to reside for the short term or long-term in a long-term care home (Ministry of Health and Long-Term Care, n.d.). Although younger adults may be eligible for admission, the average age of admission to long-term care facilities is 80 years old, therefore these options may be more relevant to elderly persons with disabilities ("Facilities for the Long-Term Care of the Elderly," 2004). Long-term care homes have been regulated under the H*omes for the Aged and Rest Homes Act*, the *Nursing Homes Act*, and the *Charitable Institutions Act*. As of July 1, 2010, short and long-term stays in long-term care facilities are regulated in accordance with the *Long-Term Care Homes Act, 2007* (***LTCHA***), which is administered by the Ministry of Health and Long-Term Care.

Under the LTCHA, a long-term care home is defined as a place that is licensed as a long-term care home under that Act, which includes a municipal home, an appropriately licensed joint home, or First Nations home (LTCHA, s. 2) (The provisions on licensing a long-term care home are at ss. 95 to 117 of the LTCHA). Services provided in long-term care homes include:

- nursing and personal care;
- regular and emergency medical care by an on-call physician;
- treatment and medication administration;
- assistance with activities of daily living;
- 24-hour supervision;
- room and board, including laundry services (special diets are also accommodated);

- pastoral services; and
- social and recreational programs.

The LTCHA generally prohibits a person who is not licensed or authorized under that Act from operating residential premises for persons requiring nursing care or in which nursing care is provided to two or more unrelated persons (LTCHA, s. 95). However, there are exemptions from this requirement, including premises falling under the jurisdiction of the *Private Hospitals Act*, and the *Public Hospitals Act*.

The LTCHA includes a Residents' Bill of Rights, which includes the right to be protected from abuse; the right not to be neglected by staff; the right to be properly sheltered, fed, clothed, groomed and cared for in a manner consistent with a person's needs; the right to live in a safe and clean environment; the right not to be restrained, except in the limited circumstances provided for under the Act; and the right to communicate in confidence, receive visitors of one's choice and consult in private with any person without interference (LTCHA, s. 3). The LTCHA also includes, but is not limited to, provisions for mandatory written care plans for each resident; services that must be available at a long-term care home (there must be both nursing services and personal support services to assist in activities of daily living); the operation of homes, including staff qualifications; the licensing of homes; funding for homes (funding may be provided by the Ministry of Health and Long-term Care); and admissions to a facility and movement to specialized units within the facility.

To be eligible for residency in a long-term care home, an individual must apply to a placement coordinator through their local CCAC. The placement coordinator must find that the following criteria are met (O. Reg. 79/10, s. 155(1)):

- the person is at least 18 years old;
- the person is an insured person under the *Health Insurance Act*;
- the person requires that nursing care be available on site 24 hours a day;
- the person either requires assistance with activities of daily living frequently throughout the day, or the person requires on-site supervision or monitoring frequently throughout the day to

ensure his or her safety or well-being;
- the publicly-funded community-based services available to the person and the other care-giving, support or companionship arrangements available to the person are not sufficient, in any combination, to meet the person's requirements; and
- the person's care requirements can be met in a long-term care home.

Further, a person who is the partner of a long stay resident is also eligible for admission if that person is at least 18 years old; insured under the *Health Insurance Act*; and if his or her care requirements can be met in a long-term care home (O. Reg. 79/10, s. 157(1)). Partner is defined as either of two persons who have lived together for at least one year and who have a close personal relationship that is of primary importance in both persons' lives (O. Reg. 79/10, s. 152).

By comparison with government operated Long-Term Care Homes, retirement homes are generally privately owned and operated. They do not receive funding from the Ministry of Health and Long-Term Care, and are not licensed or regulated by the Ministry. The regulation of privately funded homes is generally limited to those protections provided by tenancy laws under the *Residential Tenancies Act, 2006*, discussed below.

Residential Tenancies Act

The *Residential Tenancies Act* (**RTA**) (formerly the *Tenant Protection Act*) and regulations under the Act govern certain rights of tenants with developmental disabilities living in "care homes." Care homes are units occupied or intended to be occupied by persons for the purpose of receiving care services (e.g. boarding homes, retirement homes, and homes for special care). "Care services" are health care services, rehabilitative, or therapeutic services that assist with activities of daily living. Note that certain residences that provide care services, and that seem to meet the definition of a care home, are exempt from the application of the RTA. These exemptions include residences that are governed by other provincial legislation such as hospi-

tals and long-term care homes, and certain facilities established under the DSA. The exemptions from the RTA also apply to persons in custody, or confinement to accommodation for short-term respite care, and to homes where a person is intended to receive health care, rehabilitative, or therapeutic services for maximum one year (RTA, s. 5).

Care homes range in size from single family dwellings to larger institutions. Some are run for profit and others are non-profit. Care homes offer a range of services such as meals, nursing care, house-keeping, attendant care, and social programs. The landlord of the care-home determines which services will be provided ("Retirement Housing," 2004). The rights and requirements of "care homes" include (RTA, ss. 139 to 147):

- that the landlord provide an information package with details of the meals and services, before entering into a tenancy agreement;
- that until an information package is provided, the landlord cannot give notice of an increase in either rent or the cost of such services; and
- that there must be a written tenancy agreement between the tenant and landlord that sets out the care and services provided at the home and the cost of these services.

The tenancy agreement must also provide that the tenant has the right to consult a third party with respect to the agreement and to cancel the agreement within five days after the agreement has been entered into. If the landlord does not comply with the requirements of a written agreement, the Landlord and Tenant Board can order an abatement in rent.

With respect to a tenant's privacy rights, if the agreement so provides, a landlord has the right to enter a unit in a rental care home to check a tenant's condition. With written notice to the landlord, a tenant can unilaterally revoke the provision that gives the landlord right of entry.

With respect to increasing rent, a landlord must give a tenant 90 days notice for increase in rent, and rent can only be increased once every 12 months. Rent in care homes does not include the costs of meal or care services. There are no notice requirements for increases in the cost of these services, and there are no caps on the costs for such services.

A tenant of a care home can terminate tenancy by giving the landlord 30 days notice. On the other hand, with limited exception, a landlord can only terminate a care-home tenancy under the following conditions: the rental unit was occupied solely for the purpose of receiving rehabilitative or therapeutic services agreed upon by the tenant and the landlord; no other tenant in the same facility who occupied a unit for the same purpose is allowed to live in the unit beyond four years; and the period of tenancy agreed to has expired. If these conditions are met, the landlord must still give at least 28 days notice to terminate the tenancy with a daily or weekly tenant and 60 days notice for all other tenants.

Social Housing Reform Act

The *Social Housing Reform Act, 2000* (**SHRA**) and regulations under the SHRA govern the administration of "rent-geared-to-income" (**RGI**) housing and "special needs housing" in Ontario.[15] The SHRA applies to non-profit housing and non-profit housing co-operatives developed through provincial programs. It does not apply to federal non-profit and urban native housing (City of Toronto, 2008). RGI assistance is financial assistance provided for a household under a housing program to reduce the amount of rent that the household would otherwise pay to live in a unit in a housing project (SHRA, s. 2). RGI rent is calculated based on the total amount of income and the sources of income received by all members of the household.

"Special needs housing" means a unit that is either occupied by or made available for occupancy by a household in which one or more members require either accessibility modifications or provincially-funded support services in order to live independently in the community (SHRA, s. 2). A "supportive housing provider" operates a housing project that provides special needs housing (SHRA, s. 2).[16]

Service managers

The SHRA delegates the administration of RGI housing and special needs housing to "service managers," which are municipalities or other boards or commissions that represent geographic areas (i.e.

service areas) within the province (SHRA, ss. 2 and 4). The Minister of Municipal Affairs and Housing decides what geographic area is the service area for a municipality (SHRA, s. 4(2)). For example, the City of Toronto, the City of Hamilton, and other municipalities are service managers in Southern Ontario (O. Reg. 298/01, Table 11). In turn, the municipalities can delegate responsibilities under the SHRA to administrators (SHRA, s. 15). In the City of Toronto, for example, the administration of RGI housing has been delegated to Toronto Community Housing Corporation, which is a Local Housing Corporation as defined by the SHRA. Service managers may construct housing projects and alter housing projects in land that the service manager has acquired in its service area. Such alterations may include modifying units so that they will be accessible for persons with disabilities (SHRA, s. 5).

Eligibility for RGI

In order to be eligible for RGI assistance for a unit in a designated housing project, a member of the household must apply to his or her service manager with the appropriate documentation (SHRA, s. 65). The eligibility requirements for RGI assistance include the following (O. Reg. 298/01, s. 7):

- at least one member of the household is 16 years old or older and is able to live independently (i.e. the individual can perform the normal essential activities of daily living. An individual who requires and receives support services to perform these activities is considered independent);
- each member of the household is either a Canadian citizen or an applicant for permanent residency or refugee protection in Canada;
- no member of the household owes rent, money for damages, or owes a service manager reimbursement for having paid lower rent than the rent eligible for in a previous housing project tenancy (this may not apply if the service manager is satisfied that there were extenuating circumstances or the applicants intend to repay the money owed); and
- no member of the household has been convicted of an offence related to RGI assistance

(with limited exception).

A service manager may establish local eligibility rules that specify that a household is only eligible for RGI assistance if the household's gross income or the value of the household's aggregate assets is equal to or less than a specified amount (O. Reg. 298/01, s. 8).

The Regulation specifies which assets are exempt from the definition of income for the purposes of calculating RGI entitlement (O. Reg. 298/01, s. 8(12)). A household is not eligible to receive RGI assistance if a member of the household has a legal or beneficial interest in residential property inside or outside of Ontario. If an eligible household member acquires an interest in a residential property, the household member must report the interest to the service manager immediately and divest himself or herself of this interest within 180 days in order to remain eligible for RGI assistance (O. Reg. 298/01, s. 9). Note that unlike the rules under the SHRA, the rules for ODSP Income Support eligibility (discussed above) exempt a primary residence in calculating the applicant's assets. By comparison, the income level permitted for RGI assistance in a given region may be higher than permitted for ODSP support. It is important that an applicant with a disability who applies for OSDP Income Support and RGI assistance be aware that assets or income that may be allowed under one act may be prohibited, and preclude eligibility for support under another act.

The service manager determines whether the applicant is eligible for RGI assistance (SHRA, s. 66(1)), determines what type of accommodation is permissible for the household (For example, the service manager may determine that a household is eligible for a unit with a certain number of bedrooms) (SHRA, s. 67(1)), and determines the amount of RGI rent payable by an eligible household (SHRA, s. 69(1); see O. Reg. 298/01, ss. 46 to 54 for calculations). Because a household's financial needs and eligibility may change over time, the service manager continues to determine a household's ongoing eligibility for RGI assistance and accommodation (SHRA, ss. 66(2) and 67(2)).

Once a household is found eligible for RGI assistance, the service manager reviews eligibility at least once every 24 months. Once a household begins to receive RGI assistance, the service manager reviews eligibility at least once every 12 months (O. Reg. 298/01, s. 11). A household can cease to be eligible for a number of reasons, including an unreported change in income or asset level and a resulting change in rent payable (O. Reg. 298/01, s. 12).

When a household applies for RGI assistance, the service provider must provide written notice of eligibility for assistance, accommodation type, and rent payable (SHRA, ss. 66(5), 67(4), and 69(3)). Even if the service manager finds that a household is eligible for RGI assistance within a designated housing project, the service manager may not have an appropriate unit available at the time. Where the demand for RGI assistance exceeds the available units in a given region, households that are eligible for RGI assistance are put on waiting lists in accordance with priority rules established under the SHRA (SHRA, s. 68). The waiting lists are generally established on a first come fist serve basis; however, victims of abuse have priority.

Eligibility for special needs housing

As with applications for RGI assistance, a household who wants special needs housing in a designated housing project must apply to the appropriate service manager and provide the required documentation (SHRA, s. 71). A household is eligible for special needs housing if one or more of its members require accessibility modification or provincially funded support service in order to live independently in the community. A household does not need to be eligible for RGI assistance in order to be eligible for special needs housing (O. Reg. 298/01, s. 19).

The service manager determines initial and continuing eligibility both for special needs housing and for the type of accommodation appropriate for the household. The service manager must also provide written notice of eligibility and accommodation type (SHRA, ss. 72 and 73). Once a household is found eligible for special needs housing, the service manager reviews eligibility at least one every 24 months. Once a household is granted special needs housing, the service manager reviews eligibility at least once every 12 months (O. Reg. 298/01, s. 21). Eligibility ceases if the household member who initially required support no longer requires that support, or the member is no longer a part of the household (O. Reg. 298/01, s. 22). If a household is eligible, the service manager, supportive housing provider, or a lead agency, as defined by the SHRA, are responsible for establishing and administering waiting lists for Special Needs Housing, in accordance with priority rules (SHRA, s. 74).

Summary

This chapter discussed laws that govern some of the rights, benefits, and entitlements for persons with disabilities in Ontario. It included an overview of laws and regulations that govern equality rights; accessibility; consent and capacity; financial benefits and programs for persons with disabilities; and housing for persons with disabilities. However, this chapter is not exhaustive. There are other laws, some of which have not yet come into effect, which may directly or indirectly affect the rights and entitlements of persons with disabilities. These rights and entitlements develop and change over time through the actions of policy makers and legislators who enact the law, and by the intervention of courts and tribunals who interpret it.

Some of the rights discussed are automatic, such as the right not to be discriminated against; the right to be presumed capable to consent to treatment; and the right, if capable of consent, to refuse treatment. Although there is a duty on service providers to accommodate individuals with disabilities, many accommodations will not be automatic; rather, an individual might have to alert the service provider of his or her needs and request specific accommodations. Further, rights to a publicly funded or subsidized benefit or service are usually not automatic. Generally, individuals must fulfill legal requirements before they become entitled to a benefit or service. For example, persons with disabilities or financial needs must apply for and be found eligible for the income tax deductions, income support, employment support, and housing programs discussed herein. We encourage readers to learn more about their rights, exercise these rights, and apply for and take advantage of the benefits that they are entitled to.

Glossary of Acronyms

ACSD:	Assistance for Children with Severe Disabilities
CCB:	Consent and Capacity Board
CCAC:	Community Care Access Centre
CPP:	Canada Pension Plan
CPP-D:	Canada Pension Plan Disability Benefit
DAU:	Disability Adjudication Unit
DSA:	Developmental Services Act
ES:	Employment Support
HCCA:	Health Care Consent Act, 1996
ITA:	Income Tax Act
LTCHA:	Long-Term Care Homes Act, 2007
MHA:	Mental Health Act
ODSP:	Ontario Disability Support Program
ODSPA:	Ontario Disability Support Program Act, 1997
OW:	Ontario Works
PGT:	Public Guardian and Trustee
RDSP:	Registered Disability Savings Plan
RGI:	Rent-geared-to-income
RTA:	Residential Tenancies Act
SBT:	Social Benefits Tribunal
SDA:	Substitute Decisions Act, 1992
SDM:	Substitute Decision Maker
SHRA:	Social Housing Reform Act, 2000
SSAH:	Special Services At Home

Endnotes

[1] The original version of this chapter —Entitlements for People with Developmental Disabilities. (2003). In Brown, I. & Percy M. (Eds.) *Developmental Disabilities in Ontario* (2nd ed.), Toronto: Ontario Association on Developmental Disabilities — was authored by Patricia Peppin, Harry Beatty, and David Baker. The current authors have rewritten the original chapter and changed its scope and focus.

[2] Municipal governments are also bound by the Charter in that they operate on delegated authority from the provinces.

[3] See British Columbia (Public Service Employee Relations Commission) v. BCGSEU, [1999] 3 S.C.R. 3 for a discussion of mandatory eligibility requirements for fire-fighters. This case challenged fitness

requirements for fire fighters. The fitness requirements were not reasonable or bona fide for the purposes of carrying out the job in question, but had the effect of excluding women from being eligible for the job. The eligibility rules were challenged as a breach of British Columbia's human rights legislation and the Charter.

4   Please note that that the government has proposed a new regulation under the Accessibility for Ontarians with Disabilities Act. The "Proposed Integrated Accessibility Regulation" will prescribe accessibility requirements in the areas of information and communications, employment, and transportation.

5   Under the MHA, there are separate laws regarding capacity to manage property and consent to treatment that apply to patients within a psychiatric facility. The MHA governs the treatment of individuals within psychiatric facilities, as well as psychiatric assessments and voluntary, involuntary, and informal admission of individuals with mental disorders to such facilities. Among other provisions, the MHA sets out some of the legal and procedural requirements for police officers and physicians in relation to involuntarily apprehending, detaining and treating person with a mental disorder within a psychiatric facility. A discussion of the MHA is beyond the scope of this chapter. For an analysis of the MHA, see Hiltz & Szigeti, 2010, pp. 277 to 316.

6   Unless otherwise noted, all statutory sections referred to in this part of the Chapter on the SDA refer to provisions in that Act.

7   Pursuant to s. 2 of Capacity Assessment, O. Reg. 460/05 of the SDA, qualified assessors include registered physicians, nurses, occupational therapists, social workers, and psychologists who have taken a specified course and meet other enumerated criteria.

8   The prescribed forms, as well as a guide to capacity assessments, are available online from the Ministry of the Attorney General.

9   The parties before the CCB are the applicant, the assessor, and any person the CCB specifies (SDA, s. 20.2(4)).

10   The HCCA also applies to consent to admission to a long-term care home (ss. 38 to 54.1) and to personal assistance services (i.e. activities of daily living such as hygiene, dressing, elimination) for people already in a long-term care facility (ss. 55 to 69.1). This chapter, however, focuses on consent to treatment.

11   In Hillier v. Milojevic, 2010, at para. 17, Brown J. notes that appellants from the CCB to the court find it "almost impossible to secure a Legal Aid certificate for their appeal."

12   See O. Reg. 222/98, s. 28, for a full list of exempted assets, and ss. 41 to 43 for exempted income. Caution should be exercised if the recipient of ODSP benefits from other forms of social assistance. As will be discussed in the housing part of this Chapter, while an interest in residential property may be excluded from the consideration of entitlement for ODSP, if the person lives in subsidized housing, for example, an interest in residential real estate may render him or her ineligible for rental subsidy.

13   As of June 30, 2010, the maximum allowance under OW for a single recipient with no benefits was $585. Additionally, the prescribed asset value limit under OW for a single person with no dependants was $585.

14   For information about the new legislation, see Ministry of Community and Social Services (n.d.b). Some parts of the new Act came into force July 1, 2010, and others will come into force January 1, 2011 and July 1, 2011.

15   The Social Housing Reform Act will be repealed by Bill 140, "An Act to enact the Housing Services Act, 2010, repeal the Social Housing Reform Act, 2000 and make complementary and other amendments to other Acts." The purpose of the Housing Services Act, 2010 relates to the provisions of housing and homelessness services with provincial oversight. The Act will amend aspects of the Residential Tenancies Act, 2006. The text of Bill-140 is at: http://www.ontla.on.ca/bills/bills-files/39_Parliament/Session2/b140.pdf

16   Supportive Housing Providers are listed in O. Reg. 298/01, Table 2, and in O. Reg. 456/01.

For Further Thought and Discussion

1. The *Ontario Disability Support Program Act* provides at section 5(2) that a person is not eligible for income support if the person is dependant on alcohol, a drug, or some chemically

active substance that has not been prescribed, and that person's addiction is the primary cause of the person's inability to participate in activities of daily living. The courts in Ontario held that this provision discriminated on the basis of disability, in contravention of the Charter (See *Ontario (Disability Support Program) v. Tranchemontagne*, 2010, ONSC 593 (CanLII), at *http://www.canlii.org/eliisa/highlight.do?text =disability+%2Fs+alcohol&language=en&sear chTitle=Ontario&path=/en/on/onca/doc/2010/ 2010onca593/2010onca593.html*). Argue both for and against this provision in the ODSPA. That is, argue the benefits and costs of making income support available in the circumstances described in section 5(2), and argue the benefits and costs of precluding income support in the same circumstances.

2. Discuss the benefits or costs of establishing a continuing power of attorney for property, and consider the qualities that you would look for in the individual to whom you would give the power of attorney. Do the same for a power of attorney for personal care.

4. Given the various programs outlined in this chapter, discuss in the context of each of the three circumstances listed below: a) potential supports; b) the steps that you would take to try to obtain those supports; and c) possible barriers or challenges to obtaining supports.

 a. You are an unemployed adult with disabilities, and although you are physically capable of taking care of yourself, you do not have sufficient income to pay your rent and to support yourself. Right now, you are living at home with your parents, but they do not have sufficient income to continue to support you.

 b. You are an adult with a permanent disability, and you want to attend university. You do not have sufficient income for university tuition, and you are also concerned that there will be physical barriers to your attendance in classes.

 c. You have been living and working independently in the community, but you are having difficulty with activities like banking and grocery shopping. You are finding it increasingly difficult to prepare meals, wash your laundry, and bathe.

More Resources

ARCH Disability Law Centre
http://www.archdisabilitylaw.ca/
(See links to disability organizations at: *http://www.archdisabilitylaw.ca/?q=useful-links/ disability-organizations*)

CanLII
http://www.canlii.org/

COTA Health
http://www.cotahealth.ca/

e-laws Ontario
http://www.e-laws.gov.on.ca/navigation?file= home&lang=en

Hiltz, D'A., & and Szigeti, A. (2010). *A guide to consent and capacity law in Ontario.* Toronto, ON: LexisNexis.

Human Rights Tribunal of Ontario
http://www.hrto.ca

Human Rights Legal Support Centre
http://www.hrlsc.on.ca

Long-term Care Facilities in Ontario: The Advocates Manual (3rd ed.). Toronto, ON: Advocacy Centre for the Elderly.

Ministry of Community and Social Services
http://www.mcss.gov.on.ca/en/mcss/

Ministry of Health and Long-Term Care
http://www.health.gov.on.ca/

Ministry of Training, Colleges and Universities
http://www.tcu.gov.on.ca/eng/

Office of the Public Guardian and Trustee
http://www.attorneygeneral.jus.gov.on.ca/english/ family/pgt/

References

Legislation:

Accessibility for Ontarians with Disabilities Act, 2005, S.O. 2005, c. 11.

Accessibility Standards for Customer Service, O. Reg. 429/07.

Canada Pension Plan, R.S.C. 1985, c. C-8.

Canada Student Financial Assistance Act, S.C. 1994, c. 28.

Canadian Charter of Rights and Freedoms, Part I of the Constitution Act, 1982, being Schedule B to the Canada Act 1982 (U.K.), 1982, c. 11.

Charitable Institutions Act, R.S.O. 1990, c. C-9.

Community Care Access Corporations Act, 2001, S.O. 2001, c. 33.

Developmental Services Act, R.S.O. 1990, c. D-11 General, O. Reg. **272.**

Health Care Consent Act, 1996, S.O. 1996, c. 2, Sched. A.

Health Insurance Act, R.S.O. 1990, c. H-6.

Homes for the Aged and Rest Homes Act, R.S.O. 1990, c. H-13.

Human Rights Code, R.S.O. 1990, c. H-19.

Income Tax Act, R.S.C. 1985, c. 1 (5th Supp.).

Long-term Care Act, 1994, S.O. 1994, c. 26.
- Provision of Community Services, O. Reg. 386/99.
- Long-Term Care Homes Act, 2007, S.O. 2007, c. 8.
- General, O. Reg. 79/10.

Mental Health Act, R.S.O. 1990, c. M-7.

Nursing Homes Act, R.S.O. 1990, c. N-7.

Ontarians with Disabilities Act, 2001, S.O. 2001, c. 32.

Ontario Disability Support Program Act, 1997, S.O. 1997, c. 25, Sched. B
- General, O. Reg. 222/98.
- Employment Support, O. Reg. 223/98.
- Assistance for Children with Severe Disabilities, O. Reg. 224/98.

Ontario Works Act, 1997, S.O. 1997, c. 25, Sched. A.
- General, O. Reg. 134/98

Private Hospitals Act, R.S.O. 1990, c. P-24.

Public Hospitals Act, R.S.O. 1990, c. P-20.

Residential Tenancies Act, 2006, R.S.O. 2006, c. 17.
- General, O. Reg. 516/06.

Rules of Civil Procedure, R.R.O. 1990, Reg. 194.

Services and Supports to Promote the Social Inclusion of Persons with Developmental Disabilities Act, 2008, S.O. 2008, c. 14.

Social Housing Reform Act, 2000, S.O. 2000, c. 27.
- Rent-Geared-to-Income Assistance and Special Needs Housing, O. Reg. 298/01.
- Supportive Housing Providers - Section 64 of the Act, O. Reg. 456/01.

Substitute Decisions Act, 1992, S.O. 1992, c. 30.

Capacity Assessment, O. Reg. 460/05.

Other References:

Bennet v. Gotlibowicz, [2009] O.J. No. 1438 (S.C.).

British Columbia (Public Service Employee Relations Commission) v. BCGSEU, [1999] 3 S.C.R. 3.

City of Toronto – Social Housing Unit, "Rent Geared to Income Guide" (30 May 2008). Retrieved from www.toronto.ca/housing/social_housing/rgi/rgi_guide_2008edition_rev_dec_09.pdf

Community Based Services in Ontario. (2004). In G. Monticone (Ed.), *Long-term care facilities in Ontario: The advocates manual* (3rd ed.) (p. 11.1). Toronto, ON: Advocacy Centre for the Elderly.

Community Care Access Centres. (n.d.). Retrieved July 8, 2010 from http://www.ccac-ont.ca/

Entering a Long-Term Care Facility. (2004). In G. Monticone (Ed.), *Long-term care facilities in Ontario: The advocates manual* (3rd ed.) (p. 3.2). Toronto, ON: Advocacy Centre for the Elderly.

Facilities for the Long-Term Care of the Elderly and the Impact of Long-Term Care Reform. (2004). In G. Monticone (Ed.), *Long-term care facilities in Ontario: The advocates manual* (3rd ed.) (p. 2.1). Toronto, ON: Advocacy Centre for the Elderly.

Hillier v. Milojevic, [2009] O.J. No. 5786 (S.C.).

Hillier v. Milojevic, 2010 ONSC 435, [2010] O.J. No. 159 (S.C.).

Hiltz, D'A., & Szigeti, A. (2010). *A guide to consent and capacity law in Ontario.* Toronto, ON: LexisNexis.

Human Rights Tribunal of Ontario. (n.d.). Retrieved from *http://www.hrto.ca*

Human Rights Legal Support Centre. (n.d.). Retrieved from *http://www.hrlsc.on.ca*

Re Koch (1997), 33 O.R. (3d) 486 (Gen. Div).

Ministry of Community and Social Services. (n.d.a). *Ontario Disability Support Program.*

Retrieved from http://www.mcss.gov.on.ca/en/mcss/programs/social/odsp/

Ministry of Community and Social Services. (n.d.b). *About the services and supports to promote the Social Inclusion of Persons with Developmental Disabilities Act, 2010.* Retrieved from http://www.mcss.gov.on.ca/en/mcss/publications/developmentalServices/servicesSupportsSocialInclusion.aspx

Ministry of Community and Social Services. (n.d.c). *Special Services at Home.* Retrieved from http://www.mcss.gov.on.ca/en/mcss/programs/developmental/servicesAndSupport/specialServicesAtHome.aspx

Ministry of Health and Long-Term Care. (n.d.). *Seniors care: Long-term care homes.* Retrieved from http://www.health.gov.on.ca/english/public/program/ltc/15_facilities.html#top

Ministry of the Attorney General. (n.d.). *Public guardian and trustee: Capacity assessment.* Retrieved from http://www.attorneygeneral.jus.gov.on.ca/english/family/pgt/capacity.asp

Ministry of Training, Colleges and Universities. (n.d.). *Bursary for students with disabilities.* Retrieved from https://osap.gov.on.ca/OSAPPortal/en/A-ZListofAid/UCONT004257.html

Picard, E. I., & Robertson, G. B. (2007). *Legal liability of doctors and hospitals in Canada* (4th ed.). Toronto, ON: Thomson Carswell.

Retirement Housing – Care Homes. (2004). In G. Monticone (Ed.), Long-term care facilities in Ontario: The advocates manual (3rd ed.) (p. 9.1). Toronto, ON: Advocacy Centre for the Elderly.

Service Canada. (n.d.). *Canadian Pension Plan (CPP) Disability Benefits.* Retrieved from http://www.servicecanada.gc.ca/eng/isp/cpp/applicant.shtml#contrib

Starson v. Swayze (2003), 225 D.L.R. (4th) 385 (S.C.C.).

Wintermute, D. (2003a). Ontario Disability Support Program: Employment Supports Program. CLE Disability law primer: A continuing legal education program for Ontario lawyers. ARCH Disability Law Centre. Retrieved from http://www.archdisabilitylaw.ca/sites/all/files/11_odsp_employment-Support.pdf

Wintermute, D. (2003b). Ontario Disability Support Program: Income Supports. CLE Disability law primer: A continuing legal education program for Ontario lawyers. ARCH Disability Law Centre. Retrieved from http://www.archdisabilitylaw.ca/sites/all/files/10_odsp_incomeSupport.pdf

7

Self-Advocacy

Ann Fudge Schormans, Carol Krause, Kelly MacDougall and Kerr Wattie

What you will learn:

- Why it is important to hear the voices of people with developmental disabilities
- A brief history of self-advocacy
- What we mean by self-advocacy
- Talking about Self-Advocacy: Self-Advocacy Theory
- What self-advocacy is and is not
- Why self-advocacy is important

The voices of people with developmental disabilities themselves are at the heart of this chapter. Too often they are talked about and not heard. This chapter is part of an ongoing conversation with people who have disabilities about what it means to speak out and to make decisions about their lives, and about how they wish to make a difference in their own lives and in the lives of others. The forms of self-advocacy, even the term itself, will change over time. The ideas in this chapter may also come to be seen as out-dated or even as being quite obvious. And that is a good thing — it means that people with and without developmental disabilities have continued to question the meaning of disability, of self-advocacy, of having a voice and being heard. It means that they are adapting ideas to new challenges and situations. What is important is that each of us be open to lis-

tening to how people with developmental disabilities are expressing themselves and challenging the ways that they are seen, understood, and treated by non-disabled people. By breaking down barriers and working with people with developmental disabilities to build supportive spaces for people to develop confidence and skills and opportunities to exercise leadership in their own lives and the lives of others, this conversation can continue.

To do this, we must extend our understanding of *inclusion* to the spaces of research and academic writing. When people with developmental disabilities can claim their right to these spaces, they will change them and thus disrupt both how disability is understood and relations between people with and without disabilities. When, for example, the voices of people labelled developmentally disabled are included in a textbook written to teach non-disabled or differently disabled people about developmental disability, people with developmental disabilities are recognized as having knowledge that counts, that needs to be shared, and that must be listened to. This unsettles our understanding of developmental disability. It challenges our understanding of what counts as knowledge. And it turns the idea of "expert" on its head. It also changes people with developmental disabilities. When what people with developmental disabilities have to say is written down and published in textbooks, journals, and other academic texts, they may develop a different sense of their own value, abilities, and power to effect change. Having their experiences and knowledge validated, they may then also come to expect more — to expect and insist upon this type of inclusion (Fudge Schormans, 2010a). As a disability activist, Charlton (1998) demanded "nothing about us without us." His demand is for disabled people to speak and write for themselves instead of having non-disabled people such as parents, caregivers, professional and academic "experts" speak for them. It is people with disabilities who are the real experts, the real knowers (Charlton, 1998). The voices of people with developmental disabilities must be more often and more meaningfully included in research and writing about developmental disability.

This chapter is intended to be one of those inclusive spaces. It was written by four people: self-advocates Kerr Wattie and Kelly MacDougall, and Ann Fudge Schormans and Carol Krause, who are allies. As a group, we met several times to talk about what self-advocacy means and to map out what we thought should be included in this chapter. We worked separately and together to share our experiences, thoughts, and ideas about the meaning of self-advocacy. Other voices were also included: self-advocates Peter Park and Andrew Lewis shared their thoughts on rights and responsibilities. The voices of academic writers and researchers are included to provide an overview of the literature on self-advocacy. Ann and Carol worked to bring these different voices together in a way that respects each of our perspectives and also comes together as a unified piece of writing. We wished, in this chap-

ter, to "create a space where we can think and act with one another to multiply the levels of knowing upon which resistance can act" (Roets, Goodley, & Van Hove, 2007, p. 331). Ann's and Carol's role is not to speak for, but to engage with, people with disabilities, while also bringing forward some of what they themselves have learned in supporting self-advocacy. As allies, Ann and Carol are witnessing the struggles of people with developmental disabilities and working to support their self-advocacy and their efforts to change the world.

Weaving together the voices of "insiders" (self-advocates) and "outsiders" (allies and non-disabled researchers) provides different textures to this chapter. This means that different languages are brought together. For example, people with developmental disabilities themselves may sometimes have quite different ideas about self-advocacy. They may speak in different voices that change what it means to be a self-advocate or to speak out. Also, much of the theory about self-advocacy is written by non-disabled people and in a language that does not reflect the language of people with developmental disabilities. It is not written for people with developmental disabilities but for non-disabled readers, and therefore it is not always clear or accessible. Rather than trying to completely change the theoretical language that is used, this language is included to highlight that it is part of the conversation about self-advocacy. In writing this chapter for people with and without developmental disabilities, we have tried to use plainer language to share this information. It was not always easy to find simpler words, but by doing so we are reflecting our commitment to self-advocacy, and we are illustrating how people are often excluded in academic writing. In this way, the "medium is the message" — the language used tells a story. Thus, this is a story about the importance of talking *with*, rather than talking *about* people with developmental disabilities.

A Brief History Of Self-Advocacy

The concept of self-advocacy for people with developmental disabilities began to be talked about in Canada in the late 1960s and early 1970s. It is believed to have started in Sweden, with Bengt Nirje's work on *normalization*. Strongly connected to the push for de-institutionalization, which was largely started by parents of people with developmental disabilities, it was also modelled after self-advocacy efforts by women and by African Americans/Canadians in the women's and civil rights movements of the 1950s and 1960s. These civil rights movements had influenced the independent living movement for people with physical disabilities — a movement that quickly spread to include people with other disabilities as well (Shapiro, 1993; Test, Fowler, Wood, Brewer, & Eddy, 2005). The independent living movement did not, at first, include people with developmental disabilities. Nonetheless, people labelled developmentally disabled and their allies soon began to adopt self-advocacy ideas. In Canada, in1973, the British Columbia Association for the Mentally Handicapped held the first ever North American self-advocacy conference. Organized for people who had been institutionalized, this was the first time people with developmental disabilities were supported to come together to talk about their experiences and the issues important to their lives. This was followed by a conference in Oregon in the United States in 1974, and the coining of the term People First (Bersani, 1998; Shapiro, 1993).

The first People First group in Canada was formed in British Columbia in 1974. Members from this and other provincial People First groups formed an alliance with The Canadian Association for Community Living in 1979 as a means of influencing national efforts and services for people with developmental disabilities (People First of Canada, 2011a). In Ontario, self-advocacy groups started in the late 1970s (Hutton, Park, Park, & Rider, 2010). Self-advocacy groups across the country shared many similarities, but there were also differences among them — different names, goals, and organizational structures. What they had in common was a commitment to people with developmental disabilities speaking for themselves (Hutchinson, Arai, Pedlar, Lord, & Yuen, 2007), and the belief that people with developmental disabilities could be responsible for their own social organizations (Test et al., 2005). In 1991, many of these groups were brought together under the umbrella of a national self-advocacy organization — People First of Canada. This national group oversees several provincial affiliates and these, in turn, each have many local or regional groups (Hutchinson, et al., 2007). Many other self-advocacy groups, not affiliated with People First, are also operating in Ontario and across Canada.

What Do We Mean By Self-Advocacy?

The word *self-advocacy* is just that — a word. It can become a label if not used carefully. There are many different meanings of self-advocacy (Beart, Hardy, & Buchan, 2004). In a review of the literature, of what has been written about self-advocacy, Test et al. (2005) identified 25 different definitions of self-advocacy. And there are others. In many cases, these definitions came from researchers or educators. Less often, people with developmental disabilities were included in creating these meanings.

Self-Advocacy as a social movement and a skill

One of the most important ways of looking at self-advocacy is as a social movement that works much like other social movements (e.g., the civil rights movement). Understood this way, self-advocacy is both the *movement* itself — a social movement that is named, organized, and controlled by people with developmental disabilities (sometimes with support from allies) — and a *skill* that is needed for individual well-being and for the self-advocacy movement to be successful (Bersani, 1998; Test et al., 2005; Worrell, 1988).

As a social movement, self-advocacy is based on the understanding that people with developmental disabilities have historically been oppressed and deprived of social power. Simpson (1999) argued that this oppression is made plain by the term self-advocacy: "If one has to invent a special name to describe what most people take for granted, then one ought to be immediately suspicious" (p. 156). Self-advocacy is necessary, not because of people's impairments, but because labelled people have been, and continue to be, oppressed by the larger society.

Through the action of self-advocacy they engage in a process of empowerment to create social change (Worrell, 1988). This concept of self-advocacy is similar to social action approaches of community organizing that work to redistribute power and resources (Rothman & Tropman, 1987/2008). It reflects a strong ideological change — this means that it represents a shift, or change, in our ideas and understanding of developmental disability and a different identity for people labelled developmentally disabled. It uses both individual and collective (group) action to create change.

This change is instrumental. This means, for example, change in the kinds of services that are available and how these services are delivered. This change is also political and social: it is concerned with changing broad social understandings and assumptions about developmental disability, understandings and assumptions held by many non-disabled or differently disabled people in the societies in which they live. The self-advocacy movement then is a revolt against all those who have controlled or oppressed people with developmental disabilities. It has its own "history, principles, organization, conceptual reform, language, solidarity, justice, and alliances" (Bersani, 1998, p. 63; Shapiro, 1993). The goal is to achieve a number of things for people with developmental disabilities:

- Equality
- Independence and control over decision-making
- Protection through legislated civil rights
- The guarantee of basic human rights
- Meaningful participation and citizenship

As a skill, self-advocacy requires knowledge of oneself — an understanding of one's strengths, needs, interests, and preferences. It also means recognizing how one defines and understands one's own disability and how others seem to understand and respond to it. It requires:

- Learning how to make decisions and choices that affect one's life
- Developing knowledge of human rights and civil rights and responsibilities
- Being supported to develop a way to effectively

communicate with others
- Learning how to "speak" for oneself and to assert oneself (even if one cannot use speech)

Self-advocacy means learning how to speak out for what one believes in and to join with others with developmental disabilities to work towards change (Bersani, 1998; Goodley, 2000; Roets et al., 2007; Test, et al., 2005). It does *not* mean that one must learn how to do all of these things on one's own. As we will talk about further on in this chapter, self-advocacy involves education; opportunities to learn and practise, and to build on existing strengths and capacities; and supports and inclusive relationships that empower people to become successful self-advocates. Many self-advocates and their allies believe that even people with more serious disabilities can be supported to make good choices and to have greater control over their lives (Shapiro, 1993).

When asked to define self-advocacy, Kerr had this to say:

I've been advocating for many years for the rights of people who, like me, communicate in alternative ways. I was successful in changing policy in Ontario for the funding of communication devices for people on social assistance. I recently brought a case to the Ontario Human Rights Tribunal about the rights of students who communicate in alternative ways. When something is wrong, it is important to speak up and try to change things for myself and for others.

Kelly's definition is very similar:

Self-advocacy to me means standing up and fighting for yourself and for those who can't and for those who are afraid to stick up for themselves ... advocating for what I want for my life and where I want the self-advocacy movement to be because self-advocacy means speaking out for proper treatment, proper schooling, proper healthcare, proper housing, and other important issues self-advocates want and need.

She asks two questions that point to the two aspects of self-advocacy — self-advocacy as a movement and as a skill:

How are people supposed to know what self-advocates need or want to learn if people don't ask or try to learn from the self-advocates?

How is society supposed to trust self-advocates and understand them if the advocates don't speak out about what they want and need for their lives?

The consistent themes or ideas in these various understandings of self-advocacy include (Beart, et al., 2004; Bersani, 1998; People First of Canada, 2011a; People First of Ontario, 2011; Shapiro, 1993):

- Speaking for yourself
- Standing up for yourself and your rights
- Making choices and your own decisions
- Being independent or assuming as much control over your life as possible
- Helping and assisting each other
- Educating the community about the rights, strengths and abilities of people with developmental disabilities
- Making sure that what people labelled intellectually disabled have to say is heard

Talking About Self-Advocacy: Self-Advocacy Theory

Keeping in mind that people with developmental disabilities are at the heart of self-advocacy, it is important to consider the different models of disability — the different ways that developmental disability is understood — for this will also affect how people understand self-advocacy. Although these ideas of disability were not developed by people with developmental disabilities, they are important starting points because they influence the language, practices, and policies that affect labelled people.

The individual model of disability

Disability is often viewed as a personal tragedy that someone has been afflicted with or suffers from. These terms assume that disability is something negative, something that no-one would ever want to have. It assumes, too, that it is located within the person herself — that it is a function purely of the impairment. This is known as the individual model of disability (Fudge Schormans, 2010a; Goodley, 1997), or sometimes the medical model of disability (see Chapter 3). Relying on medicalized, defi-

cit-based notions of disability, it pathologizes the individual with disability. This means that it makes developmental disability — and the person with disability — a problem; it understands it to mean there is something wrong. As a consequence, the focus is on fixing, curing, or taking care of the problem of disability instead of caring about, attributing value, and finding a place for people with disabilities (Fudge Schormans, 2010b). Working from this perspective, it becomes the responsibility of more capable non-disabled persons to take care of incapable persons with disabilities. Labelled people are required to be dependent on the professional so-called expert. In this way, an individual model perspective also ignores the social/political/economic and cultural factors involved in creating disability as a problem (French Gilson & DePoy, 2002). When people operate from this theoretical lens — from this way of understanding disability — it limits their ability to see people with developmental disabilities as anything but "broken" (Fudge Schormans, 2010b).

Many people directly involved in the lives of people with developmental disabilities — including service providers, professionals, parents and caregivers, self-advocacy group advisors, teachers, and others — still view disability from an individual model perspective. When non-disabled people believe that, because of a person's impairment, their potential for growth is severely limited, and that they are not capable of understanding their circumstances, this is likely to have a negative impact on how they respond to efforts by that person to self-advocate. Rather than supporting and fostering individual growth, the support and opportunities provided to the person with a disability for decision-making, choice, and control may be limited by pessimistic and paternalistic ideas that they are not able to safely and knowledgably make decisions (Goodley, 1997; Reaume, 2002).

Kelly suggests that sometimes this is because non-disabled people want to protect people with developmental disabilities; they are afraid that they might somehow get hurt by speaking out. They think this might happen if, for example, "people don't listen to them or don't like what they have to say." She feels, however, that the most common reason for not supporting self-advocacy is because non-disabled people do not believe labelled people are capable of making decisions and taking control of their lives. Kerr agrees with this:

> *I get tired of people talking to me like I don't understand, like I'm a little kid, and they assume I'm not intelligent ... I think most of those assumptions come from a lack of knowledge, not from nastiness. But it's still painful. And those assumptions end up violating us, especially if the people who are making those assumptions have the power to make decisions which affect our lives.*

Kelly believes that when non-disabled people think labelled people have nothing to say, they actively discourage their efforts to speak. She connects this way of understanding developmental disability and self-advocacy to the question of safety:

> *When it comes to safety for self-advocates, it means feeling like you aren't going to be physically or emotionally hurt by those around you. Safety is feeling like you're in a protective environment where you are respected, feel safe, feel understood, and have people around you be empathetic to your needs.*

The social model of disability

In the late 20th century, a different way of seeing and understanding disability was put forward. Disability, these theorists argued, is created by the social, political, economic, and material barriers that non-disabled people put in place. It is constructed by non-disabled ideas about disability, by the language non-disabled people use, and by non-disabled attitudes and practices. In other words, disability is created by social environments that exclude, marginalize, stigmatize, or devalue people with impairments. This theoretical perspective diverts attention away from considering only medical explanations for the experience of disability (Young & Quibell, 2000). While an impairment (e.g., fragile X, Autism, Down syndrome) might pose certain challenges for an individual, what is thought to be more important is society's response to the person with an impairment. Thus, it is society and not the impairment that "disables" people (French Gilson & Depoy, 2002; Hutchinson, et al., 2007). Disability then is regarded

as a form of social oppression along the lines of racism, sexism, and heterosexism. It is rooted in the entrenched assumptions and practices of prejudice against people with disabilities. This has come to be called *ableism*. The process of being disabled by societal attitudes, structures, and organization is termed *disablement* (Oliver, 1990).

Self-advocacy is clearly rooted in a social model understanding of disability. In fighting against enforced dependence, infantilization, and practices that deprive people of their basic rights and exclude people, self-advocates identify the source of their troubles as being the way society responds to them. They may acknowledge that living with a developmental disability can be difficult. For example, it may make it harder to learn to read, or how to manage money or to physically care for oneself. They make plain, however, that their experience and understanding of their impairment is largely relational — it comes about primarily as a result of their relationships with other people and with the larger society. By this they mean that it is constructed in the various social, cultural, and interpersonal contexts in which the person finds him/herself. What is important to consider in determining the so-called cause and meaning of developmental disability is the way other people perceive, react to, and treat people so labelled (Charlton, 1998; Goodley, Armstrong, Sutherland, & Laurie, 2003).

This understanding is a political one. It demonstrates that people with disabilities have come to a raised consciousness, a new understanding, of themselves and the world around them — not only as people with disabilities, but also as oppressed people (Charlton, 1998). This fits with a feminist analysis that links people's personal troubles to the social, political, economic, and cultural environments in which they live. Another way to say this is that "the personal is political." It calls upon labelled people to take up the challenge of participating politically, to become politically knowledgeable and active. In contrast to an emphasis on what labelled people with developmental disabilities cannot do, the emphasis now is on what they can do (Goodley et al., 2003) — even if they might need some assistance to do it (Young & Quibell, 2000). Self-advocacy is based on the premise that labelled people have historically been oppressed and made socially powerless. Through the action of self-advocacy, they engage in a process of empowerment to create social change (Worrell, 1988). "Empowerment can be seen to exist when people believe that they possess the ability, and the right, to act effectively to influence their environments" (Lee, 1999, p. 51). It is this individual and collective political empowerment of labelled people that will bring about change in the organization of our society (Oliver, 1990). These changes will affirm the rights of people with developmental disabilities, and support full citizenship, participation, and inclusion.

When self-advocacy is understood from this social model perspective, it means that disability organizations, professionals, and staff must operate in a different way. Not all are doing so, however. Sometimes this is just out of habit. Sometimes it may just seem easier to do things *for* people with developmental disabilities instead of creating opportunities or space for people to do things for themselves. Sometimes it is because people do not know the difference between giving support and giving direction (Hutton et al., 2010). At other times, it may be something different: self-advocacy may be threatening to non-disabled people because it so radically disrupts what they think they know about the "causes" of disability and about people with disabilities (Fudge Schormans, 2010b). Individuals with developmental disabilities who are strong self-advocates are increasingly challenging the more common perceptions of labelled people: that they cannot make decisions that affect their own lives; that they need non-disabled people to guide them; that they need to be protected and taken care of (Björnsdóttir &Jóhannesson, 2009). Kelly believes it leads them to actively discourage self-advocacy "because they are afraid of what self-advocates will say."

In many situations, there is still pressure on people with developmental disabilities to act like people with developmental disabilities — to behave in the way that the individual pathology model understands and defines them. This means they are expected to act in a way that emphasizes what they cannot do. To act in a way that rationalizes their dependence on non-disabled and professional experts for care. But

self-advocates do not always do this. Because self-advocacy contradicts the idea of people with developmental disabilities as unable, it is one means of breaking free of these prescribed roles. Challenging society's understandings, it makes it necessary for non-disabled people to reconsider and rethink what they believe to be the "truth" about developmental disability and to ask themselves why they hold on so tightly to these beliefs (Fudge Schormans, 2010b). In the words of Susan Wendell (1996):

What would it mean then, in practice, to value disabilities as differences? It would certainly mean not assuming that every disability is a tragic loss or that everyone with a disability wants to be "cured." It would mean seeking out and respecting the knowledge and perspectives of people with disabilities. It would mean being willing to learn about and respect ways of being and forms of consciousness that are unfamiliar, and it would mean giving up the myths of control and the quest for perfection of the human body. (p. 84)

Elements Of Self-Advocacy

Six key elements of self-advocacy are described in the following section.

Self-advocacy is about rights

Self-advocacy for people with developmental disabilities is very concerned with the question of rights. This focus can be read in most definitions of self-advocacy, on most websites, and in academic journals and other published materials by and about self-advocates and self-advocacy. There are many provincial, national, and international legislated rights and protections in place for Canadians with developmental disabilities (see Chapters 5 and 40). There is concern, however, that such legislated rights are not necessarily enacted in the day-do-day lives of people with developmental disabilities. Nor do they appear to have been enough to bring about justice for labelled people (Young & Quibell, 2000). Peter Park, the co-founder of People First in Ontario, writes and speaks often of his experience in an institution and how institutionalization strips people who live there of any and all rights (Park,

Box 1: People First of Canada: Charter of Rights
Charter of Rights (In Plain Language)

- *The Right to life*
- *The Right to freedom*
- *The Right to control what happens to your body*
- *The Right to equal protection and equal benefit of the law*
- *The Right of choice*
- *The Right to informed consent (to know your choices)*
- *The Right to have things explained to you*
- *The Right to be heard*
- *The Right to see a lawyer of other advisor*
- *The Right to have enough money to buy food, have a place to live, and decent clothes*
- *The Right to proper medical care*
- *The Right to charge someone if they hurt you or take something of yours*
- *The Right to be educated*
- *The Right to apply for a job and be taken seriously*
- *The Right to safe working and living conditions*

Source: People First of Canada www.peoplefirstofcanada.cta/charter_rights_en.php

2011). He became involved in self-advocacy to work towards ensuring that the same human and civil rights granted to non-disabled Canadian citizens be secured for people with developmental disabilities (Park, 2011). He wrote that "citizens can experience such things as marriage, giving birth, using universities, owning property, learning to drive, being home owners, and other things. Why not people with disabilities?" (p. 2). Self-advocate Andrew Lewis shares this view, stating that he, like other labelled people, wants "the right to be treated equally — like everyone else" (Lewis, 2011, p. 2). He speaks, too, about the right to have a job of one's choice, and the right to be able to work so:

> ...*that people with developmental disabilities can pay our rent. We need to work to save money to go on trips, go shopping, and learn how to do other things by ourselves. Like cooking by yourself and doing work, and living by yourself. You need to be able to have a job to have money to pay rent, buy a house, insurance, get your licence, take a girl out and get a girlfriend, buy a car, have enough money to keep the car. Being able to have a job is very important!* (p. 2)

As these rights are still not always recognized for labelled people, many self-advocacy organizations have written their own Bill of Rights to tell service providers and others what they understand their rights to be (see, for example, Box 1). Some self-advocates — individuals and groups — have been very active in the fight to secure rights. One of the authors of this chapter, Kerr Wattie, is one such person. With the support of his mother, Kerr explains that he is currently "involved in a human rights case so that people with complex communication exceptionalities can get the education we need; and also so that all people with exceptionalities can have the expertise we need for our education."

Although the self-advocacy movement turned to "rights" as a means of addressing the inequities that have long harmed people with developmental disabilities, this may not be enough. There is awareness that, while focusing on rights has greatly affected many aspects of the lives of labelled people, there are also limits to focusing on rights. It may offer certain protections, but has been less successful in effecting dramatic social changes at the everyday level because it has not always addressed to address the misunderstandings from which these inequities arose (Young & Quibell, 2000).

Peter Park (2011) argues passionately that rights are extremely important. He also understands that achieving equality and inclusion requires more than just legislated rights. The obstacles to being recognized as citizens are, in large part, a function of how people with developmental disabilities are seen and understood — or not understood. Important here are questions of respect and value. Respect and rights are very closely connected. "If someone has their rights taken away, they are not being treated with respect," and access to rights is often the result of self-advocacy (Hutton et al., 2010, p. 109). Young and Quibell (2000) extended this, stressing the importance of others knowing, and knowing about, people with developmental disabilities to respect and value them and their rights. They argue that most non-disabled people are extremely uninformed about people with developmental disabilities. They know very little about the lives and daily realities of labelled people. Without this knowledge, they stress that "'rights' can never 'cure' societal tensions. At best they can only treat the most obvious 'symptoms'" (p. 761). People with developmental disabilities are too often still regarded only as a label, known only by their diagnosis (Park, 2011). They are, in this way, reduced to their biology (Fudge Schormans, 2005). This returns us to an individual pathology model of developmental disability. When people define someone this way, Peter Park believes they are seen as somehow less human, as being without feelings, and as not wanting or needing the same things that non-disabled people do (Park, 2011). It is only by changing existing perceptions and understandings of labelled people that meaningful change will occur. Returning to Young and Quibell (2000), they suggested that this can only come about by non-disabled people coming to a better understanding of labelled people. They argued, as well, that this is best achieved through the sharing of stories, or narratives. When self-advocates speak up and tell others about the realities of their everyday experience, this can be a powerful means of effecting change. "They do not understand us, but once we are understood, we can finally have justice. We have the

right to be understood" (p. 761).

Self-advocacy involves responsibility

Self-advocacy means not only learning about and demanding one's rights, but also recognizing that with rights come responsibilities.

We can't talk about self-advocacy without talking about rights, and we can't talk about rights without talking about responsibilities. People with disabilities have often been denied the rights of citizens, such as the right to receive minimum wage or the right to decide where to live. People still are not treated as full citizens... [But] it is a great mistake to teach people about rights alone. Every right has an equal responsibility. So with rights are responsibilities and it should be taught in this way. (Park, 2011)

For too long, people with developmental disabilities have been thought incapable of assuming the same types and levels of responsibility that are expected of non-disabled citizens. Society has then "let them off the hook." The problem with this is that it has then been used as a reason for denying them their rights (Shapiro, 1993).

Accepting responsibility can occur on a personal level. For example, Andrew Lewis (2011) wrote that while he values having the right to make his own decisions he knows, too, this means taking responsibility for those decisions, no matter what the outcome. It also involves taking responsibility (with support from other self-advocates or allies, if required) for becoming educated. One must learn about one's rights, the expectations that go along with rights, and the resources, services, and supports that are available to labelled persons. In our discussions for this chapter, we talked about how effective self-advocacy requires that self-advocates and their allies learn about the ways that oppression, discrimination, and exclusion of labelled people operates in society. It means learning about how language and representation are connected to power. Making good decisions means making informed decisions. Kelly noted that this education can happen when self-advocates talk to each other, and share stories of personal experiences: "When you hear other people's stories, it helps you learn what's wrong with the world. Sometimes you know what's wrong already, but listening to other people's stories lets you learn about their experiences. This can lead to change." Responsibility then can also take place at the group level (for members of self-advocacy groups), or at the level of the social movement. Supporting each other, helping other group members to become better able to speak out, working together to achieve personal and collective, or group, goals, demonstrates responsibility for other self-advocates. Kelly wrote that it is important that self-advocates and their allies "encourage those 'gifted' individuals to go out in their communities, to local schools, community centres, and after-school programs to inform these gifted young people that they do have something to offer."

Not everyone wants or is able to move through all of these levels of responsibility and people need to recognize that this is okay (Test et al., 2005). This is a very diverse group of people with a wide range of abilities, preferences, ideas, support needs, and experiences (Goodley, 1997). Kerr and Kelly stressed that it is important that people with developmental disabilities define for themselves what self-advocacy means for them, what word they want to use to describe who they are and the work they do. Words and meanings should come from the "bottom-up" so that people can tell others what they want to call themselves and what they want to be called.

Exercising rights and responsibilities involves risk

Self-advocacy — speaking up and taking (greater) control over one's life — means also accepting the risks that might arise from doing so. Unfortunately, people with developmental disabilities are rarely trusted to handle risk (Goodley, 1997). Often, this has resulted in non-disabled people restricting opportunities for self-advocacy because they fear it will be too difficult for the labelled person, or that the person will get hurt. But many people with developmental disabilities argue that they "are willing to take risks — like anyone else — to live like other adults around them; they want places to turn to for support but they also want the feeling of respect and self-confidence that comes from taking chances" (Shapiro, 1993, p. 192).

Self-advocacy is about change

Unfortunately, a common way of thinking about people with developmental disabilities is that they are unable to understand the world or even understand themselves. As a result, the belief is that they will not be sensitive to, nor hurt by, the ways non-disabled people treat them, and write or talk about them. They are not expected to know about society, or to notice or care about events and situations outside of themselves. They are not believed capable of having an opinion, or expressing a comment, value, or moral judgment. Or of having a shared interest, or the ability to discuss and exchange ideas, or to listen to one another. Most importantly, they are not expected to have the ability or desire to make an address to others, to tell non-disabled people what they think and feel. As a result, there is little incentive for non-disabled people to learn from them who they are, their ways of being, and the meanings they attribute to their experiences of the world (Fudge Schormans & Chambon, 2009).

An important goal of self-advocacy, both as a social movement and as a skill, is to change how people with developmental disabilities are seen by others. It does so by challenging hurtful stereotypes about labelled people as being "unable," "not capable," and "less than non-disabled others." Instead, self-advocacy makes plain that people with developmental disabilities are far more capable than they are usually given credit for. People who were previously understood to be "feebleminded, retarded, dependent, or recipients of support" are now more often seen as capable "advocates, teachers and trainers," and as "advocacy allies and even leaders" (Bersani, 1998, p. 64-65). In Kelly's words, they are "gifted." Self-advocacy asserts, too, that people with developmental disabilities can, must, and have the right to, speak for themselves — and that many self-advocates want to do so (Beart et al., 2004; Fudge Schormans, 2010a; Test et al., 2005). It begins then, not from assuming incompetence, but presuming competence — not from a belief that people with developmental disabilities are "not able," but from a belief that they are "able" (Fudge Schormans, 2010b). "The international social movement of self-advocacy of people with the label of developmental disabilities is testimony to a determination to oppose how they have been defined and treated in society" (Roets et al., p. 323). Self-advocacy is a revolution, an act of subversion. It is a way that people with developmental disabilities are rebelling against being underestimated, deprived of choices, and treated as if they were eternal children (Shapiro, 1993).

Self-advocates and their allies around the world have been involved in many different efforts to bring about change, in both big and small ways. At the smaller, personal level, people may advocate for greater control over their day-to-day lives: from the clothes they wear, to the food they eat, to who their friends are, and the activities they engage in. People may speak up for more involvement in, and power over, decision-making that affects them. For example, what school, day program, or job they have; where they live; or who they want involved in this decision-making. Joining with others, they may advocate for changes to the way disability services operate, or fight for access to a particular community service. The work of self-advocates in Ontario was an important part of the closure of Ontario's institutions. Kerr has also been instrumental in creating change in Ontario. He wrote:

> *Something that's important to me is the advocacy I do with my mother. Together we changed the policies in Ontario so that the leasing costs of communication devices are now covered for people on social assistance. Since it's so expensive to lease communication devices, this is very important for people who need them.*

At the national level, when Robert Latimer was on trial for the murder of his intellectually disabled daughter, Tracy, self-advocates across the country joined with other groups speaking for people with disabilities at the Supreme Court of Canada to oppose the murder of people with disabilities under the guise of "mercy killings" (People First of Ontario, 2011).

A powerful example of how self-advocacy by people with developmental disabilities can bring about change is the language that is used to define and describe them. Self-advocates, individually and collectively, have fought for *people-first language.*

They have also demanded that disability organizations stop using the words "mentally retarded" (see Box 2). The success of their individual and collective efforts to change language demonstrates how social activism pushes against the role of victim. A number of authors, however, suggest that we need to be very careful with language. This is because language is very much a part of the place and time in which it is used. It is also a result of the changing or different ways language gets taken up. Because of this, even the term self-advocate can be misunderstood or misused. It, too, may become a negative term over time (Goodley, 2005). At present, self-advocacy provides individuals and groups with the opportunity to unite, to pull together, under a shared identity. For many people, it is the source of a more positive identity and sense of self. It can, however, also be associated with historical and contemporary negative perceptions of people with developmental disabilities. Many disability activists (typically those with disabilities other than developmental disabilities) caution against using people-first language. They suggest that it keeps the focus on the individual and not on the ways that society is organized to oppress people with disabilities. They prefer the term disabled people, arguing that this is a more effective means of showing how disability is a political issue and keeping attention on oppressive structures, language, and practices (Titchkosky, 2001).

The self-advocacy movement has changed over time. The initial driving principle of People First of Canada was the question of voice — the right to speak for oneself. This evolved to include other aspects of personal change: the right and opportunity to develop leadership skills, and to become more effective self-advocates. It has continued to evolve to the point where the goals are more complex: service-user control, empowerment, equality, human and civil rights, full participation as citizens, and influence over policy development (Hutchinson et al., 2007).

Self-advocacy can take many forms

The Green Mountain Self-Advocates (2011) set out three stages of self-advocacy on their website. The first is "Standing up for yourself." They define this as "when people find their voice and start to use it."

Box 2: Taking Control of Language

One area where self-advocacy by people with developmental disabilities has had a significant impact is that of the language used to refer to them. This is reflected in their insistence on people-first language, and in their political action against the use of the word retarded.

People with developmental disabilities argue that people-first language forefronts the person, not the disability, thereby recognizing their humanity, their individuality, and their similarity to non-disabled people. It resists the historical tendency to see people with disabilities, not as people, but as a disability, as a diagnosis (People First of Canada, 2011b). Putting the person first, not the so-called problem of disability, tells non-disabled others that people with developmental disabilities want to be known by their names, not by their label (Park, 2011).

Self-advocates have put pressure on service agencies to stop using the word retarded to describe and name them. In the words of one self-advocate, Sam:

> *We don't like the word "retarded" — it is offensive to us! It bothers us. It is not a nice word and people shouldn't use it. Take it out! People who don't have disabilities use this word to make fun of us, to put us down. No-one should ever use this word! It is very, very hurtful! We are all supported by an agency that used to use this word. But they don't use it anymore because people with disabilities didn't like it. (Fudge Schormans, 2010b)*

People with developmental disabilities question why so many people continue to use this word, both to label them and, casually, in their day-to-day conversations. They link the prejudice inherent in popular use of the demeaning terms "retard" and "retarded" to their use as a way of having power over people so labelled. The hurt that results from this prejudice is expressed clearly in the above quotation. Yet, at the same time, Sam gives us a picture of self-advocates as powerful combatants, as people with influence. He points out the successful efforts of self-advocates to dictate the language that can, and can no longer be, used to refer to them by a service provider. With support from allies, there are now very active campaigns across North America to put an end to the use of the "R" word. (See, for example, www.r-word.org; the documentary, Offense Taken, at www.selfadvocacy.org/offensetaken/; the documentary, The "R" Word, at http://www.cacl.ca/publications-resources; and the Spread the Word channel on Youtube, at www.youtube.com/endtherword). In the United States, this campaign was instrumental in President Barak Obama's signing of a law in 2010 prohibiting U.S. statutes from using the terms retard, retarded, or mentally retarded, and replacing the term mental retardation in all US laws with the term intellectual disability.

The second — "Standing up for a friend," represents a progression: "After a person is feeling comfortable speaking up for herself or himself, you may see that they start advocating for others." The final stage is "Standing together as a group." It is their belief that "We have a stronger voice when we work and speak up together."

Kelly spoke often about the importance, but also the challenges, of becoming a self-advocate. For many people, developing the confidence to speak out is not always easy. Sometimes this is a question of safety. Sometimes it is about having (or not having) an effective means to communicate. At other times, it is about developing skills. People come to self-advocacy with different degrees of readiness. Some people will need to learn about self-advocacy. They will need the tools and the time to learn to speak for themselves. For some, joining a group will be what they want to do, and will be something they feel they can contribute to. For others, groups may hold no appeal, or may be too overwhelming. One must be careful, however, not to underestimate people with developmental disabilities. Many have demonstrated great strength and resilience over the course of their lives in an often disabling and oppressive world. They may not need to be taught to be self-advocates for they may already be practising self-advocacy in many ways. It could be that we just do not recognize these ways (Goodley, 2005).

Self-advocacy can become a collective effort where individual members "move from individual self-advocacy to advocating for others as a group of individuals with common concerns" to speaking up "for their collective wants and needs through organizations, community gatherings, and political forums" (Test et al., 2005, pp. 45, 50). This coming together supports a more positive way of identifying as a person with a developmental disability (Bersani, 1998). Kelly wrote about the different ways self-advocacy can happen in her community. These activities not only reflect this shift from individual to group to collective, they also show how many different levels of self-advocacy can be in play at the same time:

> *Self-advocacy can happen in many ways…the different ways are as follows: The "Self-Advocates Hangout," which is a group setting that lets advocates have the confidence and the skills and "circles of support" from others to advocate what we "advocates" want out of life. There are rallies so "advocates" can tell their personal stories, there are government functions so "advocates" can be heard. Last but not least, there are gatherings so "advocates" can let family, friends, staff and partners know what they need and want.*

Self-advocacy can also take place through involving labelled people in research about developmental disability. This is not about tokenism, but about meaningful participation in research that is structured on an inclusive model where people fully participate. This supports the continuing education of self-advocates — the development of research literacy and continued consciousness-raising. It also challenges how labelled people are seen and understood. People's competencies — what they can do — are revealed (Fudge Schormans, 2010a, 2010b). This type of involvement recognizes, too, the influence of research on policy and changing systems (Hutchinson et al., 2007).

Disability is a diverse experience (Goodley, 1997) and no two people experience developmental disability the same way. Similarly, it is not necessary for every individual with a developmental disability to follow the same path of self-advocacy. Just because someone does not take a leadership role in the self-advocacy movement does not mean they cannot become a successful self-advocate (Test et al., 2005). Not everyone will choose to join a self-advocates' group or become active in the larger social movement. For some, advocating for their own needs may be enough. For many people with developmental disabilities, speaking for oneself can be empowering, but it can also be very difficult (Shapiro, 1993). We shouldn't take for granted that all people with developmental disabilities can self-advocate to the same extent. To do so sets some people up for failure and for blame they may face for failing to keep up.

For people whose impairments are more serious and necessitate higher levels of support, self-determination and self-advocacy may be especially challenging. They may express themselves and make choices in more basic ways. Some members of this group need very high levels of support and may require others to speak for them for most matters: sometimes all of the time, but perhaps, only at times when illness or other issues make self-advocacy more difficult (Kittay, 2001; Shapiro, 1993). In these situations, allies can advocate for people with developmental disabilities; they can advocate with them; and they can support people to self-advocate to the fullest extent possible. Some people might be doubtful that the activities of people with more serious disabilities can be referred to as self-advocacy. Remember, however, that self-advocacy is understood to be speaking up for yourself, making choices and your own decisions, and assuming as much control over your life as possible. Carol described a situation that demonstrates how this might work and points to the powerful effect of relationships and the learning that comes from these (see Box 3).

Kelly and Kerr both stress that labelled people must be able to decide how they will engage in self-advocacy. Self-advocacy does not just emerge because someone has been told to advocate for herself or because she became a member of a self-advocates' group. It often comes about because someone believes they have been treated unfairly, that they have not been heard or even allowed to speak. Kerr and Kelly affirm the importance of labelled people making these decisions: they talk about how non-

Box 3: Carol Krause: Self-Advocacy Takes Many Forms

Some people need support to be heard. I have a friend named Jade who communicates with the language of her body and her playful spirit. As I got to know her, I grew to understand when she was hungry, when she wanted to lie down, and when she was bored and wanted to try something new. Because she does not use words and is not forceful, people do not always listen to what she is communicating. I remember a time at her home when her nurse tried to put thick winter socks on her feet. Jade kept moving her foot away, but the nurse insisted on trying to put her socks on, even though my friend enjoyed being barefoot and rubbing her feet against the bottom of her wheelchair. It was only when I stepped in and pointed out that Jade did not want to wear her socks and that it was not necessary for her to wear socks indoors that the nurse stopped.

In this situation, Jade was expressing what she wanted for her own body, but the nurse was not listening or respecting Jade's right to determine something as basic as what to wear in her own home. As a supporter of Jade, I advocated for the nurse to respond to what Jade was already communicating. Hopefully, I was translating Jade's language for her nurse, so that the next time Jade made a similar gesture, the nurse would assist Jade to make decisions about her life. Sometimes we can help people advocate for themselves in our day-to-day interactions with health care workers, family members, and staff who we work alongside. We can play a small and important role in building understanding by advocating for and with people with disabilities.

---

disabled people often try to control the self-advocacy efforts of an established group. In Kelly's words, "It is awful when you are not asked; when things are imposed upon you instead of asking for your opinion."

It is important, however, not to romanticize the autonomy of self-advocates — the independence, skills, and abilities of people with developmental disabilities. This can happen if we ignore the day-to-day experiences of oppression in the lives of labelled people (Goodley, 2005). We must not assume that increasing what individuals can do and supporting individuals to become self-advocates is, in and of itself, enough to alter their life situations. The need for self-advocacy exists only because people with disabilities live in a society that is still disabling; that is still oppressive; that is still unfair. We must "acknowledge that the main need of people with [developmental disabilities] is for society to stop oppressing them" (Simpson, 1999, p. 155). There is still a long way to go before self-advocacy is no longer necessary and no longer requires the support of allies (Goodley, 2005; Simpson, 1999).

Self-advocacy takes time

Kerr expressed his concern that, because of communication issues or other individual needs (e.g., seizures, additional disabilities), it might take time for

people to get to know you, and to become comfortable with supporting your efforts toward self-advocacy and/or your inclusion in a self-advocates' group. Both Kerr and Kelly caution non-disabled people not to underestimate just how important this knowing is for all self-advocates, but particularly those with more complex needs. Having people who know you well, who understand how you communicate, are open to finding out who you are, who are accepting and interact with you in a non-judgemental way, and thus support and encourage your self-advocacy efforts, is critical to feeling safe enough to speak up.

A sense of safety is critically important to self-advocacy and to the lives of people with developmental disabilities more generally. This is a population that faces a much higher risk of experiencing violence throughout their lives (see Chapter 40). Kelly spoke to this in our discussions, stating, "Safety for me means being able to go out without feeling like I have to look over my shoulder, wondering if I'm going to be attacked. I want to feel safe and respected in my neighbourhood and my community." An important goal of self-advocacy is to end the ways people are devalued that is at the root of this violence. Because self-advocacy groups are structured and run by self-advocates themselves, they have the potential to offer stable, safe contexts that may contrast with community experiences or with residential or daycare settings designed by others (Goodley et al., 2003). Kelly cautions that these groups may, themselves, become dangerous places. A lack of respect among group members, different personalities and interpersonal dynamics, can make this a scary space. She explained that not everyone gets along right away, has the same ideas about what self-advocacy means, or has the same goals. Some people take it more seriously than others. Some people want to own the group — they don't recognize or accept that all members share an equal role, or they don't listen to others. Kelly concluded that:

> …*in group settings there needs to be guidelines for behaviour, due to difficulty with misunderstandings with individuals. These misunderstandings take away from social change and cause fear, which in turn takes away from future endeavours that groups want as a whole.*

She feels that "safety in groups is essential for self-advocate groups to thrive!" It can take a long time to create a safe and supportive self-advocates' group. Kelly's own experience has taught her that it takes time "for the group to figure out how to do things" in a way that works for everyone. Once this happens, however, a lot of change is possible.

Self-advocacy is a skill that, like any skill, takes effort and care to develop. People often need support to develop the confidence and skills necessary to speak out in meaningful ways. Many labelled people have spent their lives being taught to think that they have no worth, that there is something wrong with them, that they should seek protection from others, and that other people should make decisions about their lives. As noted in Chapter 40, many labelled people have been taught to be compliant — taught not to speak up but to be the passive recipients of care and services. Beginning at a very early age, some people with developmental disabilities may need deliberate instruction in self-advocacy skills — they may need to learn about themselves, to identify and communicate to others what they need, and the chance to practise these skills (Test et al., 2005). However, there is often a process of unlearning that must take place first; a process where people are given the tools to

question the harmful ideas they were taught about themselves. This undoing of discriminatory and negative ideas of disability can help people understand that they have value as they are. With this understanding, people can become empowered. They can learn to make decisions and take risks. People can learn to communicate what they want and need, and to stand up for what they think is right.

Balancing the needs of the individual and the group as a whole in the process of empowerment can be a challenge. Goodley (1998) wrote that responsibility for developing skills among members can be shared by the group's non-disabled advisor and other group members. He argued that self-advocates themselves are the most important people in this process of developing their own group members' and group's skills. Kelly spoke often about how "new members can learn from more experienced members. The more experienced members become the teachers, the mentors, and they can help new members learn about becoming a self-advocate." Learning from someone who has been "down the same road" can help build skills and confidence and, she notes, also lets new self-advocates "know that they have a positive role model to look to" when in need of understanding and support. The sharing of common stories and experiences (e.g., of institutionalization, abuse and neglect, being ignored or dismissed) can be very powerful (Bersani, 1998).

Kelly, who is more actively involved in self-advocacy groups than is Kerr, spoke about how the issues facing self-advocates, and what is needed for change to happen, can be very complicated: "It takes time to figure out how things work and then figure out how to change things, all the steps that are needed." As a group, we discussed that achieving real change — in the systems that affect self-advocates' lives and in the societies in which they live — can take a tremendous amount of time.

What Self-Advocacy is Not

A number of self-advocates and allies have expressed concerns over self-advocacy: how it is understood and organized; who is (and is not) in control; and who is (and is not) included and why. Just because there are more and more self-advocacy groups and initiatives does not mean that people with developmental disabilities have more opportunities for meaningful and effective self-advocacy (Goodley, 1997; Hutton et al., 2010).

Self-advocacy is not tokenism

Without real respect for the principles of self-advocacy, the word self-advocate can become just another label used to describe people with developmental disabilities. While many in the developmental service sector are embracing self-advocacy, there is concern that this is not always as fully developed as it needs to be (Hutton et al., 2010). A lack of respect for self-advocacy, and for labelled people, still exists in this sector (Goodley, 1997; Hutton et al., 2010; Worrell, 1988). For example, self-advocates may be asked to share their stories, to sit on committees or boards of directors, but they do not always feel their contributions are valued. It may be that only one or two self-advocates are part of these committees and boards — there is a feeling of being outnumbered by the non-disabled members and, consequently, of having very little power to effect change. Sometimes self-advocates are not given the training or information they require to participate effectively in decision-making. At times, non-disabled people speak too fast or use language or terms that are not familiar to self-advocates. For these reasons, self-advocates may go along with decisions that they might not understand or agree with because "nobody wants to feel stupid" (Hutton et al., 2010, p. 112). Sometimes self-advocates feel what they have to say is being directed by others, even to the extent of being given prepared scripts to read at public events — scripts written by non-disabled people. In these "top-down" situations (Hutton et al., 2010, p. 112), they do not feel they are being supported to advocate for what is important to them. Instead, they feel they are being directed to make decisions that are good for other people — for example, for a developmental service agency (Goodley, 2005; Hutton et al., 2010; Park, 2011). Their participation, then, is not very meaningful.

Rhea (a self-advocate) has said she feels like she is a "monkey on a string." They (self-advocates) are in a role to speak for people with developmental disabilities, but the "higher-ups" are controlling what they are allowed to say. What real purpose is there for the people? Are the people actually a part of change? The bottom line is that the organizations are supposed to be there to support self-advocates, not control what they say (Hutton et al., 2010).

When people are called self-advocates without a genuine belief in their ability to be so, without a real commitment to building an opportunity for them to speak out, or a willingness to truly listen to what people have to say, people are treated as tokens (Hutton et al., 2010; Park, 2011; Shapiro, 1993). They are invited to the table but are not given the tools to speak, or the respect to be heard. This is not self-advocacy. In fact, inviting people to the table without valuing who they are and what they have to contribute can be just as harmful as not inviting them at all.

Self-advocacy is not exclusive

Self-advocacy is not just for some people with developmental disabilities. Self-advocates are not an elite group. This is something that Kerr and Kelly identified in our discussions as being necessary for understanding self-advocacy: it must be inclusive of *all* labelled people. This means, for example, that it must make room not only for people who use speech to advocate for themselves, but also for people who use other means of communicating. It is not uncommon for people with developmental disabilities to have additional communication challenges. Kelly worries that "it may be hard for people who don't speak to compete with people who can speak." We live in a culture where communication — in particular spoken and written language — is esteemed and thought to indicate someone's intelligence. As a result, people who do not speak or communicate in accepted ways are devalued and thought to be less intelligent. Over-valuing speech and written communication, however, prevents us from recognizing other forms of communication, and other indications of intelligence. A lack of speech is understood to be a barrier — to telling people what you need or want, to being heard, and to being taken seriously (Fudge Schormans, 2006). Kerr wrote:

People's attitudes and behaviour towards us often

are the result of unfair and incorrect assumptions. Such as: if you don't speak, you must not understand. Or, if you don't speak you must not be very smart. Or, if you don't speak, you must not have anything to say. If you don't speak, I need to talk to you like you're a baby. If you don't speak, you must not be able to hear very well, so I better yell. Sometimes, it's funny. But sometimes it's difficult. Such as when the assumption is: if you don't speak, it's not important to include you. Or maybe it's more accurate to say, if you don't speak, I don't know how to include you.

As Kerr is quick to point out, a lack of speech does not mean a person has nothing of value to say. Nor does it mean that non-speaking people are not active participants in their experience, understanding, and interaction with their world and with other people. Kerr stresses that it does not have to be a barrier if sufficient supports, equipment, and training are provided for alternative communication methods or if, through inclusive and supportive relationships, others take responsibility for learning how people communicate. Kelly spoke of how non-disabled people are not very creative — they rely too much on people being able to speak. She felt that this is not the only door to self-advocacy. Allies might have to help people who have difficulty communicating to find other ways to do so. For Kerr, alternative communication is the way he advocates for both himself and others; it is also the subject of much of his advocacy work (see Box 4).

To dismiss the knowledge, experience, and wishes of some people with developmental disabilities simply because they do not speak is unfair. The diverse ways that people communicate, their different "languages" need to be recognized. Photographs, concrete objects, picture symbols, gestures, consistent sounds, Facilitated Communication, and sign language are alternative means of expression for non-speaking persons. Likewise, the symbolic messages acted out in dance, art, and play may tell us a great deal. For individuals whose communication abilities are affected by more serious intellectual and/or physical impairments, their communication cues are more likely to take the form of facial expressions,

posture, or movement (Bogdan & Taylor, 1989; Mar & Sall, 1999). Again, this demands that we start from presuming communication competence and not from assuming what people cannot do.

Self-advocacy must also include the voices of people with additional disabilities and more complex needs, such as people who are dually diagnosed as having an intellectual disability and a mental health issue. Further, it must equally include, support, and value the voices of people with developmental disabilities who identify as/from different races, cultures, ethnicities, and genders. (See, for example, the work of a group of lesbian, gay, bisexual, transgender and questioning youth with developmental disabilities in the documentary *Our Compass* listed in the More Resources section at the end of this chapter.)

Nor is self-advocacy limited to being an urban phenomenon — self-advocacy is equally important in rural areas. It may, however, be more difficult to organize self-advocacy groups in rural or more remote communities. The long distances and travel requirements might pose barriers that make it necessary to consider other ways of meeting, such as meeting online. We cannot forget, however, the connection between disability and poverty — access to computers is not always easy for people with developmental disabilities and not everyone has the opportunity to develop the skills to use a computer.

Why is Self-Advocacy Important?

At its heart, self-advocacy is important because if you don't speak for yourself, others will speak for you and this may not be in your best interests.

What does self-advocacy mean to individuals — to their sense of identity, sense of self, to their personal biography, and to their personal ambition? Beart et al. (2004) noted that self-advocacy in general, but group membership in particular, has a significant impact on members' lives and self-concept. These groups give self-advocates a space to make sense of their social identity and build on existing skills and resilience. They can be a safe space to open up dialogue around developmental disability, rights, responsibilities, and identity; and they can help to create consciousness about dis-

Box 4: Kerr Wattie: Not Being Able To Speak Does Not Mean You Cannot Be A Self-Advocate!

Hi, my name is Kerr Wattie. I'm happy to be able to talk to you. First, I'd like to tell you about my communication device. It's a computer that is mounted on the back of my wheelchair. If I am giving a presentation, I decide what I want to say ahead of time so it could be programmed onto my communication device. When I touch my switch on my tray, that activates my device, and through speakers on the back of my wheelchair, I hear the menus which give me lots of choices of what I can say. When I hear what I want to say, I touch my switch again, and the synthesized voice on my communication device says it loud enough for other people to hear. I can only say what's already programmed onto my device. That's frustrating, and I want to change that.

I also have many other ways I communicate. For instance, I blink to say "yes," "I agree," or to acknowledge something somebody says. If I don't blink, my communication assistant asks if I mean to say, "no." If I do, I blink to say, "Yes, I mean 'no'!" It's a little confusing, but it works for me. That way I can answer any yes and no questions quickly. I also use my blinks to choose the words I want to say when I'm writing emails or deciding what I want to have programmed onto this device. It takes a long time, and requires a lot of patience.

There's something else that's important to know about me. I have lots of ongoing seizures that prevent me from being able to respond. You might not notice many of them because they are very subtle. I become very still, and I can't move. I can't even blink. This happens a lot, sometimes several times a minute. When the seizure is over, I'm able to move and blink and respond again.

It is difficult for me to make eye contact because I'm cortically visually impaired. That doesn't mean that I don't understand. I understand everything you say. You can talk to me as you would to any other adult. I can hear very well so it isn't necessary to speak loudly or slowly. I appreciate being addressed directly, although people often talk to my communication assistant instead of to me. I know that most people don't have experience with seizures, cortical visual impairment, and augmentative communication, so it might be easy to misinterpret who I am, what I understand, and how to communicate with me. I really like it when people take the time to get to know me.

One of the most important things in my life is my communication. When I'm provided with the supports to enable my communication I feel vital and alive. It makes a big difference in my life when I'm able to express what's important to me and to have it understood. Communication is essential in my relationships and work.

---

ability, service systems, support, and oppression (Goodley, 2003). Kelly and Kerr spoke about how they were places self-advocates could come together and share their stories and work on issues as a group. Sometimes what develops is a deep knowledge that grows out of personal experience and group dialogue. Often, this dialogue is not easy and may be quite painful. Developing a political awareness of the roots of their experience, an awareness of the extent to which labelled people — as individuals and as a group — are stigmatized, discriminated against, and oppressed, can be very difficult. It is important that we realize that many people with developmental disabilities can and do come to work with this hurt — it is not a reason for non-disabled people, in an overprotective way, to limit how people are involved with

self-advocacy (Beart, et al., 2004; Fudge Schormans, 2010b). In these instances, peer support is very valuable. Groups are also an important way to develop friendships, social connections and opportunities for people who have limited opportunities for such connections outside of these groups. Self-advocacy groups are culturally rich in the way that they provide opportunities and meanings to group members and, if tapped, they can inform professionals, caregivers, and allies (Goodley, 2003). Kelly is quite firm on this latter point. She wrote:

We need to be out there to let people know about us. We need to teach others how to understand those of us who are different and gifted so we can be part of society, because we have just as much to offer as anybody else.

All societies have particular attitudes, values, conventions, structures, and institutions that serve to privilege and include some, while at the same time devaluing and excluding others. Most of those who are privileged tend not to question this privilege. Nor do they question the seemingly "natural" ways others are excluded (Björnsdóttir & Jóhannesson, 2009). Test et al. (2005) took this up. They noted, for example, that when people develop self-advocacy skills they are more likely to have greater success with work and social and financial independence. Even though research demonstrates that children and young adults with developmental disabilities who have been supported to develop and exercise self-advocacy skills tend to move more successfully into their adult lives, these opportunities are often not part of their education. And very few people are asking why not (Test et al., 2005). Self-advocacy is about pointing out and troubling this lack of questioning. It is about disrupting the status quo. It is about challenging taken-for-granted and unquestioned ideas. It is about making the questioning more and more difficult to ignore.

Summary

People with developmental disabilities are often seen as broken people. We have all heard hurtful words about people with developmental disabilities, and have watched how labelled people are disabled as a result and continue to be oppressed. They are seen as having something wrong with them, and as not having anything important to offer their communities. Assumptions about what it means to be a person or to have abilities has restricted the opportunities labelled people have to take power over their own lives (Fudge Schormans, 2010b). They have been actively disempowered. Too often, the lived experience of people with developmental disabilities is not acknowledged; it is silenced or discredited or disqualified; or it is excluded or buried under the truth, power, and knowledge of "experts" (Roets et al., 2007). They are spoken for by non-disabled people (Fudge Schormans, 2006) and, until recently, have had almost no control or involvement over naming, defining, and describing their own experience (Reaume, 2002). Self-advocacy represents

a significant movement towards redefining people with developmental disabilities in more positive terms. While not without its problems, it seems to be making changes in the movement towards meaningfully including and valuing people who are labelled. As self-advocates, people with developmental disabilities are effectively using a range of strategies to gain authority over their lives and experiences, to improve their social position, and to achieve their aims. Björnsdóttir & Jóhannesson (2009) wrote:

By carving out space where developmental disability is gaining higher social status, people with developmental disabilities are contributing to a new social understanding of disability...Their message is, "We are here. We may be different from you, but you are also different from us." (p. 444)

However, as the theories and literature used in this chapter make clear, people without disabilities are still doing most of the talking (and writing) about developmental disability in general and about self-advocacy as well. This chapter also demonstrates that this is starting to change. As more and more self-advocates speak out, and as their voices are more often included in writings about self-advocacy, the theories and language used to explain self-advocacy will change, as will our understanding of what self-advocacy means. We end this chapter with Kelly's voice:

We as self-advocates need to stand together as a family in order for change to come around. We can't just fight as individuals, we need to stand together as one family to have our voices heard.

For Further Thought And Discussion

1. What does self-advocacy mean to you? Do you like this word? Is there another word that you think is more appropriate? Do you think this term will be able to resist becoming a pejorative term in the same way that the "R" word did?

2. What do you believe should be the "guiding principles" for self-advocacy? How do these connect to the different models for engaging self-advocates in respectful, effective and empowering ways? Which model do you think you or your agency operates from?

3. What does independence mean to you? Is independence important to you? Are there other words, such as interdependence, that people may want to use to talk about what they want for their lives?

4. Some people talk about being proud of having a disability. What does disability pride mean to you? Do you accept yourself (your son or daughter / the people you support) as you (they) are?

5. How do people from newcomer, immigrant, and other diverse communities, talk about rights and self-advocacy? Do these words have meaning for them, or are there other words that may be better? For example, family and community may be more important for some communities than individual rights.

6. How can self-advocacy groups become more inclusive?

7. What do you see as being the role of non-disabled allies in self-advocacy?

More Resources

Media Resources:

Body & Soul: Diana & Kathy: This film documents the self-advocacy activities of two people with disabilities. Diana Braun has Down syndrome and Kathy Conour has Cerebral Palsy and is non-speaking. Fearful of being shut away in a nursing home or forced into a state run institution, Diana and Kathy tirelessly advocate for the rights of people with disabilities. *Body & Soul: Diana & Kathy* moves beyond disability and activism to a story of a profound, creative friendship.
www.welcomechange.org

Credo of Support: Narrated by People First Members. *http://www.youtube.com/watch?v=wunHDfZFxXw*

Leadership and Self-Advocacy Oral History Project: Explores the life stories of 13 leaders in the American self-advocacy movement on key issues and leadership challenges.
http://bancroft.berkeley.edu/ROHO/collections/subjectarea/ics_movements/self_advocacy.html#about

Offense Taken: This film documents a community's organized response to the public use of the "R" word. *http: www.selfadvocacy.org/offensetaken/*

Our Compass: Created in 2009, Our Compass is a short documentary video that tells the previously unheard stories of a group of young, queer-identified Torontonians labelled as having developmental disabilities. In the documentary, the participants engage in discussion of topics such as dating, sex, battling stigma, and coming out, while preparing for professional portraits that will showcase the feature of their identities they are most proud of. **Contact:** Tess Vo at *tvo@griffin-centre.org*

The Freedom Tour: A documentary created by People First of Canada and People First groups in Manitoba, Saskatchewan, and Alberta, in partnership with the National Film Board, about their community efforts to close institutions.
http://www.peoplefirstofcanada.ca/images/Guide_Freedom_Tour_eng.pdf

The 'R' Word – but names will always hurt you: This documentary project, by the Canadian Association of Community Living, chronicles the struggles of people with developmental disabilities and their families to be recognized and treated as fully human with the same rights as anyone else in society. Their stories articulate the urgency to create conditions where all people can maximize their potential without fear of discrimination and dehumanization and how that process, in turn, makes us all more fully human. **Available at:**
http://www.cacl.ca/publications-resources/The%20R%20Word%20-%20Documentary%20Film%20Project

Then and Now: A film that explores the past and the future of the self-advocacy movement through the eyes of Canadians with Down syndrome. Presented by the Voices at the Table Advocacy Committee and the Canadian Down syndrome Society. **Available at:** *www.cdss.ca/eshop/publications.html*

Tying Your Own Shoes: Released in 2009, this National Film Board of Canada production "explores how it feels to be a little bit unusual." Combining the artworks of four artists with Down syndrome with footage from interviews, the film is intended to disrupt taken-for-granted understandings and stereotypes about Down syndrome. *www.nfb.ca/tyingyourownshoes*

Key Services and Supports:

*There are many websites that offer information on self-advocacy and starting a self-advocates' group. We have listed only a very small sampling of these here. Readers are encouraged to go on-line and search out these sources to determine which approach is most suitable to your own needs.

ACT, Advocating for Change Together: Run by and for people with developmental and other disabilities, this is self-advocacy in action. Through personal empowerment, disability awareness, and systems change, members work on projects, build leadership, and organize to challenge oppression, improve people's lives, and impact community. The website contains an extensive catalogue of resources developed by ACT and descriptions of the variety of workshops they offer to generate social change *http://www.selfadvocacy.org/index.htm*

Green Mountain Self-Advocates, Vermont, US: This site provides workshop materials, videos, and other resources for people wishing to learn more about self-advocacy. *http://www.gmsavt.org/*

Label Free Zone: This site has been developed by Canadian self-advocates and the National Film Board. It is a very accessible site that supports self-advocates to share opinions and stories, and upload their thoughts and videos. Self-advocates are invited to add themselves to the map, suggest a topic they might be interested in, or participate in online discussions about relationships and institutions. *http://lfz.nfb.ca/home1/*

People First of Canada: This site is a national resource for self-advocates and for those wishing to learn more about self-advocacy. *http://www.peoplefirstofcanada.ca*

People First Ontario: This site is an Ontario-based resource for self-advocates and for those wishing to learn more about self-advocacy. It is linked to the national People First of Canada site. *http://www.peoplefirstontario.com*

LiveWorkPlay: A Good Life for People with Intellectual Disabilities: A Canadian website devoted to providing information and resources around self-advocacy for people with intellectual disabilities. *http://www.self-advocacy.ca*

The Autistic Self-Advocacy Movement: Works to advance the principles of the disability rights movement in the world of autism and to empower Autistic people internationally to take control of their own lives and the future of our common community. The website includes a speakers' bureau, online community resources, writing by people on the autistic spectrum, a mailing list, and an online social support group for autistic parents. *http://www.autisticadvocacy.org/*

References

Beart, S., Hardy, G., & Buchan, L. (2004). Changing selves: A grounded theory account of belonging to a self-advocacy group for people with intellectual disabilities. *Journal of Applied Research in Intellectual Disabilities, 17*(2), 91-100.

Bersani, H. (1998). From social clubs to social movement: Landmarks in the development of the international self-advocacy movement. In L. Ward (Ed.), *Innovations in advocacy and empowerment for people with intellectual disabilities* (pp. 59-74). Lancashire, United Kingdom: Lisieux Publication.

Björnsdóttir, K., & Jóhannesson, I. A. (2009). People with intellectual disabilities in Iceland: A Bourdieuean interpretation of self-advocacy. *Intellectual and Developmental Disabilities, 47*(6), 436-446.

Bogdan, R., & Taylor, S. J. (1989). Relationships with severely disabled people: The social construction of humanness. *Social Problems, 36*(2), 135-148.

Charlton, J. I. (1998). *Nothing about us without us.* Berkeley, CA: University of California Press.

French Gilson, S., & DePoy, E. (2002). Theoretical approaches to disability content in social work education. *Journal of Social Work Education, 38*(1), 153-165.

Fudge Schormans, A. (2005). Biographical versus biological lives: Auto/biography and non-speaking persons labeled intellectually dis/abled. In J. Rak

(Ed.), *Auto/biography in Canada: Critical directions* (pp. 109-128). Waterloo, ON: Wilfrid Laurier University Press.

Fudge Schormans, A. (2006). Hearing what cannot be spoken: Social work's responsibility towards non-speaking persons labeled disabled. In N. Hall (Ed.), *Social work: Making a world of difference: Social work around the world IV in the year of IFSW's 50th Jubilee* (pp. 225-242). Bern, Switzerland: International Federation of Social Work.

Fudge Schormans, A. (2010a). Epilogues and prefaces: Research and social work and people with intellectual disabilities. *Australian Social Work, 63*(1), 51-66.

Fudge Schormans, A. (2010b). *The right or responsibility of inspection: Social work, photography, and people with intellectual disabilities.* Unpublished doctoral dissertation, University of Toronto, Toronto, ON.

Fudge Schormans, A., & Chambon, A. (in press). "Please let it not be me!" Unwounding counter life representations by persons with intellectual disability. In S. Brophy & J. Hladki (Eds.), *Embodied politics in visual autobiography.* Toronto, ON: University of Toronto Press.

Goodley, D. (1997). Locating self-advocacy in models of disability: Understanding disability in the support of self-advocates with learning difficulties. *Disability &Society, 12*(3), 367-379.

Goodley, D. (2000). *Self-advocacy in the lives of people with learning difficulties.* Buckingham, UK: Open University Press.

Goodley, D. (2005). Empowerment, self-advocacy and resilience. *Journal of IntellectualDisabilities, 9*(4), 333-343.

Goodley, D., Armstrong, A., Sutherland, K., & Laurie, L. (2003). Self-advocacy, "learning difficulties," and the social model of disability. *Mental Retardation, 41*(3), 149-160.

Green Mountain Self-Advocates. (2011). *How to start and run your own self-advocates group.* Retrieved from http://www.gmsavt.org/index.php?option=com_content&view=article&id=66&Itemid=69

Hutchinson, P., Arai, S., Pedlar, A., Lord, J., & Yuen, F. (2007). Role of Canadian user-led disability organizations in the non-profit sector. *Disability & Society, 22*(7), 701-716.

Hutton, S., Park, P., Park. R., & Rider, K. (2010). Rights, respect and tokenism: Challenges in self-advocacy. *Journal on Developmental Disabilities, 16*(1), 109-113.

Kittay, E. (2001). When caring is just and justice is caring: Justice and mental retardation. *Public Culture, 13*(3), 557-579.

Lee, B. (1999). *Pragmatics of community organization.* Mississauga, ON: Common Act Press.

Lewis, A. (March, 2011). From clients to citizens: Rights, respect and responsibilities. Panel presentation at the Shared Learning Forum, Developmental Services Toronto, Toronto, ON.

Mar, H. M., & Sall, N. (1999). Profiles of the expressive communication skills of children and adolescents with severe cognitive disabilities. *Education and Training in Mental Retardation and Developmental Disabilities, 34*(1), 77-89.

Oliver, M. (1990). *The politics of disablement.* London: Macmillan.

Park, P. (March, 2011). From clients to citizens: Rights, respect and responsibilities. Panel presentation at the Shared Learning Forum, Developmental Services Toronto, Toronto, ON.

People First of Canada. (2011a). *History.* Retrieved from www.peoplefirstofcanada.ca/start_en.php

People First of Canada. (2011b). *A word about language.* Retrieved from http://www.peoplefirstofcanada.ca/about_us_en.php

People First Ontario. (2011). *Objectives.* Retrieved from http://www.peoplefirstontario.com/mission.html

Reaume, J. (2002). Lunatic to patient to person: Nomenclature in psychiatric history and the influence of patients' activism in North America. *International Journal of Law and Psychiatry, 25,* 405-426.

Roets, G., Goodely, D., & Van Hove, G. (2007). Narrative in a nutshell: Sharing hopes, fears,and dreams with self-advocates. *Intellectual and Developmental Disabilities, 45*(5), 323-334.

Rothman J., & Tropman J. E. (1987/2008). Model of community organization and macro practice perspectives: Their mixing and phasing. In B. Lee (Ed.), *Community based social policy: Readings and resource readings* (pp. 65-90.). Hamilton, ON: McMaster University.

Simpson, M. (1999). Bodies, brains, behaviour: The return of the three stooges in learning disability. In, M. Corker & S. French (Eds.), *Disability discourse* (pp. 148-156). Buckingham, UK: Open University Press.

Shapiro, J. P. (1993). *No pity: People with disabilities forging a new civil rights movement.* New York: Three Rivers Press.

Test, D. W., Fowler, C. H., Wood, W. M., Brewer, D. M., & Eddy, S. (2005). A conceptual framework of self-advocacy for students with disabilities. *Remedial and Special Education, 26*(1), 43-54.

Titchkosky, T. (2001). Disability: A rose by any other name?: "People-first" language and Canadian society. *The Canadian Review of Sociology and Anthropology, 38*(2), 125-140.

Wendell, S. (1996). *The rejected body: Feminist philosophical reflections on disability.* New York: Routledge.

Worrell, B. (1988). *People first: Advice for advisors.* Downsview, ON: Canadian CataloguinginPublication Data.

Young, D. A., & Quibell, R. (2000). Why rights are never enough: Rights, intellectual disability and understanding. *Disability & Society, 15*(5), 747-764.

Making Services More Effective Through Research and Evaluation: An Introductory Guide

Barry J. Isaacs

What you will learn:

- How the research literature informs the support to people with developmental disabilities
- Steps to plan a program evaluation
- Contextual factors that support the use of research and program evaluation in working with people with developmental disabilities
- The need for building research and evaluation capacity in service organizations

Two excellent sources of information for improving services are the existing research literature and knowledge gained from evaluating existing interventions and programs (usually referred to as program evaluation). Yet the degree to which developmental service agencies use these sources varies. Some agencies do not use them at all because they lack the capacity to do so. In other cases, lack of knowledge or negative attitudes toward terms such as evidence-based practice (EBP) and program evaluation may discourage their use. Often there is little or no incentive or time to take advantage of the research literature or to do program evaluation. This chapter highlights the need to do both. It also dispels the misconception that EBP does not allow

for clinical judgment. Additionally, concrete steps to plan program evaluations are described, and issues of organizational capacity are discussed briefly.

Using the Research Literature

Research is one important source of information when deciding which services or supports might best meet the needs of persons with developmental disabilities. Research can be used at several levels to make decisions about services and supports. For example, it can be used by governments to decide what the most critical needs are for a population and to decide which kinds of interventions would best meet these needs. One example of this in Ontario is the funding of Intensive Behavioral Intervention programs for children with autism. On a smaller scale, hospitals or agencies, or departments within these organizations might provide — based on research evidence — specific types of interventions over others to address issues it commonly encounters with its clients. For example, there are many prepackaged social skills interventions available and an agency might decide to purchase and implement a particular one because it has been shown to be effective with the types of clients it generally serves. Research is also used by professionals at an individual client level to decide what specifically might work with a particular client who has a specific set of needs.

Any of the applications of research to inform services or supports described above might be referred to as forms of EBP. Mitchell (2011) outlined four different conceptualizations of EBP: 1) empirically supported treatments (EST), 2) integrative approaches, 3) common elements of effective evidence-based interventions, and 4) common factors and characteristics of effective programs. The EST approach is perhaps the most common view of EBP. It is characterized by the use of discrete treatments delivered in a prescribed way that are shown to be effective for particular problems with particular types of individuals. There are various names for these kinds of interventions such as empirically supported interventions (McBeath, Briggs, & Aisenberg, 2010), and empirically supported therapies (Chambless & Hollon, 1998). Rigorous evidence such as multiple, high quality, randomized controlled trials are usually required for an intervention to qualify as an EST (e.g., Chambless & Hollon, 1998). The focus on studies with random assignment of participants to treatment and non-treatment groups requires high level treatment fidelity (i.e., that interventions are delivered in a specific way) and has lead to criticisms that ESTs are impractical and have limited relevance to the diverse and often complex clients seen in many service settings (McBeath et al., 2010, Mitchell, 2011).

Second, the integrative approach to EBP focuses on the adaptation of ESTs to fit individual needs and service contexts. Sometimes under this approach contexts are also adapted to help accommodate

interventions (Mitchell, 2011). Here, there is a wider interpretation of EBP as the integration of research evidence, clinical expertise, and client values and preferences (American Psychological Association, 2005; Spring, 2007).

In a third approach to EBP, elements common to many ESTs focused on similar problems for similar populations can be identified and applied as needed based on evidence, experience, and underlying theories of change. For example, Garland, Hawly, Brookman-Frazee, and Hurlbut (2008) identified 21 elements common to at least half of a list of eight parent mediated ESTs for disruptive behaviour in children. These elements were divided into four categories:

1. Therapeutic content, such as principles of positive reinforcement
2. Treatment techniques, such as modelling
3. Aspects of working alliance, such as consensual goal setting
4. Treatment parameters, such as at least 12 sessions

In another example, researchers Chorpita, Becker, and Daleiden (2007) listed the elements that are common to childhood depression interventions. These include psycho-education, problem-solving activity scheduling, and social skills training. The identification of common elements does not necessarily replace the use of ESTs, but knowledge of common elements can, for example, guide the choice of a specific treatment manual (Chorpita et al., 2007). Another application of this approach might train clinicians on a small number of practice elements common to the most efficacious treatments, thus providing the clinicians with additional options to offer clients (Chorpita et al., 2007). Overall, this approach to practice is attractive for a number of reasons. Among these are that it allows for clinical judgement while maintaining an emphasis on evidence of effectiveness, it reduces the need to train staff in entire ESTs that may be complex and overlapping (Mitchell, 2011), and it acts as a basis for the evaluation of services by providing a list of elements it should be comprised of (Garland et al., 2008).

Finally, Mitchell (2011) identified an approach to

EBP based on common factors and characteristics of effective programs. These factors and characteristics refer to the structure and context of service provision, as opposed to specific procedures. For example, to be effective, services and supports for children should be client-centred, developmentally appropriate, address practical needs, foster good client-worker relationships, and address varied needs in a comprehensive way (Mitchell, 2011).

Whatever form of EBP is followed, the idea here is to use the core knowledge that is gained from research when setting up a new intervention, amending an intervention, or evaluating an intervention with a view to making it as effective as possible. If there is no known linkage between an intervention and research knowledge (i.e., practitioners just do not know whether or not their practice is based on theoretical and research knowledge), the four approaches to EBP described above are good ways to explore and establish such a linkage. If none exists, or if the analysis suggests improvements, appropriate amendments can be made. Box 1 provides an example of one instance where such a linkage was explored by a program operating in Ontario, and explains how the program was altered so that its practice was more evidence-based.

Although there are many gaps in available knowledge from research, there is a large and varied array of research on interventions to support persons with developmental disabilities and address many different types of needs. Developmental service agencies could adopt any one or more of the approaches to EBP described above to take advantage of this literature. To do so would require access to this literature and skills to review it that may not be available in some organizations. In these cases, agencies could develop partnerships with universities where these resources are available. Literature reviews could be generated as part of student or faculty projects serving the needs of both the agency and the university.

Program Evaluation

Besides using the existing research literature, agencies should be evaluating the services they provide. Evaluation provides accountability to those who

Box 1: EBP Based on Quality of Life Research

Since about 1990, numerous studies have been carried out in various parts of the world in quality of life. A large study in Ontario (Brown, Raphael, & Renwick, 1997) found numerous factors that were associated with better quality of life for adults with developmental disabilities, such as living in the community, living independently, exercising choice, and many others. Staff from one program in Ontario that teaches life skills to young adults with developmental disabilities read these results with interest, conducted a library search to find that studies in other countries supported the findings, and decided to use this evidence to redesign their interventions based on quality of life concepts and principles. They changed their content to cover those aspects of life that were found to be most important to people's quality of life, and they altered their process to reflect the helpful actions of quality of life (exercising choice, focussing on skills and personal interests that are pleasing, etc.). Outcomes to evaluate the success of their program were also based on quality of life research evidence: improved self-confident, statements of satisfaction and pleasure, and greater independence and self-determination. In short, this program moved toward evidence-based practice by using research evidence to amend and improve its own program.

oversee programs. It also provides information that can be used in a feedback loop to improve services. Below, a thorough discussion of program evaluation is provided, along with concrete steps for planning evaluations.

What is program evaluation?

Program evaluation is a specific type of research. Here are two definitions:

Evaluation is the systematic assessment of the operation and/or the outcomes of a program or policy, compared to a set of explicit standards, as a means of contributing to the improvement of the program or policy. (Weiss, 1998, p.4)

Program evaluation is the use of social science research procedures to systematically investigate the effectiveness of social intervention programs that is adapted to their political and organiza-

tional environments and designed to inform social action in ways that improve social conditions. (Rossi, Freeman, & Lipsey, 1999, p. 20)

Elaborating on some key elements of these definitions will help to develop a better understanding of what program evaluation is.

What is evaluated?

In this chapter, we are concerned with evaluating programs targeting people with developmental disabilities and those who care for them. Owen (2007) identified three levels at which programs operate and can be evaluated. At the *mega* level are the government offices or private boards that are ultimately responsible for the overall policies that govern programs and are concerned with their larger impacts. At the *macro* level there are the local or regional offices, agencies, divisions, and so on that are responsible for delivering the program in a specific geographic area, or are a defined group within the larger program. At the *micro* level are the individual agencies within regions, the specific services within agencies and the component parts of these services. Although evaluations of programs at the mega and macro levels are important, in this chapter we will focus on ways managers and staff can evaluate at the micro level. Examples of these are individual interventions or supports that exist within larger programs (e.g., service coordination, behaviour management, or psychotherapy), or specific components of these interventions (e.g., relaxation exercises in psychotherapy).

There are two aspects of programs that evaluations usually address. The first is *program processes*. When evaluating processes, the goal of an evaluation might be to determine if the program is being implemented as intended. Evaluation questions may include: Are certain key activities being carried out? How often are these key activities occurring? How many individuals are receiving services from the program? Sometimes, however, particularly with older programs that have not been evaluated, the goal of the evaluation may be to clarify what is going in the program. Who is the program serving? What are the key components of the program? What are the key activi-

ties and intended *outcomes* of the program?

The second aspect of programs that evaluations usually address is the achievement of *outcomes*. *Outcomes* should be distinguished from *outputs*. *Outputs* are the products or services that are delivered to program recipients (Rossi, Lipsey, & Freeman, 2004). *Outcomes* are the changes or benefits experienced by clients as a result of the program. Outcomes can be short-term such as reductions in behaviour problems or enhanced social skills. These more immediate benefits can also contribute to long-term outcomes such as improved quality of life. Program evaluation that focuses on the outcomes of a specific intervention is often referred to as research.

How are programs evaluated?

Evaluation is systematic. The approaches used in evaluation are the same as those used in social science research, such as psychology, sociology, or social work. These methods include complex experimental designs with control groups, surveys, reviews of clinical records, focus groups, and interviews. The data collected may be quantitative or qualitative. It is very important to remember that the methods used to evaluate a program must fit the program context. Some methods, such as studies with random assignment to groups, require many resources and strict adherence to program fidelity, making them impractical in many service contexts. Furthermore, these designs require some program participants to be randomly denied treatment, or at least have treatment delayed, and this can cause ethical concerns. A few simple designs are included in the following sections of this chapter that can be implemented with relative ease in community agencies.

Why do we do program evaluation?

Evaluation of services is undertaken for two main reasons. The first reason is accountability, meaning evaluation provides evidence as to whether services are reaching the goals and objectives they were meant to achieve. This is important because services cost money. If some services are not reaching their intended goals and objectives, the money to fund them might be put to more effective use elsewhere. The second reason is that evaluation provides information that can be used to make services more effective and/or more efficient. In this chapter, the evaluation approaches describes primarily address program improving effectiveness. Data from these types of evaluations, however, can also be used for accountability purposes.

Planning an evaluation

Good planning is a key to successful program evaluation. Owen (2007) and Bamberger, Rugh, and Mabry (2006) identified several issues to consider in an evaluation plan. These have been adapted below to suit the specific needs of managers, clinical personnel, and frontline staff working in developmental service agencies.

Step 1: Articulate clearly the overall purpose of the evaluation. Evaluations can have several purposes: to determine if the program is effective, if it is efficient, if it is being implemented as intended, or whether or not it should be continued or expanded. Evaluations are often undertaken to see how programs can be improved. Understanding the overall purpose of an evaluation is necessary for determining the specific evaluation questions.

Step 2: Determine who will use the information and how. The question of who will use the information and how is tied directly into the purpose of the evaluation. Results from evaluations designed to improve a service, support, or intervention will likely be used by managers and staff. Results from evaluations designed to determine whether or not a program will continue are more likely to be used only by managers or funders. Articulating clearly at the beginning who will use the information and how it will be used increases the likelihood that the results actually will be used.

Step 3: Determine the resources available for the evaluation (staff, budget etc.). Lack of resources for evaluation is a common problem in community based agencies. Often, staff lack time to participate in program evaluation, individuals with appropriate evaluations skills may be lacking, and there may be no budget for things such as computers, software, or the required measures and tests. Overcoming these issues is challenging. Often the real solutions lie at the organizational level and involve building evalu-

ation capacity and instilling a culture of evaluation, which will be discussed later in the chapter. Given these realities, each evaluation can only work within its current circumstances, and the evaluation plan must be achievable within the currently available resources. This means that the use of some types of methods, tools, or equipment may not be feasible and alternatives need to be explored. Bamburger et al. (2006) provided several recommendations for scaling back evaluation plans to meet tight budgets. It is important to remember that, during the planning stage, suggestions for possible evaluation questions and data that could be collected to answer them mount quickly (Owen, 2007). As a general recommendation, particularly if resources are scarce, evaluation questions should be prioritized and the simplest design possible, collecting only the data needed to answer the most important questions, should be used (Bamberger et al., 2006).

Step 4: Determine how much time is available to complete the evaluation. Some evaluations may have strict timelines because the information is needed by a certain date. In other cases, timelines are pre-determined. Timelines may be determined by the time period set out by funders, or those needing to have evaluation results. Another example is that the evaluation of a group intervention must, more or less, begin around the same time as the intervention and end roughly when the intervention does. The terms "more or less" and "roughly" are used purposely here because some pre-testing and follow-up may also occur. Bamberger et al. (2006) pointed out that the strategies used to meet the challenge of limited resources also address time challenges.

Thus, where there is limited time to plan and carry out an evaluation, adjustments to the overall evaluation design, methods, and the amount and nature of the data collected, might be needed. For example, organizing comparison or control groups takes time, and designs that include such features may not be possible when time and resources are limited. In other cases, interventions may be underway already before the evaluation is planned, and thus only data collected during or after the program delivery can be considered.

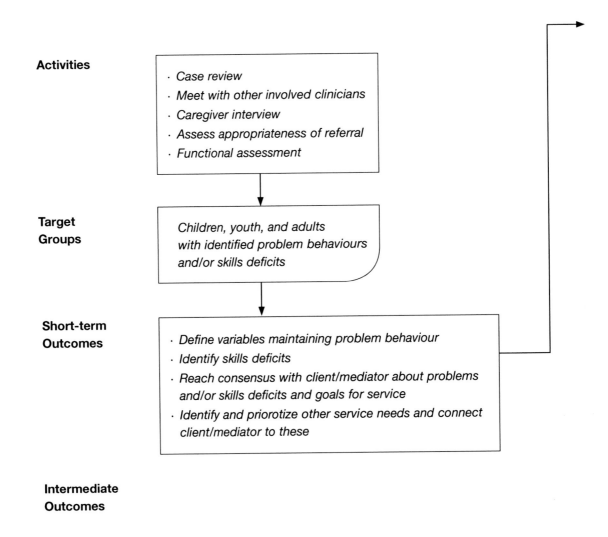

Figure 1: Logic model for a behaviour therapy service. *(Source: Barry Isaacs and the Behaviour Therapy Discipline Group, Surrey Place Centre, Toronto, Ontario.)*

Mediator Training
(Individual and Group)

Direct Intervention
(Individual and Group)

· *Identify appropriate mediator*
· *Develop intervention based on assessment*
· *Teach intervention techniques and principles*
· *Monitor progress*

· *Develop intervention based on assessment and deliver*
· *Monitor progress*

Appropriate mediator

Children, youth, and adults with identified problem behaviours and/ or skills deficits

---

· *Mediator learns and delivers intervention appropriately*
· *Increase in mediator understanding of behaviour and behavioural principles*

· *Skill acquisition: e.g. self-management, adaptive*
· *Reduction in problem issues/behaviour*

Mediator maintains, generalizes, and applies skills

· *Client maintains and generalizes skills*
· *Individualized service goals are met*

Enhanced Quality of Life
· *Personal development*
· *Improved social relations*
· *Increased community participation*
· *Improved home/school/work performance*
· *Increased independence*

Some types of evaluation activities are designed to be ongoing and therefore not time limited. In such cases, it is still wise to consider efficient methods to limit the time and resources that need to be expended.

Step 5: Identify stakeholders you will be working with to plan and carry out the evaluation. The degree to which an evaluator works with program stakeholders varies. Evaluators may act completely independently or they may involve stakeholders in the planning and execution of an evaluation (Rossi et al., 2004; Weiss, 1998). Although there are many different types of stakeholders associated with programs (e.g., policy makers, funders, even the general public), it is usually management and staff that are involved in planning and carrying out evaluation (Weiss, 1998). Service recipients may also be included. A *participatory action* approach to evaluation involves working in partnership with a variety of stakeholders, with an emphasis on service recipients, to plan, carry out, and use the results of an evaluation. This type of approach would be extremely valuable in giving people with developmental disabilities and their families a voice in program improvement (Sample, 1996).

There are many reasons for including program stakeholders. When trying to improve a service, involvement of staff and managers in the planning and execution of the evaluation will increase the likelihood that the evaluation is successful. Resistance to evaluation may be encountered because program staff and managers might see it as extra work for which they have little time, they may feel threatened by it, or they may see it as irrelevant to their work. Including these stakeholders in the planning of the evaluation increases the likelihood that evaluation questions are relevant and important to them. This, in turn, may help to foster cooperation when the evaluation is carried out and the results are used (see Weiss, 1998, pp. 101–103).

The decision about what stakeholders to include in the planning of an evaluation depends on the overall purpose, the specific evaluation questions, budget, and timelines. Often smaller, internally initiated evaluations include only program staff and managers, because this group knows the program well, has

definite ideas about the relevant questions for evaluation and program improvement, and are readily accessible. When planning an evaluation it is wise to carefully consider what would be accomplished by including various stakeholder groups (Weiss, 1998).

Step 6: Clarify the underlying program theory or logic. To carry out an evaluation, the elements of the program to be studied must be clearly defined. For example, if the purpose of the evaluation is to determine program effectiveness, then the intended outcomes of the program must be clearly articulated and agreed upon by interested stakeholders. If the program elements under study are not well defined, then some process to define them is needed. Need for this sort of clarification is common and is sometime, in and of itself, the goal of an evaluation (Owen, 2007).

Logic models are practical and straightforward tools that help to specify underlying program theory (Isaacs et al., 2009; Rossi et al., 2004). A logic model is a pictorial representation of a program. In a logic model, program elements are identified and linked. A list of the program elements often included in logic models are:

Components: Groups of closely related activities that form the main functions of the program (e.g., assessment, mediator based intervention).

Activities: The things that are done within the program components to work toward the desired outcomes.

Inputs: Resources, such as staff, that are used to carry out the program.

Outputs: A direct measure of the program activities. These include things such as the number of assessment reports, training sessions delivered, or clients supported.

Target Groups: The individuals or groups toward whom the activities are directed (e.g., clients, caregivers, professionals).

Outcomes: The intended benefits experienced by the program recipients. Often short- and long-term outcomes are specified in logic models. An example of a short-term outcome might be reduction in problem behaviour after behavioural intervention. Improved quality of life is an example of a long-term outcome for the same type of program. *Outcome* must be distinguished from *outputs*. *Outcomes* refer to change experienced by program recipients. *Outputs* are more like products that are produced by the program. Just because a client received a service *(output)* does not mean he or she experienced change *(outcome)*.

There are many formats for logic models. An example of one logic model developed to evaluate improvement in program activities and outcomes of a behaviour therapy intervention for persons with developmental disabilities is shown in Figure 1. This format was adapted from Porteous, Sheldrick, and Stewart (2002). Notice that this model does not include inputs and outputs. There are many papers on logic models, with varying formats that include other elements (Cooksy, Gill, & Kelly, 2001; Dwyer & Makin, 1997; Hernandez, 2000; McLaughlin & Jordan, 1999; Millar, Simeone, & Carnevale, 2001; Rush & Ogborne, 1991; Schalock & Bonham, 2003; W. K. Kellogg Foundation, 2004).

The information to build a logic model can come from several sources (Owen, 2007). These sources might include:

1. Program documentation such as policies and procedures
2. Literature review on the program being evaluated
3. Experts in the field the program is associated with (e.g., if a behaviour therapy intervention is being evaluated, experts in behaviour therapy)
4. Program stakeholders

Program stakeholders are a rich and important source of information, in that they know best how the program works, its subtleties and nuances, what is working well and not so well, and more. In addition, including stakeholders in the logic model building process fosters their buy-in, which is important to the success of the evaluation. Before consulting with stakeholders, however, it is best to review the literature and program documentation, and talk to others in the field. The information garnered from these other sources will inform the discussions with program stakeholders.

To build a logic model, it is important to meet with the program stakeholders identified in step 5

above to discuss and build consensus on the program (e.g., components, activities, inputs, outputs, target groups, outcomes) that will be included in the model. Then produce a draft model. Meet with the stakeholders again to discuss the model and agree on revisions. The model should then be revised and discussed again. This process continues until a final model is agreed upon (Isaacs et al., 2009). It is common for a program evaluation specialist to work with stakeholders during this process by facilitating the meetings, producing the first draft, and revising the model based on feedback.

Step 7: Specify the evaluation questions. The next step is to work with program stakeholders to specify the evaluation questions. The group or individuals who asked that the evaluation be done should definitely have input into the questions. It is also important that those who will assist in carrying out the evaluation have input, as they will be more likely to cooperate to answer evaluation questions they had a hand in formulating. For example, program staff are more likely to provide data or assist in the recruitment of program recipients if this data will be used to answer questions they think are the questions that should be asked. Not including the most appropriate stakeholders at this stage may also result in evaluation questions that are seen as irrelevant by those who should be using the information to improve the program (Weiss, 1998).

Program logic models are excellent tools for specifying evaluation questions. Working with stakeholders identified in step 5, the evaluation team can go through the logic model and discuss particular aspects of it that would be important to evaluate. Then, specific question should be developed around those aspects. Using the logic model in Figure 1, behaviour therapists and their managers might identify specific short-term outcomes such as "mediator learns and delivers intervention appropriately" and "reduction in problem behaviour/issue" as priorities for evaluation. The questions for evaluation are then:

1. Do mediators learn and deliver intervention appropriately?
2. Are significant reductions in problem behaviour/issues in clients occurring?

Another question that might arise is: What are the

most common problems/issues with which clients are presenting?

Step 8: Determine the measures to be used and develop criteria for success. The evaluation questions also specify the variables of interest. The next question is how to measure these variables. There are many types of measures that can be used. Tests, rating scales, or questionnaires (preferably with good reliability, i.e., consistent, and validity, i.e., measure what they are intended to measure), checklists, and frequency counts are just some examples. Any of these types of data may be based on reports from staff, parents, clients, or other observer reports. Data may also be found in clinical files or existing databases. Following along from the example above, behavioural problems or issues could be assessed using any number of valid and reliable scales or through caregivers counting the frequency of occurrence of the behaviours targeted for reduction.

If outcomes are being measured, criteria for success should also be established beforehand. One easy criterion when using quantitative measures, such as scales, is statistical significance. In other words, client scores on measures are significantly better after therapy than before as determined by a statistical procedure, such as a t-test. It is very important, however, to understand that statistical significance does not necessarily mean that a meaningful benefit was experienced by a client. Therefore, in some cases criteria based on clinical significance might need to be established (Hayes, Barlow, & Nelson-Gray, 1999).

Step 9: Choose an evaluation design and outline the procedures. There are several different parameters along which evaluation designs can be categorized. Broadly, designs can be distinguished by the overall approach: quantitative, qualitative, or both (i.e., mixed methods). In some respects the overall approach is determined by the measures used. Staying with our example from above, it is feasible to choose to examine parents' experiences of change in behaviour through interviews. This, however, does not mean that the overall approach will be strictly qualitative. A quantitative approach to sampling could be used, such as choosing a specific number of clients from different age groups so that the results might be representative of all clients in service. This would be in contrast to qualitative approaches that might use *snowball sampling* (asking participants to recommend other participants) and *saturation* (stopping recruitment when interviews are not revealing any new insights).

Qualitative data may be collected through a variety of methods. Interviews and focus groups are common methods used. More in-depth designs also involve observation. Qualitative approaches are useful when evaluating program processes, but can also be used to examine outcomes.

Quantitative designs may be categorized into group, and single case time series. These designs also vary in complexity. Group designs may include a comparison or control group (a group that is not exposed to the program being evaluated) that is compared to a group of individuals that get the program. Individuals might be assigned to these groups randomly or using some other method, such as date referral. Designs that do not use random assignment are referred to quasi-experimental. These designs are considered weaker than designs that employ random assignment because there are other variables besides the program that could explain the results. Including a comparison group often requires a great deal of planning and extra work. The simplest group designs do not include comparison groups. The AB, or pre-post design, in which measures are taken on program participants at the beginning and then again at the end of program, is common in applied service settings. These designs are easier to implement than comparison group designs because there are fewer participants to collect data from, and participants are likely more accessible because they are all in contact with the program being evaluated. AB designs, however, are considered a fairly weak design. That is because program recipients may have experienced some positive change (assuming their scores were better at the post measurement than pre) during the course of the program, but it is always possible that the positive change occurred for reasons other than the program (e.g., maturation, changes in the environment).

Another possible approach to evaluating outcomes

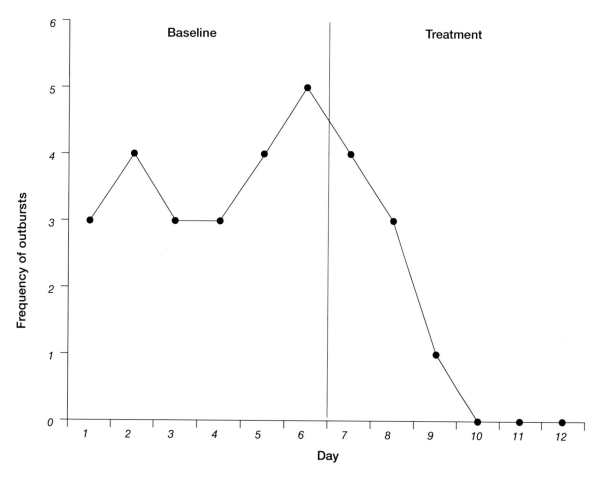

Figure 2: Graph of data evaluating an intervention to reduce aggressive outbursts using an AB time series design.

is to use single case time series designs. These designs are often used to evaluate clinical interventions. The main feature of these designs is that data is collected repeatedly, at regular intervals before an intervention begins. This period of data collection is referred to as the baseline. The collection of data at the same intervals continues throughout the intervention and may continue after the intervention stops. The assumption is that when the data are graphed, the line showing the trend during baseline will be at a different level than that representing the intervention phase. See Figure 2 for an example using an AB time-series design to evaluate an intervention to reduce aggression. Time series designs vary in complexity and there are many different types. Like

its group counterpart, the AB time series design is not considered strong because it lacks experimental control. Repeating, or replicating, the AB time series design across several individuals, however, does provide some evidence that an intervention is effective (Hayes et al., 1999). The reversal and multiple baseline, are two examples of time-series designs with good experimental control. A detailed discussion of evaluation designs is beyond the scope of this chapter. See Bamberger et al., (2006) and Rossi et al., (2004) for more discussions of group designs and qualitative approaches to evaluation, and Hayes et al. (1999) for a discussion of single case designs.

Once an overall design has been identified, the specific procedures for carrying out the evaluation and reporting the results should be developed. The following should be documented in detail:

1. What participants will be recruited and how.
2. A plan of what data will be collected, when in relation to the program (i.e., before, during, and/or after), and by whom.
3. The planned procedures for analysis (e.g., if the evaluation is a quantitative group design, the statistical tests that will be conducted should be specified).
4. How the results will be reported, to what stakeholders, and for what purpose.

Although the above steps may seem like a lot of work, it is important to remember that evaluation does not have to be complex. Here are few recommendations that might help get sustainable evaluation started in agencies:

1. Be sure there is time dedicated for evaluation.
2. Begin with small projects with simple designs.
3. Consult with an expert in evaluation. In consulting with an expert build in processes whereby the stakeholders such and program staff and managers learn about evaluation.
4. Be sure the results are reported and used.

Building Evaluation Capacity

In a previous section, the idea that the solutions to successfully engaging in evaluation lie at the organizational level was introduced. Many smaller agencies providing services to individuals with developmental disabilities, and even some larger ones, do not engage in evaluation in a way that tells us if the people they are supporting are actually experiencing positive gains. There are several reasons for this. Agencies are often not provided funding to support program evaluation. Agency staff lack the time, knowledge, and skills needed to engage in program evaluation. There may also be a view among agency staff that evaluation is not important or helpful. The concept of Evaluation Capacity Building (ECB) is concerned with addressing these issues.

The objectives of ECB are to build evaluation knowledge, increase skills, enhance evaluation resources, and foster positive attitudes toward evaluation in organizations with the goal of enabling sustainable evaluation practice (Preskill & Boyle, 2008). Preskill and Boyle (2008) developed a model that describes how EBC initiatives should be designed and implemented to maximize success. The model takes into account many factors that need to be considered, including:

- The current evaluation capacity of the organization in question (i.e., evaluation knowledge, skills, and attitudes).
- Organizations' characteristics, such as learning capacity, leadership, culture and structures.
- The motivations, expectations, and assumptions associated with a given ECB initiative.
- ECB teaching strategies, such as education and training for staff, involvement in evaluation, and technical assistance.
- Elements of sustainable evaluation practice, such as resources dedicated to evaluation, evaluation policies, and procedures and a record of using results.

Evaluation is difficult to carry out and sustain if there is little capacity in an organization for it. Thus it is important that the leadership in any organization wanting to engage in evaluation also engage in ECB. The model provided by Preskill and Boyle (2008) provides an excellent guide as to how that may be done. An organization that engages successfully in ECB should end up with a strong evaluation culture in which staff are involved in evaluation, the results are used, mistakes are tolerated and learned from, and there is willingness to change (Mayne, 2009).

Summary

Using existing research literature and engaging in program evaluation are two important sources of information to guide improvement of services and support for individuals with developmental disabilities. There are various models of evidence-based practice that allow for the integration of research evidence, clinical experience, and client characteristics and preferences, in approaches to service and supports. As well as adopting one or more of these models, developmental service agencies should also be evaluating the services they provide. Program evaluation provides accountability and information for improving services. Evaluation should have a clear purpose and be carefully planned. Issues of organizational capacity to carryout sustained evaluation should also be addressed.

For Further Thought and Discussion

1. Think of a clinical setting you have visited or worked in.
    a. To what extent is the practice there evidence-based?
    b. If it is not evidence-based, why isn't it? If it is, what factors support and encourage evidence-based practice?
    c. What program evaluation activities are carried out there?
    d. What are the barriers to program evaluation there?
2. Think of a service or support you are familiar with.
    a. What are the core components of that service?
    b. What are the short and long-term outcomes?
    c. What are some of the important evaluation questions for that service?

More Resources

The Ontario Chapter of the Canadian Evaluation Society: The Ontario chapter of the Canadian Evaluation Society provides several training courses. *http://www.evaluationontario.ca/Resources/Resources.html*

Canadian Evaluation Society
http://www.evaluationcanada.ca/site.cgi?s=1

American Evaluation Association
http://www.eval.org/

Kellogg Foundation Evaluation Handbook
http://www.wkkf.org/knowledge-center/resources/2010/W-K-Kellogg-Foundation-Evaluation-Handbook.aspx)

References

American Psychological Association. (2005). *Policy statement on evidence-based practice in psychology.* Retrieved from http://www.apa.org/practice/resources/evidence/evidence-based-statement.pdf

Bamberger, M., Rugh, J., & Mabry, L. (2006). *Real world evaluation: Working under budget, time, data and political constraints.* Thousand Oaks, CA: Sage Publications.

Brown, I., Raphael, D., & Renwick, R. (1997). *Quality of life — dream or reality? Life for people with developmental disabilities in Ontario.* Toronto, ON: Centre for Health Promotion, University of Toronto.

Chambless, D. L., & Hollon, S. D. (1998). Defining empirically supported therapies. *Journal of Consulting and Clinical Psychology, 66*(1), 7-18.

Chorpita, B. F., Becker, K. D., & Daleiden, E. L. (2007). Understanding the common elements of evidence-based paratice: Misconceptions and clinical examples. *Journal of the American Academy of Child & Adolescent Psychiatry, 46*(5), 647-652.

Cooksy, L. J., Gill, P., & Kelly, A. (2001). The program logic model as an integrative framework for a multimethod evaluation. *Evaluation and Program Planning, 24*, 119-128.

Dwyer, J. J. M., & Makin, S. (1997). Using a program logic model that focuses on performance measurement to develop a program. *Canadian Journal of Public Health, 88*(6), 421-425.

Garland, A. F., Hawley, K. M., Brookman-Frazee, L., & Hurlburt, M. S. (2008). Identifying common elements of evidence-based psychosocial treatments for children's disruptive behavior problems. *Journal of the American Academy of Child and Adolescent Psychiatry, 47*(5), 505-514.

Hayes, S. C., Barlow, D. H., & Nelson-Gray, R. O. (1999). *The scientist practitioner: Research and accoutnability in the age of managed care* (2nd ed.). Needham Heights, MA: Allyn and Bacon.

Hernandez, M. (2000). Using logic models and program theory to build outcome accoutability. *Education & Treatment of Children, 23*(1), 24-40.

Isaacs, B., Clark, C., Correia, S., & Flannery, J. (2009). Utility of logic models to plan quality of life outcome evaluations. *Journal of Policy and Practice in Intellectual Disabilities, 6*(1), 52-61.

Mayne, J. (2009). Building an evaluative culture: The key to effective evaluation and results management. *The Canadian Journal of Program Evaluation, 24*(2), 1-30.

McBeath, B., Briggs, H. E., & Aisenberg, E. (2010). Examining the premises supporting the empirically supported intervention approach to social work practice. *Social Work, 55*(4), 347-357.

McLaughlin, J. A., & Jordan, G. B. (1999). Logic models: A tool for telling your program's performance story. *Evaluation and Program Planning, 22*(1), 65-72.

Millar, A., Simeone, R. S., & Carnevale, J. T. (2001). Logic models: A systems tool for performance managment. *Evaluation and Program Planning, 24*(1), 73-81.

Mitchell, P. F. (2011). Evidence-based practice in real-world services for young people with complex needs: New opportunities suggested by recent implementation science. *Children and Youth Services Review, 33*, 207-216.

Owen, J. M. (2007). *Program evaluation: Forms and approaches.* New York: The Guilford Press.

Porteous, N. L., Sheldrick, B. J., & Stewart, P. J. (2002). Introducing program teams to logic models: Facilitating the learning process. *Canadian Journal of Program Evaluation, 17*(3), 113-141.

Preskill, H., & Boyle, S. (2008). A multidisciplinary model of evaluation capacity building. *American Journal of Evaluation, 29*(4), 443-459.

Rossi, P. H., Freeman, H. E., & Lipsey, M. W. (1999). *Evaluation: A systematic approach* (6th ed.). Thousand Oaks, CA: Sage Publications.

Rossi, P. H., Lipsey, M. W., & Freeman, H. E. (2004). *Evaluation: A systematic approach* (7th ed.). Thousand Oaks, CA: Sage Publications.

Rush, B., & Ogborne, A. (1991). Program logic models: Expanding their role and structure for program planning and evaluation. *The Canadian Journal of Program Evaluation, 6*(2), 95-106.

Sample, P. L. (1996). Beginnings: Participatory action research and adults with developmental disabilities. *Disability & Society, 11*(3), 317-332.

Schalock, R. L., & Bonham, G. S. (2003). Measuring outcomes and managing results. *Evaluation and Program Planning, 26*(3), 229-235.

Spring, B. (2007). Evidence-based practice in clinical psychology: What it is, why it matter; what you need to know. *Journal of Clinical Psychology, 63*(7), 611-631.

W. K. Kellogg Foundation. (2004). *W. K. Kellogg Foundation evaluation handbook.* Retrieved from http://www.wkkf.org/knowledge-center/resources/2010/W-K-Kellogg-Foundation-Evaluation-Handbook.aspx/

Weiss, C. H. (1998). *Evaluation* (2nd ed.). Upper Saddle River, N.J.: Prentice-Hall.

Part II

Etiology and Conditions

Introduction to Human Genetics

Maire Percy, Melissa Carter, Sheldon Z. Lewkis, Miles Thompson, and Ivan Brown

What you will learn:

- The origins of genetics and its future
- Fundamentals of human genetics
- Processes involved in cell division (mitosis, meiosis and recombination)
- Abnormalities that result in genetic disorders
- Classification and inheritance patterns of genetic disorders
- Unusual features of genetics
- Epigenetic processes

*Note: Words in **bold italics** are explained in the Special Terms section following the Summary.*

This chapter provides an introduction to some important concepts in human genetics. Genetics is the branch of biology that studies *heredity* — the passing of inherited *traits* (features that distinguish one person from another) from parents to offspring. Genetics studies how and why *traits* are transmitted from parents to children, and what causes normal and abnormal variations of inherited traits. It provides information that will help us understand our own genetic inheritance, as well as the genetic causes of certain developmental disabilities (e.g., Down syndrome).

In a more technical sense, genetics is concerned with patterns and means of inheritance of traits as well as elucidation of the functioning of genes and DNA and related molecules, including the influences of environmental factors, in health and disease.

The field of genetics is evolving rapidly, and advances have resulted in several Nobel Prizes being awarded for some of the discoveries described below. More specific information on this is included throughout the chapter, but readers are also encouraged to review the Nobel Prize website at *http://nobelprize.org/nobel_prizes/*.

Having an introductory knowledge of genetics is important for several reasons:

1. Genetics explains much of why we are the way we are. On average, each of us carries genes for at least seven serious genetic disorders (Milunsky, 1977). However, genetic processes also are influenced by environmental factors.

2. Genetics has generated a wealth of information about causes of many developmental disabilities. New knowledge about genetic causes of disabilities is leading to improved methods for

their diagnosis. Being able to diagnosis a disorder leads to better forms of intervention and treatment. This also is spurring on searches for better treatments, prevention, and even cures.

3. Genetics can help us to understand the mechanism and extent our foods and environment influence our health.

Thus, a fundamental understanding of genetics can be of benefit to everyone, particularly to those whose lives are affected by disabilities.

The Origins and Future of Genetics

The beginning of genetics as a science goes back to some observations and experiments conducted by Gregor Mendel, an Augustinian monk, born in 1822, who also taught natural science to high school students. He crossed peas of different varieties and observed that certain traits were inherited in certain proportions. His findings were first presented in 1865. For information about Mendel's discoveries, see the article by Pitman (2002) at *http:// naturalselection.0catch.com/Files/gregormendel. html/.*

The use of the word genetics as a noun was introduced by William Bateson in 1905 in a presentation that popularized Mendel's forgotten works. It is derived from the Greek word "genetikos" meaning "genitive" which is related to the word genesis or origin. Prior to Mendel's discoveries, a French naturalist and biologist — Jean Baptiste Lamarck — proposed in 1829 that characteristics developed during one's lifetime are transmitted as inheritable traits to one's offspring. Historically, this hypothesis was later discounted, but has been revived as the result of the discovery of some cellular mechanisms that are called epigenetic. The word *epigenetic* is derived from the Greek word "epi" meaning above, and literally means "above genetics."

The rediscovery of Mendel's work in the early 20th century was the first among a series of over 90 key milestones in the development of genetics as a discipline. Historically, discovery of the double helix structure of DNA in the early 1950s was arguably one of the most important scientific advances of the 20th century. For a detailed outline of historic milestones in the field of genetics, see the Dynamic Timeline website at *http://www.genome.gov/25019887/.*

Interest in genetics in the 21st century has been greatly stimulated by the *Human Genome Project* (HGP), completed in 2003. This 13-year, international research project was huge in terms of its cost and technological challenges, and in these respects has been said to rival putting man on the moon. The HGP determined the sequence of all of our DNA and identified the 25,000 genes our DNA contains. DNA (deoxyribonucleic acid) is the substance in nuclei of cells that contains the "blueprint" for the basic instructions of our structure and physiology. These genes are found in the 23 **chromosomes** of most of our cells. Red blood cells are an exception because they do not tcontain a nucleus. The term *genome* refers to the entirety of an organism's genetic information. For an introduction to HGP, see the *National Human Genome Research Institute* website at *http:// www.genome.gov/10001772/.* A sequel to the HGP is another called the Personal Genome Project (*http:// www.personalgenomes.org/project.html*). This began in 2007 and is aiming to make the cost of mapping an individuals's DNA affordable to members of the general public by 2014.

What we are still grasping to understand is how a single fertilized ovum "knows" how to develop into a complex organism containing many different types of cells. Another question is why apparently identical twins can sometimes be physically and/or psychologically different from one another (Higgins, 2008). We now know that these phenomena and others occur, in part, because of "epigenetic" biological processes that turn selective genes on or off in cells because of day-to-day experiences and interactions with the environment. Some of the instructions for turning genes on or off are inherited, and some result from interactions with the environment. So, Lamarck's idea was actually far from incorrect.

Fundamentals of Human Genetics

This section explains the relationship between DNA, chromosomes, and genes in cells, and provides an overview of how DNA functions as genetic material. Explained as well is how cells make protein using information in DNA, and differences between DNA and RNA.

Fundamental components of a cell

As shown in Figure 1, every cell has an outer *membrane*. The membrane helps the cell to hold its contents and shape. The membrane also regulates what gets into and out of the cell and it contains the cytoplasm. *Cytoplasm* is a gelatinous substance in which all of cellular metabolism, including protein production, takes place. Proteins are molecules that carry out much of the work in cells. (Hemoglobin is one very important and well-known protein; it is located in red blood cells and is involved in the transport of oxygen and carbon dioxide.) Within each cell is a structure called the nucleus, which contains 23 pairs of chromosomes (23 from your mother and 23 from your father). Each chromosome is made up of pairs of linear strands of *deoxyribose nucleic acid* (DNA) that are tightly coiled. The tight coiling of DNA results because the DNA strands wrap themselves around proteins called **histones**. Because DNA molecules are composed of two closely linked linear chains of DNA, they are said to be *double-stranded*. The DNA molecules contain short stretches of DNA called *genes*. Each gene contains information for the production of a specific protein. What we look like and how we function depends upon what proteins are made using information contained in the genes of our DNA.

The structure of DNA

The basic structure of DNA is given in Figure 2. James Watson and Francis Crick shared a Nobel Prize in Physiology or Medicine in 1962 along with their collaborator Maurice Wilkins "for their discoveries concerning the molecular structure of nucleic acids and its significance for information transfer in living material" (*http://nobelprize.org/nobel_prizes/medicine/laureates/1962/#*).

The building block of DNA molecules are nucleotides. Each *nucleotide* molecule is composed of components called a base, a sugar, and a phosphate together. These components are sometimes called groups. Different nucleotides contain different bases,

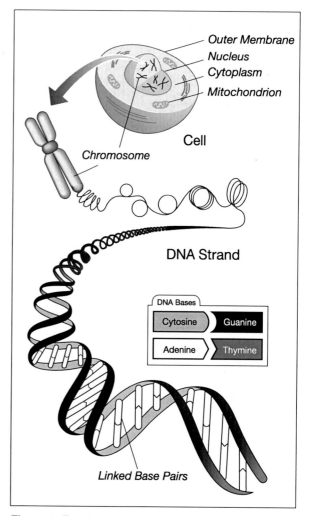

Figure 1. Fundamental components of a cell.
This diagram shows the relationship between double-stranded in a cell nucleus (genomic) DNA and chromosomes. The inset shows the four different bases in DNA and how interactions between individual bases opposite each other on the two DNA strands form rungs in the DNA "ladder." See Figure 2 for more information. (Illustration: ©2007 by Tom Dearie, Threesixty Creative; reprinted by permission.)

but identical sugar and phosphate groups. There are four different bases in DNA. They are: adenine (A), thymine (T), guanine (G), and cytosine (C). T and C groups are large, whereas A and G groups are small

The nucleotides are held together in single linear DNA strands by the phosphate groups in adjacent nucleotides. The two strands of a DNA molecule are held together by interactions between the base

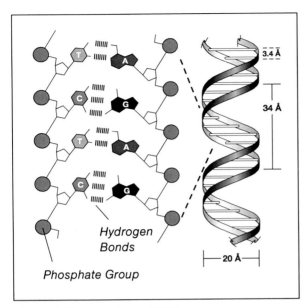

Figure 2. The structure of DNA.
Left: A two-dimensional representation of the two complementary strands of DNA, showing AT and GC base pairs (A/T and G/C are complementary base pairs). Right: The double helix model of DNA proposed by Watson and Crick (1953). The horizontal "rungs" represent the paired bases. (Source: Percy, Lewkis, & Brown, 2003. Illustration: Copyright@2007 by Tom Dearie, Threesixty Creative; reprinted by permission.)

component of a nucleotide in one DNA strand and the base of one directly opposite in the second DNA strand. An A on one side of the ladder is always paired with a T on the other side, and a G with a C (Figure 2). This base pairing makes a DNA molecule take a shape like a twisted ladder. The interconnected phosphate groups in each DNA strand form the sides of the ladders, and the interacting pairs of bases form the rungs. The linear order of nucleotides in a DNA molecule constitutes the "information coding." The order in which the four different varieties of nucleotides are strung together make the linear sequence of every gene unique. The four bases can create a code for something as complex as the development of a human through the specific ordering of pairs in the sequence.

Nuclear DNA consists of almost 6 billion (6×10^9) nucleotide (base) pairs. Every million base pairs takes up a linear space of 0.34 mm or 0.34×10^{-2} cm. So the length of DNA in each cell is 204 cm or ap-

proximately 2 metres. Because there are approximately 50 trillion (50×10^{12}) cells in the adult human body, the length of stretched out DNA in the human body is $2\times50\times10^{12}$ (100×10^{12}) metres. The extended DNA in our body would stretch from earth to the sun and back 350 times.

The DNA present in the nucleus of cells is called *genomic* DNA. Most of the text in this chapter deals with this type of DNA. DNA is also present in the cell structures called **mitochondria.** Each mitochondrion contains a circle of double-stranded DNA consisting of 16,569 nucleotide pairs. Each mitochondrion encodes several proteins and each cell has thousands of mitochondria. Mitochondrial DNA accounts for about 0.3% of total cellular DNA. Mitochondria are the "powerhouses" of the body. Proteins made from mtDNA are all subunits that take part in the important energy-generating pathway of mitochondria, known as **oxidative phosphorylation.** Mitochondria replicate themselves in a cell independently of the processes that are necessary for cell division. Mitochondria present in sperm cells get eliminated during early cell divisions after an embryo is formed. This means that the DNA in the mitochondria of most cells in the body are derived from the mother.

How information in genes of DNA results in proteins

This section provides an overview of how information in genes of DNA results in the production of specific protein molecules. What a cell does depends upon what proteins it makes. What proteins a cell makes depends upon what genes in the cell are active (turned on) or not active.

The first event in the production of a protein is the copying of the gene for that protein from the strand of a DNA molecule where it is located. The gene is copied onto a molecule of ribonucleic acid (RNA). This process is called *transcription*. Transcription takes place only from genes that are active. The second event involves a number of biochemical steps in which the cell uses information in RNA to assemble protein molecules from basic building blocks called amino acids. The process of using different RNA molecules to direct the production of different pro-

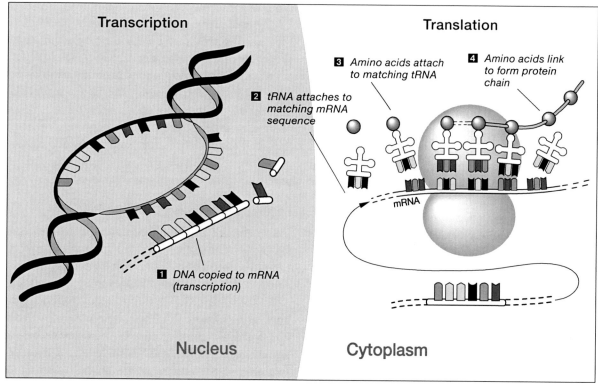

Figure 3. How protein is formed from DNA. *DNA in a gene is copied in a process called transcription into a molecule called messenger RNA (mRNA) [step 1]. This mRNA moves from the nucleus (left hand panel) into the cytoplasm (right hand panel) where it undergoes translation. Translation involves complexing of mRNA (long strand, right hand panel) with ribosomes (round structures, right hand panel). It also involves complexing of small RNA molecules called transfer RNA (tRNA) to different regions of the mRNA [step 2]. The tRNA molecules are key to translation because one end binds to a trinucleotide sequence in the mRNA molecule and the other binds to only one amino acid [step 3]. Ribosomal machinery then links amino acids attached to tRNA molecules into a linear protein chain [step 4]. The amino acids, of course, are not identical. (Source: Percy, Lewkis, & Brown, 2003. Illustration: ©2007 by Tom Dearie, Threesixty Creative; reprinted by permission.)*

tein molecules is called *translation.*

There are only about 25,000 genes in the human genome, but more than 120,000 different types of proteins. Thus, single gene contains information used to make several proteins. Moreover, we know that sometimes genes are active and result in protein production and sometimes they are inactive with no protein being produced. There is also an increasing awareness that interactions with the environment can trigger mechanisms in cells that turn genes on or off. These factors all contribute to **phenotype** (the observable physical or biochemical characteristics of an individual). More information about DNA, RNA, and protein production are given below.

How cells make proteins using information in DNA

In this section you will learn that regions of DNA corresponding to genes get copied into "working" molecules of *ribonucleic acid* (RNA) and that these RNA molecules are used by cellular machinery called **ribosomes** to make specific proteins (linear chains of building blocks called *amino acids*) (Figure 3). Also explained is how RNA differs from DNA.

As mentioned, the first step in the production of a specific protein is the copying of the gene for this protein into RNA. This RNA is called *messenger RNA* (mRNA). mRNA strands are working copies of genes located in the cell that are distinct from the genes in the DNA. Not all genes in DNA get copied into mRNA at the same time — only those that are needed by the cell. mRNA molecules then move from the cell nucleus to structures in the cell cytoplasm called ribosomes, which contain all the necessary machinery for making proteins. In order to be "read" by the ribosomal machinery, pieces of RNA that are not needed are removed. The pieces of RNA that are removed are called *introns* and those that are kept are called *exons*. RNA processed in this way is called *mature* RNA.

Within ribosomes, the mature mRNA molecule is "read" by a process called *translation* (Figure 3). Key to this process are molecules called *transfer RNAs* (tRNAs), which are essential for the ribosomal machinery to read mRNA. Translation involves the formation of complexes between the mRNA molecule and *transfer RNAs* (tRNAs). There are as many different tRNA molecules as there are amino acids. Each tRNA molecule is unique and does two important things. One end contains a unique set of 3 nucleotides (base triplets) that bind to a complementary set of 3 nucleotides in the mRNA molecule. Their other end contains a region that binds uniquely to only one of 20 different amino acids, which are the basic building blocks of proteins. Because one tRNA can bind only to one trinucleotide sequence in mRNA and only to one amino acid, the order in which different tRNAs bind to different base triplets in mRNA (which correspond to the order of unique base triplets in DNA) determines the order of amino acids in protein chains. As depicted in Figure 3, the ribosomal machinery joins amino acids attached to the tops of their respective tRNA molecules into a linear protein chain. The unique sets of base triplets in mRNA molecules (and the corresponding sets in DNA) are called *codons*. The complementary sets of base triplets in tRNA molecules are called *anti-codons*. For example, the codon ACG in DNA specifies the complementary codon CGU in mRNA, which in turn specifies incorporation of the amino acid *arginine* at that position. In 1968, the Nobel Prize in Physiology or Medicine was awarded jointly to Robert Holley, Har Gobind Khorana, and Marshall Nirenberg "for their interpretation of the genetic code and its function in protein synthesis" (*http://no-belprize.org/nobel_prizes/medicine/laureates/1968/*).

Although many genes produce only one mature species of mRNA molecule and one protein, some precursor mRNA molecules are processed in different ways to yield different species of mature mRNAs. After the protein chains are made, two or more such polypeptide chains may combine to form a single protein molecule. Proteins also may be cleaved or modified chemically — for example, by adding carbohydrate, phosphate, or certain other groups at particular sites.

Differences between DNA and RNA

As mentioned, mRNA molecules are working copies of DNA ultimately created for the purpose of protein construction. Like DNA, RNA molecules are composed of nucleotides. However, in RNA nucleotides, the sugar group is ribose rather than deoxyribose, and thymine (T) bases are replaced by uracil (U) bases. In contrast to DNA molecules, which are double-stranded, mRNA molecules are single-stranded, though these single strands fold up in complex ways. Different types of mRNA molecules and different types of proteins are produced from the same DNA sequence via a process called *alternative RNA splicing*. In this process, pieces of RNA that are not needed by a cell are removed prior to the act of translation. The process of alternative RNA splicing explains, in part, why there are many more proteins in the body than genes in the human body. Much of DNA does not code for genes; instead, it gets translated into RNA molecules that have regulatory functions. These are called microRNAs (see later section on microRNAs).

Processes Involved in Cell Division

An introduction to genetics should involve an introduction to the processes involved in cell division and in production of sperm and ova. In this section you will learn about two different forms of cell division — *mitosis and meiosis*. Also explained are the concepts of *genetic recombination* and *chromosomal nondisjunction*. Fundamental to cell division is the double-stranded nature of DNA. The sequence of bases on one strand is specified by the sequence on the other and vice versa.

All cells in the body, except for the sperm and ova (eggs) are referred to as *somatic* cells. The number of chromosomes in somatic cells (46, or 23 pairs), or the *diploid* number (sometimes indicated by 2n) is constant. Ova and sperm (also called *gametes*) have only half of the diploid number of chromosomes (23) and are said to be *haploid* (sometimes indicated by n).

In order to maintain the same number of chromosomes in cells, two types of cell division occur. *Mitosis* occurs in cells in somatic tissues during growth and repair. It ensures constancy of chromosome number in cells and constancy of genetic material. *Meiosis* is a specialized form of cell division that results in the formation of four daughter cells, each with a haploid number of chromosomes. Meiosis occurs only in *germ cells* in genital tissue and results in formation of the gametes. In males, each spermatocyte forms four functional spermatids, which develop into sperm. The formation of sperm takes place on a continual basis from the time of sexual maturity. In females, each oocyte results in the formation of only one ovum; the other three daughter cells become non-functional polar bodies. The formation of ova is largely complete at birth. Each gamete's chromosomes produced in meiosis have a unique combination of genes derived from both parents. During meiosis, each chromosome pair in a germ cell mixes the paternal and maternal genetic material in that cell by the process of *genetic recombination* (Figure 4). Thus, each unpaired chromosome in a sperm or ovum has genetic material derived from both of the chromosomes that form a pair in the germ cell. Meiosis is fundamental to sexual reproduction and ensures genetic variability of species.

Figure 4. Crossing over and recombination during meiosis. *During the early stages of cell division in meiosis, two chromosomes of a homologous pair may exchange segments in the manner shown, producing genetic variation in germ cells. This process ensures that each ovum and sperm produced will have a unique collection of alleles. This process is beneficial for survival. (Illustration: ©2007 by Tom Dearie, Threesixty Creative; reprinted by permission.)*

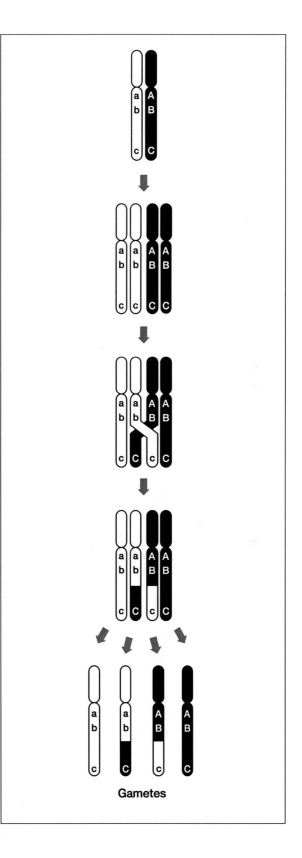

Gametes

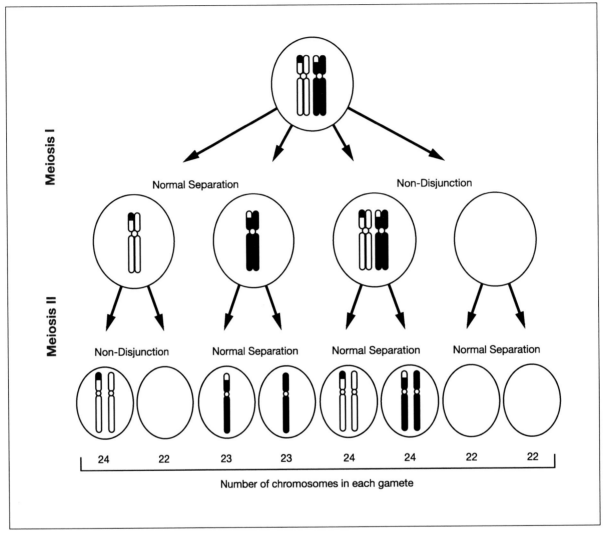

Figure 5. Diagram of normal and abnormal meiosis. *Normal meiosis delivers one sister chromatid to each gamete. But nondisjunction of sister chromatids can result in gametes receiving both or neither of a chromatid pair. The resulting gametes have too few or too many chromosomes. (Illustration: ©2007 by Tom Dearie, ThreeSixty-Creative; reprinted by permission.)*

Twenty-two of the chromosome pairs, or *autosomes*, are labelled 1-22 in decreasing order of their length (although chromosome 22 is larger than chromosome 21). One of the 23 pairs is termed the sex pair. In females, the sex pair is comprised of two X chromosomes. Conversely, males have a sex pair comprised of an X and a Y chromosome. (The X and Y chromosomes are not actually X or Y shaped.)

Figure 5 shows the process of meiosis. Sometimes, the process of meiosis is abnormal and not all the chromosomes come apart. The consequence is that one cell gets *both* **sister chromatids** that each become a chromosome, whereas the other cell gets none. This abnormal process of meiosis is called **nondisjunction**. Nondisjunction can occur during particular stages of meiosis called meiosis I or meiosis II (see Figure 5). This results in an ovum or sperm having two copies of one particular chromosome or missing a copy of that chromosome. During meiosis, translocation sometimes occurs, that is, chromosomes sometimes get attached to one another and these do not separate properly. Figure 6 provides a

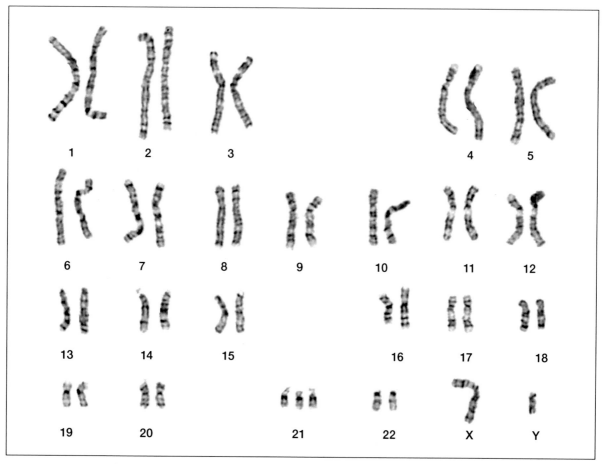

Figure 6. Photograph of chromosomes isolated from white blood cells of a male child with Down syndrome. *Chromosomes are tightly bound strands of DNA bound to proteins found in the cell nucleus. In this photograph, the chromosomes have been stained with Giemsa (G banding) in a standard fashion. They are numbered from 1-22 in order of decreasing length (except that chromosome 21 is smaller than chromosome 22), with the X and Y chromosomes shown separately. This standard arrangement of an individual's chromosomes is known as a karyotype. Healthy, typically developing individuals have 22 pairs of chromosomes plus two sex chromosomes. The presence of three chromosome 21s in this photo indicates Down syndrome. (Karyotype courtesy of Dr. Kathy Chun, North York General Hospital, Toronto.)*

photograph of chromosomes isolated from cultured white blood cells from a male child with Down syndrome, a common disorder resulting from nondisjunction of chromosome 21. See Chapter 14 for more information about Down syndrome.

As explained more fully in the second part of the next section, the cells of an individual do not always have the same genetic makeup. This is a phenomenon called *mosaicism*. Mosaicism can result from errors in cell division. However, a unique and normal type of mosaicism occurs in all females because

one of the two X chromosomes in each of their cells becomes inactivated at a very early stage of development (see below and Figure 7).

Abnormalities Resulting in Genetic Disorders

In this section, you will learn about alternative forms of genes and other abnormalities that can cause genetic disorders. Normally, we have two copies of every gene, one from our mother, the other

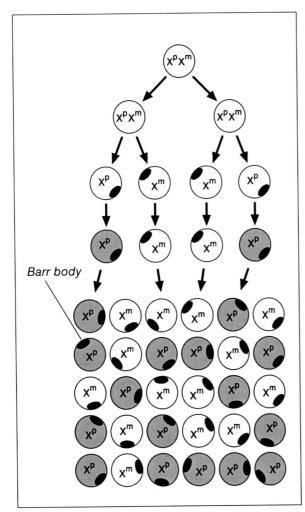

Barr body

Figure 7: The process of lyonization, or random X chromosome inactivation, in female somatic cells. *The ovals within the circles represent the Barr bodies that are formed from the inactivated paternal or maternal X chromosome. In any somatic cell in a female, either the paternally inherited X chromosome (Xp) or the maternally inherited X chromosome (Xm) may be active; which chromosome is active is usually a matter of chance. Once one X chromosome has become inactivated in a cell, this X chromosome remains inactivated in all of the descendants of that cell. (Source: Percy, Lewkis, & Brown, 2003. Illustration: Copyright@2007 by Tom Dearie, Theesixty Creative; reprinted by permission.)*

from our father. These copies sometimes are identical, but sometimes they are not. Alternative forms of a gene are called *alleles*. Different alleles code for variations in inherited characteristics such as eye colour. In some cases, allelic variation can be so abnormal that genetic disorders can result.

Mutations

Abnormalities that cause genetic disorders often result from the production of abnormal proteins as the result of errors in DNA sequences. However, in addition to malfunctioning protein, changes or errors in DNA also can result in the underexpression, overexpression, or complete absence of, proteins. Furthermore, RNA abnormalities that have no effect on protein sequence, but still be problematic.

Mutations, or errors in DNA sequence that affect protein expression or function, can occur in mtDNA as well as in genomic DNA. They occur as the result of:

- *Deletions* (loss or absence of a crucial region of DNA).
- *Duplications* (the production of one or more copies of any piece of DNA).
- *Amplification* (e.g., of regions of DNA called trinucleotide repeat regions).
- *Translocations* (transfer of a chromosomal segment to a new region).
- *Inversions* (a type of mutation in which an entire section of DNA is reversed).
- Single nucleotide changes or single nucleotide polymorphisms (SNPs) (pronounced "snips"). SNPs are DNA sequence variations resulting in a difference in a single nucleotide. SNPs are found every 100-300 nucleotides throughout the genome. They can occur in both coding regions (i.e., genes) and noncoding regions of the genome. Many SNPs have no effect on cell function, but others may affect the function of a protein and predispose people to disease or influence their response to a drug.
- Copy number variations (CNVs). Copy number variations are the most common type of genetic variation in humans. A *copy number variant* (CNV) is a segment of DNA for which differences in copy-number (number of copies of a particular region or portions of it) have been found by comparison of two or more genomes. The segment involved in a CNV may range from one kilobase to several megabases in size.

CNVs can be inherited or they may arise de novo (Morrow, 2010). Identical twins sometimes have different CNVs.

If a protein does not function properly, and if this protein is particularly important in brain cells, then brain structuring and/or physiology will be affected. Because cellular DNA is faithfully reproduced when a cell divides to produce daughter cells, mistakes that are present in a DNA molecule usually also are produced. This is the basis of inheritance of genetic forms of developmental disabilities. Generally, one gene produces one protein. However, some genes can produce more than one type of protein because different species of RNA can be produced from the same gene. Developmental disabilities that result from dysfunction or absence of only one protein are the ones for which the prospects of a cure are the most likely in the foreseeable future. One example is fragile X syndrome in which there is deficiency of FMR-1 protein.

As already mentioned and will be discussed later, epigenetic mechanisms also can affect gene function. Epigenetic modifications can be inherited, and they also can arise during development and throughout the life span in response to interaction with the environment.

Mosaicism and lyonization

It is not always the case that all somatic cells have identical chromosomes. Sometimes cells may gain or lose one or more chromosomes during the process of division. Individuals who carry somatic cells with the normal diploid number and cells that have one or more chromosomes missing or one or more extra chromosomes are said to carry more than one cell line. When individuals carry two or more different cell lines, they are said to have *mosaicism*. The development of mosaicism can occur in any dividing tissue before or after birth and throughout one's life. Mosaicism that normalizes the DNA content of a tissue or organ is beneficial. For example, as explained in Chapter 10, individuals who are mosaic for trisomy 21 — that is, who have some normal cells in their tissues along with trisomy 21 cells — may have fewer features of Down syndrome than individuals with complete trisomy 21. Errors sometimes occur in chromosomal segregation during mitosis after zygote formation in a process also resulting in mosaicism.

Another type of mosaicism occurs in all females. In females, one of the two X chromosomes in each somatic cell is inactivated, becoming the so-called "Barr body." This process has been called *lyonization* after Mary Lyon, the scientist who discovered it. Which X chromosome is inactivated (i.e., the one that originally came from the sperm or the one from the ovum) is thought to be determined randomly. Inactivation of one X chromosome in each cell of the developing embryo starts to occur about three days after fertilization, when the embryo is comprised of approximately 32 cells. Should one of the X chromosomes be defective, the process of lyonization ensures that some cells in the female always will have a normal X chromosome that is active.

This process tends to spare females from the effects of defective genes on the X chromosome. In contrast, if a gene on the X chromosome in a male is defective, there is no normal copy of that gene to compensate, as males have only one X chromosome. Lyonization explains why female carriers of an X-linked disorder are often spared from full effects of the disorder, whereas male carriers are strongly affected. *Fragile X syndrome, Duchenne muscular dystrophy,* and *Lesch-Nyhan syndrome* are examples of serious X-linked developmental disabilities. Figure 7 illustrates the process of lyonization in somatic cells of females.

Classification and Inheritance Patterns of Genetic Disorders

We have already discussed ways in which mistakes in cells can arise. Sometimes these result in genetic disorders associated with developmental and/or intellectual disability. In this section you will learn that genetic disorders are commonly classified into three types: chromosomal, single-gene, and non-Mendelian. Disorders caused by single genes are less frequent than disorders resulting from multiple genes acting on their own or in conjunction with environmental factors.

Chromosomal disorders

Chromosomal disorders/syndromes are caused by a person having too many or two few chromosomes, or by a change in the structure of a chromosome that disrupts its function. About 60% of all first-trimester miscarriages (spontaneous abortions) occur as a result of a chromosomal abnormality. The term *syndrome* refers to a set of clinically recognizable symptoms occurring together. Most chromosomal disorders are not actually inherited even though they are considered to be genetic. Rather, they occur **sporadically** (irregularly, without any pattern or order in time, with no evidence of being inherited). Examples of chromosomal disorders with an abnormal number of chromosome are: *Down syndrome* (trisomy 21), Patau syndrome (trisomy 13) Edwards syndrome (trisomy 18), **Turner** syndrome (monosomy X), and **Klinefelter syndrome** (XXY). Examples of chromosomal disorders in which there are a normal number of chromosomes but a segment of DNA is deleted include **cri-du-chat syndrome** (missing part of the short arm of chromosome 5), **Prader-Willi** and **Angelman** syndromes (missing part of the long arm of chromosome 15), and **Williams syndrome** (missing part of chromosome 7).

Single-gene disorders

Genetic disorders caused by a sequence change or chromosome abnormality affecting only one gene are called single gene disorders. Single gene disorders are sometimes called Mendelian disorders, because their inheritance pattern is predictable according to Mendel's principles. **Inborn errors of metabolism** are a subtype of single gene disorder, which occur when cells cannot produce proteins or **enzymes** needed to convert certain chemicals into others, or when cells cannot transport substances from one place to another. About 1 in 1,500 children are born with a defective enzyme that results in an inborn error of metabolism. More than 350 inborn errors of metabolism have been identified, many of which impair the function of the brain. One example of an inborn error of metabolism resulting in intellectual disability is phenylketonuria (PKU).

This disorder results from mutations in the phenylalanine hydroxylase gene. See Chapter 13 for more detail and other examples of single-gene disorders.

Single gene disorders are the easiest to diagnose since they are caused by a change in a single gene. Disorders that result from changes in single genes are inherited in one of three ways: *dominant inheritance, recessive inheritance,* and *X-linked inheritance*. Each is discussed next.

Dominant inheritance: In dominant inheritance, one affected parent of either sex has a defective gene that dominates over its normal gene counterpart. Every child has a 50 percent chance of inheriting either the defective gene (and the disease) or the normal gene from the affected parent. *Myotonic dystrophy, neurofibromatosis* and **tuberous sclerosis** are examples of autosomal dominant developmental disabilities. Myotonic dystrophy is one of several disorders caused by amplification of a nucleotide repeat region. Certain regions of DNA contain short sequences (two, three or four nucleotides) that are repeated over and over again.

Recessive inheritance: In recessive inheritance, both parents are usually healthy, but each carries a defective gene that, by itself, does not cause problems. Parents of children with autosomal recessive traits are called carriers since each parent carries one copy of the abnormal trait but does not actually show it. The disorder or disease occurs when a person receives two copies of the recessive gene (i.e., one from each parent). There is a 25 percent chance that a person will inherit two copies of the defective gene and show the abnormality, a 50 percent chance that they will be a carrier, and a 25 percent chance that they will neither be a carrier nor be affected. Some examples of autosomal recessive developmental disabilities are: Smith-Lemli-Opitz syndrome and phenylketonuria (PKU) (see Chapter 13). It is recognized that recessive genes causing certain serious genetic disorders can have beneficial functions in certain situations. For example, genes that cause sickle cell anemia and thalassemia protect against malaria infection. Genes that cause cystic fibrosis protect against typhoid.

X-linked inheritance: In X-linked disorders (sometimes called sex-linked disorders), the defective gene is carried on the X chromosome of the mother who usually shows few or no symptoms of the disorder. The disorder is expressed when a male receives the defective gene. Each male child has a 50 percent chance of being affected, while 50 percent of female children will carry the defective gene but will usually not be highly affected because of lionization. Examples of X-linked disorders are ***Duchenne muscular dystrophy, Lesch-Nyhan syndrome, and fragile X syndrome.***

Non-Mendelian genetic disorders

This is a general term that refers to any pattern of inheritance in which traits do not segregate in accordance with Mendel's simple laws of inheritance. In clinical genetics, traits that are maternally inherited or multifactorial in nature tend to be referred to as non-Mendelian.

Polygenic disorders

Polygenic disorders result from a deleterious combination of two or more genes in the absence of environmental factors. Many mental health conditions are suspected to be ***polygenic.*** Examples currently thought to be polygenic by some scientists include attention-deficit hyperactivity disorder, and schizophrenia.

Multifactorial disorders

Multifactorial disorders are caused by a combination of genetic mutations and environmental exposures. One example of a ***multifactorial*** disability is spina bifida, a neural tube defect. Spina bifida results from failure of fusion of the caudal neural tube during embryonic development. It is one of the most common malformations of human structure. Chromosomal abnormalities, single-gene disorders, and exposures to teratogens (see Chapter 10) are associated with spina bifida. Up to 70% of spina bifida cases can be prevented by maternal periconceptional folic acid supplementation. The mechanisms underlying this protective effect is unknown, but it may involve genes that regulate folate transport and metabolism. Other common examples of disorders considered to be multifactorial are: ***Alzheimer's disease***, cancer, *hypertension* (high blood pressure),

ischemic heart disease (the word ischemic refers to any form of blockage in a blood vessel), and type 2 diabetes. As noted above, multifactorial disorders tend to be referred to as non-Mendelian.

Testing for Genetic Disorders

Testing for genetic disorders involves the application of laboratory procedures to detect alterations in DNA or chromosomes. The results of such tests can be used to diagnose genetic disorders and to identify individuals who carry altered DNA but may or may not be severely affected by a disorder. Testing also can be used to determine if an individual might pass a copy of an abnormal gene to his or her child. Genetic testing can be done on cells, blood, and amniotic fluid. In this section, you will learn about different ways in which genetic abnormalities can be detected.

One approach looks for changes in chromosome number or structure under the microscope (a procedure called ***cytogenetics***). Another involves analysis of the sequence of a person's DNA. A third approach involves the application of molecular probes designed to attach to particular regions of DNA that are suspected of being altered, and then using a special procedure to visualize the molecular probes that have bound. To see how a procedure called fluorescence in situ hybridization (FISH) is used to diagnose Williams syndrome, see the images at *http://www.mun.ca/biology/scarr/Williams_Syndrome.html/*. Some genetic alterations can be detected using functional or biochemical tests that demonstrate the presence of an altered gene through the presence of abnormal proteins or no proteins at all.

Alterations in DNA gene copy number (i.e., "dosage") are associated with normal human variation, but some are responsible for genetic syndromes. A new technique called *Chromosomal Microarray Analysis* (CMA) is able to screen the entire genome in a single test. This method is being used to search for genetic abnormalities in children with autism (Miller et al., 2010). It also is being used to screen for genetic abnormalities in embryos created by in vitro fertilization (IVF) as early as 3 days of age, since 50-70% of IVF embryos are known to have chromosomal abnormalities. For an example of the application of CMA to IVF embryo analysis, see *http://blogs.nature.com/nm/spoonful/genetics/*. The Nobel Prize in Physiology or Medicine 2010 was awarded to Robert Edwards "for the development of in vitro fertilization" (*http://nobelprize.org/nobel_prizes/medicine/laureates/2010/*). For more information about genetic testing, see *What is Genetic Testing on the Genetics Home Reference website* at *http://www.ghr.nlm.nih.gov/handbook/testing/genetictesting/*.

Unusual Features of Genetics

In the previous sections, the focus was on genes in cell nuclei and two types of RNA — mRNA and tRNA. Only 10-15% of the bases in DNA make up the genes. Furthermore DNA also is present in cellular mitochondria. In this section, you will learn about mitochondrial DNA, some types of DNA once thought to be "junk," and prion disorders that are transmitted by protein and not by microorganisms containing nucleic acid. The section concludes with a brief introduction to a third type of RNA called microRNA that regulates the activity or stability of mRNA molecules.

Mitochondrial DNA variation

In contrast to our genomic DNA, which is inherited from both parents in equal proportions, mitochondrial DNA (mtDNA) is inherited only from our mother. This is because sperm cells do not contribute mitochondria to the embryo (since they are degraded upon fusion of sperm and egg). Mutations in mtDNA are transmitted to all of a woman's offspring, but none of a man's offspring. Examples of developmental disabilities resulting from mitochondrial DNA mutations are certain mitochondrial myopathies, such as MELAS (mitochondrial *encephalopathy* with lactic acidosis and stroke-like episodes), which can affect the nervous system in addition to muscle. Another mitochondrial disorder is *Leber's hereditary optic neuropathy.*

DNA satellite sequences

A large fraction of DNA (85-90%) has no identified function and is said to be "silent." Some of the remaining base sequences perform crucial functions such as helping to turn genes on and off and holding chromosomes together. DNA that does not have a specific, identified function has historically been referred to as "junk DNA."

Part of this "junk DNA" includes unusual regions called DNA *satellite sequences*. These are repetitive sequences made up of one or more of the four DNA bases — A, C, G and T — repeated over and over again. The repetitive nature of these satellite sequences makes them unstable. Satellite sequences are very prone to changing in length as they are transmitted from one generation to another. The term microsatellite is applied to very short repetitive sequences. Variations of microsatellite sequences called trinucleotide repeat regions are now known to play an important role in quite a number of disorders that affect the central nervous system. *Trinucleotide repeat regions* consist of a three nucleotide sequence repeated over and over again — for example, CGG-CGG-CGG-CGG-CGG.

It is suspected that microsatellites are involved in regulating the amount of protein produced by particular genes, and that such regulation may be important in adaptation to environmental changes. Certain trinucleotide repeat regions are known to grow in length as they are transmitted, if they become unstable. Examples of developmental disabilities that are caused by expansions of trinucleotide repeat regions are: *fragile X syndrome* and *myotonic dystrophy* (type 1). (See Ellegren, 2004; Nussbaum, McInnis & Willard, 2007; Online Mendelian Inheritance in Man (OMIM), 2011; Orr & Zoghbi, 2007). Expansion of trinucleotide repeat regions may cause particular disorders to become expressed at an earlier and earlier age and/or more severely as they are transmitted through several generations in a family (e.g., myotonic dystrophy), a phenomenon called *genetic anticipation.*

Perhaps the most important type of satellite sequence is a region of repetitive DNA located at the ends of chromosomes called *telomeric DNA*. When DNA replicates, there is difficulty copying the DNA at the chromosome ends. The impact of this problem is avoided, however, because at the ends of every chromosome is a region of satellite DNA called a telomere. With cell division, the telomeric DNA at the chromosome ends becomes shorter and shorter. If telomers become excessively short, DNA replication is negatively effected and may lead to onset of serious illness or death. Through a simple blood test, it is now possible to test for telomere length in white blood cells. If the length is found to be unduly short, then lifestyle changes are recommended. Healthy eating and exercise are known to increase the activity of the enzyme involved in telomere synthesis (these findings relate to epigenetics). The Nobel Prize in Physiology or Medicine in 2009 was awarded jointly to Elizabeth Blackburn, Carol Greider and Jack Szostak *"for the discovery of how chromosomes are protected by telomeres and the enzyme telomerase"*. (*http://nobelprize.org/nobel_prizes/medicine/laureates/2009/*).

Transposons

These are sequences of DNA that can move or transpose themselves to different regions of the genome. In the past, transposons have been considered to be a form of "junk DNA". They also have been called "jumping genes" and "selfish DNA" because their main function seems to be to replicate themselves. One type of transposon gets copied and the copy gets inserted at a new position in the genome. Another type gets cut out and moved to a new position. Transposons were first discovered by Dr. Barbara McClintock, who received The Nobel Prize in Physiology or Medicine in 1983 "for her discovery of mobile genetic elements" (*http://nobelprize.org/nobel_prizes/medicine/laureates/1983/*).

The Human Genome Project determined that a large portion of the human genome (44%) consists of transposons, though only about 0.05% are active at the present time. There is great interest in the active transposons as they continue to generate genetic diversity as well as causing genetic disease (Mills, Bennett, Iskow, & Devine, 2007).

The most common form of transposon in humans is *Alu*. The Alu sequence is about 300 bases long. There are between 300,000 and 1 million copies of Alu in the human genome. Alu insertions that have altered normal gene function have been linked with various cancers (e.g., breast cancer) and other disorders including type 2 diabetes, and neurofibromatosis.

Neurodegenerative prion disorders

A discussion of genetics would not be complete without mentioning the *prion* disorders. Prions are short proteins (peptides) that have infectious properties like bacteria or viruses even through they contain no RNA or DNA. The Nobel Prize in Physiology or Medicine 1997 was awarded to Stanley B. Prusiner "for his discovery of Prions — a new biological principle of infection" (*http://nobelprize.org/nobel_prizes/medicine/laureates/1997/*).

Prion disorders are all associated with a spongy, "swiss-cheese" appearance of the brain and a proliferation of non-neuronal brain cells called *astroglia*. Well known prion disorders in animals include *scrapie* which occurs in sheep and mice, and *bovine spongiform encephalopathy* (BSE). Human prion diseases include kuru, *Creutzfelt-Jacob disease* (CJD), *Gerstmann-Straussler disease,* and *fatal familial insomnia*. *Kuru* is a disease that was first recognized in New Guinea in the early 1900s in a group taking part in a cannibalistic ritual — eating flesh and brain tissue from dead people who were important in the community. The reason for current interest in prion disorders is that a new variant of CJD, discovered in 1990 and apparently related to BSE, has been reported in the U.K. and possibly in other countries as well. It is thought that eating beef infected with BSE resulted in transmission of CJD. BSE was nicknamed "mad cow disease" because it caused nervous, aggressive behaviour in normally peaceful animals. It is believed that cattle became infected because they were fed improperly sterilized food derived from scrapie infected sheep.

People have been cautioned not to handle scrapie infected meat and bone meal with bare hands or to inhale it. Unfortunately, prions are very resistant to heat and cannot be destroyed by autoclaving (a process of sterilization involving treatment at high temperature and pressure that is often used to decontaminate biohazardous waste, as well as surgical and dental instruments). One might ask what other animal products might be contaminated with prions — for example, gelatin, collagen, tallow, leather, and

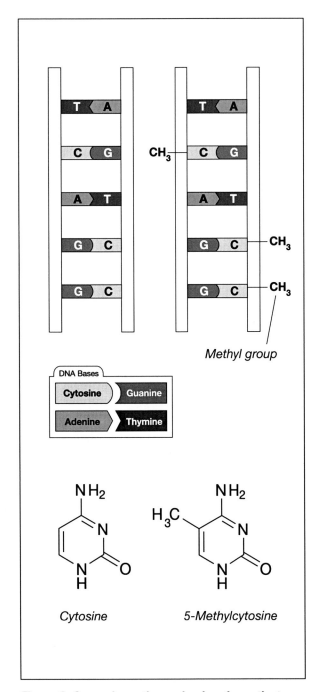

Methyl group

Figure 8. One epigenetic mechanism for activating or repressing gene activity: addition of methyl groups (CH₃) to the DNA base cytosine (C). *In this diagram, the vertical rods depict the linear backbone of the two strands of DNA. When CH₃ groups become attached to certain C residues, DNA in that region cannot be copied into mRNA. (Illustration: ©2011 by Tom Dearie, Theesixty Creative; reprinted by permission.)*

laboratory reagents such as calf serum, bovine serum albumin, and other bovine proteins.

In parts of Europe, livestock other than cattle, such as pigs, poultry, goats and sheep, have become infected by BSE (by the same means as cattle). However, BSE is currently not a major problem in the U.S. or Canada. To date, only a very small number of isolated cases of BSE have been found in cattle in these countries.

Although we do not understand exactly how, prion proteins become folded in an abnormal way that causes neighbouring prion molecules to take on the same abnormal structure. It is this abnormal folding that results in disease. For more information about prions and prion diseases, see the Genetics Home Reference website at *http://ghr.nlm.nih.gov/condition/prion-disease/*. See also Rhodes (1998).

MicroRNAs

MicroRNAs (miRNAs) are a recently discovered class of very small RNA molecules that regulate gene activity even though they are derived from non-coding DNA They act by binding to complementary sequences in regulatory regions at the ends of mRNA molecules — regions called *three prime untranslated regions* (3'UTRs). Such binding usually represses the translation of mRNA into protein or promotes mRNA degradation. MiRNAs can change the way basic processes, including cell death, cell proliferation, tissue development, and the immune response take place. Over 1000 different miRNA molecules are encoded in the human genome and each one may affect the expression of hundreds of mRNAs. Researchers are finding that the amounts of certain miRNAs produced in cells may be significantly altered in certain diseases (e.g., fragile X syndrome, **Alzheimer's disease**, and prion diseases) (Provost, 2010).

Epigenetics

As already mentioned, scientists have discovered that in addition to the master blueprint consisting of linear sequences of DNA in chromosomes, there are other sets of information that are important for cellular function. These other processes are referred to as epigenetic or epigenomic. What genes we inherit are important, but whether these genes are ac-

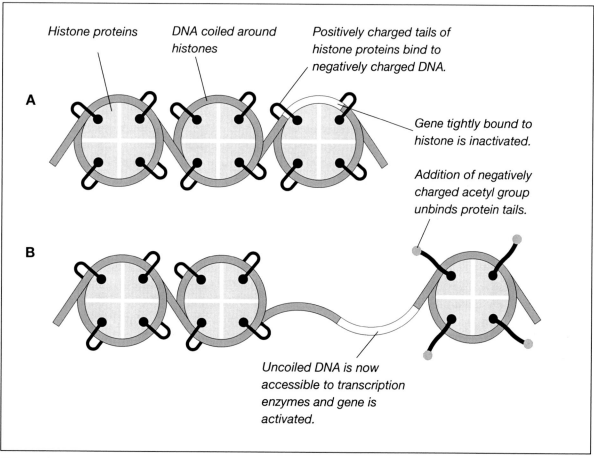

A

Histone proteins

DNA coiled around histones

Positively charged tails of histone proteins bind to negatively charged DNA.

Gene tightly bound to histone is inactivated.

Addition of negatively charged acetyl group unbinds protein tails.

B

Uncoiled DNA is now accessible to transcription enzymes and gene is activated.

Figure 9. A second epigenetic mechanism for controlling gene activity: modification of histone proteins that help to keep DNA coiled. *The top diagram (A) shows DNA interacting with histone proteins that are not modified; the tails of the histone proteins wrap themselves around the DNA. When DNA is tightly coiled it cannot be copied into RNA. The bottom panel (B) shows what happens when acetyl groups are added to the histone tails; they can no longer bind the DNA. This allows the DNA to assume a more open configuration that allows a DNA strand to be copied into RNA. (Illustration: ©2011 by Tom Dearie, Threesixty Creative; reprinted by permission.)*

tive and how active they are is critical in relation to health. The term *epigenetics* deals with any changes that affect gene activity or expression other than the linear sequence of DNA. The term *epigenomics* refers to analysis of epigenetic changes across many genes in a cell or entire organism (in this case, the human body). In this section, we will focus on epigenetic mechanisms.

Epigenetics elucidates that who we are or might become, as biological beings, is not only dependent upon the specific genes we inherit from our parents, but also upon our exposure to a wide variety of environmental factors. This knowledge represents a profound change in our understanding of the larger picture of genetics.

Even more startling, perhaps, is the emerging knowledge that the activity of some genes may undergo longterm alteration by exposure to environmental signals, although these environmental signals do not change the linear sequence of bases in the DNA. This means that if a particular gene is turned on or off by an environmental factor — adaptive or nonadaptive — such functioning or nonfunctioning might be passed on to a future generation. The positive side of this is that we apparently have the ability to acquire and pass on adaptations in attempting to survive and thrive in changing environments. The negative side of it is that harmful environmental factors may change the way genes function in negative ways that are then passed on to our children. For more information, see Lipton (2005).

Epigenetic mechanisms

In this section, we describe two cellular processes that are known to affect the activity of certain genes. The most studied process involves the addition of methyl groups to DNA and is called methylation. Methylation of DNA acts as a switch and can turn genes on or off. The second epigenetic process involves the addition of certain substances to the "tails" of the histone proteins that bind to DNA and help to keep it tightly coiled. See Figures 8 and 9 for diagrams of these two epigenetic processes.

Signals from the environment (e.g., medications, dietary factors such as low calorie diet, or exposures to environmental toxins) can activate cellular machinery that puts methyl groups on DNA or adds certain chemical groups to histone proteins, turning certain genes on or off. Epigenetic changes occur in different cells in males and females of all ages. These changes may remain through cell divisions throughout life. If they affect DNA in ova or sperm, such changes may also last for multiple generations. The best known example of epigenomic change in biology involves the process of cellular differentiation. Continued cell division in the zygote (the single fertilized egg cell), gives rise to many *different* cell types, including neurons, muscle cells, epithelium, and blood vessels. This contrasts with the simple production of copies of cells that already exist. These different cell types arise because certain genes are activated while others are inhibited. (See Bollati & Baccarelli, 2010, for a review.) The processes of lyonization and another phenomenon called *genomic imprinting*, also are considered to be epigenetic. The term genomic imprinting refers to the inactivation of certain genes on certain chromosomes inherited from either the mother or father so that only one of two inherited copies are expressed in cells. In Chapter 10, we consider how epigenetic processes are involved in development in more depth.

The *Human Epigenome Project* is now determining the locations of methyl groups in our DNA. As explained by David Allis, whereas the HMG project ...."provided the blueprint for life, the epigenome will tell us how the whole thing gets executed" (cited in Bradbury, 2003; *http://www.ncbi.nlm.nih.gov/pmc/articles/PMC300691/*).

Summary

The unusual genetic phenomena that have been described in this section are among the most profound biological discoveries of the past century. Building upon the work of Gregor Mendel, the monk who discovered the classical patterns of single gene inheritance from his studies of plants, we outline the role of mutated genomic and mitochondrial DNA, amplifications of trinucleotide repeat regions, common polymorphic variants, prions, as well as epigenetics in normal human development and disorders.

Acknowledgements

The original material for this chapter was provided by Sheldon Lewkis. The present chapter draws heavily upon material in Percy, Lewkis, & Brown (2003; 2007). Nussbaum, McInnis & Willard (2007) and The Canadian Oxford Dictionary (1998) were used as sources of some definitions of special terms. The authors are grateful to Dr. John Percy for helpful suggestions and advice.

For Future Thought and Discussion

1. How can we avoid stigmatizing those living with a genetic developmental disability while trying to prevent or eliminate the condition in others?

2. The term "environment" includes such factors as stress, diet, toxins, and use of various forms of manufactured products. What are the implications of epigenetics in terms of our relationships to such environmental factors?

3. By the year 2014, it likely will be possible for individuals in the general public to have their DNA sequenced at a reasonable cost. Would you consider having this done? Why or why not?

Special Terms

Allele: Two or more different forms of a gene at a given locus.

Alzheimer's disease: The most common form of dementia in the elderly. Brains of persons with this disorder are riddled with structures called amyloid plaques and neurofibrillary tangles.

Angelman syndrome: Initally described in 1965 by Harry Angelman. It was reported only infrequently until 1987 when a small deletion of the long arm of chromosome 15 was recognized. Up to 80% have a deletion of maternal chromosome 15, with a small number having two copies of the paternal chromosome 15 (uniparental disomy).

Astroglia: Small non-neuronal cells (astrocytes and glia, collectively called astroglia) in the brain whose functions include insulation, infection-fighting and housekeeping.

Autosome: Any chromosome other than a sex chromosome (i.e., chromosomes 1 through 22)

Bovine spongiform encephalopathy (BSE): A spongiform brain disease of cattle first identified in Britain in 1986.

Chorea: A nervous system disorder characterized by jerky involuntary movements affecting especially the shoulders, hips and face.

Chromosomes: The structures in the cell's nucleus that carry the genetic information in the form of long strands of DNA bound to proteins. They are constant in number in each species. The normal number in humans is 46: 22 pairs of autosomes and one pair of sex chromosomes (XX or XY).

Complementary base pair sequence: A linear array of nucleotide base pairs in double-stranded DNA or RNA, the sequence of which is determined by the order of nucleotides in one of the strands. In DNA, the sequence is determined by hydrogen bonding between adenosine and thymine (A-T) and guanine and cytosine (G-C). There are two hydrogen bonds in A-T pairs, and three hydrogen bonds in G-C pairs. In RNA, the sequence is determined by hydrogen bonding between adenosine and uridine (A-U) and (G-C).

Copy Number Variant (CNV): A segment of DNA for which differences in copy-number (number of copies of a particular region or portions of it) have been found by comparison of two or more genomes.

Creutzfeldt-Jakob disease (CJD): A rare human prion disorder (spongiform encephalopathy) affecting human beings, characterized by progressive dementia. It affects about 1 person in a million.

Cri-du-chat syndrome: A disorder caused by a deletion at the end of chromosome 5 that is associated with microcephaly, epicanthic folds, and a high-pitched cry. It is an example of a syndrome with intellectual disability in which a cryptic chromosomal abnormality has been defined.

Cytogenetics: The study of cell genetics, combining the methods and findings of cytology and genetics.

Degeneration: Pathological change causing impairment or destruction of function.

Dementia: Loss of mental function.

Diploid. Having two complete sets of chromosomes (2n), one from each parent. In humans, the diploid chromosome number is 46.

Dominant: This term refers to a situation in which the expression of a particular gene is the same whether it is present in two copies or in one copy.

Duchenne muscular dystrophy: An X-linked recessive disorder that affects primarily males. Nonprogressive mental retardation occurs in some patients. It is the most common type of muscular dystrophy. Serum levels of creatine kinase are grossly elevated in the early stages of the disorder. Mutations of the dystrophin gene causing this disorder have been identified.

Embryo: A human offspring in the first eight or twelve weeks from conception.

Encephalopathy: Disease of the brain.

Enzyme: A protein produced by living cells and functioning as a catalyst in a specific biochemical reaction.

Fatal familial insomnia: A form of familial prion disease that presents initially as persistent insomnia indicative of disease.

Fragile X syndrome: A common X-linked, inherited form of intellectual disability. The most common form of Fragile X syndrome is caused by a large amplification of the CGG trinucleotide repeat region of the fragile X mental retardation gene-1 (FMR-1).

Gametes or germ cells: Haploid cells that give rise

to ova (eggs) and sperm.

Genetic anticipation: A genetic phenomenon in which the symptoms of a disorder appear at an earlier age and become more severe as the disorder is passed down from one generation to another, usually due to progressive expansion of trinucleotide repeats within the causative gene.

Genetic recombination: The process by which crossing-over occurs between maternal and paternal chromatids during meiosis.

Genome: The total genetic material in the cell nucleus of an individual.

Germ cell: Cell containing half the number of chromosomes of a somatic cell and able to unite with one from the opposite sex to form a new individual; a gamete.

Gerstmann-Straussler disease (syndrome): A rare familial human prion disorder (spongiform encephalopathy) characterized by cerebellar ataxia, progressive dementia, and absent reflexes in the legs.

Haploid cell: Having only one complete set of chromosomes, usually germ cells. In humans the haploid number is 23.

Helix: An object of coiled form, either a spiral curve round an axis like a corkscrew or a coiled curve in one lane like a watchspring.

Histones: Any of several small, basic proteins commonly found in association with DNA. The word basic refers to the positive charge on these proteins.

Homologous chromosomes: Chromosomes that pair during meiosis. These have the same appearance and contain genes that govern the same functions.

Huntington's disease (or chorea): Chorea accompanied by progressive dementia.

Imprinting: The process that enables either paternal or maternal genes to function on their own in a diploid cell. The mechanism is unknown but may involve DNA methylation.

Inborn errors of metabolism: Metabolic disorders in which clinical, biochemical and pathological manifestations are the consequence of a genetically determined deficiency of a particular enzyme. Such a mutation leads to a build-up of metabolites immediately preceding the block, and/or deficiency of an important metabolite normally produced from the function of the defective gene. Inborn errors associated with mental handicap have been identified in virtually all major pathways of metabolism.

Karyotype: The term refers to photomicrographs of a set of chromosomes, arranged in a standard fashion, from a diploid cell.

Klinefelter syndrome: The syndrome associated with the karyotype 47, XXY. The first human sex chromosome abnormality to be reported. Patients are tall and thin with relatively long legs. They appear physically normal until puberty, when signs of hypogonadism become evident.

Kuru: A human prion disease (spongiform encephalopathy) resulting from cannibalism.

Leber's hereditary optic neuropathy: A disorder caused by a mutation in mitochondrial DNA that results in neurologic abnormalities, infantile encephalopathy, and transient or permanent blindness due to optic nerve damage.

Lesch-Nyhan syndrome: An X-linked metabolic genetic disorder characterized by severe behaviour disturbance and self-injury. It is caused by near absence of the enzyme hypoxanthine guanine phosphoribosyl-transferase (HPRT).

Lyonization: (Lyon hypothesis). The process by which all X chromosomes in excess of one are made genetically inactive. In the female, the decision as to which X (maternal or paternal) is inactivated is made independently for each cell, early in development, and is permanent for all descendants of that cell.

Meiosis: A process occurring in the germ cells by which gametes, containing the haploid number of chromosomes, are produced from diploid cells.

Methylation: Addition of a methyl (–CH3) moiety to a base in a DNA molecule, usually cytosine. Methylated cytosine mimics thymine and becomes a potential site for mutation. Methylation has a role in gene regulation and is one mechanism of genomic imprinting.

Mitochondria: Organelles in cells that each contain a number of copies of a small circular molecule, the mitochondrial chromosome. Mitochondrial DNA encodes 13 key structural genes as well as a number of structural ribonucleic acid RNA molecules. Mitochondria are a major source of energy production in cells.

Mitochondrial inheritance: Transmission of a mutation that is present in the mitochondrial DNA. Males and females are equally frequently and severely affected. Because mitochondrial DNA is transmitted to offspring only by mothers, mothers transmit the mutant mitochondrial chromosomes to all of their offspring, whereas affected fathers transmit the mutation to none of their offspring.

Mitosis: Somatic cell division resulting in the formation of two cells, each with the same chromosome complement as the parent cell.

Mosaicism: Having two or more cell lines of different genetic or chromosomal constitution, derived from the same zygote.

Multifactorial: Determination of a phenotype by a combination of genetic and environmental factors.

Muscular dystrophy: Hereditary progressive weakening and wasting of the muscles.

Mutation: Any permanent change in a gene sequence.

Myotonic dystrophy: An autosomal dominant disorder sometimes associated with non-progressive mental impairment. It is caused by a trinucleotide repeat expansion.

Neurofibromatosis: A dominant hereditary disorder that affects the brain and peripheral nervous system. Affected people develop skin lesions that look like coffee stains (i.e., cafe-au-lait spots), and tumours derived from nerve sheaths in any organ including the brain. Expression of this disorder is variable.

Nondisjunction: The failure of two members of a chromosome pair to disjoin during meiosis I, or two chromatids of a chromosome to disjoin during meiosis II or mitosis, so that both pass to one daughter cell and the other daughter cell receives neither.

Nucleolus: An RNA-rich, round granular structure associated with specific chromsomal sites, the nucleolus organizer regions, located at the short arms of acrocentric chromosomes in humans.

Nucleosome: The repeating nucleoprotein unit of chromatin consisting of a core of eight histone molecules wrapped by a DNA segment of about 146 base pairs in length.

Nucleus: A large, dense organelle containing the genetic material of all eukaryotic cells.

Oxidative phosphorylation: A metabolic pathway in mitochondria that results in the production of ATP, the major source of energy in cells. For an animation of this process, see *http://www.brookscole.com/ chemistry_d/templates/student_resources/shared_re-sources/animations/oxidative/oxidativephosphoryla-tion.html/.*

Penetrance: This term is used to indicate whether or not a trait that is genetically determined is manifested clinically. If the trait is always expressed whenever the responsible allele is present, the trait is fully penetrant; if the trait is expressed only in some individuals with the particular allele, the trait is incompletely penetrant; if the trait is not expressed at all, it is non-penetrant.

Phenotype: The outward observable characteristics of a cell or organism.

Phenylketonuria (PKU): Originally described by Folling in 1934. An autosomal recessive metabolic disease with many variants. Treatment with a reduced phenylalanine diet enables affected individuals to reach adulthood with considerable less intellectual impairment than untreated individuals. Neonates are screened for this condition in Canada, the U.S., and other developed countries.

Polygenic: Refers to a condition caused by a combination of multiple genetic factors.

Prader-Willi syndrome: A genetic cause of mental retardation resulting from aberrations of genomic imprinting. Fifty percent of individuals with this syndrome have a paternal deletion of chromosome 15. The remainder have two copies of maternal chromosome 15 (uniparental disomy).

Prion: A term proposed by neurologist Stanley Prusiner to identify "small proteinaceous particles which are resistant to inactivation by most procedures that modify nucleic acids". The term is meant to denote the requirement of a protein for infection; current knowledge does not allow exclusion of a small nucleic acid within the interior of the particle.

Recessive (autosomal): A characteristic of a phenotypic trait that is expressed only when the responsible gene is present in two copies.

Ribosomes: Cytoplasmic organelles composed of ribosomal RNA and protein, on which polypeptide synthesis from messenger RNA occurs.

Sclerosis: An abnormal hardening of body tissue.

Scrapie: A progressive brain disease of sheep that

frequently causes itching so intense that the animals scrape off their wool seeking relief.

Sex chromosomes: Chromosomes responsible for sex determination; in humans, the X and Y chromosomes.

Sister chromatids: Twin copies of a fully replicated chromosome containing two chromatids (threadlike strands of DNA which separate into single strands during cell division).

Smith-Lemli-Opitz syndrome: A metabolic and developmental disorder resulting from deficiency of an enzyme involved in cholesterol metabolism that affects many parts of the body.

Somatic: All cells in the body except for ova (eggs) and sperm.

Spongiform: Resembling a sponge in structure; full of holes.

Sporadic: Occurring randomly or occasionally, with no particular pattern or order in time, with no evidence of being inherited.

Trinucleotide repeat: A sequence of the same three nucleotides repeated over and over again.

Tuberous sclerosis: One of several neurocutaneous syndromes, also known as phakomatoses. These autosomal dominant disorders present with lesions both of the skin and central nervous system and may also have associated ocular and visceral abnormalities. Tuberous sclerosis is referred to as a complex disorder because it involves all tissues. In addition to the brain and retina, the skin, kidneys, heart, and lungs are most frequently involved.

Turner syndrome: 45, X and variants. The most common form is caused by a missing paternal X chromosome.

VCJD: New variant CJD is a new form of Creutzfeldt-Jakob disease believed to be transmitted by eating the tissue of cattle infected with BSE.

Wild type: Referring to a genetic locus or an allele that specifies a phenotype that predominates in natural populations or that is designated as normal in contrast with the mutant type.

Williams syndrome: A genetic syndrome associated with a distinct behavioral phenotype, caused by a deletion of a specific region of genetic material on chromosome 7. People with Williams syndrome tend to be loquacious, and unusually musical.

Zygote: A fertilized egg, the result of fusion between an ovum and a sperm.

More Resources

Genetics:

Dynamic Timeline
http://www.genome.gov/25019887

Human Genome Project Information
http://www.ornl.gov/sci/techresources/Human_Genome/home.shtml

National Institute of General Medical Sciences. The New Genetics
http://publications.nigms.nih.gov/thenewgenetics/index.html

Nobelprize.org
http://nobelprize.org/nobel_prizes/

Online Mendelian Inheritance in Man (OMIM)
http://www.ncbi.nlm.nih.gov/omim

The Personal Genome Project
http://www.wired.com/medtech/stemcells/magazine/16-08/ff_church?currentPage=1

The Personal Genome
http://thepersonalgenome.com/2009/07/documentary-film-about-personal-genome-project/

Epigenomics:

Stark, L. A. Epigenetics Online: Multimedia Teaching Resources
http://www.ncbi.nlm.nih.gov/pmc/articles/PMC2830163/

Learn.Genetics. Genetic Science Learning Center. The University of Utah
learn.genetics.utah.edu/.../epi_learns/

The NIH Common Fund. Epigenomics
http://nihroadmap.nih.gov/epigenomics/index.asp

Human Epigenome Project
http://www.epigenome.org/index.php

Prions:

Basic Concepts: Prions. Retrospectacle: A Neuroscience Blog
http://scienceblogs.com/retrospectacle/2007/02/basic_concepts_prions.php

vCJD (Variant Creutzfeldt-Jakob Disease). Centers for Disease Control
http://www.cdc.gov/ncidod/dvrd/vcjd/epidemiology.htm

References

Bollati, V., & Baccarelli, A. (2010). Environmental epigenetics. *Heredity, 105,* 105-112.

Bradbury, J. (2003). Human Epigenome Project – Up and running. *PloS Biology,* 1(3), e82. Retrieved from http://www.ncbi.nlm.nih.gov/pmc/articles/PMC300691/

The Canadian Oxford Dictionary (1998). K. Barber (Ed.). Oxford: Oxford University Press.

Dynamic Timeline. (2010). Retrieved from the website of the National Human Genome Research Institute, National Institutes of Health, at http://www.genome.gov/25019887

Ellegren, H. (2004). Microsatellites: Simple sequences with complex evolution. *Nature Reviews in Genetics,* 5(6), 435-445.

Higgins, E. S. (2008). The new genetics of mental illness. *Scientific American,* May 29.

Lipton, B. H. (2005). *The biology of belief: Unleashing the power of consciousness, matter and miracles.* New York: Hay House Inc.

Milunsky, A. (1977). *Know your genes.* Boston: Houghton Mifflin Company.

Miller, D. T., Adam, M. P., Aradhya, S., Biesecker, L. G., Brothman, A. R., Carter, N. P., et al. (2010). Consensus statement: Chromosomal microarray is a first-tier clinical diagnostic test for individuals with developmental disabilities or congenital anomalies. *American Journal of Human Genetics,* 86(5), 749764.

Mills, R. E., Bennett, E. A., Iskow, R. C., & Devine, S. (2007). Which transposable elements are active in the human genome? *Trends in Genetics,* 23(4), 183-191.

Morrow, E. M. (2010). Genomic copy number variation in disorders of cognitive development. *Journal of the American Academy of Child and Adolescent Psychiatry,* 49(11), 1091-1104.

Nussbaum, R. L., McInnis, R. R., & Willard, H. F. (2007). *Thompson & Thompson genetics in medicine* (7th ed.). Philadelphia: W. B. Saunders Co.

Orr, H. T., & Zoghbi, H. Y. (2007). Trinucleotide repeat disorders. *Annual Review of Neuroscience, 30,* 575-621.

Percy, M., Lewkis, S., & Brown, I. (2003). An introduction to genetics and development. In I. Brown & M. Percy (Eds.), *Developmental disabilities in Ontario* (2nd ed., pp. 89-108). Toronto, ON: Ontario Association on Developmental Disabilities.

Percy, M., Lewkis, S.Z, & Brown, I. (2007). Introduction to genetics and development. In I. Brown & M. Percy (Eds.), *A comprehensive guide to intellectual and developmental disabilities* (pp. 87-108). Baltimore: Paul H. Brookes Publishing Co.

Pitman, S. D. (2002). *The father of genetics.* Retrieved from http://naturalselection.0catch.com/Files/gregormendel.html

Provost, P. (2010). MicroRNAs as a molecular basis for mental retardation, Alzheimer's and prion diseases. *Brain Research, 1338,* 58-66.

Prusiner, S. B. (2001). Shattuck Lecture: Neurodegenerative diseases and prions. *New England Journal of Medicine, 344,* 1516-1526.

Rhodes, R. (1998). *Deadly feasts: Tracking the secrets of a terrifying new plague.* New York: Simon & Schuster, Inc.

Watson, J. D., & Crick, F. H. C. (1953). A structure for deoxyribose nucleic acid. *Nature, 171,* 737-738.

10

Introduction to Early Development: A Multidisciplinary Perspective

Maire Percy and Ivan Brown

What you will learn:

- Stages of development before birth
- Some important epigenetic processes in development: cellular differentiation, X-chromosome inactivation, genomic imprinting, metabolic programming, perinatal programming
- Disruption of development by teratogens
- Highlights of embryonic and fetal development and developmental milestones after birth
- Complications associated with pregnancy, labour, and birth
- Development after birth
- Approaches to prenatal detection of developmental disabilities
- Approaches to prevention, intervention and cure of developmental disabilities, including stem cell research and ethical dilemmas

It is becomingly increasingly recognized that human development is not exclusively regulated by the "blueprint" contained in our DNA (i.e., our "nature"; Chapter 9). Many different factors can affect how a child develops. Factors sometimes referred to as "environmental" include nutritional status and health care during pregnancy and afterwards, socioeconomic status, relationships during the first few months of life and during the first few years, and quality of child care, especially during the first three years of life. (For additional information about these factors, see the eHow Family website at *http://www.ehow.com/list_6384855_factors-affecting-early-child-development.html*.) Environmental factors affecting development also include exposures to toxic substances and other adverse events. What is exciting is that we are beginning to understand not just *what* factors influence development, but *how* this happens. In biology, the term *nurture* refers to the effects that various environmental influences and factors have in total on an *organism* (in this chapter an organism is a developing human body). Indeed, the ways in which *nurture* can interact with *nature* to influence who we are and who we may become is quite remarkable.

The purpose of this chapter is to provide an introduction to early development and the possibilities that exist, or that are being envisioned, for modifying this process. Such information should help individuals to make informed choices relevant to intervention, prevention, or even cures, in our field. To aid the reader, we have provided Internet resources in the text and also in the section More Resources. Chapters 9, 11, 12 and 38 contain complementary information.

Stages of Development Before Birth

This section provides an introduction to conception and the embryonic and fetal processes. Refer also to the short video clip *Human Development* at http://www.youtube.com/watch?v=UgT5rUQ9EmQ.

Conception

At birth, the ovaries of females contain precursors of all the ova they will ever produce. These immature ova are called oocytes. The testes of males from puberty onward produce new sperm continually. Sperm and ova sometimes are called *germ cells*.

Conception occurs when a sperm fertilizes an ovum and the number of chromosomes is doubled (see below). The word *sperm* comes from the Greek word "sperma" meaning seed; it refers to the reproductive cells in males. The word *ovum* refers to the reproductive cells of females; in Latin, it means egg. Mature sperm and ova are called *gametes*.

Sperm and ova contain only 23 chromosomes — half the number found in other cells of the body (46 chromosomes, arranged in 23 pairs). Of the 23 chromosomes in sperm or ova, one is the *sex chromosome*. Half of the sperm have an X sex chromosome whereas the other half have a Y sex chromosome. All ova have one X sex chromosome. If the sperm that fertilizes an ovum has an X sex chromosome, the fertilized egg will have two X sex chromosomes and will develop into a female. If the sperm has a Y sex chromosome, the fertilized egg will have one X and one Y sex chromosome and will develop into a male.

Zygotic period

Once a female egg has become fertilized, and the chromosome number increases from 23 to 46, it is known as a *zygote*. Zygotes undergo a two-week period of rapid cell division before becoming embryos. In the process of cell division, each cell doubles and divides into two daughter cells, a process called *mitosis* (see Chapter 9). This two-week stage is known as the *germinal* period of development and covers the time of conception to implantation of the embryo into the uterus.

Embryonic and fetal periods

The embryonic period refers to development occurring between weeks 2 and 8. The term fetus refers to the unborn offspring from the end of the 8th week after conception (when major structures recognizable in adults have formed) until birth. Development in the embryonic period is remarkable in the sense that cells formed during the process of mitosis from one fertilized ovum move to different places in the zygote and begin to differentiate to form different tissues in the body. Understanding how the fertilized egg can develop into all of the different tissues in the body is one of the two great challenges in human biology. (The second great challenge is how the brain works.) Some mechanisms that regulate development of the fertilized egg are described in the next section.

Some Important Processes in Prenatal Development

The DNA — and genes that are sections of DNA — that make up the chromosomes that we inherit from our parents are very important in determining how we develop. However, there is increasing recognition that development is also affected by mechanisms that regulate the activity of genes, turning them on or off. These are called *epigenetic mechanisms*. Epigenetic mechanisms do not change the sequence of the building blocks in DNA, but they instruct cells to turn certain genes "on" or "off." Below, we highlight developmental processes that occur during the embryonic and fetal stages and explain how epigenetic mechanisms are involved.

Cellular differentiation

During the zygotic stage, cells have the potential to develop into any one of many different cell types and are referred to as *pluripotent* cells (Reik, 2007). As the result of epigenetic mechanisms, methyl groups on DNA are removed or inactivated during the zygotic stage. However, after more divisions, methylation is reintroduced and cells undergo *differentiation*. This means that as cell division proceeds, the daughter cells become more and more specialized. Different types of specialized cells make different sets of proteins. It is these different sets of proteins that cause cells in different tissues to have different shapes and membranes, as well as different structures and functions (Kiefer, 2007; Leese, 2005).

Chromosome inactivation

Development also includes an epigenetic process called *X-chromosome inactivation* (or lyonization; see Chapter 9 for additional information). At an early stage in development, most genes on one or other of the two X chromosomes in cells of females become inactivated so that they do not have twice as many X chromosome genes as the male. In the past, it was thought that genetic defects on the X chromosome would only affect males and that females would be protected because they inherit two X chromosomes: if one is defective, the other can compensate for it. However, this is not always the case. In some cases, females do have symptoms of X-linked conditions (for example, Duchenne muscular dystrophy and fragile X syndrome). For more information about X-chromosome inactivation and its consequences see Chapter 9 and the X *Chromosome Genetics Home Reference* website at ghr.nlm.nih.gov/chromosome=X.

Genomic imprinting

Another epigenetic process called *genomic imprinting* is also important in development. Genes can occur in alternative forms that are known as *alleles*. For most genes, alleles inherited from the mother and from the father are both expressed. However, this is not the case for the relatively small groups of genes located on certain chromosomes that are subject to genomic imprinting. Genomic imprinting occurs during sperm and ova formation and this persists throughout embryonic and fetal development. What happens in genomic imprinting is that methyl groups are added to certain regions of certain genes,

causing them to be "turned off." In these cases, genes on the maternal allele are expressed because the paternal allele is imprinted (and thus "turned off"), or genes on the paternal allele are expressed because the maternal allele is imprinted. Because genomic imprinting affects some genes, genetic information is needed from both a mother and a father for normal development of offspring. On the other hand, interference with genomic imprinting can result in developmental disorders such as Prader Willi and Angelman syndromes (see Chapter 13). For an introduction to genomic imprinting see the following websites: *National Human Genome Research Institute* at *http://www.genome.gov/27532724* and Learn.Genetics at *Learn.Genetics.utah.edu*.

Metabolic programming

Development is affected by factors other than those discussed above. There is evidence that a wide range of environmental factors acting during critical periods of early development can affect health in adults. For example, if a woman does not have adequate nutrition prior to conception, her child might develop high blood pressure, heart disease, or diabetes later in life. This hypothesis was originally proposed in the 1980s by the physician and epidemiologist, Dr. David Barker. This idea evolved into *the fetal origins theory*, and it presently is called *metabolic programming*. Epigenetic processes also are involved in this physiological process, but our understanding of this area is in its infancy. (See Fowden & Forhead (2009) and Wong-Goodrich et al. (2008) for more information.)

Perinatal programming

The concept of metabolic programming has since expanded into an idea called *perinatal programming*. Physicians and researchers are now exploring the idea that environmental factors including the ways in which mothers, fathers and other persons interact with a baby, bacterial and viral infections, and nutritional deficiencies after birth, can change the way a baby's brain genes express themselves, the way a baby develops, and even result in neurodevelopmental disorders, including memory disorders. For example, there is evidence that having the flu dur-

Table 1: Highlights of Embryonic and Fetal Development

Conception	*Takes place in one of the fallopian tubes midway through the menstrual cycle.*
3 weeks	*The blastocyst implants in the uterus; the primitive placenta produces the pregnancy hormone human chorionic gonadotrophin. The blastocyst is a berry-like structure consisting of an outer cell mass (trophoblast), an inner cell mass, and the cavity.*
4 weeks	*The embryo consists of two layers — the epiblast and hypoblast — from which all body parts develop. The primitive placenta also is made of two layers. Present at this time are the amniotic sac, the amniotic fluid, and the yolk sac. The future brain and nervous system are visible after approximately 4 weeks of gestation.*
5 weeks	*The embryo is approximately 1 millimetre (mm) across. It is made of three layers — the ectoderm, mesoderm, and endoderm. The ectoderm gives rise to the neural tube (which gives rise to brain, spinal cord, nerves, and backbone), skin, hair, nails, mammary and sweat glands, and tooth enamel. The mesoderm gives rise to the heart and circulatory system, muscles, cartilage, bone, and subcutaneous tissue. The endoderm gives rise to the lungs, intestine, rudimentary urinary system, thyroid, liver, and pancreas. The primitive placenta and umbilical cord are already delivering oxygen and nourishment.*
6 weeks	*The embryo is 4-5 mm across. The head appears large; dark spots mark where the eyes and nostrils will be; shallow pits on the sides of the head mark developing ears; arms and legs appear as protruding buds; hands and feet look like paddles with webbing between the digits. Below the opening that will be the mouth are small folds from where the neck and lower jaw develop. The heart is already beating 100-130 beats per minute. Blood is beginning to circulate. The intestines are developing. Tiny breathing passages appear where the lungs will be. Muscle fibres are beginning to form.*

Sources: Harding and Bocking (2006); University of Maryland Medical Center (2011); The Visible Embryo (n.d.).

ing pregnancy is associated with an increased risk of schizophrenia or autism in offspring. Interestingly, animal studies have shown how the impact of a mother's "love" — maternal licking and grooming — affects behaviour in later generations. Rat pups that are frequently licked and groomed by their mothers (or a surrogate mother) appear to have lower stress, are more social, have greater cognitive skills and are more responsive to reward motivations than those that are not. Furthermore, the rats that receive such affection pass on this trait to their own offspring (Champagne, 2008). It is believed that the hormone *oxytocin* is responsible for positive maternal behav-

iour, and that licking and grooming triggers the production of proteins called growth factors in the rat pups. These growth factors, in turn, prevent certain genes in the brains of the rat pups from becoming methylated. There currently is much interest in determining if similar mechanisms affect human health and behaviours (Galbally, Lewis, Ijzendoorn, & Permezel, 2011).

Highlights of embryonic and fetal development

Table 1 lists some of the highlights of embryonic and fetal development. *The Visible Embryo* web site (*http://www.visembryo.com*) enables one to navi-

7 weeks	*The embryo is approximately 0.5 inches (in.) long.*
2 months	*The embryo is the size of a lima bean. It moves and shifts constantly. It has distinct, slightly webbed, fingers.*
3 months	*The fetus is approximately 2 in. long. The skin is transparent; the face is becoming human-like.*
4 months	*The fetus is approximately 4.5 in. long. The heart pumps approximately 25 quarts of blood per day. The body is covered with downy hair.*
5 months	*The fetus is approximately 10 in. long from head to heel. A protective substance coats the skin.*
6 months	*The fetus is approximately 12 in. long and weighs approximately 1 pound (lb). The skin is red, still transparent, and wrinkled. The lips, eyebrows and eyelids are distinct.*
7 months	*The fetus is approximately 15 in. long and weighs approximately 2.25 lb. Body fat begins to form.*
8 months	*The fetus weighs approximately 4 lb. It may have "peach fuzz" on the head. It may have turned its head down in preparation for birth.*
9 months	*At birth, the baby is approximately 18 in. long and weighs approximately 6 lb, but weight at birth is variable*

gate through the 40 weeks of pregnancy and see the unique changes in each stage of human development shown in this table.

Disruption of Prenatal Development by Teratogens

Typical fetal development depends on the mother's good health and nutritional status. Because pregnancy is a period of rapid growth for both mother and fetus, both mother and fetus are vulnerable to disruptions in the supply of nutrients and micronutrients in the diet. Fetal growth and development can be adversely affected by many different factors, including teratogens. The word teratogen is derived from the Greek words "terato" (monster) and "gen" (to give rise to). Teratogens are factors that interfere with normal embryonic and fetal differentiation, and teratology is the study of congenital anomalies (those present at birth) and their causes, whether they are genetic or environmental in origin (Arndt, Stodgell, & Rodier, 2005). It is suspected that many teratogens exert their effects via epigenetic mechanisms.

A large number of teratogenic agents have been identified (see below and also Table 2). These include *diethylstilbestrol* (a drug used to prevent miscar-

Table 2: Some Known Teratogens

Drugs and environmental chemicals	**Drugs:** *alcohol; vitamin A derivatives (13-cis-retinoic acid, isotretinoin (Accutane); etretinate); certain sedative and anxiety reducing drugs (temazepam (Restoril; Normisson), nitrazepam (Mogadon), nimetazepam (Ermin); certain anticancer drugs (aminopterin, busulfan; cyclophosphamide); androgenic hormones (testosterone); blood pressure medications (captopril, enalapril); coumarin (blood thinner); diethylstilbestrol (synthetic estrogen); anticonvulsants (diphenylhydantoin (Phenytoin, Dilantin, Epanutin), trimethadione, valproic acid); lithium; methimazole (anti-thyroid drug); penicillamine (copper-binding drug used to treat rheumatoid arthritis and Wilson's disease); tetracyclines (antibiotic); thalidomide* **Environmental chemicals:** *chlorobiphenyls (PCBs, used as plasticizers, lubricants, dielectrics); dioxin; ethidium bromide (chemical often used in molecular biology labs); hexachlorobenzene (fungicide); hexachlorophene (disinfectant); organic mercury; uranium; methoxyethyl ethers (type of organic solvent); and many others*
Ionizing radiation	*atomic weapons, radioactive iodine, radiation therapy*
Infections	*cytomegalovirus (a type of herpesvirus that causes enlargement of epithelial cells, especially the salivary glands); intrauterine herpes simplex virus (cold sore virus) infection; parvovirus B-19 (causes several different autoimmune diseases); rubella virus (German measles); syphilis (a sexually transmitted disease); toxoplasmosis (a parasitic disease passed from animals to humans, often not causing symptoms); Venezuelan equine encephalitis virus (causes a mosquito-borne disease)*
Metabolic imbalance	*alcoholism, iodine deficiency, diabetes, folic acid deficiency, elevated body temperature due to failed body regulation, unmanaged phenylketonuria (Chapter 13), lupus erythymatosis (a type of autoimmune disease), virilizing tumours (tumours that produce male hormones causing growth of facial hair)*
Tobacco, alcohol, caffeine	*smoking, alcohol use, and consumption of caffeine*

Sources: List of Known and Suspected Teratogens, Oxford University (2011); Shepard & Lemire (2007).

riages and premature deliveries in the 1950s, 1960s and early 1970s and also used in some countries as an emergency contraceptive or "morning after pill" to prevent implantation of a fertilized ovum in the womb); *thalidomide* (a drug used to treat morning sickness in the early 1960s in Canada); *Agent Orange* (a toxic agent used to defoliate trees, especially during the Vietnam war); *valproic acid* (an anticonvulsant); and *misoprostol* (a drug originally developed to prevent stomach ulcers in people who take certain arthritis or pain medications, including aspirin, but which also has been used in some countries to induce abortion). The *rubella virus* (which causes German measles) also is teratogenic. In addition, alcohol is a teratogen, and use of large amounts of alcohol during pregnancy can result in Fetal Alcohol Spectrum Disorder (see Chapter 19). *Isotretinoin* (13-cis-retinoic acid, a vitamin A derivative) which is often used to treat severe acne, is a strong teratogen: a single dose taken by a pregnant woman may result in serious birth defects. Because of this effect, most countries have systems in place to ensure that isotretinoin is not given to pregnant women and that the patients are aware how important it is to prevent pregnancy during, and at least one month after, treatment. Whether isotretinoin also affects sperm is controversial; on the basis of adverse effects in studies with rats, birth control is advocated for males undergoing high dose, or prolonged treatment for acne (Gencoglan, & Tosun, 2010). Excessive exposures to mercury are problematic during prenatal development and throughout life. There also is evidence that excessive exposures to aluminum can be problematic. See the Health Canada websites for information about mercury (*http://www.hc-sc.gc.ca/hl-vs/iyh-vsv/environ/merc-eng.php*) and aluminum (*http://www.hc-sc.gc.ca/fn-an/securit/addit/aluminum-eng.php)* toxicity. See also Chapter 12.

Examples of effects caused by teratogens include some cases of cleft lip and/or palate, *anencephaly* (a neural tube defect in which a large part of the brain and skull are missing), or *ventricular septal defects* (one or more holes in the wall of the heart located between the two ventricles), which are medically serious abnormalities present at birth. By interfering with the development of the brain and nervous system, teratogens also can result in developmental disability. It is important to note that at least five teratogens are associated with increased risk of autism; these include maternal rubella infection, ethanol, thalidomide, valproic acid and misoprostol (Arndt et al., 2005). Fetal death, prematurity, growth retardation, and unexplained *dysmorphology* (structural abnormalities) are all suggestive of teratogenic effects. The study of teratogens also is important because disorders resulting from them can be prevented by education of the community. Four factors that are important in teratogenicity are as follows:

1. Embryo/fetus age, or the gestational age of the fetus at the time of the exposure to the teratogen. Different organs of the body are forming at different times; therefore, the sensitivity to the teratogen and the organ affected by the teratogen will vary. Generally, the *embryonic stage* (i.e., the first trimester, or the period of 18-54-60 days of gestation) is a time of greater vulnerability than the *fetal period* (i.e., the second and third trimesters). For a period of approximately 2 weeks from the time of conception until implantation, teratogenic insults to the embryo are likely to result either in miscarriage (or resorption) or in intact survival. Because the embryo is undifferentiated at this stage, repair and recovery can occur through multiplication of pluripotent cells. If the teratogen persists beyond this period, however, congenital malformations may result.

2. Dosage of the teratogen.

3. Fetal genotype. This may make the fetus more or less resistant to the teratogen.

4. Maternal genotype. Pregnant women differ in their ability to detoxify teratogens.

By considering the sequence of events involved in normal embryonic and fetal development, it is easy to see how teratogens may have different effects depending upon when they are encountered. Women who are planning to become pregnant or who are pregnant should get advice from their doctors or prenatal clinics about what potential teratogens to avoid, and if there are any potential problems associated with prescription medications or over the counter substances they may be taking or consider using. For additional information see the Motherisk website at *http://www.motherisk.org/women/index.jsp.*

Complications Associated with Pregnancy, Labour and Birth

Many pregnancies are uneventful. However, sometimes there are complications that occur during a pregnancy, or during labour and the birth process itself that can affect a baby's health and development and/or result in physical or intellectual disability. These are discussed below. To note is that good health care can avert complications in mothers and babies, or lessen their effects, in many instances.

Complications of pregnancy

Complications of pregnancy refer to problems experienced by the mother, the fetus, or both. Some of the most common complications include *ectopic pregnancy* (a pregnancy that is not in the uterus), *Rh negative disease* (this occurs if the mother has Rh negative blood and the father has Rh positive blood; see Chapter 38), *group B streptococcus infection* (the bacteria causing this infection is often present in the gastrointestinal tract, but sometimes can be passed on to a baby), preterm labour, and low gestational birth weight. For information about these conditions and interventions for them see the *American Pregnancy Association* website at *http://www.americanpregnancy.org/pregnancycomplications/*. See also Chapter 12.

Complications of labour and delivery

Occasionally, women who have had normal pregnancies can experience complications during labour or delivery. Such complications can deprive the baby of oxygen or increase the risk of acquiring an infection and result in developmental delay, intellectual disability, and/or physical disabilities. Examples of labour or delivery complications include premature labour and premature delivery, a labour that lasts too long, abnormal presentation of the baby in the birth canal, premature rupture of the membranes around the baby, or *umbilical prolapse* in which the umbilical cord precedes the baby into the birth canal. For more information about these conditions and interventions for them, refer to the WebMD site at *http://www.webmd.com/baby/understanding-labor-delivery-complications-basics?page=2*. See also Chapters 9, 12, and 38.

Complications associated with premature birth

Babies born before the 37th week of gestation are said to be *premature*. There are many complications associated with premature birth that can result in physical, developmental or intellectual disability. These include immature lungs, increased risk of acquiring pneumonia, other infections, jaundice, *intraventricular hemorrhage* (hemorrhage into the ventricles of the brain; see Chapter 12), inability to maintain normal body temperature, and immature digestive tracts. For more information about these disorders and interventions for them, see the American Pregnancy Association website at *http://www.americanpregnancy.org/labornbirth/complicationspremature.htm*. See also Chapter 38.

Development After Birth

There are countless books and other resources readily available on the development and care of babies. Although these vary in quality, friends, relatives, and baby care specialists can help select those that are the most reliable and useful. The best materials are those that reflect current medical and developmental knowledge, are in keeping with current health care and child rearing practices, describe health problems that babies might encounter, clearly explain the expected stages of development, and provide practical advice for caregivers.

Development during the first year

During the first year of life, a baby grows and develops rapidly. The child's weight doubles by age 5-6 months and triples by his or her first birthday. Some of the major achievements in the development of a baby are called developmental milestones. Many organizations have published developmental checklists. For example, see the *Developmental Health Watch* website at *http://www.earlyinterventioncanada.com/pdf/Developmental_Milestones.pdf* that provides milestones typically observed from 3 months after birth to 5 years of age. See also More Resources.

It must be emphasized that there is considerable variation among babies in their development rate; however, a substantial deviation from the norm, especially in walking or talking, sometimes may reflect a problem with brain development and the presence of developmental disability. The time of onset of developmental disability depends on its nature. Symptoms may be evident at birth or manifest later in childhood. Children who have conditions such as *encephalitis* or *meningitis* (infections of the brain) may suddenly show signs of cognitive impairment or cognitive difficulties. Early intervention programs are very important in helping babies and young children to reach developmental milestones. See also Chapter 38 and More Resources for additional information.

Development throughout the lifespan

Until the early 20th century, the process of development from birth to adulthood was largely ignored, and children tended to be viewed as little adults. It is now recognized that from birth into early childhood, children go through cognitive, emotional, physical, social, and educational growth. Many different theories have been proposed to account for childhood development. More recently there is an emphasis on identifying typical ages at which various milestones occur. For an introduction to child development theory, see the *Video Child Development Theorists* at *http://www.youtube.com/watch?v=15HncOVohTo.* See also the section on More Resources for information about development through the lifespan.

Approaches to Prenatal Detection of Developmental Disabilities

As discussed above and in Chapter 12, particularly, various genetic and environmental factors can affect development and result in physical and/or developmental disabilities. There are a number of ways that certain disorders resulting in disability can be detected before an infant is born. These include ultrasound scans and maternal serum screening, as well as amniocentesis, chorionic villus sampling, and percutaneous umbilical cord sampling. See also Chapter 38.

Ultrasound scans and maternal serum screening

As many as 9 in 10 pregnant women use some form of prenatal screening. The most common form of prenatal screening is to look directly at the fetus with ultrasound, or sound wave, scans. Ultrasound is usually done to determine an accurate gestational age, but the procedure also will pick up certain types of physical abnormalities such as a gross brain defect, a very large or very small head, poor fetal growth, and certain abnormal features that suggest the presence of Down syndrome (see Chapter 14). It also will detect the presence of twins, triplets, or even more babies. Since the beginning of the 21st century, major improvement in ultrasound imaging resolution continues to take place. Although ultrasound scans conducted prior to 1992 were considered not to be harmful to fetuses, the safety of newer technologies simply is not known. Fetuses are now being examined at early and vulnerable stages of development, and the acoustic energy applied now is considerably greater than that used previously (Houston, Odibo, & Macones, 2009). The lack of evidence about ultrasound scan safety should not be taken to mean that it is safe.

Screening for Down syndrome and neural tube defects (e.g., spina bifida) can be done using a blood sample from a pregnant woman at 15–17 weeks of gestation for a process called maternal serum screening. Several substances can be measured in such blood samples in order to determine the risk that the woman may be carrying a baby with these conditions. Some prenatal clinics offer pregnant women screening for Down syndrome using both ultrasound and maternal serum testing. Because such testing is associated with false positive and false negative rates, some pregnant women choose to have diagnostic testing for Down syndrome using an invasive test that analyzes cells from the fetus (see next section). See also Chapter 38.

Amniocentesis, chorionic villus sampling, and percutaneous umbilical blood sampling

Women at risk of having a child with a birth defect, and women older than the age of 35 (who are at increased risk of having a child with Down syndrome), may choose to have amniocentesis (analysis of the fluid and or fetal cells gathered from the womb's amniotic fluid), chorionic villus sampling (CVS; analysis of cells from the placenta), or percutaneous umbilical blood sampling (PUBS; analysis of blood from the umbilical cord) (see Figure 1). Tests that can be done on such samples include analysis for the presence of particular proteins, as well as analysis of cells in the samples or that are cultured from the samples, under the microscope for the presence of extra or missing chromosomes, or structurally altered chromosomes. Certain biochemical errors, such as a reduced level of a particular enzyme that results in a particular disorder, can be detected by measuring levels of certain metabolites or measuring the activity of particular enzymes in cells. As explained in Chapter 9, to look for particular defects in DNA extracted from cells, long stretches of DNA along the chromosomes can now be copied billions of times in a procedure called the *polymerase chain reaction* (PCR). The PCR reaction is so sensitive that it can detect different types of genetic defects in single cells. Furthermore, as explained in Chapter 9, the application of microarray procedures has the potential for identifying defects in DNA or RNA in amniotic fluid, and samples obtained using CVS or PUBS procedures very quickly.

Amniocentesis, CVS and PUBS have relative advantages and disadvantages. Amniocentesis is usually performed in the second *trimester* of pregnancy, between the 15th and 18th weeks, though it can be done throughout weeks 12 through 20. Amniocentesis before the 14th week is associated with a risk of miscarriage (0.25% to 0.5%). By the second trimester, there is enough amniotic fluid surrounding the baby to make it easier for the doctor to take an adequate sample without putting the fetus at risk. Because cells from the amniotic fluid are usually cultured to get a large sample of the baby's cells, results from amniocentesis often take up to two weeks to obtain.

In comparison to amniocentesis, CVS can be performed between the 10th and 12th weeks of pregnancy. The risk of miscarriage associated with CVS (0.5% to 1%) is slightly higher than in amniocente-

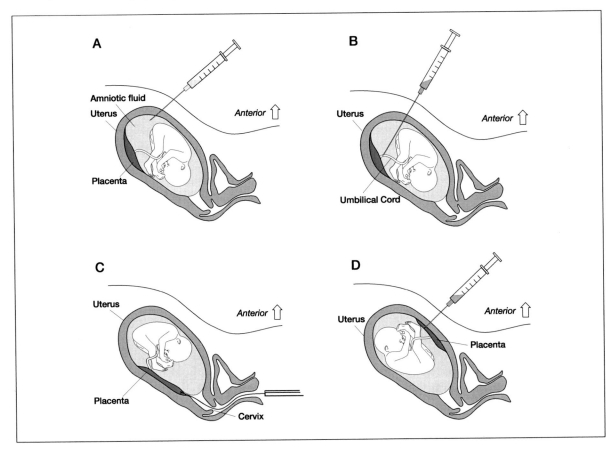

Figure 1. Amniocentesis (panel A), percutaneous umbilical cord sampling (panel B), and chorionic villus sampling (panels C and D). *Illustration ©2007 Tom Dearie, Threesixty Creative; reprinted by permission.*

sis. CVS has been associated with the occurrence of limb defects in babies, but this happens rarely, and mainly when the test is carried out before the10th week of pregnancy.

PUBS is done at 18 weeks of pregnancy or later, when diagnostic information cannot be obtained through ultrasound, amniocentesis, or CVS, or results from these tests were not conclusive. In contrast to these procedures, PUBS cannot detect neural tube defects, but it can detect chromosomal abnormalities, hemophilia and anemia, some metabolic disorders, infections such as toxoplasmosis and rubella, and causes of some structural problems such as intrauterine growth restriction. Results from PUBS usually are available within 72 hours. PUBS also can be used to give blood transfusions to the fetus and to administer medication directly. This procedure is considered to be safe, though invasive. The miscarriage rate associated with PUBS is 1%-2%.

Approaches to Prevention, Intervention, and Cure

Future issues in the area of genetics and development include the prevention and cure of genetic disorders as well as the use of cloning and stem cells. Inherent in these topics are various ethical and social issues, including the ethical, legal, and social concerns arising from new genetics findings.

Prevention via genetic counselling

The availability of technology that can detect genetic defects causing developmental disabilities is a blessing to many parents. Knowing the exact cause of the problem helps parents to understand the likely outcome for their child and to choose the best intervention. Such information is absolutely essential for researchers to develop rational treatments or even cures. It also provides people with choices for family planning. For example, after undergoing genetic counselling, parents may choose not to have a family or to have a therapeutic abortion if a life-threatening problem is identified in the fetus.

Sex selection techniques based on in vitro fertilization can reduce the risk of giving birth to a baby with X-linked disorders. If couples know that they carry genes for life threatening illnesses that they do not want to pass on to their children, they can choose to have a procedure called *preimplantation genetic diagnosis*. This procedure begins with a process called *in vitro fertilization*. This involves mixing sperm from the father with ova from the mother in a dish in the laboratory rather than having fertilization occur within the mother's body after intercourse. Single cells from the fertilized ova are then subjected to DNA analysis for a large number of disorders. Only those ova that do not show evidence of genetic defects are implanted. A few thousand of these procedures have already been performed for couples who have genetic defects causing life-threatening conditions. In Europe and a few centres in the United States, in vitro fertilization using washed sperm is being used to reduce the chance of HIV infection in a baby whose father is HIV positive.

As discussed in other chapters, some persons with developmental disability receive a genetic diagnosis. Although there are many benefits that can result from genetic diagnosis, there also are ethical concerns. Some women would never consider having a therapeutic abortion. Others feel great relief at receiving a genetic diagnosis. Yet, they must think carefully about whether they should tell other biological members of their family about the disorder and how they should communicate the information. Professionals should be sensitive to the attitudes of individuals and support the choices that they make. Another concern is whether it is really ethical to test children for genetic disorders when there is no cure for them. In addition, assigning a genetic diagnosis can have unexpected consequences in the sense that once a diagnosis is made, the information is filed in the health records of the child and will probably be available for life to all future health professionals. This may be extremely helpful in many cases, but children and adults sometimes experience discrimination because of "labels" given to them by professionals. It has also been the case that, despite universal health care in Canada, people with genetic disorders may still have problems obtaining extra health insurance or assistance with paying for such things as corrective surgery or dental work arising from a disability. For example, the authors know of some families that have mortgaged their lives away to pay for removal of benign tumours and correction of non-life threatening facial or jaw disfigurement resulting from neurofibromatosis (see Chapter 13).

Fetal surgery

Some potentially life-threatening conditions diagnosed before birth are suitable for surgical intervention in utero. Surgical interventions have included intrauterine blood transfusion, operations on the placenta and umbilical cord, clearance of congenital diaphragmatic hernia associated with occlusion of lung growth, and treatment of urinary obstruction. Even non-lethal conditions such as repair of *myelomeningocoele* (protrusion of the spinal membranes and spinal cord through a hole in the vertebral column) are now considered a potential indication. Although many fetal interventions are investigational, randomized clinical trials have established the safety and potential of some types of fetal therapy (Deprest et al., 2010).

Gene therapy

In the past, only a few genetic disorders could be detected and treated early enough to prevent disease. However, as explained in Chapter 9, the Human Genome Project is significantly increasing our ability to discover more effective therapies and prevent inherited disease. It is anticipated that future advancements in genetic technology known as *gene therapy* will actually be able to correct certain human genetic diseases, thereby improving the lives of children and their families. This technology is only beginning to develop and, although extremely promising, has not yet advanced to the point where interventions are developed and available.

There are two types of gene therapy: *germ line* gene therapy and *somatic cell* therapy. The former refers to therapy in which germ cells (sperm or ova) are modified by the introduction of functional genes into their genomes. In this case, change due to therapy would be heritable and passed on to later generations. In somatic gene therapy, the therapeutic genes are transferred into the somatic cells (all

body cells that are not germs cells) of a patient, and any effects will be restricted to the individual patient only and not transmitted to offspring.

Many jurisdictions presently do not allow germ line gene therapy, so that discussion of gene therapy usually refers to correction of genetic disease by modification of the somatic genome. *Somatic* gene therapy approaches include:

- Replacement of the defective gene with normal DNA to reverse the genetic defect
- Transplantation of cells that have been genetically engineered to express molecules that are missing
- Transplantation of stem cells or of tissues produced from stem cells

As mentioned, the development of gene therapies is still in the infancy stage. It is believed that such therapies are likely to have most benefit for people who have single-gene disorders associated with a severe phenotype. Examples of the latter include Lesch-Nyhan disease, and phenylketonuria (PKU) (see Chapter 13). Gene therapy is far less likely to provide treatment of mild developmental disability which accounts for 87 percent of all cases. Therapy that involves the transplantation of stem cells (or tissues derived from stem cells) is a particularly exciting area of research. For example, results from research reported by the Foundation Fighting Blindness (2011) describe a variety of promising ways that stem cell therapy can result in restored functioning of the cells of the retina on the back part of the eye socket (Taylor et al., 2011). See also Alenzi, Lotfy, Tamimi, & Wyse, 2010.

Cloning

A major achievement in the field of biology has been the ability to clone — or to produce genetically identical copies of cells or organisms. In 1952, a tadpole was cloned. For many years, scientists have been able to grow colonies or clones of cells in tissue culture or in animal hosts. The first report of cloning a mammal was in 1997. This involved the creation of the beloved "Dolly, the sheep" by a process called *reproductive cloning* or *nuclear transfer technology*. Genetic material from the nucleus of a cell derived from the udder of an adult sheep was transferred into an egg whose nucleus (containing its genetic material) had been removed. The reconstructed egg containing the DNA from the donor cell was then treated with chemicals in order to stimulate cell division. Once the cloned embryo had reached a suitable stage, it was transferred to the uterus of a female host where it continued to develop until birth. Strictly speaking, Dolly was not 100% genetically identical to the sheep from which the udder cell DNA was derived, because the egg from which the nucleus was removed still contained *mitochondria* (the energy-generating organelles of cells) which carry their own DNA segments (see Chapter 9). Since Dolly, researchers have used nuclear transfer technology to clone a number of different animals including sheep, goats, cows, mice, pigs, cats, rabbits, and a gaur.

As explained in more detail below, the discovery of stem cells has led to an activity called *therapeutic cloning*. This refers to the production of human embryos for use in research. The purpose of such cloning is to generate a supply of stem cells for the study of human development, the replacement of damaged tissues and organs, and the treatment of disease. Stem cells are important to biomedical researchers because they can be used to generate virtually any type of specialized cell in the human body. However, extraction of stem cells from a 5-day old embryo results in its destruction, raising ethical concerns. Furthermore, using in vitro fertilization technology, it may become possible for parents to choose the traits they would like to see in their child. This process of human *reproductive cloning* should be distinguished from therapy — choosing only healthy embryos, or embryos of a particular gender, for implantation. Reproductive cloning has not yet been carried out, and is illegal in many countries.

Another human cloning concept includes *replacement cloning*, a combination of therapeutic and reproductive cloning. In this approach, replacement cloning would entail the replacement of an extensively damaged, failed, or failing body part or parts (through cloned replacement), possibly followed by whole or partial brain transplant.

Stem cells

Stem cells are primitive cells that have the capacity to self-renew as well as to differentiate into one or more mature cell types. As of 2010, four different types of stem cells have been described. To note is that the first three types are able to provoke an immune response unless they are derived from the individual who needs the stem cell treatment.

Embryonic stem cells are taken from the inner cell mass of an embryo after 5 days of cell division. They are *pluripotent* (i.e., can differentiate into approximately 200 different cell types), and into cells of the three germ cell layers. Because of their capacity of unlimited expansion and pluripotency, they are potentially useful in regenerative medicine. Because they have long *telomeres* (regions of DNA located at the ends of chromosomes), they are classified as "young" cells. Being derived from embryonic tissue, however, there are ethical objections associated with their investigation and applications, because extraction of stem cells destroys the embryo.

Tissue or adult stem cells produce cells specific to the tissue in which they are found. They are relatively unspecialized and are predetermined to give rise to specific cell types when they differentiate. Their regenerative power is not strong in comparison to embryonic stem cells, and they are not "young." However, their use is not subject to ethical objection.

Induced pluripotent stem cells (ipSCs) are created by genetically engineering normal adult cells to revert to embryonic stem cell status. They are "young," but because they are derived from adult cells, they are not subject to ethical objection. To create these cells, adenoviruses are injected into the cell. Adenoviruses do not change the DNA of their host. They go into the nucleus of the host and work directly on the proteins without altering the chromosomes (Stadtfeld, Nagaya, Utikal, Weir, & Hochedlinger, 2008). *Parthenogenic stem cells* are obtained from unfertilized oocytes, the cells that, if allowed to develop, would become ova. They are, by definition, young. These cells are not associated with ethical objections associated with the use of embryonic tissue, but there is now ethical debate as to whether oocyte donors should be financially compensated for their contributions (Baylis & McLeod, 2007).

Recently, a Canadian group discovered a way to differentiate adult skin cells into blood cells without the need to program them to a primordial state (Szabo et al., 2010). In this approach, patients could have small pieces of their own skin removed, cultured in vitro and then differentiated into blood cells of their own genetic makeup. Potentially, these cells could then be used for blood transfusion without the concern of immune rejection. Once such blood cells can be produced in sufficient numbers, this protocol can be tested in humans. For information about stem cells and how the field is advancing, see the Learn.Genetics website at *learn.genetics.utah. edu/content/tech/stemcells/*.

Ethical and moral implications

For different reasons, many people find some or all of the preceding concepts to be ethically and morally problematic, unacceptable, or completely wrong. The process of inclusion (the philosophy and practice of including all people who belong to a society in the functioning of the society) and *prevention* (the philosophy and practice of applying current knowledge about the causes of developmental disabilities to preventing them) are conflicting trends in the field of developmental disabilities. Because radical decisions have been made by some governments in the past, including involuntary sterilization during the eugenics movement, and the practice of allowing infants born with Down syndrome to die from lack of medical treatment, it is imperative that the scientific and medical communities and governments hear the views of consumers and families about ethical issues that involve new genetic findings. Fortunately, as part of the Human Genome Project, research is now being conducted on such topics as discrimination in insurance and employment, genetic testing, screening and counselling, and genetic therapies to cure developmental disability.

Summary

Embryonic and fetal development are dependent upon many factors that can include nurture as well as nature. Good nutrition and maternal health, pre-natally and perinatally, are key to the development of a healthy baby and to good health later in life. Early intervention programs are very important in helping babies and young children to reach developmental milestones. Readers also have been introduced to topical issues in the area of genetics and development. These include screening for genetic disorders, as well as future approaches for their prevention and cure including potential applications of cloning and stem cells, issues about which some individuals have strong moral objection, and which are topics of continued ethical and moral debate.

For Further Thought and Discussion

1. What are some risks and benefits associated with fetal screening using ultrasound?
2. The under-nutrition of women during pregnancy is a world-wide problem that is not receiving enough attention or support. What steps might be taken, and by whom, to address this universal problem?
3. Check the Health Canada websites given in the text for information about consequences of excessive exposures to mercury and aluminum. Is there enough information on these sites for people to make decisions about how to reduce their own exposures and those of their babies to these metals? If not, what actions might concerned citizens take to increase awareness of potential hazards that might result from excessive exposures to these metals?
4. The frequency of developmental disabilities is known to be higher in areas of poverty than in affluent areas. What factors might account for this finding?

More Resources

Websites:

Developmental Milestones, Centers for Disease Control and Prevention
http://www.cdc.gov/ncbddd/actearly/milestones/index.html

Developmental Milestones, Todays Parent
http://www.todaysparent.com/toddler/article.
jsp?content=3237&page=1

The Foundation Fighting Blindness
*http://www.ffb.ca//research/research_news/ipsc_*
transplant.html

FFA Research Fact Sheet – Stem Cell Therapy
http://www.ffb.ca/patient_resources/factsheets/
stem_cells.html

Genetic Information Nondiscrimination Act (GINA) of 2008
http://www.genome.gov/24519851

List of known and suspected teratogens
http://msds.chem.ox.ac.uk/teratogens.html

Mount Sinai Hospital. Prenatal Diagnosis and Medical Genetics
http://www.mountsinai.on.ca/care/pdmg

UNSW Embryology
http://embryology.med.unsw.edu.au/Medicine/
images/hcriticaldev.gif

YourChild Development & Behavior Resources, University of Michigan Health System
http://www.med.umich.edu/yourchild/topics/
devmile.htm

Books:

Boyd, D. A., Bee, H. L., & Johnson, P. (2008). *Lifespan development*. Third Canadian Edition with MyDevelopmentLab. Newmarket, ON: Pearson Education.

Santrock, J., MacKenzie-Rivers, A., Leung, K. H., & Malcomson, T. (2008). *Life-span development* (3rd Canadian ed.). Toronto, ON: McGraw-Hill Ryerson Higher Education.

References

Alenzi, F. Q., Lotfy, M., Tamimi, W. G., & Wyse, R. K. (2010). Review: Stem cells and gene therapy. *Laboratory Hematology, 16*(3), 53-73.

Arndt, T. L., Stodgell, C. J., & Rodier, P. M. (2005). The teratology of autism. *International Journal of Developmental Neuroscience, 23*(2-3), 189-199.

Baylis, F., & McLeod, C. (2007). Selling of eggs for research. *Journal of Medical Ethics, 33*, 726-731. Retrieved from http://www.noveltechethics.ca/pictures/File/publications/2007/JME_Stem_Cell_Debate_2007.pdf

Champagne, F. A. (2008). Epigenetic mechanisms and the transgenerational effects of maternal care. *Frontiers in Neuroendocrinology, 29*(3), 386-397.

Deprest, J. A., Flake, A.W., Gratacos, E., Ville, Y., Hecher, K., Nicolaides, K., et al. (2010). The making of fetal surgery. *Prenatal Diagnosis, 30*(7), 653-667.

Foundation Fighting Blindness. (2011). Retrieved from http://www.ffb.ca/index.html

Fowden, A. L., & Forhead, A. J. (2009). Hormones as epigenetic signals in developmental programming. *Experimental Physiology, 94*(6), 607-625.

Galbally, M., Lewis, A.J., Ijzendoorn, M., & Permezel. M. (2011). The role of oxytocin in mother-infant relations: A systematic review of human studies. *Harvard Reviews in Psychiatry, 19*(1), 1-14.

Gencoglan, G., & Tosun, M. (2010). Effects of isotretinoin on spermatogenesis of rats. *Cutaneous and Ocular Toxicology,* Oct 26.

Harding, R., & Bocking, A. D. (Eds.). (2006). *Fetal growth and development.* Cambridge, UK: Cambridge University Press.

Houston, L. E., Odibo, A. O., & Macones, G. A. (2009). The safety of obstetrical ultrasound: A review. *Prenatal Diagnosis, 29*(13), 1204-1212.

Kiefer, J. C. (2007). Epigenetics in development. *Developmental Dynamics, 236*(4), 1144-1156.

Leese, H. J. (2005). Rewards and risks of human embryo creation: A personal view. *Reproduction, Fertility, and Development, 17*(3), 387-391.

List of Known and Suspected Teratogens, Oxford University. (2010). Retrieved from http://msds.chem.ox.ac.uk/teratogens.html

Reik, W. (2007). Review article. Stability and flexibility of epigenetic gene regulation in mammalian development. *Nature, 447*(7143), 425-432.

Shepard, T. H., & Lemire, R. J. (2007). *Catalog of teratogenic agents* (12th ed.). Baltimore: Johns Hopkins University Press.

Stadtfeld, M., Nagaya, M., Utikal, J., Weir, G., & Hochedlinger, K. (2008). *Induced pluripotent stem cells generated without viral integration.* Science, Published Online September 25, 2008. DOI: 10.1126/science.1162494

Szabo, E., Rampalli, S., Risueno, R. M., Schnerch, A., Mitchell, R., Fiebig-Comyn, A. et al. (2010). Conversion of human fibroblasts to multilineage blood progenitors. *Nature, 468*, 521-526.

Tucker, B.A., Park, I. H., Qi, S. D., Klassen, H. J., Jiang, C., Yao, J., et al. (2011). Transplantation of adult mouse iPS cell-derived photoreceptor precursors restores retinal structure and function in degenerative mice. *PLoS One, 6*(4), e18992.

University of Maryland Medical Center. (2011). Retrieved from http://www.umm.edu/ency/article/002398.htm

The Visible Embryo. (n.d). Retrieved from http://www.visembryo.com

Wong-Goodrich, S. J., Glenn, M. J., Mellott, T. J., Blusztajn, J. K., Meck, W. H, & Williams, C. L. (2008). Spatial memory and hippocampal plasticity are differentially sensitive to the availability of choline in adulthood as a function of choline supply in utero. *Brain Research, 1237*, 153-166.

11

Introduction to the Nervous Systems

William MacKay and Maire Percy

What you will learn:

- What the central nervous system is (the brain, spinal cord, and cerebrospinal fluid)
- How the brain is supplied with blood
- What the peripheral nervous system is (the sympathetic and autonomic nervous systems, and the enteric nervous system of the gut)
- Introduction to brain structure and function (including cells of the brain and synapses, neurotransmitters, external and internal parts of the brain, differences between the male and female brain, and importance in development)
- Future directions in brain and neuroscience research

*Note: Words in **bold italics** are explained in the Special Terms section following the Summary.*

The purpose of this chapter is to provide an introduction to the central and peripheral nervous systems. Problems with the development and functioning of the central nervous system or the peripheral nervous system — or both — can result in developmental or other disabilities. These may be shown as difficulties in many areas of day-to-day functioning, such as communication, learning, behaviour, and motor ability.

Over the past 20 years, we have learned that our thoughts and interactions with the environment can affect the structure and function of our brains, even into old age. The implications for persons with different types of nervous system injury or intellectual

and developmental disabilities are indeed profound (Arrowsmith School, n.d. ; Doidge, 2007; Eaton, 2011; Restak, 1999).

Central Nervous System

The *central nervous system* (CNS) is divided into two parts: the brain and the spinal cord. The brain is protected by the skull and the spinal cord is protected by the vertebrae of the spinal column. A set of membranes called the **meninges** covers the brain and spinal cord surfaces; these protect and nourish the CNS. Fluid in the brain and spinal cord called *cerebrospinal fluid* (CSF) protects these tissues from trauma. CSF is made by the choroid plexus, a ribbon of tissue that is highly *vascularized* (i.e., contains a lot of blood vessels) and lines the CSF-filled **ventri-**

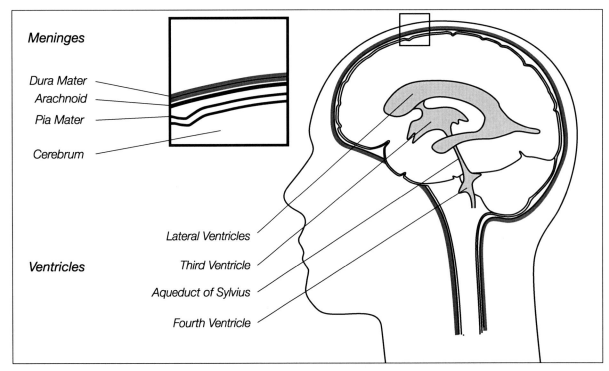

Figure 1. Meninges and ventricles of the brain. *(Illustration: Copyright@2007 by Tom Dearie, Threesixty Creative; reprinted by permission.)*

cles of the brain. The ventricles are a set of four cavities in the brain that connect with one another and with the central canal of the spinal cord (see Figure 1 for an illustration of the ventricles).

The brain and the spinal cord

The brain is the supervisory centre of the nervous system and the most complex body organ. The various parts of the brain work together to enable perception and thoughts, and to coordinate behaviours and body maintenance. The brain resembles a mushroom: the giant *cerebrum* forms the cap; the lower part (the **brainstem**), which is continuous with the spinal cord, forms the stalk.

The average adult human brain weighs 1.3 to 1.4 kilograms (kg) (about 3 lb). It contains approximately 100 billion nerve cells (*neurons*) and trillions of three different types of non-neural support cells called **glia**: 1) *Microglia* are the "garbage disposal" cells of the brain; 2) Astrocytes provide nutritional support to neurons (e.g., lactate and glutamine molecules); and 3) *Oligodendrocytes* encircle the *axons*

(long processes of neurons that conduct impulses away from the nerve cell body) of many neurons to form **myelin** sheaths. (Myelin is an insulating material that increases the rate of signal transmission through neurons.)

Brain tissue contains gray and white matter. **Gray matter** is composed of the bodies of neurons, dendrites (processes that lead impulses toward the nerve cell body), and some other supporting tissue. **White matter** largely consists of myelinated axons. In general, gray matter is responsible for information processing and white matter for information transmission. Intelligence in males correlates to the amount of gray matter in specific areas of the cerebral cortex, whereas intelligence in females correlates better to specific volumes of white matter (Haier, Jung, Yeo, Head, & Alkire, 2005).

The *spinal cord* is the main information pathway connecting the brain and the peripheral nervous system (PNS) (see below). It consists largely of white matter arranged in tracts of longitudinal fibres around a central core of gray matter; the gray matter surrounds a small, longitudinal canal that is filled with CSF and is continuous with the ventricles of the brain. In adult men and women, the spinal cord length is about 43 and 45 centimetres (cm), respectively, and the weight is 35-40 grams (g) (Gray, 1918).

How the brain is supplied with blood

Survival of the brain depends on its receiving (via the circulation of blood) an adequate supply of fuel (mainly glucose), other nutrients, and oxygen. The front part of the brain is supplied with blood by the internal carotid arteries, which branch and become the anterior and middle cerebral arteries. The back part of the brain is supplied with blood by the vertebral arteries, which merge to become the basilar artery. These arteries are joined together by smaller connections to form the *Circle of Willis* (see Figure 2). (See also the North Harris College Biology Department website (*http://www.apchute.com/cardio/circle. htm*) for an animation of blood flow through the Circle of Willis). The small arteries of the Circle of Willis are a frequent site of *infarction* (area of coagulated tissue death due to a local obstruction of circulation and lack of oxygen). Reduced blood flow in the cerebral arteries radiating out from the Circle of Willis is a common cause of *stroke* (death of brain cells in a restricted region due to either infarction or hemorrhage (excessive loss of blood from blood vessels.) Venous drainage occurs via deep veins and sinuses that finally drain into the internal jugular veins. In a healthy brain, a mechanism called *autoregulation* allows blood flow to stay constant even when physiologic conditions change radically. However, when the heart does not function properly (as in heart failure) or when the volume of blood in the body becomes significantly decreased, the blood supply to the brain may not be sufficient, a factor suspected of contributing to the development of dementia, including Alzheimer's disease (see Chapter 37).

Cerebrospinal fluid

The volume of CSF in adults is normally constant at about 140 millilitres (ml), although approximately 550 ml are produced every day. To prevent buildup *of intracranial pressure* (pressure inside the skull), the CSF flows out of the fourth ventricle into the

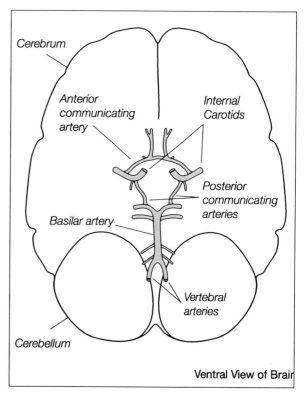

Figure 2. Circle of Willis. *In the brain, anterior and posterior as well as right and left arteries join to create an interconnected blood supply in a structure called the Circle of Willis. (Illustration: Copyright@2007 by Tom Dearie, Threesixty Creative; reprinted by permission.)*

subarachnoid space (the area under the *arachnoid mater*, which is the middle membrane of the brain meninges) to eventually drain either into the venous or lymphatic system. The *venous system* is comprised of blood vessels that carry blood towards the heart; most veins carry blood that has been deoxygenated (exceptions are the pulmonary and umbilical veins which carry oxygenated blood). The *lymphatic system* is the key system for protecting against invaders that have entered the body such as bacteria, viruses, and fungi. It consists of capillaries that drain into a system of collecting vessels that carry lymph back into the blood stream, and lymph nodes that filter the lymph. Lymph is a clear fluid related to plasma that carries *lymphocytes* (white cells) involved in fighting infection. For more information, see *http://www. newworldencyclopedia.org/entry/Lymphatic_system/*

CSF is made by filtration, diffusion, and active

Table 1: Some Contrasting and Complementary Effects of Sympathetic and Parasympathetic Arousal

Sympathetic nervous system	Parasympathetic nervous system
Pupil dilation and opening of the eyelids	*Pupil constriction*
Stimulation of the sweat glands	*Activation of the salivary glands*
Constriction of blood vessels in the skin and gut	*Promotion of urination*
Increase of the heart rate	*Decrease of the heart rate*
Dilation of the bronchial tubes	*Constriction of the bronchial tubes*
Inhibition of the secretions in the digestive system	*Stimulation of intestinal movement and secretions of the stomach*
Ejaculation of semen	*Penile erection*

transport of substances from the blood. It washes away waste products of metabolism, drugs, and other substances that may gain access to the brain from the blood. CSF is clear and colorless; it contains only a few lymphocytes, small amounts of protein, glucose, potassium, and relatively large amounts of *sodium chloride* (salt). When the intracranial pressure is increased (e.g., as a result of brain injury, hydrocephalus (buildup of fluid inside the skull), or a brain tumour), this can cause changes in behaviour, agitation, confusion, decreased response, and coma.

Analysis of the CSF can give clues in cases of CNS disease. Total protein is increased in infections and viral diseases, and CSF cell counts increase in cases of **meningitis** (inflammation of the meninges; Chapter 13) or *encephalitis* (infections of the brain). (General sources: Bear, Connors, & Paradiso, 2001; Matthews, 2001.)

Peripheral Nervous System

The peripheral nervous system (PNS) is divided into three parts: the somatic nervous system, the autonomic nervous system, and the enteric nervous system of the gut. These are explained below. For

more information see *http://faculty.washington.edu/chudler/nsdivide.html#pns/* .

Somatic nervous system

The *somatic nervous system* is the part of the PNS that is concerned with voluntary muscle movement and for processing sensory information that arrives as the result of external stimuli (hearing, touch, and sight). It consists of the *afferent nerve network*, which includes most sensory nerves leading to the CNS, and the *efferent nerve network*, which includes all motor nerves leading from CNS to the muscles. (**Afferent** means carrying impulses toward the CNS; **efferent** means leading away.) See *http://faculty.washington.edu/chudler/nsdivide.html#pns* for a diagram of the somatic motor system.

The brain typically processes the information from the afferent network and responds through the efferent nerve network to elicit a response in the muscles. Sometimes, however, the brain does not fully process the information before a **reflex arc** within the spinal cord triggers a movement. (A reflex arc refers to the neural pathway that a nerve impulse follows. In its simplest form, this consists of a sensory nerve, a motor nerve, and the synapse between.)

Reflex arcs coordinate stereotyped reactions that are either protective in dangerous situations or regulatory. The term *regulatory* refers to the maintenance of a specific motoric function, be it postural balance, finger grip, or eye position. Certain stimuli, such as touching a hot surface, stimulate activity in a protective reflex arc. Nerve impulses travel up the afferent nerve, through several interneurons in the spinal cord, to eventually activate selected motor (efferent) neurons. (*Interneurons* are connector neurons that process signals from one or more sensory neurons and relay signals to motor neurons.) Finally, the reflex signal travels down the appropriate efferent nerves to jerk the hand away from the hot surface. This automatic response system results in reactions that are much quicker than is possible with consciously willed responses, and better scaled to the magnitude of the stimulus.

Autonomic nervous system

The *autonomic nervous system* controls smooth muscles, both in *viscera* (internal organs) and in blood vessels, and it controls the secretions of glands (e.g., adrenal, thyroid, salivary). It is involved in functions such as blood pressure, heart rate, breathing, digestion, excretion, body temperature, and copulation. The effector channels of the autonomic system are classified as either sympathetic or parasympathetic. See *http://faculty.washington.edu/chudler/auto.html/*.

The sympathetic system prepares the body for sudden stresses. Efferents of the sympathetic nervous system originate in the thoracic (chest area) segments of the spinal cord and are distributed to various parts of the body via the sympathetic chain of **ganglia** on either side of the vertebral column. (The term ganglia refers to PNS structures containing a collection of nerve cell bodies.) Sympathetic nerves also contain sensory afferents conveying metabolic information from internal organs to the CNS. The sympathetic nervous system prepares the body for activities associated with fight or flight; it prepares for stressful events ranging from facing a violent confrontation to running from danger. In the *fight-or-flight reaction*, adrenalin and noradrenalin (hormones released by the medulla of the two adrenal glands) cause various parts of the body to respond in much the same way as the sympathetic nervous system.

Because adrenalin and noradrenalin are released into the blood stream, they continue to exert effects after a stressful event has stopped. In the fight-or-flight reaction, blood sugar is increased, extra red blood cells are released from the spleen, peripheral blood vessels constrict, the pulse quickens, blood pressure elevates, and digestion stops.

The *parasympathetic* system prepares the body for rest and helps the digestive tract to work. Efferents of the parasympathetic nervous system originate in the brainstem and in the lowest segments of the spinal cord. Neurological functions located here include those necessary for survival (e.g., breathing, digestion, heart rate, and blood pressure) and for arousal (being awake and alert). Sensory afferents mingle with efferents in parasympathetic nerves. The main nerves of the parasympathetic system are the large *vagus nerves*. These convey information about blood pressure, levels of carbon dioxide in the blood, and the amount of food in the stomach to the CNS. Parasympathetic function is largely nutritive, restorative, and restful; it will bring the body back from any emergency state that the sympathetic nervous system creates.

As noted above, the sympathetic and parasympathetic systems are structurally distinct entities. Some functions of these two systems oppose one another — as in a push-pull balancing act — but other functions are complementary in nature (see Table 1).

Reflexes also operate within the autonomic nervous system, generally to regulate homeostatic functions such as blood pressure or body temperature. Moreover, many afferents within autonomic nerves transmit pain information. In the CNS, information about organ pain often converges with pain signals from surface areas of the body. As a result, the source of the information sometimes gets confused. This is called *referred pain*. One example is the referred pain that some people feel in the shoulders and arms when they are having a heart attack.

The autonomic nervous system influences all aspects of digestion including gut motility, ion transport associated with secretion and absorption, and

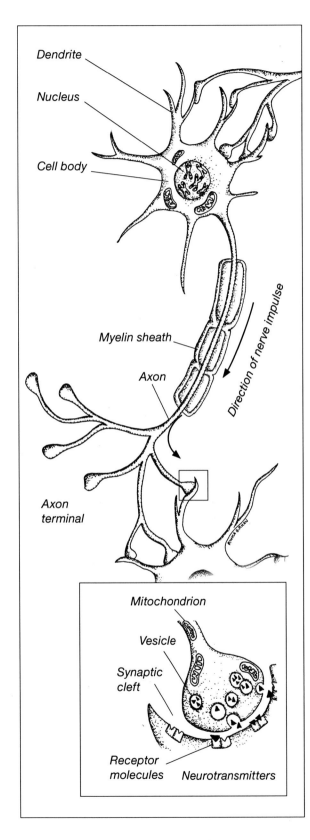

Dendrite

Nucleus

Cell body

Myelin sheath

Axon

Direction of nerve impulse

Axon terminal

Mitochondrion

Vesicle

Synaptic cleft

Receptor molecules

Neurotransmitters

gastrointestinal blood flow. Much of the control of the gastrointestinal system results from the feedback of digestive system hormones acting both on vagal afferents and directly on the CNS. However, the gastrointestinal tract also has its own, local nervous system referred to as the *enteric nervous system* (Grundy & Schemann, 2005).

Enteric nervous system

The enteric nervous system contains as many neurons as the spinal cord. It is primarily composed of two networks of neurons extending from the esophagus to the anus, both of which are imbedded in the wall of the digestive tract and innervate the gastrointestinal muscles, pancreas, and gall bladder (i.e., viscera). Disorders of the gastrointestinal system, such as *celiac disease* (an inability to tolerate a protein called gluten that is found in many grains) and *Helicobacter pylori* infection (a common cause of ulcers in the gastrointestinal tract), or the intestinal inflammation that is common in people with autism, must involve the enteric nervous system. Feeling sick to the stomach or "having butterflies" when nervous are effects of a psychological disturbance to the enteric nervous system. (General sources: Bear et al., 2001; Matthews, 2001.)

Figure 3. Diagrammatic representation of a neuron and a chemical synapse. *Neurons are specialized cells in the brain. If a single neuron is magnified approximately 1,000 times, it looks like an uprooted tree. The "branches" at one end of the neuron are dendrites, and the long "trunk" is the axon. Dendrites and axons connect with neighbouring cells. Dendrites receive signals from other cells. Axons pass signals on to other cells. The transfer of signals from axons to dendrites occurs at specialized junctions, or synapses. The narrow gap between an axon terminal and a dendrite is called the synaptic cleft. A neuron signals information by transmitting electrical impulses along its axon. When impulses reach the end of the axon, they trigger the release of neurotransmitters that are stored in pouches called vesicles. The neurotransmitters released from vesicles rapidly diffuse across the synaptic cleft and bind to receptor molecules in the postsynaptic membrane of the dendrite (Source: Percy, Lewkis, & Brown, 2003. Illustration kindly provided by Rivka Birkan and Simon Wong.)*

Brain Function and Structure

There are various elements of brain function and structure. These are explored in the following sections.

Cells of the brain and synapses

The functional units of all nervous systems are: 1) nerve cells or *neurons* that transmit and process information via electrochemical signalling, and 2) the glia that perform "housekeeping" functions such as insulation, infection-fighting, maintainance of ion balance, and transfer of nutrients between brain capillaries and neurons. The anatomical and biochemical connections between neurons are called *synapses*. There are two types of synapses: chemical and electrical. At *chemical synapses*, communication between two cells is mediated by specialized molecules, or neurotransmitters (see the Neurotransmitters section later in this chapter). At *electrical synapses*, structures called *gap junctions* join cells, and signals are transmitted via ion currents without involvement of neurotransmitters. Specialized membranes of nerve cell axons enable them to conduct electrical impulses over long distances. The conduction of electrical impulses depends on the ability of axonal membranes to undergo rapid changes in permeability to small, positively charged ions. Conduction of impulses along axonal membranes consumes relatively little energy when compared with synaptic signal transmission. The needed energy is largely derived from the aerobic metabolism of lactate and glutamine, supplied to neurons by astrocytes. In turn, the astrocytes are ultimately dependent on glucose from the bloodstream. Consequently, the brain is very sensitive to disruption of a regular supply of glucose and of oxygen.

Interference with any major metabolic system in the brain can deprive it of essential nutrients and other regulators that are required for its function (Restak, 1999). Therefore, it is not surprising that inborn errors of metabolism, or certain types of genetic disorders, very often result in developmental disability associated with brain dysfunction. In an infant, the developing brain is continually forming and reforming synapses. A synaptic connection is preferentially made between neurons that are simultaneously active. When frequently stimulated, synapses become stronger. Signalling chemicals are sent out that make the connections stronger and more permanent. A diagram of a neuron and a chemical synapse is given in Figure 3. A cross-section of the human brain showing interconnections between neurons (*interneurons*) is shown in Figure 4.

Neurotransmitters

Neurotransmitters are classified into two broad categories depending on the effects that they trigger when they bind to specific receptors on the ***postsynaptic*** cell — ionotropic and metabotropic. (The term post-synaptic refers to the surface of the cell on the opposite side of the synapse from the synaptic terminal of the stimulating neuron (see Fig. 3). The post-synaptic neuron contains receptor proteins and degradative enzymes for the neurotransmitter.) First, at ***ionotropic*** synapses, binding of a neurotransmitter or hormone causes the opening of diffusion channels through the *postsynaptic* membrane of a target neuron. Ion diffusion through the open channels then generates a postsynaptic potential, which may be either excitatory or inhibitory, depending on the properties of the channel. Ionotropic transmitters are glutamate, gamma aminobutyric acid (GABA), glycine, acetylcholine, and serotonin. Glutamate is the main excitatory transmitter; GABA is the main inhibitory transmitter. Second, these same transmitters and many others — including catecholamines, peptides and fatty acid amides — can bind to ***metabotropic*** receptors. Metabotrophic receptors do not have ion channels as part of the receptor. Instead they are coupled to molecules called G-proteins. Transmitter binding to metabotropic receptors initiates a cascade of enzyme activations or deactivations in the postsynaptic neuron that results in changes of the levels of "second messenger" molecules and subsequently other signalling agents. Responses at ionotropic synapses are fast, whereas those at metabotropic synapses can persist for minutes. In general, metabotropic receptor activation has a modulatory effect, suppressing or enhancing adjacent ionotropic transmission. Some metabotropic transmitters are gases, such as nitric oxide,

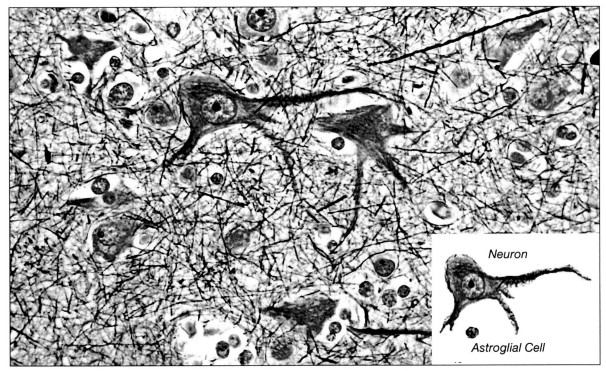

Figure 4. Cross-section of the cortex (outer region) of the human brain showing interconnections between neurons (the neuronal network). *In this photograph, a small section of a normal human brain cortex has been fixed and stained with Bielchowsky silver stain. The large triangular cells with an oval nucleus are the neurons. The neurons are connected to one another by an intricate network of long processes (dendrites and axons, see Figure 3). Small non-neuronal cells are either astrocytes or microglia. (Source: Percy, Lewkis & Brown, 2003. Photo kindly provided by Dr. Catherine Bergeron, Centre for Research in Neurodegenerative Disease, University of Toronto.)*

which cannot be stored in vesicles. Instead they are synthesized when an electrical impulse arrives at the end of the axon, and then they promptly diffuse everywhere in the vicinity. (See the Neuroscience, Fourth Edition website at *http://www.sinauer.com/neuroscience4e/animations5.1.html* for a demonstration of ionotropic and metabotropic transmission.) (General sources: Bear et al., 2001; Matthews, 2001.)

Parts of the brain

The brain has both external and internal parts. These are described next.

External structure: The brainstem provides the connection between the brain and the spinal cord. It controls many vital and involuntary body functions such as blood pressure, breathing, and pulse; coordinates posture and locomotion; and regulates the level of consciousness. The cerebellum is a structure that greatly improves the fine temporal control of all body movements, from postural balance to speech and manual skills.

Figure 5 illustrates the lobes of the brain. These include the frontal lobes, parietal lobes, temporal lobes, occipital lobes, and the olfactory bulbs. The *frontal lobes* control personality, expression of emotion, motivation, planning, and initiation of motor actions. They also inhibit inappropriate or impulsive action. Moreover, they store information and affect a person's ability to concentrate, plan strategically, and think in abstract terms. The *parietal lobes* control a person's awareness of his or her body parts and his or her position in space. In addition, they mediate physical sensations such as touch, *kinesthesia* (sense of body posture and movement), temperature, and pain. The *temporal lobes* embody memory, intellectual abilities, and impulse control. They also process visual and auditory input, making these lobes essential for object and color recognition, language comprehension, and music appreciation. The *occipital lobes* are the site of entry-level processing of visual information. This information is transmitted to the inferior temporal lobes for object recognition (ventral visual pathway), and to the parietal lobes for recognition of spatial relationships and direction (dorsal visual pathway). The *olfactory bulbs* (not shown in the diagram) are narrow extensions from the undersurface of the frontal lobes, one on each side of the midline. They are useful to entry-level processing of odorous stimuli. Neurogenesis (creation of new neurons) in the adult brain takes place continually in the olfactory bulbs, and also in the dentate gyrus region of the hippocampus. (General source: Bear et al., 2001.)

Inner structure: Figure 6 shows the brain's inner structure. The *amygdala* is an almond-shaped neural structure in the anterior part of the temporal lobe of the cerebrum. It is intimately connected with the hypothalamus, the hippocampus, and the cingulate gyrus. As part of the limbic system, the amygdala plays an important role in motivation and emotional behaviour. (The **limbic system** is part of the brain that controls our emotions. For example, if someone is about to be attacked, this system first produces fear, then rage.) It consists of a complex set of structures located on both sides of the thalamus, just under the cerebrum. It includes the hypothalamus, the hippocampus, the amygdala, and several other areas located nearby. The amygdala is primarily responsible for emotions, and also plays an important role in the formation of memories. Interestingly, the hypothalamus produces a hormone called *oxytocin*. This is best known for its role in inducing labour. However, it has been nicknamed the "cuddle hormone," since in animal models it plays a role in the expression of maternal, sexual, social, stress and feeding behaviours, as well as in learning and memory (Ross & Young, 2009). The *basal ganglia* are large structures toward the centre of the brain that surround the thalamus. The basal ganglia have both limbic and motor functions. They participate in making decisions, integrating feelings, and habit formation. They are involved with setting the body's

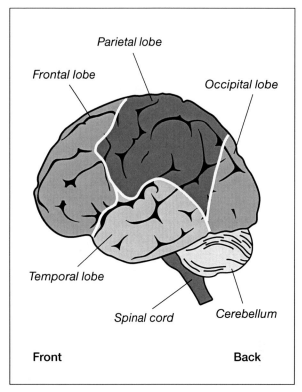

Figure 5. Major subdivisions of the cerebral cortex.
Source: Understanding the Brain — The Birth of a Learning Science, Volume 2, @ OECCD 2007; reprinted by permission.

idle or anxiety level. In addition, the basal ganglia help to modulate motivation and are likely involved with feelings of pleasure and ecstasy. Closely associated with the basal ganglia is a small region in the upper brain stem known as the *substantia nigra* ("black substance"). It contains neurons that produce and release dopamine, a neurotransmitter that acts within the basal ganglia to facilitate both movement-related and reward-related signals.

The cerebral cortex is the highest brain part in terms of abstraction and uniqueness to humans. Phylogenetically, it is the most recent addition to the brain, and in human development it is the last brain area to fully mature. It governs thoughts, senses, and skilled body motion. It consists of two (left and right) highly folded sheets of gray matter, called *hemispheres*. Each hemisphere has a temporal, frontal, parietal, and occipital lobe, plus an olfactory bulb.

The *hippocampus* forms the medial (middle) edge

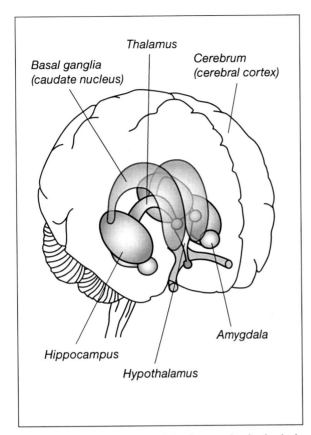

Thalamus

Basal ganglia
(caudate nucleus)

Cerebrum
(cerebral cortex)

Amygdala

Hippocampus

Hypothalamus

Figure 6. Inner structure of the human brain, including the limbic system. *Source: Understanding the Brain - The Birth of a Learning Science, Volume 2, @OECD 2007); reprinted by permission.*

of the temporal lobe in both hemispheres, and is essential for memory and learning. The hippocampus contains the *dentate gyrus*, one of two brain regions in which neurogenesis is known to take place in adults. As already mentioned, the hippocampus is a component of the limbic system as well.

The thalamus and *hypothalamus* serve as the interface between the brainstem and cerebrum; they are located just above the brainstem. The hypothalamus oversees the endocrine system to regulate thirst, hunger, body temperature, sleep, moods, sex drive, and the release of hormones from various glands. The hypothalamus controls the hypothalamic-pituitary-adrenal (HPA) axis (for more details, see the Hypothalamic-Pituitary-Adrenal Axis and Stress section). In general, the hypothalamus communicates with the body via the autonomic nervous system and the pituitary gland (or "master gland"), which produces hormones that are important in regulating growth and metabolism. As mentioned, the hypothalamus is part of the limbic system which mediates emotional experience, and autonomic behaviours.

The *thalamus* is located in the centre of the brain, beneath the cerebral hemispheres and next to the third ventricle. It is formed of gray matter and can be thought of as a processing station for nerve impulses being sent to the cerebral cortex or basal ganglia. (General source: Bear et al., 2001.)

Effects of developmental stage on brain structure and function

Since the mid-1990s, evidence from genetic research and studies of the brain, especially brain imaging (see the Measuring Brain Activity and Structure section), has shown that many developmental disabilities, including learning difficulties, have a neurobiological basis. This means that such disabilities result from changes in the structure or function of the brain or both. Compared with other organs, the human brain develops over a long period of time.

Before birth to the second year of life: Development begins in the first weeks after conception, with most of the basic brain structure completed before birth. The brain is very vulnerable to environmental changes in early pregnancy and during the brain growth spurt that begins in the last trimester of pregnancy and extends to the end of the second year in life. Factors such as lack of oxygen, lack of essential fatty acids or folic acid and other vital nutrients, infections, drugs, toxins (including maternal use of alcohol), stress, and lack of stimulation can particularly affect normal development of the brain. Developing fetuses and babies are much more vulnerable to toxins than adults for the following reasons:

- Their brains are developing rapidly
- Chemical exposures have a bigger effect on fetuses and babies than on adults simply because of body size difference
- Their blood-brain barriers are not mature and allow substances to enter the CNS that adult brains would exclude
- Their systems for detoxifying and excreting

chemicals are not fully developed
- They have more years than adults during which a problem caused by an exposure can develop (General sources: Environmental Working Group, 2005; Matthews, 2000; Restak, 1999).

A child's brain is characterized by plasticity. Plasticity means that connections between neurons can form, strengthen, weaken, or disappear, depending on the nature and duration of environmental and other experiences. Between 10 and 18 months, a baby's emotions begin to develop. Emotion involves the entire nervous system, but two parts of the nervous system are particularly important for emotion: the limbic system (see Figure 6) and the autonomic nervous system (see the preceding Peripheral Nervous System section). The limbic system not only plays an important role in emotional life and how people respond to stress but it also is important in the formation of memories. Emotion and sensory perception (smelling, hearing, seeing, feeling, and tasting) are vital for survival, growth, development, and the experience of bodily pleasure. Learning between the ages of 3 and 10 years plays a key role in establishing connections in the child's brain. Positive experiences affect brain development in a positive way. Conversely, both acute and chronic stress can adversely affect brain development and function. Severe stress, particularly that which lasts a long time, can adversely affect a child's brain development and functioning when he or she becomes an adult. (General sources: Als et al., 2003; Bear et al., 2001; DeBord, n.d.; Eisenberg, 1999; Greenspan, 1997; Ito, 2004; Lewis, 2004; Restak, 1999; Shore, 1997; National Dissemination Center for Children with Disabilities, n.d.)

Adolescence: Puberty is said to be as critical a time for typical brain development as are the growth spurts in the fetal or baby brain. Puberty is marked by striking changes in neuroendocrine function. In particular, levels of steroidal gonadal hormones increase markedly. These steroidal hormones have profound effects on the structure and function of the maturing nervous system, and they influence the development of various steroid-dependent behaviours characteristic of adulthood (e.g., sexuality). They also affect stress reactivity. Changes in neuronal

circuitry in adolescence involve steroid hormone-induced sculpting of certain synapses and the pruning of others. Because the areas of the brain involved in emotion mature earlier than those involved in judgement and reasoning, adolescents tend to make decisions more impulsively than adults, who balance emotion with reason and use both abilities to reach decisions. (General sources: Restak, 1999; Romeo, 2005; Sisk & Foster, 2004.)

Aging: The brain in older individuals is characterized by challenges with memory, and more time is needed to learn new information. Yet, intelligence, abstract thinking, and verbal expression tend to remain the same with age. Life experiences provide older people with wisdom, making them more rational and flexible. Lifestyle is thought to be very important in the preservation of memory with aging. Mental and physical exercise promote increased blood circulation to the brain, stimulate the production of molecules that keep neurons healthy and disease-resistant, and maintain important synaptic connections. Good nutrition also is extremely important, especially a rich and varied supply of antioxidants. (General sources: Allen, Bruss, & Damasio, 2005; Bengmark, 2006; Grady & Craik, 2000; Hess, 2005; Restak, 1999.)

The right brain and the left brain

The two hemispheres of the cerebral cortex are linked by the *corpus callosum*, the band of white matter through which the hemispheres communicate and coordinate. Generally, the right hemisphere controls the left side of the body and the left hemisphere controls the right side. When the left brain has been damaged, some of the lost functions can be taken over by the right brain (Gazzaniga, 2005). Nevertheless, the two hemispheres have some separate specializations. The left hemisphere predominates in reasoning ability (i.e., the detailed sequential thinking common in science and mathematics), and in written and spoken language. In contrast, the right hemisphere predominates in spatial or integrative tasks, insight, imagination, and appreciation of art and music. Generally speaking, the left brain excels at information processing based on fine distinctions in temporal order and the right brain tends to ignore precise timing in favour of details regarding how information is grouped together.

The male brain and the female brain

There has been much controversy as to whether there are structural and functional differences between the brain in males and females. A few hypothalamic centres concerned with sex hormones are clearly different. Although there are no significant differences in general intelligence between males and females, there is evidence that women have more white matter and men more gray matter correlated to intellectual skill. Although there may be other explanations, it has been suggested that such differences may help to explain why men tend to be better in tasks requiring local processing and enhanced systemizing (e.g., mathematics), whereas women tend to excel at integrating and assimilating information as required for empathy and language proficiency. In a study by Haier et al. (2005), 84% of gray matter correlated to intelligence was found in the frontal region in women, as compared to 45% in men. In contrast, 86% of white matter correlated to intelligence was found in the frontal region in women, as compared to 0% in men. The more frontally focussed basis of intelligence processing in women may explain why brain injuries affecting the frontal lobes tend to be more detrimental to cognitive performance in women than in men. (General sources: Haier et al., 2005; Legato, 2005.)

Relationship between brain changes and developmental disabilities

Because the developing human brain is much more vulnerable to toxic insult than the mature brain, this insult affects not only those processes upon which development is dependent but also some processes that are programmed to start later. Research on the role of neurotoxicants as factors in developmental disabilities is growing. In one study by the Environmental Working Group (2005), 285 environmental toxins were found in the blood of newborn babies. Of these, 217 were known neurotoxins. In order to develop properly, the brain must be well-fed and protected from neurotoxicants. Injury to the brain also may markedly affect brain development, or

function, or both. For example, embryonic or fetal exposure to alcohol can result in injury to cells and, in turn, a markedly smaller brain and brain development that is affected in many different ways. Brain injury may result from traumatic injuries to tissue from an external impact to the head, from nontraumatic injuries caused by any change in the supply of blood or oxygen that the brain receives, or from tumours. Injury to the brain can affect function and development. See Chapters 12 and 35 for more information about traumatic brain injury.

Aberrations of development that affect brain morphology, circuitry, or both, and that involve the *serotonergic system* (regions of the brain that release or respond to the neurotransmitter serotonin) may account for morphological changes in the frontal lobes, hippocampus, temporal lobes, amygdala, and cerebellum of children with autism (Whitaker-Azmitia, 2005). A theory has been proposed that autism represents an extreme of the male pattern of brain structure and function (impaired empathizing and enhanced systemizing). It has been proposed that high levels of testosterone present in the amniotic fluid — as the result of genetic or environmental factors or both — strengthen effects of maternal exposure to environmental mercury, which is present, for example, in certain types of fish (Baron-Cohen, Knickmeyer, & Belmonte, 2005; Geier & Geier, 2005).

Neurological aberrations of development may also account for changes in frontal-striatal circuitry and problems in executive functioning in people with attention-deficit/hyperactivity disorder (Willis & Werler, 2005). They may also be responsible for brain changes that are characteristic of schizophrenia, Williams syndrome, fetal alcohol syndrome, and numerous other disorders (NICHCY, n.d; Thompson et al., 2005).

Systems and processes affecting brain development and function

The blood-brain barrier, as well as the HPA axis and stress, affect brain development and function. Each topic is explored next.

Blood-brain barrier: Typical brain function depends on the integrity of the so-called blood-brain barrier (BBB; Francis, van Beek, Canova, Neal, &

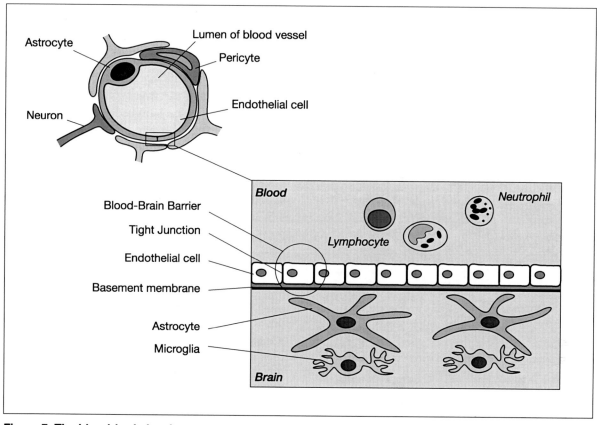

Figure 7. The blood-brain barrier. *(From Francis, K., van Beek, J., Canova, C., et al. (2003, May 23). Innate immunity and brain inflammation: The key role of complement. Expert Reviews in Molecular Medicine, 3. Reprinted with the permission of Cambridge University Press.)*

Gasque, 2003; see Figure 7). The BBB is made of the closely knit sheets of endothelial cells that form the walls of blood vessels in the brain. The BBB separates the brain and surrounding tissues that contain neurons, astrocytes, and microglia from circulating blood; tightly regulates the transport of nutrients and signalling molecules into the brain; and maintains proper biochemical conditions for normal brain function. It normally blocks circulating bacteria and viruses (pathogens) from entering the brain and thus acts as a sentry to defend against infection. If a pathogen gains entry to the endothelial cells, genes are activated that produce protein factors that recruit white blood cells to the brain to fight the infection. Group B streptococcus (Doran, Liu, & Nizet, 2003) and HIV (McArthur, 2004) are two pathogens that manage to gain access to the BBB. The former results in meningitis, which can result

in developmental disability; the latter can lead to dementia and different types of neuropathy. Group B strep is a common resident of the gastrointestinal and vaginal tracts of adults. Although such colonization normally is not a problem, strep B infection is the most common cause of blood infection and meningitis in newborns. Fortunately, most cases of group B strep disease in newborns can be prevented by giving pregnant women known to carry strep B antibiotics during labour. The BBB of fetuses and babies are not fully formed and may explain in part why their brains are so vulnerable to the effects of infection and toxic substances. See Matthews (2001) for more information on the BBB.

Hypothalamic-Pituitary-Adrenal Axis and stress: The HPA axis (see Figure 8) is a communication system between the hypothalamus and pituitary gland, which are in the brain, and the adrenal glands,

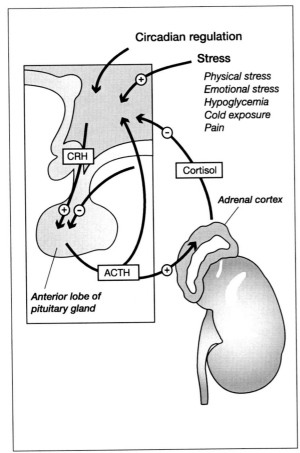

Figure 8. The hypothalamic-pituitary-adrenal axis.
(From Kirk, L.F., Jr., Hash, R.B., Kanner, H.P., et al. (2000). Cushing's disease: clinical manifestations and diagnostic evaluation. American Family Physician, 52(5), 1121. Original artwork@2000 D. Klemm. Reprinted by permission.)

which are located just above the kidneys. Various types of stress (psychological, emotional, and physical — including the tissue injury associated with infection, hypoglycemia, cold exposure, and pain) activate the HPA axis in the CNS and the sympathetic nervous system in the PNS. As explained at the end of this section, there is increasing evidence that abnormal functioning of the HPA axis, resulting from experiencing severe stress prenatally or postnatally, is involved in different types of developmental disabilities, in challenging behaviour, and in mental illnesses (which generally are more prevalent in people with developmental disability), as well as in certain physical illnesses such as cardiovascular

disease. Conversely, there also is evidence that in an appropriate environment, the HPA axis will develop typically or can be normalized (see also the Psychoneuroimmunology section).

It sometimes is said that chronic stress activates the CNS whereas acute stress activates the PNS, but this segregation is too simplistic. The two function in parallel as a double-barrelled neural-endocrine defense system. Activation of the HPA axis may be involved in a complex way with the serotonergic system, which acts functionally as part of the sympathetic nervous system. Proper functioning of the HPA axis plays an important role in development, health, and resistance to stress (see Figure 8). Activation of the HPA axis ultimately results in the release of the hormone *cortisol* from the cortex of the two adrenal glands. Cortisol increases the level of blood sugar and increases the vascular tone, resulting in increased blood pressure. Blood sugar is increased because cortisol promotes the conversion of protein from muscle, glycogen from the liver, and fatty acids from fat tissue into intermediates that get converted into glucose. Cortisol also alters the balance of cells in the blood. It results in lowered numbers of lymphocytes (including T cells), eosinophils, basophils, monocytes, and macrophages but in increased numbers of neutrophils and red blood cells. It also increases the blood hemoglobin level. The paraventricular nucleus of the hypothalamus releases corticotropin-releasing hormone (CRH). In turn, CRH acts on the pituitary gland, which releases adrenocorticotrophic hormone (ACTH). ACTH then causes the adrenal cortex to release cortisol. It is this combined system of CRH-ACTH-cortisol release that is referred to as the *HPA axis*. Positive and negative feedback occurs at various sites in the brain to ensure that cortisol production stays within certain limits, depending on the body's requirements. Excessive cortisol production has a negative effect on the immune system, suppressing the production of *cytokines* (immunoregulatory proteins) such as IL-1, IL-2, IL-6, and TNF-alpha, which are produced by *cells of the immune system* (lymphocytes, macrophages, monocytes, neutrophils in the peripheral circulation and microglia in the CNS).

Appropriate responsiveness of the stress system to

stressors is necessary for a sense of well-being, adequate performance of tasks, and positive social interactions. In contrast, inappropriate responsiveness of the stress system may impair growth and development and may account for a number of endocrine, metabolic, autoimmune, and psychiatric disorders that affect intellect, development, or both. Studies in rodents and nonhuman primates have shown that maternal stress during pregnancy can influence the developing fetus and can result in a delay of motor and cognitive development, impaired adaptation to stressful situations, small birth size, and an increased risk of cardiovascular disease in later life. It is thought that excessive cortisol production in the mother affects the way in which the HPA axis functions in the fetus. Understanding how maternal stress adversely affects fetal development and health outcomes later in life may hold the key to the development of therapeutic interventions aimed at reversing such adverse effects. There also is evidence that stress after birth can alter functioning of the HPA axis. For example, individuals with posttraumatic stress disorder as the result of sexual abuse have enhanced sensitization of the HPA axis (Duval et al., 2004). Furthermore, chronic excess cortisol secretion is believed to damage the hypothalamus and affect the normal sleep–wake cycle. (General sources: Andrews & Matthews, 2004; Buitelaar, Huizink, Mulder, de Medina, & Visser, 2003; Matthews, 2000; Matthews, 2001; Van den Bergh, Mulder, Mennes, & Glover, 2005.)

Future Directions in Brain and Neuroscience Research

As explained in other chapters in this book, millions of people in all countries of the world are affected each year by different types of intellectual and developmental disabilities; impairments of speech, language, and hearing; spinal cord injuries; depressive disorders; and epileptic seizures, as well as by traumatic brain injury, strokes, and neurodegenerative brain diseases such as Alzheimer's disease. Researchers have come a long way in understanding how the brain works and what causes brain and nervous system malfunction and disease. Nonetheless,

many mysteries still remain. New advances are being facilitated by the development of powerful microscopes, molecular genetics, brain imaging devices, animal models for human neurodevelopmental and neurological disorders, and the discovery of biological processes that respond to one's environment and affect brain development and function. These provide hope for future treatments and cures. The next sections highlight developments in four areas that hold promise for providing new insights into typical brain function and the neurodevelopmental or neurological basis of developmental disabilities and related brain disorders.

Measuring brain activity and structure

Three different approaches are providing quantitative information about functions of the brain and which areas are involved in different intellectual, developmental, and related disabilities. One very important approach involves the analysis of brain tissue donated to organizations called "brain banks" (Kretzschmar, 2009; Perl et al., 2000). Many different histochemical, biochemical, molecular biological, and biophysical techniques can be applied to brain tissues collected at autopsy. Computer-assisted analysis of brain images taken with powerful microscopes (image analysis) enables the results to be expressed quantitatively.

The second approach involves the application of different neuroimaging techniques and electrophysiological techniques to study the brain in living persons. One type of neuroimaging technique is a computed tomography (CT) scan, which involves passing a beam of X rays through the head. A computer then reconstructs an image of each slice or brain section, allowing structural abnormalities to be detected. Magnetic resonance imaging (MRI) is a technique that involves the application of a strong magnetic field, pulsed electromagnetic fields, and radiowaves to excite hydrogen nuclei (protons) to produce an image in the region of interest. Functional neuroimaging techniques — including positron emission tomography (PET), single photon emission computed tomography (SPECT), regional cerebral blood flow (rCBF), and functional magnetic resonance imaging (fMRI) — are used to measure brain activity while individuals are engaged in tasks such as reading. PET requires the injection of radioactive materials and involves the acquisition of physiologic images based on the detection of radiation from the emission of positrons. SPECT involves the injection of a radioactive chemical that emits gamma rays. The test differs from a PET scan in that the chemical stays in the blood stream rather than being absorbed by surrounding tissues, thereby limiting the images to areas where blood flows. SPECT scans are cheaper and more readily available than higher resolution PET scans. Similar to a PET scan, rCBF uses an inert radioactive element (usually the gas xenon), which is dissolved in the blood by being inhaled. As the blood flow increases or decreases, the radioactivity serves as a marker of the amount of the blood flow. fMRI is a variant of MRI that relies on the magnetic properties of blood to reveal images of blood flow as it is occurring. Electrophysiological techniques record electrical activity of the brain through electrodes or magnetometers. These techniques include electro-encephalograms (EEGs), magnetoencephalograms (MEGs), event related potentials (ERPs), and averaged evoked potentials (AEPs).

The third approach to providing quantitative information involves quantitative neuropsychological assessments. These assessments include a variety of tests of cognitive/intellectual, language, visual-perceptual, scholastic, motor, sensory, and emotional/behavioural abilities and functions.

The coordinated application of all three approaches is proving to be key in identifying physiological, neurocognitive, and neurobehavioural consequences of single-gene mutations associated with developmental disability (see Ebstein, Israel, Chew, Zhong, & Knafo, 2010). It also is key to identifying the neurobiological basis of cognitive and behavioural differences in males and females, of multifactorial developmental disabilities, and of mental illnesses. As an example, Rett syndrome is a neurodevelopmental disorder that affects mainly girls. It results from a mutation in the methyl-CpG-binding protein (MECP2), which encodes a transcriptional repressor (a protein that suppresses the production of certain RNA molecules). Neuropsychological and neurobehavioural testing has shown that children with Rett syndrome have significant intellectual disability and behaviours frequently associated with autism. The application of PET imaging using radioactive fluorodeoxyglucose has shown that glucose uptake differs in specific regions of the brain of individuals with Rett syndrome compared with those in typically developing individuals, individuals with autism, individuals with Down syndrome, and individuals with Alzheimer's disease (Villemagne et al., 2002). Furthermore, studies of postmortem brain tissue from young adult females with Rett syndrome have revealed abnormalities in the density of excitatory (glutamate) and inhibitory GABA synaptic receptors (Johnston, Blue, & Naidu, 2005). This information thus supports the hypothesis that Rett syndrome is a genetic disorder associated with intellectual disability that affects the uptake of glucose in specific regions of the brain and the development of synapses, especially synapses that use glutamate and GABA as neurotransmitters. (See Chapter 13 for more information about Rett syndrome.) (General sources: Fiedorowicz, 2002; Mathias, 1996; Thompson et al., 2005.)

Neurogenesis and neuroplasticity

For many years it was thought that the formation of new neurons (*neurogenesis*) did not take place in the brain after birth. As well, it had been assumed that beyond childhood, it was not possible for the brain to form new neuronal networks, and that certain functions were hardwired in specific regions of the brain. We now know that this is not the case. New neuron formation has been demonstrated in the dentate gyrus region of the hippocampus and also in the olfactory lobes. Furthermore, it is increasingly recognized that the brain is more flexible and able to change than previously thought, not only in children but also in adults. New therapies and exercises have been able to counter conditions that include strokes, balance disorders, learning disabilities, brain and spinal cord injuries, as well as age-related cognitive decline. (See Arrowsmith Schools, n.d.; Doidge, 2007; Eaton, 2011; Mackowiak, Chocyk, Markowicz-Kula, & Wedzony, 2004; Matthews, 2001; Prickaerts, Koopmans, Blokland, & Scheepens, 2004; Restak, 2001; Vessal & Darian-Smith, 2010 .)

Nurturing positive brain development

Animal studies have shown that environmental restriction or deprivation early in development can induce social, cognitive, affective, and motor deviations similar to those associated with autism. Conversely, rearing animals in larger, more complex environments results in enhanced brain structure and function, including increased brain weight, dendritic branching, neurogenesis, and gene expression, as well as improved learning and memory. On the basis of this information, there is much interest in identifying ways to nurture a child's developing brain. People (especially parents and other caregivers) are key features of an infant's environment; their protection, nurturing behaviour, and stimulation shape early development.

Adults can undertake a number of different activities to help children's brains develop to the fullest potential. These can include giving consistent loving care, physically touching infants, paying attention to hearing and language, looking for teachable moments and using them to advantage, using music to develop math skills, making emotional connections relaxed rather than stressful, and behaving in the ways that parents would like their children to behave (as behaviours of adults are mirrored in children). It is also key to remember that optimum development of the brain and nervous systems requires proper nutrition, avoidance of exposure to environmental toxins, and avoidance of injury. (For more information see Als et al., 2003; Charmandari, Kino, Souvatzoglou, & Chrousos, 2003; DeBord, n.d.; Eisenberg, 1999; Greenspan, 1997; Lewis, 2004; Shore, 1997; Thompson, 2001.)

Psychoneuroimmunology

The discipline of psychoneuroimmunology is the study of interactions between a person's perception of the surrounding world and his or her stress level, behaviour, brain functioning, and *immune system* (which is the body's defense against external infection and aberrant cell division). As of 2011, there is ample evidence that communication exists between the brain, and other body systems including different tissues in the body, the stress response, and the immune system. Extensive communication among these different compartments is maintained by neurotransmitters; hormones; and various other signalling neurochemicals, such as peptides, endorphins, enkephalins, and cytokines. These molecules carry messages from cells in the brain to the immune system and to other tissues in the body and from the immune system and other tissues back to the brain. They generate metabolic responses by binding to receptors in cell membranes. Chronic stress-related interactions between the brain and immune system is now thought to be very relevant to mental health disorders, to the effects of stress on adults' physical health, and to the effects of various stressors on premature babies and babies of low birth weight who are at high risk of developmental disability. The HPA axis (see Figure 8) is one component of this complex communication system. (For more information see Adamson-Macedo, 2004; Cohen, 2006; Fleshner & Laudenslager, 2004.)

Summary

This chapter provides background for a better understanding of the neurodevelopmental basis of the developmental disabilities covered in other chapters of this book. It is hoped that the material also will stimulate the development of new research directions in the field of developmental disability that will benefit from the combined expertise and insights of basic scientists, clinicians, and theoreticians in all relevant disciplines. In addition, this chapter's material should alert readers to their potential as concerned citizens to ensure that their food supplies and environment are conducive to having a healthy brain and nervous systems.

Special Terms

Afferent: Carrying inward to a central organ or section.

Astrocyte: Star shaped, non-neuronal "support" cell in the brain.

Brainstem: The lower extension of the brain where it connects to the spinal cord.

Cerebrospinal fluid: The serum-like fluid that fills

the ventricles of the brain and the cavity of the spinal cord.

Efferent: Directed away from a central organ or section.

Ganglia: A group of nerve cell bodies, usually external to the brain or spinal cord.

Glia: Non-neuronal support cells in the brain (microglia, astrocytes and oligodendrocytes).

Gray matter: Brownish-gray tissue of the brain and spinal cord that contains the nerve cell bodies, dendrites, and some supportive tissues.

Ionotropic receptor: A receptor that opens when a hormone or neurotransmitter binds to it and allows ions to flow through it.

Limbic system: The set of structures in the brain that regulate emotion and autonomic responses.

Meninges: A set of membranes covering the surface of the brain and spinal cord.

Meningitis: Inflammation of the protective membranes (i.e., the meninges) covering the brain or spinal cord.

Metabotropic receptors: Those that are indirectly activated by the action of neurotransmitters or other signals as the result of G-protein activation.

Microglia: A non-neuronal "support" cell of the central nervous system that is phagocytic and functions as a "garbage disposal unit."

Myelin: Material located around the axons of some neurons that is electrically insulating and increased the speed of an electrical impulse.

Neuroplasticity: This term refers to the ability of the brain and nervous system in all species to change structurally and functionally as a result of input from the "environment."

Oligodendrocytes: A non-neuronal cell in the central nervous system that produces myelin.

Post-synaptic: The surface of the cell on the opposite side of the synapse from the synaptic terminal of the stimulating neuron that contains receptor proteins and degradative enzymes for the neurotransmitter.

Reflex arc: The nerve pathway involved in a reflex action. In its simplist form, this consists of a sensory nerve, a motor nerve, and the synapse between them. A reflex is an involuntary response such as a sneeze or a blink or hiccup.

Serotonergic: Related to the neurotransmitter serotonin. The serotonergic system is not just related to the brain and nervous systems, but is widespread throughout the body.

Ventricles: The system of open fluid-filled spaces in the brain: The fluid that fills these spaces is called the cerebrospinal fluid.

White matter: Whitish tissue of the brain and spinal cord that consists mainly of myelinated axons.

For Further Thought and Discussion

1. List five ways in which parents can help their babies' brains develop and function typically. Explain why these approaches lead to good brain health and development.
2. What actions can concerned citizens take to ensure that neurotoxic substances are not a threat to daily living?
3. Why do environmental hazards place babies' brains more at risk than adults' brains?
4. How can the average citizen help researchers to better understand brain function and development?

More Resources

Websites:

Arrowsmith School
http://www.arrowsmithschool.org/index.html

CBC documentary. The brain that changes itself
http://www.cbc.ca/documentaries/ natureofthings/2008/brainchangesitself/

Electronic atlas of the developing human brain
http://www.ncl.ac.uk/ihg/EADHB/atlasbox.html

Institute of Human Genetics, Newcastle, & MRC Human Genetics Unit, Edinburgh. (2009).
Electronic atlas of the developing human brain.
http://www.ncl.ac.uk/ihg/EADHB/atlasbox.html

National Dissemination Center for Children with Disabilities (NICHCY). (n.d.). Understanding how the brain learns.
http://www.nichcy.org/EducateChildren/effective/ Pages/brain101.aspx

Neuroscience For Kids
http://faculty.washington.edu/chudler/introb.html

Secret Life of the Brain

http://www.pbs.org/wnet/brain/about.html

Understanding the brain-The birth of a learning science. (2007).

books.google.ca/books?isbn=9264029125

Books:

Doidge, N. (2007). *The brain that changes itself.* London: Penguin Group, Inc.

Eaton, H. (2011). *Stories of children with learning disabilities and attention disorders who changed their lives by improving their cognitive function.* Vancouver, BC: Glia Press Publishing.

Reztak, R., & Grubin, D. (2001). *The secret life of the brain.* Washington, DC: Joseph Henry Press.

References

Adamson-Macedo, E. N. (2004). Neonatal health psychology [NNHP]: Theories and practice. *Neuro Endocrinology Letters, 25*(Suppl. 1), 9-34.

Allen, J. S., Bruss, J., & Damasio, H. (2005). The aging brain: The cognitive reserve hypothesis and hominid evolution. *American Journal of Human Biology, 17*(6), 673-689.

Als, H., Gilkerson, L., Duffy, F. H., McAnulty, G. B., Buehler, D. M., Vandenberg, K., et al. (2003). A three-center, randomized, controlled trial of individualized developmental care for very low birth weight preterm infants: Medical, neurodevelopmental, parenting, and caregiving effects. *Journal of Developmental and Behavioral Pediatrics, 24,* 399-408.

Andrews, M. H., & Matthews, S. G. (2004). Programming of the hypothalamo-pituitary-adrenal axis: Serotonergic involvement. *Stress, 7,* 15-27.

Arrowsmith School (n.d.). Retrieved from http://www.arrowsmithschool.org/index.html

Baron-Cohen, S., Knickmeyer, R. C., & Belmonte, M. K. (2005). Sex differences in the brain: Implications for explaining autism. *Science, 310*(5749), 819-823.

Bear, M. F., Connors, B. W., & Paradiso, M. A. (2001). *Neuroscience: Exploring the brain* (2nd ed.). Philadelphia: Lippincott Williams & Wilkins.

Bengmark, S. (2006). Impact of nutrition on ageing and disease. *Current Opinion in Clinical Nutrition and Metabolic Care, 9*(1), 2-7.

Buitelaar, J. K., Huizink, A. C., Mulder, E. J., de Medina, P. G., & Visser, G. H. (2003). Prenatal stress and cognitive development and temperament in infants. *Neurobiology of Aging, 24*(Suppl. 1), S53-S60.

Charmandari, E., Kino, T., Souvatzoglou, E., & Chrousos, G. P. (2003). Pediatric stress: Hormonal mediators and human development. *Hormone Research, 59,* 161-179.

Cohen, N. (2006). The uses and abuses of psycho-neuroimmunology: A global overview. *Brain, Behavior and Immunity, 20,* 99-112.

DeBord, K. (1997). *Brain development* [Extension Publication]. Raleigh, NC: North Carolina Cooperative Extension Service.

Doidge, N. (2007). *The brain that changes itself.* London: Penguin Group, Inc.

Doran, K. S., Liu, G. Y., & Nizet, V. (2003). Group B streptococcal beta-hemolysin/cytolysin activates neutrophil signaling pathways in brain endothelium and contributes to development of meningitis. *Journal of Clinical Investigation, 112,* 736-744.

Duval, F., Crocq, M. A., Guillon, M. S., Mokrani, M. C., Monreal, J., Bailey, P., et al. (2004). Increased adrenocorticotropin suppression after dexamethasone administration in sexually abused adolescents with posttraumatic stress disorder. *Annals of the New York Academy of Sciences, 1032,* 273-275.

Eaton, H. (2011). *Stories of children with learning disabilities and attention disorders who changed their lives by improving their cognitive function.* Vancouver, BC: Glia Press Publishing.

Ebstein, R. P., Israel, S., Chew, S. H., Zhong, S., & Knafo, A. (2010). Genetics of human social behavior. *Neuron, 65*(6), 831-844.

Eisenberg, L. (1999). Experience, brain, and behavior: The importance of a head start. *Pediatrics, 103*(5, Pt. 1), 1031-1035.

Environmental Working Group. (2005, July 14). *Body burden: The pollution in newborns.* Retrieved from http://www.ewg.org/reports/bodyburden2

Fiedorowicz, C., Benezra, E., MacDonald, W., McElgunn, Wilson, A., & Kaplan, B. (2002). The neurobiological basis of learning disabilities: An update. *Learning Disabilities: A Multidisciplinary Focus, 11*(2), 61-73.

Fleshner, M., & Laudenslager, M. L. (2004). Psycho-neuroimmunology: Then and now. *Behavioral and Cognitive Neuroscience Reviews, 3*(2), 114–130.

Francis, K., van Beek, J., Canova, C., Neal, J. W., & Gasque, P. (2003, May 23). Innate immunity and brain inflammation: The key role of complement. *Expert Reviews in Molecular Medicine, 5*(15), 1-19.

Gazzaniga, M. S. (2005). Forty-five years of split-brain research and still going strong. *Nature Reviews. Neuroscience, 6*(8), 53-59.

Geier, M. R., & Geier, D. A. (2005). The potential importance of steroids in the treatment of autistic spectrum disorders and other disorders involving mercury toxicity. *Medical Hypotheses, 64*(5), 946-954.

Grady, C. L., & Craik, F. I. (2000). Changes in memory processing with age. *Current Opinion in Neurobiology, 10*(2), 224-231.

Gray, H. (1918). The spinal cord or medulla spinalis. In *Anatomy of the human body.* Retrieved from http://www.bartleby.com/107/185.html

Greenspan, S. (1997). *Growth of the mind.* New York: Addison Wesley.

Grundy, D., & Schemann, M. (2005). Enteric nervous system. *Current Opinion in Gastroenterology, 21*, 176-182.

Haier, R. J., Jung, R. E., Yeo, R. A., Head, K., & Alkire, M. T. (2005). The neuroanatomy of general intelligence: Sex matters. *Neuroimage, 25*(1), 320-327.

Hess, T. M. (2005). Memory and aging in context. *Psychology Bulletin, 131*(3), 383-406.

Institute of Human Genetics, Newcastle, & MRC Human Genetics Unit, Edinburgh. (2009). *Electronic atlas of the developing human brain.* Retrieved from http://www.ncl.ac.uk/ihg/EADHB/atlasbox.html

Ito, M. (2004). 'Nurturing the brain' as an emerging research field involving child neurology. *Brain & Development, 26*, 429-433.

Johnston, M. V., Blue, M. E., & Naidu, S. (2005). Rett syndrome and neuronal development. *Journal of Child Neurology, 20*(9), 759-763.

Kirk, L. F. Jr., Hash, R. B., Katner, H. P., & Jones, T. (2000). Cushing's disease: Clinical manifestations and diagnostic evaluation. *American Family Physician, 62*(5), 1119-1127, 1133-1134.

Kretzschmar, H. (2009). Brain banking: Opportunities, challenges and meaning for the future. *Nature Reviews Neuroscience, 10*, 70-78, doi:10.1038/nrn2535

Legato, M. J. (2005). Men, women, and brains: What's hardwired, what's learned, and what's controversial. *Gender Medicine, 2*(2), 59-61.

Lewis, M. H. (2004). Environmental complexity and central nervous system development and function. *Mental Retardation and Developmental Disabilities Research Reviews, 10*, 91-95.

Mackowiak, M., Chocyk, A., Markowicz-Kula, K., & Wedzony, K. (2004). Neurogenesis in the adult. *Polish Journal of Pharmacology, 56*, 673-687.

Mathias, R. (1996). *The basics of brain imaging.* NIDA Notes, 11(5), Retrieved from http://archives.drugabuse.gov/nida_notes/nnvol11n5/Basics.html

Matthews, G. G. (2001). *Neurobiology: Molecules, cells and systems* (2nd ed.). Cambridge, United Kingdom: Blackwell Science.

Matthews, S. G. (2000). Antenatal glucocorticoids and programming of the developing CNS. *Pediatric Research, 47*, 291-300.

McArthur, J. C. (2004). HIV dementia: An evolving disease. *Journal of Neuroimmunology, 157*, 3-10.

National Dissemination Center for Children with Disabilities (NICHCY). (n.d.). *Understanding how the brain learns.* Retrieved from http://www.nichcy.org/EducateChildren/effective/Pages/brain101.aspx

Organisation for Economic Co-operation and Development (OECD). (n.d.). *Major subdivisions of the cerebral cortex.* Retrieved from http://www.oecd.org/dataoecd/50/25/15355617.gif

Percy, M., Lewkis, S., & Brown, I. (2003). An introduction to genetics and development. In I. Brown & M. Percy (Eds.), In *Developmental disabilities in Ontario* (2nd ed.) (pp. 89-116). Toronto, ON: Ontario Association on Developmental Disabilities.

Perl, D. P., Good, P. F., Bussiere, T., Morrison, J. H., Erwin, J. M., & Hof, P. R. (2000). Practical approaches to stereology in the setting of aging- and disease-related brain banks. *Journal of Chemical Neuroanatomy, 20*(1), 7-19.

Prickaerts, J., Koopmans, G., Blokland, A., & Scheepens, A. (2004). Learning and adult neurogenesis: Survival with or without proliferation? *Neurobiology of Learning and Memory, 81*, 1-11.

Restak, R. M. (1999). *The secret life of the brain.* New York: Canada Press.

Romeo, R. D. (2005). Neuroendocrine and behavioral development during puberty: A tale of two axes. *Vitamins and Hormones, 71*, 1-25.

Ross, H. E., & Young, L. J. (2009). Oxytocin and the neural mechanisms regulating social cognition and affiliative behavior. *Frontiers in Neuroendocrinology, 30*(4), 534-547.

Shore, R. (1997). *Rethinking the brain: New insights into early development.* New York: Families and Work Institute.

Sisk, C. L., & Foster, D. L. (2004). The neural basis of puberty and adolescence. *Nature Neuroscience, 7*(10), 1040-1047.

Thompson, R. A. (2001). Development in the first years of life. *Future Child, 11*(1), 20-33.

Thompson, P. M., Sowell, E. R., Gogtay, N., Giedd, J. N., Vidal, C. N., Hayashi, K. M., et al. (2005). Structural MRI and brain development. *International Review of Neurobiology, 67*, 285-323.

Van den Bergh, B. R., Mulder, E. J., Mennes, M., & Glover, V. (2005). Antenatal maternal anxiety and stress and the neurobehavioural development of the fetus and child: Links and possible mechanisms. A review. *Neuroscience and Biobehavioral Reviews, 29*, 237-258.

Vessal, M., & Darian-Smith, C. (2010) Adult neurogenesis occurs in primate sensorimotor cortex following cervical dorsal rhizotomy. *Journal of Neuroscience, 30*(25), 8613-8623.

Villemagne, P. M., Naidu, S., Villemagne, V. L., Yaster, M., Wagner, H. N., Jr., Harris, J. C., et al. (2002). Brain glucose metabolism in Rett Syndrome. *Pediatric Neurology, 27*(2), 117-122.

Whitaker-Azmitia, P. M. (2005). Behavioral and cellular consequences of increasing serotonergic activity during brain development: A role in autism? *International Journal of Developmental Neuroscience, 23*, 75-83.

Willis, W. G., & Weiler, M. D. (2005). Neural substrates of childhood attention-deficit/hyperactivity disorder: Electroencephalographic and magnetic resonance imaging evidence. *Developmental Neuropsychology, 27*, 135-182.

12

Factors that Cause or Contribute to Developmental Disabilities

Maire Percy and Ivan Brown

What you will learn:

- The importance of understanding factors that cause or contribute to developmental disabilities
- Classification of factors causing or contributing to developmental disabilities
- Genetic and environmental factors causing or contributing to developmental disabilities
- Mental health disorders and their relation to developmental disabilities
- Implications of epigenetic changes for people with developmental disabilities

The purpose of this chapter is to draw awareness to the complexity of genetic and environmental factors that cause or contribute to developmental disabilities. Although an understanding of this topic necessitates looking at the biology of disability, a much broader multidisciplinary perspective is required for the issues of quality of life, prevention, helpful interventions, reduction in occurrence, or even cures, to be addressed in the most effective ways.

Importance of Understanding Factors that Cause or Contribute to Developmental Disability

Everyone who works with children who have developmental delay knows that the child's condition can cause some parents anxiety. Right from the beginning, most parents want to know all they can

about the condition. What specifically caused the problem? What can be done to enable the child to have the best possible quality of life and to develop to his or her potential? Can the problem be prevented in the future?

There are several important reasons for understanding what causes or contributes to developmental disability:

1. *Some developmental disabilities that result from certain genetic or hormone disorders can actually be prevented.* For example, intellectual impairment resulting from certain genetic disorders called inborn errors of metabolism (e.g., phenylketonuria or PKU) can be prevented in large part by early dietary intervention, drugs, or stem cell therapy. Intellectual impairment resulting from congenital hypothyroidism, a common hormone disorder, can largely be prevented by treatment as soon as possible after birth.

Table 1: Fetal Vulnerability at Different Stages of Development

Developmental Stage[1]	Developmental Features	Possible Outcome
Fertilization	*Restoration of diploid number* *Establishment of sex* *Triggering of first cleavage division*	
1st week	*Embryo is transported from site of fertilization to site of implantation in the uterus; formation of blastula*	*50-70% of pregnancies end in spontaneous abortions within the first two weeks due to:* *· chromosomal abnormalities, which result in 60% of miscarriages* *· implantation failure* *· maternal immune response* *· physical teratogens such as heat, X-rays, ionizing radiation*
2nd Week	*Embryo implants into lining of uterus; amniotic cavity and primitive yolk sac formed*	
3rd–8th Week	*Organogenesis – beginning of the development of body form*	*Chemical teratogens and metabolic upsets may produce major malformations*
Second trimester	*Multiplication of neurons*	
Third trimester to 18 or 24 months after birth	*Brain growth spurt – glial cell multiplication, dendritic arborization, synaptogenesis, and myelination*	*Brain very vulnerable to malnutrition, endogenous and environmental poisons and hormonal imbalances; in utero effects of teratogens may include minor malformations and neurobehavioral and/or neurocognitive function issues*

1. *Pregnancy is measured from the start of a woman's last menstrual period. It usually lasts 40 weeks or about 9 calendar months. The first trimester lasts from 0 to 13 weeks, the second from 14 to 27 weeks, and the third from 28 to 40 weeks.*

Sources: *Dionne Laslo-Baker, personal communication; Percy (2007).*

2. *If the cause of a disability is inherited (e.g., fragile X syndrome), families have a right to know this information and to be able to plan their families in the most informed way.* Families may choose not to have children, to adopt, to therapeutically abort an affected fetus, or to have an unaffected child through assisted reproductive technology.

3. *Some developmental disabilities that result from certain environmental hazards can be prevented.* Such disorders include brain injury from avoidable car accidents incurred as the result of drunk driving; avoidable falls; child battering; maternal alcohol use during pregnancy; maternal smoking during pregnancy; folic acid deficiency; hypothyroidism resulting from iodine deficiency in the soil; and various other malnutrition challenges.

4. *In the absence of preventive measures, various*

approaches can help individuals with particular disabilities to develop to their maximum potential. One example is intensive early behavioural intervention for severe autism. Some, though not all, children who take part in this intervention experience less disruptive or obvious symptoms and can be included in regular education classrooms (Chapter 16). Another example is medical intervention to improve concentration in attention-deficit/hyperactivity disorder (Chapter 35). See Chapters 13 and 22 for a range of interventions that can benefit all aspects of quality of life for people with developmental disability. Families — often highly motivated to find information, supports, and services — can both teach and learn from professionals.

5. *Knowledge about causes of developmental disabilities will lead to the development of better interventions and treatments or, in some cases, prevention, or even cures.* This objective must be based on clear and complete information about the disability, gathered from a broad range of disciplines and perspectives. For example, there is evidence that from a public health perspective children born to mothers with a low level of education benefit from early intervention and prevention efforts (Chapman, Scott, & Stanton-Chapman, 2008).

Etiology

This section describes what etiology means, explains why the prenatal period is particularly critical to etiology, and identifies level of disability as a factor in our ability to determine etiology.

What etiology means

The term *etiology* is derived from the Greek word meaning "the study of cause." In this chapter, the term refers to the study of factors that cause or contribute to the occurrence of different types of developmental disability. Many such factors have been identified, but in 30% -50% of cases, the cause remains unknown (Curry et al., 1997; Percy, 2007). A full understanding of etiology requires knowing not only what factors are involved, but also when

such factors have an effect upon the developing embryo, fetus, or child; their severity; and the duration of time over which they act. Etiology is also an important start in the process of understanding what interventions might help children develop to the best of their potential.

Prenatal vulnerability and etiology

The developing fetus is very susceptible to specific causes and contributing factors at certain developmental stages. Substances and agents that induce the production of physical deformities in the fetus, including the central nervous system, are called teratogens (Chapter 10). Table 1 shows the vulnerability of the fetus to different factors causing developmental disabilities.

Etiology and level of disability

Etiological factors have been easier to identify in people with severe disabilities than in people with milder levels. In a survey conducted by Bodensteiner and Schaefer (1995), a primary cause was identified in 85% of those with a severe disability. Genetic abnormalities were found in 30%; injury from teratogens and pre-, peri-, and post-natal injuries in 15-29%; central nervous system abnormalities and malformations in 10-25%; identifiable multiple congenital anomalies in 4-5%; and endocrine and metabolic causes in 3-5%. In Arvio & Silanpaa's (2003) study of a Finnish population, a primary cause was found in an even higher percentage of people with severe developmental disability.

General Classification System of Etiological Factors

Factors that cause or contribute to developmental disabilities may broadly be classified as being general or specific. Within each of these two classifications, causal and contributing factors may be genetic or environmental. Table 2 outlines this general classification system of factors.

The causes of developmental disabilities are still unknown for up to half of people diagnosed. Nevertheless, it is helpful to know the relative importance of each of the four main etiological factors of

Table 2: General Classification of Factors that Cause or Contribute to Developmental Disabilities

Etiological Classification	More General Causes	Specific Causes
Genetic	*Common variants (alleles) of one or more genes that affect the clinical expression of a disability*	*Chromosome (or part of chromosome) or single gene aberrations that cause a particular type of disability.*
Environmental	*Adverse environmental and social circumstances.* *Poor educational experiences.* *Adverse maternal behaviours.* *(e.g. smoking, substance abuse)* *Complications of prematurity.*	*Particular physical hazards or chemical teratogens that result in disability before, during, or after birth, including malnutrition.*

Source: Percy (2007).

this classification system. Table 3 shows the percentages of people with developmental disabilities caused by each of the four etiological factors (U.S. data).

Although the classification system in Tables 2 and 3 suggests that developmental disabilities can be neatly placed into one of four quadrants, this is not necessarily the case. The nature and degree of developmental disability in individuals may, at times, be the result of both genetic and environmental causes. For example, Prader-Willi syndrome is a disorder with a genetic cause; however, if a person with Prader-Willi syndrome lives in an environment that does not promote good physical, social, or emotional development, environmental causes may exacerbate the disability. This is because, as we are beginning to understand, "gene expression can be mediated by circumstances" (Motluk, 2011, p. 26). Thus, there is "grey area" and overlap, but the four quadrants of the general classification system in Table 2 represent a clear way to think about something as complex as the many causes and contributing factors of developmental disability.

General genetic factors

Chromosomal aberration (deviation from the expected or "normal") or a genetic mutation can result in the expression of a disability that varies slightly or considerably from one person to another. The reason for this variation in expression, in part, is thought to result from effects of genes that do not cause the disability per se. Genes that have such effects are sometimes referred to as *general genetic factors* or *background genes*. Consider, for example, Down syndrome which is usually caused by having three copies of chromosome 21 instead of two (Chapter14). Some but not all people with Down syndrome are born with congenital heart defects. To explain such variation we would have said, until recently, that heart abnormalities resulted, in part, from general genetic factors. But sometimes — as is the case here with Down syndrome and heart defects — the specific causal gene just has not been identified. As of 2011, we have evidence that variants of folate pathway genes contribute to the risk of congenital heart defects among people with Down syndrome (Locke et al., 2010). (Folate is a B vitamin; folate deficiency is a strong risk factor for neural tube defects.) Consider also the disorder of neurofibromatosis type 1 (Chapter 13). This is characterized by wide variation of clinical manifestation, even within a family. Reasons for the extreme variability, even within a family, are not known, but have

Table 3: Relative Importance of Factors Causing Developmental Disabilities, Mild to Severe

Etiological Factor	% of People with Developmental Disability
Unknown	*30–50*
Structural central nervous system *(cause not specified)*	*7–17*
General Genetic*	
General, Environmental	
Cultural-familial intellectual disability	*3–12*
Complications of prematurity	*2–10*
Specific, Genetic	
Aberrant Chromosomes	*4–34*
Known harmful single genes	*3–9*
Recognizable syndromes	*3–7*
Metabolic or endocrine causes	*1–5*
Provisionally uniques syndromes	*1–5*
Specific, Environmental	
Specific physical hazards or teratogens	*5–13*

* No data available. As noted in the text, we are using this term to "explain" unusual variability of clinical expression that occurs in certain disorders (e.g., Down syndrome, neurofibromatosis type 1).

As noted in the text, the relative importance of different factors causing developmental disabilities varies markedly from one country to another. The data depicted above, derived from sources in the U.S., do not capture the devastation resulting from iron deficiency, iodine deficiency, and malnutrition in some countries. Technological advances in genetics and in brain imaging are leading to a reduction in the % of people with an unknown cause of developmental disability and to relative increases in the % with structural CNS abnormalities or with specific genetic causes. Causes of almost all cases of global developmental disability can be determined using neuroimaging, genetic studies, and metabolic testing. Up to half of the causes of mild developmental disability are not known.

Sources: Curry et al. (1997); Percy (2007).

Table 4: The Most Common Specific Genetic Developmental Disabilities

Diagnosis	Type of Disorder	Genetic Basis	Incedence/ 1000 live births
Down syndrome	*Chromosomal*	*Extra chromosome 21*	*1.3*
*Fragile X syndrome	*Single gene (FMR-1 is involved most commonly)*	*Triplet repeat disorder, X-linked*	*0.6 (males) 0.4 (females)*
Turner syndrome	*Chromosomal*	*Missing X or part of an X in females*	*0.2-0.4*
Trisomy 18	*Chromosomal*	*Extra chromosome 18*	*0.3*
Duchenne muscular dystrophy	*Single gene (Dystrophin)*	*X-linked recessive*	*0.15*
Trisomy 13	*Chromosomal*	*Extra chromosome 13*	*0.125*
Tuberous sclerosis	*Single gene (Tuberin)*	*Autosomal dominant*	*0.1*
Klinefelter syndrome	*Chromosomal*	*Extra X in males*	*0.1*
Phenylketonuria	*Single gene (Phenylalanine hydroxylase, & cofactors involved in phenylalanine metabolism)*	*Autosomal recessive*	*0.067*

been attributed, in part, to general genetic factors or background genes.

General environmental factors

There are a number of *general environmental factors* that cause or contribute to developmental disabilities in ways that are not precisely understood. These result from a wide variety of adverse biological, social, and learning circumstances that have not been specifically identified. Biological factors include the general effects on our bodies of such things as toxins (chemicals), other pollutants, stress, substance abuse, disease, and poor nutrition. There are many more examples. Social factors arise from poor community and family interaction such as lack of child stimulation and adult responsiveness, abuse, poor moral and emotional development, little or stressful social interaction, and lack of self-esteem and hope for the future. Educational factors include not having access to adequate learning opportunities or not being able to benefit from available learning opportunities, especially early in life, and these can have serious and long-lasting effects on the cognitive and other functioning of individuals. As mentioned in Chapter 1, we live today in a complex world where lifelong learning is increasingly necessary to adapt to changing environments, and disability is increased if ongoing learning cannot occur.

Diagnosis	Type of Disorder	Genetic Basis	Incedence/ 1000 live births
Cri du chat syndrome	*Chromosomal deletion*	*Small deletion on chr. 5*	*0.05*
Williams syndrome	*Chromosomal deletion (Elastin is one gene involved)*	*Small deletion on chr. 7*	*0.02-0.05*
Galactosemia	*Single gene (GALT, GALK, or epimerase)*	*Autosomal recessive*	*0.017*
Hunter syndrome	*Single gene (Lysosomal hydroxylase)*	*X-linked*	*0.015-0.03*
Lesch-Nyhan	*Single gene (HPRT)*	*X-linked recessive*	*0.003-0.1*
*Prader-Willi syndrome	*Genomic imprinting defect (SNRPN)*	*Chromosome 15*	*0.01-0.1*
*Angelman syndrome	*Genomic imprinting defect (UBE3A)*	*Chromosome 15*	*unknown*

As explained in the text of this chapter, the prevalences of intellectual disability resulting from fetal alcohol spectrum disorder, autistic spectrum disorders, iron and iodine deficiencies, and malnutrition are far more common than for specific genetic disabilities.

*, disorders associated with aberrant epigenetic processes. Other examples of developmental disabilities characterized by abnormal epigenetic processes are: Rett syndrome, Rubinstein-Taybi syndrome, Coffin Lowry syndrome, and alpha thalassaemia/mental retardation X-linked syndrome (Bell & Spector, 2011). See Future Directions in the text for additional information

Sources: Chapter 13; Percy (2007).

More specific to disability, early intensive behavioural intervention (IBI) for people with autism spectrum disorder (Chapter 16) can be a very helpful learning intervention, and lack of access to it at a critical period of development in early childhood appears to have permanent negative effects on cognitive and social development.

Many general environmental factors often occur at the same time, partly because they contribute to one another. When they occur together or in greater numbers, the risk for contributing to disability is probably greater. An example of this comes from studies of low socioeconomic status (SES), which leads to the presence of many other risk factors. In

one study, poor SES of parents resulted in children's poorer health and a reduced capacity to benefit from the economic and social advances experienced by the rest of society (Najman et al., 2004). Many studies have examined the effects of low family income, parental (particularly maternal) education, and occupational status. Others have looked at lack of access to medical care, healthy food, physical activities, and so forth. There appears to be a strong relationship between low SES, and the presence of mild intellectual impairment, especially among those who have multiple risk factors (Murphy, Boyle, Schendel, Decouflé, & Yeargin-Allsopp, 1998), although this relationship is not clearly understood (Stromme &

Magnus, 2000). However, because it does exist, it seems that the effects of low SES may be transmitted from one generation to another.

It should be noted that not all disabilities are affected by SES. Down syndrome, for example, occurs evenly across all socioeconomic groups. For reasons that are not understood, studies of severe disability and autism have found some inverse relationship with SES (Durkin et al., 2010; Stromme & Magnus, 2000).

Although not mentioned above among the biological factors, parental age may be considered to be a general environmental factor. For example, it is well known that the risk for Down syndrome increases with the age of the mother. Beyond this, one study found that advanced paternal age was associated with an increased risk of autism, schizophrenia, bipolar disorder, dyslexia, lower intelligence, and subtle impairments on tests of neurocognitive ability (Saha et al., 2009). Ethnic background is another biological factor that can affect the severity or prevalence of some developmental disabilities. Reasons for this are complex and not clearly understood, but relate at least to culture, lifestyle, environments, and genetics inheritance. One example is that vegetarian diets of certain ethic groups are often iron deficient. Iron deficiency during pregnancy can result in serious anemia in a newborn and lead to cognitive problems. Below we provide examples of correlations between specific ethnic backgrounds and specific developmental disabilities resulting from specific genetic factors.

Specific genetic factors

The term specific genetic factors refers to abnormalities of genes or chromosomes that have significant effects on cellular function and actually cause particular developmental disabilities. This term includes alterations in the usual number of chromosomes that cause a disability such as Down syndrome or Klinefelter syndrome (for more examples, see Chapter 13). Table 4 lists the most common, specific genetic causes of developmental disabilities and their approximate prevalences. As of 2004, approximately 7,500 different genetic disorders were known. Of these, about 1,200 were associated with

cognitive disability (Moser, 2004). As of 2011, the number of genetic disorders identified has risen to approximately 20,000. Genetic factors that result in syndromes (sets of characteristics that occur together) may have consequences that are behavioural, physical, or a combination thereof (Chapter 13). Within given syndromes, there may be considerable variability of expression of the disorder. This is because a syndrome is not always caused by exactly the same type of genetic abnormality. As well, people have different background genes, they are exposed to different environmental effects, and genetic abnormalities sometimes are expressed differently in males and females.

In this section, specific genetic factors are discussed under two topics: specific genetic factors that cause developmental disabilities, and conditions caused by specific genetic disabilities. It also discusses some factors that affect the prevalence of specific genetic disabilities.

Specific genetic factors that cause developmental disabilities: Genetic disabilities may be inherited or arise spontaneously through the occurrence of new mutations in genes (i.e., sporadically). Disabilities arising sporadically from new mutations are far more common than inherited ones. Males contribute more mutations than females to their offspring because their sperm are formed from cells that have gone through many more cell divisions than the oocytes (eggs) of females. See Chapter 10 for information about ways in which genetic disabilities can be inherited or acquired. In some cases, it matters whether the mutation comes from the mother or father; if this is the case, the genes involved are said to be imprinted (Chapters 9 & 10). Imprinted genes likely have evolved over time in mammals to fine-tune the growth of the fetus. Imprinted genes inherited from the father tend to enhance growth, whereas imprinted genes inherited from the mother appear to suppress growth (Butler, 2002; Franklin & Mansuy, 2011). The prevalence of developmental disability is higher in males than in females. This is likely because there are many genes affecting cognitive function on the X-chromosome. Because females have two X chromosomes and males have only one (Chapter 10), they tend to be protected against effects of deleterious X-linked mutations.

Conditions caused by specific genetic disabilities: This section briefly describes several of the most common genetic forms of developmental disabilities that are presented in Table 4. See also Chapter 13 and other chapters in this book.

Down syndrome is the most common developmental disability resulting from an aberration of chromosome number (Chapter 14). It is usually caused by the presence of an additional chromosome 21 and is referred to as *trisomy 21* (i.e., having 3 copies of chromosome 21 instead of the usual 2 copies). Most cases are not inherited and occur spontaneously without a family history. The birth incidence of Down syndrome increases markedly after a maternal age of 35. Trisomy 18, or Edwards syndrome, and trisomy 13, or Patau's syndrome, are other common autosomal trisomies. Many babies with the latter two syndromes are stillborn or die in the perinatal period. Fragile X syndrome is the most common inherited developmental disability (Chapter 18). (Down syndrome occurs more frequently, but is not usually inherited.) Fragile X is caused by inherited mutations that result in the absence of a protein called FMR1. It is an extraordinary disability, because it is caused by unstable mutations in a single gene that tend to become larger and larger when they are passed on by females. Many people carry fragile X mutations but are unaware that this is the case (Chapter 18). Numerous other disabilities associated with neurodegeneration now are known to be caused by similar unstable mutations (Chapter 10).

Inherited genetic metabolic disorders include PKU, galactosemia, Hunter syndrome, and Lesch-Nyhan syndrome; these are caused by defects in single genes regulating the metabolism of an amino acid, a sugar, a *mucopolysaccharide* (complex carbohydrate), and a *purine nucleotide* (DNA building block), respectively. Abnormalities in the number of sex chromosomes (Turner syndrome and Klinefelter syndrome) tend to result in mild disabilities and physical anomalies.

Two genomic imprinting disorders, Prader-Willi and Angelman syndromes, are very different disabilities caused by small deletions in exactly the same region of chromosome 15, or by duplication of one chromosome 15 and loss of the other. Prader-Willi syndrome is often caused by deletions in the paternal chromosome 15 or by duplication of the maternal chromosome 15. Angelman syndrome is often caused by deletions in the maternal chromosome 15 or by duplication of the paternal chromosome 15. Not shown in Table 4 is congenital hypothyroidism that does not result from iodine deficiency and is primarily genetic in origin; this affects approximately 1 in 4,000 newborns in North America. (See Chapter 13 for more information about these syndromes and conditions).

Some factors that affect the prevalence of specific genetic disabilities: Ethnic origin may influence the chances of a child being affected by, or being a carrier of, a genetic disability. For example, there is a high frequency of Tay-Sachs disease (a fatal genetic disorder in which harmful quantities of a fatty substance called a ganglioside GM2 accumulate in the nerve cells of the brain) among *Ashkenazic* (central, northern or eastern European) Jews but not among *Sephardic* (Spanish, Porguguese, or Middle Eastern) Jews (Charrow et al., 2004), whereas PKU is mostly found in Caucasians and is rare in people of (or descended from) African or Asian ethnic groups (Chapter 13). Fragile X syndrome is reported to be particularly common in Finland and in Québec (Chapter 18). Disorders that have a high prevalence in certain ethnic groups, regardless of where they live now, result from probable common ancestry, which explains why there are many more people in these groups who carry a gene for the disorder than in the general population.

Survival advantage is a consequence of traits for some genetic disabilities. In some, recessive mutant genes that are harmful when present in two copies have some advantage when they are singularly expressed. *Sickle cell anemia* (a condition in which red blood cells that are sickle shaped rather than round) and *beta-thalassemia* (a disorder in which the body cannot make the beta chains of hemoglobin, the red cell protein that carries oxygen and carbon dioxide in the blood) are two recessive genetic disorders that are sometimes associated with developmental disability in which being the carrier of one

Table 5: The Most Common Specific Environmental Causes of Developmental Disabilities

Classification	Contribution to Developmental Disability
Prenatal causes	
Preconceptual and prenatal malnutrition including iodine deficienc	*Suspected of being the major factor, but impact varies from one population to anothery*
Folic acid deficiency	*Neural tube defects are caused in large part by folic acid deficiency*
Maternal behaviors and exposures Alcohol abuse	*Possibly up to 1% of children are affected; impact varies from one population to another*
Perinatal causes	
Asphyxia	*5% of all intellectual impairment*
Intrauterine infections	*3-5% of all intellectual impairment*
Postnatal causes	
Head trauma due to child battering, motor vehicle accidents, and falls	*3-15% of all intellectual impairment 52% of postnatal intellectual impairment*
Near drownings	*4% of postnatal intellectual impairment*
Stroke (mainly from sickle cell anemia)	*7% of postnatal intellectual impairment*
Brain tumors	*1% of postnatal intellectual impairment*
Infections (congenital cytomegalovirus infection affects 40,000 newborns/year in the U.S.)	*33% of postnatal intellectual impairment*

Although the term intellectual disability is used here, data for this table are drawn primarily from U.S.-based studies where the term mental retardation has been used to describe the population See Chapter 13 for more detail about asphyxia, brain injury, stroke, and infections (e.g., meningitis).

Source: Percy (2007).

mutant gene has an advantage. The trait for sickle-cell anemia, found in many people of African origin, is connected with a resistance to malaria; two sickle cell genes result in the expression of anemia and resistance to malaria while a carrier possessing a single sickle cell gene is resistant to malaria and lacks the anemia. The trait of beta-thalassemia, found in people of Mediterranean origin, similarly is connected with a resistance to malaria. Treatment for the anemia in both disorders requires blood transfusions, which leads to iron overload and organ failure if the body iron load is not normalized by treatment with drugs that remove iron from the body.

Specific environmental factors

Numerous specific environmental factors can cause or contribute to developmental disabilities. The main ones are listed in Table 5 according to three stages of fetal/child development: *prenatal* (before birth), *perinatal* (encompassing a certain period of time before and after birth as well as the time during birth), and *postnatal* (after birth). The following sections elaborate on some common environmental causes of developmental disability, some of which are largely preventable.

Malnutrition: This is suspected of being a cause or contributing factor to developmental disability associated with cognitive impairment in a large proportion of affected individuals. Pre-conceptual malnutrition may be the largest culprit (Chapter 38). Although adults are remarkably resistant to effects of malnutrition, the developing fetal brain is very susceptible. Protein-energy undernutrition and deficiencies of certain vitamins (folic acid, B12, vitamin A) and minerals (e.g., iodide and iron) are problems not only in underdeveloped countries but in developed countries, including Canada and the U.S. (Deitchler, Mason, Mathys, Winichagoon, & Tuazon, 2004). As of 2010, one-quarter of the world's population under 5 years of age was found to be underweight (UNICEF Nutrition, 2010). During 2008-2009, 1 in 16 newborns in Canada were found to be underweight (Canadian Institute for Health Information (CIHI), 2010). Underweight is defined as having a birth weight of less than 2500 g (or 5.5 lb). In North America, there are many regional programs to address the challenge of how to prevent low birth weight babies (e.g., the Healthiest Babies Possible (HBP) Program in Toronto, 2007; see also Chapter 38.) Below, we discuss several specific factors that contribute to malnutrition.

1. *Protein-energy undernutrition.* This term refers to a reduced protein intake over an extended period of time (Agarwal, 2011). This eventually leads to depletion of the tissue protein reserve, and lowering of blood protein levels, compromising proper function of nerve, muscle, and intellectual function. The latter may be irreversible if protein deprivation occurs during periods of brain development. Economic, social, and cultural factors (bad feeding habits, superstitions, and belief in information that is incorrect) all contribute to protein malnutrition in many countries. Infants and young children

are very vulnerable. There are two disorders of protein calorie malnutrition — marasmus and kwashiorkor. Which form develops depends upon the relative availability of nonprotein and protein sources of energy. In *marasmus* there is severe deficiency of calories in the diet, including calories from protein. This results in severe growth failure and emaciation. *Kwashiorkor* results from premature abandonment from breast feeding, usually when a second child is born and replaces the first born at the mother's breast. Children with kwashiorkor have an odd reddish orange color of the hair, as well as a characteristic red skin rash. In kwashiorkor, the total calorie intake may be adequate, but there is a deficiency of protein in the diet. Kwashiorkor often is associated with a maize-based diet. (See The Merck Manual at http://www.merckmanuals.com/professional/sec01/ch002/ch002b.html for more information about these types of malnutrition.) Protein calorie malnutrition results in more severe infections than would occur in a state of adequate nutrition.

2. *Folic acid and related deficiencies.* As explained in Chapter 38, *folate* or *folacin* is a water soluble B vitamin that is needed by everyone for our bodies to make new cells. A folic acid deficiency may result from low dietary intake of folic acid (eating the wrong foods) and/or as the result of one's genetic makeup. Folic acid deficiency is a risk factor for neural tube defects such as *spina bifida* (a birth defect in the bony encasement of the spinal cord) and *anencephaly* (a birth defect characterized by missing or a very reduced amount of brain tissue). Pregnant women (especially those who have diabetes, epilepsy, or a family history of neural tube defects), should take a daily folic acid supplement before and during pregnancy to reduce the risk of having a baby with a neural tube defect. The U.S., Canada, and some other countries fortify grain products, such as bread and pasta, with folic acid. For more information about folic acid, see the Office of Dietary Supplements (ODS) website at *http://ods.od.nih.gov/factsheets/Folate-HealthProfessional/*.

3. *Vitamin A deficiency and excess.* Vitamin A (retinol) is a fat soluble vitamin that is found mainly in fish liver oils, liver, egg yolks, butter, and cream. Vitamin A precursors (e.g., carotene) are found in green leafy and yellow vegetables. Vitamin A is crucial for normal nervous system development and is particularly important for proper function of the immune system. Vitamin A deficiency(VAD) is the leading cause of preventable blindness in children and raises the risk of disease and death from severe infections accompanied by diarrhea and measles. In pregnant women, VAD causes night blindness and may increase the risk of maternal mortality. For pregnant women in high risk areas, VAD can occur during the last trimester, when demand by both the unborn child and the mother is highest. VAD may also be associated with elevated mother-to-child transmission of HIV. Secondary VAD results when vitamin A precursors cannot be converted into vitamin A, or with absorption, storage or transport of vitamin A (as in celiac disease or intestinal infections). VAD is a public health problem in 118 countries, especially in Africa and Southern and Eastern Asia. It is common in protein-energy malnutrition.

   More of vitamin A is not necessarily better. Too much is toxic and can result in death. Women of child bearing age need to be very careful. Women who are pregnant should carefully check the amount of vitamin A in their multivitamins and consult with their doctor to make sure the dose is safe. For more information about vitamin A see the ODS website *http://ods.od.nih. gov/factsheets/VitaminA-HealthProfessional/*

4. *Iodine deficiency.* Iodide is a trace mineral used by the thyroid gland to produce the important thyroid hormone called thyroxine. Thyroid dysfunction resulting from iodine deficiency disorder is the single most common cause of preventable developmental disability and brain damage in the world. In North America, iodine deficiency is not usually a problem because salt is usually iodized. Surprisingly, iodine deficiency still is a problem in some developed countries such as Switzerland and Germany. Iodine defi-

ciency in children can cause stunted growth; apathy; difficulty with movement, speech, and hearing; and intellectual impairment. Iodine deficiency in pregnant women causes miscarriages and stillbirths; if the fetus survives, severe maternal iodine deficiency slows fetal growth and brain development. Infants with iodine deficiency are usually given L-thyroxine for a week plus iodide to quickly restore a euthyroid state. Iodide supplementation is then continued.

   More iodide is not necessarily better. Chronic iodine toxicity results when iodide intake is 20 times greater than the daily requirement. Paradoxically, too much iodide can lead to hypothyroidism as can too little. For more information see the Chapter 13 and the ODS website at *http://ods.od.nih.gov/factsheets/Iodine -QuickFacts/*.

5. *Iron deficiency.* Iron, a trace metal that is essential for life, is absorbed in the intestines. It comes in two forms: heme iron (found in meats), which is well absorbed, and nonheme iron (found in leafy vegetables such as spinach), which is not as well absorbed. Most of the iron we consume goes to form *hemoglobin*, the substance that helps red blood cells transport oxygen from the lungs to the rest of the body. The rest of the iron is stored for future needs and mobilized when dietary intake is inadequate. Because iron also plays a key role in helping to prepare the immune system do its job, a deficiency may lead to colds. Low iron levels can also cause fatigue, pallor, and listlessness — hallmarks of anemia.

   In developing countries, 66% of children and women, ages 15-44 years, have this problem. In developed countries, 10-20% of women of childbearing age are anemic (Zlotkin, 2004). Complications of iron deficiency anemia in infants and children include: developmental delays; behaviour disturbances such as decreased motor activity; social interaction and attention to tasks; compulsive eating of non-food items (pica) and ice; and irreversible impairment of learning ability. In adults, iron deficiency anemia can result in a low capacity to perform physically demanding labour. Iron deficiency anemia also contributes to lead poisoning in children by increasing the gastrointestinal tract's ability to absorb heavy metals including lead. Iron deficiency anemia is associated with conditions that may independently affect infant and child development. Iron deficiency during pregnancy contributes to maternal mortality and fetus/infant mortality in the perinatal period. During the first two trimesters of pregnancy, it is associated with increased risk for preterm delivery and for delivering a low birth weight infant.

Iron deficiency can result from poor diet (especially vegetarian), parasitic diseases (especially worm and malaria infections), and abnormal uterine bleeding. Iron therapy in anemic children, can often, but not always, improve behaviour and cognitive performance, lead to normal growth and hinder infections. However, excessive iron can be damaging. Too much supplemental iron in a malnourished child or in people from certain ethnic backgrounds promotes fatal infections since the excess iron is available for pathogen use (Moalem, Weinberg, & Percy, 2003). As well, excessive body iron resulting from excessive iron therapy, repeated blood transfusions, or iron overload resulting from a genetic condition called hemochromatosis is problematic. For more information see the ODS website at *http://ods.od.nih.gov/factsheets/Iron-HealthProfessional/*.

Toxic threats: Toxic threats to a child's environment and development can have adverse outcomes ranging from severe developmental disability to more subtle changes such as problems with attention, memory, learning, social behaviour and I.Q., depending on timing and dose of the toxic threat. Furthermore, infants and children have unique patterns of exposure and special vulnerabilities to pesticides (Landrigan, Kimmel, Correa, & Eskenazi, 2004). Toxic threats include exposures to lead, mercury, polychlorinated biphenyls (PCBs), dioxins, pesticides, ionizing radiation and environmental tobacco smoke, as well as maternal use of alcohol, tobacco, marijuana, and cocaine (see Dufault et al., 2009; Graff, Murphy, Ekvall, & Gagnon, 2006).

Many chemicals produced in large amounts may have some effect on neurodevelopment, but only 12 of among 3,000 have been tested. Other exposures currently suspected of being a threat include maternal consumption of antidepressants and anti-anxiety drugs, and maternal exposure to dental X-rays. By learning about different types of toxic threats and their sources, by taking efforts to avoid them, and by promoting hand washing and good dietary habits, caregivers and parents can play an important role in reducing exposures to toxicants present in consumer products. Many places are undertaking initiatives to reduce sources of toxic threats in the environment. (See More Resources for links to websites providing more information on these topics.)

Maternal metabolic effects: Certain metabolic abnormalities in the mother may have harmful effects on the developing fetus. Such effects are being called "gestational programming" (Chapter 10; Ross & Desai, 2005). Two specific metabolic effects are described below.

Maternal obesity during pregnancy is associated with a greatly increased risk of neural tube defects such as spina bifida and anencephaly (Stothard, Tennant, Bell, & Rankin, 2009). Obesity is becoming a world-wide epidemic. Associated with obesity is the occurrence of Type 2 diabetes, a disorder in which the level of blood sugar is excessively high. Some women have diabetes before they become pregnant. Others develop it during pregnancy, a form called gestational diabetes. About 3% of pregnant women have problems with their blood sugar. It presently is not clear whether it is obesity or high blood sugar that results in the neural tube defects. Babies born to mothers with diabetes tend to be very large. This poses risks to their health and to the mothers who may require delivery by Caesarean section. Further, babies born to diabetic mothers may have cognitive dysfunction and also develop diabetes themselves. It is important that pregnant women control their blood sugar levels.

Abnormal thyroid function in a pregnant mother, in the fetus, or in the newborn all have repercussions on neuropsycho-developmental development. There are three sets of clinical disorders that affect fetal development: those that affect the infant only, those that affect only the maternal thyroid gland, and iodine deficiency which affects maternal and fetal thyroid function. Hypothyroidism in pregnant women is associated with an increased risk of miscarriage, hypertension, pre-eclampsia, abruptio placentae, low birth weight infants, still births, and fetal distress in labour. Children born to mothers with untreated hypothyroidism during pregnancy score lower on I.Q. tests than children of healthy mothers. Thus it is important for pregnant mothers with hypothyroidism to be adequately treated during their pregnancy. Congenital hypothyroidism of the fetus affects approximately 1 in 4,000 newborn babies, resulting in permanent developmental delay and growth defects. In Canada, the U.S., and other developed countries, newborns are screened for hypothyroidism, and are given early thyroid replacement therapy to prevent severe developmental disability. Causes of this disorder can be genetic or environmental (e.g., caused by iodine-deficiency) (Chapter 13).

Infection: Intrauterine and perinatal TORCH infections (Toxoplasmosis, Rubella, Cytomegalovirus (CMV), Herpes and other infections such as syphilis, varicella-zoster, and parvovirus B19) used to cause a larger percentage of developmental disabilities in children (Stegman & Carey, 2002). With the availability of improved vaccines, prevention methods, and early identification, these infections in many instances can now be prevented or treated early enough to prevent damage to the central nervous system of the fetus. The application of antibiotics to cut umbilical cords prevents much newborn infection. Currently, there is an unfortunate resurgence of some vaccine-preventable diseases in North America due to immigration from countries that do not promote vaccination. New challenges also include pediatric HIV, and perinatal bacterial infections with Group B streptococcus, and Listeria monocytogenes. There is also concern that unidentified multiple organisms causing bacterial vaginal infections may be causing intellectual impairment in some children (Murphy et al., 1998).

Preterm delivery and low birth weight: *Preterm delivery* (birth occurring before 36 weeks of gestation) is associated with increased risk for developmental disabilities. The more premature or underweight the newborn, the greater the risks of illness (infection, respiratory distress or other problems); disabilities such as cerebral palsy and learning problems, hearing and vision problems; and death. Factors that predispose to prematurity are multiple births regardless of the cause, placental failure, and excess amniotic fluid. Preterm delivery is known to place the immature brain at risk of hemorrhage and tissue damage resulting from this. Low birth weight also is associated with increased risk for developmental disability, even if a baby is full term. The frequency of preterm and low birth weight babies is increasing in Canada. This may, in part, be related to the use of in vitro fertilization and/or to women having babies at a later age than before (Canadian Institute for Health Information (CIHI), 2007; Percy, 2007).

Premature cutting of the umbilical cord: For over 200 years, there has been an awareness that the umbilical cord should be cut after the baby has drawn its first breath and after the cord stops pulsating. However, since 1980, cords are often clamped as soon as possible after birth or following delivery of the fetal head in order to obtain cord blood samples for diagnosis of asphyxia. Although this practice is saving lives and reducing law suits, evidence is mounting that it is resulting in developmental disabilities later in life (Park et al., 2011). There is increasing recognition that delayed cord clamping should be encouraged. It increases the baby's blood volume, counters anemia, and serves as the first natural stem cell transfer (Tolosa et al., 2011).

Postnatal brain injury: Postnatal brain injury (injury after birth) causes of intellectual impairment are the most identifiable and should be the most preventable. Accidents resulting from drunk driving are the leading cause of brain injury in adults in North America. Brain injury also is incurred in falls, shaken baby syndrome, bicycle accidents, and accidents using guns, riding scooters, and taking part in sports. Leading causes in children include meningitis and child battering (including shaken baby syndrome). Surveillance and intervention activities could prevent many cases of brain injury. See Chapter 35 for more information about brain injury and Chapter 13 for more information about meningitis and shaken baby syndrome.

Mental Health Disorders and Relation with Developmental Disabilities

There is a complex relationship among the causes and contributing factors of developmental disabilities, psychiatric illnesses, and behaviour disturbances (Chapters 35 and 36). Psychiatric illnesses and behaviour disturbances (sometimes called mental ill-health disorders) occur in people in the general population who do not have developmental disabilities; however, for reasons undetermined, certain psychiatric illnesses and behaviour disturbances have been consistently found to affect a much higher proportion of people with developmental disabilities than people in the general population (Chapter 35). Thus environmental or genetic risk factors for developmental disabilities also may be risk factors for mental ill-health disorders. To note is that psychiatric illnesses, difficult behaviours, and mental ill-health disorders are functional classifications and not etiological diagnoses.

Autistic Spectrum Disorders (ASDs)

Although described elsewhere in this volume (Chapters 16 & 17), the ASDs are highlighted here because of concern that their prevalence may be increasing. Recent studies of monozygotic and fraternal twins indicate that both nature and nurture contribute to ASDs. As much as 55% of the risk of autism has been attributed to environment, and 40% to genes. Environmental factors may include multiple births, older fathers, exposure to medications or infection during pregnancy, and mothers' use of antidepressants like Prozac and Zooloft during pregnancy (Gardener, Spiegelman, & Burka, 2011). There is concern that excessive exposures to neurotoxins such as lead, mercury, polychlorinated biphenyls (PCBs), fluoride, cadmium, and aluminum may be ASD risk factors (Blaylock, 2009; Obrenovich, Shamberger, & Lonsdale, 2011; Winneke, 2011). Concern has been raised about potential overloading of babies with aluminum as the result of ambitious vaccination schedules (Tomljenovic & Shaw, 2011). Because adequate amounts of vitamin D are essential for normal brain development, some researchers are asking if vitamin D deficiency is involved in the ASDs. This question was prompted by the finding of high rates of ASDs in immigrants who moved from an equatorial country to two northern latitude locations (Dealberto, 2011; Glaser, 2009). In the absence of proof of causation, preventing excessive exposures to potential risk factors for ASD and ensuring adequate vitamin D intake in pregnant women and babies are advocated.

Importance of Education About Causes of Developmental Disabilities

Information about factors causing or predisposing to disability should be made accessible to the public, professionals, families, and governments. Four important reasons for promoting education about causes of developmental disabilities are:

1. Deficiencies in education at the professional level can have adverse effects on the management of people with developmental disabilities and well being of families. For example, it would be tragic if a family were not informed of the likely cause of a neural tube defect (i.e., folic acid deficiency) so that the risk of recurrence could be reduced in a subsequent pregnancy, or if a newborn were suffering from anemia that was not corrected by administration of an iron supplement. Educating professionals and the public about factors that cause or contribute to specific disabilities increases awareness of intervention options and how to prevent recurrences. Family physicians, in particular, should all receive basic training and clinical experience in developmental disabilities. In turn, professionals should listen to primary caregivers who often are the ones most knowledgeable about the people they look after, about their disabilities, and about the help that they need.

2. There may be complex ethical, legal and social issues associated with a diagnosis that can interfere with obtaining medical or life insurance, or with employment. Professionals and families need to be aware of the consequences. On one hand, finding out the cause of a disability (e.g., fragile X syndrome; Chapter 18) is key for obtaining supports or disability pensions. On the other

hand, finding out that the disability is associated with a characteristic prognosis that benefits from costly intervention (e.g., Hurler syndrome; Chapter 13) may lead to difficulties in obtaining health or life insurance for the individual and/ or their family. Knowledge that having a genetic mutation may result in a debilitating disorder at a later age (e.g., the person is a paternal carrier of fragile X syndrome and at risk of developing Parkinson-like disease at a relatively early age (Chapter 18)), may lead to discrimination in the workplace. Input from people with disabilities and families to policy makers will help establish acceptable guidelines and laws.

3. Policies about services and service delivery may not be realistic, or may not be driven by the needs of individuals. Professionals and families need to be aware of the needs of the persons with the disabilities. One example came from the closing of institutions in Ontario over the past few decades. This was undeniably beneficial for many people, especially for those with mild disabilities. However, there were individuals with severe physical disabilities, with mental ill-health in addition to developmental disability, or with severe behaviour problems, for whom immediate community integration posed more of a challenge. This resulted in the policy being somewhat more difficult to put into practice than first anticipated. Policy makers also need to be familiar with strategies that are working in other places, to ensure that the best possible options for services and methods of service delivery become available.

4. Health professionals are often reluctant to treat people with developmental disabilities because they are not paid adequately to do so. Unfortunately, lack of appropriate intervention can lead to escalating health care and other costs in the future. Policy makers need to be educated about the importance of determining the primary causes of developmental disabilities, and the importance of intervention and prevention in the field. They also need to ensure that health professionals are adequately compensated for this work.

Future Directions

Tremendous strides have been made in the last eight years with respect to the ability and feasibility of detecting abnormalities in DNA in individuals (Chapter 9). A procedure called microarray based comparative genomic hybridization (aCGH) can identify microscopic and submicroscopic chromosomal imbalances (Chapter 9; Thiesen, 2008). It has led to the discovery of many new syndromes and is now being used in the diagnosis of unknown causes of developmental disabilities (Gropman & Batshaw, 2010). However, the causes of more than half of all people with developmental disabilities are still not known.

The recognition that environmental factors also are etiologically involved in developmental disabilities has created awareness of the complexity of the biological mechanisms that result in developmental disabilities. In Chapters 9 and 10, we explained how environment factors and our behaviours can signal cells to turn certain genes on or off by epigenetic mechanisms that control the way DNA is folded. Hence there is increasing interest in investigation of the role of aberrant epigenetic mechanisms in developmental disabilities and also in disorders of mental ill-health like schizophrenia that are more common in developmental disabilities than in the general population. Such interest has been further fuelled by the fact that at least 20 genetic forms of developmental disabilities are now known to be associated with abnormal epigenetic processes (see Table 4 for examples). Studies of these disorders are revealing how important it is for epigenetic processes to be tightly regulated for neurocognitive and neurobehavioural functions to be normal. As well, insights about what aspects of cognitive function and behaviour are genetic and what are not also are coming from comparison studies of identical twins, who are genetic photocopies of each other, with fraternal twins whose genes are different but upbringings are very similar (Bell & Spector, 2011). Because epigenetic processes are potentially reversible and theoretically amenable to manipulation, there is optimism that new forms of pharmacological intervention directed at modification of epigenetic processes may be a fruitful avenue for intervention in developmental disabilities and certain disorders of mental ill-health (Gropman & Batshaw, 2010; Urdinguio, Sanchez-Mut, & Esteller, 2009).

Summary

Over the last decade, there have been amazing advances in technology that are enabling the discovery of more and more genetic causes of developmental disabilities, and also to a better understanding of the ways in which environmental factors are involved. Environmental factors include not only malnutrition and deficiencies of specific nutritional factors (e.g., folic acid, iodine, and possibly vitamin D), but also excessive exposures to heavy metals (e.g., lead, mercury, and aluminum), toxic environmental factors (e.g., PCBs), and socioeconomic factors including parental education level and age. Biomedical information alone is not sufficient to address issues of prevention and reoccurrence, potential complications, and prospective treatment strategies. Hence a multidisplinary perspective is essential. Thus, there is a great need for better communication and cooperation among policy makers, professionals dedicated to the care of individuals with developmental disabilities, the public, and researchers. The information in this chapter provides readers with a background to help them better understand the factors that cause and/or contribute to developmental disabilities and why such information is important.

For Future Thought And Discussion

1. What can be done to target and educate prospective mothers about the dangers of folic acid deficiency, drinking, smoking, preterm birth, low birthweight babies, and other preventable causes of developmental disabilities?
2. What actions might be taken to curb brain injury due to drunk driving, accidental falls, and child battering?
3. What actions might policy makers take to ensure that health professionals are appropriately paid for providing services to people with developmental disabilities?
4. What strategies should be undertaken to create awareness of toxic threats to the health of babies and children?

More Resources

Websites:

The Arc. Causes and Prevention of Intellectual Disabilities
www.thearc.org/page.aspx?pid=2453

AAIDD. Environmental Health Initiative
www.aamr.org/ehi/content_323.cfm?NavID=105

CDC. Centers for Disease Control and Prevention (Environmental Health)
http://www.cdc.gov/Environmental/

CDC. Centers for Disease Control and Prevention. National Center on Birth Defects and Developmental Disabilities
www.cdc.gov/ncbddd/index.html

Environmental Toxins and Disabilities. A Concern Throughout the Life Span
www.aaidd.org/ehi/media Patient_Education_ Handout _v2.pdf

EPA. United States Environmental Protection Agency
www.epa.gov/epahome/children.htm

HSC. Hospital for Sick Children (Aboutkidshealth)
www.aboutkidshealth.ca/En/HealthAZ/Pages/ default.aspx?name=a

ICCIDD. International Council for the Control of Iodine Deficiency Disorders
www.iccidd.org/

ODS. Office of Dietary Supplements, National Institutes of Health
http://ods.od.nih.gov/

OMIM. Online Mendelian Inheritance in Man
www.ncbi.nlm.nih.gov/omim

SickKids Motherisk
www.motherisk.org/women/index.jsp

Thyroid Disease Manager
www.thyroidmanager.org/

WHO. World Health Organization — Nutrition Health Topics
www.who.int/nutrition/topics/en/

X-Linked Mental Retardation Genes Update
Website
http://xlmr.interfree.it/home.htm

Articles:

Mercola, J. (2010). *BPA toxins put newborns, mothers at risk.* Retrieved from http://www.huffingtonpost.com/dr-mercola/bpa-toxins-puts-newborns_b_457590.html

Mercola, J. (2011). *How to avoid the top ten most common toxins.* Retrieved from http://articles.mercola.com/sites/articles/archive/2005/02/19/common-toxins.aspx

Polley, B., Wheeler, K., & Percy, M. (2009). Most pressing environmental hazards affecting children and youth and the connection with intellectual and developmental disability. Results from Canadian high school focus groups. *Journal on Developmental Disabilities, 15*(2), 114-124. Retrieved from http://www.oadd.org/index.php?page=616

Williams, C. (2011). *The environmental causes of intellectual disability.* Retrieved from Understanding Disability and Health website at http://www.intellectualdisability.info/diagnosis/the-environmental-causes-of-intellectual-disabilities

References

Agarwal, C. (2011). Protein-calorie (energy) malnutrition. *PEDIATRIC ONCALL.* Retrieved from http://www.pediatriconcall.com/fordoctor/diseasesandcondition/Diet_diseases/Protein.asp

Arvio, M., & Sillanpaa, M. (2003). Prevalence, aetiology and comorbidity of severe and profound intellectual disability in Finland. *Journal of Intellectual Disabilities Research, 47*(Pt 2), 108-112.

Bell, J. T, & Spector, T. D. (2011). A twin approach to unraveling epigenetics. *Trends in Genetics, 27*(3), 116-125.

Blaylock, R. L. (2009). A possible central mechanism in autism spectrum disorders, part 3: The role of excitotoxin food additives and the synergistic effects of other environmental toxins. *Alternative Therapies in Health and Medicine, 15*(2), 56-60.

Bodensteiner, J. B., & Schaefer G. B. (1995). Evaluation of the patient with idiopathic mental retardation. *Journal of Neuropsychiatry, 7*, 361-370.

Butler, M. G. (2002). Imprinting disorders: Non-Mendelian mechanisms affecting growth. *Journal of Pediatric Endocrinology and Metabolism, 15* (Suppl. 5), 1279-1288.

Canadian Institute for Health Information (CIHI). (2007). *Giving birth in Canada: Regional trends from 2001-2002 to 2005-2006.* Retrieved from http://www.cihi.ca/CIHI-ext-portal/internet/en/Document/health+system+performance/indicators/health/RELEASE_18M

Chapman, D. A, Scott, K. G., & Stanton-Chapman, T. L. (2008). Public health approach to the study of mental retardation. *American Journal of Mental Retardation, 113*(2), 102-116.

Charrow, J. (2004). Ashkenazi Jewish genetic disorders. *Familial Cancer, 3*, 201-206.

Cocco, S., Diaz, G., Stancampiano, R., Diana, A., Carta, M., Curreli, R., Sarais, L., & Fadda, F. (2002). Vitamin A deficiency produces spatial learning and memory impairment in rats. *Neuroscience, 115*, 475-482.

Curry, C. J., Stevenson, R. E., Aughton, D., Byrne, J., Carey, J. C., Cassidy, S., Cunniff, C., Graham J. M. Jr., Jones, M. C., Kaback, M. M., Moeschler, J., Schaefer, G. B., Schwartz, S., Tarleton, J., & Opitz, J. (1997). Evaluation of mental retardation: Recommendations of a Consensus Conference: American College of Medical Genetics. *American Journal of Medical Genetics, 72*, 468-477.

Dealberto, M. J. (2011). Prevalence of autism according to maternal immigrant status and ethnic origin. *Acta Psychiatrica Scandinavica, 123*(5), 339-348.

Deitchler, M., Mason, J., Mathys, E., Winichagoon, P., & Tuazon, M. A. (2004). Lessons from successful micronutrient programs. Part I: program initiation. *Food Nutrition Bulletin, 25*(1), 5-29.

Dufault, R., Schnoll, R., Lukiw, W. J., Leblanc, B., Cornett, C., Patrick, L., Wallinga, D., Gilbert, S. G., & Crider, R. (2009). Mercury exposure, nutritional deficiencies and metabolic disruptions may affect learning in children. *Behavioral and Brain Functions, 5*, 44.

Durkin, M. S., Maenner, M. J., Meaney, F. J., Levy, S. E., DiGuiseppi, C., et al. (2010). Socioeconomic inequality in the prevalence of autism spectrum disorder: Evidence from a U.S. cross-sectional study. *PLoS ONE, 5*(7), e11551.

Franklin, T. B., & Mansuy, I. M. (2011). The involvement of epigenetic defects in mental retardation. *Neurobiology of Learning and Memory, 96*(1), 61-67.

Gardener, H., Spiegelman, D., & Buka, S. L. (2011). Perinatal and neonatal risk factors for autism: A comprehensive meta-analysis. *Pediatrics*, July 11. [Epub ahead of print].

Glaser, G. (April 24, 2009). What if vitamin D deficiency is a cause of autism? *Scientific American.* Retrieved from http://www.scientificamerican.com/article.cfm?id=vitamin-d-and-autism

Graff, J. C., Murphy, L., Ekvall, S., & Gagnon, M. (2006). Toxic chemical exposures and children with intellectual and developmental disabilities. *Pediatric Nursing, 32*(6), 596-603. Retrieved from http://www.medscape.com/viewarticle/552359

Gropman, A. L., & Batshaw, M. L. (2010). Epigenetics, copy number variation, and other molecular mechanisms underlying neurodevelopmental disabilities: New insights and diagnostic approaches. *Journal of Developmental & Behavioral Pediatrics, 31*(7), 582-591.

Hamdan, F. F., Gauthier, J., Araki, Y., Lin, D.-T., Yoshizawa, Y., Higashi, K., et al. (2011). Excess of de novo deleterious mutations in genes associated with glutamatergic systems in nonsyndromic intellectual disability. *The American Journal of Human Genetics, 88* (3), 306.

Healthiest Babies Possible (HBP). (2007). Retrieved from http://www.toronto.ca/health/hbpp/hbpp.htm

Kaufman, L., Ayub, M., & Vincent, J. B. (2010). The genetic basis of non-syndromic intellectual disability: A review. *Journal of Neurodevelopmental Disorders, 2*(4), 182–209.

Landrigan, P. J., Kimmel, C. A., Correa, A., & Eskenazi, B. (2004). Children's health and the environment: Public health issues and challenges for risk assessment. *Environmental Health Perspectives, 112*, 257-265.

Laslo, D. (1999). Embryonic neurodevelopment, neural tube defects, and folic acid. *PSL1062S Seminar, April 23*, University of Toronto.

Locke, A. E., Dooley, K. J., Tinker, S. W., Cheong, S. Y., Feingold, E., Allen, E. G., et al. (2010). Variation in folate pathway genes contributes to risk of congenital heart defects among individuals with Down syndrome. *Genetic Epidemiology, 34*(6), 613-623.

Moalem, S., Weinberg, E. D., & Percy, M. E. (2004). Hemochromatosis and the enigma of misplaced iron: Implications for infectious disease and survival. *Biometals, 17*, 135-139.

Morley, G. M. (2004). Immediate cord clamping: The primary injury. Retrieved from http://www.cordclamping.com/ZICCthe%20PrimeInjury.doc/

Moser, H. W. (2004). Genetic causes of mental retardation. *Annals of the New York Academy of Sciences, 1038*, 44-48.

Motluk, A. (2011). Unlocking our potential. *U of T Magazine, Summer*, 25-29.

Murphy, C. C., Boyle, C., Schendel, D., Decouflé, P., & Yeargin-Allsopp, M. (1998). Epidemiology of mental retardation in children. *Mental Retardation and Developmental Disabilities Research Reviews, 4*, 6-13.

Najman, J. M., Aird, R., Bor, W., O'Callaghan, M., Williams, G. M., & Shuttlewood, G. J. (2004). The generational transmission of socioeconomic inequalities in child cognitive development and emotional health. *Social Science & Medicine, 58*(6), 1147-1158.

Obrenovich, M. E., Shamberger, R. J., & Lonsdale, D. (2011). Altered heavy metals and transketolase found in autistic spectrum disorder. *Biological Trace Element Research*. July 14 [Epub ahead of print].

Oriá, R .B., Patrick, P. D., Oriá, M. E. B., Lorntz, B., Thompson, M. R., Azevedo, O.G. R., et al. (2010). ApoE polymorphisms and diarrheal outcomes in Brazilian shanty town children. *Brazilian Journal of Medical and Biological Research, 43*(3), 249-256.

Percy, M. (2007). Factors that cause or contribute to intellectual and developmental disabilities. In I. Brown & M. Percy (Eds.), *A comprehensive guide to intellectual & developmental disabilities* (pp. 125-148). Baltimore: Paul H. Brookes Publishing Co.

Ross, M. G., & Desai, M. (2005). Gestational programming: Population survival effects of drought and famine during pregnancy. *American Journal of Physiology. Regulatory, Integrative and Comparative Physiology, 288*, R25-R33.

Saha, S., Barnett, A. G., Foldi, C., Burne, T. H., Eyles, D. W., Buka, S. L., et al. (2009). Advanced paternal age is associated with impaired neuro-cognitive outcomes during infancy and childhood. *PLoS Med, 6*(3), e40.

Stegmann, B. J., & Carey, J. C. (2002). TORCH Infections. Toxoplasmosis, Other (syphilis, vari-cella-zoster, parvovirus B19), Rubella, Cytomega-lovirus (CMV), and Herpes infections. *Current Women's Health Reports, 2*, 253-258.

Stothard, K. J., Tennant, P. W., Bell, R., & Rankin, J. (2009). Maternal overweight and obesity and the risk of congenital anomalies: A systematic review and meta-analysis. *JAMA, 301*(6), 636-650.

Stromme, P., & Magnus, P. (2000). Correlations between socioeconomic status, IQ and aetiology in mental retardation: A population-based study of Norwegian children. *Social Psychiatry and Psychiatric Epidemiology, 35*, 12-18.

Thiesen, A. (2008). Microarray-based comparative genomic hybridization (aCGH). *Nature Education, 1*(1). Retrieved from http://www.nature.com/scitable/topicpage/microarray-based-comparative-genomic-hybridization-acgh-45432

Tolosa, J. N., Park, D. H., Eve, D. J., Klasko, S. K., Borlongan, C. V., & Sanberg, P. R. (2010). Mankind's first natural stem cell transplant. *Journal of Cellular and Molecular Medicine, 14*(3), 488-495.

Tomljenovic, L., & Shaw, C. A. (2011). Aluminum vaccine adjuvants: Are they safe? *Current Medicinal Chemistry, 18*(17), 2630-2637.

UNICEF-Nutrition. (2010). Retrieved from http://www.unicef.org/nutrition/

Urdinguio, R. G., Sanchez-Mut, J. V., Esteller, M. (2009). Epigenetic mechanisms in neurological diseases: Genes, syndromes, and therapies. *Lancet Neurology, 8*(11),1056-72.

Williams, L. O., & Decoufle, P. (1999). Is maternal age a risk factor for mental retardation among children? *American Journal of Epidemiology, 149*, 814-823.

Winneke, G. (2011). Developmental aspects of environmental neurotoxicology: Lessons from lead and polychlorinated biphenyls. *Journal of Neurological Sciences,* June 14. Available at http://www.unbound-medicine.com/medline/ebm/record/21679971/full_citation/Developmental_aspects_of_environ-mental_neurotoxicology:_Lessons_from_lead_and_polychlorinated_biphenyls_

Zlotkin, S. (2004). A new approach to control of anemia in "at risk" infants and children around the world. Ryley-Jeffs memorial lecture. *Canadian Journal of Dietetic and Practical Research, 65*, 136-138.

13

Other Syndromes and Disorders Associated with Developmental Disabilities

Miles Thompson and Maire Percy

What you will learn:

- Common syndromes and disorders associated with developmental disabilities that are not presented in detail in other chapters in this text
- Physical and behavioural characteristics, causes, prevalence or incidence, and intervention issues applicable to each syndrome or disorder
- Relevant resources, both specific and general, that will provide more information about the syndromes and disorders described, and others not described, including internet sites, books, and published articles that will promote independent learning

*Note: Words in **bold italics** are explained in the Special Terms section following the Summary.*

The word *syndrome* refers to *a complex of concurrent signs and symptoms that are characteristic of a particular condition or disorder*. Each syndrome has its own cause or causes, and each has distinctive physical, cognitive, and behavioural profiles. Professionals need to be aware of syndrome characteristics in order to make the best treatment and education decisions. In this chapter, the focus is on 32 of the most common syndromes and disorders associated with developmental disability that are not emphasized in other chapters.

Introductory material about each syndrome or disorder is presented in alphabetical order. Summary information for each one is organized in table for-

mat to enable readers to quickly focus on and compare their particular causes and characteristics.

This chapter is intended to promote interest for life-long learning in this area. There are many syndromes and disorders that have not been covered here, and facts about them may be investigated and listed in a similar way to those presented in this chapter. Many other syndromes and disorders will be uncovered and described in coming years. At the end of the chapter, more resources for specific syndromes and a list of general resources are provided.

How people come to have syndromes and disorders

As explained in Chapters 9 and 12, syndromes and disorders may occur for different reasons and result from genetic and/or environmental factors (including toxic exposures, accident, injury and infection). Genetic disorders can occur as the result of genetic inheritance from one or both parents, or occur by accident during the formation of eggs and sperm, or during development as cells divide. In each of the syndromes or conditions described below, how people come to have it are mentioned ¾ if it is known. In this chapter, syndromes and disorders are listed alphabetically. Table 1 lists them by type and identifies those that may have autistic features, microcephaly, or seizures.

Angelman Syndrome

Harry Angelman, an English physician, first described this syndrome in three children who had a stiff and jerky gait, absent speech, excessive laughter, and seizures. It is sometimes called "happy puppet" syndrome because of the inappropriate laughter and puppet-like gait. It is caused by abnormality of chromosome 15 in the same region as in Prader-Willi syndrome, but the two syndromes are clinically distinct. It usually occurs as the result of a new genetic mutation (*de novo)*, but sometimes is inherited in an *autosomal dominant* fashion (only *one* copy of the genetic abnormality from one parent is needed for the disorder to be expressed).

Physical characteristics:
- Malformed (*dysmorphic*) facial features that develop by the age of two years include a wide and smiling mouth, pointed chin, prominent tongue, wide-spaced teeth, large jaw, and deep set eyes.
- Approximately half of all affected individuals have fair-colored hair and skin, and most have blue eyes.
- Head circumference is usually below the 50th percentile; approximately one-fourth of affected individuals have a small head (are *microcephalic*).

Prevalence:
- 1:10,000 to 1:20,000 live births, but the condition is underdiagnosed.

Genotype or cause:
- Mutations or deletions in the maternally inherited UBE3 gene on chromosome 15. UBE3

encodes a protein called E3 ubiquitin ligase. Maternal copies of UBE3 are expressed in most tissues; only the maternal copy is expressed in neurons.
- When E3 is not made, then certain proteins in the brain are not degraded.

Functional and behavioural characteristics:
- Severe to profound developmental delay evident in all cases by 6 to 12 months.
- Children laugh frequently and inappropriately, but are sociable; hand flapping may occur.
- Puppet-like gait (wide-base gait and stiff legs).
- Grabbing and hair pulling is frequently seen.
- Tend to like water.
- Sleep disturbances are common.
- Profound speech impairment and delay occur in 98% of cases, and absent speech in 88%; an ability to comprehend is better than ability to express.
- May have problems with eye focussing as the result of an imbalance in the eye muscles — a condition called alternating or intermittent strabismus; this means that the eye is turned abnormally only some of the time.
- Seizures with characteristic recordings of electrical activity of the brain (*electroencephalograms or EEGs*) occur in approximately 80% of individuals.

Intervention approaches and issues:
- Genetic counselling.
- Seizure management in primary care; trials with more than one anticonvulsant.
- Drug therapy (*pharmacotherapy*) and behaviour management for sleep disturbances.
- Sign language may be required for communication.
- Identification and treatment of behaviour problems.

22q11.2 Deletion Syndrome

This syndrome results from a small deletion (*microdeletion*) on the long arm of chromosome 22. It also is known by several other names: DiGeorge syndrome (DGS), velocardiofacial (Shprintzen) syndrome (VCFS), velofacial hypoplasia (Sedlackova syndrome), conotruncal anomaly face syndrome (CTAF), Caylor cardiofacial syndrome, and autosomal dominant Opitz G/BBB syndrome. In the past, it was also called CATCH 22. The term *velocardiofacial* is derived from the Latin words *velum* meaning palate, *cardia* meaning heart, and **facies** meaning having to do with the face. The disorder usually occurs de novo, but can be inherited in an autosomal dominant fashion.

Physical characteristics:
- Variable dysmorphic features are stable but present at birth. They include palate abnormalities, and velopharyngeal incompetence.
- Characteristic facies: round face, almond-shaped eyes, bulbous nose, posteriorly rotated and malformed large ears.
- 74% have congenital heart defects (conotruncal malformations: tetralogy of Fallot, interrupted aorta, ventricular septal defect, and truncus arteriosus; see Chapter 14).
- Immune deficiency in 77% of individuals.
- Calcium deficiency (hypocalcemia), underactive parathyroid gland (hypoparathyroidism), floppy muscles (**hypotonia**), kidney (**renal**) anomalies; recurrent ear infections, including middle ear infection that may lead to hearing loss (otitis media); growth hormone deficiency (leading to short stature); skeletal abnormalities including curvature of the spine (**scoliosis**); vision problems; autoimmune disorders; and seizures.

Prevalence:
- 1:4,000 to 1:6,395 live births, but condition is underdiagnosed.

Genotype or cause:
- Small deletion on the long arm of chromosome 22, specifically 22q11.2.
- Chance of inheritance is only 10-15% when one parent possesses the deletion.

Functional and behavioural characteristics:
- Wide spectrum of characteristics (**phenotype**).
- Difficulty planning and executing speech that is not the result of muscular disturbance (**apraxia**).
- Developmental delays.
- Learning disabilities, with verbal skills being better preserved than non-verbal skills; pronounced deficit in visual-spatial memory.
- Psychiatric illnesses: schizophrenia in 25%, major depression, bipolar disorder, obsessive-compulsive disorder, and alcoholism are common.

Intervention approaches and issues:
- Genetic counselling: when the disorder is inherited, the parent possessing the deletion often displays mild features and is diagnosed after the child.
- Management of congenital heart disease, immune deficiency and other health risks.

Congenital Hypothyroidism

The failure of normal infant development can result from a deficiency of iodine or, sometimes, other micronutrients. When iodine deficiency is *not* involved, the following problems can occur: the thyroid gland is absent or almost absent (thyroid gland *agenesis*) or development is faulty (thyroid gland *dysgenesis*); production of thyroid hormones (T3 or T4) is defective (T3 and T4 levels are controlled by a hormone produced by the pituitary gland called thyroid stimulating hormone, TSH). Of those with thyroid gland abnormalities, approximately: 40% have under-developed or absent thyroid glands; 40% have ectopic thyroid glands (under the tongue or at the far side of the neck); and 20% have deficient production of thyroid hormones. Thyroid hormone deficiency can result from TSH or T3 and/or T4 deficiencies resulting from an underactive thyroid gland. In rare instances, a normal gland does not make enough thyroid hormone because of insufficient TSH. Congenital hypothyroidism can be transient or permanent. 15-20% of hypothyroid infants require temporary treatment. Some thyroid hormone biosynthesis defects are **autosomal recessive** (one copy of the genetic abnormality is inherited from each parent who normally do not have the disease.)

Physical characteristics:
Features may include:
- Arrested physical growth.
- Puffy face; thick neck due to enlargement of the thyroid gland (**goitre**).
- Dry, swollen skin.

Table 1: Syndromes and Disorders: Associated Features*

Syndrome	Associated Features	Autistic Traits	Microcephaly
Genetic, Autosomal			
Angelman Syndrome	*Puppet-like gait*		Yes
22q11.2 Deletion Syndrome	*Palate abnormalities*		
Congenital Hypothyroidism (when iodine deficiency is not the cause)	*Arrested physical growth*		
Cornelia de Lange Syndrome (some cases are X-linked)	*Long eyelashes; bushy eyebrows that meet*	Yes	
Cri Du Chat Syndrome	*High pitched cry*		Yes
Hurler Syndrome	*Coarse facial features*		
Mabry Syndrome	*Facial seizures, facial dysmorphology, short terminal phalange on each fingers*	Yes	
Neuronal Migration Disorders (some cases are X-linked; others may result from intrauterine infection or insult)	*Cranio-facial abnormalities*		
Neurofibromatosis	*Abnormalities of skin and nerves*		
Noonan Syndrome	*Short stature, facial abnormalities, congenital heart defects*	Yes	
Phenylketonuria	*Fair skin, blue eyes, blond hair; eczema; peculiar odour of urine*	Yes	Yes (mild)
Prader-Willi Syndrome	*Small stature, obesity, small hands and feet*	Yes	
Progressive Myoclonus Epilepsy	*Onset of severe progressive epilepsy after apparently normal development*		

* The features included do not occur in all individuals with the specified disorders, and are not diagnostic. Note how many of the syndromes and disorders are associated with autistic traits, microcephaly, or seizures. See text for detail.

Syndrome	Seizures	Stereotypic Behaviour	Self-Injurious Behaviour	Tooth Defects
Angelman Syndrome	Yes			Wide-spaced teeth
22q11.2 Deletion Syndrome	Yes			
Congenital Hypothyroidism (when iodine deficiency is not the cause)				
Cornelia de Lange Syndrome (some cases are X-linked)				
Cri Du Chat Syndrome		Yes	Yes	
Hurler Syndrome				
Mabry Syndrome	Yes			
Neuronal Migration Disorders (some cases are X-linked; others may result from intrauterine infection or insult)	Yes			
Neurofibromatosis	Yes			
Noonan Syndrome				
Phenylketonuria	Yes	Yes	Yes	
Prader-Willi Syndrome			Yes	
Progressive Myoclonus Epilepsy	Yes			

Table 1: Syndromes and Disorders: Associated Features* *continued*

Syndrome	Associated Features	Autistic Traits	Microcephaly
Genetic, Autosomal *cont'd*			
Sanfillipo Syndrome	*Normal development for first 1-2 years, followed by coarsening of facial features, abnormal growth*	Yes	
Smith-Lemli-Opitz Syndrome	*Craniofacial, limb or skeletal, uro-genital, and internal organ abnor-malities*	Yes	Yes
Smith-Magenis Syndrome	*Unusual behavioural and physical characteristics*	Yes	
Tuberous Sclerosis	*Abnormalities of skin and nerves*	Yes	
Williams Syndrome	*Cardiovascular problems; elfin-like face*		Yes
Genetic, X-linked			
Cornelia de Lange Syndrome	*Long eyelashes; bushy eyebrows that meet*		Yes
Hunter Syndrome	*Coarse facial features*		
Klinefelter Syndrome	*Hypogonadism in males*		
Lesch-Nyhan Syndrome	*Orange-coloured crystals in baby's diaper or urine*		
Neuronal Migration Disorders	*Cranio-facial abnormalities*		
Rett Syndrome	*Regressive form of autism in girls*	Yes	
Turner Syndrome	*Sexual infantilism, short stature, webbed neck, and elbows that are turned in.*		

* *The features included do not occur in all individuals with the specified disorders, and are not diagnostic. Note how many of the syndromes and disorders are associated with autistic traits, microcephaly, or seizures. See text for detail.*

Syndrome	Seizures	Stereotypic Behaviour	Self-Injurious Behaviour	Tooth Defects
Sanfillipo Syndrome				
Smith-Lemli-Opitz Syndrome			Yes	
Smith-Magenis Syndrome		Yes	Yes	
Tuberous Sclerosis	Yes		Yes	Tooth enamel defects
Williams Syndrome				Wide-spaced teeth
Cornelia de Lange Syndrome				
Hunter Syndrome				Wide spaces between erupting teeth
Klinefelter Syndrome				
Lesch-Nyhan Syndrome			Yes	
Neuronal Migration Disorders	Yes			
Rett Syndrome				
Turner Syndrome				

Table 1: Syndromes and Disorders: Associated Features* *continued*

Syndrome	Associated Features	Autistic Traits	Microcephaly
Other			
Congenital Hypothyroidism (from iodine deficiency)	*Arrested physical growth*		
Congenital Rubella (from infection during pregnancy)	*Can result in vision, hearing, and other health problems*	Yes	Yes
Hypoxic-Ischemic Encephalopathy/ Neonatal Encephalopathy	*Suspect when there is a poor Apgar score at birth*		
Intraventricular Hemorrhage	*Suspect when apnea occurs*		
Meningitis	*Symptoms can include high fever, headache, stiff neck, nausea, and vomiting*		
Neuronal Migration Disorders	*Cranio-facial abnormalities*		
Pediatric stroke	*Symptoms can include seizures, lethargy, decreased consciousness in newborns; Acute focal neurological deficits in older children*		
Shaken Baby Syndrome	*Symptoms can include lethargy, vomiting, reduced consciousness, hypothermia*		
Traumatic Brain Injury	*Suspect after a head injury*		
Unknown			
Developmental Coordination Disorder	*Clumsiness*		
Sturge-Weber Syndrome	*Port-wine stain on face*		
Tourette Syndrome	*Multiple tics*		

* *The features included do not occur in all individuals with the specified disorders, and are not diagnostic. Note how many of the syndromes and disorders are associated with autistic traits, microcephaly, or seizures. See text for detail.*

Syndrome	Seizures	Stereotypic Behaviour	Self-Injurious Behaviour	Tooth Defects
Congenital Hypothyroidism (from iodine deficiency)				
Congenital Rubella (from infection during pregnancy)				
Hypoxic-Ischemic Encephalopathy/ Neonatal Encephalopathy	Yes			
Intraventricular Hemorrhage	Yes			
Meningitis	Yes			
Neuronal Migration Disorders	Yes			
Pediatric stroke	Yes			
Shaken Baby Syndrome	Yes			
Traumatic Brain Injury	Yes			
Developmental Coordination Disorder				
Sturge-Weber Syndrome	Yes			
Tourette Syndrome			Yes	

- Large abdomen.
- Protrusion of internal organs through a weakening in the wall of the abdomen near the navel (umbilical **hernia**).
- Yellowish colour of the skin and whites of the eyes (**jaundice**).
- Feeding difficulties.
- Respiratory difficulties aggravated by a large tongue.
- Cold, mottled arms and legs.

Prevalence:
- Iodine deficiency is the leading cause of developmental disabilities worldwide (up to 10% of Chinese are affected by iodine deficiency). Too much iodine can also result in hypothyroidism.
- In iodine replete areas, 1:3,000 to 1:4,000 newborns are affected; more females are affected than males.

Genotype or cause:
- Iodine deficiency.
- When iodine deficiency is not involved, the disorder can result from various mutations that affect the function of the thyroid.

Functional and behavioural characteristics:
- Lower intellectual functioning that develops progressively with age.
- Sluggishness, sleepiness, poor cry.

Intervention approaches and issues:
- Genetic counselling.
- Early detection and treatment impedes progression; newborns should be screened for iodine deficiency and thyroid hormone deficiency.
- Treat for iodine deficiency if relevant; treat for thyroid hormone deficiency if level of TSH is high and levels of thyroid hormones (T4 or T3, or both) are low.

Congenital Rubella Syndrome

Rubella (German measles) infection during the first three months of pregnancy (*first trimester*) results in fetal rubella infection causing the child to be born with developmental disability, and other health problems. In 1941, Normann Gregg, an Australian eye doctor, observed large numbers of persons with white pupils (clouding of the eye lens

as the result of *cataracts*) and other birth defects in children after rubella outbreaks. In 1964 and 1965, there was a world-wide epidemic of rubella. In the U.S. epidemic, approximately 20,000 children were born with two or more of the symptoms listed below, which came to be known as congenital rubella syndrome, or CRS. Almost all cases arise de novo.

Physical characteristics:
- Central nervous system problems: microcephaly and developmental disabilities.
- Hearing impairment; visual impairments: cataracts, increased pressure within the eye (*glaucoma*), or inflammation of the vascular layer of the eye (*choroid coat*) or the light-sensitive layer (*retina*).
- Congenital heart disease.
- Additional medical problems may develop, such as diabetes.

Prevalence:
- A serious problem in unvaccinated areas; 100,000 cases per year world-wide.

Genotype or cause:
- Mother (and fetus) infected with rubella during early pregnancy.

Functional and behavioural characteristics:
- Developmental disabilities.
- In one study of 243 children, 15% had reactive bad behaviour disorder and 7% had autism.

Intervention approaches and issues:
- Primary preventive action is immunization between 9 and 15 months of age; women should avoid pregnancy for at least 28 days after immunization.
- Rubella vaccines consist of either single antigen vaccines or in combination with mumps vaccine or measles and mumps vaccine (MMR).

Cornelia de Lange Syndrome

Cornelia de Lange syndrome (CdLS) is a congenital syndrome that was named after Cornelia de Lange, a Dutch pediatrician who described the syndrome it in two children in 1933. Winfried Brachmann wrote about a similar syndrome in 1916. Most physical and behavioural characteristics are present at or shortly after birth, but not all are required for diagnosis. Another disorder called Mabry syndrome can mask as CdLS. To distinguish between CdLS and Mabry syndromes, the level of the enzyme alkaline phosphatase should be measured in the serum. If this is elevated, then the disorder is Mabry syndrome. The majority of cases of CdLS result from new mutations. Very occasionally, transmission has been observed to be autosomal dominant or *X-linked* dominant. (In X-linked disorders, the genetic mutation is on the X chromosome; in most disorders, females are not as severely affected as males because their normal X chromosome protects them. In CdLS, males and females are affected similarly by the X-linked mutation; in this disorder, the condition thus is said to be X-linked dominant.)

Physical characteristics:
- Facies: thin down-turned lips, low set ears, long eyelashes, bushy eyebrows that meet, drooping upper eyelid (*ptosis*), abnormal separation of eyes (*hypertelorism*).
- Disproportionately flat head (*brachycephaly*).
- Small hands and feet, and webbing or fusing (*syndactylism*) of toes in the feet.
- Reverse flow of stomach contents into the esophagus (*gastroesophageal reflux disease, GERD*); aspiration pneumonia risk.
- Congenital heart defects.
- Hearing deficits.
- Skin often has a marbled (bluish, mottled) appearance on the arms and legs; body hair.

Prevalence:
- 1:10,000 to 1:30,000 live births; affects males and females equally. Is underdiagnosed and tends to be misdiagnosed.

Genotype or cause:
- Most cases result from new mutations.
- Gene mutations on chromosomes 5, 10 and X can result in the disorder. Some mutations affect *cohesion*, a complex that regulates the separation of sister chromatids during cell division.

Functional and behavioural characteristics:
- Delays in cognitive development; communication delays.
- Associated autistic features, seizures, self-injury, hyperactivity, aggression, and sleep disturbances.
- Parents report that their children laugh, are charming, and interact with others.
- Strengths include perceptual organization, visuospatial memory, and fine motor skills.

Intervention approaches and issues:
- Genetic counselling.
- Speech therapy or sign language, or both, may be required.
- Pharmacotherapy and behaviour management may help with sleep disturbances, hyperactivity, and aggression.
- Management of GERD through diet, medication, and elevating the child after eating.
- Surgery allowing feeding through a G-tube (*gastrostomy*) may be required

Cri Du Chat Syndrome

Cri du chat syndrome (also known as 5p-syndrome after the de novo chromosome 5 short (p) arm defect) was first described in 1964 by Dr. Jerome Lejeune. Lejeune was a French geneticist who also discovered the chromosomal abnormality characteristic of Down syndrome. Cri du chat is named after the infantile, high pitched, cat-like cry by which it is characterized.

Physical characteristics:
- Early hypotonia.
- The skin fold from the root of the nose extending to the inner end of the eyebrow (*epicanthic fold*) may be prominent; microcephaly, and low set ears.

Prevalence:
- 1:15,000 to 1:50,000 live births.
- Genotype or cause:
- Deletion of variable size on the short (p) arm of chromosome 5, called a 5p deletion.
- Functional and behavioural characteristics:
- Infantile, high-pitched, cat-like cry.
- Severe motor, language, and developmental delay.
- Repetitive (*stereotypic*) behaviours have been observed and hyperactivity is common.
- Occasional aggressive and self-injurious behavior; more typically friendly demeanour.

- 75% of affected individuals are easily distracted, restless and excessively active.

Intervention approaches and issues:

- Genetic counselling.
- Intensive early intervention to improve speech, motor, and self-help skills.
- Clinicians may consider medication to treat hyperactivity.

Developmental Coordination Disorder (DCD)

Children exhibit poor motor coordination (e.g., tying shoe-laces). DCD was introduced into the DSM III-R (Diagnostic and Statistical Manual of Mental Disorders, Third Edition, Revised) in 1987. DCD was previously known as developmental dyspraxia, sensorimotor dysfunction, perceptual-motor problem, minor neurological dysfunction, minimal brain dysfunction, and "clumsiness."

Physical characteristics:

- Motor coordination below that expected for children of the same age.
- Deficits that interfere with daily activities are not due to other neurological disorders such as cerebral palsy, total paralysis of arm, leg and trunk on one side of the body (*hemiplegia*), or muscular dystrophy.

Prevalence:

- 5-6 % in school-aged children; more frequent in males than females.

Genotype or cause:

- Unknown.
- Atypical brain development or abnormal fatty acid metabolism hypotheses.

Functional and behavioural characteristics:

- Children may have any or all of the following deficits:
- Poor balance and control affects motor tasks (writing, dressing, catching, or kicking a ball).
- Delayed motor development: sitting, crawling, walking.
- Increased reliance on visual information.
- Difficulties with motor imagery, visual memory, and in learning new skills.
- Academic skills, such as writing, reading, spelling, and mathematics, are compromised.
- Decreased social skills, and lack of confidence.

Co-occurring conditions:

- Attention-deficit (ADD), attention-deficit/ hyperactivity disorder (ADHD) in 41% of cases.
- Learning disability, such as difficulty with the brain's ability to translate written messages taken in by the eye into meaningful language (*dyslexia*), occurs in 38% of individuals.

Intervention approaches and issues:

- The intervention must be tailored individually to each child.
- Most interventions do not generalize to other tasks (sensory integration intervention, process oriented treatment, perceptual motor training, and task-specific training).
- Recent cognitive approaches have a problem-solving framework, although this is unvalidated.

Hunter Syndrome/ Mucopolysaccharidosis Type II (Mps II)

Hunter syndrome is a mucopolysaccharidosis (MPS) type II (MPS II) lysosomal storage disorder. It interferes with the body's ability to break down and recycle certain complex carbohydrates, which build up in tissues and organs. It was first described in 1917 by Charles Hunter, a Scottish-Canadian physician. There are two forms of this disorder: a severe, early-onset form, and a mild, late-onset form. The severe form is typically diagnosed at 18 to 36 months. The mild form appears later and is less severe. Typically, there is recessive X-linked inheritance, and consequently, is usually only seen in males, but rare cases in females have been reported. Refer to the sections on Hurler Syndrome and Sanfilippo Syndrome for more information.

Physical characteristics:

- Normal at birth except for noisy breathing and hernias near the navel (umbilical) or groin (inguinal), or both.
- Features develop around age 2 (severe form), and later for the mild form: they include coarse facial features, large head, frontal skull protu-

berance (*frontal bossing*), and enlarged tongue.

- Enlarged cavities of brain through which the cerebrospinal fluid flows (*ventricles*) due to cerebrospinal fluid accumulation (*hydrocephaly*).
- Slowed growth rate; wide spaces between erupting teeth.
- Claw hands and abnormal bone development in the collar area; carpal tunnel syndrome; stiffening of joints.
- Enlargement of liver and spleen (*hepatosplenomegaly*); thickened heart valves.
- Upper airway obstruction due to thickened airways.

Prevalence:

- 1:16,000 to 1:30,000 live births for all MPS disorders (1:65,000 to 1:320,000 for MPS II)
- Increased incidence in Israel; usually only affects males.

Genotype or cause:

- X-linked disorder resulting from different mutations in the iduronate-2-sulphatase (IDS) gene, which results in lack of the enzyme iduronate sulfatase.

Functional or behavioural characteristics:

- The severe, early-onset form of the syndrome is characterized by mental deterioration, sever mental delay, aggressive behaviour, and hyperactivity.
- The mild, late-onset form is characterized by mild to no mental deficiency.
- Susceptibility to ear infections, colds, and meningitis, which can lead to deafness.

Intervention approaches and issues:

- Genetic counselling; no consensus on effective treatments; unusual anesthetic sensitivity.
- Current treatment is primarily supportive: hearing aids, physical therapy, and selected surgical procedures (bone marrow transplantation lessens the effects of MPS disorders). Elaprase (idursulfase) is the first prescription medication approved for treatment.
- In the severe form, death occurs at approximately 10 to 15 years of age from cardiac or respiratory failure; in the mild form, individuals survive.

Hurler/Hurler-Scheie/Scheie Syndrome/Gargoylism/Mps I

Hurler syndrome, also known as mucopolysaccharidosis type I (MPS I), or gargoylism, was named after the German pediatrician who described it in 1919. Hurler-Scheie or Scheie syndrome, refers to less severe forms of the syndrome. All three syndromes are due to a defect in the same enzyme. Hurler syndrome has an autosomal recessive mode of inheritance.

Physical characteristics:

- Facies include coarse facial features, thick coarse hair and eyebrows (*gargoylism*).
- Skeletal abnormalities include dwarfism, forward curvature of the spine (*kyphosis*), a broad hand with short fingers, and stiff joints from abnormal shortening of muscle tissue making them resistant to passive stretching (*contractures*).
- Hepatosplenomegaly.
- Structural abnormalities of the heart.
- Clouding of corneas.
- Umbilical and inguinal hernias.
- Conductive hearing loss in most individuals.

Prevalence:

- 1:16,000 to 1: 30,000 live births for all MPS disorders (1:76,000 to 1:150,000 for MPS I).

Genotype or cause:

- Mutations in the alpha-L-iduronidase gene located on chromosome 4 (4p16.3). These disrupt the function of alpha-L-iduronidase.

Functional and behavioural characteristics:

- Cognitive development is initially normal; progressive learning disorders are evident later.

Co-occurring conditions:

- Severe respiratory tract infections.

Intervention approaches and issues:

- Genetic counselling.
- Supplemental oxygen for breathing difficulties, continuous positive airway pressure (CPAP) machines for interrupted breathing during sleep (*sleep apnea*), tracheotomy for breathing difficulty, physical therapy for joint stiffness, and heart valve replacement.
- Severe MPS I is treated with palliative support,

hematopoetic stem cell transplantation, enzyme replacement therapy.

- Death is common in the second decade (heart failure and severe respiratory tract infections).
- Patients with MPS may have unusual sensitivity to anesthesia.

Hypoxic-Ischemic Encephalopathy/Neonatal Encephalopathy

Hypoxic-Ischemic Encephalopathy (HIE), also known as Neonatal Encephalopathy (NE), is an acquired clinical neurologic syndrome that involves acute brain injury due to severe restriction of oxygen supply (*asphyxia*). It is usually caused by subnormal oxygen concentration (*hypoxia*) and inadequate blood supply (*ischemia*) often resulting in reduced cerebral blood flow. The damage includes neuronal death (*necrosis*) in the region (called the *infarc*t) resulting from a metabolic shift from aerobic to anaerobic. Infants are damaged faster than adults (1 to 2 hours versus 1 to 2 days). HIE accounts for 25% of full term neonatal mortality. In severe HIE, 50% of affected infants die. HIE is the most common cause of disabling conditions such as cerebral palsy, seizures, behavioural problems, learning disability, and intellectual deficits. Rapid identification of HIE is paramount, especially in infants, since the therapeutic window is small. The outcome is not always predictable from the severity of the injury. 80% of cases suffer serious complications.

Physical characteristics:
- The following must be present for diagnosis of HIE in a newborn:
- Low pH (pH <7) of umbilical artery blood.
- An Apgar score of 0 to 3 for more than 5 minutes. (The *Apgar score* is a rating, based on heart rate, skin color, breathing, response to stimulus, and muscle tone; 10 is normal).
- Neurological symptoms such as seizures, coma, and hypotonia.
- Multiple organ involvement (e.g., kidney, lungs, liver, heart).

Prevalence:
- 6:1,000 live births in industrialized countries;

higher in developing countries.
- Affects males and females equally.

Genotype or cause:
- Prolonged partial asphyxia due to disturbances in blood flow to the brain.
- Brief intrapartum events leading to asphyxia such as placental abruption.

Functional or behavioural characteristics:
- Mild HIE
- Muscle tone increases slightly and deep tendon reflexes are brisk.
- Transient behavioural abnormalities (e.g., poor feeding, irritability).
- By 3 to 4 days, central nervous system examination findings are normal.
- Moderately Severe HIE
- Drowsiness (*lethargia*) with significant hypotonia and diminished deep tendon reflexes.
- Grasping, sucking and *Moro reflexes* are sluggish or absent; the Moro reflex normally protects against falling — it includes a "startled" look, the arms move sideways, the palms are up and the thumbs are flexed).
- Occasional periods of temporary breathing stoppage (*apnea*)
- Seizures within first 24 hrs of the hypoxic period; initial well-being but sudden deterioration.
- Severe HIE
- Stupor or coma.
- Irregular breathing — ventilatory support may be needed.
- Generalized hypotonia and depressed deep tendon reflexes.
- Neonatal reflexes absent; disturbed eye motion (dilated, fixed, or altered pupil reaction to light).
- Increased frequency of seizures 2 to 3 days after their onset.
- Irregular heartbeat and blood pressure.

Intervention approaches and issues:
- 1-2 hrs after birth is critical to success; there is no uniform standard of care.
- Neurological assessment and treatment of seizures; CT scans may be used sparingly (they cause injury to the developing brain).
- Maintenance of ventilation, perfusion, and

metabolic status.

- Prevention of hypoxia and too much carbon dioxide in the blood (*hypercapnia*) and too little carbon dioxide in the blood (*hypocapnia*).
- Maintenance of blood gases (by intubation and artificial ventilation), and acid-base status. In some (but not all) cases, compensation by the lungs or kidneys corrects pH imbalance.
- Maintenance of mean blood pressure above 35 mm Hg with medications.
- Focal cooling of brain by 3° to 6°C reduces extent of tissue injury.
- Evaluation of neurological functioning.

Intraventricular Hemorrhage (IVH)

Intraventricular hemorrhage (IVH) refers to bleeding from fragile blood vessels within brain tissue into the brain ventricles. Bleeding puts pressure on nerve cells and can damage them. IVH is most common in premature babies. Most cases occur within the first three days of life, but cases in adults have been reported.

Physical characteristics:
- Temporary stoppage of breathing (*apnea*).
- Slow heart rate (*bradycardia*).
- Pale or blue coloring (*cyanosis*).
- Weak suck.
- High-pitched cry.
- Seizures.
- Swelling or bulging of the "soft spots" between the bones of the baby's head (*fontanelles*).
- Low number of red blood cells in peripheral circulation (*anemia*).
- IVH is graded from 1 to 4 according to the severity of the bleeding; small amounts of bleeding (grades 1 to 2) do not usually cause any long-term damage; grades 3 to 4 cause long-term problems such as hydrocephalus.

Prevalence:
- 3-10% of all intracerebral hemorrhages in the U.S.
- 50% in very low birth weight (<1500g) or pre-term (<35 weeks of gestation) infants (U.S.).

Genotype or cause:
Head trauma; insertion or removal of a ventricular catheter (to drain fluid from the ventricles); intraventricular vascular malformation; bulging wall of a blood vessel (*aneurism*); tumour; high blood pressure (**hypertension)**; or bleeding predisposition.

Other causes include rapid ventricle volume expansion; asynchrony between mechanically delivered and spontaneous breaths in infants on ventilators; blood clotting disorders; oxygen deficiency and/or poor blood flow to the brain; respiratory disturbances; too much blood acid (*acidosis*); infusions of hypertonic solution (e.g. sodium bicarbonate); anemia; vacuum-assisted delivery; frequent handling, and tracheal suctioning (to remove mucus).

Functional and behavioural characteristics:
- Grade 1 and 2 hemorrhages: prognosis is good; neurodevelopment is slightly hindered.
- Grade 3 hemorrhage without white matter disease (disease characterized by damage to, or destruction of, the electrically insulating myelin sheath of neurons (demyelination)): mortality is less than 10%; cognitive or motor disorder is 30-40%.
- Grade 4: mortality approaches 80-90%; severe cognitive and motor conditions.

Intervention approaches and issues:
- For adults, treatment involves ventricular drainage and administration of a drug to remove the blood clots.
- Treatment of infants involves supportive care for cardiovascular, respiratory, or neurological complications, including treatment of lung conditions and infections; blood transfusions; seizure treatment; treatment for hydrocephalus by spinal taps.
- Before a premature birth, giving a pregnant woman corticosteroids reduces the risk.

Klinefelter Syndrome

Klinefelter syndrome is also known as Klinefelter-Reifenstein-Albright syndrome, after the three men who described it in 1942 in nine men who had enlarged breasts, sparse facial and body hair, small testes, and the inability to produce sperm. In 1959, Klinefelter syndrome was associated with an extra sex chromosome (genotype XXY) instead of the usual male sex complement (genotype XY). This syndrome usually occurs de novo.

Physical characteristics:

- Physical phenotype is variable; most common cause of infertility in males.
- Small testes, small penis, inadequate testosterone (*hypogonadism*).
- Swelling of breast tissue in puberty (*gynecomastia*) in about half.
- Tall with slim stature, long legs, and a tendency for truncal obesity.
- Female distribution of body fat in adults, sparse facial and body hair.
- Hypotonia, motor skill difficulties.

Prevalence:

- 1:500 to 1:1,000 live male births; one fifth of males at fertility clinics.

Genotype or cause:

- Most commonly, males have three sex chromosomes (X,X,Y) instead of two (X,Y); some are mosaic for this abnormality (i.e., have normal (X,Y) and abnormal (X,X,Y) cell lines; see Chapter 9).
- 50-60% of cases result from chromosomal nondisjunction during meiosis I in older mothers (see Chapter 9).

Functional and behavioural characteristics:

- 80% of XXY males have average to superior intelligence.
- Intellectual disability is rare; when this occurs, I.Q. is lower by only 10 or 15 points.
- Problems with expressive language, psychiatric disorders, poor social skills, anxiety, and low self esteem.

Co-occurring conditions:

- Hypothyroidism, breast cancer, osteoporosis, leg ulcers, depression, dental problems, varicose veins, mitral valve prolapse.
- Risk for autoimmune disorders, including type 2 diabetes and inflammation of the thyroid (*thyroiditis*).

Intervention approaches and issues:

- Testosterone replacement helps with development and maintenance of masculine characteristics (e.g., loss of libido, decreased energy, increased abdominal fat); may have positive effects on language or behavioural problems; no effect on infertility but eases puberty.
- Special education is helpful in some cases; many go on to post-secondary education.
- Intracytoplasmic sperm injection (a single sperm recovered from a testicular biopsy injected into a mature oocyte) offers an opportunity for procreation.
- Syndrome-specific care should complement standard preventative health care.

Lesch-Nyhan Syndrome

This is an inheritable disorder that affects how the body builds and breaks down *purines* (compounds in RNA and DNA). The syndrome was first discovered by Michael Lesch and William Nyhan (an American cardiologist and an American pediatrician, respectively) in 1964, when they described two affected brothers. The underlying enzyme defect was discovered in 1967 and the responsible gene was discovered in 1985. Lesch-Nyhan syndrome is characterized by diffuse effects throughout the central nervous system and specific effects in the basal ganglia. It has an X-linked recessive mode of inheritance; therefore, the syndrome is seen mainly in males.

Physical and health characteristics:

Development is typical in the prenatal period and in first 2-3 months of the neonatal period. The first symptoms is likely to be presence of urate crystals (orange-coloured, crystal-like deposits resembling orange sand) in the child's diaper or urine.

An increased urate to creatinine ratio in the blood or urine; a ratio of more than 2:1 indicates dysfunction. Urate is the breakdown product of dietary purines formed by action of the enzyme xanthine oxidase; creatinine is a by-product of muscular exertion and a marker of kidney function.

Reflex sensitivity is increased.

Prevalence:

- 1 in 380,000 live births.
- Affects males almost exclusively.

Genotype or cause:

- Mutation in the X chromosome gene for

hypoxanthine-guanine phosphoribosyltransferase (HPRT).

Functional and behavioural characteristics:

- Symptoms first present by 3-6 months and include unusual irritability and nervous system impairment (child can't lift head or sit up).
- By end of first year, atypical motor development is evident: writhing motions (***athetosis)*** and spasmodic movement of limbs and facial muscles (*chorea*).
- Most children never can walk.
- Tendency for compulsive self-injury.
- Kidney stones and kidney damage.
- Joints are tender and swollen (*gout*).
- Presence of neurological dysfunction resembling athetoid cerebral palsy (that resulting from damage to the cerebellum or basal ganglia.)

Intervention approaches and issues:

- No known interventions for neurological effects.
- Allopurinol is used to lower urate concentrations.
- Lithotripsy to break up kidney stones
- Parkinson disease medications and tranquilizers to control involuntary movements.
- Filing of teeth and use of restraints to limit self-injury.
- With proper management, affected individuals can survive until their 20s or 30s.

Mabry Syndrome

This profound developmental disability was first identified as *hyperphosphatasia* (high alkaline phosphatase levels in the serum) with neurologic deficit by Charleton Mabry in 1970. The syndrome is a diagnosis of exclusion for Cornelia deLange syndrome — since the facial dysmorphology and bone abnormalities are strikingly similar. The two syndromes can be distinguished because the Mabry syndrome is always accompanied by elevated serum *alkaline phosphatase* (an enzyme associated with bone metabolism). Miles Thompson named the syndrome in 2010. It consists of the trio of facial seizures, facial dysmorphology, and short terminal phalange of each finger (*brachytelephalangy*). The condition is observable in the first year of life. In 2010, the disorder was found to result from mutations in the phosphoinositol glycan (PIG) anchor biosynthesis gene (PIGV). The disorder is inherited in an autosomal recessive fashion. Other syndromes and disorders result from disruption of other genes in the PIG pathway.

Physical characteristics:

- Facies: thin, down-turned lips, hypertelorism, bulbous nose.
- In approximately half of the cases, the features may be coarsened — a feature often associated with the accumulation of material in cells (*vacuolar storage*). This stored material has been reported in some cases.
- Hypotonia and frequent difficulty with feeding.
- Aspiration pneumonia is a risk.

Prevalence:

- Fewer than 1:30,000 live births; affects males and females equally.

Genotype or cause:

A recessive disorder. Half of known cases result from inheritance mutations in the phosphoinositol glycan (PIG) anchor, type V (PIGV) gene on chromosome 1.

This gene codes for an enzyme critical to the production of the PIG anchor — a tether for alkaline phosphatase. The absence of the tether results in excessive secretion of alkaline phosphatase.

Mutations in other genes in the PIG biosynthesis pathway may account for other cases.

Functional and behavioural characteristics:

- Delays in mental development; communication delays.
- May be associated with autistic features, seizures.

Intervention approaches and issues:

- Genetic counselling.
- Speech therapy may be required.
- Anticonvulsant therapy for seizures.
- Pharmacotherapy for seizures; behaviour management may help.
- Management of GERD may be required.

Meningitis (particularly bacterial meningitis)

An infection of the membranes surrounding the brain (*meninges*; Chapter 12) and the fluid surrounding the brain and spinal cord. There are two types of meningitis: viral and bacterial. In general, viral meningitis is less severe and can resolve without treatment, while bacterial meningitis can be quite serious and may result in brain damage, learning disability, and even death. Over 50 types of bacteria can cause meningitis, and the agent varies with age. The bacteria responsible for the majority of meningitis cases are *Nisseria meningicoccus*, *Haemophilus influenzae* type b, and *Streptococcus pneumoniae*.

Physical characteristics:
- High fever, headache, stiff neck, nausea, and vomiting.
- Approximately one-third of children have seizures; 75% have a red or purple rash caused by meningococcal bacteria.
- Symptoms persist for hours to days and worsen with time.

Prevalence:
- 13:100,000 affected yearly in industrialized countries; more common in developing countries.

Genotype or cause:
- Genetic factors predispose to susceptibility and outcome.
- Often secondary to a bacterial infection in another part of the body such as the respiratory tract, urinary tract, or the ear. The disease is contagious and can be spread by contact.

Functional and behavioural characteristics:
- Infants show increasing distress when held and rocked; appear disoriented and drowsy.
- If the disease is not treated, serious complications may result, including developmental disability, epilepsy, visual, speech and hearing disabilities, cognitive impairment, and death.

Intervention approaches and issues:
- Many forms of meningitis can be prevented by vaccination.
- Utility of antibiotics is dependent on early diagnosis; treat for any ensuing complications.

Neuronal Migration Disorders

Result from the failure, during embryonic development, to form the neocortex (and subsequent formation and organization of the cerebral cortex) by neuronal migration. *Lissencephaly* (LIS) literally means smooth brain, and has traditionally been separated into two classes: classical (previously type I LIS) and cobblestone complex (previously type II LIS). Classical LIS is the more prevalent and presents in two common ways: isolated lissencephaly sequence (ILS) and Miller-Dieker syndrome (MDS). Other manifestations of classical LIS include X-linked lissencephaly (XLIS)/subcortical band heterotopia (SBH), and X-linked lissencephaly with abnormal genitalia (XLAG). MDS and ILS share a common genetic pathway, and exhibit similar symptoms. MDS generally occurs as the result of a de novo chromosomal deletion. In rare cases it can be associated with an interchange of material between two chromosomes (*familial reciprocal translocation*). ILS also mainly occurs de novo, but some cases autosomal recessive. Both disorders primarily affect the cortex, while MDS also affects the cranium and facial tissues.

Physical characteristics:
- Magnetic resonance imaging (MRI) demonstrates a very thick cortex (10-20mm), malformations of the ridges on the surface of the cerebellum (*gyri*) that are more severe in the posterior brain regions, and a prominent cell-sparse zone in the cortex (more severe in MDS than in LIS).
- MDS has characteristic cranio-facial anomalies, including a broad and high forehead, subtle indentation of the temples, slightly upturned nose, thin upper lip, and small jaw.

Prevalence:
- Classical LIS is reported at 11.7:1,000,000 live births in 1991 before extensive MRI use.

Genotype or cause:
Can result from viral infections of the uterus or the fetus during the first trimester, insufficient blood supply to the fetal brain early in pregnancy, and genetic causes (chromosome 17 mutations, the X chromosomes, and the reelin gene on chromosome 7).

Functional and behavioural characteristics:

- Severe developmental delay, seizures, and mortality in early childhood; more severe in MDS; gradient of severity in ILS, which correlates with the mutation type and location.
- Feeding problems are common, and include gagging while feeding, refusal of feeding, spitting up, and weight loss.
- Aspiration and reflux places patients are at risk of recurrent pneumonia.

Intervention approaches and issues:

- Management is symptomatic; use of a nasogastric tube and g-tube may alleviate feeding problems; use of medication to control seizures. These approaches have increased life expectancy to adolescence.
- Genetic counselling is important when there is risk of recurrence, such as in the case of a familial reciprocal translocation.

Neurofibromatosis

Neurofibromatosis was once known as "elephant man disease." This genetic syndrome was described in 1768 by Mark Akenside and, in 1882, by German pathologist Friedrich Daniel von Recklinghausen, who described autopsy findings in a female and male. There are two types of neurofibromatosis: neurofibromatosis Type 1 (NF1), or von Recklinghausen disease, which describes 85% of cases, and neurofibromatosis Type 2 (NF2), which describes 15% of cases. The disorder arises de novo, but can be inherited in an autosomal dominant manner. Refer to Sturge-Weber Syndrome and Tuberous Sclerosis Complex/Syndrome for related disorders.

Physical characteristics:

Neurofibromatosis Type 1:

- Two or more of the following:
- 6 or more coffee-with-cream/light brown skin spots (*café au lait spots*).
- 2 or more tumours that grow on a nerve or nerve tissue under the skin (*neurofibromas*), or 1 involving many nerves (*plexiform neurofibroma*).
- Multiple freckles in axillary (arm pit) or inguinal (groin) region.

- Lesions on the bone (*osseous lesions*); deformation of certain bones other than the spine.
- Tumours of the optic nerve (*optic gliomas*).
- 2 or more abnormally pigmented areas in the iris (coloured part of the eye) (*hamartomas*)
- Severe scoliosis.
- First degree relative (parent, child, or sibling) with NF1.

Neurofibromatosis Type 2:

- Either one of the following:
- Bilateral benign tumours of the cochlear vestibular nerves (*acoustic neuromas*).
- First degree relative (parent, child, or sibling) with NF2, plus one of the following: unilateral acoustic neuroma at below 30 years of age; any 2 of: benign tumour of the brain meninges (*meningioma*); tumour of the brain glial cells (*glioma*); a usually benign tumour of the peripheral nerve fibres that is composed of Schwann cells (*schwannoma*); or juvenile cortical cataract (affecting the cortex of the lens).

Prevalence:

- Neurofibromatosis Type 1 — 1:3,000 to 1:4,000 live births.
- Neurofibromatosis Type 2 — 1:30,000 to 1:40,000 live births.

Genotype or Cause:

- Neurofibromatosis Type 1: mutation in neurofibromin gene on chromosome 17. Neurofibromin functions as a tumour suppressor.
- Neurofibromatosis Type 2: mutation in the merlin gene on chromosome 22. Merlin also is involved in tumour suppression.

Functional and behavioural characteristics:

Neurofibromatosis Type 1:

- Depends on the system affected.
- May include seizures, intellectual compromise, blindness, deafness, movement disorders, dislocations, endocrine abnormalities, autonomic involvement, bowel irregularities, and hypertension.

Neurofibromatosis Type 2:

- Depends on the system affected.
- Acoustic neuromas present with high frequency; problems in the inner ear or auditory

nerve resulting in *sensorineural hearing loss*, dizziness (*vertigo*), ringing of the ears (*tinnitus*), and facial paralysis.

- Cataracts lead to blindness.
- Spinal tumours cause pain and paraplegia or quadriplegia.

Intervention approaches and issues:

- Genetic counselling for familial cases of NF1 and NF2.
- Neurofibromatosis Type 1: depends on organ system involved.
- Neurofibromatosis Type 2: surgical removal or radiotherapy for acoustic neuromas.

Noonan Syndrome (NS)

Noonan syndrome (NS) is a genetic disorder characterized by short stature, facial anomalies, and congenital heart defects that is similar to Turner syndrome, except that it occurs in both sexes and there is no chromosomal abnormality. A male with webbing of the neck, incomplete folding of the ears, and a low posterior hair line was first reported in 1883 by Koblinsky. Further characteristics of the syndrome were described by Jacqueline Noonan and Dorothy Ehmke in 1963. The syndrome arises de novo and is inherited in an autosomal dominant manner.

Physical characteristics:

- Short stature.
- Facial anomalies include hypertelorism, drooping of eyelids (*ptosis*), slanted *palpebral fissures* (area of the eye between the eyelids), *epicanthic folds*, *micrognathia* (small jaw), ear abnormalities (low set, prominent, and abnormally rotated), and neck webbing.
- Skeletal abnormalities, including abnormalities of the elbow in which the forearm deviates away from the midline of the body (*cubitus valgus*) and incompletely formed vertebrae in the back (*hemivertebrae*) leading to scoliosis.
- Congenital heart disease (pulmonary valve stenosis is the most common problem); cardiac defect is right-sided in contrast to Turner syndrome where it is left-sided.
- Gonadal defects vary from severe to normal;

defects include undescended testes (*cryptorchidism*); puberty can be delayed.
- Enlargement of liver and spleen (*hepatosplenomegaly*) and abnormal bleeding.

Prevalence:

- 1:1,000 to 1:2,500 live births.

Genotype or cause:

- Mutations in at least 7 different genes have been identified. These mutations cause problems with cell division, cell movement and cell differentiation. About 50% have mutations in the PTPN11 gene.

Functional and behavioural characteristics:

- No specific behavioural phenotype; some autistic-like features.
- Mild to moderate mental delay in about 33% of affected individuals..
- The prevalence of progressive high-frequency sensorineural hearing loss may be as high as 50%.
- Children may exhibit stubbornness, clumsiness, mood problems, communication problems, and/or "fussy" eating.
- Co-occurring conditions:
- Some PTPN11 mutations are associated with a risk of developing mild juvenile myelomonocytic leukemia.

Intervention approaches and issues:

- If no serious heart problem exists, life expectancy should be normal.
- Assessment is necessary to identify any delays and allow for intervention.
- Mildly affected individuals should respond well to traditional educational methods.
- Audiologic evaluation of high-frequency sensorineural hearing loss.

Pediatric Stroke

Of the two types of stroke, hemorrhagic stroke and ischemic stroke, hemorrhagic stroke is less common but more frequently fatal than ischemic stroke. The majority of information presented, therefore, pertains to ischemic stroke, which occurs when blood supply is reduced to a part of the brain due to occlusion of a blood vessel. In *arterial ischemic stroke*

(AIS), occlusion in the artery is usually due to a blood clot that forms, breaks off and travels through the bloodstream to another part of the body (*thromboembolism*), and that results in a localized area of ischemic necrosis caused by vascular blockage (*infarct*). Infants under 28 days of age make up 25% of pediatric AIS patients.

Physical characteristics:

Newborns:
- Presence of seizures, lethargy, or decreased consciousness.

Older infants and children:
- Acute focal neurological deficit, usually motor, speech, or visual, as well as one or more of the following: weakness or inability to move a body part; numbness or loss of sensation; decreased or lost vision (may be partial); speech difficulties; inability to recognize or identify familiar things; sudden headache; loss of coordination; dizziness (**vertigo**); swallowing difficulties; sleepy, stupourous, lethargic, comatose, or unconscious.

Prevalence:
- 6 cases/100,000/year in children under age 15 years; more males affected than females.

Genotype or cause:

There are a number of causes; about half the children with first-ever AIS have a known pre-disposing cause; the following genetic disorders predispose:
- Sickle cell disease: autosomal recessive red blood cell disease; confers malaria resistance.
- Homocystinuria: autosomal recessive disorder resulting from a deficiency of the amino acid, cystathionine.
- Fabry disease: one of several disorders called lysosomal storage disorders.
- Progeria: a rare disorder that accelerates the aging process about 7-fold.
- Neurofibromatosis: see this chapter.
- Coagulation disorders: the most common inherited blood abnormality that results in blood clots (*Factor V Leiden*) results in activated protein C resistance.

Risk factors for pediatric stroke:
- Congenital heart disease.
- Acquired heart disease: rheumatic heart disease; infection of prosthetic heart valve; bacterial edocarditis (infection of valve); arrhythmia; and other conditions.
- Systemic vascular disease: systemic hypertension; volume depletion or systemic hypotension; diabetes; and other conditions.
- Vasculitis (inflammation of blood vessels as the result of meningitis or systemic infection); chronic inflammation of connective tissue (*systemic lupus erythematosus*).
- Any disorder of blood vessels (vasculopathies).
- Blood vessel constricting (*vasospastic*) disorders resulting from ergot (fungal parasite in the heads of grains) poisoning, or nitric oxide poisoning.
- Disorders of blood and blood cell producing organs (*hematologic disorders*) and disorders affecting blood clotting (coagulopathies) such as leukemia, vitamin K deficiency, congenital coagulation defects, and others).
- Structural abnormalities of the cerebrovascular system.
- Trauma (e.g., child abuse, obstruction of a blood vessel by a blood clot, air bubble, fat deposit, other foreign substance, penetrating intracranial trauma, and others).

Functional and behavioural characteristics:
- Post-stroke behaviours and functional deficits depend on the location of the brain infarct.
- Long-term neurological deficits can occur after childhood AIS in 60-85% of cases.
- Most frequent neurological impairment is one-sided weakness (**hemiparesis**), but other residual deficits include speech, learning, and behaviour problems.

Intervention approaches and issues:
- No clinical trials have been completed in pediatric stroke; treatment is experimental.
- Initial strategies for AIS aim to reduce the size of the infarct.
- For older children antithrombotic agents (e.g., antiplatelet drugs such as aspirin which prevent platelets from clumping) and anticoagulants (e.g., heparin or warfarin) prevent clots from forming or enlarging, and reduce the 20-30% risk of recurrence of AIS.

- Rehabilitation (school re-integration); neuropsychology, occupational and physiotherapy.

Phenylketonuria (PKU)

This disorder was first described by Norwegian physiologist, Ivar Asbjorn Folling, in 1934, and named phenylketonuria (PKU) by Lionel Penrose. It is a rare autosomal recessive disorder in which the essential amino acid phenylalanine is not properly metabolized. High levels of phenylalanine and its derivatives are toxic to the central nervous system and cause brain damage. Treatment involves elimination of phenylalanine from the diet. PKU is characterized by paleness of skin, eyes and hair, eczema, cognitive delay, and a characteristic odor of the urine due to high levels of the amino acid phenylalanine in the blood and the metabolite phenylketone in the urine. The accepted as the upper limit of phenylalanine in blood plasma for preschoolers is 360 micromol/L. Women with PKU are likely to have children with congenital and cognitive abnormalities unless they adhere to the diet before conception through to delivery.

Physical characteristics:
- Fair skin, blond hair, blue eyes.
- Eczema (skin rashes).
- No dysmorphism except for possible mild microcephaly; growth normal.
- Characteristic odor of the urine is due to high levels of the amino acid phenylalanine in the blood and excretion of the metabolite phenylketone in the urine.

Prevalence:
- 1:15,000 live births in the U.S.; in Turkey the incidence is 1:2,600 live births; high incidence also in the Yemenite Jews, northern and eastern Europe, Italy, and China.

Genotype or cause:
- Mutations in the phenylalanine hydroxylase (PAH) gene on chromosome 12. Phenylalanine cannot be converted to tyrosine because PAH is non-functional; a deficiency of tetrahydrobiopterin also causes some cases. Tetrahydrobiopterin is a co-factor for an enzyme that breaks down phenylalanine.

Functional and behavioural characteristics:
- If untreated, developmental delay is observable by mid-infancy.
- Severe behavioural disturbances include hyperactivity, destructiveness, impulsiveness, uncontrolled rage attacks, and self-injury.
- Possible autistic disorder and schizophrenia-like symptoms.
- Tonic clonic seizures in about 25% of affected children.
- Exaggerated reflexes (*hyperreflexia*) in about 50% of affected individuals.
- Spastic cerebral palsy may also appear.
- Involuntary twisting of upper extremities (*athetosis*), hand posturing, and behavioural stereotypy.

Intervention approaches and issues:
- No symptoms if a phenylalanine-free diet is started before 3 weeks of age; if started between 3 and 6 weeks, there are mild effects of disorder; after 6 months, there is little benefit.
- With treatment: normal life-span, but lower than average intellectual functioning.
- Dietary restriction should be followed until 10 years of age (life-time diet is recommended).
- Aspartame is a potent source of phenylalanine and should be avoided.

Prader-Willi Syndrome (PWS)/ Prader-Labhart-Willi Syndrome

This syndrome was first described in Switzerland in 1956 by Andrea Prader, Alexis Labhardt and Heinrich Willi on the basis of nine children with the tetrad of small stature, intellectual disability, obesity, and small hands and feet. Prader and Willi reviewed the condition in 1961, expanded the phenotype, and drew attention to the presence of hypotonia in infancy and the development of diabetes mellitus in later childhood. Most cases of this syndrome arise de novo, but some have an autosomal dominant mode of inheritance.

Physical characteristics:
- Dysmorphic facies.
- Commonly blond to light brown hair, blue eyes, and sun-sensitive, fair skin.

- Hypotonia in newborns, poor sucking response, weak cry and feeding difficulties; overeating between six months and two years of age.
- Obesity after infancy; *Pickwickian syndrome* (severe obesity impairs breathing, leading to drowsiness), blue colour due to decreased oxygen (*cyanosis*), and possibly heart failure.
- Short stature.
- Undescended testicle(s) (*cryptorchidism*) and small testes, small penis, inadequate testosterone production (hypogonadism).
- Small hands and feet.
- Increased occurrence of scoliosis and other orthopedic problems.
- Likely have a hypothalamic growth hormone deficiency.

Prevalence:
- 1:8,000 to 1:25,000 live births; same frequency in males and females.

Genotype or cause:
- A genetic imprinting disorder. Loss of some genes in a specific region of chromosome 15 inherited from the father. This is a problem, because these genes are *active* (turned on) only in the paternal copy of the chromosome.

Functional and behavioural characteristics:
- Majority of individuals exhibit mild to moderate developmental delay.
- Typical behavioural patterns include irritability, anger, temper tantrums, stubbornness, low frustration tolerance, anxiety, compulsive eating (*hyperphagia*), and self-injurious behaviour (skin picking is the most common).
- Obsessive compulsive disorder (including nonfood-related behaviour) is common.
- Food-related behaviours include food seeking, overeating, and hoarding.
- Other maladaptive behaviour includes argumentativeness and aggression.
- Difficulty in sequential processing and short-term memory (visual and motor).
- Relative strengths in expressive vocabulary, long term memory, visual memory, and visual spatial integration (e.g., an unusual interest in jigsaw puzzles).

Co-occurring conditions:
- Obesity may cause other complications such as heart failure and diabetes.

Intervention approaches and issues:
- Genetic counselling.
- Life expectancy into the fifties is dependent upon weight management.
- Dietary, behavioural, pharmacological, and family intervention: physiotherapy with passive exercises and frequent change in position to prevent disuse atrophy and joint contractures, as well as pharmacological interventions.
- Growth hormone is being tried on an experimental basis.

Progressive Myoclonus Epilepsy (PME)

Progressive myoclonus epilepsy (PME) describes a group of rare catastrophic epilepsies affecting children and adolescents. PMEs include Unverricht-Lundborg disease, Lafora's disease, five forms of neuronal ceroid lipofuscinosis (NCL), myoclonic epilepsy with ragged red fibers (MERRF) and sialidosis (a disorder in which a lysosomal enzyme called neuraminidase is missing; this enzyme is involved in the first stage of breakdown of large carbohydrate groups, removing sialic acid residues). The term Batten disease originally referred to the juvenile form of NCL, but it is being increasingly used to describe all forms of NCL. PME is associated with myoclonus (sudden, brief, jerky, shock-like, involuntary movements), tonic-clonic seizures (seizures with contraction of all skeletal muscles and loss of consciousness; formerly called "grand mal" seizures), and neurological decline. All types of PME are genetic. Most have an autosomal recessive mode of inheritance and one affects mitochondrial DNA.

Physical characteristics:
- Generalized or multifocal myoclonus (stimulus sensitive).
- Tonic-clonic ("grand mal") seizures.
- Cognitive deterioration.
- EEG abnormalities.

Prevalence:
- 1% of all epilepsy cases in childhood and adolescence.

Genotype or cause:

Different variants of the syndrome are associated with genetic errors at different loci, chromosoems, or genes, as listed below:

Unverricht-Lundborg Disease:
EPM1/21q22.3/cystatin B

Lafora's Disease:
EPM2A/6q24/laforin
EPM2B/6p22/malin

NCL – Infantile:
CLN1/1p32/palmitoyl-protein thioesterase 1

NCL – Late infantile:
CLN2/11p15/tripeptidyl peptidase 1

NCL – Finnish variant:
CLN5/13q22/novel membrane protein

NCL – Juvenile:
CLN3/16p12/novel membrane protein

NCL – Northern epilepsy:
CLN8/8p23/novel membrane protein

MERRF:
MTTK/mtDNA/tRNALys

Sialidosis:
NEU/6p21/neuraminidase 1

Functional and behavioural characteristics:
- Mental deterioration and dementia.
- Iimpaired ability to coordinate voluntary movements (*cerebellar ataxia*).
- Deafness, blindness (*sensory-neural deficits*).
- Degeneration or destruction of the optic nerve (*optic atrophy*) and *macular "spots"* (blind spots in the central part of the retina).

Intervention approaches and issues:
- Anti-epileptic medication useful in controlling myoclonus and seizures.
- Therapeutic approaches for mitochondrial disease include vitamins (B, C, E), enzyme cofactors (co-enzyme Q10), and antioxidants.

Rett Syndrome

Rett syndrome was originally described in 1966 by Andreas Rett, an Austrian pediatrician, but it was not known worldwide until two decades later following a report by Bengt Hagberg and colleagues, describing 35 affected girls from Sweden, Portugal, and France. Most cases of Rett syndrome occur de novo. This disorder also has an X-linked dominant mode of inheritance, which is usually lethal in males. Because females have two X chromosomes, one provides enough normal protein for survival.

Physical characteristics:
- Normal development for first 6 to 18 months.
- Hypotonia — a first sign.
- Slowing head growth beginning at approximately 2 to 6 months of age, with gray matter atrophy, leading to acquired microcephaly.
- Shaky, unsteady, or stiff gait.
- Scoliosis.
- Poor circulation leading to cold and bluish arms and legs, and small feet.
- Excessive saliva and drooling.
- Disease development progresses through four stages.

Prevalence:
- 1:23,000 live births in U.S.; 1:10,000 to 1:45,000 live births internationally.

Genotype or cause:
- Mutation of gene encoding methyl-CpG-binding protein 2 (MeCP2) on the X chromosome; MeCP2 binds methylated DNA regulating gene expression and chromatin structure.
- Mutations have also been found in males and children with autism and mental delay.

Functional and behavioural characteristics:
- Autistic behaviours.
- Developmental regression (e.g., slowing of head growth).
- Severe language regression, loss of communication skills.
- Impairment involving planning, executing, and sequencing motor movements (apraxia).
- Seizures; loss of normal sleep patterns and sleep disturbances.
- Breathing abnormalities.
- Gastrointestinal complaints include severe constipation and GERD.

Intervention approaches and issues:
- Physical and occupational therapy to slow the progression.

• Speech therapy; music therapy as an adjunct.

Sanfilippo Syndrome

Sanfilippo syndrome was recognized by American physician Sylvester Sanfilippo and colleagues in 1963. Sanfilippo syndrome is the most common form of the mucopolysaccharide (MPS) disorders. It is a lysosomal storage disorder resulting from deficiency in one of the enzymes needed to break down heparan sulfate (a glycosaminoglycan which is found in the extra-cellular matrix and on cell surface glycoproteins). The MPSs are ubiquitous and, therefore, multiple organ systems can be involved. Like Hurler syndrome (MPS-I) and Hunter syndrome (MPS-II), Sanfilippo syndrome (MPS-III) can result in severe cognitive delay. The mode of inheritance of Sanfilippo syndrome is autosomal recessive.

Physical characteristics:

• Children develop normally for the first year or two; as more and more cells become damaged, symptoms appear.

• Difficult diagnosis because MPSs are not present in urine.

• Mild dysmorphism and coarsening of facial features; hairiness.

• Incomplete/defective bone formation.

• Corneal clouding and hepatosplenomegaly in rare cases.

Prevalence:

• 1:16,000 to 1:30,000 live births for all MPS disorders.

• MPS III accounts for approximately 50% or all cases of MPS diagnosed and has a combined prevalence of 1:53,000 to 1:280,000 live births.

• Four enzyme deficiencies cause Sanfilippo, resulting in types A, B, C, and D. Prevalence of type A is 1:24,000 to1:89,000 (the most severe and common). Type B is the second most common.

Genotype or cause:

• Deficiency of one of four enzymes necessary to degrade heparan sulfate (a sulfated polysaccharide that consists of alternating hexuronate and glucosamine units).

• Type A: deficiency of heparan sulfatase.

• Type B: deficiency of N-acetyl-alpha-D-glucosaminidase (NAG).

• Type C: deficiency of acetyl coA-alpha-glucose N-acetyl transferase.

• Type D: deficiency of N-acetyl glucosamine 6-sulfate sulfatase.

• In each case, a partially broken-down sugar, or mucopolysaccharide, accumulates in the brain and other tissues, causing progressive damage to appearance and development.

Functional and behavioural characteristics:

• Severe cognitive disability; joint stiffness; often difficult to manage.

• Symptoms can mimic those of autism.

• Severe behavioural disturbances can include hyperactivity, aggression and sleep disturbances; some affected children chew objects.

• Loss of language and hearing; intellectual deterioration and dementia.

Intervention approaches and issues:

• Genetic counselling.

• Symptomatic treatment is needed.

• Bone marrow transplants (see Hunter Syndrome and Hurler Syndrome).

• Tend to have short life spans (10 to 20 years); pneumonia is common.

• Some people with a mild form of type B live well into adulthood.

• Patients with MPS may have unusual sensitivity to anesthesia.

Shaken Baby Syndrome (SBS)

Head injuries are the leading cause of traumatic death and the leading cause of child abuse fatalities. These shaking events usually result from tension and frustration in parents or caregivers, generated by a baby's crying. SBS refers to a cluster of clinical findings in infants, including retinal hemorrhages, subdural and subarachnoid hemorrhages, and little or no evidence of external cranial trauma. Since the infant is unable to give a history and the caregiver may be unwilling or unable to be truthful, there is often delayed diagnosis. As well, many people have been wrongly accused of causing SBS. Advances in imaging have been helpful in detailing the extent of intracranial injury, directing neurosurgical intervention, and determining when injuries occurred.

Physical characteristics:
- A triad of symptoms — retinal hemorrhage, subdural hematoma (and/or subarachnoid hemorrhage), and acute encephalopathy is indicative of the syndrome, but these features can also result from other causes.
- The symptoms usually occur in the absence of any external trauma to the head, face and neck and with inadequate history or report by caregiver.

Prevalence:
- An estimated 50,000 cases occur each year in the U.S.
- Victims range in age from a few days to 5 years (average 6-8 months).
- The leading cause of death in children less than 4 years in the U.S.

Cause:
- Vigorous shaking of an infant by the arms, legs, chest, or shoulders such that the brain rotates more than the surrounding skull and dura; not attributable to play or falls.
- Males tend to predominate as the perpetrators in 65-90% of cases.

Functional and behavioural characteristics:
- Less severe cases include vomiting, poor feeding, lethargy or irritability, hypothermia, increased sleeping, difficulty arousing, or failure to vocalize.
- More severe cases include seizures, transient cessation of respiration (*apnea*), relatively slow heart action (*bradycardia*), complete cardiovascular collapse.

Intervention approaches and issues:
- To treat an SBS victim, interdisciplinary intervention by clinical teams and community programs is imperative and costly.
- Effective prevention strategies include increasing public awareness regarding the consequences of shaking a child, and educating healthcare professionals to identify infants at high risk for abuse.

Smith-Lemli-Opitz syndrome (SLOS)

Smith-Lemli-Opitz syndrome (SLOS) is characterized by a deficiency of plasma cholesterol as well as the presence of high levels of the precursor 7-dehydrocholesterol reductase (7DHC), which is toxic at high concentrations. It was first described in three unrelated boys in 1964 by David Weyhe Smith, Luc Lemli, and the American Pediatrician John Marius Opitz. DHCR7 converts 7-dehydrocholesterol (7DHC) into cholesterol. Severity of the disease generally correlates with plasma sterol concentration. Very severely affected individuals are subject to multiple congenital malformations and are often miscarried or die within the first few weeks of life. Morphogenic abnormalities are predominantly located in the following systems: craniofacial, limb or skeletal, urogenital, and internal organs such as the heart. The syndrome has an autosomal recessive mode of inheritance.

Physical characteristics:
- Severely affected individuals often present with these characteristics:
- Intrauterine growth retardation, low weight, shortness of stature.
- Dysmorphic facial features (cleft palate, anteverted nostrils), microcephaly
- Genital anomalies.
- Joining or webbing of two or more fingers or toes (*syndactyly*) or having more than the normal number of fingers or toes (*polydactyly*).
- Cardiac malformation.

Prevalence:
- Incidence is 1:20,000 to 1:60,000 live births; as many as 1:30 people carry one mutant gene, suggesting an incidence of 1:5,000 to 1:18,000. Incidence may be lower than expected due to fetal loss.
- More frequent in Eastern Europe; least frequent in Asian and African populations.
- Equally prevalent among males and females.

Genotype or cause:
- Mutations in the DHCR7 gene located on chromosome 11.

Functional and behavioural characteristics:
- Neuropsychiatric and neurodevelopmental

abnormalities are frequent.

- Antisocial, self-destructive, hyperactive, or aggressive behaviour.
- Withdrawal or autism, or both.
- Borderline normal intelligence to profound mental delay; language impairment.
- Hearing deficits.

Intervention approaches and issues:

- Medical treatment for some of the malformations include surgery for congenital heart defects, repair of polydactyly, and hearing aids for hearing deficits.
- Dietary cholesterol supplementation is under evaluation.

Smith-Magenis Syndrome (SMS)

This rare group of children was described in the 1980s by Ann Smith, a genetic counsellor, and Ellen Magenis, a physician and chromosome expert. A variety of unusual physical and behavioural characteristics have been found in people with SMS. This syndrome typically occurs de novo, but can have an autosomal dominant mode of inheritance.

Physical characteristics:

- Disproportionately short head (*brachycephaly*), broad face, broad nasal bridge, flat mid-face, posteriorly rotated or low set ears, short broad hands, upper limb deformity, eye problems including strabismus, and severe nearsightedness(*myopia*).
- Low muscle tone and feeding problems in infancy.
- Short stature.
- Prominent jaw in older children and adults.
- Abnormalities of the palate, with or without cleft lip.
- Downturned mouth.
- Chronic ear infections and hearing impairments.
- Short fingers and toes.
- Heart defects and murmurs.
- Urinary system problems.
- Scoliosis; unusual walking pattern (*gait*).

Prevalence:

- 1:25,000 live births in the U.S., but condition is under-recognized and underdiagnosed.

Genotype or cause:

- Most cases are associated with a chromosome 17 deletion. Loss of the retinoic acid induced 1 (RAI1) protein seems to be associated with most of the characteristic features of the main features of the syndrome.

Functional and behavioural characteristics:

- Moderate cognitive impairment; speech and language delays.
- Some, but not all those affected, show maladaptive behaviours including hyperactivity, sleep problems (frequent awakenings), and autistic features.
- An abnormal movement described as "self-hugging" posture.
- A tendency to repeat the same questions (e.g., "What's your name?").
- Aggression, self-injury, head banging, hand biting, pulling out fingernails and toenails, and insertion of foreign bodies or objects into bodily orifices (*polyembolokilamania*).
- Individuals are at risk of stereotypic movement disorders.
- Described as very appealing and affectionate.

Intervention approaches and issues:

- Behavioural intervention as part of family services.
- Psychotropic drugs for modifying behaviours; therapeutic management of sleep disorders.
- Speech therapy, occupational therapy, physical therapy, orthopedic intervention.
- Support from families, schools, work, and residential service providers.

Sturge-Weber Syndrome (SWS)

In 1879, English physician William Allen Sturge clearly described the main clinical manifestations in a young girl and deduced that they resulted from a vascular lesion or birth mark. In 1922, Frederick Parkes Weber described the radiographic features of the syndrome for the first time. This syndrome occurs de novo, and rarely more than once in a family. Refer to the sections entitled Neurofibromatosis and Tuberous Sclerosis Complex/Syndrome for information on related disorders.

Physical characteristics:

- Characterized by a port-wine stain birthmark (*angiomatous facial malformation*).
- There is overgrowth of capillaries around the trigeminal nerve just below the surface of the face on the same side as the birthmark; brain tissue beneath the growth may not receive adequate perfusion.
- Other physical symptoms may include:
  - A weakening or loss of the use of one side of the body (hemiparesis), may develop opposite to the port-wine stain.
  - An enlarging of the eye (*buphthalmos*) that has been affected by the stain.
  - Increased pressure within the eye (*glaucoma*) resulting in damage to the optic disk and gradual loss of vision.

Prevalence:

- Disease is sporadic, prevalence has not been estimated.
- Males and females are affected equally.

Genotype or cause:

- Unknown.

Functional and behavioural characteristics:

- Seizures often occur, usually begin between 2 and 7 months of age.
- Varying degrees of developmental delay in motor and cognitive skills.

Intervention approaches and issues:

- Laser treatment to lighten or to remove port-wine stains in young children.
- Diagnosis of glaucoma and intracranial involvement is fundamental.
- Early neuroimaging features are important to recognize.
- Management of associated neurologic and ocular abnormalities.
- Anticonvulsants are used to control seizures.
- Vagus nerve stimulator (VNS) implants (leading to an anti-epileptic effect) in children over 12 years of age; surgery.
- Physical and occupational therapy.
- Special education.

Tourette Syndrome

In 1885, French neurologist Georges Albert Édouard Brutus Gilles de la Tourette described a condition involving multiple tics, involuntary movements, involuntary repetition of a word or sentence just spoken by another person (*echolalia*), and involuntary utterance of vulgar or obscene words (*coprolalia*). Tourette syndrome, named after its discoverer, is a childhood onset neurological disorder characterized by motor and vocal tics.

Physical characteristics:

- Not relevant.

Prevalence:

- 1:2,000 live births in the U.S.; incidence is higher children with special education; 3 to 4 times more common in males than females.

Genotype or cause:

- A combination of genetic and environmental factors likely are involved.
- May involve nerves linking the basal ganglia to the frontal cortex (*striatocortical circuits*).

Functional and behavioural characteristics:

- Symptoms begin between the ages of 2 and 15 years; most by age of 11.
- Affected individuals exhibit head and facial tics, vocalizations (throat clearing, barking, snorting, grunting, coughing, word accentuation, and others).
- Other movement symptoms touching, hitting, jumping, and smelling objects, involuntary and inappropriate obscene remarks, obsessive compulsive behaviours, hyperactivity, attention-deficit disorder and learning disabilities, self-injury, inappropriate sexual activity, exhibitionism, and antisocial behaviour.
- Sleep disorders are common.

Intervention approaches and issues:

- Critical to work with family; modification of the work and home environment.
- Traditional antipsychotic drugs (*neuroleptics*) are standard; non-neuroleptic drugs, behavioural therapies, and surgical approaches may apply.
- Treatment of tics may result in more disability than the tics themselves.

- Remissions may occur without the use of medication; 30 to 40% of children have total remission; another 30% exhibit substantial improvement.

Traumatic Brain Injury

Traumatic brain injury (TBI) occurs as a result of either direct or indirect forces to the brain matter and is divided into two phases of injury. The primary phase includes damage to the brain and its structures as a direct result of the force of the injury. The secondary phase consists of a cascade of physiological, cellular, and molecular events that exacerbate the primary injury. Structures that may be damaged during the primary phase of injury include the skull, the frontal, and temporal lobes. Tissues and cells that are affected by the secondary phase include all cells and tissue types in the brain.

Physical characteristics:
- TBI abnormalities include swelling (*edema*) of the brain, bruising of the tissue (*hematomas*), diffuse axonal injury lesions, hemorrhage, and neuronal death from lack of oxygen.

Prevalence:
- Each year more than 1.6 million people in North America sustain TBIs resulting in 80,000 severe neurological disabilities and 52,000 deaths.

Genotype or cause:
- Falls; bicycle, sports, and motor vehicle accidents.
- Direct injury is immediate and results from the force of an object striking or penetrating the head. Indirect injury results from acceleration or deceleration generated by movements of areas of the brain against one another of the brain against the skull.

Functional and behavioural characteristics:
- Symptoms may include amnesia, headaches, confusion, dizziness, blurred vision, fatigue or lethargy, a change in sleep patterns, behaviour and mood changes, and attention deficit.
- Moderate or severe TBI patients experience repeated vomiting or nausea, convulsions, slurred speech, weakness or numbness in the extremities, and loss of coordination.
- Permanent cognitive, communication, sensory, behavioural and mental health problems; Alzheimer's and Parkinson diseases; post-traumatic dementia or epilepsy; stroke; and dysfunction of the autonomic nervous system.

Intervention approaches and issues:
- In addition to rehabilitation, successful intervention requires the support and patience of family members, community members, and clinicians.
- For children, school-based behavioural treatments, teaching, and reinforcement of metacognitive thinking strategies.

Tuberous Sclerosis (TS) Complex/Syndrome

Tuberous sclerosis (TS) complex/syndrome is one of the group of congenital and hereditary diseases called *phacomatoses* or *neurocutaneous syndrome*s that include neurofibromatosis, tuberous sclerosis, Sturge-Weber syndrome, and ataxia-telangiectasia. TS is haracterized by the development of benign tumour-like malformations (*hamartomas*), in various tissues). In 1880, French neurologist, Désiré-Magloire Bourneville, formally described a condition with onset in the first decade of life. TS is characterized by the classic triad of epilepsy, low cognitive functioning, and benign tumours of the sebaceous glands (*adenoma sebaceum*). TS usually occurs de novo, but may be inherited in an autosomal dominant fashion.

Physical characteristics:
- Benign tumours or growths on brain, face and organs (especially the kidneys, heart, liver, spleen and lungs).
- Between 2 and 5 years of age, facial growths appear as small, bright red or brownish nodules occurring in a butterfly distribution on nose and cheeks.
- Areas of decreased pigmentation (*hypopigmentation)* on the arms, trunk, and legs at birth.
- Tooth enamel defects.
- Tumours under the fingernails (*periungual fibromas*) occur in 50% of cases.

- Skin plaques (irregularly thickened, slightly elevated soft plaques usually noted over the lower back (*lumbosacral area*) called *Shagreen patches*) occur in about 70%.
- Benign tumours (single or multiple) composed of striated muscle fibres may be present on the heart (*cardiac rhabdomyoma*).

Prevalence:
- 1:5,800 to 1:30,000 live births.

Genotype or cause:
- TSC1 and TSC2 mutations, encoding the proteins hamartin and tuberin, respectively.
- TSC1 maps to chromosome 9; TSC2 maps to chromosome 16.
- Hamartin helps control cell growth and size; it may function as a tumour suppressor.
- Tuberin interacts with hamartin.

Functional and behavioural characteristics:
- Convulsions occur in approximately 80% of cases.
- Mild to severe developmental disabilities are apparent in 70% of cases.
- Associated with behaviour disturbances (is one cause of autism and Asperger syndrome) and socially unacceptable behaviours (hyperactivity, screaming, destructiveness, and self-mutilation).
- Sleep disorders are common (e.g., night walking, and early morning waking).

Intervention approaches and issues:
- Medication for seizures; pharmacological interventions.
- Surgery or plastic surgery for skin conditions.
- Psychoeducational and behavioural therapy.
- Individuals with mild cases may live productive lives.
- Severe mental impairments and seizures require medical and psychosocial treatment.

Turner Syndrome

Turner syndrome was first described by Henry Hubert Turner in 1938 as a condition consisting of sexual infantilism, short stature, webbed neck, and elbows that are turned in (*cubitus valgus*). Also known as chromosome XO syndrome, Turner syndrome only affects females. Individuals with Turner syndrome are also prone to cardiovascular, kidney and thyroid problems, skeletal disorders such as scoliosis or dislocated hips, and hearing and ear disturbances. Turner syndrome arises de novo.

Physical characteristics:
- Early characteristics: low birth weight; fluid retention (*edema*) on back of hands and feet; loose skin folds at nape of neck.
- Later-developing characteristics: short stature, webbing of the neck, low posterior hairline, small jaw (*mandible*), prominent ears, epicanthic folds, high-arched palate; broad chest and wide spaced nipples, elbow abnormality (see above), hyperconvex fingernails, defective embryonic development of the ovaries (*ovarian dysgenesis*) resulting in absence of menstrual periods (*amenorrhea*) and infertility, sensorineural hearing loss, and relative smallness of the jaw (*micrognathia*).

Prevalence:
- 1:2,500 to 1:5,000 live female births; common cause of miscarriages.

Genotype or cause:
- Genetic condition specific to females caused by an X-chromosome abnormality, often a missing paternal X chromosome (genotype XO).

Functional and behavioural characteristics:
- Intelligence is typically in the normal to low range, with developmental disability occurring in fewer than 10% of those affected.
- May have ADHD; poor right-left directionality; impaired social cognition and low self-esteem; increased risk of depression and anorexia nervosa; learning difficulties (e.g., inability to write properly (*dysgraphia*) or to do math (*dyscalculia*); problems with visual-spatial organization (e.g., impaired shape copying); and psychomotor delays or disabilities.

Co-occurring conditions:
- Most individuals do not menstruate, cannot become pregnant, and may lack other secondary sex characteristics such as breast development.
- High rate of colour blindness, short stature, chronic middle ear infections, kidney and uri-

nary tract abnormalities, and narrowing of the aorta of the heart (*coarctation*).

- Abnormalities of the ear lobes are associated with progressive sensorineural hearing loss in the second decade of life.

Intervention approaches and issues:

- Growth hormone, either alone or with a low dose of androgen, will increase growth velocity and probably also final adult height.
- Estrogen replacement therapy (ERT) will promote development of secondary sexual characteristics, and maintain good tissue and bone integrity. ERT has been associated with risk of breast cancer and blood clots, amongst other problems.
- Reproductive technologies (with donor egg) may help assist pregnancy.
- Hypertension in adulthood may need treatment.
- Psychiatric symptoms may be decreased by medical and psychological treatments for the short stature and ovarian impairments.
- New information is ideally presented verbally to affected individuals.
- Normal life expectancy.

Williams Syndrome

Williams syndrome was first identified by New Zealand cardiologist J.C.P. Williams and colleagues in 1961 on the basis of a pattern of cardiovascular anomalies. In 1978, the syndrome was recognized to include specific heart defects (in about 80% of cases), developmental disabilities, and unusual facial features. Williams syndrome usually occurs de novo, but when transmitted has an autosomal dominant mode of inheritance.

Physical characteristics:

- Facial features include: broad forehead, medial eyebrow flare, depressed nasal bridge, star-like pattern in the iris, wide spaced teeth, and full lips; face is frequently described as "elfin-like."
- Low birth weight; growth delay; mild microcephaly.
- Renal and cardiovascular irregularities.
- Difficulties in feeding, digestion, constipation,

and failure to thrive in infancy.

- Hypertension, narrowing or stricture above the aortic heart valve (*supravalvular aortic stenosis*), narrowing of the pulmonary heart valve (*supravalvular aortic stenosis*), and high levels of calcium in the blood (**hypercalcemia)** with increased urination and water intake.
- There may be narrowing of the ureter (*supravalvular aortic stenosis*), and pouches in the bladder (*bladder diverticula*).
- Contractures in the legs are common.

Prevalence:

- 1:20,000 to 1:50,000 live births.

Genotype or cause:

- Microdeletions on chromosome 7 involve about 20 genes.
- A submicroscopic deletion of variable size on chromosome band 7q11.23, that includes the elastin gene, is present in 95-98% of affected individuals.

Functional and behavioural phenotype:

- Developmental delays; severely disabled to average mental ability.
- Auditory sensitivity.
- Increased risk of anxiety and ADHD.
- Despite lower overall intellectual and visuospatial functioning, higher level language abilities are evident; those affected display "cocktail party speech."
- Emotional and behavioural difficulties can include irritability, poor concentration, temper tantrums, overactivity, eating difficulties, poor peer relationships, and sleep disturbances.
- Inappropriate attention seeking behaviour.
- Affected children show lack of social constraints (friendliness toward adult strangers).

Co-occurring conditions:

- High frequency of middle ear infections.

Intervention approaches and issues:

- Children respond better to verbal teaching methods.
- Early speech, language and occupational therapy.
- Sociability needs to be appropriately directed (risk of exploitation due to their friendly nature).

- Individuals and families may require help from mental health professionals.
- Most affected adults live and work in supervised settings.
- Life expectancy may be lessened if congenital heart disease is present.

Summary

This chapter is a guide to basic information about more than 30 syndromes and disorders not covered in other chapters. For each, background (historical) information, physical and behavioural characteristics, causes, prevalence or incidence, and applicable intervention issues are presented.

Acknowledgements

This chapter draws upon material originally presented in Percy et al., 2007. The previous contributions of Karolina Machalek and other authors of this article are recognized.

Special terms

Apraxia: Impairment involving planning, executing and sequencing motor movements

Autosomal dominant: A form of inheritance in which the abnormality is inherited from only one parent in order for the disorder to be expressed. Often, one of the parents has the disorder.

Autosomal recessive: A form of inheritance in which the abnormality must be inherited from both parents in order for the disease to be expressed. The parents usually do not have the disease.

Congenital heart defects: Heart defects that are present at birth. See Chapter 14.

Cubitus valgus: Deformity of the elbow in which the forearm deviates away from the midline of the body.

De novo: Occuring as a new event without being inherited.

Dysmorphic: Malformed.

Electroencephalogram (EEG): a test that measures and records the electrical activity of the brain.

Epicanthic fold: A fold of skin of the upper eyelid that partially covers the corner of the eye.

Facies: Having to do with the face.

Gastroesophageal reflux disease (GERD): Reverse flow of stomach contents into the esophagus.

Gastrostomy (g)-tube: A gastric feeding tube inserted into a small incision in the abdomen into the stomach, for the long-term feeding of persons who cannot swallow.

Hemiparesis: Paralysis on one side of the body.

Hernia: A weak spot in the abdominal wall. Locations are often near the navel (umbilical) or in the groin (inguinal).

Hypercalcemia: Elevated levels of calcium in the blood (usually serum).

Hypertelorism: Abnormally wide space between the eyes.

Hypertension: High blood pressure.

Hypogonadism: A condition in which the sex glands produce no or little sex hormones. The sex glands in men and women are the testes and ovaries, respectively.

Hypotonia: Floppy muscles as the result of decreased muscle tone.

Microcephaly: Having a small head.

Pharmacotherapy: Drug therapy.

Phenotype: The observable physical, behavioural, or biochemical characteristics of an organism, as determined by both genetic and environmental factors.

Renal: Having to do with the kidney.

Scoliosis: Lateral curvature of the spine.

Sensorineural hearing loss: Hearing loss resulting from damage to the auditory nerve; sometime called "nerve deafness."

Stereotypic: Repetitive

Strabismus: A condition in which the eyes are not properly aligned with one another. Sometimes referred to as cross-eyed (eye points inwards) or wall-eyed (eye points outwards).

Ventricles: Cavities in the brain through which the cerebrospinal fluid flows.

Vertigo: Dizziness.

X-linked: A form of inheritance in which the abnormal gene is located on the X chromosome. In most X-linked disorders, females are not affected as severely as males, because their normal X chromosome tends to be protective.

Syndrome Specific Resources

Angelman Syndrome

Canadian Angelman Society. (n.d.). Retrieved from http://www.angelmancanada.org/

Mabb, A. M., Judson, M. C., Zylka, M. J., & Philpot, B. D. (2011). Angelman syndrome: insights into genomic imprinting and neurodevelopmental phenotypes. *Trends in Neuroscience, 34*(6), 293-303.

Williams, C. A. (2010). The behavioral phenotype of the Angelman syndrome. *American Journal of Medical Genetics C: Seminars in Medical Genetics, 154C*(4), 432-437.

22q11.2 Deletion Syndrome

Bassett, A. S., McDonald-McGinn, D. M., Devriendt, K., Digilio, M. C., Goldenberg, P., Habel, A., et al. (2011). The International 22q11.2 Deletion Syndrome Consortium: Practical guidelines for managing patients with 22q11.2 deletion syndrome. *Journal of Pediatrics*, May 11.

National Institute on Deafness and Other Communication Disorders. (2005). *Velocardiofacial syndrome*. Retrieved from http://www.nidcd.nih.gov/health/voice/velocario.asp

Congenital Hypothyroidism

Grosse, S. D., & Van Vliet, G. (2011). Prevention of intellectual disability through screening for congenital hypothyroidism: How much and at what level? *Archives of Disease in Childhood, 96*(4), 374-379.

Murray, M. A. (Summer, 2009). Primary TSH screen for congenital hypothyroidism. *Newborn Screening and Congenital Hypothyroidism 2*(1), 1-5. Retrieved from http://health.utah.gov/newbornscreening/Disorders/English/CHYP/Newsletter_CHYP_En.pdf

Thyroid Foundation of America. (2004). *Congenital hypothyroidism*. Retrieved from http://www.tsh.org/disorders/pregnancy/newborns.html

Congenital Rubella Syndrome

Duszak, R. S. (2009). Congenital rubella syndrome — major review. *Optometry, 80*(1), 36-43.

Libbey, J. E., Sweeten, T. L., McMahon, W. M., & Fujinami, R. S. (2005). Autistic disorder and viral infections. *Journal of Neurovirology, 11*, 1-10.

MedlinePlus. *Congenital rubella*. (2011). Retrieved from http://www.nlm.nih.gov/medlineplus/ency/article/001658.htm

Cornelia de Lange or de Lange Syndrome

Cornelia de Lange Syndrome (CdLS) Foundation, Inc. (2010). Retrieved from http://www.cdlsusa.org/

Liu, J., & Krantz, I. D. (2009). Cornelia de Lange syndrome, cohesin, and beyond. *Clinical Genetics, 76*(4), 303-314.

Cri du Chat Syndrome

Orphanet Encyclopedia. (2011). *Monosomy 5p*. Retrieved from http://www.orpha.net/consor/cgi-bin/OC_Exp.php?lng=EN&Expert=281

Cerruti Mainardi, P. (2006). Cri du chat syndrome. *Orphanet Journal of Rare Diseases, 1*, 33.

Developmental Coordination Disorder (DCD)

American Psychiatric Association (2000). *Diagnostic and statistical manual of mental disorders* (Revised, 4th ed.). Washington, DC: Author.

CanChild, Centre for Childhood Disability Research (Canada). (2011). *Developmental coordination disorder*. Retrieved from http://dcd.canchild.ca/en/

Dewey, D., & Wilson, B. N. (2001). Developmental coordination disorder: What is it? *Physical & Occupational Therapy in Pediatrics, 20*, 5-27.

Hunter Syndrome/Mucopolysaccharidosis Type II (MPS II)

The Canadian Society for Mucopolysaccharide and Related Diseases, Inc. (n.d.). *Links to MPS and related websites*. Retrieved from http://www.mps-society.ca/

National Library of Medicine and the National Institutes of Health. (2011). Hunter syndrome. *Medline Plus Encyclopedia*. Retrieved from http://www.nlm.nih.gov/medlineplus/ency/article/001203.htm

Hurler/Hurler-Scheie/Scheie Syndrome/Gargoylism/MPS I

Beck, M. (2003, September). Mucopolysccharidosis

I. *Orphanet Encyclopedia.* Retrieved from http://www.orpha.net/data/patho/GB/uk-MPS1.pdf

Muenzer, J., Wraith, J. E., & Clarke, L. A. (2009). International Consensus Panel on Management and Treatment of Mucopolysaccharidosis I. Mucopolysaccharidosis I: Management and treatment guidelines. *Pediatrics, 123*(1), 19-29.

U.S. National Library of Medicine and the National Institutes of Health. (2011). Hurler syndrome. *Medline Plus Encyclopedia.* Retrieved from http://www.nlm.nih.gov/medlineplus/ency/article/001204.htm

Hypoxic-Ischemic Encephalopathy (HIE)/ Neonatal Encephalopathy (NE)

Medscape. *Hypoxic-ischemic encephalopathy.* (2011). Retrieved from http://emedicine.medscape.com/article/973501-overview

Newborn Services Clinical Guideline. Neonatal encephalopathy (NE). (2004). Retrieved from http://www.adhb.govt.nz/newborn/guidelines/neurology/NE.htm

Selway, L. D. (2010). State of the science: Hypoxic ischemic encephalopathy and hypothermic intervention for neonates. *Advances in Neonatal Care, 10*(2), 60-6; quiz 67-68.

Intraventricular Hemorrhage (IVH)

Annibale, D. J., & Hill, J. (2011). Periventricular hemorrhage-intraventricular hemorrhage. *eMedicine.* Retrieved from http://emedicine.medscape.com/article/976654-overview

Engelhard, H. H., Andrews, C. O., Slavin, K. V., & Charbel, F. T. (2003). Current management of intraventricular hemorrhage. *Surgical Neurology, 60,* 15-22.

Stamford Hospital – The Regional Center for Health. (2011). *High-risk newborn – intraventricular hemorrhage.* Retrieved from http://www.stamfordhospital.org/health-information/health-library/content.aspx?pageid=P06951

Klinefelter Syndrome

The American Association for Klinefelter Syndrome Information and Support (AAKSI). (n.d.). Retrieved from http://www.aaksis.org/about.cfm

Giltay, J. C., & Maiburg, M. C. (2010). Klinefelter syndrome: Clinical and molecular aspects. *Expert Reviews of Molecular Diagnostics, 10*(6), 765-776.

Knowledge, Support and Action (KS@A). (2011). Retrieved from http://www.genetic.org/

Lesch-Nyhan Syndrome

Jinnah, H. A. (2009).Lesch-Nyhan disease: From mechanism to model and back again. *Disease Models and Mechanisms, 2*(3-4), 116-121.

Nyhan, W. L., O'Neill, J. P., Jinnah, H. A., & Harris, J. C. (2000; updated 2010). Lesch-Nyhan syndrome. In: R.A. Pagon, T. D. Bird, C.R. Dolan, & K. Stephens (Eds.), *GeneReviews* [Internet]. Seattle (WA): University of Washington, Seattle. Retrieved from: http://www.ncbi.nlm.nih.gov/bookshelf/br.fcgi?book=gene&part=lns

National Institute of Neurological Disorders and Stroke. (2007). *NINDS Lesch-Nyhan syndrome information page.* Retrieved from http://www.ninds.nih.gov/disorders/lesch_nyhan/lesch_nyhan.htm

Mabry Syndrome

Thompson, M. D., Nezarati, M. M., Gillessen-Kaesbach, G., Meinecke, P., Mendoza, R., Mornet, E., et al. (2010). Hyperphosphatasia with seizures, neurologic deficit, and characteristic facial features: Five new patients with Mabry syndrome. *American Journal of Medical Genetics A, 152A,* 1661-1669.

Krawitz, P. M., Schweiger, M. R., Rödelsperger, C., Marcelis, C., Kölsch, U., Meisel, C., et al. (2010). Identity-by-descent filtering of exome sequence data identifies PIGV mutations in hyperphosphatasia mental retardation syndrome. *Nature Genetics, 42,* 827-829.

Meningitis

Meningitis Research Foundation of Canada. (n.d.). Retrieved from http://www.meningitis.ca/en/

Swartz, M. N. (2004). Bacterial meningitis: A review of the past 90 years. *New England Journal of Medicine, 351,* 1826-1828.

World Health Organization. (2011). *Meningitis.* Retrieved from http://www.who.int/topics/meningitis/en/

Neuronal Migration Disorders

Kato, M., & Dobyns, W. B. (2003). Lissencephaly and the molecular basis of neuronal migration. *Human Molecular Genetics, 12,* R89-R96.

Liu, J. S. (2011). Molecular genetics of neuronal migration disorders. *Current Neurology and Neuroscience Reports, 11*(2) 171-178.

National Institute of Neurological Disorders and Stroke. (2011). *NINDS Neuronal Migration Disorders Information Page.* Retrieved from http://www.ninds.nih.gov/disorders/neuronal_migration/neuronal_migration.htm

Neurofibromatosis

Evans, D. G. R. (2009). Neurofibromatosis type 2 (NF2): A clinical and molecular review. *Orphanet Journal of Rare Diseases, 4,* 16.

National Institute of Neurological Disorders and Stroke. (2011). *Neurofibromatosis fact sheet.* Retrieved, from http://www.ninds.nih.gov/disorders/neurofibromatosis/detail_neurofibromatosis.htm

Neurofibromatosis Society of Ontario. (n.d.). Retrieved from http://www.nfon.ca/nf_info.php

Noonan Syndrome (NS)

Disease Directory.net. (2011). *Diseases: Genetic disorders.* Retrieved from http://www.diseasedirectory.net/Genetic_Disorders/default.aspx

Jongmans, M., Sistermans, E. A., Rikken, A., Nillesen, W. M., Tamminga, R., Patton, M., et al. (2005). Genotypic and phenotypic characterization of Noonan syndrome: New data and review of the literature. *American Journal of Medical Genetics A, 134,* 165-170.

National Organization for Rare Disorders (NORD). (2011). *Noonan syndrome.* Retrieved from http://www.rarediseases.org/rare-disease-information/rare-diseases/byID/412/viewAbstract

Pediatric Stroke

Children's Hemiplegia and Stroke Association. (2010). Retrieved from http://www.chasa.org

Roach, E. S., deVeber, G., Riela, A. R., & Wiznitzer, M. (2011). Recognition and treatment of stroke in children. *Child Neurology Society Ad Hoc Committee on Stroke in Children.* Retrieved from http://www.ninds.nih.gov/news_and_events/proceedings/stroke_proceedings/childneurology.htm

U.S. National Library of Medicine and the National Institutes of Health. (2010). *Cerebral hemorrhage. MDGuidelines.* Retrieved from www.mdguidelines.com/cerebral-hemorrhage

Phenylketonuria (PKU)

Blau, N., van Spronsen, F. J., & Levy, H. L. (2010). Phenylketonuria. *Lancet, 376*(9750), 1417-1427.

Centerwall, S. A., & Centerwall, W. R. (2000). The discovery of phenylketonuria: The story of a young couple, two retarded children, and a scientist. *Pediatrics, 105,* 89-103.

Scriver, C. R. (2007). The PAH gene, phenylketonuria, and a paradigm shift. *Human Mutation 28*(9), 831-845. Retrieved from http://bh4.org/pdf/scriver07.pdf

U.S. National Library of Medicine and the National Institutes of Health. (2011). *Phenylketonuria. Medline Plus.* Retrieved from http://www.nlm.nih.gov/medlineplus/phenylketonuria.html

Prader-Willi Syndrome (PWS)/Prader-Labhart-Willi Syndrome

Eiholzer, U., & Whitman, B. Y. (2004). A comprehensive team approach to the management of patients with Prader-Willi syndrome. *Journal of Pediatric Endocrinology and Metabolism, 17,* 1153-1175.

Jin, D. K. (2011). Systematic review of the clinical and genetic aspects of Prader-Willi syndrome. *Korean Journal of Pediatrics, 54*(2), 55-63.

Prader-Willi Syndrome Association (U.S.A). (n.d.). Retrieved from http://www.pwsausa.org

Progressive Myoclonus Epilepsies (PME)

de Siqueira, L. F. (2010). Progressive myoclonic epilepsies: Review of clinical, molecular and therapeutic aspects. *Journal of Neurology, 257*(10), 1612-1619.

National Institute of Neurological Disorders and Stroke. (2011). *Seizures and epilepsy: Hope through research.* Retrieved from http://www.ninds.nih.gov/disorders/epilepsy/detail_epilepsy.htm

Zupanc, M., & Legros, B. (2004). Progressive myoclonic epilepsy. *The Cerebellum, 3,* 156-171.

Rett Syndrome

Rett Syndrome Research Foundation. (2011). Retrieved from http://www.rsrf.org

Weaving, L. S., Ellaway, C. J., Gecz, J., & Christodoulou, J. (2005). Rett syndrome: Clinical review and genetic update. *Medical Genetics, 42,* 1-7.

U.S. National Library of Medicine and the National Institutes of Health. (2011). Rett syndrome. *Medline Plus Encyclopedia.* Retrieved from http://www.nlm.nih.gov/medlineplus/ency/article/001536.htm

Sanfilippo Syndrome

de Ruijter, J., Valstar, M. J., & Wijburg, F. (2011). A. Mucopolysaccharidosis type III (Sanfilippo Syndrome): Emerging treatment strategies. *Current Pharmaceutical Biotechnology, 2*(6), 923-930.

National MPS Society. (2009). Retrieved from http://www.mpssociety.org/mps3.html

Society for Mucopolysaccharide Diseases (U.K.). (2009). Retrieved from http://www.mpssociety.co.uk

Shaken Baby Syndrome (SBS)

National Center on Shaken Baby Syndrome. (n.d.). Retrieved from http://www.dontshake.org/sbs.php?topNavID=2&subNavID=10

Gabaeff, S. C. (2011). Challenging the pathophysiologic connection between subdural hematoma, retinal hemorrhage and shaken baby syndrome. *Western Journal of Emergency Medicine, 12*(2), 144-158.

Shaken Baby Syndrome Controversy. (n.d.). Retrieved from http://shakenbabysyndromecontroversy.blogspot.com/

Smith-Lemli-Opitz Syndrome (SLOS)

Jira, P. E., Waterham, H. R., Wanders R. J., Smeitink, J. A., Sengers, R. C., & Wevers, R. A. (2003). Smith-Lemli-Opitz syndrome and the DHCR7 gene. *Annals of Human Genetics, 67,* 269-280.

Porter, F. D. (2008). Smith-Lemli-Opitz syndrome: Pathogenesis, diagnosis and management. *European Journal of Human Genetics, 16*(5), 535-541.

Smith-Lemli-Opitz/RSH Foundation. (2011). Retrieved from http://www.smithlemliopitz.org/

Smith-Magenis Syndrome (SMS)

PRISMS: Parents & Researchers Interested in Smith-Magenis Syndrome. (2011). Retrieved from http://www.prisms.org/

Shelley, B. P., & Robertson, M. M. (2005). The neuropsychiatry and multisystem features of the Smith-Magenis syndrome: A review. *The Journal of Neuropsychiatry and Clinical Neurosciences, 17,* 91-97.

Spilsbury, J., & Mohanty, K. (2003). The orthopaedic manifestations of Smith-Magenis syndrome. *Journal of Pediatric Orthopedics Part B, 12,* 22-26.

Sturge-Weber Syndrome (SWS)

Comi, A. M. (2011). Presentation, diagnosis, pathophysiology, and treatment of the neurological features of Sturge-Weber syndrome. *Neurologist, 17*(4), 179-184.

Sturge-Weber Foundation (Canada) Inc. (2008). Retrieved from http://www.sturge-weber.ca/

University Hospitals of Cleveland Comprehensive Epilepsy Program. (2011). Retrieved from http://www.epilepsy.uhhs.com/

Tourette Syndrome

Singer, H. S. (2005). Tourette's syndrome: From behaviour to biology. *Lancet Neurology, 4,* 149-159.

National Tourette Syndrome Association, Inc. (n.d.). Retrieved from http://www.tsa-usa.org/index.html

Bloch, M., State, M., & Pittenger, C. (2011). Recent advances in Tourette syndrome. *Current Opinion in Neurology, 24*(2), 119-125.

Traumatic Brain Injury

National Institute of Neurological Disorders and Stroke. (2011). *Traumatic brain injury: Hope through research.* Retrieved from http://www.ninds.nih.gov/disorders/tbi/detail_tbi.htm

Sosin, D. M., Sniezek, J. E., & Thurman D. J. (1996) Incidence of mild and moderate brain injury in the United States, 1991. *Brain Injury, 10,* 47-54.

Zatzick, D. F., Rivara, F. P., Jurkovich, G. J., Hoge, C. W., Wang, J., Fan, M. Y., et al. (2010). Multisite investigation of traumatic brain injuries, posttraumatic stress disorder, and self-reported health and cognitive impairments. *Archives of General Psychi-*

atry, 67(12), 1291-1300.

Tuberous Sclerosis (TS) Complex/Syndrome

Au, K. S., Williams, A. T., Gambello, M. J., & Northrup, H. (2004). Molecular genetic basis of tuberous sclerosis complex: From bench to bedside. *Journal of Childhood Neurology, 19*, 699-709.

Maria. B. L., Deidrick, K. M., Roach, E. S., & Gutmann, D. H. (2004). Tuberous sclerosis complex: Pathogenesis, diagnosis, strategies, therapies, and future research directions. *Journal of Childhood Neurology, 19*, 632-642.

Tuberous Sclerosis Alliance. (2010). Retrieved from http://www.tsalliance.org/index.aspx

Turner Syndrome

Sybert, V. P., & McCauley, E. (2004). Turner's syndrome. *New England Journal of Medicine, 351*, 1227-1238.

Turner Syndrome Society of the United States. (2011). Retrieved from http://www.turner-syndrome-us.org/

U.S. National Library of Medicine and the National Institutes of Health. (2011). Hormone replacement therapy (HRT). *Medline Plus Encyclopedia.* Retrieved from http://www.nlm.nih.gov/medlineplus/ency/article/007111.htm

Williams Syndrome

Laws, G., & Bishop, D. (2004). Pragmatic language impairment and social deficits in Williams syndrome: A comparison with Down's syndrome and specific language impairment. *International Journal of Language & Communication Disorders, 39*, 45-64.

Mervis, C. B. (2003). Williams syndrome: 15 years of psychological research. *Developmental Neuropsychology, 23*, 1-12.

The Williams Syndrome Association. (2011). Retrieved from http://www.williams-syndrome.org/

More Resources

Websites:

American Association on Intellectual and Developmental Disabilities (AAIDD)
www.aaidd.org/content_185.cfm?navID=62

Disease Directory.net
www.diseasedirectory.net/Genetic_Disorders/default.aspx

GeneTests (NCBI)
www.ncbi.nlm.nih.gov/sites/GeneTests/?db=GeneTests

Human Genome Project Information. Genetic Disease Information – pronto!
www.ornl.gov/sci/techresources/Human_Genome/medicine/assist.shtml

Human Genome Variation (HGV) Society. Guidelines and Recommendations
www.hgvs.org/rec.html

The MAGIC Foundation
www.magicfoundation.org/www

National Center for Biotechnology Information
www.ncbi.nlm.nih.gov/

National Human Genome Research Institute
Talking glossary of genetic terms.
www.genome.gov/glossary/index.cfm?

OMIM. Online Mendelian Inheritance in Man
www.ncbi.nlm.nih.gov/sites/entrez?db=omim

OMMBID. The Online Metabolic and Molecular Bases of Inherited Diseases
www.ommbid.com/

Specific Disabilities and Syndromes
www.autreat.com/other_specific.html

Support for Families of Children with Disabilities
www.supportforfamilies.org/internetguide/specdisab.htm

TIDE-BC. Changing Paradigms to Improve Child Health
www.tidebc.org/

University of Western Ontario Developmental Disabilities Division
http://ddd.uwo.ca/

U.S. National Library of Medicine and the National Institutes of Health.
Medical Dictionary.
ww.nlm.nih.gov/medlineplus/mplusdictionary.html

Whonamedit
www.whonamedit.com/

Books:

Accardo P. J. (Ed.). (2008). *Capute and Accardo's*

neurodevelopmental disabilities in infancy and childhood (3rd ed.). Baltimore: Paul H. Brookes Publishing Co.

Accardo, P. J., Whitman, B. Y., Accardo, J. A., Bodurtha, J. N., Farrell, A., Goelz, T., et al. (2011). *Dictionary of developmental disabilities terminology* (3rd ed.). Baltimore: Paul H. Brookes Publishing Co.

American Psychiatric Association. (2000). *Diagnostic and statistical manual of mental disorders* (4th ed., text rev.). Washington, DC: Author.

Baraitser, M., & Winter, R. M. (1996). *Color atlas of congenital malformation syndromes*. London: Mosby-Wolfe.

Batshaw, M. L. (2001). *When your child has a disability: A complete sourcebook of daily and medical care, revised edition*. Baltimore: Paul H. Brookes Publishing Co.

Batshaw, M. L., Pelligrino, L., & Roizen, N. L. (2007). *Children with disabilities* (6th ed.). Baltimore: Paul H. Brookes Publishing Co.

Griffiths, D., & King, R. (Eds.). (2004). *Demystifying syndromes: Clinical and educational implications of common syndromes associated with persons with intellectual disabilities*. Kingston, NY: The NADD Press.

Harris, J. C. (2006). *Intellectual disability: Understanding its development, causes, classification, evaluation, and treatment (Developmental perspectives in psychiatry)*. New York: Oxford University Press.

Jones, K. L. (Ed.). (2006). *Smith's recognizable patterns of human malformation* (6th ed.). Philadelphia: Elsevier Saunders.

Jung, J. H. (2010). *Genetic syndromes in communication disorders* (2nd ed). Austin, TX: Pro-Ed Publishing.

Nickel, R. E., & Desch, L. W. (2000). *The physicians guide to caring for children with disabilities and chronic conditions*. Baltimore: Paul H. Brookes Publishing Co.

Rubin, L. I., & Crocker, A. C. (Eds.). (2006). *Medical care for children and adults with developmental disabilities*. Baltimore: Paul H. Brookes Publishing Co.

Ryan, R. M. (2001). *Handbook of mental health care for persons with developmental disabilities*. Evergreen, CO: S & B Publishing.

Shapiro, B. K., & Accardo, P. J. (2010). *Neurogenetic syndromes: Behavioral issues and their treatment*. Baltimore: Paul H. Brookes Publishing Co.

Articles:

Connors, S. L., Levitt, P., Matthews, S. G., Slotkin, T. A., Johnston, M. V., Kinney, H. C., et al. (2008). Fetal mechanisms in neurodevelopmental disorders. *Pediatric Neurology 38*(3), 163-176.

Di Nuovo, S., & Buono, S. (2011). Behavioral phenotypes of genetic syndromes with intellectual disability: Comparison of adaptive profiles. *Psychiatry Research*, Apr 18.

Grey, I. M., & Hastings, R. P. (2005). Evidence-based practices in intellectual disability and behaviour disorders. *Current Opinion in Psychiatry, 18*(5), 469-475.

Hodapp, R. M., & Dykens, E. M. (2009). Intellectual disabilities and child psychiatry: Looking to the future. *The Journal of Child Psychology and Psychiatry, 50*(1-2), 99-107.

Harris, J. C. (2010). Advances in understanding behavioral phenotypes in neurogenetic syndromes. *American Journal of Medical Genetics C: Seminars in Medical Genetics, 154C*(4), 389-399.

Hässler, F., & Reis, O. (2010). Pharmacotherapy of disruptive behavior in mentally retarded subjects: A review of the current literature. *Developmental Disabilities Research Reviews, 16*(3):265-272.

Matson, J. L., & Mahan, S. (2010). Antipsychotic drug side effects for persons with intellectual disability. *Research in Developmental Disabilities, 31*(6), 1570-1576.

Oliver, C., & Richards, C. (2010). Self-injurious behaviour in people with intellectual disability. *Current Opinion in Psychiatry, 23*(5), 412-416.

Percy, M. (2007). Other syndromes and disorders associated with intellectual and developmental disabilities. In I. Brown & M. Percy (Eds.), *A comprehensive guide to intellectual and developmental disabilities* (pp. 229-268). Baltimore: Paul H. Brookes Publishing Co.

Rowles, B. M., & Findling, R. L. (2010). Review of pharmacotherapy options for the treatment of attention-deficit/hyperactivity disorder (ADHD) and ADHD-like symptoms in children and adolescents with developmental disorders. *Developmental Disabilities Research Reviews, 16*(3), 273-282.

Valkenburg, A. J., van Dijk, M., de Klein, A., van den Anker, J. N, & Tibboel, D. (2010). Pain management in intellectually disabled children: Assessment, treatment, and translational research. *Developmental Disabilities Research Reviews, 16*(3), 248-257.

14

Down Syndrome: Characteristics and Health Issues

Maire Percy, Jane Summers, and John Lovering

What you will learn:

- Causes of Down syndrome
- Diagnosis of Down syndrome
- Physical characteristics of individuals with Down syndrome
- Communication and achievement issues in Down syndrome
- Some medical conditions that are common in Down syndrome
- Mental health issues in Down syndrome
- Treatments, interventions and preventions for these medical conditions
- Recent research advances and future direction

This chapter is dedicated to the memory of our colleague and friend, Dr. John Lovering, developmental pediatrician, whose breadth of knowledge and insight have provided, and continue to provide, the fundamentals for this chapter.

Note: *Words in **bold italics** are explained in the Special Terms section following the Summary.*

Down syndrome is the most common genetic cause of moderate developmental disability. In North America, it occurs in about one live born child in 800 to 1,000. Although its existence may have been documented in classical art, it was first formally described by John Langdon Down in 1866 (Berg, 2003; Berg & Korossy, 2001; Down, 1866). This advance reflected the growing recognition that

mental health conditions and cognitive disabilities are different, and that each requires different types of care and interventions. Since that time, there has been an increasing awareness of the many causes of developmental disability and a vast expansion of our knowledge about Down syndrome. The purpose of this chapter is to familiarize readers with the complexities of Down syndrome, and to highlight how preventive strategies can result in remarkable quality of life for people with this condition.

Causes of Down Syndrome

The chromosomal basis of Down syndrome was established independently in 1959 by groups headed by Patricia Jacobs and Jerome Lejeune. Approximately 95% of individuals with Down syn-

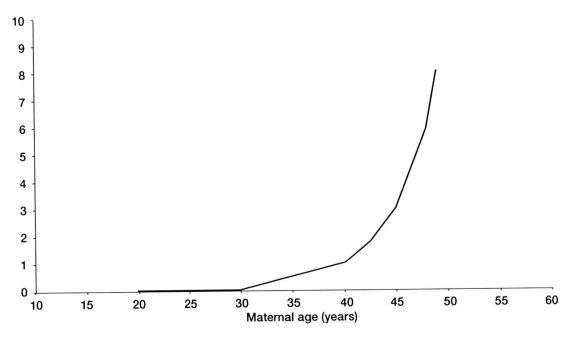

Figure 1. Percentage of live births with Down syndrome and mother's age in years

Source: Behman (1992, p. 284).

drome have an extra chromosome 21 (trisomy 21), for a total of three instead of the normal two. The extra chromosome 21 results from a process called ***non-disjunction***, which causes an ovum in a female or a sperm in a male to have two chromosome 21s instead of the usual one. The risk of non-disjunction that results in a child having trisomy 21 has been shown to increase with advancing maternal age (Figure 1), and significantly increases after the age of 35 years. About 85% of cases of trisomy 21 result from maternal errors in ***meiosis***; about 15% result from paternal meiotic errors.

Although most cases of Down syndrome are caused by trisomy 21, about 4% are caused by a critical extra part of chromosome 21 being attached to another chromosome (usually to a chromosome 14 or a chromosome 22, but sometimes to 13, 15 or another 21); in this case the hybrid chromosome is called a translocation chromosome. For normal females or males who carry such a translocation chromosome, the risk of having a child with Down syndrome is 10-15%, or 3-8%, respectively, even when they are young adults.

A third cause of Down syndrome is an internal duplication of some critical genes on one of the two chromosome 21s. A fourth cause is *mosaicism* for chromosome 21. Individuals affected in this way usually have two cell lines — some cells have three chromosome 21s, while other cells have two. The proportion of these two kinds of cells may vary from one tissue to another (e.g., be different in white blood cells and in skin cells). Only about 1% of individuals identified with Down syndrome have mosaicism. Mosaicism for Down syndrome is difficult to diagnose and people with this disorder tend to be less severely affected than those with trisomy 21 (Fishler & Koch, 1991). To note is that although increasing maternal age is a strong risk factor for Down syndrome, the majority of babies with Down syndrome are born to young mothers. (See also Chen, 2011; Lovering & Percy, 2007.)

Diagnosis of Down Syndrome

Down syndrome often is diagnosed during pregnancy (see Chapter 38). Fetal ultrasound analysis looks for fetal abnormalities that are characteristic of

Down syndrome. If an accurate diagnosis of Down syndrome is desired, then it is possible to examine fetal chromosomes by *karyotyping*, or to study the fetal DNA using the *polymerase chain reaction*. Both of these latter procedures can be applied to tissue samples obtained by *chorionic villus sampling or by amniocentesis*. Because there is a slight risk of miscarriage or of causing damage to the fetus, chronionic villus sampling and amniocentesis usually are recommended only if the mother is over age 35, has had another child with Down syndrome, has had an abnormal ultrasound or serum test to detect Down syndrome, or has a family history of the condition. All prenatal testing requires informed consent.

Karyotyping can also be done shortly after birth if Down syndrome is suspected. It may take 2 to 3 weeks to get the complete results of this test. As well, a health professional is able to provide an opinion about the likelihood that a baby has Down syndrome without chromosomal or DNA analysis (Devlin & Morrison, 2004). This opinion is based on the baby's appearance, the results of a physical exam, family history, and results of ultrasound and the serum screening test if done during the pregnancy. (See also Chapter 38; Chen, 2011; Lovering & Percy, 2007.)

The Down Syndrome Phenotype

Physical characteristics

There is considerable variability in the appearance of individuals with Down syndrome. Not all of the features described below are always present and some may disappear over time. Many of these features are also seen in the general population, but at a lower frequency than in people with Down syndrome and fewer of them occur in any one person. Hereditary factors also influence the physical appearance of children and adults with Down syndrome.

Physical features that are commonly present in individuals with Down syndrome are called the Down syndrome phenotype (Roizen & Patterson, 2003). These include:

- Brachycephaly (short, broad head)
- Bradydactyly (short fingers)
- Broad hands
- Duodenal atresia (complete obliteration of the *duodenal lumen*)
- Epicanthal folds (the skin fold of the upper eyelid that covers the inner corner of the eye)
- 5th finger clinodactyly (curving in of the little finger)
- Flat nasal bridge
- Hypotonia (low muscle tone, often involving low muscle strength)
- Intellectual disability
- Lax ligaments
- Open mouth
- Short stature
- Wide gap between the 1st & 2nd toes

Other features may include: grey-white raised Brushfield spots on the surface of the iris that have no clinical significance and require no treatment; small ears often with a low and oblique placement on the face; narrowing of the ear canals and absent or incompletely attached ear lobes; lips that may gradually become more prominent with fissuring and thickening (in cold weather the lips are prone to chapping); a tongue that protrudes; a neck that appears short and widened (extra folds of skin at the back of the neck are sometimes seen in newborn babies, but these gradually disappear); hernias around the navel; and a single transverse palmar crease on at least one hand.

Growth

Children with Down syndrome usually grow less quickly than other children. This seems to hold from before birth to adolescence, but the differences in growth velocity are most evident in the first few years of life. Growth velocity during middle childhood tends to more closely parallel growth changes in children who do not have Down syndrome. The cause of short stature in children with Down syndrome is unclear but may result from a number of causes, including having the extra chromosome 21, having a resulting deficiency of growth hormone, celiac disease, or significant hypothyroidism. Environment and heredity may be factors as well. Children reared in institutional settings tend to be shorter than those living at home, probably as the result of poorer nutrition.

In view of the consistent findings in the growth patterns of children with Down syndrome, special growth charts have been constructed. These help in following the physical development of children with Down syndrome. If concerns arise around the youngster's pattern of growth or weight, the use of standard charts helps identify and follow unusual trends in height and weight. (See Growth Charts in More Resources.)

Life expectancy

Life expectancy for people with Down syndrome in North America has shown dramatic increases over the past 50 years as the result of improved medical care (e.g., use of antibiotics, correction of congenital heart disease, and treatment of leukemia). Data from a variety of studies have been summarized in graphical form in Figure 2 to demonstrate this change through the first 10 years of life (Berg,

Karlinsky, & Holland, 1993).

In British Columbia, where accurate figures have been maintained since 1952 from numerous sources, the survival rate for individuals with Down syndrome at 30 years of age has been estimated to be 72% (Baird & Sadovnick, 1987). It is somewhat higher when one considers those without congenital heart disease, a leading cause of sickness and death, particularly in the first year of life. Baird & Sadovnick pointed out that the survival rate in the general population at age 30 is 97%. In moderate developmental disability other than Down syndrome, it is 92%. In Down syndrome, the survival rate appears to plateau from about the age of 5-40 years. After age 40, the rate decreases.

The importance of a physically active lifestyle to prevent deterioration of health cannot be overemphasized (Rimmer, Heller, Wang, & Valerio, 2004). One indication that this does occur is that many people with Down syndrome take part in the Special Olympics.

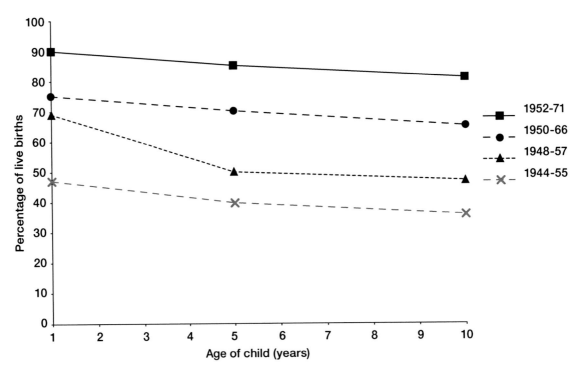

Figure 2. Percentage of live births with Down syndrome surviving through childhood
Source: Berg, Karlinsky, & Holland (1993).

Communication and Achievement Issues

General issues

Chapman and Hesketh (2001) pointed out that, relative to people without Down syndrome, those with Down syndrome are characterized by a delay in non-verbal cognitive development, specific deficits in speech and language production and deficits in short term auditory memory, but fewer adaptive behavioural problems. There is no critical period for the acquisition of communication in Down syndrome. Speech and language skills continue to develop even into adulthood, although at a slower pace than in typically developing people. Language skills are less well developed than visuospatial skills and difficulties are present in both speech and language. The majority of individuals with Down syndrome read at some level (Cupples & Iacono, 2000), and reading skills can develop beyond mental age abilities.

Some people with Down syndrome have had remarkable achievements. For example, Chris Burke is a well-known actor who also has co-authored a book and is editor-in-chief of a magazine for children and young adults with Down syndrome. Chris also has a band and gives inspirational speeches. (See Chris' website at *http://www.chrisburke.org/* for more information.) Cathy Lemon is a young woman living in Ontario whose passion for baking and dreams inspired formation of the Lemon & Allspice Cookery in 1998. As the result of increased demand for similar opportunities, the Common Ground Co-operative was created in 2000. In 2011, five businesses with over sixty partners and seven job coaches are providing long-term employment. (See the Common Ground website at *http://ckc. tcf.ca/org/common-ground-co-operative* for more information.)

Speech

Speech intelligibility in Down syndrome is adversely affected by two neurological factors:
- Dysarthria (difficulty with the strength and precision of muscle movements, leading to thick and imprecise articulation)
- Apraxia (the inability to program, combine, organize and sequence muscle movements)

Other conditions common in Down syndrome affect intelligibility and clarity of speech. These include mouth breathing, enlargement of the tonsils and adenoids that block the nasal airways, velopharyngeal incompetence (difficulty forming a seal between the pharynx and nasal passages), and relative macroglossia (a tongue that is too large for the size of the oral cavity). Mid-facial ***hypoplasia***, hypotonicity of the oral cavity, high arched palate, and irregular and delayed dentition also play a role. In addition, phonological processes may be substantially delayed. All children make errors and inconsistencies in pronouncing words, but these are more common in children with Down syndrome and persist into adolescence and adulthood.

Expressive language

The expressive language skills in children with Down syndrome do not keep pace with cognitive skill development (Chapman & Hesketh, 2001), a finding evident in most children with Down syndrome by the age of three years. In addition to having syntactic difficulties (difficulties with the grammatical arrangement of words, showing their connection and relation), problems with short-term memory and auditory processing impair the development of expressive language. In contrast, the onset of babbling, with its patterns of syllables, the emergence of first words (8-45 months), and the content of the first 50 words (a preponderance of nouns over verbs) are similar to those of typically developing children matched for mental age. Signing can be taught through the second cognitive year and is a particularly helpful intervention in improving vocabulary development and language skills. Young children 2-3 years of age can learn to read a large number of words. Over the age of 20-24 months, children with or without Down syndrome use two-word utterances similarly. After that, expressive syntax differs significantly; in particular, children with Down syndrome have difficulties in verb agreement and use pronouns less frequently.

Receptive language

Vocabulary comprehension is a relative strength in adolescents with Down syndrome and acquisition of skills in this area is similar to children without Down syndrome matched for mental age. Adults with Down syndrome have more difficulty with syntax comprehension, a problem that begins in adolescence (Kernan, 1990).

Developmental and learning profile

Individuals with Down syndrome demonstrate a specific profile of strengths and weaknesses. In addition to stronger receptive than expressive language abilities, their visuo-spatial memory is better developed than auditory verbal short-term memory (Jarrold, Nadel, & Vicari, 2009), and implicit long-term memory is superior to explicit long-term memory (Vicari, 2001). Many of these patterns start to emerge in early childhood and become more pronounced as children get older (Fidler, Most, Booth-LaForce, & Kelly, 2008). A strong visual memory and good visual imitation skills can be very helpful, in terms of promoting greater competence in self-care and work-related skills. However, they can also overshadow weaker auditory processing abilities and lead to inappropriate expectations and poor performance when spoken instructions are not accompanied by visual cues (McGuire & Chicoine, 2006). Motor impairments are another aspect of their developmental profile and include low muscle tone and deficits in fine and gross motor skills (Fidler, Most, & Philofsky, 2008).

The popular view of individuals with Down syndrome is that they are friendly and sociable. Basic aspects of social-emotional functioning are relatively well developed in young children with Down syndrome, who may be particularly adept at showing empathy or an ability to engage others (Fidler, Most, & Philofsky, 2008). However, impairments in more advanced social-cognitive skills such as social referencing may become evident as children get older (Cebula, Moore, & Wishart, 2010). An interesting phenomenon has been identified among children with Down syndrome, whereby they may "misuse" their social skills to delay, avoid or terminate learn-ing tasks or situations that are potentially difficult or challenging. This type of "counterproductive" learning style can have a deleterious effect on their ongoing educational opportunities (Wishart, 2001).

Interventions

Early intervention is extremely important in the first six years, as cognitive and communication skills lag behind personal-social and adaptive skills. Intervention improves the style of mothers' interaction, which in turn benefits the child's receptive language. Because sign, picture communication, and reading fall into the visual domain and are relative strengths, it is often helpful if they form the primary focus in intervention. Group therapy has proven to be a valuable form of intervention in improving language in childhood and early adulthood. Language intervention should continue throughout adolescence and into early adulthood as there is evidence that individuals show ongoing progress (Chapman & Hesketh, 2001). Fidler (2005) pointed out that much more work needs to be done to link the results of behaviour phenotype research to intervention efforts, so that knowledge of specific patterns of strength and weakness and learning style in individuals with Down syndrome can assist with the selection of treatment elements to maximize their learning outcomes. Specific teaching procedures that may help improve children's motivation to engage in learning tasks and maintain task persistence could include the use of errorless learning approaches, providing a high ratio of easy-to-difficult tasks, and pairing verbal instruction with visual supports (Feeley & Jones, 2008; Fidler, Most, & Philofsky, 2008).

Medical Health Concerns

The medical conditions found in people with Down syndrome are, for the most part, no different than those found in individuals without Down syndrome. There is, however, clear evidence of increased risk for a variety of health concerns. These altered risks are thought to result, in part, from the chromosomal nature of the condition and the effect it has on developmental processes. One can antici-

Table 1: The Most Common Forms of Congenital Heart Disease in Down Syndrome

Atrioventricular canal	60%
Atrial septal defects	
Ventricular septal defects	30%
Patent ductus arteriosus	
Tetralogy of Fallot	7%

pate these problems before they have an opportunity to produce significant illness. Individuals with Down syndrome should be followed on a regular basis by a physician who is interested in the care of individuals with Down syndrome. The following are the most common considerations in the health care of individuals with Down syndrome. The content is not exhaustive and the reader is referred to the More Resources section of this chapter for additional information.

Heart disease

Children with Down syndrome have a significantly increased risk of congenital heart disease (CHD); as many as 40-50% are affected, compared to about 3% in the general population. Improvements in the treatment of CHD have had a dramatic impact on the life expectancy of children with Down syndrome. An association between heart defects and ocular abnormalities in children has been noted (Bromham, Woodhase, Cregg, Webb, & Fraser, 2002).

In the most common form of CHD, the endocardial cushion fails to fuse with the membranous septa of the walls of the heart chambers (Figure 3). This results in a canal and a lack of separation of the four chambers of the heart. In an atrial septal defect, there is a defect or "hole" of variable size in the septum, allowing communication between the left and right-sided atrials, or low-pressure chambers of the heart. Table 1 lists the most common forms of CHD in Down syndrome and the approximate frequencies of their occurrence.

An infant with Down syndrome must have a cardiovascular examination because of the high risk of CHD. The examination usually includes an ***electrocardiogram***, a chest X-ray, and an ***echocardiogram***. Early diagnosis and surgery, where necessary, are important in the prevention of complications. The results of treatment are as successful in children with Down syndrome as in those without Down syndrome (80-90% survival rates).

In adults, there is higher prevalence of ***aortic regurgitation*** and ***mitral valve prolapse***, presumably related to connective tissue abnormalities. Adults with Down syndrome appear to have lowered blood pressure and a reduced likelihood of atherosclerosis (lesions of medium-sized arteries that contain fatty deposits including cholesterol). This has the effect of protecting the individual from strokes and heart attacks in adult life.

Gastrointestinal obstructions and abnormalities

Gastrointestinal obstructions affect many individuals with Down syndrome (Langman, 1963). There is an association between gastrointestinal obstructions and cardiac disease; about 70% of children with gastrointestinal defects also have some form of congenital heart disease. The most common gastrointestinal obstructions are:

- Esophageal atresia with tracheoesophageal fistula
- Esophageal reflux
- Duodenal atresia or stenosis
- Hirschsprung disease
- Imperforate anus

Celiac disease (an autoimmune disorder) and *Helicobacter pylori* (a gastrointestinal infection) are very common gastrointestinal abnormalities in people with Down syndrome; unfortunately, they are underrecognized and underdiagnosed.

Gastrointestinal obstructions: These disorders affect about 10% of children with Down syndrome. They are second only to congenital heart disease as causes of infant mortality. An understanding of these disorders requires a short discussion of em-

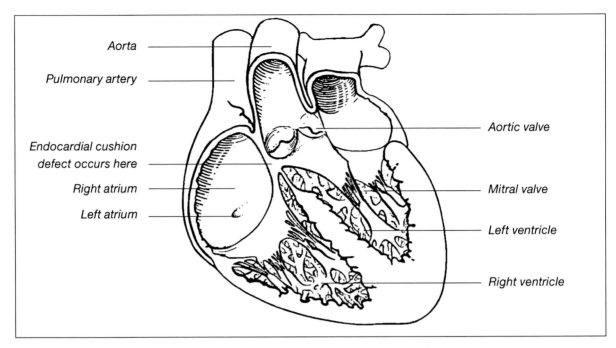

Figure 3. Cross-section of the heart showing its chambers and great vessels

Source: Medical Illustrations Library (1994).

bryology. During fetal development, the lumen of the bowel is patent (open) and then is obliterated as tissue forms. During the 4th to 6th weeks of gestation, a process of recanalization (reopening of the lumen) of the gastrointestinal tract takes place. If this process fails at any point, an obstruction remains. There may be associated interference in the separation between the trachea and esophagus leading to a persistent communication between the two, known as a tracheoesophageal fistula. The finding of an imperforate anus is also related to deficiencies in the process of recanalization.

Esophageal atresia and tracheoesophageal fistula: The trachea, or windpipe, carries air to the lungs. The esophagus carries food to the stomach. The term esophageal atresia means that the esophagus is blocked to a greater or lesser degree. The term tracheoesophageal fistula means that the trachea and esophagus are connected. Sometimes during development, these two tubes do not separate completely, but remain connected by a short passage. When this happens, air enters the gastrointestinal system, causing the bowels to distend, and mucus is

breathed into the lungs causing aspiration pneumonia and breathing problems. In the diagrams depicting the most common forms of tracheoesophageal fistula (Figure 4), A represents about 87% of these anomalies, while B and C represent 8% and 4%, respectively (Behrman, 1992). The most common signs of this condition include respiratory distress and drooling. Early diagnosis is important, and appropriate treatment limits the degree of respiratory compromise. An attempt to pass a firm feeding tube into the stomach will meet resistance when an esophageal atresia or obstruction is present. X-rays will establish the level of the atresia and the most likely location of the fistula. If the blind ends are not separated by too great a distance, a primary anastomosis (connection) can be done. Otherwise, several staged surgical interventions over time are required. The most common complications include leaks around the anastomosis, which may result in chronic lung disease and reflux or regurgitation.

Gastroesophageal reflux: Gastroesophageal reflux is the movement of stomach contents up the esophagus toward the mouth, rather than down through

Box 1: Symptoms of Celiac Disease

Intestinal

- *Abdominal pain, abdominal distention, diarrhea, lactose intolerance, nausea & vomiting, stools that float, weight loss*

Non-intestinal

- *Anemia; bone & joint pain; bone disease; breathlessness; bruising; dental enamel discoloration; depression; fatigue; growth delay (children); hair loss; hypoglycemia; irritability and behaviour changes; malnutrition; mouth ulcers; muscle cramps; nosebleed; seizures; other neurological abnormalities; skin diseases (dermatitis herpetiformis); swelling (general or abdominal); vitamin or mineral deficiency*

the digestive system (peristalsis). Problems such as choking and difficulty swallowing often occur with these strictures. It may be difficult to move from a fluid to a solid diet and failure to thrive may occur if the problem persists. Up to one-half of children will require dilatation to gradually improve the patency of the esophagus. Reflux can usually be managed medically with small feedings, antacids and other newer agents such as cimetidine.

Duodenal atresia: This is a form of intestinal obstruction that causes symptoms such as vomiting and, depending on the level of the blockage, abdominal distention and bile-stained vomitus. X-rays are often helpful in the diagnosis, and the treatment is surgical. Feeding difficulties are common after the surgery but gradually abate.

Hirshsprung disease (aganglionic megacolon): In this condition, which is commonly associated with Down syndrome, there is an absence of "ganglion cells" in a portion of the large intestine. The result is an inability of the bowel muscle to relax and produce normal peristaltic movement, and severe constipation results. With the obstruction that this causes, newborn babies do not pass meconium (the dark green mucilaginous substance present in the intestine of the full-term baby) in the first 24 hours as expected, and they go on to develop vomiting and abdominal distention. Some babies also

develop bloody diarrhea and generalized infection. Sometimes Hirshsprung disease is so severe that the bowel must be put to rest and a colostomy (the surgical creation of a new opening of the colon on the surface of the body) carried out. Before surgery, intravenous feeding may be necessary to boost the child's weight. Such surgery is not done before the child is one year old. Patience is required to eventually achieve normal bowel function and eradicate bowel accidents.

Celiac disease (CD): CD is much more common in the general population than previously believed, and more common in Down syndrome than in the general population. In the general population, prevalences of CD are 0.5-1%. In Down syndrome, prevalences are reported to be 3-7% (U.S.) and 7-16% (Europe) (Roizen & Patterson, 2003). In CD, there is sensitivity to gluten, a protein commonly found in foods containing oats, barley, rye and wheat. In addition to bread, cookies and other baked products, packaged and processed foods are especially problematic. Those with CD have an impaired ability to absorb water and many important nutrients. CD is often diagnosed in the general population between 6 months and 2 years of age, while this diagnosis often occurs much later in children and adults with Down syndrome. As shown in Box 1, CD often is associated with intestinal symptoms. However, sometimes the symptoms are more subtle, or it is associated with non-intestinal symptoms including dermatitis herpetiformis, a chronic benign skin disorder associated with a burning, itching rash. An intestinal infection with ***Giardia lamblia*** may produce symp-

Box 2: Symptoms of *Helicobacter pylori* Infection

Children

- *Nausea, vomiting, abdominal pain*

Older children and adults

- *Gnawing or burning pain in abdomen below ribs and above navel that is relieved by eating, drinking milk, and taking antacid.*

toms that are similar to those of CD. In CD, characteristic changes occur in the lining of the small bowel that can be detected with an intestinal biopsy. As well, certain antibodies are present in the blood that can be detected with sensitive blood tests.

The most important component of the treatment for CD is the institution of a gluten-free diet (Hill, 2006). This regimen is difficult to maintain without cooperation and commitment and is especially troublesome for children. It must be adhered to throughout adulthood. Vitamin supplementation and the help of support groups are additional aspects of intervention. Health care guidelines for individuals with Down syndrome recommend screening at 2-3 years of age to reduce growth failures, gastrointestinal symptoms, behaviour problems and intestinal lymphoma associated with CD. (For more information about CD, see Percy & Probst, 2007; Chapter 32.)

Helicobacter pylori **infection:** Infection with the microorganism *Helicobacter pylori* is common in the general population, but it occurs twice as fre-quently in people with various forms of intellectual disability, including Down syndrome (Wallace, Webb, & Schluter, 2002). It is a cause of gastritis, ulcers, and some types of gastrointestinal cancer. Symptoms associated with this infection are listed in Box 2. Diagnosis of helicobacter infection includes blood tests for antibodies, breath tests, stool tests, and sometimes endoscopy. Treatment involves administration of 1 or 2 antibiotics and antacid for 10 days to 2 weeks.

Ear, nose and throat problems

Individuals with Down syndrome have underdeveloped midfacial structures and a reduced distance from the back to the front of the skull. Anatomic variations are often present in association with these findings. The oral cavity is often relatively small, and this may cause the tongue to protrude. It is common to find dysfunction of the middle ear and Eustachian tube, the connection between the middle ear and the nasopharynx.

Infections are common, much moreso than in the

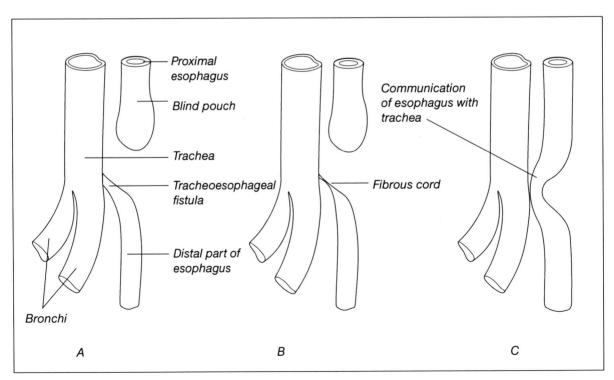

Figure 4. The most common forms of tracheosophageal fistula

Source: After Langman (1963, p. 218).

general population, and these affect the chest as well as structures of the ear, nose and throat. In Down syndrome, the external ear canal is often narrow and can be easily impacted with cerumen (earwax).

Hearing loss also occurs frequently (Shott, Joseph, & Heithaus, 2001). Otitis media (middle ear infection) with effusion (accumulation of sticky thick fluid in the middle ear) is the most common cause. This results in what is called a *conductive hearing loss* and affects 60-90% of individuals with Down syndrome. In conductive hearing loss, the transmission of sound through the ear canal to the tiny bones in the middle ear and then to the nerve connections of the inner ear is in some way impeded. Less commonly, the neural pathway is affected, producing what is known as a *sensorineural* hearing loss. Some individuals have a combination of both types of hearing problems. A cross-section of the human ear is shown in Figure 5.

Routine screening of hearing (audiometry), and aggressive treatment are important to maintain optimal language and cognitive development. Removal of earwax is a simple but often very important procedure that can be done in the family doctor's office. The placement of ventilating tubes through the eardrum may be required when standard treatment of middle ear infection and effusion is unsuccessful. Monitoring by an audiologist every 6-12 months and by an Ear Nose & Throat specialist is advisable. Many individuals with Down syndrome benefit from hearing aids or some form of amplification (such as desktop and personal frequency modulated systems), and experts recognize the role for a team of health care professionals in these circumstances. Sometimes the surgical removal of adenoids and/or tonsils is carried out, but the decision to do this needs to be made carefully, as the reduced size of the nasopharynx may make the adenoids appear large when they are not. Persons with large adenoids are at higher risk for velopharyngeal incompetence, a condition that leads to a hypernasal voice.

Oral health

The oral cavity is typically small in people with Down syndrome, and relative macroglossia is common. This may lead to protrusion of the tongue and

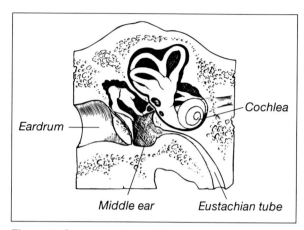

Figure 5. Cross-section of the human ear
Source: Medical Illustration Library (1994).

a tendency to keep the mouth open. Occasionally, surgical intervention is used to reduce the size of the tongue.

Malocclusion of teeth is very common and occurs in most individuals with Down syndrome. Occlusion refers to the alignment of teeth and the way that the upper and lower teeth fit together (bite). Malocclusion means the teeth are not aligned properly. Types of malocclusion include cross bite, crowded teeth, misaligned teeth, open bite, overbite and underbite. Malocclusion is the most common reason for referral to an orthodontist. Most malocclusion is mild enough not to require treatment. If a severe misalignment is present, orthodontics and/or oral surgery may be required. Caries (dental cavities) have been found in some studies to occur less frequently in people with Down syndrome than in others with or without other forms of intellectual disabilities. However, when other factors are taken into consideration, such as diet, numbers of teeth and spacing of teeth, these differences are not characteristic of Down syndrome. Good oral hygiene is very important. Both primary and permanent teeth often erupt one to two years later than expected. Because of this, permanent teeth often erupt in front of, or behind the primary teeth. Teeth are often missing, particularly the upper lateral incisors, and less frequently, second bicuspids and lower incisors.

Marked, rapid and early onset of periodontal (gum) disease, is a concern in the dental care of individuals with Down syndrome. Periodontal disease may result in the teeth losing their attachment to alveolar bone, leading to a loss of teeth. Gingivitis and gingival bleeding are common in children with Down syndrome and there is often more plaque and calculus than in children with other forms of intellectual disability. Diet, oral hygiene and immunodeficiency are all factors in the evolution of these dental problems. Routine tooth brushing combined with dental visits every 6 months can prevent periodontal disease and associated tooth loss (Buckley, 2003; Fiske & Shafik, 2001.)

Skin conditions

A number of skin conditions are common in people with Down syndrome (Schepis, Barone, Siragusa, Pettinato, & Romano, 2002). These include:

Alopecia areata: This is the name for a condition in which round patches of hair loss (scalp, beard area, eyebrows or eyelashes) appear suddenly. The hair-growing tissue is attacked by the patient's own immune cells for unknown reasons. There is a tendency for spontaneous recovery.

Atopic dermatitis: Atopic dermatitis, commonly referred to as eczema, is a chronic skin disorder categorized by scaly and itching rashes. Red scaly patches can occur on the flexor surfaces of the arm, creases of the elbow, backs of the knee, the ankles,

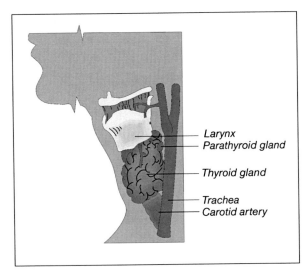

Figure 6. Cross-section of the neck
Source: Corel Gallery 2 (1995).

Box 3: Symptoms of Thyroid Dysfunction

General population

- *Weakness, lethargy, fatigue; dry skin, coarse hair; cold intolerance, constipation, weight gain; muscle cramps; edema of eyelids, face, legs; hoarseness, hearing loss; menorrhagia; slowing of return phase of reflexes (e.g., knee jerk); bradycardia*

Down syndrome

- *Physical symptoms of hypothyroidism are not often evident; a possible relation with hepatitis B virus infection*

wrists and cheeks. The skin is itchy and becomes thickened. Oilated oatmeal in the bath and hydrophilic lotions are often helpful. Medications such as antihistamines, antibiotics, and topical corticosteroids may be necessary to deal with inflammation and infection.

Cheilitis: This term refers to inflammation and cracking of the lips that involves red scaling and crusting. It is more common in males than females with Down syndrome. Zinc oxide or white petrolatum may be used to treat the condition.

Xerosis: This is the term for dry skin. There is often a gradual change in the skin of individuals with Down syndrome. The skin is soft and velvety in infancy, but by mid-adolescence it becomes dry and scaly in about 70% of individuals. Symptoms of itching develop and, because of thickening and cracking, the skin becomes prone to infections and may heal slowly. Moisturizers and emollients are helpful; oilated Aveeno can be added to bath water and the individual should avoid the use of soaps that dry the skin.

Scrotal tongue: This disorder is a benign condition that is characterized by numerous shallow or deep grooves or furrows (fissures) on the back (dorsal) surface of the tongue. The surface furrows may differ in size and depth, radiate outward, and cause the tongue to have a wrinkled appearance. This condition is present in 3-5% of the general population, but occurs in nearly all persons with Down syndrome.

Other disorders: Syringomas (benign tumors of the sweat glands), milia-like calcinosis, folliculitis (inflammation of the hair follicles), and elastosis perforans serpiginosa (a rare disorder occurring more frequently in males than females in which abnormal elastic fibres are expelled through the dermis) also occur in Down syndrome (Schepis et al., 2002).

Eye conditions

Several conditions related to the eyes are common in people with Down syndrome (van Splunder, Stilma, Bernsen, & Evenhuis, 2004). These include:

Brushfield spots: These white to light yellow nodules or speckles at the periphery of the iris are common, particularly when the iris is blue or hazel in color. They are benign and require no treatment.

Blepharitis: Inflammation of the eyelid occurs in up to half of individuals with Down syndrome. Daily cleansing of lid margins helps to reduce the likelihood of this condition.

Keratoconus: A cone-shaped cornea occurs in 5-8% of individuals with Down syndrome, and may occur acutely. Keratoconus is a frequent cause of blindness in Down syndrome, second only to complications related to cataract surgery. Non-penetrating corneal grafting is recommended as the procedure of choice in this disorder (Haugen, Hovding, Eide, & Bertelsen, 2001).

Cataracts: This condition refers to opacity of the lens of the eye. In people with Down syndrome, cataracts may occur in the form of gray flaky opacities near the surface of the lens. Cataracts are not uncommon in childhood, but they become more common as the individual ages. Some investigators believe that virtually all elderly individuals with Down syndrome have some degree of cataract formation. When visual acuity decreases substantially, surgical removal of the cataract is carried out.

Strabismus: This refers to a deviation of one or both eyes that cannot be voluntarily overcome. The presence of epicanthic folds sometimes gives the appearance of the eyes converging inwards; as the bridge of the nose develops and the epicanthic folds become less prominent or disappear altogether, strabismus may disappear. True strabismus is, however, common in Down syndrome. The condition is treated in the same way as in children without Down syndrome, using patching, eyeglasses, or surgery if these interventions are unsuccessful. Treatment is important, as reduced visual acuity may develop in the normal eye if its vision is involuntarily suppressed to avoid double vision.

Nystagmus: In nystagmus, the eye beats back and forth involuntarily, usually in a horizontal direction in a fine rapid pendular fashion. These oscillating movements often first occur in the first year of life and may improve over time. No definitive treatment is available.

Refractive errors: These are common, affecting more than one half of people with Down syndrome. Myopia, or shortsightedness, is the most common cause of the higher degrees of refractive errors. This occurs when the distance between the front and back of the eyeball is increased. As a result, the focussed image lies in front of the retina. Here, the individual is able to see well at close range but must use corrective lenses to clearly see objects far away. The prescribed lenses are concave in shape. The reverse is true in hyperopia, or farsightedness. Here, a convex lens is required to see objects close to the eye. Astigmatism is another cause of refractive errors; in this condition the cornea is misshapen or uneven. Corrective lenses compensate for astigmatism.

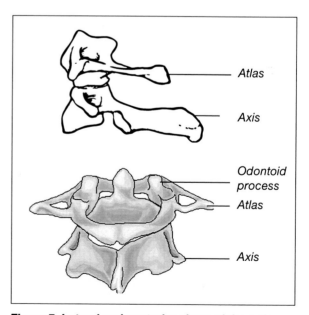

Figure 7. Lateral and posterior views of the articulated atlas and axis

Source: Corel Gallery 2 (1995).

Thyroid abnormalities

Thyroid abnormalities are common in Down syndrome. The thyroid gland is responsible for the production and secretion of thyroid hormones (T3, triiodothyronine, and/or T4, thyroxine, the most active thyroid hormone), which mediate a variety of cellular functions (Figure 6). Falling levels of thyroxine cause the pituitary gland to produce increasing levels of thyroid stimulating hormone or thyrotropin (TSH). The thyroid gland responds by producing more thyroxine. Some children are born with hypothyroidism. This is known as *congenital hypothyroidism*; it can be an inherited condition or transient. In most developed countries, newborns are screened for congenital hypothyroidism and a treatment program with thyroid hormone supplement is implemented to prevent the development of intellectual disability. In some countries, congenital hypothyroidism that is the result of iodine deficiency is very high.

The most common form of acquired hypothyroidism in Down syndrome, as in the general population, is *hypothyroid autoimmune thyroiditis* (also known as lymphocytic thyroiditis or Hashimoto's thyroiditis). In this disorder, autoimmunity causes the body to fail to recognize its own tissue and it mounts an autoimmune response that destroys cells in the thyroid gland. Circulating autoantibodies to the thyroid gland may be found to support this diagnosis. Autoimmune thyroiditis is frequently associated with normal thyroid function, at least in the early stages of the disease.

Compensated hypothyroidism is a condition that is associated with normal or only slightly reduced levels of T3 and/or T4) and elevated TSH. The individual is usually asymptomatic and, although some studies have suggested lower than normal rates of growth and development, many physicians refrain from treatment with L-thyroxine until there is clinical and laboratory evidence of hypothyroidism.

Congenital hypothyroidism is about 28 times more common in Down syndrome than in the general population as detected in newborn screening tests (0.7% permanent, 0.3% transient). Past the newborn stage, as many as 85% of infants under the age of 12 months have elevated TSH but, after this age, the prevalence of elevated TSH decreases. Levels of thyroid hormone (T3 and T4) tend to decrease with advancing age. Hypothyroid autoimmune thyroiditis affects 13-63% of adults with Down syndrome. Overt hyperthyroidism also can occur in Down syndrome, but this disorder is not common.

Signs and symptoms of abnormally low thyroid function are shown in Box 3. The presence or absence of symptoms does not always predict thyroid status. People with Down syndrome who have abnormally low thyroid often do not show the classical symptoms. There may be a connection between thyroiditis and hepatitis B virus (HBV) infection. In one study, the frequency of thyroiditis in those Down syndrome patients who were also carriers of the HBV surface antigen, HbsAg, was found to be threefold higher than the frequency of thyroid disease in those patients with Down syndrome who were not carriers of HBsAg (65% vs. 23%) (May & Kawanishi, 1996).

Health guidelines in some countries recommend reviewing results of the newborn thyroid function screen, then repeating thyroid function tests at the age of 6 months and 12 months, and then annually (Hardy et al., 2004; Roizen & Patterson, 2003). If a TSH value is high or low, then T4 or T3 should be measured; if either of the latter are normal, then autoantibodies to thyroid should be measured.

Some guidelines have recommended that treatment for hypothyroidism should be started only if the TSH is high and T4 and/or T3 is low, or if the TSH is high, T4 or T3 is normal, and autoantibodies to thyroid are present. Treatment for hyperthyroidism should be started if the TSH is low and T4 and/or T3 are high.

Diabetes mellitus

Diabetes is more prevalent in Down syndrome than in the general population, but not known are the relative prevalences of Type 1 and Type 2 diabetes. In an epidemiological study, Anwar, Walker, and Frier (1998) calculated the prevalence of Type 1 diabetes in Down syndrome to fall between 1.4 and 10.6%, which was higher than expected. Differences in glycemic control between subjects with Down syndrome and those without were not significant, despite less stringent insulin regimens in the subjects with Down syndrome.

Hematological abnormalities

Abnormalities found in the elements of the blood of individuals with Down syndrome do not differ substantially from the general population, but there are some problems that are much more common.

Red blood cell abnormalities: The numbers and size of red blood cells in newborns with Down syndrome are often increased (erythrocytosis and macrocytosis, respectively). The mechanisms that cause these conditions are unknown. In most babies, the number and size of red blood cells returns to normal at about one month of age, but in babies with Down syndrome this time may be reduced to about three weeks. Macrocytosis also occurs in adults with Down syndrome.

White blood cell abnormalities: People with Down syndrome tend to have a normal response to infectious processes, but there often is an increase in the number of circulating white blood cells, especially in the neutrophils, the most common form of granulocytes. Granulocytes are white blood cells that help to protect the body from infection. They are able to envelop microorganisms such as bacteria, draw them into the cell and surround them by the cell membrane (phagocytosis). The "captured" bacteria are then killed by an enzymatic process.

Platelet abnormalities: Platelets are blood cells that play a role in the blood clotting process. A reduction in the platelet count (thrombocytopenia) may be found in newborns with Down syndrome as a mild and insignificant occurrence that resolves spontaneously. The physician must, however, consider the possibility of less benign conditions, including transient myelodysplasia or leukemia. Transient elevated platelet counts may also be seen in infants.

Leukemia: This is a type of cancer in which white blood cells displace normal blood. This leads to infection, shortage of red blood cells (anemia), bleeding and other disorders, and can often be fatal. Children with Down syndrome have a higher likelihood of developing leukemia than children without Down syndrome. *Myeloid leukemia* is especially common in Down syndrome. Studies suggest that there is a 10-30% increase in risk. Infants and young children are also much more likely to have a form of leukemia called *acute non-lymphoblastic leukemia* (ANLL) and, in particular, *acute megakaryoblastic leukemia* (AMKL), which affects precursor cells of platelets. In fact, this disease is several hundred times more common in people with Down syndrome than in the general population (Zipursky, 1996). The reason for this is unclear, but again it may have something to do with the increase in gene dosage from the extra chromosomal material. Immature "blast" cells are not normally present in circulating blood.

Myelodysplasia is a condition in which these immature cells appear in the peripheral blood but are seen in smaller numbers than would be considered a frank leukemia. Infants in the first few months sometimes develop transient myelodysplasia, which resolves between one to three months without treatment. There is, however, a 20% chance that this will later reappear as AMKL, so follow-up is important. Many hematologists/oncologists begin treatment before the threshold of 30% immature cells appears in a blood smear. Part of the initial evaluation of a child for leukemia includes a bone marrow biopsy. A condition known as *myelofibrosis* commonly accompanies AMKL and increases the amount of fibrous tissue in the bone marrow. This interferes with the aspiration of a sample for microscopic analysis. Treatment of leukemia with alkylating agents, such as methotrexate, frequently produces concerning side effects in people with Down syndrome. Sores in the mouth and gastrointestinal tract, and suppression of bone marrow function are the most common such side effects. Treatment regimens have recently been modified in order to avoid these drugs, and often include administration of cytosine arabinoside (ARA-C) and daunorubricin instead. Although patients with Down syndrome are unusually sensitive to treatments with alkylating agents, children with acute myeloid leukemia have significantly higher event-free survival rates compared to children without Down syndrome when treated with ARA-C (Gamis, 2005; Hitzler & Zipursky, 2005).

Testicular cancer

Evidence for a suspected association of Down syndrome and testicular cancer continues to accumulate. Along with genetically determined malformations in many other organs in trisomy 21, the gonads also undergo maldevelopment, thus creating the conditions for step one of germ cell tumor oncogenesis in utero. Physicians caring for patients with Down syndrome should be aware of the possible association with testicular neoplasms (Goldacre, Wotton, Seagroatt, & Yeates, 2004). Various other types of solid tumors may occur less frequently in Down syndrome than in the general population (Hasle, 2001).

Obesity

Prevention of obesity is an important goal in Down syndrome (Roizen & Patterson, 2003). Infants with Down syndrome tend to be light for their height, but by age 3-4 years children are often overweight. Efforts to prevent such weight gain should begin by the age of 2 years and include:

- A total calorie intake that is less than the recommended daily allowance
- Foods that are high in nutrients, high in fiber and low in calories and fat
- Supplementary vitamins and minerals, especially calcium and vitamin D
- Encouragement to eat sensibly
- Participation in physical and social activities

Arthritis and walking problems

People with Down syndrome are susceptible to arthritis and other disorders that lead to walking problems (Roizen & Patterson, 2003). These include:
- A juvenile rheumatoid arthritis-like disorder in 1.2% of children and adolescents associated with joint subluxations and with dislocations of the cervical spine, patella and other joints. (A subluxation is the condition of a bone in a joint or a vertebra that has lost its juxtaposition with the one above or the one below and which impinges on nerves and interferes with the transmission of impulses over or through the affected nerve.)

- Chaplinesque gait resulting from external rotation of the hips, knees in flexion and valgus (twisted away from the center of the body), and tibias that are externally rotated.
- Pes planovalgus (flat feet) with marked pronation of the foot (turning in of the foot so that the inner edge bears too much weight).
- Severe bunions and hammer toe deformities.
- Plantar fasciitis (inflammation of the plantar fascia, a tight band of tissue on the bottom of the foot extending from the heel bone to the back of the toes).
- Pedal (foot) arthritis associated with severe flat feet.

Management may include consultation with an orthopedic specialist or a podiatrist.

Atlantoaxial instability

The first description of this condition dates back to 3,500-4,000 BC. It was first reported in the medical literature in 1961 as an abnormality associated with Down syndrome. The prevalence varies, but it is about 15%. Atlantoaxial instability became much more visible in 1983 when the Special Olympics required cervical spine X-rays of all entrants with Down syndrome. In 1995, however, the Committee on Sports Medicine and Fitness of the American Academy of Pediatrics published a position paper on this topic that included several arguments that disfavour such screening. Nevertheless, screening for atlantoaxial instability is considered prudent.

The second cervical vertebra, the axis, has a finger-like extension on its upper and front surface called the odontoid process, or dens (Figure 7). A transverse ligament holds the odontoid process against the front inner surface of the first cervical vertebra above it, the atlas. Presumably as the result of laxity of this ligament in Down syndrome, the odontoid process is able to rock and/or slide backwards when the neck moves, especially when the head flexes forwards. The odontoid process in this circumstance impinges to some extent on the spinal canal that lies directly behind it, and therefore on the spinal cord and on the various nerve roots that emerge from it in this area.

Most children with atlantoaxial instability have no symptoms or signs, but there are reports of catastrophic neurological events. About 1% of individuals with Down syndrome have neurological signs, such as stiff neck, problems with walking, numbness, tingling, or weakness.

X-rays of the cervical spine in three positions, neutral, flexion, and extension, are typically carried out to measure the distance between the odontoid process and the atlas. An interval or space of <5 mm is usually felt to be the acceptable threshold, although higher values are used by some. When this instability is found, the individual is advised — as a precaution — not to engage in activities where there is a high risk of extreme neck flexion. The presence of neurological symptoms raises the possibility of a stabilizing surgical procedure in which the two vertebrae are fused together to avoid serious damage to the spinal cord. Activities to avoid include:

- Gymnastics
- Diving
- Pentathlon
- Butterfly stroke in swimming
- Diving start in swimming
- High jump
- Soccer
- Alpine skiing

Screening for atlantoaxial instability is recommended by most authorities and should be initiated when the child enters an educational or day care program where organized physical activities are first introduced. The screening includes a history to assess any symptoms of atlantoaxial instability, a neurological examination and laboratory investigations, in particular neck X-rays in neutral, flexion and extension. In appropriate circumstances, *CT* or *MRI* scans aid in the diagnosis. Nerve conduction studies (somatosensory evoked potentials) may also be helpful in the assessment. Evaluation is also recommended prior to surgery when the anesthetist may need to flex the patient's neck both to ensure a patent airway and prior to intubation. At 9-10 years of age, if the child is introduced to the Special Olympics or other sports programs, another evaluation is recommended.

The presence of atlantoaxial instability requires monitoring over time. In most instances, no intervention is required other than avoidance of activities that are likely to produce undue stress on the neck. There are instances in which the interval distance gradually changes: it may normalize, or it may even increase. The presence of any neurological symptoms requires immediate reassessment in order to evaluate the need for neurosurgical intervention.

Hypotonia

Virtually all children with Down syndrome have central *hypotonia*. This is apparent in early infancy, affecting certain physiological reflexes (***Moro, parachute***), but shows gradual improvement over time. The term hypotonia refers to reduced muscle tone or resistance to passive movement. It is a common finding in young children with Down syndrome and has a variety of consequences in early development. Hypotonia itself is not dangerous.

Seizures

Although there has been controversy in the medical literature over the prevalence of seizures in Down syndrome in the past, many experts agree that individuals with Down syndrome are more prone to seizures than those in the general population. Approximately 6-8% of individuals appear to be affected overall. This is particularly true of adults, although infants and children are also affected. There appear to be two or three peak age ranges of onset of seizures (i.e., a bimodal or trimodal distribution). The first occurs in infancy over the first year of life. Infantile ***spasms*** and *tonic-clonic seizures*, often with ***myoclonus***, are the most common form of epilepsy. Pueschel and Pueschel (1992) reported that 40% of seizures in Down syndrome occur during this time period. There is a suggestion in the literature that febrile seizures are less common in Down syndrome, although studies vary in this regard.

About 40% of individuals with Down syndrome who have seizures are first affected in the second peak age range: late adolescence or early adulthood. Seizures in this age range are more often tonic-clonic or partial in nature. However, these also may

Table 2: Diagnosed Disorders for 148 adults with Down Syndrome who Presented with a Decline in Function

Disorder	Frequency	Percent of Diagnosed Disorders (%)
Mood	*76*	*31*
Anxiety	*31*	*13*
Obsessive-compulsive	*29*	*12*
Behaviour	*23*	*9*
Hypothyroid	*22*	*9*
Adjustment	*12*	*5*
Alzheimer's	*11*	*4*
B12 Deficiency	*7*	*3*
Menopause	*7*	*3*
Attention Deficit / Hyperactive	*6*	*2*
Gastrointestinal or Urinary	*6*	*2*
Sensory Impairment	*6*	*2*
Psychotic	*4*	*2*
Other Medical Conditions *(Includes Parkinsonism, hyperthyroidism, and seizure disorder.)*	*4*	*2*
Cardiac Conditions	*3*	*1*
Total	*247*	*100*

After Chicoine, McGuire & Rubin (1999).

be complex, that is, a seizure with impairment, distortion or loss of consciousness.

There is a third age range when onset of seizures often occurs. This is associated with dementia of the Alzheimer type (DAT). Some authors report that up to 75% of individuals with this type of dementia have associated seizure disorders. Treatment depends on the nature of the seizures, and is as successful in Down syndrome as in the general population.

Reproductive health

Roizen and Patterson (2003) have summarized important medical issues that are related to reproductive health for people with Down syndrome. These include:

Fertility issues and need for sexual education programs: In adolescent girls and boys with Down syndrome, the physical features of puberty and age of onset of puberty are similar to those of other adolescents. Some people with Down syndrome marry. Even if they do not, they may wish to be sexually active. Fertility is reduced in both men and women with Down syndrome, but moreso in men. With rare exceptions, men with Down syndrome cannot father a child. In any pregnancy, women with Down syndrome have a 50% chance of having a child with Down syndrome, but many affected fetuses are miscarried (Bovicelli, Orsini, Rizzo, Montacuri, & Bacchetta, 1982). Responsibility within a sexual relationship includes mutual consent, contraception, and prevention of sexually transmitted diseases (including HIV). All of these topics need to be the subject of sexual education programs for both men and women with Down syndrome.

Earlier menopause in women: The onset of menopause for women with Down syndrome is earlier (47.1 years), than for women with intellectual disability who do not have Down syndrome (49.3 years), or for women without intellectual disability (51 years) (Schupf et al., 2007).

Menstrual problems in women: As for women in the general population, it is recommended that women with Down syndrome who are sexually active or who have menstrual problems have a pelvic examination. To help with control of menstrual hygiene, family skill training, behavioural support,

Box 7: Guidelines for Medical Management in Down Syndrome

Assessment of newborns
- *Congenital heart disease*
- *Hearing assessment*
- *Ophthalmological assessment*

Prevention
- *Obesity*
- *Periodontal disease*
- *HBV infection*

Monitoring
- *Celiac disease*
- *Thyroid function*

Vigilance
- *Arthritis*
- *Atlantoaxial subluxation*
- *Diabetes mellitus*
- *Leukemia*
- *Sleep disorders*
- *Seizures*
- *Testicular cancer*

Other
- *Behaviour problems including autism, sleep disorders and dementia of the Alzheimer type*
- *Dermatological problems*
- *Development*
- *Sexuality and reproductive health*

After Roizen & Patterson (2003).

and hormone treatment may be successful. Again, as in the general population, women with Down syndrome may experience premenstrual syndrome (PMS). This may manifest in difficult behaviours such as temper tantrums, social withdrawal, or seizures at (or just before) the time of menses. Women with Down syndrome who experience PMS may benefit from typical treatments for this condition (Johnson, 2004).

Mental Health Issues

Level of functioning

Individuals with Down syndrome are considered to have developmental disabilities, but have a wide range of functioning in all areas of development, including intellectual functioning. Most individuals with Down syndrome function in the mild to moderate range of intellectual disability; severe intellectual disability is less common (Weijerman & DeWinter, 2010).

Behavioural issues and dual diagnosis

Traditional stereotypes of behaviour in Down syndrome include a friendly, affectionate and outgoing personality and a stubborn obsessional temperament with resistance to change. This view is an oversimplification of reality. Individuals with Down syndrome are at lower risk for significant psychopathology than other individuals with similar levels of developmental disabilities; however, they are at higher risk for behaviour problems and for developing certain types of psychopathology than non-delayed individuals (Dykens, Shah, Sagun, Beck, & King, 2002; Fidler, Most, Booth-Laforce, & Kelly, 2006; Roizen & Patterson, 2003). Behavioural concerns among preschool-aged children with Down syndrome include tantrums, non-compliance, impulsivity, and increased motor activity (Capone, Goyal, Ares, & Lannigan, 2006). Pre-pubertal children with Down syndrome may manifest a variety of psychiatric disorders, including attention deficit hyperactivity disorder (ADHD), oppositional-defiant and disruptive behaviour disorders, and autism-spectrum and stereotypy movement disorders (Capone et al., 2006). Compared to individuals with "typical" Down syndrome, those with Down syndrome and co-morbid (co-occurring) autism spectrum disorder have more significant cognitive impairment (Capone, Grados, Kaufmann, Bernad-Ripoll, & Jewell, 2005; Carter, Capone, & Kaufmann, 2008) and differing patterns of region-specific brain growth (Carter et al., 2008). A different pattern of symptomatology emerges among adolescents with Down syndrome, characterized by a decrease in "externalizing" problems such as aggression and an increase in "internalizing" problems like withdrawal (Dykens et al., 2002). In young adults, depression, obsessive-compulsive disorder, and psychotic-like disorder tend to be diagnosed (Capone et al., 2006). McGuire and Chicoine (2006) cautioned against interpreting the tendency of many adults with Down syndrome to engage in self-talk and invent imaginary friends as signs of psychosis, pointing out that these behaviours may serve a number of useful functions by providing a means to vent emotions, process events, and produce social stimulation.

Older people with Down syndrome are at increased risk of developing dementia of the Alzheimer type (DAT) much earlier than people in the general population. As in the general population, the frequency of dementia in Down syndrome increases with increasing age. Not everyone with Down syndrome develops dementia. Chicoine, McGuire, and Rubin (1999) reported that decline in function does not always signify the development of DAT (Table 2), particularly in those under 40 years of age. It is crucial to attempt to determine if a decline in function has a reversible cause. A separate chapter in this volume is dedicated to dementia (chapter 37).

Sleep disorders

Sleep disorders are common in Down syndrome (see the online article by Wood and Sacks, 2004, for a review). Two sleep problems are particularly common in children with Down syndrome in comparison to those in children with other types of developmental disability: *physical or breathing-related sleep problems (especially sleep apnoea)*, and *behavioural sleep problems*. Sleep apnoea is characterized by abnormal pauses in breathing or instances of abnormally slow breathing during sleep. Obstructive sleep apnoea and central sleep apnoea are the two main types. Obstructive sleep apnoea results from partial obstruction of the upper airways, which tend to be quite small in children with Down syndrome, and from enlarged tonsils and/or adenoids. This type of obstruction is usually treated by surgery, although this approach is not always effective. Obesity also can contribute to sleep disordered breathing (Ng & Chan, 2004). Central sleep apnoea occurs less frequently and is considered to be a neurological disorder. This latter condition can be harder to treat, but an affected child may benefit from wearing an oxygen mask at night. Children suspected of having sleep apnoea should be evaluated at a sleep laboratory. Sleep masks that deliver positive airway pressure also may help, although these can be uncomfortable. Behavioural sleep problems can be managed successfully using behaviour modification techniques (see Wood & Sacks, 2004).

In addition to the strategies mentioned above, sleep problems in Down syndrome have been successfully treated with:

- Niaprazine, a histamine H1-receptor antagonist with sedative properties
- The pineal gland hormone, melatonin
- Behavioural interventions
- Sedatives and hypnotics are not advised

Assessment and Management

Assessment, monitoring, prevention, and vigilance play a part in management of newborns, children, adolescents, and adults with Down syndrome. Roizen and Patterson (2003) have prepared a set of guidelines for the medical management in Down syndrome under these headings based on recommendations from a number of sources. A summary of their guidelines with modifications is given in Box 7.

Recent Research Developments and Future Advances

A review of Down syndrome would not be complete without reference to some ground-breaking advances in basic research that have been made over the past few years. A highlight of the early 21st century has been the Human Genome Project. This has resulted in the determination of the DNA sequence of the entire chromosome 21; 225 genes already have been identified and 329 more are predicted to exist (Hattori et al., 2000; Roizen & Patterson, 2003). Surprisingly, much of the DNA of chromosome 21 has been found not to be in genes; it does, however, result in the production of RNA molecules whose functions are not known. Of the known genes, 16

have a role in energy and reactive oxygen species metabolism, 9 may affect brain development, neuronal loss and Alzheimer type neuropathology, and 6 have a role in folate and methyl group metabolism (Roizen & Patterson, 2003).

Researchers have realized that it is a mistake to assume that the clinical features of Down syndrome are only due to a few chromosome 21 genes that are overexpressed (Olson, Richtsmeier, Lesz, & Reeves, 2004). Furthermore, the gene products that are overexpressed in Down syndrome are not the same for everyone because many chromosome 21 genes have a number of different allelic variants. Such allelic variation may explain why some people with Down syndrome, but not others, are born with congenital heart disease, gastrointestinal abnormalities, or develop autoimmune thyroiditis. How the overexpressed gene products of chromosome 21 interact with normally expressed gene products on other chromosomes is a key issue already under intensive investigation.

A number of different mouse models for Down syndrome have been developed (Antonarakis et al., 2004). These mice carry various regions of mouse chromosome 16, which is the homologue of human chromosome 21, and have different types of abnormalities of brain and behaviours. Further, it is now possible to construct mice, through genetic engineering, that lack particular chromosome 21 genes, or that have excesses of normal or mutant human chromosome 21 genes. From such mouse models, we will be able to identify functions of the genes on chromosome 21 that are important in cognition and behaviour, immunity, predisposition to and protection against certain cancers, functions of chromosome 21 RNA that do not get translated into protein, how chromosome 21 genes "talk" to one another and to genes on other chromosomes, and the causes of the non-disjunction that result in trisomy 21. Along with such information, such mouse models will aid enormously in the identification of genes and molecular processes affecting the development of dementia and with the testing of new drugs and medicines for treatment of dementia and other behavioural disorders affected by chromosome 21 genes.

Last but not least, some large clinical trials designed to improve health and quality of life for people with Down syndrome on the basis of published research data are being conducted to objectively determine treatment outcomes. One randomized trial showed no benefit to treatment with antioxidants and folinic acid (Ellis et al., 2008). Another study is testing the ability of high doses of vitamin E to slow down deterioration of neurocognitive and neurobehavioural function in aging persons with Down syndrome (*http://clinicaltrials.gov/ct2/show/NCT00056329*).

All of these basic and clinical advances alluded to above will provide information that should help people with Down syndrome to have a better quality of life. In particular, they should lead to the development of new strategies that will increase longevity, that will at least ameliorate the development of intellectual disability and various aspects of the Down syndrome phenotype in children, and possibly even prevent development of dementia of the Alzheimer type in older persons with Down syndrome.

Summary

People with Down syndrome are at risk for numerous medical complications that can, to a large extent, be treated or prevented and lead to high quality of life. Health professionals have played a more extensive and energetic role in the overall care and support for individuals with Down syndrome, as they have become more familiar with their medical and non-medical needs. This awareness has led to a more anticipatory and preventative approach. Medical conditions are now treated earlier and there is the potential for a shorter course of treatment and fewer complications. The hope for the future lies in the emergence of new interventions as we learn more and more about Down syndrome and its etiology. This process will develop partly through research efforts focused on these same illnesses that are found in the general population. The information provided in this chapter provides optimism that the quality of life for people with Down syndrome and their potential for achievement will continue to increase in the future.

For Further Thought and Discussion

1. What preventive strategies should be undertaken to improve the quality of life for people with Down syndrome? Who should take the initiative for preventive care?
2. What medical conditions are most likely to cause serious or life threatening problems for individuals with Down syndrome?
3. There has been a gradual increase in the longevity of individuals with Down syndrome over the past few decades in some countries. What changes in the provision of health care are responsible for this? Why has longevity not increased in some ethnic groups? What should be done to remedy this situation?

Special Terms

Amniocentesis: This is a prenatal test that involves sampling and analyzing the amniotic fluid which is the fluid that surrounds a baby in the uterus (see Chapter 38). The test is done between 15 and 18 weeks after a woman's last menstrual period.

Aortic regurgitation: The backflow of blood from the aorta into the left ventricle, owing to imperfect functioning of the aortic semilunar valve.

Chorionic villus sampling (CVS): This is a prenatal test that involves taking a tiny tissue sample from outside the sac where the fetus develops (see Chapter 38). The tissue is tested to diagnose or rule out certain birth defects. The test generally is performed between 10 and 12 weeks after a woman's last menstrual period.

CT. Computerized tomography: A series of detailed pictures of areas inside the body taken from different angles; the pictures are created by a computer linked to an X-ray machine.

Duodenal lumen: Duodenum is the first part of the small intestine. The term lumen refers to the inner, open region of the duodenum.

Echocardiogram: A record produced by echocardiography, the use of ultrasound waves, to investigate the action of the heart.

Electrocardiogram: A record produced by an electrocardiograph, used in the diagnosis of heart disease. The electrocardiograph is an instrument that displays the electric activity of the heart by means of electrodes attached to the skin.

Hypoplasia: Underdevelopment of an organ or tissue because of loss of cells.

Karyotype: An organized profile of a person's chromosomes. In a karyotype, chromosomes are arranged and numbered by size, from largest to smallest. This arrangement helps scientists quickly identify chromosomal alterations that may result in a genetic disorder. See Chapter 9 for a karyotype of a child with Down syndrome.

Meiosis: The type of cell division that produces ova and sperm.

Mitosis: The process by which a eukaryotic cell separates the chromosomes in its cell nucleus into two identical sets in two new nuclei.

Mitral valve prolapse: Billowing of one or both mitral valve leaflets into the left atrium at the end of each active contraction of the heart.

Moro response: This is an infantile startle response that disappears after a few months. It may be demonstrated by placing the infant face up on a soft, padded surface. The head is gently lifted with enough traction to just begin to remove the body weight from the pad (Note: the infant's body should not be lifted off the pad, only the weight removed). The head is then released suddenly, allowed to fall backward momentarily, but quickly supported again (not allowed to bang on the padding). The infant may have a "startled" look, and the arms fling out sideways with the palms up and the thumbs flexed. As the reflex ends the infant draws the arms back to the body, elbows flexed, and then relaxes.

MRI. Magnetic resonance imaging: A form of medical imaging that employs a combination of radio frequency energy and a powerful magnetic field.

Myoclonus: Jerking, involuntary movements of the arms and legs; may occur normally during sleep.

Non-disjunction: The failure of chromosome pairs to separate during cell division.

Parachute reflex: This occurs in the slightly older infant. It is elicited by holding the child upright then rotating the body quickly face forward (as if falling). The arms are reflexively extended as if to break a fall even though this reflex appears long before walking.

Polymerase chain reaction (PCR): A molecular technique for rapidly creating many extra copies of a sequence of DNA.

Spasms: Sudden, involuntary muscle contractions.

Tonic clonic seizure: This type of seizure is characterized by sudden loss of consciousness and jerking of the body musculature that may last for up to a few minutes. After a grand mal seizure, a patient may exhibit various behaviours, ranging from regaining consciousness, confusion, disorientation, absence of memory of the immediate events, to further seizures.

More Resources

Organizations:

Canadian Down Syndrome Association
http://www.dsao.ca/

Directory of Down Syndrome Sites (US and International)
http://www.downsyndrome.com/

Down Syndrome Association of Ontario
http://www.dsao.ca/

Down Syndrome Association of Toronto
http://dsat.ca/index.asp

Down Syndrome International
http://www.down-syndrome-int.org/

Down Syndrome Quarterly
http://www.denison.edu/collaborations/dsq/

Down Syndrome Research Foundation
http://www.dsrf.org/home/

Education and Health Issues:

American Academy of Pediatrics: Health Supervision for Children with Down syndrome
http://aappolicy.aappublications.org/cgi/content/full/pediatrics;107/2/442

Down Syndrome: Health Issues (compiled by Len Leshin)
http://www.ds-health.com/

Esbensen. A.J. (2010). Health conditions associated with aging and end of life of adults with Down syndrome. *International Review of Research in Mental Retardation, 39*(C), 107-126.

Forster-Gibson, C., & Berg, J. M. (2010). Health Watch Table — Down Syndrome-Adult. Retrieved from http://www.surreyplace.on.ca/Documents/10%20-%20Health%20Watch%20Table%20Down%20Syndrome%20Feb.9.2011_PAPER.pdf

Pueschel, S. M. (2006). *Adults with Down syndrome.* Baltimore: Paul H. Brookes Publishing Co.

Wallace, R., & Dalton, A. J. (2006). Clinicians' guide to physical health problems of older adults with Down syndrome. *Journal on Developmental Disabilities, 12*(1) (Suppl. 1), 92 pages http://oadd.org/index.php?page=249

Growth Charts:

Cronk, C. E., Crocker A. C., Pueschel, S. M., Shea, A. M., Zackai, E., Pickens, G., et al. (1988). Growth charts for children with Down syndrome: 1 month to 18 years of age. *Pediatrics, 81,* 102-110. Retrieved from http://aappolicy.aappublications.org/cgi/content/full/pediatrics;107/2/442

Myrelid, A., Gustafsson, J., Ollars, B., & Anneren, G. (2002). Growth charts for Down's syndrome from birth to 18 years of age. *Archives of Disease in Childhood, 87,* 97-103. Retrieved from http://www.ncbi.nlm.nih.gov/pmc/articles/PMC1719180/pdf/v087p00097.pdf

Richards, G. Growth charts for children with Down syndrome
http://www.growthcharts.com/

References

Antonarakis, S. E., Lyle, R., Dermitzakis, E. T., Reymond, A., & Deutsch, S.(2004). Chromosome 21 and Down syndrome: From genomics to pathophysiology. Nature Reviews. *Genetics, 5,* 725-738.

Anwar, A. J., Walker, J. D., & Frier, B. M. (1998). Type 1 diabetes mellitus and Down's syndrome: Prevalence, management and diabetic complications. *Diabetic Medicine, 15,* 160-163.

Baird, P. A., & Sadovnick, A. D. (1987). Life expectancy in Down syndrome. *Journal of Pediatrics, 110,* 849-854.

Behrman, R. E. (Ed.). (1992). *Nelson textbook of pediatrics* (14th ed.). Philadelphia: W. B. Saunders Company.

Berg, J. M. (2003). Down syndrome before Down: A postscript. *American Journal of Medical Genetics A, 116,* 97-98.

Berg, J. M., Karlinsky, H., & Holland, A. J. (1993). *Alzheimer disease, Down syndrome, and their relationship.* Oxford, NY: Oxford University Press.

Berg, J. M., & Korossy, M. (2001). Down syndrome before Down: A retrospect. *American Journal of Medical Genetics, 102,* 205-211.

Bovicelli, L., Orsini, L. F., Rizzo, N., Montacuti, V., & Bacchetta, M. (1982). Reproduction in Down syndrome. *Obstetrics & Gynecology, 59*(6 Suppl.), 13S-17S.

Bromham, N. R., Woodhouse, J. M., Cregg, M., Webb, E., & Fraser, W. I. (2002). Heart defects and ocular anomalies in children with Down's syndrome. *British Journal of Ophthalmology, 86*(12), 1367-1368.

Buckley, S. J. (2003). *The significance of hearing loss for children with Down syndrome.* Retrieved from http://clinicaltrials.gov/ct2/show/NCT00056329

Capone, G., Goyal, P., Ares, W., & Lannigan, E. (2006). Neurobehavioural disorders in children, adolescents and young adults with Down Syndrome. *American Journal of Medical Genetics, 142C,* 158-172.

Capone, G. T., Grados, M. A., Kaufmann, W. E., Bernad-Ripoll, S., & Jewell, A., (2005). Down syndrome and comorbid autism-spectrum disorder: Characterization using the Aberrant Behavior Checklist. *American Journal of Medical Genetics, 134A,* 373-380.

Carter, J., Capone, G., &, Kaufmann, W. (2008). Neuroanatomic correlates of autism and stereotypy in children with Down syndrome. *NeuroReport, 19*(6), 653-656.

Cebula, K. R., Moore, D. G., & Wishart, J. G. (2010). Social cognition in children with Down's syndrome: Challenges to research and theory building. *Journal of Intellectual Disability Research, 54*(2), 113-134.

Chapman, R. S., & Hesketh, L. J. (2001). Language, cognition, and short-term memory in individuals with Down syndrome. *Down Syndrome Research and Practice, 7*(1), 1-7.

Chen, H. (2011). *Genetics of Down syndrome.* eMed-

icine. Retrieved from http://emedicine.medscape. com/article/943216-overview

Chicoine, B., McGuire, D., & Rubin, S. (1999). Adults with Down syndrome: Speciality clinic perspectives. In M. Janicki & A. Dalton (Eds.), *Dementia aging and intellectual disabilities. A handbook* (pp. 278-291). London: Taylor and Francis. Retrieved from http://www.ds-health.com/adults. htm

Corel Gallery 2. (1995). Ottawa, ON: Corel Corporation.

Cupples, L., & Iacono, T. (2000). Phonological awareness and oral reading skill in children with Down syndrome. *Journal of Speech, Language and Hearing Research, 43*, 595-608.

Devlin, L., & & Morrison, P. J. (2004). Accuracy of the clinical diagnosis of Down syndrome. *Ulster Medical Journal, 73*, 4-12.

Down, J. L. H. (1866). Observations on an ethnic classification of idiots. *London Hospital Reports, 3*, 259.

Dykens, E. M., Shah, B., Sagun, J., Beck, T., & King, B. H. (2002). Maladaptive behaviour in children and adolescents with Down's syndrome. *Journal of Intellectual Disabilities Research, 46*(Pt 6), 484-492.

Ellis, J. M., Tan, H. K., Gilbert, R. E., Muller, D. P., Henley, W., Moy, R, et al. (2008). Supplementation with antioxidants and folinic acid for children with Down's syndrome: Randomised controlled trial. *British Medical Journal, 336*(7644), 594-597.

Feeley, K. M, & Jones, E. A. (2008). Strategies to address challenging behaviour in young children with Down syndrome. *Down Syndrome Research and Practice, 12*(2), 153-163.

Fidler, D. J. (2005). The emerging Down syndrome behavioral phenotype in early childhood: Implications for practice. *Infants & Young Children, 18*(2), 86-103.

Fidler, D. J., Most, D. E., Booth-LaForce, C., & Kelly, J. F. (2006). Temperament and behaviour problems in young children with Down syndrome at 12, 30, and 45 months. *Down Syndrome Research and Practice, 10*(1), 23-29.

Fidler, D. J., Most, D. E., Booth-LaForce, C., & Kelly, J. F. (2008). Emerging social strengths in young children with Down syndrome. *Infants and Young Children, 21*(3), 207-220.

Fidler, D. J., Most, D. E., & Philofsky, A. D. (2008). The Down syndrome behavioural phenotype: Taking a developmental approach. *Down Syndrome Research and Practice*. Retrieved from http://www. down-syndrome.org/reviews/2069/

Fishler, K., & Koch, R. (1991). Mental development in Down syndrome mosaicism. *American Journal on Mental Retardation, 96*, 345-351.

Fiske, J., & Shafik, H. H. (2001). Down's syndrome and oral care. *Dental Update, 28*, 148-156.

Gamis, A. S. (2005). Acute myeloid leukemia and Down syndrome evolution of modern therapy – state of the art review. *Pediatric Blood & Cancer, 44*, 13-20.

Goldacre, M. J., Wotton, C. J., Seagroatt, V., & Yeates, D. (2004). Cancers and immune related diseases associated with Down's syndrome: A record linkage study. *Archives of Disease in Childhood, 89*(11), 1014-1017.

Hardy, O., Worley, G., Lee, M. M., Chaing, S., Mackey, J., Crissman, B., & Kishnani, P. S. (2004). Hypothyroidism in Down syndrome: Screening guidelines and testing methodology. *American Journal of Medical Genetics, 124A*, 436-437.

Hasle H. (2001). Pattern of malignant disorders in individuals with Down's syndrome. *The Lancet Oncology, 2*, 429-436.

Hattori, M, Fujiyama, A., Taylor, T. D., Watanabe, H., Yada, T., Park, H. S. et al. (2000). Chromosome 21 mapping and sequencing consortium. The DNA sequence of human chromosome 21. *Nature, 405*(6784), 311-319.

Haugen, O. H., Hovding, G., Eide, G. E., & Bertelsen, T. (2001). Corneal grafting for keratoconus in mentally retarded patients. *Acta Ophthalmologica Scandinavica, 79*, 609-615.

Hill, I. D. (2006). Management of celiac disease in childhood and adolescence: Unique challenges and strategies. *Current Treatment Options in Gastroenterology, 9*(5), 399-408.

Hitzler, J. K., & Zipursky, A. (2005). Origins of leukaemia in children with Down syndrome. *Nature Reviews: Cancer, 5*, 11-20.

Jarrold, C., Nadel, L., & Vicari, S. (2009). Memory and neuropsychology in Down syndrome.

Down Syndrome Research & Practice, 12(3). Retrieved from http://www.down-syndrome.org/research-practice/12/3/

Johnson, S. R. (2004). Premenstrual syndrome, premenstrual dysphoric disorder, and beyond: A clinical primer for practitioners. *Obstetrics & Gynecology, 104,* 845-859.

Kernan, K. T. (1990). Comprehension of syntactically indicated sequence by Down's syndrome and other mentally retarded adults. *Journal of Intellectual Disability Research, 34*(2), 169-178.

Langman, J. (1963). *Medical embryology.* Baltimore: The Williams & Wilkins Company.

Lovering, J., & Percy, M. (2007). Down syndrome. In I. Brown & M. Percy (Eds.), *A comprehensive guide to intellectual and developmental disabilities* (pp. 139-172). Baltimore: Paul H. Brookes Publishing Co.

May, P., & Kawanishi, H. (1996). Chronic hepatitis B infection and autoimmune thyroiditis in Down syndrome. *Journal of Clinican Gastroenterology, 23,* 181-184.

Medical Illustration Library. (1994). Baltimore: Williams & Wilkins.

McGuire, D., & Chicoine, B. (2006). *Mental wellness in adults with Down syndrome: A guide to emotional and behavioral strengths and challenges.* Bethesda, MD: Woodbine House.

Ng, D. K., & Chan, C. H. (2004). Obesity is an important risk factor for sleep disordered breathing in children with Down syndrome. *Sleep, 27,* 1023-1024.

Olson, L. E., Richtsmeier, J. T., Lesz, J., & Reeves, R. H. (2004). A chromosome 21 critical region does not cause specific Down syndrome phenotypes. *Science, 306*(5696), 687-690.

Percy, M., & Probst, E. (2008). Celiac disease: Its many faces and relevance to developmental disabilities. *Journal on Developmental disabilities, 14*(2), 105-110. Retrieved from http://oadd.org/index.php?page=287

Pueschel, S. M., & Pueschel, J. K. (1992). *Biomedical concerns in persons with Down syndrome.* Baltimore: Paul H. Brookes Publishing Co.

Rimmer, J. H, Heller, T., Wang, E., & Valerio, I. (2004). Improvements in physical fitness in adults with Down syndrome. *American Journal on Mental Retardation, 109,* 165-174.

Roizen, N. J., & Patterson, D. (2003). Down's syndrome. *The Lancet, 361,* 1281-1291.

Schepis, C., Barone, C., Siragusa, M., Pettinato, R., & Romano, C. (2002). An updated survey on skin conditions in Down syndrome. *Dermatology, 205,* 234-238.

Schupf, N., Zigman, W., Kapell, D., Lee, J. H., Kline, J., & Levin, B. (2007). Early menopause in women with Down's syndrome. *Journal of Intellectual Disability Research, 41*(Pt 3), 264-267.

Shott, S. R., Joseph, A., & Heithaus, D. (2001). Hearing loss in children with Down syndrome. *International Journal of Pediatric Otorhinolaryngology, 61,* 199-205.

van Splunder, J., Stilma, J. S., Bernsen, R. M., & Evenhuis, H. M. (2004). Prevalence of ocular diagnoses found on screening 1539 adults with intellectual disabilities. *Ophthalmology, 111,* 1457-1463.

Vicari, S. (2001). Implicit versus explicit memory function in children with Down and Williams syndrome. *Down Syndrome Research and Practice, 7,* 35-40.

Vitamin E in aging persons with Down syndrome. (2008). Retrieved from http://clinicaltrials.gov/ct2/show/NCT00056329

Wallace, R. A., Webb, P. M., & Schluter, P. J. (2002). Environmental, medical, behavioural and disability factors associated with Helicobacter pylori infection in adults with intellectual disability. *Journal of Intellectual Disability Research, 46*(Pt 1), 51-60.

Weijerman, M. E., & de Winter, J. P. (2010). Clinical practice: The care of children with Down syndrome. *European Journal of Pediatrics, 169*(12), 1445-1452.

Wishart, J. (2001). Motivation and learning styles in young children with Down syndrome. *Down Syndrome Research & Practice, 7*(2), 47-51

Wood, A., & Sacks, B. (2004). Overcoming sleep problems for children with Down syndrome. *Down Syndrome News and Update, 3*(4), 118-127. doi:10.3104/reviews.320

Zipursky, A. (1996). The treatment of children with acute megakaryoblastic leukemia who have Down syndrome [editorial comment]. *Journal of Pediatric and Hematological Oncology, 18,* 10-12.

Cerebral Palsy

Darcy Fehlings and Carolyn I. Hunt

What you will learn:

- What cerebral palsy is and what impact it has on an individual's development and activities of daily living
- Different types of cerebral palsy
- Risk factors for cerebral palsy
- Medical complications associated with cerebral palsy
- Treatment and rehabilitation approaches for individuals with cerebral palsy

*Note: Words in **bold italics** are explained in the Special Terms section following the Summary.*

Case Scenario

Jessica is a 3½ year old girl who attends an integrated day care in the heart of the city. She has a twin sister, Kayla, who also attends the centre. Jessica loves to play at the sand station. She loves building blocks and she especially enjoys story time. Kayla's favourite activity is going out on to the playground. She always helps Jessica get her walker out the door so that they can go outside and have fun! Jessica loves to play and since she has learned to use her walker outside, nobody has been able to catch her! Jessica has spastic diplegia, a form of cerebral palsy, and uses a walker for mobility most of the time. She is having a little bit of difficulty learning her letters but is an enthusiastic participant at the day

care, and all the children love her. Their mother, Cindy, is so proud of her twins. Who would have guessed they would have grown to be so big and strong, after being premature and weighing just 1½ pounds each at birth?

What is Cerebral Palsy?

Cerebral palsy (CP) is a commonly used term that refers to a group of motor disorders. The current definition of CP is a group of permanent disorders of the development of movement and posture causing activity limitations that are attributed to non-progressive disturbances that occurred in the developing fetal or infant brain. The motor disorders are often accompanied by disturbances of sensation, perception, cognition, communication, and behaviour; by epilepsy; or by secondary musculoskeletal problems (Rosenbaum et al., 2007, p. 9). The five

Table 1. Risk Factors for Cerebral Palsy

Prenatal (Before Birth)	Perinatal (During Birth)	Postnatal (After Birth)
Congenital malformations of the brain	Premature separation of the placenta from the uterus	Asphyxia (secondary to choking or near drowning)
Congenital infections (e.g., Rubella [German measles], Cytomegalovirus*)	Neonatal encephalopathy	
Exposure to chemicals/toxins (e.g., alcohol, cocaine and crack)	Cord prolapse	Head injury
Prematurity/low birth weight	Brain hemorrhage or infarction (stroke)	Brain infections (such as meningitis and encephalitis)
Inflammation of the placenta, or amniotic fluid (chorioamnionitis)		
Stroke		
Twins/multiple births		
Toxemia (high blood pressure during pregnancy)		

* Cytomegalovirus — see special terms

main features of CP are:

- Onset that is before, during, or after birth (usually before 5 years of age)
- Damage to the brain, or an abnormality of the developing brain
- Motor difficulties that are secondary to brain damage or abnormal development
- Decreased control of movements with poor motor co-ordination, balance, or abnormal movements (or a combination of these features)
- A condition that is non-progressive but permanent

A child is often suspected of having CP in the first year of life if his or her motor milestones are delayed (late in sitting, crawling, and walking). Parents may also notice that their baby has an abnormal way of moving, such as commando crawling (crawling by pulling the body forward with the arms and dragging the legs behind), or that their child always stands or walks on his or her toes. There is a common misconception that all people with CP have intellectual delays. Although this is sometimes the case, many children with CP have normal intellectual skills.

Cerebral palsy is diagnosed by assessing abnormalities in muscle tone (such as stiffness) and motor function. A diagnosis of CP is usually made by a pediatrician. Pediatricians typically take a careful history and review any potential risk factors for CP. They also carry out a physical examination, concentrating on the neurological examination and watching how the child is moving. They may want to order a special picture of the brain (by *CT Scan* or *MRI*). Often, a diagnosis cannot be made until the child has reached his or her second birthday, as some children have motor stiffness and delays in the first year that improve by the second year.

How common is cerebral palsy?

Cerebral palsy is quite common. In developed countries the prevalence is estimated to be 2.0 to 2.5 for every 1000 children (Kuban & Leviton, 1994; Murphy, Yeargin-Allsopp, Decoufle, & Drews, 1993; Stanley, Blair, & Alberman, 2000). The prevalence of CP has remained very stable despite improvements in obstetrical care.

What causes cerebral palsy?

A combination of genetic vulnerability interacting with environmental stressors leads to the development of CP. The presence of multiple risk factors markedly increases the risk. Possible risk factors are listed in Table 1. It is often assumed that most children who develop CP have had a difficult birth. With more research, however, it appears that only a small percentage of children with CP have effects related to their delivery (Cummins, Nelson, Grether, & Velie, 1993; Nelson, 1996, 2008).

Birth asphyxia (another term for this is neonatal encephalopathy), a condition in which the baby experiences a low oxygen level during delivery (sometimes resulting in delayed crying and poor respiratory effort at birth), is associated with the subsequent development of CP. However, birth asphyxia often appears to be a secondary symptom of an otherwise sick baby, and thus is not the primary cause of CP in the majority of cases. One study of children with CP found that 78% did not have birth asphyxia (Torfs, van den Berg, Oechsli, & Cummins, 1990). Of the 22% who did have birth asphyxia, all had prenatal risk factors as well.

There are three main types of CP: Spastic, Dyskinetic, and Ataxic (Surveillance of Cerebral Palsy in Europe [SCPE], 2000). Spasticity refers to extra stiffness in the muscles associated with increased reflexes and can be further sub-divided into bilateral (limbs on both sides of the body are involved) or unilateral (limbs on one side of the

Table 2. Types of Cerebral Palsy

Spastic
  Bilateral
      Spastic quadriplegia
      Spastic diplegia
  Unilateral
      Spastic hemiplegia

Dyskinetic
  Dystonic
  Choreoathetotic

Ataxia

Mixed

body are involved). Another term for unilateral spastic CP is hemiplegia. When the spastic CP is bilateral, it often involves both legs and the term for this is spastic diplegia; if all four limbs are involved, this is spastic quadriplegia. Dyskinetic CP is characterized by involuntary movements and consists of two subtypes: dystonic and choreoathetotic. The dystonic subtype consists of marked fluctuation in tone and a stiffness to the movement. Individuals with dystonic CP get stuck in abnormal postures. Choreoathetotic CP is associated with hyperkinetic (increased activity) involuntary movements. Ataxic CP is associated with poor balance and decreased muscle co-ordination. Mixed CP occurs when there is a combination of at least two sub-types.

Impact of Cerebral Palsy on Development

Movement

One of the defining features of CP is difficulty controlling and planning motor movements in the parts of the body that are affected. There is wide variability in movement function, with some individuals being completely independent, and others requiring a manual or electric wheelchair for mobility. Most individuals with hemiplegia and spastic diplegia are able to walk. A higher percentage of individuals with spastic quadriplegia, or dyskinetic CP, use a wheelchair for mobility. (The term spastic quadriplegia refers to a form of CP in which all four limbs

Table 3. Gross Motor Function Classification System (Children Ages 6 to 12 Years)

Level I	*Walks without restrictions; limitations in more advanced motor skills*
Level II	*Walks without assistive devices; limitations walking outdoors and in the community*
Level III	*Walks with assistive mobility devices; limitations walking outdoors and in the community*
Level IV	*Self-mobility with limitations; children are transported or use power mobility outdoors and in the community*
Level V	*Self-mobility is extremely limited even with the use of assistive technology*

and the trunk are affected. Dyskinetic CP refers to a form characterized by uncontrolled, slow, and writhing movements.) Researchers from McMaster University in Hamilton, Ontario have created a new classification system, which classifies CP according to gross motor function, and divides CP into five ability levels (Table 3; Palisano et al., 1997). Jessica, from the anecdote at the beginning of this chapter, has Level III CP.

Hand control and activities of daily living

People with CP vary from being completely independent in their activities of daily living (ADL) to being dependent for their care. Their degree of independence often relates to the motor control they have in their hands. Those with hemiplegia can become very good at doing tasks with one hand and achieve a great deal of independence. People with spastic diplegia can have some overflow tone into their hands, but many can also achieve independence in their ADL. They can also have more subtle difficulties with hand control, such as slower written output. Compared to the other types of CP, there are higher rates of dependence in ADL in individuals with spastic quadriplegia or dyskinetic CP.

The Manual Ability Classification System (MACS), similar to the Gross Motor Function Classification System (GMFCS), describes the ability of the individual to do activities with their hands from level I \9independent) to level V (dependent) (Eliasson et al., 2006).

Learning and developmental disabilities

People with CP can have typical intelligence, but they are at a greater risk of developmental challenges, and are more likely to have slowness in their learning (developmental disability). Reported rates of slower intellectual development associated with CP vary from 30% to 60% (Evans, Evans, & Alberman, 1990). Individuals with CP can have both a physical disability as well as an intellectual disability, although this is not always the case.

Speech/language

Many people with CP are able to speak fluently and clearly. Some have difficulty with articulation, which can make speech difficult for a listener to understand. Others may be unable to speak because of motor problems and require alternate strategies, such as picture or symbol displays. This is more likely to be the case for people with dyskinetic CP, since some have language learning disabilities.

Medical Problems Associated with Cerebral Palsy

People with CP are at risk for medical complications. The main medical complications include:

- Seizures (seen in approximately 20-30%)
- Visual impairment
- Strabismus (turning in or out of the eye)
- Hearing loss
- Dental cavities
- Drooling
- Swallowing difficulties
- Poor growth/nutrition
- Aspiration pneumonia
- Reflux
- Constipation
- Orthopedic complications

The medical complications associated with CP

require careful monitoring and active treatment. A developmental pediatrician is a physician who has specialized training in developmental problems, such as CP and other areas, and will co-ordinate care of children who are medically complex and have a diagnosis of CP.

Seizures occur when there is an episodic excess of electrical activity in the brain (often arising from an area that has been injured). This can lead to shaking of the arms and legs and a loss of consciousness. Seizures are usually treated with anticonvulsants that help to prevent or decrease their frequency and severity. Strabismus (more commonly known as lazy eye) is usually treated with eye surgery that helps to align both eyes. Hearing loss can often be helped with a hearing aid. If there is persisting fluid in the middle ear, secondary to recurrent ear infections, the fluid can be drained with a small tube inserted into the eardrum. Drooling often improves with age and training. If it persists past five years of age, a small surgical procedure that moves the saliva ducts farther back in the mouth can be done.

Feeding difficulties — especially difficulties with swallowing — are commonly seen in people with spastic quadriplegia, or dyskinetic CP. It takes good muscle co-ordination to swallow food, particularly thin liquids such as juice. When the swallowing is poor, food can be taken into the lungs and can create an aspiration pneumonia. It can also decrease the total amount of food and calories being taken in, which can cause poor nutrition and delayed growth. Thickening liquids and watching the physical position of individuals when they are eating can help (sitting up in a comfortable supported seat is best). Sometimes a feeding tube (gastrostomy tube [g-tube]) placed in the stomach is required. Parents and caregivers are able to manage a g-tube in a home environment.

Orthopedic (bone) complications are frequently seen in CP. They often require surgical intervention by an orthopedic surgeon (bone doctor). The extra stiffness in the muscle decreases the muscle growth. This can lead to joint contractures that can impact on the individual's gait (walking pattern). The surgeon does an operation that lengthens the tendon of the muscle to help to increase flexibility. For instance, with a heel cord lengthening, a child can go from always standing on his or her toes, to being able to bring the heel down to the floor. A significant complication of the extra stiffness can be subluxation (a partial sliding out) of the hip joint. The surgeon can lengthen the muscles around the hip and reshape the bones of the hip to try to prevent a complete dislocation of the hip.

Treatment (Rehabilitation) for People with Cerebral Palsy

The focus of rehabilitation for people with CP is on health, wellness, and participation. The aim is to help people with CP achieve their developmental potential. Many health professionals can be involved: nurses, occupational therapists, orthopedic surgeons, orthotists, pediatricians, physiotherapists, psychologists, recreation consultants, social workers, speech therapists, teachers, and others. With so many people on the "team," things can get confusing. Families tell us that it is very important to co-ordinate services, to provide long-term continuity of care, and to focus on the whole individual and his or her family, rather than just on problems or medical issues. In the rehabilitation field, this is called "family-centred care."

There are many different treatments available for people with CP. Increasingly, it is recognized that treatment needs to be "evidence based" (showing that it does some good, and that this outweighs any harmful side effects). This applies to "standard" therapies as well as to "alternative" therapies. Some types of commonly used treatments are listed in Table 4.

New Directions in Management and Prevention

Advances in management

Over the last 15 years, the use of ***botulinum toxin*** to help manage spasticity has become a treatment option for individuals with CP (Fehlings et al., 2010; Love et al., 2010). When botulinum toxin is injected into an affected muscle, it causes partial temporary paralysis of this muscle. It decreases the muscle tone for about 3 months following the injection. This can

Table 4. Examples of Rehabilitation Therapies

Developmental Area	Example of Treatment	Health Professional Involved
Gross Motor Function	*Physiotherapy to teach stretching to maintain flexibility, improve muscle strength, and work on functional movements (i.e., walking, sitting, rolling)*	*Physiotherapist* *Orthotist* *Physician*
	Use of special equipment such as walkers to help promote independence in walking	
	Use of wheelchairs (manual and electric) to help promote mobility	
	Use of splints, braces (a commonly used brace is an ankle-foot orthosis that helps the individual put his/her heel on the floor)	
	Spasticity management (Butler & Campbell, 2000; Goldstein, 2007)	
Fine Motor Function/ Activities of Daily Living	*Stretching and strengthening activities to promote hand control, splinting (a commonly used splint for the hand is a neopryne splint that helps to keep a still thumb out of the palm to make grasping objects easier)*	*Occupational therapist* *Writing Aids Clinics (staffed by occupational therapists)*
	Assessment for equipment to make activities of daily living easier (examples include handle bars near toilets and baths, commode chairs, seating with trays to create a stable work/play area, lifting systems)	
	Home renovations to promote wheelchair accessibility	
	Computer assisted writing aids	

allow the affected muscle to relax and move more easily, and provides an opportunity to strengthen the opposing muscles. Botulinum toxin can also relieve painful muscle spasms (Lundy, Doherty, & Fairhurst, 2009). Injections can be paired with casting to increase the range of motion of the joint (Blackmore, Boettcher-Hunt, Jordan, & Chan, 2007)

For individuals with hemiplegia, therapists are always looking for ways to improve function of the affected hand and limb. Evidence suggests that if the unaffected limb is temporarily constrained via a splint/or cast, there will be improvements in function in the affected limb (Hoare, Imms, Carey, & Wasiak, 2007). Researchers are currently trying to determine what combination of constraint therapy vs. bi-manual (two-handed) activities produce the

Developmental Area	Example of Treatment	Health Professional Involved
Speech and Language	*Parent training to teach parents of young children how to encourage language development (an example is the* **Hanen Program***)* *Speech and language therapy to improve articulation and promote language development* *Augmentative communication systems used for individuals who are not able to speak effectively (examples can include a communication book with picture symbols that the individual will look at or point to, and voice output computer systems)*	*Speech and language therapists* *Augmentative communication clinics (staffed by speech therapists and occupational therapists)*
Learning/Cognitive Development	*Infant stimulation programs for children under 2 years of age* *Nursery school programs for children aged 2-4 years that include therapy consultation* *Special education* *Psychology assessment to evaluate learning strengths and weaknesses to assist with school and vocational planning* *Vocational programs to provide training and support to individuals with special needs to enter the workplace*	*Early childhood educators* *Schoolboards/teachers/psychologists* *Programs are often staffed by teachers/occupational therapists/psychologists*
Psychosocial Development/Wellness	*Support to family and siblings* *Participation in recreational and extracurricular activities* *Promotion of peer interactions*	*Social worker* *Recreational therapist*

best result (Boyd et al., 2010).

Transitions

Transitioning from a supportive school environment and children's treatment centre to adult life in the community with employment and relationship opportunities can be challenging (Logan, 1997). Adults with CP report feeling isolated and have more difficulty accessing employment opportunities and establishing long-term relationships with a life partner (Stevenson, Pharoah, & Stevenson, 1997). There also are challenges associated with health care needs in the transition to adulthood. Furthermore, it is not uncommon for persons with CP to experience a gradual decline in mobility as they move through adulthood (Young et al., 2006).

Research is needed to determine how these issues can be addressed or prevented.

Will we ever be able to prevent CP?

A major focus of today's research is aimed at increasing participation of individuals with disabilities in the community. However, it does not mean that we should not continue to look for strategies to minimize the amount of disability experienced by an individual. There are currently two promising therapies that are new.

Magnesium sulphate therapy: Preterm birth is a significant risk factor for CP. There now is evidence that treating women at risk of having a preterm baby with magnesium sulphate substantially reduces the risk of CP in their infants. Why exposure of preterm babies to magnesium sulphate in the antenatal or immediate newborn period may be neuroprotective is not clear, but it may reduce the amount and severity of *hypoxic ischemic injury* that may lead to CP (Doyle, Crowther, Middleton, Marret, & Rouse, 2009).

Cooling: The second strategy is the use of a cooling bed for 72 hours for treatment in the immediate newborn period if a child is suspected of having hypoxic ischemic injury that may lead to CP. Studies have shown that cooling may reduce the severity of CP (Schulzke, Rao, & Patole, 2007).

Services Available in Ontario for People with Cerebral Palsy

People with CP and their families use many different services. Many of the services and resources that are commonly used in Ontario are provided through the Ontario Association of Children's Rehabilitation Services (OACRS) organizations. These organizations are funded through the Ontario government and provide multi-disciplinary wide-ranging services for children with rehabilitation needs.

Listing of OACRS organizations:

Ontario Association of Children's Rehabilitation Services: 150 Kilgour Road, Toronto, ON, M4G 1R8. Tel: (416) 424-3864; Fax: (416) 467-7083; *www.oacrs.com*

Members of OACRS:

Bloorview Kids Rehab (Toronto)
Child Development Centre – Hotel Dieu Hospital (Kingston)
Children's Rehabilitation Centre – Algoma (Sault Ste. Marie)
Children's Treatment Centre Sudbury Regional Hospital
Children's Treatment network of Simcoe-York
ErinoakKids Centre for Treatment and Development (Halton/Peel/Dufferin)
George Jeffery Children's Centre (Thunder Bay)
Grandview Children's Centre (Oshawa)
John McGivney Children's Centre (Windsor)
KidsAbility Centre for Child Development (Waterloo)
Lansdowne Children's Centre (Brantford)
McMaster Children's hospital – Developmental Paediatrics & Rehabilitation (Hamilton)
Niagara Peninsula Children's Centre
One Kids Place/La Place Des Enfants (North Bay)
Ottawa Children's Treatment Centre
Pathways Health Centre for Children (Sarnia)
Quinte Children's Treatment Centre (Belleville)
Thames Valley Children's Centre (London)

Additional commonly used services/resources in Ontario:

Discoverability (helps with transitional planning after high school): 44 Applan Drive, North York, ON, M2J 2P9. Tel: (416) 395-4896; Fax: (416) 395-3710
Easter Seal Society: *www.easterseals.org* Tel: 1-866-630-3336
West Park Hospital (an adult rehabilitation facility): 82 Buttonwood Ave., Toronto, ON, M6M 2J5 Tel: (416) 243-3600; Fax: (416) 243-8947
Ontario Federation for Cerebral Palsy: 104-1630 Lawrence Ave. W., Toronto, ON, M6L 1C5 Tel: (416) 244-9666; Fax: (416) 244 6543
Speech Foundation of Ontario (can provide a list of speech therapists): 10 Buchan Court, north York, ON, M2J 1V2. Tel: (416) 491-7771; Fax: (416) 491-7215
Hanen Centre: 252 Bloor St. W., Suite 3-390,

Toronto, ON, M5S 1V5. Tel: (416) 921-1073; Fax: (416) 921-1225

March of Dimes: 10 Overlea Blvd., Toronto, ON, M4H 1A4. Tel: (416) 425-3463; Fax: (416) 425-1920

Summary

People with CP have motor difficulties secondary to damage or an abnormality of the developing brain. It is a common condition with prevalence rates of 2 to 2.5 for every 1000 children. Having CP can impact on many areas of the individual's development and function. There is a high association with a co-existing developmental disability (30-60%) and medical complications. Rehabilitation often requires the teamwork of many different social service and health professionals working together with individuals who have CP and their families to maximize developmental potential and promote quality of life.

For Further Thought and Discussion

1. What are the best types of service delivery models for people with CP?
2. Discuss the importance of providing treatments that are evidenced based. How can this be promoted in organizations in Ontario?
3. A new drug used for women who are pregnant is considered by some to have the potential to be associated with the baby developing CP. How would you evaluate this drug as a potential risk factor?
4. What can you do personally to promote universal accessibility for people with disabilities?

Special Terms

Botulinum toxin: A neurotoxin that blocks the synaptic release of acetylcholine from cholinergic nerve terminals mainly at the neuromuscular junction, resulting in irreversible loss of motor end plates

CT scan: Computerized axial tomography scan — a process in which an X-ray scanner makes many sweeps of the body and the results are processed by computer to give a cross-sectional image.

Cytomegalovirus: A kind of herpesvirus that usually produces very mild symptoms in an infected person but may cause severe neurological damage in the newborn and in people with weakened immune systems.

Hanen program: Program(s) in which groups of parents or educators learn how to create and take advantage of everyday opportunities to promote language development so that language learning becomes an ongoing, enjoyable and natural part of a child's life.

Hypoxic ischemic injury: Injury resulting from a lack of oxygen, which causes damage to brain cells and the spinal cord.

MRI: Magnetic resonance imaging — a form of medical imaging using the nuclear magnetic resonance of protons in the body.

More Resources

The American Academy for Cerebral Palsy and Developmental Medicine: 6300 N. River Road, Suite 727, Rosemont, IL 60018-4226, U.S.A. Tel: (847) 698-1635; Fax: (847) 823-0536

Miller, F., & Bachrach, S. (1995). *Cerebral palsy: A complete guide to caregiving.* Baltimore: The Johns Hopkins University Press.

References

Blackmore, A. M., Boettcher-Hunt, E., Jordan, M. & Chan, M. D. (2007). A systematic review of the effects of casting on equines in children with cerebral palsy: An evidence report of the AACPDM. *Developmental Medicine & Child Neurology, 49*(10), 781-790.

Boyd, R., Sakzewski, L., Ziviani, J., Abbott, D. F., Badawy, R., Gilmore, R., Provan, K., Tournier, J. D., Macdonell, R. A., & Jackson, G. D. (2010). INCITE: A randomised trial comparing constraint induced movement therapy and bimanual training in children with congenital hemiplegia. *BMC Neurology, 10,* 4.

Butler, C., & Campbell, S. (2000). Evidence of the effects of intrathecal baclofen for spastic and dystonic cerebral palsy. *Developmental Medicine & Child Neurology, 42,* 634-645.

Cummins, S. K., Nelson, K. B., Grether, J. K., & Velie, E. M. (1993). Cerebral palsy in four northern California counties, births 1983 through 1985. *The Journal of Pediatrics, 123*, 230-237.

Doyle, L. W., Crowther, C. A., Middleton, P., Marret, S. & Rouse, D. (2009). Magnesium sulphate for women at risk of preterm birth for neuroprotection of the fetus. *Cochrane Database of Systematic Reviews, Issue 1*, DOI: 10.1002/14651858. CD004661.pub3.

Eliasson, A. C., Krumlinde-Sundholm, L., Rosblad, B., Beckung, E., Arner, M., Ohrvall, A. M., & Rosenbaum P. (2006). The manual ability classification system (MACS) for children with cerebral palsy: Scale development and evidence of validity and reliability. *Developmental Medicine & Child Neurology, 48*(7), 549-554.

Evans, P. M., Evans, S. J. W., & Alberman, E. (1990). Cerebral palsy: Why we must plan for survival. *Archives of Disease in Childhood, 65*, 1329-1333.

Fehlings, D., Novak, I., Berweck, S., Hoare, B., Stott, N., & Russo, R. (2010). Botulinum toxin assessment, intervention and follow-up for paediatric upper limb hypertonicity: International consensus statement. *European Journal of Neurology, 17*(2), 38-56.

Goldstein, E. (2001). Spasticity management: An overview. *Journal of Child Neurology*, 16, 16-23.

Hoare, B, Imms, C, Carey, L., & Wasiak J. (2007). Constraint-induced movement therapy in the treatment of the upper limb in children with hemiplegic cerebral palsy: A Cochrane systematic review. *Clinical Rehabilitation, 21*, 675-685.

Kuban, K., & Leviton, A. (1994). Cerebral palsy. *The New England Journal of Medicine, 330*(3), 188-195.

Logan, S. (1997). In the UK the transition from youth to adulthood of people with cerebral palsy is poorly planned and co-ordinated. *Child: Care, Health & Development, 23*(6), 480-482.

Love, S. C., Noval, I., Kentish, M., Desloovere, K., Heinen, F., Molenaers, G., O'Flaherty, S., & Graham, H. K. (2010). Botulinum toxin assessment, intervention and after-care for lower limb spasticity in children with cerebral palsy: International consensus statement. *European Journal of Neurology, 17*(2), 9-37.

Lundy, C., Doherty, G., & Fairhurst, C. (2009). Botulinum toxin type A injections can be an effective treatment for pain in children with hip spasms and cerebral palsy. *Developmental Medicine & Child Neurology, 51*, 705-710.

Murphy, C. C., Yeargin-Allsopp, M., Decoufle, P., & Drews, C. D. (1993). Prevalence of cerebral palsy among ten-year-old children in metropolitan Atlanta, 1985 through 1987. *The Journal of Pediatrics, 123*(5), S13-S20.

Nelson, K. (2008). Causative factors in cerebral palsy. *Clinical Obstetrics and Gynecology, 51*(4), 749-762.

Nelson, K. B. (1996). Epidemiology and etiology of cerebral palsy. In A. J. Capute, & P. J. Accardo (Eds.), *Developmental disabilities in infancy and childhood (2nd ed.): Volume 2, The spectrum of developmental disabilities* (pp. 73-79). Baltimore: York Press.

Palisano, R., Rosenbaum, P., Walter, S., Russell, D., Wood, E., & Galuppi, B. (1997). Development and reliability of a system to classify gross motor function in children with cerebral palsy. *Developmental Medicine & Child Neurology, 39*(4), 214-223.

Rosenbaum, P., Paneth, N., Leviton, A., Goldstein, M., Bax, M., Damiano, D., Dan., B., & Jacobsson, G. (2007). A report: The definition and classification of cerebral palsy April 2006. *Developmental Medicine Child Neurology Suppl., 109*, 8-14.

Schulzke, S. M., Rao, S., & Patole, S. K. (2007). A systematic review of cooling for neuroprotection in neonates with hypoxic ischemic encephalopathy—are we there yet? *BMC Pediatrics, 7*, 30, DOI:10.1186/1471-2431-7-30.

Stanley, F. J., Blair, E., & Alberman, E. (2000). Cerebral palsies. *Epidemiology and causal pathways*. London: Mac Keith Press.

Stevenson, C. J., Pharoah, P., & Stevenson, R. (1997). Cerebral Palsy—the transition from youth to adulthood. *Developmental Medicine & Child Neurology, 39*(5), 336-442.

Surveillance of Cerebral Palsy in Europe (SCPE). (2000). Surveillance of cerebral palsy in Europe: A collaboration of cerebral palsy surveys and registers. *Developmental Medicine and Child Neurology, 42*, 816-824.

Torfs, C. P., van den Berg, B. J., Oechsli, F. W., &

Cummins, S. (1990). Prenatal and perinatal factors in the etiology of cerebral palsy. *The Journal of Pediatrics, 116,* 615-619.

Young, N., McCormick, A., Mills, W., Barden, W., Boydell, K., Law, M., Wedge, J., Fehlings, D., Mukherjee, S., Rumney, P., & Williams, J. (2006). The transition study: A look at youth and adults with cerebral palsy, spina bifida and acquired brain injury. *Physical and Occupational Therapy Pediatrics, 26*(4), 25-45.

16

Autism and Related Disabilities

Adrienne Perry, Alvin Loh, Melissa Carter, Glen Dunlap,
Anne Black, and Kerry Wells

What you will learn:

- What autism and other pervasive developmental disorders are
- Treatments and interventions for autism
- Medical issues in autism
- Evidence-based interventions
- Alternative interventions
- Large systems challenges

It is often said that no two people with autism are alike. The three examples in Box 1 demonstrate a number of important things about autism from the outset:

1. Autism may seem very different from one person to another, depending on the person's age, level of cognitive functioning, personality, medical issues, and particular pattern of symptoms and behaviours.
2. Children and adults with autism can be found in a variety of environments including: school programs (both segregated and integrated), children's mental health and treatment agencies, residential settings, health care settings, and generic community settings.
3. Having a child with autism has far-reaching effects on the parents and other family members, with different issues arising at different stages in the family life cycle.

Autism and Pervasive Developmental Disorders

Autism was first described by Leo Kanner in 1943. Since that time, our understanding of autism has changed and grown. Autism is not an illness or a disease; it is a behaviourally defined syndrome, which means that its definition is based on a pattern of symptoms, not on a blood test or certain physical features. There have been many different definitions of autism and sets of diagnostic criteria in the past, but at the present time most professionals have adopted the same definition, which comes from the Diagnostic and Statistical Manual of Mental Disorders, Fourth Edition, Text Revision (DSM-IV-TR; American Psychiatric Association (APA), 2000). The Fifth Edition of the DSM is underway at the time of writing, and this will likely result in some changes in the way we talk about autism (see American Psychiatric

Box 1: Three Profiles of Autism

Ben Loves Trains

Ben is 2½ and he loves trains. He is content to play with them alone for hours. Yet he doesn't seem to really understand that they are trains. He doesn't pretend to make them go on the track or have crashes or imagine what the cars are carrying or talk as he plays alone. He just lines them up in the same way every time. He gets very upset if anyone rearranges his trains. Sometimes he carries a train around with him and rubs it against his chin or waves it in front of his eyes. He never brings a train to show his father, never points to the trains to show his sister. In fact, he completely ignores his sister. He doesn't talk to her, doesn't look at her, no matter how hard she tries to be a good big sister. Ben doesn't talk at all, rarely looks at other people, and rarely smiles. His mother suspects something is wrong, but her doctor told her Ben is probably just slow talking and will outgrow the other odd behaviour. He will be starting nursery school soon and his mother hopes that will turn him around.

Carolyn Just Wants To Be Friends

Carolyn is 12 and is great at puzzles. She can do them just as fast whether they are picture side up or upside down! She struggles with her school work, especially language, arts and social studies, but is pretty good at spelling and math and has an excellent memory. She was in special education classes when she was younger but is now in a regular class. She seems to be very friendly and talkative, though a bit immature. She goes up and asks questions of anyone she comes in contact with, even if they're not interested in talking to her. She doesn't know how to relate to other kids very well, but really wants to be friends. She is enrolled in a social skills group at a local treatment agency. Her mother worries about what is in store for Carolyn as a teenager and adult. Though she has come so far, from the 3-year-old who used to repeat back nursery rhymes and TV commercials, she still has some very pervasive difficulties.

Jeff Got A Job

Jeff is 23 and has lived, for the past two years, in a group home with four other young men who have developmental disabilities. Jeff just got a job in a warehouse. Although he has the skills needed to do the actual work, Jeff still needs a lot of support and the employer insists a staff person is with him at all times. One reason is that he sometimes has seizures at work. Also, he has a hard time when asked to do new things or when the jobs are slightly different than what he is used to and when he gets frustrated he will bang his head and scream. At the group home, three staff members work with Jeff and his housemates to teach them how to cook, clean their rooms, and do their laundry. Jeff's parents are pleased with how well he has adjusted to the group home and his new job. It was very hard for them to place their son out of their home, but Jeff's father has some serious health problems and his mother was just not able to look after both of them.

Association, 2010, for ongoing updates).

Autistic Disorder (usually just called autism) is the most well known of the five disorders that DSM-IV-TR describes under the general category of Pervasive Developmental Disorders (or PDDs). See the circular depiction in Figure 2. All of the PDDs involve pervasive difficulties (that is, severe impairments across many areas of development). The three broad areas of particular difficulty are:

1. Reciprocal social interaction and play
2. Verbal and nonverbal communication
3. Repetitive and unusual behaviour and/or interests

The term Autism Spectrum Disorder (ASD) is being used more frequently in recent years (and will likely be the term used in DSM-V) to express the idea that there is a spectrum of conditions or a continuum of autistic-like symptoms (Wing, 1988). Some people use the term ASD to mean all the PDDs but usually, in effect, it means an Autistic Disorder, PDD-NOS, and Asperger's syndrome (discussed further below). Instead of a group of related disorders within a category (that's the DSM concept of the PDDs), this spectrum idea suggests there is a continuum of severity of autistic symptoms, as well as a range of developmental level. It is important to realize that ASD is a much

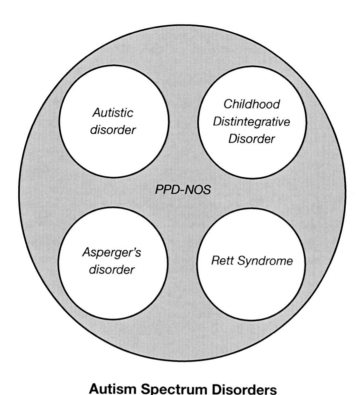

Autism Spectrum Disorders

Autistic disorder	PDD-NOS	Asperger's disorder

Level of Intellectual Functioning

Profound	Severe	Moderate	Mild	Low Average	Average	Above average

Figure 1. Autism disorders and level of intellectual function.

broader concept than just autism. See the lower part of Figure 2 for a graphic of one popular way of thinking about the Spectrum idea.

Autism: definition and description

Table 1 shows a brief summary of the DSM-IV-TR definition of Autistic Disorder. First, we will describe how each of the three areas of difficulty is expressed in autism (in some depth), and then we will briefly mention the other PDDs and related terms.

Autism involves, first and foremost, *pervasive difficulties in reciprocal social interaction*. This social deficit does not necessarily involve withdrawing from social contact but is, rather, a difficulty developing and sustaining relationships with other people. Children with autism may prefer isolation and ignore other people, may be unresponsive or aloof when others try to interact with them, often show no interest in playing with other children, and rarely initiate social contact. Some children do seem more sociable (e.g., may like hugs) but this is usually "on their own terms" and not very reciprocal. People with autism often have multiple deficits in "non-verbals." These include such things as eye contact that may be very brief, odd, or almost nonexistent; infrequent smiling or other facial expression; or

Table 1: DSM-IV-TR (APA, 2000) Definition of Autistic Disorder

1) *Qualitative Social Impairments*
   · *impaired nonverbals*
   · *poor peer relationships*
   · *lack of spontaneous social sharing*
   · *lack of social/emotional reciprocity*

2) *Qualitative Communication Impairments*
   · *no speech or delayed speech*
   · *(if verbal) impaired conversational skills*
   · *unusual, repetitive speech*
   · *lack of pretend and social play*

3) *Repetitive and Unusual Behaviours and Interests*
   · *preoccupations, narrow interests*
   · *rigid adherence to routines and rituals*
   · *stereotypic self-stimulatory behaviour*
   · *preoccupations with parts of objects*

Of the 12 criteria, at least 6 must be present, including:
   · *at least 2 from section 1;*
   · *1 from section 2; and*
   · *1 from section 3.*

Criteria must be judged relative to developmental level.

Some delays or abnormalities must be present before age 3.

great difficulty with the use of gestures and behaviours to engage the attention of another person in a social context ("joint attention"). They tend not to display spontaneous social sharing, such as showing others something they have made or pointing out things of interest. Even high functioning people with autism have great difficulty thinking about the feelings and thoughts of other people (this is sometimes described as lacking a "theory of mind"). For example, they may appear not to notice if another person is hurt or upset, and don't seem to have empathy for others. This makes true mutual friendships extremely difficult for people with autism. In fact, having very poor or no peer relationships is one of the defining features of the disorder.

The second area of difficulty (see Table 1) is pervasive *impairments in verbal and nonverbal communication.* About 1 in 3 people with autism cannot talk at all (sometimes called nonverbal or "mute"). Others do speak, at least to some extent, and many use a variety of other communication systems such as pictures or signs to communicate their wants and needs. Even people with good speech have difficulty using it in socially appropriate ways, such as having a real two-way conversation. Some children exhibit "echolalia," which is repeating back the words of others, either right away (immediate echolalia) or some time later (delayed echolalia). Although this may seem strange, it can be quite meaningful if the function of the echoed speech is understood. For example, they may repeat back a question when they don't understand it or don't know the answer. Other people with autism may use gibberish or funny made up words. They often seem to confuse pronouns (like saying "you" instead of "I"). The play of children with autism is also very problematic. In addition to the social difficulties mentioned above, they often have difficulty with imitation and usually do not engage in symbolic or pretend play (like pretending to give the doll a drink). They may have a good memory but seem to have little imagination. For example, a child with autism may open and close the window of a playhouse, where another child might be pretending to sell ice cream cones in the playhouse. Sometimes children with autism appear to have imaginative play but the play scenario is repetitive in nature, lasting for weeks or months, and often involving their restricted interest.

A pattern of *restricted, repetitive, and unusual behaviours and interests* is the third area of difficulty seen in Table 1. People with autism may show obsessive preoccupations (like arranging the books on the coffee table a certain way) or intense interest in one topic (such as the call letters of radio stations). They frequently have great difficulty coping with change and transitions and they like things in their environment to stay the same. For example, changing the school bus route to avoid construction or even hanging a new picture on the wall may be upsetting enough to precipitate a tantrum in some children. Repetitive or "stereotyped" behaviours (often assumed to be self-stimulatory) are common and are often the most noticeably odd thing you will see in a person with autism (though they may not be obvious at all in very young children). These include things like rocking, flapping of hands, and other unusual body movements. They may also involve peculiar use of objects, such as jiggling, spinning, tapping, or rubbing things constantly. They may not use toys and objects in the way they were intended and sometimes get fixated on one small part of a toy, such as staring at the spinning wheels of a toy car (rather than making the car move).

As you can see from the formula at the bottom of Table 1, there are many different combinations of characteristics that could meet the definition. It is important to understand that not all people with a diagnosis of autism have all the symptoms listed. Individuals with autism vary widely in ability, behaviour, activity level, and personality. Furthermore, just because someone doesn't have a particular symptom on the list doesn't necessarily mean that he or she doesn't have autism. For example, absent or disordered eye contact is often characteristic of children with autism, but some people with autism may have relatively good eye contact. There are general social difficulties, but children may well enjoy rough-and-tumble play, for example (just because they do doesn't rule out autism). On the other hand, simply exhibiting one or two of the symptoms on the list does not mean that the person has autism. The whole pattern of symptoms must be considered. Furthermore, each of the characteristics listed has to be judged abnormal relative to the person's developmental level. That is, children with autism are not just delayed (though they often are delayed as well, as we will discuss shortly), but rather their development is disordered. For example, their speech is not just immature, but is unusual; their play is not just delayed, it is different.

Part of the definition states that the onset of autism is before age 3. In fact, most children with autism have probably had the condition from birth. Peculiarities can be seen on early home videos, whether or not the parents recognized them or professionals diagnosed them appropriately. As infants and toddlers, children later diagnosed with autism may be unresponsive to their name, may not point to draw another person's attention, may show unusual

or absent facial expression, may not look at people, may not talk or not form two-word combinations by age 2, and may show minor attentional and motor difficulties. However, there is a subgroup of children who appear to have a normal early infancy, and then regress as toddlers, losing the ability to say words they had learned, for example. Early screening is very important and parents should be respected and believed when they suspect something is wrong. Many parents have been told to "wait and see" or that "he'll likely grow out of it," but this is bad advice. Children should be referred as soon as possible for a comprehensive diagnostic assessment and, in locations where there is a long waiting list for that assessment, it may be wise to begin intervention even before a formal diagnosis is obtained (some ideas of how to get started are discussed below in the early intervention section).

Diagnostic assessments and medical tests

The diagnosis of autism is a complex task and should only be done by an experienced professional (usually a psychologist, developmental pediatrician, neurologist, or child psychiatrist) or a multi-disciplinary team, based on some combination of: direct observation of the child (often using an observational measures such as the *Autism Diagnostic Observation Schedule* or ADOS or the *Childhood Autism Rating Scale* or CARS), history and diagnostic interviews with parents (such as the *Autism Diagnostic Interview-Revised* or the ADI-R), completion of rating scales designed to measure autism (such as the *Gilliam Autism Rating Scale* (2nd ed.) or GARS), and assessment of the child's developmental level (intelligence level and adaptive behaviour). A proper diagnostic assessment may be necessary to access services or funding, but should also help promote a better understanding of the child, help answer the family's questions, and guide intervention efforts. For more in-depth information about best practices in the screening, assessment, and diagnosis of autism, please see clinical practice parameters described in Filipek et al. (1999), the New York Guidelines (New York State Department of Health, 1999), National Research Council (2001), Perry and Condillac (2003), Sattler and Hoge (2006), and

Table 2: Some Genetic and Metabolic Disorders That May Have Features of Autism

Fragile X syndrome

Rett syndrome

Tuberous sclerosis

Neurofibromatosis type 1

CHARGE syndrome

22q11.2 microdeletion syndrome

Smith-Lemli-Optiz syndrome

Phenylketonuria

Creatine deficiency disorders

Disorders of purine and pyrimidine metabolism

Mitochondrial cytopathies

Nachshen et al. (2008).

When a child is diagnosed with autism, it is important that the physician rule out a possible associated genetic or metabolic disorder. A list of such conditions is found in Table 2. Although the majority of children with autism do *not* have such a disorder, some children could have and it is important to diagnose these other syndromes to increase potential options for treatment. The diagnosis of a genetic disorder will also provide parents with information about the chance that their subsequent children will also be affected. For example, if a diagnosis of fragile X syndrome is made, the recurrence risk is 50%. Compared to fragile X syndrome, the recurrence risk for idiopathic autism is between 5 and 10 percent, and increases with the number of children affected in the same family. However, caution must be used in quoting recurrence risks, as autism could co-occur with a genetic condition just by chance.

The medical evaluation for a child with autism includes blood tests for common genetic conditions (such as fragile X syndrome) as well as for conditions that have features similar to those seen in autism (e.g., Rett syndrome). A physical examination can also reveal clues to a specific diagnosis (e.g., children

with tuberous sclerosis or neurofibromatosis type 1 have characteristic patches of altered skin pigmentation). Screening tests, such as chromosome analysis for genetic imbalances, and tests of metabolite levels in blood and urine, occasionally detect a genetic or metabolic condition in children with autism. A relatively new technology to screen the genetic material for small imbalances, known as array comparative genomic hybridization (Li & Andersson, 2009), has revealed previously unrecognized genetic syndromes associated with autism, such as 16p11.2 deletion syndrome. Recent studies with this newer technology have reported that approximately 12% of children with autism have abnormalities, compared to the previous standard of 5% (Shih et al., 2010). An MRI of the brain may be helpful in some children with autism, although most often the brain is found to be structurally normal. Likewise, an EEG is suggested if there are symptoms compatible with seizures.

How common is autism?

Autism is not a rare disorder! The prevalence of autism proper is at least 2 in every 1000 children. For the whole PDD category, it is at least 6 in every 1000 or 1 per 166 children (Fombonne, 2009). It is much more common in boys than in girls (about 4 boys to every girl). Autism occurs in all cultures and all social classes. More recent studies suggest that the prevalence may be even higher, approaching 1 per 100 (ADDM, 2009), but it is important to remember that this number refers to the whole spectrum and that autism proper is a much smaller number. The frequency of PDDs seems to be increasing, and certainly the demand for services and educational resources is increasing significantly. However, we do not know whether this is a real increase in incidence or whether it is due to the different definitions of autism now being used, the narrowness or breadth of diagnoses examined in the studies (i.e., did they include related PDDs or only autism, did they include developmental disabilities), the recognition of earlier diagnosis, the greater awareness of autism among community professionals and the public, and the increased resources (in some jurisdictions) for intervention (Fombonne, 2009).

What is the connection between autism and developmental disabilities?

Autism often co-occurs with other medical disorders and diagnoses. The most common of these is intellectual or developmental disabilities (or mental retardation, or developmental handicap, or cognitive/intellectual impairment, all of which mean the same thing in this context). It is for this reason that a chapter on autism has been included in this book. Approximately three-quarters of people with autism also have some degree of cognitive impairment (APA, 2000; NRC, 2001) but it is important to realize that this is not necessarily true for other forms of PDD (see below) or for the whole autism spectrum. Level of cognitive ability or impairment is also sometimes referred to as the person's "level of functioning." It is important to understand, when providing support or intervention, that autism can be more or less severe, as can be the degree of cognitive impairment.

Although there may be overall delays, the cognitive profiles of people with autism are somewhat different from those of other individuals with developmental disabilities (this is the "not just delayed, but disordered" idea again). In general, people with autism show an uneven pattern of skills. A lot of people with autism have peak skills (also called splinter skills or "islets of ability"), which are characteristic strengths in their cognitive profile. They are usually better at nonverbal reasoning tasks like puzzles and copying designs as well as rote memory; they have much greater difficulty with tasks requiring abstract verbal reasoning and comprehension of social situations. Some people with autism are very good at spelling and reading decoding (pronouncing words), even scoring well above their expected age or grade level. This is sometimes called hyperlexia. It is important to recognize that understanding or comprehension is usually very poor in these individuals and that hyperlexia is not an indication of a high level of intelligence. Also, there are "autistic savants" who have amazing abilities in music, arithmetic calculations, or drawing. This is very rare (probably less than 1% of people with autism have savant skills) and does not mean the person is a

genius. In fact, they may be quite "low functioning" in most other areas of life.

What causes autism?

The causes of autism are complex and it is thought that many factors interact to cause the symptoms of autism. Although we do not have all the answers yet, we can say that: 1) autism is not caused by poor parenting (this is an old idea that has been totally discredited), and 2) autism is a biological disorder but there is probably no one single, straightforward cause. Physicians often classify children with autism into two categories, based on whether or not the cause is known. Primary or "idiopathic" autism makes up about 80-95% of individuals with autism. The term idiopathic means that no identifiable cause can be found. The second category, secondary or syndromic autism is much less common. These individuals have a medical condition, usually genetic in origin, which accounts for their autistic features, such as those mentioned earlier and listed in Table 1.

Research increasingly shows that genetics is a major contributing factor. A family history of autism increases the possibility of having a child with autism but none of the usual genetic mechanisms seems to explain autism. There are likely many different genes involved. Identical twins are much more likely than fraternal twins to have autism. The fact that this doesn't always happen, however, indicates that there must be other (non-genetic) factors involved.

The interactions between genetic and environmental factors in autism may result in structural differences and altered connectivity of the brain in individuals with autism. The brain has been shown to be larger in children with autism (Courchesne et al., 2001; Hazlett et al., 2005). This increased brain size is the result of an increase in the volume of grey and white matter in the brain. As individuals with autism mature, the difference in brain size disappears so that by adulthood the brain size has normalized or is smaller. Some studies have found that parts of the cerebellum are smaller in autism, and that the amygdala (a ganglion near the part of the brain involved in emotions of fear and aggression) is larger in younger children with autism and normal in adults (Stanfield et al., 2007). Some studies of the brain have shown impaired connectivity between regions of the brain important for social and higher level processing (Minshew & Williams, 2007). Taken altogether, the findings suggest that autism is a brain-based biological disorder.

Environmental factors, particularly prenatal and early childhood exposure to micro-organisms (e.g., the rubella virus), drugs (such as valproic acid), and toxins (notably lead and mercury), have been proposed to be associated with an increased risk of autism. It has been suggested that individuals with autism have a genetic vulnerability to the damage inflicted by these toxins. Also, some toxins may cause genetic mutations that predispose to autism. Others might disrupt normal gene expression without actually changing the DNA. Still, if or how environmental exposure contributes to the development of autism is largely unknown. There are no definite answers in this area at this time, but research is ongoing.

The controversy over the measles, mumps, and rubella (MMR) vaccines (which some people had suggested was a cause of autism) has been settled by numerous studies that demonstrate that neither the vaccine itself, nor thimerosal, a form of mercury formerly used as a preservative in other childhood vaccines, contribute to the risk of developing autism (Elliman & Bedford, 2007). Thus, we can say that vaccines do not cause autism.

In summary, there may be a number of different subgroups of autism with different causes, some of which are genetic, and some of which are associated with other known disorders. A great deal of research is going on in this area and we may have better answers in the future. Unfortunately, for parents who, understandably, want to know why autism occurred in their child, the current reality is that a particular cause may never be identified in a particular child.

What are the other related disorders?

As we said earlier, autism is the most well-known of the PDDs and, for this reason, it is the one we are focussing on in this chapter. But for the sake of completeness, we will briefly mention the other PDDs described in DSM-IV-TR and related terms here, as they compare to Autistic Disorder. You may want to refer back to Figure 2.

Rett Disorder : Typically, girls with Rett Disorder or Rett's syndrome (it seems to affect only girls) experience a regression at 6 to 24 months of age, after a period of apparently normal development. They generally cease making social contact and also lose normal hand use and develop characteristic hand wringing mannerisms. They are very incapacitated cognitively and also have some physical complications (see Perry, 1991). Rett Disorder is quite rare (Fombonne, 2003). The majority of girls with Rett syndrome have a mutation in a gene on the X chromosome called *MECP2,* and genetic testing for this mutation is readily available.

Childhood Disintegrative Disorder: Children with Childhood Disintegrative Disorder look similar to children with severe autism. However, this disorder has a much later onset, with a period of normal development until age 3 or 4 (or even later), followed by a regression and loss of skills. It is very rare, occurring in about 2 per 100,000 children (Fombonne, 2009) and is not well understood.

Asperger Disorder : People with Asperger Disorder or Asperger's syndrome have many similarities to people with autism but have relatively intact language and cognitive abilities (that is, they are higher functioning). The DSM-IV-TR criteria specify there must be qualitative impairment in reciprocal social interaction (the same four criteria as in Autistic Disorder) and restricted and repetitive interests, but no clinically significant difficulties with cognition or language, although they may have great difficulty using their knowledge and speech appropriately in social situations. Asperger's syndrome is often not diagnosed until the child is school-aged and the social difficulties become more apparent. There is some controversy among experts about whether Asperger's syndrome is really the same thing as high-functioning autism (that is, people with autism who have higher cognitive levels) and it seems likely that the DSM-V may no longer make this distinction.

Pervasive Developmental Disorder – Not Otherwise Specified (PDD-NOS): The term Pervasive Developmental Disorder is a rather confusing term that is meant to be used for individuals who are within the overall PDD category but do not meet the criteria for any of the other four disorders (the space in between the four specific disorders shown in the large circle in Figure 2). In practice, this term is most often used for milder or atypical disorders, so it basically means mild autism. Sometimes, however, clinicians use PDD-NOS when the age of onset is late or unclear; when the child is very low functioning and it is difficult to differentially diagnose the autism symptoms relative to developmental level; or in situations where the child is very young and the professional is reluctant to give the autism label. Note that the term PDD by itself is not really a diagnosis (it is the general category), but it is sometimes used to mean PDD-NOS. There are no official criteria for PDD-NOS; it just means the autism criteria are not quite fulfilled. The lack of specific diagnostic criteria is unfortunate, because PDD-NOS seems to be quite common, more common than Autistic Disorder, in fact (Fombonne, 2009). You may also hear (or read in reports) these children described as autistic-like, developmentally delayed with autistic features, autism/PDD, ASD, autistic tendencies, and so on. For most practical purposes, such as educational or behavioural supports with these individuals, the distinction between Autism and PDD-NOS is not very meaningful, as interventions should be individualized for the person, taking into account their particular abilities and disabilities.

Treatment and Intervention In Autism

Autism is, in most cases, a lifelong disorder. However, better diagnosis, better intervention, and better education programs are making a real difference. The future for children with autism today is much more optimistic than was the case in the past. Still, many of them will continue to need significant supports throughout their lives.

Treatment of common medical disorders in autism

As of 2011, there is no one medical treatment for the core symptoms of autism, but there are common health issues which may require medical treatment.

Epilepsy

Epilepsy is the tendency to have seizures, which are brief episodes of synchronous electrical activity in the brain. Seizures may produce convulsions, disturbance of consciousness, or other physical symptoms. Epilepsy is diagnosed in up to one-third of individuals with autism, and children with epilepsy are more likely to have autistic features than children without epilepsy. Seizures are more likely to occur in children with a syndromic form of autism, and in those with intellectual disability. Diagnosis of epilepsy in children with autism may be difficult, as some of the behaviours exhibited (such as staring, unresponsiveness, or repetitive behaviour) may resemble seizures. EEG can distinguish between seizures and autistic behaviour by recording electrical activity from the surface of the brain. Interestingly, some children with autism have abnormal EEG results despite never having a witnessed seizure. The treatment of epilepsy in autism is the same as for the general population. Anticonvulsant medication is used to prevent or reduce seizures. Controlling epilepsy with medication does not typically result in the improvement of core symptoms of autism, but can help with learning and concentration if appropriate dosing is used.

Sleep problems

Sleep problems are prevalent in children and adolescents with developmental disabilities, and those with autism seem to be particularly vulnerable, with up to two-thirds of parents reporting a sleep problem at some point in the child's life. The most common problem among children with autism is insomnia, particularly "settling down" to sleep and staying asleep through the night. This appears to be true regardless of age or cognitive level (Richdale & Schreck, 2009). The causes of sleep problems in autism are unknown, but some have suggested abnormalities in melatonin production or pattern of release, causing circadian rhythm disruptions. It is likely that sleep problems in autism result from a number of factors including co-morbid conditions (e.g., anxiety, depression, hyperactivity), medications, and poor sleep habits (such as co-sleeping with parents). Methods for managing sleep problems in autism include those used in the general pediatric population, such as improving sleep hygiene (e.g., establishing a non-stimulating bedtime routine, eliminating caffeine). Melatonin can be taken in pill form before bedtime, and is safe and tolerated well. Studies of melatonin use in individuals with autism have shown favourable results, but there are some children who do not respond. Some medications used primarily to target ADHD symptoms (e.g., clonidine) or aggression (atypical antipsychotics) can improve sleep when given prior to bedtime because of their sedative properties. In severe cases of insomnia, sedating medications ("sleeping pills") can be used on an occasional basis as a last resort.

Gastrointestinal issues

Based on parent report, gastrointestinal complaints are common in children with autism. However, it is uncertain whether these complaints are actually more frequent in children with autism than in typical children or children with developmental delays (Buie et al., 2010). Common complaints include constipation, diarrhea, vomiting, abdominal cramping and bloating, and dietary sensitivities (e.g., to milk proteins). These are common childhood complaints, with a wide array of possible causes. It is difficult to tease out the relationship between gastrointestinal issues and autism due to impaired communication skills, and behavioural issues that may affect eating (e.g., intolerance of certain food textures) and toileting habits. Research into gastrointestinal complaints in autism has not yet revealed any convincing pathology or effective treatments. In general, children with autism are not malnourished, do not have vitamin or mineral deficiencies (or excesses), and do not have a higher than expected incidence of food allergies, celiac disease, or inflammatory bowel disease. Studies reporting chronic gastrointestinal tract inflammation suffer from bias and lack of control group data. However, the lack of evidence of specific gut pathology in autism has not dissuaded some researchers from attempting to treat behavioural problems using elimination diets, under the assumption that gastrointestinal complaints aggravate the behavioural manifestations of

autism. High quality experimental studies involving controlled trials of secretin (a hormone produced in the duodenum in response gastric emptying) administration to children with autism showed no improvement in behaviour compared to placebo. It has become a popular practice among parents to place children with autism on gluten- and casein-free diets but research has produced mixed results.

Early intervention in autism

Behavioural early intervention programs (some of which started as far back as the 1960s) have been shown to produce significant improvements in children's cognitive level, language, and ability to function in school. In fact, a significant minority of these children improve so much that they would no longer be said to have autism or a developmental disability (Green, 1996). These children are sometimes described as "recovered" although this term is quite controversial. Other children, especially those who are initially lower functioning, can be expected to improve significantly but not to the same extent.

The most well-known of these behavioural early intervention programs was developed by Lovaas in California. It has been around the longest (the first children treated have now been followed well into adulthood), their results are very impressive (47% best outcome), and they have done good research (although some people have criticized it). In the last 10 to 20 years, a number of other programs have been developed along the same lines, and some of these have also done research to show their effectiveness. There are some differences among these programs in the settings where the intervention takes place (home-based, clinic-based, school-based), the specific methods used, the type of children, and so on. We do not have enough evidence yet to say whether any specific variation is better than any other, but there are certain basic similarities among the effective ones. Common features of these successful programs (based partly on Powers, 1992) are:

- *They begin in the preschool years* (usually age 2 to 4) and the evidence suggests "best outcomes" are much more likely if children begin very young.
- *They are intensive* (often 20 to 40 hours per

week for 1 to 2 years).

- *They use structured behavioural teaching principles* (reinforcement, task analysis, shaping, repetition and practice). See Martin & Pear (2010) for a good basic text on these methods.
- *They are comprehensive* (provide teaching in all areas of development including language, play, social skills, academics, self-help skills, etc.).
- *They are individualized* (specific goals and methods are individualized based on thorough developmental assessment, child's strengths and weaknesses, and preferences).
- *They use highly trained staff,* who receive frequent direct supervision from a highly trained supervisor (usually a psychologist and/or Board Certified Behaviour Analyst) and also usually involve parents in the treatment.
- *They involve some integration* with typically developing peers.

What kinds of things would a child learn in a behavioural early intervention program? How do you get started? Table 2 gives you some idea of the early stages of a developmentally-based curriculum that might provide the sequence of early skills to be taught, even if a child is not yet formally diagnosed. For more specific details and programs, see Koegel and LaZebnik (2004), Lovaas (2002), Maurice, Green, and Luce (1996), and Maurice, Green, and Foxx (2001).

There has been debate among professionals about the best theoretical background for preschool autism programs. Some have characterized this debate as "behavioural" vs. "developmental" (NRC, 2001), but clearly both are important. It is our observation that, over the past 10 years or so, there has been a gradual coming together and recognition of the similarities across approaches, rather than focusing on the differences. Dunlap (1999) suggested four main messages about the current state of the field. First, although there are differences among approaches, there is a growing consensus on critical ingredients in early intervention, (e.g., all promote or teach active engagement of the child with other people). Second, there are very few studies that involve direct comparisons of one approach

to another with similar children, so it is difficult to say one theory, approach, or program is better than another in any overall sense. However, we believe it is likely that future research will help establish that certain approaches may be better for certain types of children and families. Third, having acknowledged the lack of comparison studies, we do think it important to point out that the vast majority of the early intervention programs that have documented evidence of effectiveness are based on principles of applied behaviour analysis (ABA). There is great variation, however, in where and how the principles are implemented (e.g., discrete trial training, incidental teaching, pivotal response training, verbal behaviour approach, etc.). Fourth, it is crucial to consider the family perspective, not only in assess-

Table 3: Early Intervention Strategies for Parents and Therapists

Intervene in social aloofness & self-stimulatory behaviour

Work on motivation — learning to learn
- *find effective means of reinforcement (primary like food at first if needed)*

Teach attending & co-operating
- *sitting, looking, following instructions, trying*

Teach imitation
- *gross motor, fine motor*
- *vocal, verbal*
- *social, parallel play*

Teach pointing
- *requesting — shape "autistic leading" into pointing*
- *receptive — to teach vocabulary*
- *pointing to show — practice with prompts & commenting*

Teach toy play
- *means-end toys*
- *functional use*
- *symbolic use i.e., pretend play*

Teach social play
- *turn-taking*
- *social interaction games*
- *practice greetings & routines*
- *parallel play*
- *sharing*

ment and goal selection, but in terms of finding the best match of intervention approaches that suits the family's beliefs, values, and culture, and does not inadvertently damage the family by undermining their parenting and adding to their stress.

Even with the best early intervention, however, the majority of children with autism will not improve enough to function without supports in school and in adult life. Older children and adults can still continue to benefit from a similar approach involving structured teaching and individualized goals in a comprehensive range of areas of functioning (Howlin, 1997; Smith, 1990). Teaching vocational skills and life skills becomes more important as individuals with autism get older. These skills need to be learned and applied in a variety of environments. In addition, some other characteristics of autism have implications for intervention with older children and adults. We will examine some of these briefly in the next sections.

Educational Intervention in Autism

Children and adolescents with autism have a right to an "appropriate" publicly-funded education in many places, including Ontario. However, there is considerable variability throughout Ontario, as there is in different countries, states, and provinces, in the resources and expertise available, philosophical approaches between and within different school districts, legislation and appeal processes and so on. Children with autism certainly present a challenge to educational systems but it is important to remember that they are, first and foremost, students who need to be taught. All the specialized interventions and treatments that may be needed are really just specialized ways of teaching children what they need to know to grow and develop.

As with the other forms of intervention discussed in this chapter, we believe that educational programming should be evidence-based and effective. Compared to the early intervention literature, there is not the same body of research literature and consensus panels to guide educators and others working with school-aged individuals with autism. However, there are hundreds of small studies that look at specific intervention approaches to teach specific skills

in individuals or small groups of children and adolescents. Iovannone, Dunlap, Huber, and Kincaid (2003) reviewed the literature regarding effective educational practices for children with ASD over age 5 and formulated six core elements that are evidence-based and that should be included in a comprehensive educational intervention program for any student with autism. Programs should be: 1) individualized, 2) systematic, 3) structured, 4) have specific autism-related curriculum goals, 5) use positive behavioural supports, and 6) involve families. We will discuss each of these in turn.

1. First, effective supports should be *individualized*. Given the individual differences among students with autism in terms of the symptoms and characteristics described earlier, as well as behaviours and functioning levels, it stands to reason that educational programs need to be individually tailored to suit the child, not the "label" of autism. Further, individualization needs to take into account the student's likes and dislikes, strengths and weaknesses, and his or her motivation. In part, this means instructional materials and tasks should be interesting to the student, perhaps tapping into particular interests or strengths he or she has (e.g., for a child who loves puzzles, use a map puzzle to learn geography).

   Appropriate individualized motivational systems (that is, reinforcement) are crucial to help children with autism learn. Reinforcement does not just mean using candies to reward correct responses. It could include check marks or stickers for correct answers in written work, frequent praise for working quietly without disruptive behaviour, hugs and tickles for a spontaneous social initiative, and effective use of activity reinforcers and treats. Also, giving students certain choices among activities or choices of reinforcers to work for assists with motivation for task-related behaviour and minimizes problem behaviour.

   People with autism may have difficulty paying attention or paying attention to the things we want them to (e.g., they may pay attention to a small, irrelevant detail in a picture, and "miss the point"). They may have difficulty processing multiple cues at the same time (like the shape of puzzle pieces and the pattern on them). They may have trouble shifting their attention from one thing to another. What sometimes helps is to have people point to what you want them to look at, or have them move their whole body when you are trying to get them to attend to something new. Often you need to remind them to look at what they're doing (during dressing tasks for example).

In some cases, "sensory issues" need to be taken into account in planning intervention programs. People with autism may experience sensations in unusual ways, such as being overly sensitive to certain sounds, disliking certain textures, or having trouble processing two senses at the same time. They may use sensations to soothe themselves or decrease anxiety or to gain a sense of control of their world. Working effectively with a person with autism requires knowing the person well and taking these possible sensory preferences and sensitivities into account.

2. Effective educational intervention is *systematic*, that is, carefully planned and structured, and constantly evaluated and modified based on data. Most of the published literature reviewed by Iovannone et al. (2003) is based on principles derived from applied behaviour analysis (ABA), but these studies can be very different from each other in terms of specific methodologies. They include such diverse approaches as self-management training to promote independent academic work, in vivo training to teach grocery shopping skills, and discrete trial training to teach academic skills. All involve data collection and analysis. It may be difficult to collect certain kinds of data in school settings (such as the trial-by-trial data that is often used in preschool programs). What is important is that enough data on the child's skills be taken to answer questions such as: How do you know he has learned "blue"? When do we move on to the next set of reading words? Has she mastered appropriate greetings? There should be enough data of a reasonable sort so that data-based decisions can be made.

3. Children with autism need a *structured environment*. That means the structure of the day (or of

a task or lesson) is predictable and understandable for the student. There are a number of supportive strategies that may be helpful such as providing pictorial schedules, visual cues for a task sequence, warnings before transitions to new tasks or environments are about to happen, and so on. Many people with autism (but not all) respond well to visual cues and teaching aids. Pictures are especially useful, in addition to their use as communication tools (see below). They can be used to prompt an activity (such as matching cutlery to an outline on the table to teach table setting), to provide helpful structure and predictability (such as a picture activity schedule of the tasks expected of the person over the day), and to help break a task down into easier to understand steps (e.g., pictures of the sequence of making a sandwich). Pictures can also help people be more independent if they can use the pictures to cue themselves rather than waiting for someone to remind them verbally what to do next.

4. Within the individualized approach, there should be a *functional curriculum that addresses the specific characteristics of autism*. This means there should be explicit teaching of social and communication skills that are functional, that is, meaningful and useful for the child's life. Social abilities are crucial in all aspects of life and the child with autism is particularly disadvantaged in this domain. Sometimes very basic social skills (such as taking turns) and specific social skills (like asking other children to join in a game) must be taught and practised in real-life settings, including school and home. The nature of the specific instructional targets may vary a great deal, depending on the child.

Improving communication skills is likely to be a goal for all people with autism, regardless of their age or functioning level. For people with good verbal skills, intervention will focus more on reciprocal conversation skills and social routines to help the person use his or her speech for social communication purposes. For nonverbal or minimally verbal individuals, there are various other means of communication, known collectively as Alternative and Augmentative Communication. These include nonsymbolic gestures (like leading you by the hand to what they want), learned cultural gestures (like waving), and formal systems of symbolic gestures (sign language). Sign language can be helpful at times, as long as people in the environment understand what the person with autism is signing. There are also various graphic systems including miniature objects, photographs, drawings, symbols, and printed words. These can be used in "low tech" ways (such as a person carrying a wallet or binder of pictures) or "high tech" ways (such as a computerized speech synthesizers that say words when certain keys are pressed). One of the most popular and well-researched systems is the Picture Exchange Communication System (PECS; Bondy & Frost, 2002) in which a child gives a photograph to a communicative partner, in exchange for a desired object. Different communication systems have different advantages and disadvantages for different people with autism. Parents sometimes worry that learning one of these other systems will discourage the development of speech but, if anything, the opposite is true — they may help the child later speak as well as communicate their needs at the time (at least for PECS and for sign language).

It is important to remember, however, that finding the one best system is not likely to suddenly make a nonverbal person diagnosed with autism be able to communicate at a sophisticated level, because of their underlying cognitive level. The real goal is not so much to increase vocabulary or teach speech or the rules of grammar, but rather for people with autism to learn to communicate about things that are relevant in their lives, and in ways that are effective in their environments. For example, it is more important (and more functional) that the child has the ability to ask for a drink when thirsty (using a sign or picture) than to name 100 flash cards of obscure objects.

5. Effective school-based intervention includes a *functional approach to understanding the child's problem behaviour.* Some people with autism may exhibit severe problem behaviours, such as aggression and self-injurious behaviour. These behaviours are not part of the definition of autism, but may be related to the difficulties people with autism have with communication, adapting to change, and understanding social situations, as well to as their level of functioning. Thus, helping students with these problems is a crucial part of their educational program. See the section below regarding behavioural and pharmacological interventions for problem behaviour.

6. Active *family involvement* is crucial to the effectiveness of educational intervention. Parents should be involved in assessing and determining goals for the child's individual learning plan, should have input into the methods and motivational strategies used (they have often discovered the best strategies already), and could help determine progress (e.g., by reporting how well skills are generalized to the home setting). There should be frequent communication between home and school. In some cases, parents can supplement the teaching at home by either helping the child practise specific skills or by doing informal generalization (e.g., helping the child use the skill in a different setting and with different people). Transitions to school, between schools, and from school to post-school adult life are often very stressful for families, and everyone involved needs to work respectfully and collaboratively. Having a child with autism is one of the hardest things that can happen to a family. Although most families cope remarkably well most of the time, some really struggle at times, and all have some tough challenges along the way. For a summary of family needs and issues at different family life cycle stages see Perry and Condillac (2003). See also the chapter on families in this book. Much of it applies to families of children with autism too. For more information about families and positive behaviour support, see Lucyshyn, Dunlap, and Albin (2002), a book written about and with parents.

Treatment of problem behaviour

As noted above, some individuals with autism exhibit aggression, self-injurious behaviour, destructiveness, and tantrums. The treatment of these behaviours has been quite controversial in the history of autism. In the past, it was believed to be best to try to eliminate such behaviour by punishment, extinction, or medication. Fortunately, our methods of assessing and intervening in these problem behaviours have improved considerably in the past two decades, a great deal of research has accumulated, and practices have changed, as well as policies and legislation in some places.

The overall approach we recommend is known as Positive Behaviour Support (see Jackson & Veeneman Panyan, 2002; Koegel, Koegel, & Dunlap, 1996; Sailor, Dunlap, Sugai, & Horner, 2009). First, it is important to try to rule out any medical issues (e.g., a child who is "biting" his hand may have a toothache, or an adolescent who bangs the side of his head may have an earache). There may well be sleep problems or gastro-intestinal issues as discussed above. These need to be investigated and treated first and foremost. Also, the environment and the nature of the schoolwork or other activities the individual is expected to do need to be examined. Is the classroom too loud and distracting? Are the tasks too boring or far too difficult for the student? Sometimes, it is quite easy to prevent the problematic behaviour by attending to these environmental factors.

If these things have been considered and the behaviour persists, a behavioural support plan may need to be developed and it should be based on the concept of a functional assessment (or functional behavioural assessment). Note that the term "functional" is used here in a slightly different way than above. In this case, it refers to the function of the behaviour or why the behaviour is happening. Behaviours like this don't happen "out of the blue" for no reason; it is our job to figure out the reason(s). For example, is it the only way the person has of getting something they want? Is it effective at getting you to stop something they do not like? Has the behaviour been reinforced by other people's attention? It is only once we figure out the function of the behaviour that we can design an intervention plan to reduce or change it.

There are many behaviour therapy strategies that can be used, but one of the most important principles is to teach the person alternative behaviours and skills to use instead of the problem behaviour (like teaching them to sign "break," teaching them to raise their hand to get your attention when they are finished a task and don't know what to do next). Also, there are a variety of positive reinforcement-based approaches that involve differentially reinforcing the absence of the problem behaviour (pay attention to them when they are behaving appropriately), reinforcing the presence of the new replacement skill (oh, good, you raised your hand, I'll be right there), reinforcing other incompatible behaviours, and so on. Ultimately, the goal is for the natural environment (peers, other school personnel) to take over reinforcing appropriate behaviour so that it becomes natural. See chapter 24 and Martin and Pear (2010) for more detail.

Individuals with autism often benefit from multimodal treatments that include medication in addition to educational or behavioural intervention (Myers & Johnson, 2007). Research suggests that combined treatments of medication and behavioural strategies lead to greater reduction of maladaptive behaviour compared to medication alone. However, it is often challenging for community physicians and mental health professionals to work together toward a combined behavioural and pharmacological treatment plan.

The majority of the medications used in the autism populations have been borrowed from other psychiatric disorders. To avoid side effects, physicians generally follow the rule "Start Low, Go Slow." When considering whether to start a medication, often the profile of the child's behaviours is considered, including each target symptom, the need for monitoring a specific medication for side effects with blood testing, and the family history of mental health issues and response to similar classes of medications. A list of target symptoms, medications, and studies can be found in pharmacotherapy reviews by Myers (2007) and Myers and Johnson (2007).

- For aggression with marked irritability, medications in the atypical antipsychotic class have shown efficacy in studies of children with autism and intellectual disabilities (Jesner, Aref-Adib, & Coren, 2007). However, the drawbacks of atypical antipsychotics are their side effects, including increased appetite and weight gain, sedation, as well effects on cholesterol, blood sugar, prolactin and liver enzymes.

- For symptoms of repetitive behaviour and anxiety, some studies using Selective Serotonin Reuptake Inhibitors (SSRIs), such as fluoxetine and citalopram, have shown small improvements in symptoms (Hollander et al., 2005). Large well controlled studies of citalopram have demonstrated no differences with placebo but it must be noted that the placebo response was very large in these studies.
- As in typical children with ADHD, symptoms of hyperactivity and impulsivity have shown improvements with stimulant treatment (e.g., methylphenidate), but the proportion of responders is often smaller (50%-60%) (RUPP, 2005). Small studies with non stimulant medication, atomoxetine, have also shown some benefit.

Complementary and alternative medicine and controversial intervention approaches

So far in this chapter, we have been describing psychosocial and medical treatments that have been shown through research to be effective — that is, they are *"evidence-based."* However, many families and service providers find themselves tempted by new types of treatment they hear about from the internet or on television. Unfortunately, these other forms of intervention may not be evidence-based. For a review of the scientific evidence on a number of therapies, see the New York State Department of Health's guidelines (1999), National Research Council (2001), and Perry and Condillac (2003). Most recently, the National Autism Center (2009) has presented a user-friendly, but thorough, review of the evidence base for a large number of psychosocial interventions.

These approaches are sometimes referred to as Complementary and Alternative Medicine (CAM) therapies (Myers, 2007). These CAM therapies can be categorized into "nonbiological" (e.g., auditory integration therapy, music therapy) and "biological" (e.g., vitamins, dietary supplements, restriction diets, detoxification therapies, gastrointestinal treatments) (Levy & Hyman, 2005). Many of these CAM therapies are not evidence-based. There are two different ways an approach can be said to be not evidence-based. One way occurs when there have been a reasonable number of high quality studies which show that the approach does not work (e.g., facilitated communication, secretin). For these interventions, we can say the evidence shows they do not work and, furthermore, there may be harmful side effects. The other way in which a treatment may not be evidence-based is when there are no research studies showing its effectiveness, or there are only one or two very poor quality studies. In this case, we can draw no conclusions one way or the other. Then we have to use clinical judgment and common sense, considering the potential gains but also the possible risks. Some of these approaches do have significant risk of harm (e.g., chelation). If you are working in the autism field, it is important to know that many therapies have been inadequately evaluated and therefore evidence-based recommendations to support or refute their use are not possible. Most professionals prioritize evidence-based therapy, and are reluctant to support alternative therapies that may not be effective, may have unknown side effects and financial and emotional costs for individuals with autism and their families.

However, when we consider the viewpoints of families who feel that they are losing time waiting for evidence to support a treatment, there are some principles that support a consideration of unproven therapies, ideally in a research context, where side effects and benefits can be closely monitored. Autism spectrum disorders are likely caused by a variety of genetic and possibly environmental factors, and one biological therapy is unlikely to "cure" most individuals with ASD. It is possible, though, that some biological therapies may be helpful for particular individuals with a specific "cause" of ASD, but at present researchers are still looking to identify these "causes" or "biomarkers" that can indicate which subgroup of ASD might be responsive to which therapy. As families of individuals with ASD often use alternative biological therapies, it is helpful for clinicians to understand the rationale, side effects, and initial evidence proposed by advocates of unproven biological therapies. A summary of these can be found on the website of a CAM advocate, Dr. Jim Adams, a supporter of the "Defeat Autism Now" philosophy: *http://www.autism.com/treatable/adams_biomed_summary.pdf.*

In the autism field, new treatment methods tend to spring up regularly but, unfortunately, they usually do not turn out to be as exciting as originally hoped. Parents and others who care about children and adults with autism naturally wish a "cure" would be possible. So, people are vulnerable to being disappointed when a new treatment turns out not to be very effective, which is what usually happens unfortunately. On the other hand, valid new treatments and techniques may be found in the future, and we need to keep an open mind, as well as maintain an appropriate level of hope about the future of the person with autism we care about (that is, we should be both optimistic and realistic). The following are some points to keep in mind and some questions you should ask if you come across a controversial or unproven treatment technique (based partly on Freeman, 1997; Green, 1996):

- Be open-minded but skeptical (don't rush to jump on every bandwagon).
- Ask about the theory behind it and decide whether it makes sense based on what is known about autism.
- Ask what research has been done to demonstrate its effectiveness.
- Beware if it is being promoted as a "miracle," "cure," or "breakthrough."
- Beware if it is claimed to work for everyone and/or is done the same way for everyone, rather than being based on an individualized assessment.
- Ask whether it is monitored and changed regularly based on some form of data.
- Ask what harm it could do, what side effects or risks might be possible.
- Ask who is qualified to provide the treatment and/or what training and supervision the person receives.
- Consider the costs in money, time, and energy to the person with autism, family, and staff.

- Do a risk/benefit analysis taking all above points into consideration.
- If trying an unproven technique don't discontinue other approaches known to be beneficial (don't put all your eggs in one basket) and try to evaluate its effectiveness systematically.

Large Systems Challenges

Autism presents a conspicuous challenge to educational, social service, and health care systems. Families, professionals, and policy-makers alike struggle with several recent realities (Dunlap & Fox, 2004). First, the increasing prevalence and broader understanding of Autism Spectrum Disorders is putting tremendous pressure on the whole service system. Second, there is a heightened level of parent advocacy, litigation, and demand for services that are appropriate and effective. Third, in many jurisdictions there are new regulations or policies that begin to address these issues, and even considerable new financial resources in some cases, but the capacity-building required is slow to happen (that is, large scale recruiting and training, spreading of knowledge about autism throughout the system, and so on). We believe there are several very important issues that systems need to address in the near future:

- Assessment and diagnosis of autism (and related disorders) still happen late and inconsistently in different places, with excellent centres in some locations (usually in large urban hospitals) and sketchy resources in other places. Some professionals are not well-informed about autism and may hesitate to label young children. Families may travel long distances, go through misdiagnosis, apparently contradictory diagnoses, and long waiting periods. A recent trend is overdiagnosis of autism, which is seen as a "ticket" to funding for intervention for children with non-autistic developmental problems. Even when diagnosis is well done, the child's developmental assessment is often inadequate. Given the progress that has been made in articulating best practices for assessment and diagnosis of autism (Filipek et al., 1999; NRC, 2001; Perry & Condillac, 2003), systems must be adequately funded and organized to conduct comprehensive multi-disciplinary assessments that result in early, accurate diagnoses and these assessments should feed directly into early intervention programs. In some locales, this will require greater cooperation across professions and across funding silos (e.g., health and education) than presently exists.

- In terms of intervention, systems must be structured to be both comprehensive and flexible, to allow for the wide range of needs of children, adolescents, and adults with autism and their families. No one particular model (such as a certain specialized autism classroom) is going to be appropriate for all children with autism because they are so different from one another. Rather, a range of evidence-based approaches — educational/behavioural, integrated with medical care, individually tailored to the child — is needed and systems have to be suitably organized to deliver intervention with this in mind.

- There needs to be greater cooperation, collaboration, and continuity across systems and agencies and less debate about "whose job it is" to deliver services. The successful care of a child with autism requires the relationship between an experienced team of clinicians working co-operatively with each child and family. Researchers are evaluating the impact of a network of physicians and other clinicians, in a model of comprehensive and chronic care, such as the Autism Treatment Network (ATN) (Coury, Jones, Klatka, Winklosky, & Perrin, 2009). A key target area of the ATN is to build capacity in community physicians through the construction of evidenced based clinical guidelines for various aspects of medical care, for example, the management of sleep difficulties in children with ASD.

- From the family's point of view, the arbitrary divisions among services by diagnostic label, age, or particular symptom are often nonsensical and inefficient. Because of all the different services, agencies, and schools a family must deal with, there are many transition points in the lives of children with autism and their families, and the number and difficulty of these should be reduced whenever possible. Given that not all can be avoided, transition planning must be addressed more systematically and earlier.

- Services for adults are, in many jurisdictions, in particularly short supply and parents of adults are often exhausted from "fighting the system" for many years. There is a shortage of appropriate day programs, vocational programs, and meaningful work for adults with autism in most communities. Adolescents and adults (and some children) may require residential placement outside the family home at some point. There are shortages of spaces and long wait lists for these placements in many cases.

- Accurate information about autism, about interventions, about local service systems, and about supports for families is crucial. Great progress has been made in some locations in the past decade or so, but in many areas, families flounder with misinformation or lack of information. The internet can be both a blessing and a curse in this respect. It is important to help families (and staff) critically evaluate such information. Recent initiatives such as the National Autism Centre's Standards are a helpful example of making evidence-based information available in a user-friendly way.

- Some family support services are in short supply, particularly service coordination and respite care. Service coordination (or case management) is important to help families navigate the system, which is complex and poorly integrated in many locales. There is a need for greater funding for in-home respite and more out-of-home respite spaces which accept children with autism, especially those with behavioural and medical needs.

- Intervention for challenging behaviour must be integrated with a skill development focus and a medical approach, into the overall program for the person with autism. The difference among treatment, education, therapy, intervention, and rehabilitation is purely semantic. What we call it doesn't matter; what matters is that we do it.

- Well-trained staff are needed at all levels of the system. Even if financial resources were multiplied a hundred-fold, it would not overcome the reality that there is a critical shortage of trained professionals. See the NRC (2001) recommendations regarding training of teachers and support staff in the education system. Senior level clinicians to supervise early intervention programs, and consult to school and adult programs, are also in short supply and it takes at least a decade to train and mentor these professionals. We need to do so in greater numbers, as soon as possible.
- Partly because of the tendency for less optimally trained people to fill the gap provided by the large service demand, professional organizations have proposed standards for consumers to use in choosing professionals (e.g., *http://www.abainternational.org/Special_Interests/AutGuidelines.pdf*) or are promoting a formal certification process which assures consumers and employers that, at least, core behavioural content has been mastered (e.g., *www.bacb.com*), though it is not specific to autism.

There is no doubt these are formidable challenges! Yet, this is also a time of exciting opportunities: opportunities to make a very real difference in the lives of individuals with autism, their families, students, paraprofessionals and professionals, and with policy makers and legislators. We have come a long way, but we still have a long way to go.

Summary

Autism is a Pervasive Developmental Disorder involving severe difficulties in social relationships, severe difficulties in communication, and unusual repetitive behaviours. In addition, many people with autism also have an intellectual disability. People with autism vary a great deal depending on their age, level of cognitive functioning, medical needs, and particular symptoms. Autism is a biological disorder, but there is probably no single cause. Rather, there may be different subgroups with different causes. For young children, intensive behavioural early intervention programs can make a very significant difference. Older children may continue to need comprehensive, structured intervention and education. It is important to give the person a functional communication system(s) and to take their attentional and sensory difficulties into account. Problem behaviours need to be well-understood and treated carefully based on a functional approach. New and controversial treatments should be approached with a healthy skepticism. Families of people with autism have many challenges to face and may need a variety of supports. Autism presents a number of significant challenges to large systems. Future research into evidence-based models of care and in many of the areas discussed in this chapter will be necessary to continue to improve the quality of life for individuals with autism and their families.

For Further Thought and Discussion

1. Select one of the treatment approaches currently being used in the field of autism. Explain this approach and evaluate the extent to which it would be considered evidence-based.
2. Tim is 3 years old. He is described by his mother as having been a good baby. In fact, he seemed more contented when left alone. His mom recalls that he didn't smile and didn't seem to recognize her as a young infant. He walked at nine months and has always been very agile, rarely falling or hurting himself. He has not yet begun to speak and does not yet dress or feed himself. His parents report that he does not seem to be interested in their love and affection. His lack of speech and responsiveness continue along with an increase in unusual behaviours. He spends much of the day picking up pieces of lint, which he drops in the air and then watches intently as they fall to the floor. He also licks the back of his hands and stares at the saliva. The family doctor is concerned about his developmental delays and has made a referral to an early intervention program. You are the early intervention worker who has been assigned to work with Tim and his family.
   a. What behaviours of Tim's are consistent with the diagnosis of autistic disorder?

What steps would you take to ensure that a complete and accurate diagnosis was made?

b. What issues do you think the family might be facing as they receive a diagnosis of Tim's disorder? What supports would you provide for the family in response to the issues you have identified? Be specific.

c. Would you begin to work with Tim before receiving a diagnosis? Explain your answer (why or why not).

d. What areas of functioning you would work on with Tim? Detail some specific strategies that might be used to enhance Tim's functioning in each of these areas.

3. For many individuals diagnosed with autistic disorder the prognosis is poor. Many families initially maintain their children at home. Others, however, seek out-of-home placement for their child with autism. What factors do you think might prevent a family seeking out-of-home care for their child and why? What supports and services do you think families would require if they were to continue to maintain their child at home and why?

4. Autism is viewed by some as being like an illness from which people can recover. Intellectual/developmental disability, on the other hand, tends to be seen as an unchanging characteristic of the person. Do you agree with this position and why? Is it justified to spend more money per child to treat autism than to treat children with other developmental disabilities?

More Resources

Books and Articles:

Gillberg, C., & Coleman, M. (2000). *The biology of the autistic syndromes* (3rd ed.). London: Mac Keith Press.

Howlin, P. (1997). *Autism: Preparing for adulthood.* London: Routledge.

Koegel, R. L., & Koegel, L. K. (Eds.). (1995). *Teaching children with autism: Strategies for initiating positive interactions and improving learning opportunities.* Baltimore: Paul H. Brookes Co.

Maurice, C. Green, G., & Foxx, R.M. (Eds.). (2001). *Making a difference: Behavioral intervention for autism.* Austin, TX: Pro-ed.

Maurice, C., Green, G., & Luce, S. C. (Eds.). (1996). *Behavioral intervention for young children with autism: A manual for parents and professionals.* Austin, TX: Pro-ed.

Powers, M. D. (2000). *Children with autism: A parents' guide* (2nd ed.). Bethesda, MD: Woodbine House.

Quill, K. A. (Ed.). (1995). *Teaching children with autism: Strategies to enhance communication and socialization.* New York: Delmar.

Siegel, B. (1996). *The world of the autistic child: Understanding and treating autistic spectrum disorders.* New York: Oxford University Press.

Smith, M. D. (1990). *Autism and life in the community: Successful interventions for behavioral challenges.* Baltimore: Pau H. Brookes Co.

Volkmar, F. R., Paul, R., Klin, A., & Cohen, D. J. (Eds.). (2005). *Handbook of autism and pervasive developmental disorders* (3rd ed.) vol. 1. and vol. 2. New York: Wiley.

Wetherby, A. M., & Prizant, B. M. (Eds.). (2000). *Autism spectrum disorders: A transactional developmental perspective.* Communication and Language Intervention Series, vol. 9. Baltimore: Paul H. Brookes Co.

Wing, L. (1996). *The autistic spectrum: A guide for parents and professionals.* London: Constable.

Websites:

National Institutes of Health: *http://www.nichd.nih.gov/autism*

Autism Society of America: *http://www.autism-society.org/*

Association for Science in Autism Treatment: *http://www.asatonline.org*

Canadian Autism Intervention Research Network (CAIRN): *http://www.cairn-site.com/en/research4.html*

Autism Treatment Network (ATN): *http://www.autismspeaks.org/science/programs/atn/index.php*

Autism Speaks — Science Updates: *http://www.autismspeaks.org/science/science_news/index.php*

Families for Effective Autism Treatment: *http://www.feat.org/*

National Autism Center (National Standards Report): *http://www.nationalautismcenter.org*

Scholarly Journals:

Journal of Autism and Developmental Disorders (Plenum Press)

Autism: International Journal of Research and Practice (Sage)

Research in Autism Spectrum Disorders (Elsevier)

Focus on Autism and Other Developmental Disabilities (Sage)

Molecular Autism (Biomed)

References

Autism and Developmental Disabilities Monitoring Network Surveillance [ADDM]. (2009). *Prevalence of autism spectrum disorders. MMWR surveillance summary* (vol. 58) (pp. 1–20). Atlanta, GA: Centers for Disease Control and Prevention.

American Psychiatric Association. (2000). *Diagnostic and statistical manual of mental disorders* (4th ed., text rev.). Washington, DC: Author.

American Psychiatric Association. (2010). *DSM-5: The future of psychiatric diagnosis.* Retrieved from http://www.dsm5.org/Pages/Default.aspx

Bondy, A. S., & Frost, L. A. (2002). *The Picture Exchange Communication System Training Manual* (2nd ed.). Cherry Hill, NJ: Pyramid Educational Consultants.

Buie, T., Campbell, D. B., Fuchs, G. J., Furuta, G. T., Levy, J., Vandewater, J., et al. (2010). Evaluation, diagnosis, and treatment of gastrointestinal disorders in individuals with ASDs: A consensus report. *Pediatrics, 125 Suppl 1,* S1-18.

Coury, D., Jones, N. E., Klatka, K., Winklosky, B., & Perrin, J. M. (2009). Healthcare for children with autism: The autism treatment network. *Current Opinion in Pediatrics, 21,* 828-832.

Courchesne, E., Karns, C. M., Davis, H. R., et al. (2001). Unusual brain growth patterns in early life in patients with autistic disorder: an MRI study. *Neurology, 57,* 245-254.

Dunlap, G. (1999). Consensus, engagement, and family involvement for young children with autism. *Journal of the Association for People with Severe Handicaps, 24,* 222-225.

Dunlap, G., & Fox, L. (2004). The challenge of autism from a large systems perspective. [Unpublished manuscript.]

Elliman, D., & Bedford, H. (2007). MMR: Where are we now? *Archives of Disease in Children, 92,* 1055-1057.

Filipek, P. A., Accardo, P. J., Baranek, G. T., Cook, E. H., Dawson, G., Gordon, B., et al. (1999). The screening and diagnosis of autism spectrum disorders. *Journal of Autism and Developmental Disorders, 29,* 439-484.

Fombonne, E. (2003). Epidemiological surveys of autism and other pervasive developmental disorders: An update. *Journal of Autism and Developmental Disorders, 33,* 365-382.

Fombonne, E. (2009). Epidemiology of pervasive developmental disorders. *Pediatric Research, 65,* 591-598.

Freeman, B. J. (1997). Guidelines for evaluating intervention programs for children with autism. *Journal of Autism and Developmental Disorders, 27,* 641-651.

Green, G. (1996). Early behavioral intervention for autism: What does the research tell us? In C. Maurice, G. Green, & S. C. Luce, (Eds.), *Behavioral intervention for young children with autism: A manual for parents and professionals* (pp. 29-44). Austin, TX: Pro-ed.

Hazlett, H. C., Poe, M., Gerig, G., Smith, R. G., Provenzale, J., Ross, A., et al. (2005). Magnetic resonance imaging and head circumference study of brain size in autism: Birth through age 2 years. *Archives of General Psychiatry, 62,* 1366-1376.

Hollander, E., Phillips, A., Chaplin, W., Zagursky, K., Novotny, S., Wasserman, S., & Iyengar, R. (2005). A placebo controlled crossover trial of liquid fluoxetine on repetitive behaviors in childhood and adolescent autism. *Neuropsychopharmacology, 30,* 582-589.

Howlin, P. (1997). *Autism: Preparing for adulthood.* London: Routledge.

Iovannone, R., Dunlap, G., Huber, H., & Kincaid, D. (2003). Effective educational practices for students with Autism Spectrum Disorders. *Focus on Autism and Other Developmental Disabilities, 18,* 150-165.

Jackson, L., & Veeneman Panyan, M. (2002). *Positive behavioural support in the classroom: Principles and practice.* Baltimore: Paul H. Brookes Co.

Jesner, O. S., Aref-Adib, M., & Coren, E. (2007). Risperidone for autism spectrum disorder. *Cochrane Database of Systematic Reviews,* Issue 1. Art. No.: CD005040. DOI: 10.1002/14651858.CD005040.pub2

Koegel, L. K., Koegel, R. L., & Dunlap, G. (Eds.). (1996). *Positive behavior support: Including people with difficult behavior in the community.* Baltimore: Paul H. Brookes Co.

Koegel, L. K., & LaZebnik, C. (2004). *Overcoming autism: Finding the answers, strategies, and hope that can transform a child's life.* New York: Viking.

Levy, S. E., & Hyman S. L. (2005). Novel treatments for autistic spectrum disorders. *Mental Retardation and Developmental Disabilities Research Reviews, 11,* 131–142.

Li, M. M., & Andersson, H. C. (2009). Clinical application of microarray-based molecular cytogenetics: An emerging new era of genomic medicine. *The Journal of Pediatrics, 155,* 311-317.

Lovaas, O. I., (2002). *Teaching individuals with developmental delays: Basic intervention techniques.* Austin, TX: Pro-ed.

Lucyshyn, J., Dunlap, G., & Albin, R. W. (Eds.). (2002). *Families and positive behavior support: Addressing problem behaviors in family contexts.* Baltimore: Paul H. Brookes Co.

Martin, G., & Pear, J. (2010). *Behavior modification: What it is and how to do it* (9th ed.). Upper Saddle River, NJ: Prentice-Hall.

Maurice, C., Green, G., & Foxx, R. M. (Eds.). (2001). *Making a difference: Behavioral intervention for autism.* Austin, TX: Pro-ed.

Maurice, C., Green, G., & Luce, S. C. (Eds.). (1996). *Behavioral intervention for young children with autism: A manual for parents and professionals.* Austin, TX: Pro-ed.

Minshew, N., & Williams, D. (2007). The new neurobiology of autism: Cortex, connectivity, and neuronal organization. *Archives of Neurology, 64,* 945-950.

Myers, S. M., & Johnson, C. P. (2007). American Academy of Pediatrics, Council on Children With Disabilities: Management of children with autism spectrum disorders. *Pediatrics, 120,* 1162–1182.

Myers, S. M. (2007). The status for pharmacotherapy in Autism Spectrum Disorders. *Expert Opinion in Pharmacotherapy, 8,* 1579-1603.

Nachshen, J., Garcin, N., Moxness, K., Tremblay, Y., Hutchinson, P., Lachance, A. et al. (2008). *Screening, assessment, and diagnosis of Autism Spectrum Disorders in young children: Canadian best practice guidelines.* Montreal, QB: Miriam Foundation.

National Autism Center. (2009). *National Standards Report.* Randolph, MA: Author.

National Research Council. (2001). *Educating children with autism.* Committee on Education and Interventions for Children with Autism. Division of Behavioral and Social Sciences and Education. Washington, DC: National Academy Press.

New York State Department of Health. (1999). *Autism/pervasive developmental disorders. Clinical practice guideline technical report.* New York: Author.

Perry, A. (1991). Rett syndrome: A comprehensive review of the literature. *American Journal on Mental Retardation, 96,* 275-290.

Perry, A., & Condillac, R. A. (2003). *Evidence-based practices for children and adolescents with Autism Spectrum Disorders: Review of the literature and practice guide.* Toronto, ON: Children's Mental Health Ontario.

Powers, M. D. (1992). Early intervention for children with autism. In D. E. Berkell (Ed.), *Autism: Identification, education, and treatment* (pp. 225-252). Hillsdale, NJ: Lawrence Erlbaum.

Richdale, A. L., & Schreck, K. A. (2009). Sleep problems in autism spectrum disorders: prevalence, nature, & possible biopsychosocial aetiologies. *Sleep Medicine Reviews, 13,* 403-411.

Research Units on Pediatric Psychopharmacology Autism Network [RUPP]. (2005). Randomized, controlled, crossover trial of methylphenidate in pervasive developmental disorders with hyperactivity. *Archives of General Psychiatry, 62,* 1266-1274.

Sailor, W., Dunlap, G., Sugai, G., & Horner, R. (Eds). (2009). *Handbook of positive behavior sup-*

port. New York: Springer.

Sattler, J. M., & Hogue, R. D. (2006). *Assessment of children: Behavioral, social, and clinical foundations* (5th ed.). San Diego, CA: Author.

Shih, P., Shen, M., Ottl, B., Keehn, B., Gaffrey, M. S., & Muller, R. (2010). Atypical network connectivity for imitation in autism spectrum disorder. *Neuropsychologia, 48,* 2931-2939.

Smith, M. D. (1990). *Autism and life in the community: Successful interventions for behavioral challenges.* Baltimore: Paul H. Brookes Co.

Stanfield, A. C., McIntosh, A. M., Spencer, M. D., Philip, R., Gaur, S., & Lawrie, S. M. (2007). Towards a neuroanatomy of autism: A systematic review and meta-analysis of structural magnetic resonance imaging studies. *European Psychiatry, 23,* 289–299.

Wing, L. (1988). The continuum of autistic disorders. In E. Schopler & G. B. Mesibov (Eds.), *Diagnosis and assessment in autism* (pp. 91-110). New York: Plenum.

17

Individuals with Asperger Syndrome: A Lifespan Perspective

Kevin P. Stoddart and Barbara Muskat

What you will learn:

- Asperger syndrome (AS) has only been recently been described
- The characteristics of AS, its prevalence, and possible causes
- Diagnostic and support needs in five stages of life
- Current needs in AS research
- Ontario resources for AS

In a 1944 paper, Viennese pediatrician Hans Asperger described a group of boys with normal intelligence and good language development, but with significant educational, social and communication difficulties. Asperger's findings were largely unknown until their translation into English by Uta Frith and inclusion in her book in 1991 (Asperger, 1944, 1991; Frith, 1991). Lorna Wing also provided early case descriptions of similar children and adults whom she saw in London, England (Wing, 1981, 1991). In Ontario, Peter Szatmari played a significant role in bringing Asperger syndrome (AS) to light. In the early 1990s some Ontario children were among the first diagnosed with AS in Canada. Szatmari and his colleagues proposed several characteristics that were thought to be a part of AS, such as solitary behaviour, impaired social interaction, non-verbal communication, and odd speech (Szatmari, 1991, 1992; Szatmari, Bartolucci, & Bremner, 1989;

Szatmari, Bremner, & Nagy, 1989). In 1994, diagnostic criteria for Asperger's Disorder were first included in the *Diagnostic and Statistical Manual of Mental Disorders* (DSM-IV; APA, 1994) section on Pervasive Developmental Disorders, and remain unchanged in the DSM-IV-TR (APA, 2000; Table 1).

This chapter provides an introduction to AS. It highlights that AS is a condition that can be identified at any life stage, and that has implications for individual functioning in many areas across the lifespan. After we discuss the characteristics of AS, its relationship to other Autism Spectrum Disorders (ASDs), prevalence and possible causes, we detail the assessment and support needs at five developmental stages: preschool children, school aged children, adolescents and young adults, middle-aged adults, and older adults. A developmental lifespan framework is helpful in understanding the challenges that individuals with AS experience at various ages. As noted by Stoddart (2005a):

A common occurrence in clinical practice is that many children or adults diagnosed with AS are identified in response to a developmental crisis. They are not able to fulfill the social or developmental expectations of various life stages because of a lack of internal or external resources and because of specific challenges related to the syndrome. A frequent cause of distress for individuals with AS is their realization that they are lagging developmentally behind their peers in key transitional tasks. (p. 19)

Asperger Syndrome: Characteristics, Prevalence and Causes

People with AS have some unique characteristics, but also share some characteristics with others who have been diagnosed in the broader category *Autism Spectrum Disorder*. Recent research has demonstrated that this disorder is much more common than previously thought, although its causes are still largely unknown.

Characteristics

The features of AS include impairments in social interaction; difficulties in the use of nonverbal cues; problems developing peer relationships; lack of social or emotional reciprocity; restricted, repetitive and stereotyped patterns of behaviour, interests, and activities; and delays in social, occupational or other important areas of functioning (see Table 1 for diagnostic criteria). According to *DSM-IV-TR* (APA, 2000), AS has characteristics that distinguish it from Autistic Disorder (AD). The two are mainly differentiated by the presence of language and, sometimes, cognitive difficulties. Individuals with AS do not have the delays in development of language that define AD. In addition, individuals with AS always have average or above average intelligence. Other Pervasive Developmental Disorders (PDDs) currently include Autistic Disorder, Rett's Disorder, Childhood Disintegrative Disorder, and Pervasive Developmental Disorder - Not Otherwise Specified. Autistic Disorder is described in Chapter 16 of this volume. In this chapter, instead of PDD,

we use the more commonly used term Autism Spectrum Disorders (ASDs), which emphasizes that there can be a range of functioning and co-occurring conditions associated with social impairments and a restricted range of interests — the two core features in this spectrum of conditions.

There has been continuing debate in the scientific community over the usefulness and accuracy of the differentiation between AS and so-called "high-functioning autism" (Mayes, Calhoun, & Crites, 2001; Volkmar, Klin, Schultz, Rubin, & Bronin, 2001). The focus of this controversy has been on the merits of distinguishing AD and AS as unique conditions or, alternatively, as merely a continuum of variations in symptom presentation within a larger spectrum of conditions. Although there are rationales for both viewpoints, it appears that the category of AS may be eliminated from the next version of the DSM, the *DSM-5* which is currently under development (APA, 2011; Ghaziuddin, 2010). Although there has been no conclusive empirical evidence to differentiate the two as separate and distinct conditions, the inclusion of AS in the DSM has meant that many individuals (especially adults) have received a diagnosis of AS and appropriate support, when they may not have otherwise (Stoddart, Burke, & King, 2011).

Prevalence

The estimated prevalence of ASDs has grown significantly over the past 20 years. Recent surveys of parental reports of ASDs found a prevalence of 1.1% of children ages 3-17, or 1 out of 91 children (Kogan et al., 2009). Rice et al. (2010) argued that ASD prevalence estimates are approximately 6 to 7 per 1,000. Recent studies in Japan (Honda, Shimizu, Imai, & Nitto, 2005), Sweden (Kadesjö, Gillberg, & Hagberg, 1999), and the United Kingdom (Baird et al., 2006) have shown an ASD prevalence of more than 1%, and as high as 2.7% in Norway (Posserud, Lundervold, & Gillberg, 2006). Rice noted that fewer than half of children in these studies have cognitive impairment, compared with the 75% estimated to have intellectual disabilities in the past.

Although the epidemiology of ASDs in adults has been less understood, a recent U.K. study found that

Table 1: Diagnostic Criteria for Asperger's Disorder

A. *Qualitative impairment in social interaction, as manifested by at least two of the following:*

    i.   *marked impairments in the use of multiple nonverbal behaviors such as eye-to-eye gaze, facial expression, body posture, and gestures to regulate social interaction*

    ii.   *failure to develop peer relationships appropriate to developmental level*

    iii.   *a lack of spontaneous seeking to share enjoyment, interest or achievements with other people, (e.g., by a lack of showing, bringing, or pointing out objects of interest to other people)*

    iv.   *lack of social or emotional reciprocity*

B. *Restricted repetitive and stereotyped patterns of behavior, interests and activities, as manifested by at least one of the following:*

    i.   *encompassing preoccupation with one or more stereotyped and restricted patterns of interest that is abnormal either in intensity or focus*

    ii.   *apparently inflexible adherence to specific, nonfunctional routines or rituals*

    iii.   *stereotyped and repetitive motor mannerisms (e.g., hand or finger flapping or twisting, or complex whole-body movements)*

    iv.   *persistent preoccupation with parts of objects*

C. *The disturbance causes clinically significant impairments in social, occupational, or other important areas of functioning.*

D. *There is no clinically significant general delay in language (e.g., single words used by age 2 years, communicative phrases used by age 3 years).*

E. *There is no clinically significant delay in cognitive development or in the development of age-appropriate self help skills, adaptive behavior (other than in social interaction), and curiosity about the environment in childhood.*

F. *Criteria are not met for another specific Pervasive Developmental Disorder or Schizophrenia.*

Source: DSM-IV-TR (APA, 2000, p. 84). Printed by permission of the American Psychiatric Association.

ASDs affect about 1% of the adult English household population, which is similar to recent findings for children (Brugha et al., 2011). What is remarkable is that none of the individuals who were diagnosed as part of this study previously had received a diagnosis of ASD. This suggests that there has not been an actual increase in the prevalence of ASDs, but rather that there has been poor detection of ASDs in the past. This study requires replication in other countries, but is consistent with the clinical experiences of the authors in Ontario. That is, many adults who meet criteria for ASD have yet to be diagnosed, especially those with the so-called "milder variations" of the disorder (Stoddart et al., 2011). Undiagnosed adults living with ASDs may have

previously received services in the developmental services sector or the mental health system and be experiencing legal, social, emotional, relationship, or employment problems.

Although there has clearly been a rise in the number of individuals being diagnosed with ASD, there is conjecture about the cause(s) for the increase. Possible reasons include increased awareness of ASD by professionals and parents, and a better understanding that the spectrum is wider than once thought. These factors may be leading to more individuals undergoing diagnostic assessment (Fombonne, 2008; Stoddart et al., 2011). Changes in diagnostic classification, diagnostic precision, differing types of screening methods, and the size of the population screened may also account for differing rates found in previous studies. Rice and colleagues (2010) argued that an increase in ASD symptoms cannot be ruled out, and may not be entirely explained by improved case ascertainment.

Causes of ASD

The cause(s) of ASDs are still unknown. However, research has focussed on examining differences in the structure and functioning of the brain. There is also rapidly growing evidence to support a genetic component to ASDs, as it has been observed that autistic-like traits and ASDs run in families. Researchers have not identified a specific gene for autism, and it is unlikely that this will ever be the case; rather, recent findings point to a likelihood of a large group of genes that may make an individual vulnerable to developing ASD (e.g., Pinto et al., 2010; see also Chapter 16).

Assessment and Support Needs Across the Lifespan

Although Asperger syndrome is a lived reality at all stages of life, the assessment and support needs are somewhat different for people of different ages. Here, five age groups are discussed.

AS in preschool children

Unlike more severe forms of ASD, AS may not be noticed until later in a child's development. Parents may first see signs of delayed motor development and unusual patterns of language use. Children with AS may walk late and may show signs of clumsiness. While children with AS do not generally display language delays, their speech may have an odd inflection, be monotone, or be louder than required. They often display obsessive interest in a single object or topic to the exclusion of others. Children with AS are sometimes described as "little professors" because of their significant knowledge of a single topic, their strong expressive language skills, and their strong cognitive abilities. Socially, they may have difficulty playing with other children, especially in group situations, when their idea of how to play or activity of choice does not match that of other children. Sensory

sensitivities may be observed, such as when a child refuses to wear certain types of clothing, responds in an extreme manner to a sound or a touch, agrees to eat only specific foods, or interacts in unusual sensory ways with objects (e.g., smelling toys).

Concerned parents often bring their child to the family doctor or pediatrician, who may conduct an assessment of the child's development. Some physicians, not recognizing that unusual development or behaviours are symptomatic of an ASD, tell parents that their child will outgrow their difficulties (Howlin & Asgharian, 1999). But parents' concerns might lead to further assessment or referrals to a developmental pediatrician, psychologist, or specialty child development team. An assessment team for AS may include a psychologist, neurologist, psychiatrist, occupational therapist, and speech-language pathologist. There is no agreed-upon standardized screening tool for AS in children; however, there are several instruments that are commonly in use (Campbell, 2005). Often, diagnosticians use instruments and methods used to screen for other ASDs.

Usually, assessment begins with a review of the child's medical and developmental history. Assessment may also include examination of the child's intellectual/cognitive functioning, motor coordination, and speech and language skills. Reports may be sought from the child's preschool or childcare setting related to overall development and interaction with peers. Particular attention is given to the child's ability to engage in non-verbal forms of communication (gaze and gestures); use of non-literal language (metaphor, irony, absurdities, and humour); patterns of inflection, and volume modulation; pragmatics (e.g., turn-taking and sensitivity to verbal cues); and the content, clarity, and coherence of conversations.

Following a diagnosis of AS, professionals involved should take time to discuss the findings and their implications with parents. Some parents may feel relieved to have an explanation for their child's struggles; others may experience shock at hearing the diagnosis and may undergo a period of sadness and mourning. It is important for parents to work through these feelings, through discussions as a couple, with family and friends, or with a professional if needed (Bradford, 2010; Stoddart, Muskat, & Mishna, 2005). It may also be helpful for parents to seek out sources of information about AS, available in books or online. Some parents also find support in groups designed specifically for parents of children with AS (Banach, Iudice, Conway, & Couse, 2010).

Despite their social differences, children with AS should be encouraged to take part in social activities. In early childhood, the child should be enrolled either in integrated preschool programs or in specialized programs that directly target the child's social development needs. Assistance with social communication may be helpful for these children. This intervention is typically delivered by speech and language therapists. Targets for intervention include modulation of tone of voice, use of social language, and help in conversational skills (e.g., starting and ending conversations, turn taking). Occupational or physical therapists may assist with gross and fine motor difficulties (i.e., coordination, balance, and movement), sensory sensitivities, or handwriting skills.

AS in school-aged children

For school-aged children with AS, there is usually a need for intervention in the school setting to ensure the child's educational program is meeting academic needs and learning styles, and is adapted to sensory sensitivities such as noise level. Transition periods at school, such as the times before and after school, lunchtime, and recess, can be difficult for children with AS. Recess can produce particular challenges as children with AS may be subject to teasing and bullying by other children because of their odd mannerisms. It is best if parents and school officials jointly plan to provide a safe environment for these children. Suggested strategies include extra monitoring by adults, use of peer buddies, and development of special interest clubs at school that fit the unique interests of these children.

Accommodations for the child with AS are provided after the student is diagnosed and identified as exceptional and an Individual Education Plan (IEP) is introduced (see Chapter 41). It is the responsibility of school personnel, parents, and other professionals to monitor the implementation and success of the IEP and make any necessary changes to it throughout the child's school years (Ontario Ministry of Education, 2011). Although parents are sometimes concerned about disclosing diagnostic or assessment results to the school for fear that it will stigmatize their children, most consider this disclosure to be helpful in generating useful approaches to the students' social, academic, and emotional needs. Accommodations may not only relate to the core features of AS, but also address the co-existing characteristics that are seen in some school-aged children with AS and identified through the assessment process, such as learning disabilities (LDs), anxiety, or attention deficit hyperactivity disorder (ADHD). Often, these issues emerge in the early grades or may be exacerbated by increasing academic, behavioural or social demands, and may require additional assessment and remediation.

Social skills groups are commonly recommended to help children with AS learn how to interact with their peers. Unfortunately, there has been little research carried out to show that social skills can be taught effectively to children or youth with ASDs, maintained over time, and generalized across environments (Rao, Beidel, & Murray, 2008). Groups that help these children and youth to feel less socially isolated and marginalized have, however, been highly valued by children and youth with AS and their families. Such programs offer children with AS an opportunity to meet with others, and to develop friendships with children who are similarly affected (Marriage, Gordon, & Brandt, 1995; Mishna & Muskat, 1998). As children with AS get older, it is recommended that they be enrolled in programs such as boy scouts or girl guides, special interest clubs, or community recreation programs. In recent years, there has been an increase in the number of specialized summer camp programs designed for children with ASDs. While these may be suitable for some children with AS, others may do just as well in mainstream camp programs with the assistance of a social coach or a one-to-one camp counsellor.

As mentioned, children with AS may experience some co-existing conditions. These include learning disabilities, neurological problems, tic disorders, and attention deficit hyperactivity disorder. In addition, children with AS may struggle with anxiety, depression, obsessive-compulsive disorder, and problems with emotional regulation (Bryson, Corrigan, McDonald, & Holmes, 2008; Ghaziuddin, 2002; Stoddart, 1999). They also frequently have problems with friendship, loneliness, depression, and social anxiety (Myles, Barnhill, Hagiwara, Griswald, & Simpson, 2001). Clinicians unfamiliar with AS may diagnose these children with attentional or anxiety issues only, and not recognize the diagnostic features of AS. The use of medication to address anxiety or depression, and individual and group therapeutic approaches, are helpful for some children. There is also developing evidence about the usefulness of cognitive behaviour therapy (Wood et al., 2009) and individual therapy to address emotional and behavioural challenges. Individual sessions with older children may offer an opportunity to discuss their diagnosis and often troubling social experiences with peers.

Parents of children and youth with AS report lower quality of life, particularly in the areas of their own psychological well-being, social relationships, and health (Mugno, Ruta, D-Arrigo, & Mazzone, 2007). This has been attributed to the stressors associated with parenting this population, including dealing with challenging behaviours, constant monitoring of children's health and safety, and difficulties finding suitable education and services that address and accommodate the needs of a child with AS. Community services for children with AS have been described as limited, and systems as difficult to navigate in Ontario (Boydell, 2008). Parents of newly diagnosed children typically need help in finding services and finding their way through the maze of limited public and private services, often of unknown quality. Parents should be informed by professionals about interventions that may be helpful for their child.

AS in adolescents and young adults

Some individuals with AS receive their first diagnosis in adolescence or in the early adult years. By this time, the principal characteristics of AS, such as a restricted range of interests and poor social skills,

have usually been noted over a number of years. These individuals may display extraordinary skills in specific areas and significant shortfalls in others. This uneven skill profile can be puzzling to parents or clinicians who are unfamiliar with the symptoms of the syndrome, as well as to the youth themselves.

The expression and impact of the characteristics of AS throughout childhood can be significant on a young person's development. As noted, teenagers with undiagnosed AS may have been diagnosed with other disorders that are part of the clinical presentation of AS, such as ADHD, anxiety, or depression. Mental health problems are common in adolescents with AS who are seen in clinical settings (Stoddart, 1999). The tendency to display mental health problems may be exacerbated by adolescents' emerging awareness that they are different from their peers. Adolescents may have gravitated towards interests that are solitary in nature (such as computer or video games) and, as a result, they may feel socially isolated. All adolescents face an increasing academic workload, the need for organizational skills, unstructured and unsupervised social interactions, and transitions in school and lifestyle. For the adolescent with AS, these demands may be experienced as overwhelming. For this reason, they may need the mediating influence of supports and understanding from peers, family, and school personnel. School and peer pressures, if left unchecked, can precipitate depression and anxiety and involvement in risky behaviours (Stoddart, 2005b; 2011).

A few approaches may be helpful for adolescents or young adults with AS. With a well-monitored plan for use of medication to address mental health symptoms, individual therapy can be effective for adolescents or young adults, as it gives them the opportunity to discuss their diagnosis and social experiences with peers (Stoddart, 1999; 2005b). Although there has been debate about the pitfalls of discussing AS with children, teens and young adults, and fear among parents about disclosing an AS diagnosis with their teen, such knowledge usually comes as a relief to adolescents. Deciding when and how to tell children about their diagnosis is a difficult decision, and parents may need to seek professional support such as individual or parent counselling. Social skills groups may be helpful to teach adolescents with ASDs to interact in conventional ways with their peers. Activity-based community groups can also provide a more naturalistic setting for learning and practising social interaction skills. Family therapy from a clinician knowledgeable about AS and co-existing conditions can be helpful in more clearly defining roles of parents and youth, managing conflict, and planning collaboratively with the adolescent or young adult for their future (Stoddart 1999; 2005b).

A developmental challenge facing all adolescents is the process of individuation, separation, gaining independence from parents, and affiliating with a peer group. Adolescents are also faced with questions about their sexuality, sexual expression, and drug and alcohol use. In an attempt to belong, adolescents with AS may choose or be easily lured toward drug or alcohol use, unhealthy sexual behaviours, or inappropriate and illegal behaviours in the community. This may result in a decline in school performance or even contact with police and the legal system. Proactive socio-sexual education programs in schools and in programs for youth at risk are a priority, and may need tailoring to the specific needs of youth with AS (Stoddart, 2011). Increasingly, we are seeing youth and adults with AS who have been charged with criminal offenses. These have included possession of marijuana, public intoxication, theft, fraud, identity theft, attempted murder, driving while impaired by alcohol, physical assault, sexual assault/interference, and stalking. Many of these individuals would probably not have been involved in these acts if they had the appropriate diagnosis, services, and supports available to them at an earlier age.

A complicating issue for teens and young adults who have been diagnosed with AS is locating and accessing assessment and treatment services that understand the needs of this population. Unfortunately, children's services in Ontario end at the age of 18 and there is little assistance for transitioning to the adult services sector. This lack of transitional services is especially critical, given that young adults with AS have great difficulty coping, even with parental help, let alone thinking about living independently. This requires making decisions about a career, involvement in post-secondary education, or managing living arrangements — all which can be very difficult for people with AS. Some services, recognizing that consistent and knowledgeable service provision into adulthood can be extremely helpful, do provide support across life stages (The Redpath Centre, 2011).

AS in middle-aged adults

An increasing number of individuals receive a diagnosis of AS in adulthood. While they may have been struggling throughout their lives, their problems may be increasingly apparent as they move through adulthood. They may struggle with what appear to be mental health problems or extended periods of social isolation, and their search for a cause of their struggles may lead them to professionals who recognize and diagnose AS. Some adults find out about the symptoms of AS through the Internet or the media and come to diagnosticians seeking a confirmation of their suspicions. These adults may also be found in vocations that rely on a very circumscribed area of knowledge, such as computer programming, engineering, or accounting. Other adults may discover AS symptoms in themselves subsequent to their child being diagnosed with an ASD (Stoddart, 2005a; Stoddart et al., 2011). Most often, adults who are diagnosed with AS in adulthood are relieved to finally have an explanation for their puzzling characteristics. Such information can also be helpful to family members or spouses to better understand their relative's behaviours and struggles with relationships.

Some adults with AS become involved in life partner relationships, and family and marital clinicians are beginning to see in their practices increasing numbers of couples where one or both partners have AS. In this regard, separation and divorce are not uncommon (Stoddart et al., 2011). A literature is evolving that describes the experience of having intimate relationships with somebody with AS, and the professional roles required to facilitate relationships for affected adults (e.g., Hendrickx and Newton, 2007; Slater-Walker & Slater-Walker, 2002). Additional literature is needed on parenting when a parent has AS. In addition to coping with their own issues, parents with AS sometimes face the challenges of raising children with AS or other neurodevelopmental conditions (Willey, 1999).

It is difficult for service providers and adults with AS to decide in which service sectors they will be best served. Since, by definition, adults with AS do not have an overall cognitive delay (although there may be significant delays in day-to-day functioning and specific aspects of cognition), they are a unique population in the developmental services sector. To further complicate matters, they may not have mental health issues that fit the current approaches that are available in the adult psychiatric service system. Although some individuals with AS do not have the specific diagnosis of a learning disability, their learning styles are unique. They may have traits in common with adults with learning disabilities, but there are very few services in Ontario for this group of adults. There have been recent policy changes in Ontario intended to address this need, but services have not yet developed. Thus, many adults with AS have to pay for private services to address their social, emotional, vocational and relational needs.

AS in older adults

The question of autism and AS in older people has received little attention in the literature (Stoddart et al., 2011). It is highly probable, however, that many in the aging population who have exhibited life-long problems in social functioning, experienced long-standing mental health problems, or demonstrated a restricted range of interests, have AS that has gone unrecognized. Clinicians who support older people need to consider the potential for ASDs in this older population. Grandparents of children diagnosed with ASDs are sometimes recognized as "loners," or "eccentric" by family members, yet there may be no explanation for these characteristics until their grandchild's diagnosis. Many such people have had successful careers, or have specific and focused interests and activities. Realization that a grandparent may have AS can potentially lead to a better understanding of their social, behavioural and emotional presentation.

There are some reports of older individuals identified as having AS. For example, one report noted that 14 parents of patients with ASDs were diagnosed as a result of their children's diagnoses. At the time of publication, the parents were ages 37-77

years; six were over 50 (Ritvo, Ritvo, Freeman, & Mason-Brothers, 1994). Similarly, James, Mukaetova-Ladinska, Reichelt, Briel, and Scully (2006) presented a case series of five elderly adults who met criteria for AS. All were males who had a history of interpersonal problems, dating back to their early school years.

Retirement is often characterized by less structure in day-to-day living and more social isolation. Both these factors may have negative effects on individuals with ASDs. With few interests and friends, retirement may be a difficult stage of life. We currently know little about the health needs of older adults with ASDs or about the life expectancy of individuals with AS, and it is important to consider the possible effects of other existing medical conditions, isolation, and poor medical attention, diet, and exercise. The collaboration of service providers from various service sectors, including health and residential services for the elderly, is essential.

Areas for Further Research

There are many areas of research that require attention in the field of AS. Two general areas are highlighted here. The first is related to the specific characteristics of AS. Two specific questions are: Is AS qualitatively different from high-functioning autism? and What can we learn from less severe variants of AS such as those symptoms found in relatives of those with AS? A second general area for research relates to intervention: Are social skills groups useful for teaching interactional abilities to this population? What are the outcomes of other interventions such as medication (e.g., Selective Serotonin Reuptake Inhibitors, otherwise known as SSRI's), individual psychotherapy, dietary restrictions, social integration, or attention to sensory problems? Under what conditions are these interventions most successful?

Summary

Awareness of the symptoms of AS has increased considerably in Ontario since its inclusion in the DSM-IV (APA, 1994), yet much work remains for clinicians and researchers. Unquestionably, AS is becoming more readily recognized in children, adolescents, and adults due to public education, better assessment approaches, and inclusion of AS in the DSM. Through diagnosis and appropriate treatment planning, approaches can be implemented in response to the specific problems experienced by individuals with AS at all life stages. Although inroads made in the field have brought relief for many, the lack of sufficient AS specific services continues to be a problem. Through individual, clinician, and parent initiatives, strong public advocacy is raising the profile of this condition and, as a consequence, will hopefully lead to increases in public services and funding.

For Further Thought and Discussion

1. What are the key characteristics of AS?
2. Why is it helpful to have agreement on the diagnostic criteria for AS?
3. Why is diagnosis important at each life stage?
4. What are some other psychosocial problems that may exist for individuals at each life stage?

More Resources

Websites:

Autism Ontario
www.autismontario.ca

Autism Society Canada
www.autismsocietycanada.ca

Geneva Centre for Autism
www.autism.net

Kerry's Place Autism Services
www.kerrysplace.org

The Redpath Centre
www.redpathcentre.ca

Further reading:

Attwood, T. (2007). *The complete guide to Asperger's syndrome.* London: Jessica Kingsley Publishers.

Frith, U. (Ed.). (1991). Autism and Asperger syndrome. Cambridge: Cambridge University Press.

Stoddart, K. P. (Ed.). (2005). *Children, youth and adults with Asperger syndrome: Integrating multiple perspectives.* London: Jessica Kingsley Publishers.

Stoddart, K. P., Burke, L., & King, R. (2011). *Asperger syndrome in adulthood: A comprehensive guide for clinicians.* New York: Norton Professional Books.

Szatmari, P. (2004). *A mind apart: Understanding children with autism and Asperger syndrome.* New York: Guildford Press.

Willey, L. H. (1999). *Pretending to be normal: Living with Asperger's syndrome.* London: Jessica Kingsley Publishers.

References

American Psychiatric Association (APA). (1994). *The diagnostic and statistical manual of mental disorders,* (4th ed.). Washington, DC: Author.

American Psychiatric Association (APA). (2000). *Diagnostic and statistical manual of mental disorders: DSM-IV-TR* (4th ed., text rev.). Washington, DC: American Psychiatric Association.

American Psychiatric Association (APA). (2011). *DSM-5 development.* Retrieved from www.dsm5.org.

Asperger, H. (1944). Die "autistischen psychopathen" im kindeslater. *Archive fur Psychiatrie un Nervenkrankheiten, 117,* 76-136.

Asperger, H. (1991). "Autistic psychopathy" in childhood. In U. Frith (Ed.), *Autism and Asperger syndrome* (pp. 37-92). Cambridge: Cambridge University Press.

Baird, G., Simonoff, E., Pickles, A., Chandler, S., Loucas, T., Meldrum, D., et al. (2006). Prevalence of disorders of the autism spectrum in a population cohort of children in South Thames: The Special Needs and Autism Project (SNAP). *Lancet, 368,* 210-215.

Banach, M., Iudice, J., Conway, L., & Couse, L. J. (2010). Family support and empowerment: Post autism diagnosis support group for parents. *Social Work with Groups, 33*(1), 69-83.

Boydell, K. (2008). *A patchwork quilt: Mothers' perspectives on the needs of children and youth with Asperger's syndrome.* Toronto, ON: East Metro Youth Services.

Bradford, K. (2010). Supporting families dealing with Autism and Asperger's disorders. *Journal of Family Psychotherapy, 21*(2), 149-156.

Brugha, T. S., McManus, S., Bankart, J., Scott, F., Purdon, S., Smith, J., Bebbington, P., Jenkins, R., & Meltzer, H. (2011). Epidemiology of Autism Spectrum Disorders in adults in the community in England. *Archives of General Psychiatry, 68*(5), 459-466.

Bryson, S. A., Corrigan, S. K., McDonald, T. P., & Holmes, C. (2008). Characteristics of children with autism spectrum disorders who received services through community mental health centers. *Autism: International Journal of Research and Practice, 12*(1), 65-82.

Campbell, J. M. (2005). Diagnostic assessment of Asperger's disorder: A review of five third-party rating scales. *Journal of Autism and Developmental Disorders, 35*(1), 25-35.

Fombonne, E. (2008). Is autism getting commoner? *British Journal of Psychiatry, 193*(1), 59.

Frith, U. (Ed.). (1991). *Autism and Asperger syndrome.* Cambridge, United Kingdom: Cambridge University Press.

Ghaziuddin, M. (2002). Asperger syndrome: Associated psychiatric and medical conditions. *Focus on Autism and Other Developmental Disabilities, 17*, 138-144.

Ghaziuddin, M. (2010). Brief report: Should the DSM V drop Asperger syndrome? *Journal of Autism and Developmental Disorders, 40*(9), 1146-1148.

Hendrickx, S., & Newton, K. (2007). *Asperger syndrome: A love story.* London: Jessica Kingsley Publishers.

Honda, H., Shimizu , Y., Imai, M., & Nitto, Y. (2005). Cumulative incidence of childhood autism: A total population study of better accuracy and precision. *Developmental Medicine and Child Neurology, 47*(1), 10-18.

Howlin, P., & Asgharian, A. (1999). The diagnosis of autism and Asperger syndrome: Findings from a survey of 770 families. *Developmental Medicine and Child Neurology, 41*, 834-839.

James, I. A., Mukaetova-Ladinska, E., Reichelt, F. K., Briel, R., & Scully, A. (2006). Diagnosing Aspergers syndrome in the elderly: A series of case presentations. *International Journal of Geriatric Psychiatry, 21*(10), 951-960.

Kadesjö, B., Gillberg, C., & Hagberg, B. (1999). Brief report: Autism and Asperger syndrome in seven-year-old children: A total population study. *Journal of Autism and Developmental Disorders, 29*(4), 327-331.

Kogan, M. D., Blumberg, S. J., Shieve, L. A., Boyle, C. A., Perrin, J. M., Ghandour, R. M., Singh, G. K., Strickland, B. B., Trevathan, E., & van Dyke, P. C. (2009). Prevalence of parent-reported diagnosis of Autism Spectrum Disorder among children in the US, 2007. *Pediatrics, 124*(5), 1395-1403.

Marriage, K. J., Gordon, V., & Brandt, L. (1995). A social skills group for boys with Asperger's syndrome. *Australian & New Zealand Journal of Psychiatry, 29*(1), 58-62.

Mayes, S. D., Calhoun, S. L., & Crites, D. L. (2001). Does DSM-IV Asperger's disorder exist? *Journal of Abnormal Child Psychology, 29*(3), 263-271.

Mishna, F., & Muskat, B. (1998). Group therapy for boys with features of Asperger syndrome and concurrent learning disabilities: Finding a peer group. *Journal of Child and Adolescent Group Therapy, 8*(3), 97-114.

Mugno, D., Ruta, L., D-Arrigo, V. G., & Mazzone, L. (2007). Impairment of quality of life in parents of children and adolescents with pervasive developmental disorder. *Health and Quality of Life Outcomes, 5*, 22.

Myles, B. S., Barnhill, G., Hagiwara, T., Griswald, D. E., & Simpson, R. L. (2001). A synthesis of studies on the intellectual, academic, social/emotional & sensory characteristics of children and youth with Asperger syndrome. *Education and Training in Mental Retardation and Developmental Disabilities, 36*(3), 304-311.

Ontario Ministry of Education. (2011). Ontario Ministry of Education. Retrieved from www.edu.gov.on.ca

Pinto, D., Pagnamenta, A. T., Klei, L., Anney, R., Merico, D., Regan, R., et al. (2010). Functional impact of global rare copy number variation in autism spectrum disorders. *Nature, 466*(7304), 368-372.

Posserud, M. B., Lundervold, A. J., & Gillberg, C. (2006). Autistic features in a total population of 7-9-year-old children assessed by the ASSQ (Autism Spectrum Screening Questionnaire). *Journal of Child Psychology and Psychiatry, 47*(2), 167-175.

Rao, P., Beidel, D., & Murray, M. (2008). Social skills interventions for children with Asperger's syndrome or high-functioning Autism: A review and recommendations. *Journal of Autism and Developmental Disorders, 38*(2), 353-361.

Redpath Centre. (2011). *The Redpath Centre Website*. Retrieved from www.redpathcentre.ca.

Rice, C., Nicholas, J., Baio, J., Pettygrove, S., Lee, L.-C., Van Naarden Braun, K., et al. (2010). Changes in autism spectrum disorder prevalence in 4 areas of the United States. *Disability and Health Journal, 3*(3), 186-201.

Ritvo, E. R., Ritvo, R., Freeman, B. J., & Mason-Brothers, A. (1994). Clinical characteristics of mild autism in adults. *Comprehensive Psychiatry, 35*(2), 149-156.

Slater-Walker, G., & Slater-Walker, C. (2002). *An Asperger marriage*. London: Jessica Kingsley.

Stoddart, K. P. (1999). Adolescents with Asperger syndrome: Three case studies of individual and family therapy. *Autism: International Journal of Research and Practice, 3*(3), 225-271.

Stoddart, K. P. (2005a). Introduction to Asperger syndrome: A developmental lifespan perspective. In K. P. Stoddart (Ed.), *Children, youth and adults with Asperger syndrome: Integrating multiple perspectives* (pp. 13-29). London: Jessica Kingsley Publishers.

Stoddart, K. P. (2005b). Young adults with Asperger syndrome: Psychosocial issue and interventions. In K. P. Stoddart (Ed.), *Children, youth and adults with Asperger syndrome: Integrating multiple perspectives* (pp. 84-97). London: Jessica Kingsley Publishers.

Stoddart, K. P. (2011). *Opening keynote: Sexuality and youth at risk*. 1st Annual York Region Day Treatment Conference, January 31 2011, Maple, Ontario.

Stoddart, K. P., Burke, L., & King, R. (2011). *Asperger syndrome in adulthood: A comprehensive guide for clinicians*. New York: Norton Professional Books.

Stoddart, K. P., Muskat, B., & Mishna, F. (2005). Children and adolescents with Asperger syndrome: Social work assessment and intervention. In K. P. Stoddart (Ed.), *Children, youth and adults with Asperger syndrome: Integrating multiple perspectives* (pp. 155-167). London: Jessica Kingsley Publishers.

Szatmari, P. (1991). Asperger's syndrome: Diagnosis, treatment, and outcome. *Psychiatric Clinics of North America, 14*(1), 81-93.

Szatmari, P. (1992). Asperger's syndrome. *Current Opinion in Pediatrics, 4*, 616-622.

Szatmari, P., Bartolucci, G., & Bremner, R. (1989). Asperger's syndrome and autism: Comparison of early history and outcome. *Developmental Medicine and Child Neurology, 31*, 709-720.

Szatmari, P., Bremner, R., & Nagy, J. (1989). Asperger's syndrome: A review of clinical features. *Canadian Journal of Psychiatry, 34*(6), 554-560.

Volkmar, F. R., Klin, A., Schultz, R. T., Rubin, E., & Bronin, R. (2001). Asperger disorder. *American Journal of Psychiatry, 157*, 262-267.

Willey, L. H. (1999). *Pretending to be normal: Living with Asperger's syndrome*. London: Jessica Kingsley Publishers.

Wing, L. (1981). Asperger's syndrome: A clinical account. *Psychological Medicine, 11*, 115-129.

Wing, L. (1991). The relationship between Asperger's syndrome and Kanner's autism. In U. Frith (Ed.), *Autism and Asperger syndrome* (pp. 93-121). Cambridge: Cambridge University Press.

Wood, J. J., Drahota, A., Sze, K., Har, K., Chiu, A., & Langer, D. A. (2009). Cognitive behavioral therapy for anxiety in children with autism spectrum disorders: A randomized, control trial. *The Journal of Child Psychology and Psychiatry, 50*(3), 224-234.

18

Fragile X Syndrome

Cynthia J Forster-Gibson and Jeanette Jeltje Anne Holden

What you will learn:

- The nature of fragile X syndrome, and how it affects individuals
- The genetics of fragile X, the pattern of heredity, and genetic testing
- How fragile X syndrome affects families
- The needs and services for people with fragile X syndrome
- Some interesting areas of fragile X syndrome research

*Note: Words in **bold italics** are explained in the Special Terms section following the Summary.*

Fragile X syndrome (FXS) is the most common known inherited form of intellectual disability worldwide. Some effects of this syndrome include intellectual and developmental disabilities, characteristic physical features and atypical behaviours, and other health effects as discussed later in this chapter.

The Nature of Fragile X Syndrome

The number of people reported to have FXS varies greatly, from one in 1,200 to 6,000 males and one in 2,500 to 10,000 females in the general population. The prevalence of unaffected carriers of an abnormal fragile X gene in the province of Ontario has not yet been determined. Studies in Quebec and in Israel suggest that the frequency of carrier females is about 1 in 250.

The gene for FXS is located on the X chromosome. This gene is called FMR1 (Fragile X Mental Retardation 1). Mutations of the FMR1 gene usually result from an increase in size of a specific region of the gene (described below). Small increases in size may have little to no effect, while larger increases may cause severe cognitive disability and physical changes (FXS). Males with FXS typically need specialized help at school, supported employment and assistance with community living. Females with FXS usually have milder cognitive impairment and fewer clinical features (see Figures 1 and 2, Tables 1 and 2). Individuals who have an abnormal FMR1 gene of any size are called carriers.

Public awareness about FXS is limited. Even health care professionals, educators, and other service providers may have little information about this

Figure 1. Preschool male affected with Fragile X syndrome.

Figure 2. School-aged female affected with Fragile X syndrome.

syndrome. This lack of information can create additional difficulties for fragile X families. The effects of FXS on a family are not limited to the individual with the syndrome, but can influence family planning and affect education, health care, financial planning, and life planning for siblings, other family members and future descendents.

At this time, there is no cure for FXS. Researchers from around the world are actively carrying out research aimed at finding a cure or improving treatment for this syndrome.

Why is it called fragile X syndrome?

The term fragile X syndrome comes from the observation of a fragile site (a small break) on the tip of the X-chromosome of males and some females who have this disorder (see Figure 3). The fragile site distinguishes persons with FXS from those with other causes of developmental disability.

How fragile X syndrome affects individuals

The effects of the fragile X *gene mutation* (summarized in Tables 1 and 2) vary from one person to another. (See Garber, Bisootsak, & Warren, 2008 for a review.) Most males with FXS have some degree of cognitive impairment and many have behavioural

problems, including aggression and anxiety and, in about one-third, autistic behaviours. The physical features include a long face with prominent jaw and ears, high arched palate, flat feet and loose joints. Most females who are affected by FXS have only mild impairment, including learning difficulties, anxiety and shyness, and some physical features that become more evident with age. These characteristics, common to individuals with FXS, are part of the "phenotype" of FXS.

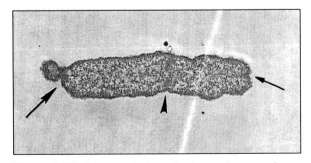

Figure 3. First transmission electron micrograph of a fragile X chromosome. *The FMR1 gene is located in the constricted region near the left end of the chromosome, and is denoted by the largest arrow. (This scanning EM image was kindly provided by Dr. G. Y. Wen and Dr. E. C. Jenkins of the New York State Institute for Basic Research in Developmental Disabilities (Wen et al., 1997)).*

Table 1: Characteristics of Males with Fragile X Syndrome (Full Mutation)*

Characteristic	Childhood	Adolescence	Adulthood
Physical	*Large protruding ears, single crease on palm, flat feet, loose joints, strabismus*	*Long narrow face, large protruding ears, prominent jaw, large testicles, single crease on palm, high arched palate, flat feet, loose joints, scoliosis*	*Long narrow face, large protruding ears, prominent jaw, large testicles, single crease on palm, high arched palate, flat feet, loose joints, short stature, scoliosis*
Behavioural	*Hyperactivity, autistic-like features, shyness, social anxiety, sensitivity to touch/sound, hand-biting, poor eye contact, aggressive outbursts*	*Social anxiety, sensitivity to touch/sound, hand-flapping or hand-biting, poor eye contact, repetitive speech, aggressive outbursts*	*Shyness, social anxiety, sensitivity to touch/sound, hand-biting, poor eye contact, aggressive outbursts*
Learning	*Cognitive delay, attention difficulty, with or without hyperactivity*	*Mild to severe developmental disability*	*Mild to severe developmental disability*
Health	*General good health, otitis media, sinusitis, orthopaedic problems, club foot deformity, minor heart anomalies, kidney dysfunction, orthodontic problems, strabismus*	*General good health Watch for high blood pressure, bladder infections, sleep apnea, heart valve problems (MVP)*	*General good health Watch for high blood pressure, bladder infections, sleep apnea, heart valve problems (MVP)*
Neurological	*Hypotonia, seizures*	*Hypotonia, seizures*	*Hypotonia, seizures*

* These characteristics are not always present

Fragile X sub-phenotypes

The term phenotype refers to the characteristics that are common to a particular genetic disorder. Some persons with FXS belong to a sub-group of FXS with a phenotype that resembles another genetic disorder. These sub-groups include:

Obesity phenotype: Truncal obesity, short broad hands and feet, hyperpigmentation, small genitals; occasionally referred to as Prader-Willi-like phenotype because some of these characteristics resemble another genetic disorder called Prader-Willi syndrome.

Overgrowth phenotype: Above average birthweight; increased head circumference; includes extreme overall body overgrowth; increased height in childhood and adulthood. This phenotype resembles Sotos syndrome and has been referred to as "Sotos-like."

Table 2. Characteristics of Females Affected by Fragile X Syndrome (Full Mutation)*

Characteristic	Childhood	Adolescence	Adulthood
Physical	*High arched palate, knock knees, flat feet, loose joints*	*High arched palate, knock knees, flat feet, loose joints, early puberty*	*High arched palate, knock knees, flat feet, loose joints, early menopause*
Behavioural	*Shyness, anxiety*	*Shyness, anxiety*	*Shyness, anxiety*
Learning	*Learning disabilities, mild/moderate developmental delay*	*Mild/moderate developmental delay*	*Mild/moderate developmental delay*
Health	*General good health; sometimes: ear infections, strabismus*	*General good health*	*General good health*
Neurological	*Seizures*	*Seizures*	*Seizures*

* These characteristics are not always present

Autistic phenotype: Children with FXS can be very shy and display stereotypies such as hand flapping, resembling the behaviours seen in children with autism (see Chapter 16 for more information about autism). Approximately 25% of boys with FXS meet full criteria for a diagnosis of autism and many more have some of the features of autism (Bailey et al., 1998).

The Genetics of Fragile X

The discovery of the fragile site and its association with developmental disabilities directed researchers to the place on the X-chromosome where they could look for the gene responsible for this syndrome (see Figure 3). This gene, called the Fragile X Mental Retardation-1 (FMR1) gene, was identified in 1991. Everyone has a copy of the FMR1 gene on his or her X-chromosomes. However, persons with FXS have an abnormal (or mutant) FMR1 gene. What researchers found in 1991 is that persons with FXS actually have a larger FMR1 gene than those in the general population.

The following genetic information is included for two reasons: 1) to provide a more in-depth understanding of the nature of the fragile X gene mutation; and 2) to provide an appreciation for the complexity of information that fragile X families encounter when they receive a diagnosis of FXS in a family member.

GENETIC EFFECTS OF FXS

The effects of fragile X and the *pattern of heredity* are influenced by: 1) the size of the FMR1 gene; 2) the gender of the parent; and 3) the gender of the child.

Size of the FMR1 gene

DNA is made up of four different bases (molecules) called adenine, thymine, cytosine and guanine (A, T, C and G) (see Chapter 9 for additional details). The fragile X gene mutation is a change in the gene that results in the gene having extra bases. The extra bases in this gene come in sets of three, CGG CGG CGG etc., called triplet repeats. The number of triplet repeats can be classified into one of four categories: normal, full mutation, premutation, and intermediate or grey zone (Figure 4).

Normal FMR1 repeats: (approximately 6-54 copies of the CGG repeat). Everyone in the general population has an FMR1 gene on the X chromosome. When the number of CGG-repeats within the FMR1 gene is between 6 and 54, individuals are said to have a normal FMR1 gene.

Full mutation: (more than 200 repeats). When the number of copies of the CGG-repeat exceeds 200, the mutation is described as being a full mutation. The full mutation prevents the gene from producing the protein that it codes for. Genes with 200 repeats or with 2000 repeats are basically "equal" — the FMR1 protein is not made in either case. This causes the clinical phenotype associated with FXS. Almost all males with a full mutation are affected with FXS. Approximately half of all females with a full mutation are affected. Whether a female is affected or not depends to some extent on whether the X chromosome with the mutant FMR1 gene is active or inactive in cells that need the FMR1 protein in order to function properly. If, in a female, the active X-chromosome in the majority of cells in the brain, for example, has the mutant FMR1 gene, this would result in the girl being affected. (Remember that although females have two X chromosomes, only one in each cell is active. Which one is active and which one is not is determined at an early stage of cell division in the embryo. For additional information about X-inactivation, see Chapter 9.) Females who have the full mutation will either pass their mutated gene or their normal gene to sons or daughters. The mutation size in the sperm of males with a full mutation contracts to a premutation size. Any daughter they have will be a premutation carrier.

Premutation: (approximately 55-200 repeats). Individuals with FMR1 genes having 55-200 repeats are said to have a premutation. Males and females with the premutation do not have FXS. They may be called premutation carriers. Whether premutation carriers have cognitive or behavioural differences is an area of controversy (Hunter, Abramowitz, Rusin, & Sherman, 2009). Some female carriers develop premature ovarian failure (early menopause and changes in their menstrual cycle) and older male and female carriers sometimes develop the Fragile X Tremor Ataxia Syndrome (FXTAS), a condition that is sometimes said to look like Parkinson's disease.

Depending on the size of the repeat, if a female carrier of a premutation passes this gene to her child, it may expand to a full mutation or remain within the premutation size (see Figure 5). Premutations in the

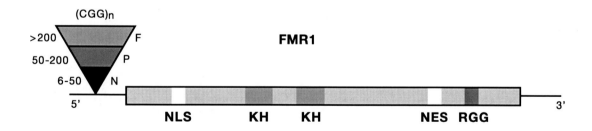

Figure 4. Schematic representation of the FMR1 gene. *The coding region of the FMR1 that specifies FMR1 RNA is depicted by the horizontal rectangular bar. Noncoding regions of the gene called untranslated regions (UTRs) are depicted by the horizontal lines on either side of the bar. The region called the 5'UTR is denoted by 5' and that called the 3'UTR is denoted by 3'. The CGG repeat region that is expanded in fragile X syndrome is located in the 5'UTR. The relative sizes of the CGG repeat region are shown for healthy individuals that do not have fragile X (5-50 repeats), for people who have a premutation (50-200 repeats), and for people who have a full mutation (>200 repeats). The terms NLS, KH, NES, and RGG refer to regions of FMR1 DNA that affect important functions of FMR1 protein. The KH and RGG regions of FMR1 protein are involved in RNA binding. The NES region helps the protein to move from the cell nucleus to the cytoplasm. The NLS region helps the protein to move from the cytoplasm to the cell nucleus. (From Oostra, B. A., Hoogeneen, A. T., & Willemsen, R. (n.d.). Fragile X syndrome and FMR1. Retrieved August 12, 2010, from http://www2.eur.nl/fgg/kgen/research/fmr1.html, reprinted by permission.)*

55-65 repeat range rarely expand to full mutations, but those that are greater than about 80 repeats almost always do. Thus the risk for a carrier mother to have a child who is affected with FXS depends to a large extent on the size of the repeat within her mutated FMR1 gene. Males with the premutation pass the premutation on to all of their daughters. The chance of the mutation expanding to a full mutation is extremely small.

Intermediate or grey zone: (approximately 45-54 repeats). Persons with an intermediate size repeat may or may not have an FMR1 mutation. Researchers believe that some grey zone repeats are small premutations, although the risk that a female with a grey zone FMR1 gene has of having a child affected with FXS is extremely low. As of 2008, the latter situation had never been observed in several hundreds of cases of transmission of grey zone alleles that have been studied. Further, the FMR1 gene had never been observed to expand from a grey zone allele to a premutation allele in thousands of families with FXS that had been studied; in all cases, the full mutation could only

be traced back to premutations. However, in 2009, Fernandez-Carvajal et al. described a family in which a grey-zone allele expanded to the full mutation range in two generations. Thus, if a grey zone allele can become a full mutation allele, it probably takes many generations.

The gender of the parent

Thousands of families with FXS have been studied to determine the likelihood that premutation and full mutation carriers will have affected offspring. The findings indicate that when the FMR1 premutation is passed from fathers to daughters, it has a very low probability of expanding to a full mutation. However, when the same size premutation is carried in mothers and is passed to either sons or daughters, it often expands to a full mutation (see Figure 5).

The gender of the child

Males with a full mutation are almost always affected with FXS. Not all females with a full mutation are affected, and those who are affected are generally less affected than males.

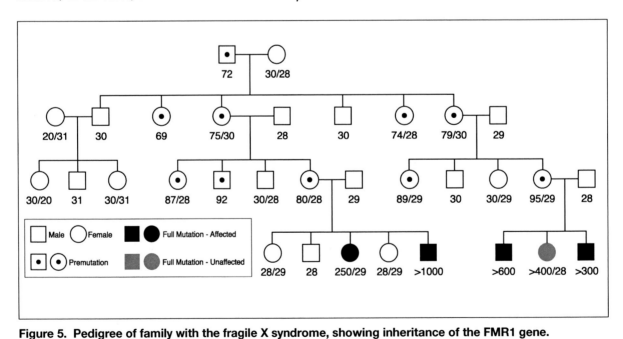

Figure 5. Pedigree of family with the fragile X syndrome, showing inheritance of the FMR1 gene.
The numbers under the pedigree symbols indicate the number of CGG-repeats in the FMR1 gene on each chromosome. Females have two X chromosomes, and hence have two FMR1 genes; males have a single X chromosome, and hence a single FMR1 gene. Sons inherit the X chromosome (and FMR1 gene) from their mothers and Y chromosome from their fathers. Daughters receive X chromosomes from both their mothers and fathers.

GENETIC TESTING FOR FXS

Chromosome test

Until 1991, genetic testing for the FXS relied on the examination of chromosomes to search for the little break or fragile site at the end of the X-chromosome. Although this test was an important step in distinguishing fragile X from other causes of developmental disability, the test was not always reliable, and sometimes resulted in misdiagnoses.

Gene test

Since the discovery of the FMR1 gene in 1991, two tests have been developed: PCR (polymerase chain reaction) and Southern blotting. Both gene tests examine the number of repeats in the FMR1 genes from individuals, using a small sample of blood or even a swab of cells from the inside of the cheek. The PCR test is more accurate for determining the number of repeats, especially when the number is less than about 200. It is difficult to determine accurately the number of repeats when the size is much larger than that. However, since males with 200 repeats are as affected as those with 4500 repeats, having accurate numbers for full mutations is not necessary. A simple method of doing PCR to determine the number of repeats in the FMR1 gene using only a small spot of blood was developed, making the test very inexpensive (Holden, Chalifoux, Wing, DiTullio, & Julien-Inalsingh, 1996), and enabling the study of large populations.

Who is eligible for testing?

Anyone with a family history of FXS, or anyone who has a developmental disability or an Autism Spectrum Disorder of unknown cause, is eligible for testing. The family history in Figure 5 illustrates no instances of developmental disability prior to the youngest generation. However, genetic testing of other family members revealed the FMR1 premutation in several family members, and that expansion had occurred in each generation until it reached the full mutation in five members of the last generation. Four of the five are affected with FXS, with one daughter being unaffected. Since all individuals with FXS inherit an abnormal FMR1 gene from a parent,

all relatives of an affected individual are eligible for testing and should be offered testing.

FXS often appears in a family unexpectedly. This is because small premutations, which have been present in the family for several generations, expand in size, finally reaching a size that is clinically significant (i.e., produces symptoms in the person having the mutation).

The accuracy of fragile X testing

Testing for the standard FMR1 mutation (i.e., expansion of the number of CGG-repeats) using the gene test is extremely precise and approaches 100% accuracy.

The cost of testing

There are no fees for genetic services provided through Ontario hospitals to residents of the province.

When to provide testing

Genetic testing can be performed for individuals at any age, as well as for the developing fetus. The decision to have genetic testing for oneself, for a child, or for a relative is a personal choice and can evoke a variety of emotions. Professional assistance can be helpful when dealing with such challenging issues. The testing of children who are not old enough to provide their own consent is a controversial issue. Genetic testing should only be done with appropriate counselling.

How Families Are Affected When a Member Has FXS

Families in which at least one member has FXS face unique challenges. In dealing with these challenges, family members experience a range of emotions, including joy, pride, and love, but also a sense of loss, fear, guilt, and other difficult emotions. A recent study involving several fragile X families in Ontario revealed various areas of stress experienced by families (Nachshen & Minnes, 2005). These include:

- Getting a second opinion
- Assisted community living

- Explaining fragile X to others
- Meeting personal needs
- Dealing with professionals
- Spouse/sibling relationships
- Being part of a neighbourhood
- Nurturing friendships
- Difficulties with the education system
- Sexuality issues
- Problems with integration into a normal classroom
- Employment
- Finding recreation
- Long term planning

These areas of stress reflect the need for public awareness about FXS and more information for professionals in the health care and education systems, particularly in areas such as:

- Ways in which fragile X families cope with many of these stresses
- Experiences of students with FXS
- Experiences of teachers
- Experiences of students who share classrooms with students who have fragile X
- Experiences of women who are carriers of the fragile X premutation

Needs and Services for People with FXS

Healthcare needs

Although persons with FXS do not all have medical complications, some children with FXS are at higher risk for some problems than unaffected children of the same age. Table 3 summarizes some of the problems that might arise, as well as how the problems might be manifested and what assessments or management tools should be implemented. For example, recurrent otitis media is common in boys with FXS, and tubes to drain fluid from the middle ear may be indicated.

A tool to help primary care providers looking after all persons with FXS has been developed. This tool gives information about health problems in FXS and suggests approaches to management. The tool is called a *Health Watch Table* and is available at www.surreyplace.on.ca in the Clinical Programs section.

Educational needs

In Ontario, all students with developmental disabilities are eligible for integration into regular classrooms but may require special assistance. Students with FXS sometimes benefit from short periods away from regular classroom activity. Teachers can benefit from accessing information on educational strategies designed specifically for children with FXS (*National Fragile X Foundation, Education,* at website *www.nfxf.org/html/home.shtml*).

Services and supports for individuals with FXS in Ontario

Using the estimates reported at the beginning of this chapter, there are probably 2,000-8,000 males and 500-4,000 females with FXS in Ontario. Ontario, like other provinces in Canada, typically provides for the health care needs of children and adults with FXS through family physicians. Family physicians then refer fragile X families and affected individuals to specialized services as required.

Interventions may include behavioural or medical therapies to modify sleep disturbances, hyperactivity, and short attention span and address other concerns. Specialized services include:

- Assessment of fine motor or gross motor functioning
- Assessment of speech and language development
- Assessment of learning abilities
- Behavioural assessment
- Occupational therapy (OT) or physiotherapy (PT)

Health professionals involved in such service provision include:

- Pediatricians (especially developmental pediatricians)
- Psychologists/psychiatrists
- Speech/language pathologists
- Behavioural consultants
- Occupational therapists
- Physiotherapists
- Psychometrists

Table 3. Checklist of Possible Health Care Needs of Persons with Fragile X*

Problem Area	Clinical Expression	Assessment/Management
Feeding difficulties	*Poor weight gain*	*Feeding team*
Eyes	*Squint/refractive errors*	*See pediatric ophthalmologist early if eyes are not straight or if there is a suggestion of poor vision*
Ears and hearing	*Chronic otitis media (ear infection or ear ache), conductive hearing loss*	*Early treatment, hearing assessment, Ear Nose Throat consult re ventilation tubes*
Dental	*Caries, malocclusion*	*Initial dental examination by age 2 (may require sedation)*
Musculoskeletal	*Low muscle tone, flat feet, scoliosis, loose joints*	*Physiotherapist, orthopaedic or occupational therapist*
Cardiovascular	*Cardiac murmurs/clicks, high blood pressure*	*Echocardiogram, cardiologist*
Genitourinary	*Bed-wetting, late toilet training, urinary tract infections, hernia, large testes*	*Behavioural interventions, medication, renal ultrasound, reassurance*
Endocrine	*Early puberty, early menopause*	*Endocrinologist, genetic counselling, medications*
Central nervous system	*Seizure disorder, cognitive delay, low muscle tone, behaviour disorders, psychiatric disorders*	*Pediatric neurologist, EEG/anticonvulsant medication, early developmental assessment, psychology assessment*

* All health care should be co-ordinated by one primary physician

Special intervention strategies for people with FXS

Several intervention strategies have been developed to help reduce difficult behaviours in special circumstances and improve the quality of life for individuals with FXS. Changes in routine may result in behavioural outbursts, much like the response of children with autism to change. Loud noises and bright lights can be distracting and cause problems in a learning environment. Some examples of behavioural disturbances and how to deal with them are illustrated in Table 4.

Table 4. Examples of What May Cause Behavioural Disturbances and How to Avoid Them

Types of Behavioural Disturbances	Strategies to Try
Changes in routine *Has the routine suddenly changed?* *Is there a new teacher?* *Have seating arrangements been changed?*	*Keep the routine as predictable as possible. Introduce changes regularly. Give appropriate notice of changes. (Note: excessive amount of notice may cause anxiety.)*
Loud noises *Are there loud or unpredictable noises?* *Did the alarm go off?* *Does someone have a beeper?*	*Keep unpredictable sounds (alarms, pagers, etc.) to a minimum. Avoid loud or abrupt noises. Use soothing uninterrupted sounds, such as quiet steady hums, classical music, tapes of nature.*
Lights *Is the lighting too bright?* *Are there flashing lights?*	*Natural daylight is preferable to fluorescent lighting. Reduce brightness-use pink or other soft tone light bulbs.*
Crowds *Are there too many people around?* *Are they too close together?*	*Maintain a sense of spaciousness-avoid crowds. Choose aisle seats or back sections for more space and an easy exit.*

Programs and services beneficial to children with FXS

Five types of beneficial programs and services are outlined below.

Infant development/stimulation programs: From birth to two years of age, such programs provide in-home support with suggestions for parents on how to manage a child with a developmental disability. This program is generally available through the local health unit or hospital.

Hanen program: The Hanen program is a language training program for parents to provide the best environment for their child's development or communication skills, and is generally available at health units/hospitals.

Nursery/day care placements: Day-care placements can help by providing a stimulating environment with peers. Some agencies have subsidies for children with special needs.

Preschool development services: These services provide support of a worker in the home or day care with suggestions for activities to stimulate development. Such services are also helpful in planning transition to school.

Programs in schools: Provincially supported programs in the schools provide occupational therapy and physiotherapy, as well as support for speech and language development. (See Wilson, Stackhouse, O'Connor, & Hagerman, 1994, for more information about educating children with FXS.)

Community programs to facilitate child development

Services for children with developmental disabilities in Ontario vary among communities. Child development centres are part of hospital services, health units or specialized day care centres, depending on the size of the community. These resources include government financial assistance, respite care, and behaviour management. Listings of services can often be found at community libraries and in community listings on the internet.

The Fragile X Research Foundation of Canada (*www.fragilexcanada.ca*) promotes awareness of Fragile X syndrome, funds research and provides access to support through newsletters, an annual "Family Fun Day" and on-line discussion groups. The headquarters for this organization are in Brampton, Ontario. In conjunction with Surrey Place Centre, they also provide a dedicated Fragile X clinic to assess and treat patients with FXS. The clinic has begun to conduct clinical trials of new treatments for FXS.

Fragile X Research

Every two years, researchers from around the world come together to discuss their research findings. The 8th International Workshop on the Fragile X Syndrome and X-linked Mental Retardation took place in Picton, Ontario in 1997. The proceedings of this workshop were published in the American Journal of Medical Genetics (Holden et al., 1999). The 14th International Workshop was held in Brazil in 2009, and the next will be held in 2011 in Berlin. In addition, the National Fragile X Foundation (U.S.) holds an International Fragile X Conference in alternate years to the Fragile X Workshops. This conference is for families, care providers, professionals, and researchers (www.fragilex.org). In 2010, the conference was held in Detroit, Michigan.

Some areas of current research are described below.

The FMR1 protein (FMRP): The FMR1 gene codes for the FMR1 protein, which is lacking in persons with FXS. It is particularly abundant in neurons in the brain and may play a role in modulating the signalling that occurs between neurons. Researchers are now learning the precise role of FMRP in different cells of our bodies. For a review, see Pfeiffer and Huber (2009).

Strategies designed to maximize functioning of individuals with fragile X syndrome: These include a wide range of treatments, including psychopharmacology (reviewed by Hagerman et al., 2009). The identification of appropriate medical therapies has been influenced by research into the effect of FMR1 mutations in FXS. The identification of the fragile X gene, FMR1, and its product, FMRP, have allowed researchers to begin to understand how the lack of FMRP leads to certain aspects of FXS. Much of this research has been done using animal models, which allow for research that cannot be attempted on human subjects. Mice with the fragile X gene mutation have

been developed and are being used to explore treatments for fragile X. For example, Bilousova et al. (2009) have been able to show potential benefit in using an antibiotic (minocycline) to reduce anxiety in a mouse model of fragile X. Other work by Wang et al. (2008) in Toronto has suggested an important role for dopamine regulation in FXS, also using a mouse model. Clinical trials of some of these agents, including minocycline, are on-going in Canada, through Dr. Carlo Paribello (President of the Fragile X Research Foundation of Canada, *www.fragilexcanada.ca*).

Premature ovarian failure (also called Primary Ovarian Insufficiency): Women with premutations can have irregular menses, decreased fertility and may go into menopause at an early age, leading to concerns about family planning and health. It is important for women with premutations who are experiencing very irregular or no menses to consult their physician and be tested to determine whether they should be considering any therapy, such as hormone replacement. One of the researchers in this field is Stephanie Sherman at Emory University in Georgia (Crawford & Sherman, 2004).

Parkinson-like disease: Older adults who have the premutation, may develop a neurological condition that is sometimes described as being like Parkinson's disease. This is called the Fragile X Tremor Ataxia Syndrome (FXTAS). It is more common in males but can also occur in females. It does not occur in full mutation carriers. This has been reviewed by Brouwer, Willemsen, and Oostra (2009).

Distributions of FMR1 alleles and prevalence of mutant alleles in different populations: Several studies are looking at the prevalence of the fragile X full mutation, premutation and grey zone alleles in different populations. This may shed light on how the normal fragile X gene becomes a premutation. Recent scientific articles on different populations include studies in India, Taiwan, South America, Indonesia, Tasmania, and other locations. Crawford and Sherman (2004) have reviewed some of the on-going research in this area and describe some of the difficulties encountered in prevalence studies of fragile X gene mutations.

Educational strategies: Dr. Marcia Braden (Colorado) (*http://www.marciabraden.com/index.html*)

is studying learning and behaviour management strategies for students with FXS and has developed the logo teaching program. Dr. Michelle Mazzocco (Maryland) is examining math skills in girls with fragile X in order to adapt math programs to optimize learning in these girls (Murphy & Mazzocco, 2008). Increasing our understanding of learning difficulties for fragile X students is important in devising effective learning strategies.

Healthcare concerns: Dr. Patricia Minnes, Department of Psychology, Queen's University, has been working with fragile X families for several years and is currently studying parents' concerns about, and views on, enhancing healthcare of their children with FXS (Minnes & Steiner, 2009).

Summary

FXS is one cause of developmental disability in males and females. This syndrome is hereditary, with females usually being less affected than males. Affected individuals generally have good health but can require specialized services or medication. Health care services are provided through family physicians and pediatricians. Regular public education for individuals with FXS is available in Ontario, but affected individuals often require special education assistance.

Families of individuals affected with FXS frequently experience challenges associated with raising a child with a developmental disability, as well as finding information, services, and support. Family members generally encounter a lack of awareness of fragile X in the community and among professionals. Unaffected family members can also carry the fragile X mutation, and this often affects their family planning decisions. Research, public awareness and support for FXS are growing in Ontario and in Canada.

For Further Thought and Discussion

1. Labelling. Parents of students with fragile X do not always inform teachers and other students about the fragile X diagnosis. Discuss possible advantages and disadvantages of sharing or not sharing this information.
2. Screening for the premutation in females. If fragile X carrier women were identified, they could be offered the option of prenatal diagnosis and pregnancy termination. Should screening be carried out? To whom should screening be available (e.g., newborn females, teenagers, pregnant women, etc)? Should the cost of screening be a health-care responsibility?
3. Pregnancy termination for females. Prenatal screening can identify the size of the mutation in a female fetus but cannot predict whether or not she will be affected. Should a pregnancy termination be offered for a female fetus with the fragile X full mutation?

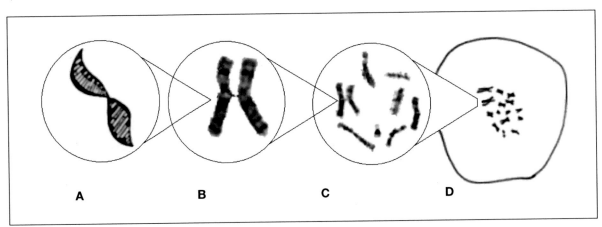

Figure 6. The relationship between DNA and chromosomes. *DNA (panel A) is tightly coiled and bound with proteins to form chromosomes (panel B). The chromosomes are located within the nucleus (panel C) of the cell (panel D).*

4. The right to know, the right to not know, and the duty to disclose. When a person receives a diagnosis of fragile X, other family members also have a high probability of carrying the mutation. Genetic counsellors recommend that family members tell their relatives about fragile X so that they too can avail themselves of genetic counselling and testing for the mutation. Geneticists and genetic counsellors often encounter family members who, for a variety of reasons, have chosen not to tell other relatives about fragile X. Should this task be left to the family member who received the diagnosis? If the genetics department knows the names of the extended family members, do they have an obligation to tell them about the fragile X diagnosis? Would this be a violation of confidentiality?

5. Gene therapy for FXS: Several research initiatives are looking at the possibility of gene therapy for FXS. This involves the delivery of a working copy of the fragile X gene into the cells of the brain in the hope that the gene would make the needed protein and reverse the cognitive disabilities associated with this syndrome. Discuss arguments for and/or against such therapy.

Acknowledgements

The authors wish to thank the following people for their comments and contributions to this chapter: P. Frost, J. Henderson, A. Holmes, B.A. Lee, R. Lokkesmoe, P. Minnes, J. Naschen, S. Stone, R. Wiens, and M. Wing.

Special Terms

The following list provides an overview of genetic terms used in discussions of Fragile X. For additional information on genetics and development, see Chapters 9 and 10.

Cells: Our bodies are made of cells which form our skin, muscles, nerves, bones and all of our organs. Each cell contains genetic material (DNA) that determines the kind of cell it is, and how it works.

Chromosomes: Very large strands of DNA tightly coiled inside the cell (Figure 6). Human chromosomes have 20,000 to 25,000 genes coding for proteins distributed on the 23 pairs of chromosomes. Each cell contains 46 chromosomes (2 sets of 23 chromosomes each). Chromosomes come in pairs: one copy from our mother; the other from our father. Each sperm and each ovum (egg) has only 1 copy of each of the 23 chromosomes. When the sperm fertilizes the egg, the total number of 46 chromosomes is restored. This is why children have some characteristics of each parent. The largest chromosome is called #1; the smallest, #22. The 23rd pair is called the sex chromosomes because they determine the male or female gender. The sex chromosomes are designated by an X and a Y. Males (XY) inherit an X chromosome from their mothers and a Y chromosome from their fathers. Females (XX) inherit two X chromosomes, one from each parent. The mutation that causes FXS is located on the X chromosome. The name fragile X was adopted because the chromosome appeared to be broken or fragile.

DNA: A blueprint or code of instructions for the entire body that is organized into units called genes. Under a powerful microscope, DNA would look like a ladder. The rungs of the ladder are the bases (molecules) called A, T, C and G, repeated in varying sequences. When this long strand of DNA is coiled up it is called a chromosome (see Figure 6). Example of sequences of DNA bases from part of a gene:

GATCGGCGGCTAGCGGTATTAGCAGTTT

Genes: Units of DNA that instruct the cells of our body to make proteins. It is the sequence of the bases that distinguishes one gene from another. There are thousands of genes on each human chromosome. Genes are regulated, meaning they are either turned on or off. A gene can be "turned on" and may make protein in one cell type (e.g., blood), but be "turned off" in other cells (e.g., brain, muscle) when not needed. Genes determine all aspects of our development, (appearance, eye colour, behaviour, blood type). However, life experiences and the environment modify the effects of genes.

Gene mutation: For a gene to be working well, the correct bases must be present and in the right sequence. If a gene is mutated (bases are missing, extra, or in the wrong place), the protein coded for will also be incorrect, and may result in abnormal development or ill health in that individual.

Fragile X carrier: Fragile X carrier is a genetic term used to refer to males and females who have an FMR1 gene mutation.

Normal transmitting male: Is a term used to refer to males with a premutation or males with a larger mutation who are not clinically affected.

Pattern of heredity: Refers to the way in which a genetic condition is passed from one generation to the next. It can be transmitted through the genetic material of the mother only, the father only, or the genetic material of both parents. Many genetic conditions are also due to genetic changes that occur for the first time in an individual and are not inherited from the genetic material of either parent. The pattern of heredity for fragile X is X-linked. This means the gene for this disorder is on the X chromosome.

Syndrome: A combination of traits or characteristics resulting from a single cause. FXS, arising from triplet repeat expansion in the FMR1 gene, results in a combination of learning disabilities, joint flexibility, large ears, etc.

More Resources

Resources in Canada:

Fragile X Research Foundation of Canada
167 Queen St W, Brampton, Ont., Canada L6Y 1M5
Tel: 905-453-9366;
E-mail: *info@fragilexcanada.ca*
Website: *www.fragilexcanada.ca*

Canadian Association for Research and Education in Intellectual Disability/Association canadienne pour la recherché et l'enseignement en deficience intellectuelle (CARE-ID/ACREDI)
Website: *www.care-id.com*

Resources in U.S.A.:

National Fragile X Foundation
1441 York St., Suite 303, Denver Colorado
80206-2127
Tel: 1-800-688-8765
Website: *www.nfxf.org*

FRAXA Research Foundation
Tel: 978-462-1866; Fax: (978) 463-9985;
E-mail: *info@fraxa.org*
Website: *www.fraxa.org*

References

Bailey, D. B., Jr., Mesibov, G. B., Hatton, D. D., Clark, R. D., Roberts, J. E., Mayhew, L. (1998). Autistic behavior in young boys with fragile X syndrome. *Journal of Autism and Developmental Disorders, 28(6), 499-508.*

Bilousova, T. V., Dansie, L., Ngo, M., Aye, J., Charles, J. R. Ethell, D. W., et al. (2009). Minocycline promotes dendritic spine maturation and improves behavioural performance in the fragile X mouse model. *Journal of Medical Genetics, 46(2), 94-102.*

Brouwer, J. R., Willemsen, R., & Oostra, B. A. (2009). The FMR1 gene and fragile X-associated tremor/ataxia syndrome. *American Journal of Medical Genetics, 150B(6), 782-798.*

Crawford, D., & Sherman, S. L. (2004). Fragile X syndrome: Application of gene identification to clinical diagnosis and population screening. In M. J. Khoury, J. Little, & W. Burke (Eds.), *Human genome epidemiology: A scientific foundation for using genetic information to improve health and prevent disease* (chapter 23). Oxford: Oxford University Press. Retrieved August 12, 2010, from http://www.cdc.gov/genomics/resources/books/HuGE/chap23.htm

Fernandez-Carvajal, I., Lopez Posadas, B., Pan, R., Raske, C., Hagerman, P.J., & Tassone, F. (2009). Expansion of an FMR1 grey-zone allele to a full mutation in two generations. *Journal of Molecular Diagnostics, 11(4), 306-310.*

Garber, K. B., Visootsak, J., & Warren, S. T. (2008). Fragile X syndrome. *European Journal of Human Genetics, 16(6), 666-762.*

Hagerman, R. J., Berry-Kravis, E., Kaufmann, W. E., Ono, M. Y., Tartaglie, N., Lachiewicz, A., et al. (2009). Advances in the treatment of fragile X syndrome. *Pediatrics, 123, 378-390.*

Holden, J. J. A., Chalifoux, M., Wing, M., DiTullio, K., & Julien-Inalsingh, C. (1996). The fragile-X syndrome: Current understanding and testing procedures. *Journal on Developmental Disabilities, 2*(1), 82-90.

Holden, J. J. A., Percy, M., Allingham-Hawkins, D., Brown, W. T., Chiurazzi, P., Fisch, G., et al. (1999). Eighth international workshop on the fragile X syndrome and X-linked mental retardation. *American Journal of Medical Genetics, 83,* 221-236.

Hunter, J. E., Abramowitz, A., Rusin, M., & Sherman, S, (2009). Is there evidence for neuropsychological and neurobehavioural phenotypes among adults without FXTAS who carry the FMR1 premutation? A review of current literature. *Genetics in Medicine, 11*(2), 79-89.

Minnes, P., & Steiner, K. (2009). Parent views on enhancing the quality of health care for their children with fragile X syndrome, autism or Down syndrome. *Child: Care, Health and Development, 35*(2), 250-256.

Murphy, M. M., & Mazzocco, M. M. (2008) Rote numeric skills may mask underlying mathematical disabilities in girls with fragile X syndrome. *Developmental Neuropsychology, 33,* 345-364.

Nachshen, J. S., & Minnes, P. (2005). Empowerment in parents of school-aged childen with and without developmental disabilities. *Journal of Intellectual Disability Research, 49,* 889-904.

Pfeiffer, B. E., & Huber, K. M. (2009). The state of synapses in fragile X syndrome. *Neuroscientist, 15,* 549-567.

Wang, H., Wu, L.-J., Kim, S. S., Lee, F. J. S., Gong, B., Toyoda, H., et al., (2008). FMRP acts as a key messenger for dopamine modulation in the forebrain. *Neuron, 59*(4), 634-637.

Wen, G. Y., Jenkins, E. C., Yao, X.-L., Yoon, D., Brown, W. T., & Wisniewski, H. M. (1997). Transmission electron microcopy of chromosomes by longitudinal section preparation: Application to fragile X chromosome analysis. *American Journal of Medical Genetics, 68,* 445-449.

Wilson, P., Stackhouse, T., O'Connor, R., Scharfenaker, S., & Hagerman, R. (1994). *Issues and strategies for educating children with fragile X syndrome.* A Monograph (pp. 13-18, 47-52). Dillon, CO: Spectra Publishing Co., Inc.

19

Fetal Alcohol Spectrum Disorder. Part I: Triumphs and Challenges

Irena Nulman and Ariel Pulver

What you will learn:

- Brief history of Fetal Alcohol Spectrum Disorder (FASD)
- Epidemiology of FASD
- Effects of alcohol use during pregnanay
- Diagnosing FASD
- How mother's alcohol use affects the child
- Psychiatric abnormalities
- Screening and prevention
- Interventions

The topic of Fetal Alcohol Spectrum Disorder is not black and white. Hence, this section is written in academic style with detail provided to inform readers about the evidence on which particular statements are made. To obtain an overall perspective of the field before reading this chapter, please refer to Table 1 entitled FASD at a Glance. Refer to Chapter 10 for information about development and Chapter 11 for information about the brain and nervous systems.

The recreational effects of alcohol have been enjoyed by almost every ethnic group throughout human history, making it legal and culturally accepted. Therefore, it is a part of the lifestyles of many women of childbearing age throughout the world. In fact, in Canada, 76.8% of women reported drinking within the past year (Canadian Centre on Substance Abuse, 2004). On average, 49% of women drink some alcohol during pregnancy (Abel, 1998).

Alcohol consumption during pregnancy can be toxic for central nervous system development in the fetus, and is associated with problems in both physical and mental development. Alcohol use during pregnancy, resulting in Fetal Alcohol Spectrum Disorder (FASD), is currently a common cause of developmental disability in babies and young children. A diagnosis of FASD is based upon the finding of growth retardation, facial anomalies,

Table 1: Fetal Alcohol Spectrum Disorder at a Glance

Overview of facts	• *Includes behavioural and cognitive dysfunction, sometimes associated with growth and physical abnormalities linked with heavy drinking* • *Is a leading preventable cause of developmental delay in children* • *May affect 1% of fetuses* • *Is completely preventable with alcohol abstinence* • *Is a marker of alcohol abuse during gestation*
How alcohol affects the fetus	• *Is toxic to the embryo and the fetus* • *Is converted to acetaldehyde, which is toxic to the embryo and fetus* • *Deprives the fetus of oxygen; in particular, it constricts the umbilical cord vessels* • *Has deleterious effects on fetal metabolism* • *Causes an increase in fatty acid alcohol complexes in the meconium (first neonatal stool)*
Main effects of FASD by age	*Early childhood* • *Neurodevelopmental delay and possible physical abnormalities* • *Psychiatric symptoms* • *Attachment insecurity* *Childhood and adolescence* • *Behavioral, cognitive, and learning impairments* • *Significant psychiatric comorbidities (co-existing conditions)* • *Secondary disabilities, such as disruptive school experiences, trouble with the law, confinement (inpatient treatment for mental health problems or alcohol/drug problems, or incarceration for a crime), inappropriate sexual behaviour, alcohol and drug problems, dependent living, and unemployment* • *Low adaptability and impaired judgment* *Adulthood* • *Mental health problems* • *Major problems with adaptive behaviour*

but most importantly, signs of neuropsychological dysfunction. Long-term neurocognitive and neurobehavioural deficits in these children often contribute to debilitating psychiatric conditions and poor quality of life. Since the syndrome was first recognized, considerable progress has been made in understanding alcohol's *teratogenic effects* (interference with normal fetal development), defining diagnostic categories for FASD, developing screening tools, and identifying biological markers to substantiate alcohol exposure — all of which have helped to identify and diagnose more children who have been exposed to alcohol's toxic effects in utero. Research since about 2000 has mostly focussed on psychological markers and management of affected children.

Key risk factors for FASD	• *Maternal heavy drinking and binge drinking*
	• *Maternal high blood alcohol levels*
	• *Maternal high alcohol consumption and unplanned pregnancy*
	• *Genetic and environmental factors that affect fetal and childhood development in the context of maternal alcohol consumption*
Intervention	• *Focus on early diagnosis*
	• *Use a multidisciplinary approach*
	• *Focus on early intervention to address the development of secondary disabilities*
Prevention	• *Prevent alcohol abuse and treat those with problematic use*
	• *Increase societal awareness of fetal alcohol related abnormalities*
	• *Educate women about the consequences of drinking alcohol while pregnant and treat alcohol dependency*
	• *Encourage women to stop drinking alcohol while trying to get pregnant or during pregnancy and treat alcohol dependency*
	• *Consider alternatives to continuing pregnancy*
	• *Use effective contraception if educational and treatment efforts are unsuccessful*

A Brief History

The Bible first made note of fetal alcohol toxicity, but the initial scientific report came in 1968 by Lemoine and associates, who reported on pregnancy outcomes of incarcerated alcoholic women in France (Lemoine, Harousseau, Borteyru, & Menuet, 1968). The term Fetal Alcohol Syndrome (FAS) was coined in 1973 by Jones and Smith who described a distinct group of physical abnormalities in children following alcohol exposure during pregnancy (Jones & Smith, 1973). Jones, Smith, Ulleland, and Streissguth (1973) noted that children exposed in utero to alcohol had a similar pattern of craniofacial defects associated with growth and developmental delay that began before birth. Since Jones and Smith originated the definition, the criteria for diagnosis of FAS has been based on the presence of the following three features: 1) growth retardation prior to and/or following birth, 2) characteristic facial abnormalities (for example, small palpebral fissures, long and thin upper lip, flattened mid face and upper jaw area (see Figure 1), and 3) complex long-term neurobehavioral and cognitive impairments.

Since 1973, there have been numerous *epidemiological* and original research endeavours that have aimed to describe the negative effects that have been observed in children exposed to alcohol during gestation. (Epidemiology refers to the study of patterns of health and illnesses and associated factors at the population level.) The available research and clinical observations were summarized in a set of diagnostic categories in 1996 by a designated committee of the Institute of Medicine in the United States (Institute of Medicine, 1996). The committee decided to classify the spectrum of clinical presentations into Fetal Alcohol Syndrome (FAS), Partial Fetal Alcohol Syndrome (pFAS), alcohol related birth defects (ARBD), and Alcohol Related Neurodevelopmental Disorder (ARND). ARND has replaced the term Fetal Alcohol Effects (FAE), which was used to describe children who did not fit the characteristic triad of features, but had since fallen out of use due to its limited clinical relevance. Fetal Alcohol Spectrum Disorder (FASD) is the umbrella term that includes the above diagnostic categories as suggested by Streissguth and O'Malley (2000). (Definitions of the various terms related to FASD are explained in the section *Diagnosis of Fetal Alcohol Spectrum Disorder* in a later section of this chapter.)

Epidemiology of FASD

Abel (1998) reviewed the available epidemiological studies on FAS and presented calculations for the incidence of FAS based on geographical, ethnic and socio-economic variables. He estimated, after an analysis of 29 prospective studies, a mean (average) incidence of 0.97 cases per 1,000 live births in the general obstetric population. However, the incidence appears to vary both among and within countries. (Note that the term *incidence* is distinct from *prevalence*. Incidence is a measurement of the number of *new* individuals who are identified as having the condition during a particular period of time. Prevalence is a measurement of *all* individuals affected by the condition at, or within, a particular period of time.)

Sampson et al. (1997) estimated 1% of the pediatric population (i.e., *the prevalence*) to be affected by in utero alcohol toxicity. Canadian estimates of FASD prevalence are similar and are approximately 1% (Canadian Pediatric Society Statement, 2002; Chudley et al., 2005; Roberts & Nanson, 2000). More recently, the prevalence of FAS in the United States has been estimated at 0.2-0.7%, while the prevalence of the entire spectrum is about 10 times more, and may be as high as 2-5% (May et al., 2009). FAS results from heavy prenatal alcohol exposure, the reality that led Abel (1998) to rename FAS as Fetal Alcohol Abuse Syndrome while maintaining the same acronym. Within this subpopulation of "heavy" drink-

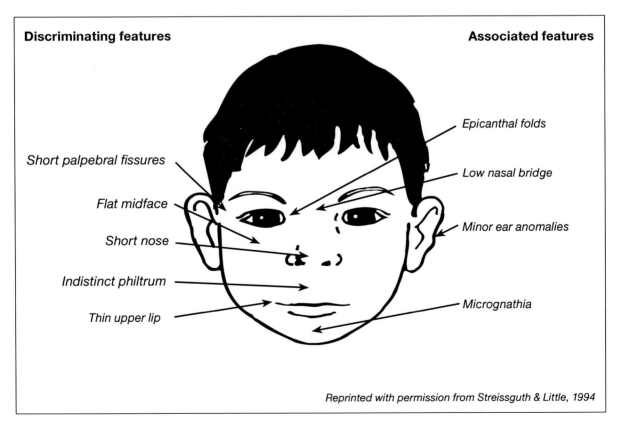

Discriminating features   Associated features

Short palpebral fissures
Flat midface
Short nose
Indistinct philtrum
Thin upper lip

Epicanthal folds
Low nasal bridge
Minor ear anomalies
Micrognathia

Reprinted with permission from Streissguth & Little, 1994

Figure 1. Faces in fetal alcohol syndrome in the young child.

ers, Abel's review of the literature (1995) found the incidence of FAS to be 4.3 per 100 live births in alcohol dependent and abusing women.

The incidence and prevalence of FASD are still to be clearly defined due to numerous methodological issues, such as variation in study design, failure to include confounding factors, targeting of specific populations, and different reporting practices. Alcohol consumption during pregnancy is challenging to document as it is mostly based on self-report from mothers of children who have been diagnosed with FASD, and this may not be reliable since women are understandably sometimes unwilling to report this information. Thus, self-reports of alcohol use may be underestimated because some women are reluctant to admit to alcohol use (Public Health Agency of Canada, 2009).

FASD is not only very common, but is very costly to our society. The annual financial burden of FASD in Canada has been estimated at 5.3 billion dollars (Stade et al., 2009). Per individual, the costs related to healthcare, education, and social services amounts to approximately $1.4 million (Sarkar et al., 2009). Early identification of alcohol-affected children could facilitate the delivery of helpful support services with the hope of decreasing or eliminating the costly and debilitating secondary disabilities (Streissguth, Bookstein, Sampson, & Barr, 1996b; Streissguth et al., 2004). The net cost resulting from prenatal alcohol exposure is considerably higher than the cost of FAS alone. Clearly, the damaging effects of prenatal alcohol exposure need to be reduced.

Alcohol Use in Pregnancy

An understanding of FASD in general must begin with understanding the patterns of use of alcohol by women just prior to or during pregnancy, and the effects of alcohol on the developing fetus.

Characteristics of women who use alcohol

In the 2005 Canadian Community Health Survey, 10.5% of women who had given birth in the preceding five years reported drinking alcohol during pregnancy (Public Health Agency of Canada, 2008). Notably, 62.4% of women consumed alcohol dur-

ing the three months prior to pregnancy or before realizing they were pregnant. By comparison, in a 2009 U.S. survey, 30.3% of all women reported some alcohol consumption during pregnancy, with 8.3% reporting binge drinking (Ethen, 2009). Drinking rates declined considerably after the first month of pregnancy, during which 22.5% of women reported drinking; 2.7% of women reported drinking during all trimesters, and 7.9% reported drinking in the third trimester. Women who engaged in binge drinking prior to conception were more likely to drink during pregnancy as well (Ethen, 2009).

It is crucial to understand the various lifestyle factors in the context of alcohol use in pregnancy. *This awareness helps us understand what things pose risks for a mother and fetus during pregnancy, and what things might act to protect them.* Pregnant women who use alcohol may be single mothers, experience changes in custody of their other children, and have low socioeconomic status (Public Health Agency of Canada, 2005). They often have unplanned pregnancies, limited access to *perinatal* care services (services supporting the period of time just before and just after birth), poor nutrition, shelter insecurity, low literacy, cognitive impairments, and low self-esteem. Women who use alcohol while pregnant may also have experienced childhood stress, abuse, or neglect themselves. They may have mental health problems (e.g., depression, bipolar disorder, or schizophrenia) or physical health issues (e.g., sexually transmitted infections, or anemia). They may use other substances, or may have experienced violence, trauma, sexual exploitation, or incarceration (Public Health Agency of Canada, 2005).

When considering alcohol's toxic effects on the developing fetus, it is important to consider the above factors, which may themselves detract substantially from a healthy pregnancy. For example, women who are alcohol-dependent may use other substances (Gladstone, Levy, Nulman, & Koren, 1997). Analyses of *meconium* (the first fecal excretion of a newborn child) and hair from newborns revealed that those who were heavily exposed to alcohol in utero were twice as likely to be exposed to opiates and more than three times as likely to be exposed to amphetamines (Shor, Nulman, Kulaga,

& Koren, 2010). A recent study demonstrated more severe neurological abnormalities in children exposed in pregnancy to a combination of methamphetamines and alcohol than to alcohol alone (Sowell et al., 2010). In this sample, approximately half of women who used methamphetamine also used alcohol. Moreover, there is strong evidence of interaction effects between alcohol use and smoking during pregnancy. Combined use of tobacco and alcohol in pregnancy increases the risk of babies being small for their age compared with alcohol use alone, and increases the risk for low birth weight, microcephaly (abnormal smallness of the head), and hearing difficulties (Aliyu et al., 2009; Olsen, Pereira, Da, & Olsen, 1991). Awareness of the extent of alcohol consumption in the context of the mother's lifestyle, co-existing mental and physical health problems, and other substance use is imperative to identify, diagnose, and manage children who might have been exposed to alcohol before birth.

Other factors that may influence the development and presentation of FASD include the amount of alcohol consumed, and the timing and pattern of alcohol exposure. Genetic factors, mental ill-health of a parent, as well as the rate at which mother and fetus metabolize and eliminate alcohol from the body, rates of transport of nutrients across the placenta, and alteration in uterine blood flow also influence the risk and severity of fetal alcohol-induced damage. These factors are discussed in more detail below.

Timing of exposure

Many women may not be aware of their pregnancy for the first four to six weeks (Zieman, 2009). Unintended pregnancies are most common in those aged 15-19 (82% are unintended) and least common in those aged 35-39 (29% are unintended pregnancies) (Finer & Henshaw, 2006). Importantly, the 15-19 year old group is also at highest risk of binge drinking (Ahmad, Flight, Singh, Poole, & Dell, 2008). Girls and young women who have unplanned pregnancies often unknowingly consume high levels of alcohol during the first trimester — the very time when the fetus is most vulnerable to adverse effects from alcohol exposure (Sulik, Johnston,

Draft, Russel, & Dehart, 1986). A recent study found a fourfold increased risk of alcohol-related birth defects following heavy alcohol use in the 1st trimester (O'Leary, Nassar, Kurinczuk, de Klerk, & Geelhoed, 2010). Alcohol exposure during *gastrulation* (the first 3-5 weeks post-conception) may disrupt brain formation (Miller, 2007; Mooney & Miller 2007) and the child's future neurocognitive and behavioural functioning.

The critical period of neuroepithelial cell proliferation occurs during 7 to 20 weeks of gestation (Suzuki, 2007), when most areas of the nervous system begin to differentiate and neuronal migration takes place (Guerri, Bazinet, & Riley, 2009). The brain develops particularly quickly during the last trimester; therefore exposure at this stage may significantly change brain architecture and head size. However, research has shown that *microcephaly* (small head size) may result from alcohol toxicity at any time during the pregnancy.

Alcohol exposure during the second trimester has been associated with an increased risk for miscarriages and growth impairments. Intrauterine growth retardation is a term that describes fetuses that are small in weight, length, and/or head size for their gestational age. This decreased weight is not just temporary, and there is rarely a "catch-up" to normal levels.

Patterns of exposure

Drinking patterns are typically described in the academic literature as: on average, daily, weekly, or monthly alcohol intake. However, the definitions of mild, moderate, and heavy use vary considerably among studies, making generalizations and comparisons difficult. Moreover, accurate measurement of alcohol exposure is highly problematic. As mentioned, self-report currently is the chief way to obtain this crucial information. Precise self-report is tricky because it requires: 1) remembering (often years later) the amount, type, and frequency used in a particular nine month period; and 2) admitting to something that is known to be harmful, and that the mother may already know has affected her child.

It is now evident that drinking patterns in pregnancy, such as binging, play a crucial role in predicting teratogenic effects. A teratogen is an agent that can disturb the development of an embryo or a fetus, and thus teratogenic effects of alcohol are disturbances to the development of an embryo or fetus. Binge drinking for women has been defined as four or more drinks per occasion, over the course of 1.5-2 hours. Among women of reproductive age who are not pregnant, 10-12% report binge drinking, as binge drinking is associated with social events among women of reproductive age. Research indicates that a single binge exposure with a high *blood alcohol concentration (BAC)* during a critical time in pregnancy may be toxic to the fetus (Streissguth, Bookstein, & Barr, 1996a). Peak BACs are a function of both the dose and rate of alcohol consumption. Therefore, a very different pattern of BACs would be achieved by two different sets of activities: spreading 10 drinks throughout the day from morning to evening, and binging on 10 drinks in about 2 hours (Gladstone, Nulman, & Koren, 1996). Compared with daily amounts of alcohol consumed in a slower or more spread out manner, alcohol consumed in a binge pattern can rapidly produce high BACs in the mother and the fetus. This important finding has been incorporated into the Canadian Alcohol Use and Pregnancy Consensus Guidelines (Carson et al., 2010), which notes that metabolic activity is slower in the fetus than in the mother; while the BAC in the mother may have attenuated, it may still remain high in the fetus. Thus, there may be a critical individual threshold of BAC required to induce neurotoxicity. Differences in drinking rate and patterns may explain, in part, the large variability in the clinical presentation of FASD, and inconsistency in research reports. For example, Strandberg-Larsen and colleagues found that drinking more than four alcoholic beverages a week or binging on three or more occasions during pregnancy is associated with increased risk of infant deaths (Strandberg-Larsen, Grønboek, Andersen, Andersen, & Olsen, 2009) and O'Leary found an increased risk for preterm birth (O'Leary, Nassar, Kurinczuk, & Bower, 2009). However, an earlier systematic review found no significant effects of binge drinking on pre or post natal physical development (Henderson, Kesmodel, & Gray, 2007b).

A prospective, longitudinal study by Streissguth et al. (1996a) investigated children exposed in utero to a moderate amount of alcohol, characteristic of social drinking. This study examined three types of teratogenic outcomes: deficits in growth, morphology (body form and structure), and function, all of which were evident in children with FAS. They reported that the most persistent effects of prenatal alcohol exposure, observed from the first day of life through 14 years, were problems in neurobehavioural functioning. Learning problems were observed from 7 through 14 years, but problems with attention and speed of information processing were observable over the entire 14-year period. Stronger effects were associated with higher level of alcohol use and, in the school-age years, more with binge-type drinking patterns. While children of social drinkers who binge do not display intellectual or language impairments when compared to unexposed children, they do show more behavioural problems (Nulman et al., 2004).

The issue of a safe-amount of alcohol becomes cloudier when considering the conflicting findings of low consumption. Some studies have found a link between low levels of drinking and increased externalizing behaviours and aggression (Sood et al., 2001), learning (Olson et al., 1997), and other mental health problems (Sayal, Heron, & Golding, 2007) in children exposed to alcohol prenatally. However, other research has not found such adverse effects in children exposed to low level drinking in gestation (Kelly et al., 2009; Robinson et al., 2010; Rodriguez et al., 2009). Similarly, a meta-analysis of 46 relevant articles did not find any consistent evidence for adverse effects of low-moderate prenatal alcohol exposure (Henderson, Gray, & Brocklehurst, 2007a). In fact, a recent study found that mild drinking during pregnancy may be associated with more positive child behavioural outcomes than complete abstinence from alcohol (Robinson et al., 2010). It must be noted that many of these studies have significant methodological issues, making decisions about any "safe amount" difficult to render. In 2003, the U.S. National Institute of Alcohol Abuse and Alcoholism stated that low-moderate drinking in pregnancy "does not seem to be associated with an increased risk of fetal physical malformations, but may have behavioral or neurocognitive consequences."

Before messages about a safe amount of prenatal alcohol are publicized, future studies must be careful to control for confounding factors such as socioeconomic status (SES) and parental psychopathology, obtain data from multiple sources including the child, parents and teachers, and use a comprehensive assessment strategy (Todorow, Moore, & Koren, 2010).

The recent Canadian Alcohol Use and Pregnancy Consensus Clinical Guidelines from the Society of Obstetrics and Gynaecology, 2010, clearly state that:

> *There is insufficient evidence regarding fetal safety or harm at low levels of alcohol consumption in pregnancy. There is insufficient evidence to define any threshold for low-level drinking in pregnancy. Abstinence is the prudent choice for a woman who is or might become pregnant. (p. S10)*

How Does Alcohol Affect the Child?

Alcohol can affect children in a variety of ways and, as such, there is great variability in the presence and/or degree of abnormality in alcohol-exposed children. An affected child may have an IQ ranging from normal to very low, and may have physical features that range from normal appearance to evident anomalies. Likewise, a child exposed to alcohol prenatally may present with normal growth and physical features, but have slight or significant behavioural and/or cognitive abnormalities. Consequently, when the phenotype is "incomplete" or "atypical" or the clinician is inexperienced in making this diagnosis, FAS may be misdiagnosed.

CNS abnormalities resulting from in utero exposure to alcohol are mediated by a number of factors. Alcohol can affect most areas of brain development and, although it is not yet possible to detail the mechanisms by which alcohol affects each stage of development, the mechanism of action is likely to be the result of several forces acting together. As alcohol crosses the placenta and blood brain barrier (the cells that line the walls of blood vessels in the brain), it can be directly toxic to the fetus. The major *metabolite* of alcohol (the substance into which alcohol is converted), *acetaldehyde*, is also toxic to the fetus. (Acetaldehyde is actually more toxic than alcohol itself.) In addition, alcohol can affect the fetus indirectly through its secondary effects, such as insufficient oxygen supply due to constriction of vessels in the umbilical cord. Alcohol may induce changes in the activity of certain genes, a factor that may be responsible for at least some of the developmental abnormalities observed in FAS.

Factors such as increased *prostaglandin* levels may lead to a reduction in the rate of cell division and a possible decrease in the weight of the fetal brain. (Prostaglandins are particular types of fatty acids that can affect the biological activities of every organ system.) Other effects of alcohol may also contribute to fetal brain damage. For example, high levels of alcohol in the blood increase the liver's demand for oxygen, resulting in oxygen deprivation of other organs. As well, alcohol may impair oxygen unloading from *hemoglobin* (a protein in the body that carries oxygen) by lowering the *pH* of the blood (i.e., making the blood more acidic). (pH is a term used to describe the acidity or basicity of an aqueous solution.) Finally, experiments with embryonic stem cells of the mouse show that alcohol exposure triggers cell death by a process called "*apoptosis*" (the breakage of cells into fragments), a factor potentially also causing brain damage in the developing fetus (Arzumanyan, Anni, Rubin, & Rubin, 2009). In addition, there are numerous other factors such as *free radical* damage, and the inhibition of the enzyme *aldehyde dehydrogenase*, that could contribute to alcohol's teratogenic effects. (Free radicals are very reactive atoms, molecules or ions that carry an unpaired electron, making them very reactive. Aldehyde is a toxic by-product of alcohol degradation and is kept at low levels by the action of aldehyde dehydrogenase.)

Exposure to alcohol during gestation is associated with significant effects on the shape, volume, and surface area of particular brain regions, as well as reduced white matter and increased grey matter densities in corresponding areas (Guerri et al., 2009; see Chapter 11 for diagrams of the brain). Thus, certain areas, including the parietal lobe, portions of the frontal lobe, and the cerebellum may be particularly vulnerable to alcohol exposure. There are also disproportionate reductions in other brain regions, including the cranial and cerebral areas as well as the corpus callosum and caudate nucleus (Spadoni, McGee, Fryer, & Riley, 2007; see also Sulik, 2005, for a review of effects of alcohol in the developing mouse). Abnormalities in the corpus callosum have been linked with deficencies in the coordination of both hands, attention, verbal learning ability, and executive functioning. Cerebellum defects may explain motor deficiencies and attention regulation problems (Guerri et al., 2009). Moreover, functional abnormalities in neurotransmitter and metabolic activity as well as in cerebral blood flow may contribute to the impairments associated with FASD (Clark, Li, Conry, & Loock, 2000; Fagerlund et al., 2007; Guerri et al., 2009). In one study, children with FAS were found to display increased non-righthandedness and lack of right ear advantage in speech perception as compared to unaffected children (Domellöf, Rönnqvist, Titran, Esseily, & Fagard, 2009). Functional MRI (a form of imaging that reveals changes in blood flow to local vasculature when neural activity changes) studies also suggest that the region of the brain thought to mediate inhibitory control (the frontal-striatal circuitry) is sensitive to alcohol teratogenesis (Fryer et al., 2007b; Sowell et al., 2007). It is important to note that the majority of the studies did not use a control group, and therefore these results must be interpreted with caution.

Effects of alcohol on brain development are complex in the sense that some are direct and others are not. Streissguth et al. (1996b) defined these effects as *primary* and *secondary disabilities*. *Primary disabilities* are those that are inborn and a direct consequence of the teratogenic effects of alcohol, while *secondary disabilities* are those that an individual is not born with, but that develop as a consequence of, the primary disability. Secondary disabilities are the most common and clinically-relevant aspects of FASD. These may include significant cognitive and developmental delay, antisocial behaviours, learning disabilities, poor adaptation skills, and psychiatric illnesses.

Some investigations of intellect in individuals with FAS revealed IQs ranging in the 70s (Streissguth et al., 1996b). Meanwhile, children with ARND obtained either similar scores or much higher IQs, reaching up to 120. A significant body of literature, as summarized by Kodituwakku (2009), supports Streissguth's findings (Adnams et al., 2001; Korkman, Kettunen, & Autti-Rämö, 2003). Moreover, a recent study compared the verbal, performance and full scale IQ scores of children with FAS to those of children exposed to psychotropic drugs in pregnancy. The study revealed that the children with FAS scored significantly worse on verbal, performance and full scale IQ than those exposed to psychotropic drugs alone (Dalen, Bruarøy, Wentzel-Larsen, & Laegreid, 2009), suggesting that alcohol is more neurotoxic.

Significant deficits in attention and information processing have also been identified (Coles, Platzman, Lynch, & Freides, 2002; Dalen et al., 2009; Lee, Mattson, & Riley, 2004). Tasks requiring active rather than automatic processing may be particularly taxing for children with FASD (Burden, Jacobson, & Jacobson, 2005). Executive functioning, which includes planning, inhibition, organization and strategic thinking may be challenging as well (Rasmussen, 2005). Individuals with FASD may also face difficulties with visual processing (Guerri et al., 2009; Mattson, Calarco, & Lang, 2006), learning, memory (Coles, Lynch, Kable, Johnson, & Goldstein, 2010), number processing, motor dysfunction (Mattson, Riley, Gramling, Delis, & Jones, 1998), and social cognition, all of which may persist into adulthood (Connor, Sampson, Streissguth, Bookstein, & Barr, 2006). Children exposed to alcohol prenatally have decreased academic achievement and higher rates of learning disabilities than non-exposed children, possibly relating to verbal and nonverbal learning and memory (Howell, Lynch, Platzman, Smith, & Coles, 2006; Mattson & Roebuck, 2002). Although children with and without the physical signs of alcohol toxicity may have similar intellectual deficits, cognitive impairments are not the hallmark elements of an FASD diagnosis. Behavioural dysfunction and mental health problems are much more salient features in this population.

Although cognitive deficits are over-represented among FASD-affected children, mental functioning varies widely and some of these children may function at a sufficient academic level at school, even though they may have behaviour problems. Children with FASD frequently display antisocial behaviours (Nash et al., 2006; Rasmussen, Andrew, Zwaigenbaum, & Tough, 2008a; Sood et al., 2001; Spohr, Willms, & Steinhausen, 2007). In a study investigating the behavioural profiles of children exposed to low and moderate/heavy alcohol in pregnancy, both groups of alcohol-exposed children displayed more deleterious *externalizing* (aggressive and delinquent) and *internalizing* (anxious/depressed and withdrawn) behaviours than those with no exposure; however, maternal psychopathology was the greatest predictor for behaviour (Sood et al., 2001). Insecure attachment has also been associated with FASD (O'Connor, Sigman, & Kasari,1992).

Children with FASD tend to lie more regularly than unaffected children (Rasmussen, Talwar, Loomes, & Andrew, 2008b). In fact, Nash et al. (2006) found that children exposed to alcohol had higher rates of delinquent behaviours such as lying, cheating, stealing and bullying than children with ADHD. Moreover, aggression and delinquency have been shown to even worsen later in life for affected children (Spohr et al., 2007). Youth exposed to alcohol show lower moral maturity than matched controls, specifically related to moral value judgments having to do with relationships with others. This may contribute to the increased deliquency observed in these children (Schonfeld, Mattson, & Riley, 2005). Their high rates of social and behavioural problems may stem from challenges with social and emotional processing (Greenbaum, Stevens, Nash, Koren, & Rovet, 2009) and they may make poor peer choices (Schonfeld et al., 2005). Adaptive skills are frequently underdeveloped in those with FASD (Carr, Agnihotri, & Keightley, 2010) and people may lack adequate personal and social skills to navigate independently through life (Spohr et al., 2007). Their poor social adaptability often leads these children to display disruptive behaviour in school, engage in inappropriate sexual behaviour, have drug problems, depend on others, and experience unemployment.

Disrupted school experiences are also prevalent in 61% of adults and adolescents with FAS or FAE. Moreover, 60% have trouble with the law, 50% experience confinement (detention, jail, prison, or psy-

chiatric inpatient), 49% show inappropriate sexual behaviours repeatedly, and 35% have alcohol/drug problems (Streissguth et al., 2004). Research suggests that avoidance of these problems is 2-4 times more likely if diagnosed at an earlier age and by rearing exposed children in stable home environments (Streissguth et al., 2004).

Psychiatric Difficulties

Children exposed to alcohol prenatally are at particular risk for developing psychiatric conditions. In an early study, Streissguth et al. (1996b) found that 94% of their sample experienced psychiatric problems. Another more recent study has found that 87% of children exposed to heavy prenatal alcohol met the criteria for psychiatric diagnosis of FASD (O'Connor et al., 2002). Heavy prenatal alcohol exposure is greatly associated with a number of common disorders included in the DSM-IV — in particular ADHD (94.87%) and Oppositional Defiant Disorder (38.46%) (Fryer, McGee, Matt, Riley, & Mattson, 2007a; see also Chapter 35). Children with FASD often experience depression and anxiety (Stade, Stevens, Ungar, Beyene, & Koren, 2006). Some research suggests that 61% receive a mood disorder diagnosis: 26% experienced major depressive disorder or adjustment disorder with depressed mood and 35% meet criteria for bipolar disorder. Considering that mental health has a strong family connection, it is difficult to disentangle the effects of parental psychopathology from the effects of in utero alcohol toxicity. It appears that a child's behavioural phenotype may be confounded by both (Staroselsky et al., 2009).

Diagnosing FASD

FASD is complex and may be expressed in a variety of ways. Research in previous decades has demonstrated that, in prenatally alcohol-exposed individuals, the presence and/or degree of abnormalities can vary considerably in physical features that range from normal to obvious malformations. Those with full expression of FAS comprise only a very small proportion of all the individuals affected

Table 2: Categories of FAS Effects

FAS with confirmed maternal alcohol exposure:	1. *Confirmed maternal alcohol use;*
	2. *Characteristic pattern of facial anomalies such as short palpebral fissures and premaxillary abnormalities (flat upper lip, flattened philtrum, flat midface);*
	3. *Evidence of growth retardation in at least one of the following: a) low birth weight for gestational age, b) decelerating weight over time not due to nutrition, and c) disproportional low weight to height ratio; and*
	4. *Evidence of CNS (central nervous system) neurodevelopmental abnormailites in at least one of the following: a) decreased cranial size at birth, b) structural brain abnormalities (e.g., microcephaly, cerebellar hypoplasia (a disorder in which the cerebellum is not completely mature at birth), partial or complete agenesis of the corpus callosum (partial or complete absence of this brain structure), or c) neurologic hard signs (physical, concrete evidence of changes in brain structure), or soft signs (e.g., impaired fine motor skills, neurosensory hearing loss, poor tandem gait, or poor hand eye coordination).*
FAS without confirmed maternal alcohol exposure:	*Includes 2, 3, and 4 from above*
Partial FAS with confirmed maternal alcohol exposure:	1. *Confirmed maternal alcohol exposure;*
	2. *Evidence of some components of the pattern of characteristic facial anomalies; Either: 3 or 4 from above; or*
	3. *Evidence of a complex pattern of behaviour or cognitive abnormalities inconsistent with developmental level and cannot be explained by familial background or environment alone.*
Alcohol-related effects	***Alcohol-related birth defects (ARBD):*** *Describes children with characteristic cardiac (heart), skeletal (bone), kidney, ocular (vision), auditory (hearing), or other physical anomalies.*
	Alcohol-related neurodevelopmental disorder (ARND): *Describes children without growth impairments or facial dysmorphology, but who have salient neurodevelopmental deficits. This category requires the presence of evidence of growth retardation and/or CNS neurodevelopmental abnormalities, as described in FAS above. A diagnosis of ARND represents a different, but not necessarily less severe, spectrum of abnormalities than a diagnosis of FAS. A specific psychological and behavioural phenotype unique for ARND has yet to be made clear and the degree of severity of these abnormalities varies considerably.*

by fetal alcohol exposure.

Children prenatally exposed to alcohol may present with severe growth restriction, birth defects, characteristic facial dysmorphology (characteristic abnormal face structure, or "look"), and intellectual disability while other affected children may have normal growth, an absence of alcohol-related facial features, and normal intellect but stable deficits in brain function. Many problems associated with fetal alcohol exposure may be subtle and go undetected, or fall elsewhere on the spectrum.

It is sometimes difficult to pinpoint alcohol exposure as the cause of a child's behaviour or other characteristics. Many of the characteristics seen in FASD are not specific for alcohol toxicity and are often observed in other childhood disorders as well. Moreover, specific psychological markers for FASD have not yet been defined. Finally, the phenotype (observable characteristics of an individual, including physical appearance and/or behaviour) of FASD varies with age as the child moves through childhood into adolescence and adulthood.

The most recent and comprehensive advancement in diagnosis was undertaken by the Institute of Medicine of the National Academy of Sciences Committee to Study Fetal Alcohol Syndrome (Institute of Medicine, 1996) and has been incorporated into the Canadian Guidelines for diagnosis (Chudley et al., 2005). Except for FAS, the confirmation of use of alcohol by mothers during pregnancy is essential for all diagnostic categories listed in Table 2.

Diagnosis issues

Proper diagnosis of FASD requires a medical assessment by a multi-disciplinary team. The assessment should use several sources of information to identify features that might be associated with prenatal alcohol toxicity and those associated with other things. The assessment involves a general physical and neurological examination — including growth, head size, and facial measurements — testing for genetic syndromes, and assessment of mental health disorders or other medical conditions that mimic the clinical presentation of FASD.

Astley and Clarren developed and reviewed a 4-digit Diagnostic Code using data from the Washington State Fetal Alcohol Syndrome Diagnostic and Prevention Network of clinics. The code is made of 4 digits chosen to reflect the severity of expression of the 4 key diagnostic features of FASD: growth deficiency, FAS facial phenotype, central nervous system damage or dysfunction, and gestational exposure to alcohol (Astley, 2004).

Because the vast majority of children do not present with growth or facial dysmorphology, the diagnosis mostly relies on detailed neurocognitive and behavioural assessment. Therefore, newborns who might be suspected of having FASD should be monitored for their developmental progress, and the diagnosis should be finalized as early as neurocognitive tests can be applied.

Two issues that present problems with the diagnosis of FASD are whether the so-called characteristic FAS face shown in Figure 1 is present among all ancestries, and whether such characteristics change with age. A new procedure based on analysis of facial images, called "landmark-based morphometric analysis" has recently addressed these issues. When applied to a mixed ancestry population, this procedure has confirmed that the FAS face is characterized by small palpebral fissures, a thin upper lip and midface hypoplasia, but found that FAS facial anomalies diminish with age (Mutsvanga, Meintjes, Viljoen, & Douglas, 2010). Furthermore, a recent study by Clarren, Chudley, Wong, Friesen, and Brant (2010) determined that, if measured properly, palpebral fissure length among students up to grade 10 does not vary by race, but may by gender and age. (Means and standard deviations from this study are now available in figure form to aid with FASD diagnosis.) Although impaired growth and facial anomalies may normalize and become less apparent with age, enduring brain effects with their corresponding disabilities comprise the hallmark and most unfortunate aspect of fetal alcohol abnormalities.

Screening and Prevention

Maternal alcohol consumption must be determined in order to best counsel women to ensure the safest pregnancy. Screening for alcohol use in women of childbearing age must continue to be routinely discussed between health care professionals and their patients. However, only 62% of professionals who treat women of reproductive age use standardized screening tools (Tough, Clarke, Hicks, & Cook, 2006; Tough, Ediger, Hicks, & Clarke, 2008). For those who drink heavily and are at risk of affecting their baby, gathering information about their alcohol use is crucial in order to create an appropriate intervention to minimize harm and to diagnose babies early on. There is evidence that even brief motivational intervention can have a significant effect on reducing at risk drinking patterns as well as improve practices of effective contraception (Floyd et al., 2007).

Three levels of screening were described by Carson et al. (2010). Level 1 involves motivational interviewing or supportive dialogue used by health care providers to talk to women about alcohol use in practice. A woman-centred approach, using open-ended questions, may be most effective. Level 2 involves the use of structured questionnaires to better specify the pattern and severity of alcohol use. Level 3 involves use of laboratory techniques to confirm the presence/absence of a substance. However, laboratory testing can be costly and may be a delicate issue between the patient and her health care practitioner.

Alcohol is metabolized quickly. Thus, while blood and urine tests can show recent alcohol use, they cannot tell us about longer-term use. However, biological markers can provide factual information about longer-term exposure. For example, compounds called *fatty acid ethyl esters (FAEE)* found in the baby's hair or in the meconium may confirm alcohol use in the second part of pregnancy (Klein, Chan, & Koren, 2002; Koren, Hutson, & Gareri, 2008; Kulaga, Pragst, Fulga, & Koren, 2009). Moreover, recent animal research has explored changes in *gene expression* (changes in concentrations of certain messenger RNAs or protein products encoded by certain genes) in the placenta as potential plausible markers for prenatal maternal alcohol exposure (Rosenberg et al., 2010), although more research is required to determine its applicability in humans. The above mentioned biomarkers, although useful to substantiate exposure, are insufficient to form an FASD diagnosis. Physical and psychological assessments must be performed by experienced professionals prior to diagnosing, considering that even among the children of heavy drinkers, many remain spared from alcohol's teratogenic effects (Sampson et al., 1997).

Primary prevention efforts target the universal level, striving to ensure that society as a whole is aware of the hazards associated with using alcohol, particularly during pregnancy. The choice to refrain from alcohol use prior to and during pregnancy is the goal of primary prevention. Although prevention and treatment of maternal alcohol abuse are difficult and often unsuccessful, effective contraception is a more discernible focus for primary pre-

vention efforts. Health care providers should make asking about alcohol use routine. This will lessen the feeling of being judged on the part of the pregnant women because the questions will not be specific to her pregnancy (Carson, 2010).

Secondary prevention efforts are initiated after heavy alcohol consumption in early pregnancy is recognized. The woman should be informed about the risks posed to her fetus to date and potential risks if alcohol use is continued. Optimal management of alcohol cessation should be emphasized if the woman chooses to continue her pregnancy and, in extreme cases, pregnancy termination may be an option for her consideration. At-risk women should be encouraged to reduce alcohol consumption, and guided to seek prenatal care.

Tertiary prevention efforts focus on early intervention and screening of children with FASD in an attempt to prevent the development of secondary disabilities. These strategies target society at large, cultural and community groups, as well as medical and public health professionals. The pediatrician's involvement in FASD should focus on prevention, early diagnosis, and multidisciplinary care. To date, educational approaches including advertising campaigns, public service announcements, and labels on alcoholic beverages have proven to be inadequate in reducing prenatal alcohol use. More effective plans should use educational strategies as a part of a more comprehensive plan (Gray, 2011).

Interventions for FASD

Increasing attention has been given to screening at-risk children, and developing appropriate management strategies for FASD. Some health care providers have sometimes been reluctant to provide diagnosis of FASD because of the lack of treatment options following diagnosis (Jirikowic, Gelo, & Astley, 2010; Kodituwakku, 2010). The large majority of available tactics have been derived from interventions for other disabilities without appropriate adjustments for the unique needs of children and families affected by prenatal alcohol exposure (Bertrand, 2009). Scientific publications on this topic are scarce; however over the past decade, many efforts have been directed towards developing systematic and scientifically validated interventions.

One of the research projects focused on social skills training based on the child friendship training program (Frankel, 2005), including social network formation, in-home play dates, and conflict avoidance and negotiation, to improve peer friendships for children with FASD (O'Connor et al., 2006). A second intervention investigated the effect of sociocognitive habilitation on improving mathematical abilities of alcohol-affected children by providing short-term intensive individual attention and instruction. Participants who were in the mathematics treatment group performed significantly better than children who received standard psychoeducational interventions (Kable, Coles, & Taddeo, 2007; Coles, Kable, & Taddeo, 2009). A third strategy involved effective teaching of safety skills using computer games involving incremental steps and appropriate feedback (Coles, Strickland, Padgett, & Belmoff, 2007). Children were able to retain and verbally express the knowledge they learned and were able to generalize it to real life situations. Rehearsal training has also been shown to help working memory deficits in children with FASD (Loomes, Rasmussen, Pei, Manji, & Andrew, 2008).

To improve executive functioning in children with FASD, researchers have used components of the Alert Program© (Williams & Shellenberger, 1996), including use of the metaphor of a car engine to describe the concept of self-regulation; for example, children can make their bodies run in high, low, or "just right" gear. As a result, children experienced significant improvement in executive functioning skills (Chasnoff, Well, & Bailey at Children's Research Circle, Chicago, IL, in Bertrand, 2009). A behavioural consultation intervention called Families Moving Forward (FMF) has also been evaluated with respect to improving caregiver self-efficacy, meeting needs of the family and reducing child behaviour issues. The goal of FMF is to modify parental attitudes and responses to their child's behaviour in a "parent-friendly" way. Data suggests a positive re-framing of parenting attitudes and resultant improvement in child behaviours (Olson et al., in Bertrand, 2009).

In sum, children with FASD seem to learn skills best through explicit instruction and do not benefit as much from observational learning. However, the population affected by FASD is highly heterogeneous and interventions for individuals must be developed to correspond each person's characteristics and learning styles (Bertrand, 2009).

The above studies were implemented within community-based services in special education, therapy and counselling and, importantly, included parents as participants and collaborators. However, it remains to be seen if the interventions have long-term effects or if children are able to retain skills and apply them to multiple domains (Bertrand, 2009). Pharmacotherapy for children with FASD also warrants consideration. This is because these children often experience co-existing disorders that may inhibit progress with behavioural interventions (Kodituwakku, 2009). Therefore a combination of pharmacotherapy with behavioural interventions may produce the most effective results.

FASD is not simply a childhood disorder; there is a long-term progression into adulthood in which maladaptive behaviours pose a risk for the development of secondary disabilities. The costs of fetal alcohol abnormalities are extraordinarily high for society as a whole, the education and health care systems, the family, and the individual affected. Health care professionals must be better advocates for children with FASD, helping them to find a support system able to meet their special needs. It is crucial that community health care programs initiate primary prevention efforts, as the effects of alcohol consumption during pregnancy on children are completely preventable.

Summary

Alcohol is in most cases legal and socially acceptable, so it is used on a much larger scale than another other known noxious substances. Alcohol is currently the most widely used substance resulting in fetal malformation and intellectual disability. FASD in a child reflects maternal alcohol use, and it is a permanent condition for which there is no specific treatment. Prenatal exposure to alcohol, even when used in moderate doses, can create a variety of extensive problems.

The cognitive and neurobehavioural impairment in FASD has a wide range of clinical presentations that also can occur with numerous other disorders. It is closely associated with mental health disorders. Potential secondary disability includes various social, behavioural and learning problems. Screening for maternal alcohol abuse and fetal exposure can lead to early diagnosis and early intervention.

There have been significant advances in understanding alcohol's harmful effects, but it is not yet fully clear how the timing of alcohol exposure, socio-economic status, prenatal care, maternal health, genetic susceptibility, and other factors contribute to FASD. The economic costs of FASD are extraordinarily high for society as a whole, for the education and health care systems, and for those individuals affected and their families.

For Further Thought and Discussion

1. To what degree are the criteria for diagnosing FAS, ARBD, and ARND useful?
2. What methods can support the confirmation of alcohol abuse in pregnancy?
3. Review the several risk factors for developing FASD. What preventive measures could be initiated for each?
4. Can a stimulating environment compensate for prenatal damage due to alcohol exposure? What intervention program might you suggest for a child with FAS or ARND?
5. What might constitute an effective public health prevention program for FASD? Whom should such a program target?
6. What should the direction be for future research?

More Resources

Breaking the Cycle
Tel: 416-364-7373

Canadian Centre on Substance Abuse (CCSA)
www.ccsa.ca/fas

FAS Bookshelf Inc.
www.fasbookshelf.com

FAS Link- Fetal Alcohol Disorders Society

www.faslink.org

FAS World Toronto
Tel: 416-264-8222; www.fasworld.com

FASD Connections
www.fasdconnections.ca

FASD Justice
www.fasdjustice.on.ca

FASD Ontario Network of Expertise (FASD ONE)
Email: info@fasdontario.ca; www.fasontario.ca

The FASD Centre for Excellence
www.fasdcenter.samhsa.gov/fasdDb/expertRecomd/cfm

FASD Durham Committee, Resources for Exceptional Children
Tel: 905-427-8862 ext. 346

Healthy Generations Family Support Program
Tel: 807-737-1447; www.clsiouxlookout.com/fasd/htm

Journal of FAS, International
www.motherisk.org/FAS/index.jsp

Layman's Terms of Reference
http://www.janetchristie.ca/docs/terminology.pdf

Motherisk FASD Clinic
Tel: 416-813-7392

Motherisk Alcohol Information Line
Tel: 1-877-FAS-INFO

Toronto FASD Leadership Team, Child Welfare Institute
Tel: 416-924-4640 ext. 2780

References

Abel, E. L. (1995). An update on incidence of FAS: FAS is not an equal opportunity birth defect. *Neurotoxicology and Teratology, 17,* 437-443.

Abel, E. L. (1998). Why fetal alcohol abuse syndrome? In E. L. Abel (Ed.), *Fetal alcohol abuse syndrome* (pp. 7-8). New York: Plenum Press.

Adnams, C. M., Kodituwakku, P. W., Hay, A., Molteno, C. D., Viljoen, D., & May, P. A. (2001). Patterns of cognitive-motor development in children with fetal alcohol syndrome from a community in South Africa. *Alcoholism: Clinical and Experimental Research, 25*(4), 557-562.

Ahmad, N., Flight, F., Singh, V., Poole, N., & Dell, C. A. (2008). *Canadian addiction survey (CAS): Focus on gender.* Ottawa, ON: Health Canada.

Aliyu, M. H., Wilson, R. E., Zoorob, R., Brown, K., Alio, A. P., Clayton, H., & Salihu, H. M. (2009). Prenatal alcohol consumption and fetal growth restriction: Potentiation effect by concomitant smoking. *Nicotine & Tobacco Research, 11*(1), 36-43.

Arzumanyan, A., Anni, H., Rubin, R., & Rubin, E. (2009). Effects of ethanol on mouse embryonic stem cells. *Alcoholism: Clinical and Experimental Research, 33*(12), 2172-2179.

Astley, S. J. (2004). *Diagnostic guide for fetal alcohol spectrum disorders: The 4-digit diagnostic code* (3rd ed.). Seattle, WA: University of Washington Publication Services.

Bertrand, J. (2009). Interventions for children with Fetal Alcohol Spectrum Disorders Research Consortium (2009). Interventions for children with fetal alcohol spectrum disorders (FASDs): Overview of findings for five innovative research projects. *Research in Developmental Disabilities, 30*(5), 986-1006.

Burden, M. J., Jacobson, S.W., & Jacobson, J. L. (2005). Relation of prenatal alcohol exposure to cognitive processing speed and efficiency in childhood. *Alcoholism: Clinical and Experimental Research, 29*, 1473-1483.

Canadian Alcohol Use and Pregnancy Consensus Clinical Guidelines from the Society of Obstetrics and Gynaecology. (2010). *Journal of Obstetrics and Gynaecology Canada, 32*(8) (Suppl. 3), S1-S32. Retrieved from http://www.sogc.org/guidelines/documents/gui245CPG1008E.pdf

Canadian Centre on Substance Abuse. (2004). *Canadian addiction survey: A national survey of Canadians' use of alcohol and other drugs - prevalence of use and related harms.* Ottawa, ON: Author.

Canadian Pediatric Society Statement (CPS). (2002). Fetal alcohol syndrome. *Pediatric Child Health, 7*, 161-174.

Carr, J. L., Agnihotri, S., & Keightley, M. (2010). Sensory processing and adaptive behavior deficits of children across the fetal alcohol spectrum disorder continuum. *Alcoholism: Clinical and Experimental Research, 34*(6), 1022-1032.

Carson, G., Vitale Cox, L., Crane, J., Croteau, P., Graves, L., Kluka, S., et al. (2010). Alcohol use and pregnancy consensus clinical guidelines. *Journal of Obstetrics and Gynaecology Canada, 32*(8 Suppl. 3), S1-S31.

Chudley, A., Conry, J., Cook, J., Loock, C., Rosales, T., & LeBlanc, N. (2005). Public Health Agency of Canada's National Advisory Committee on Fetal Alcohol Spectrum Disorder. Fetal alcohol spectrum disorder: Canadian guideline for diagnosis. *Canadian Medical Association Journal, 172*, S1-S21.

Clark, C. M., Li, D., Conry, J., & Loock, C. (2000). Structural and functional brain integrity of fetal alcohol syndrome in nonretarded cases. *Pediatrics, 105*, 1096-1069.

Clarren, S. K., Chudley, A. E., Wong, L., Friesen, J., & Brant, R. (2010). Normal distribution of palpebral fissure lengths in Canadian school age children. *Canadian Journal of Clinical Pharmacology, 17*(1), e67-78.

Coles, C. D., Kable, J. A., & Taddeo, E. (2009). Math performance and behavior problems in children affected by prenatal alcohol exposure: Intervention and follow-up. *Journal of Developmental and Behavioral Pediatrics, 30*(1), 7-15.

Coles, C. D., Lynch, M. E., Kable, J. A., Johnson, K. C., & Goldstein, F. C. (2010). Verbal and nonverbal memory in adults prenatally exposed to alcohol. *Alcoholism: Clinical and Experimental Research, 34*(5), 897-906. Epub 2010 Mar 3.

Coles, C. D., Platzman, K. A., Lynch, M. E., & Freides, D. (2002). Auditory and visual sustained attention in adolescents prenatally exposed to alcohol. *Alcoholism: Clinical and Experimental Research, 26*(2), 263-271.

Coles, C. D., Strickland, D. C., Padgett, L., & Bellmoff, L. (2007). Games that "work": Using computer games to teach alcohol-affected children about fire and street safety. *Research in Developmental Disabilities, 28*, 518-530.

Connor, P. D., Sampson, P. D., Streissguth, A. P., Bookstein, F. L., & Barr, H. M. (2006). Effects of prenatal alcohol exposure on fine motor coordination and balance: A study of two adult samples. *Neuropsychologia, 44*(5),744-751.

Dalen, K., Bruarøy, S., Wentzel-Larsen, T., & Laegreid, L. M. (2009). Cognitive functioning in children prenatally exposed to alcohol and psychotropic drugs. *Neuropediatrics, 40*(4), 162-167.

Domellöf, E., Rönnqvist, L., Titran, M., Esseily, R., & Fagard, J. (2009). Atypical functional lateralization in children with fetal alcohol syndrome. *Developmental Psychobiology, 51*(8), 696-705.

Ethen, M. K., Ramadhani, R., Scheuerle, A. E., Canfield, M. A., Wyszynski, D. F., Druschel, C. M., & Romitti, P. A. (2009). Alcohol consumption by women before and during pregnancy. *Maternal and Child Health Journal, 13*(2), 274-285.

Fagerlund, A., Heikkinen, S., Autti-Rämö, I., Korkman, M., Timonen, M., Kuusi, T., et al. (2006). Brain metabolic alterations in adolescents and young adults with fetal alcohol spectrum disorders. *Alcoholism: Clinical and Experimental Research, 30*, 2097-2104.

Finer, L. B., & Henshaw, S. K. (2006). Disparities in rates of unintended pregnancy in the United States, 1994 and 2001. *Perspectives on Sexual and Reproductive Health, 38*(2), 90-96.

Floyd, R. L., Sobell, M., Velasquez, M. M., Ingersoll, K., Nettleman, M., & Sobell, L., et al. Project CHOICES Efficacy Study Group. (2007). Preventing alcohol-exposed pregnancies: A randomized controlled trial. *American Journal of Preventive Medicine, 32*(1), 1-10.

Frankel, F. (2005). Parent-assisted children's friendship training. In E. D. Hibbis & P. S. Jensen (Eds.), *Psychosocial treatments for child and adolescent disorders: Empirically based approaches* (pp. 693-715). Washington, DC: American Psychological Association.

Fryer, S. L., McGee, C. L., Matt, G. E., Riley, E. P., & Mattson, S. N. (2007a). Evaluation of psychopathological conditions in children with heavy prenatal alcohol exposure. *Pediatrics, 119*(3), e733-741.

Fryer, S. L., Tapert, S. F., Mattson, S. N., Paulus, M. P., Spadoni, A. D., & Riley, E. P. (2007b). Prenatal alcohol exposure affects frontal-striatal BOLD response during inhibitory control. *Alcoholism: Clinical and Experimental Research, 31*, 1415-1424.

Gladstone, J., Levy, M., Nulman, I., & Koren G. (1997). Characteristics of pregnant women who

engage in binge alcohol consumption. *Canadian Medical Association Journal, 156*, 789-794.

Gladstone, J., Nulman, I., & Koren, G. (1996). Reproductive risks of binge drinking during pregnancy. *Reproductive Toxicology, 10*, 3-13.

Gray, R. (2011). Epidemiology of drug and alcohol use during pregnancy. In P. M. Preece & E. P. Riley (Eds.), *Alcohol, drugs and medication in pregnancy: The long-term outcome for the child* (pp. 11-22). London: Mac Keith Press.

Greenbaum, R. L., Stevens, S. A., Nash, K., Koren, G., & Rovet, J. (2009). Social cognitive and emotion processing abilities of children with fetal alcohol spectrum disorders: A comparison with attention deficit hyperactivity disorder. *Alcoholism: Clinical and Experimental Research, 33*(10), 1656-1670.

Guerri, C., Bazinet, A., & Riley, E. P. (2009). Foetal alcohol spectrum disorders and alterations in brain and behavior. *Alcohol and Alcoholism, 44*(2), 108-114.

Henderson, J., Gray, R., & Brocklehurst, P. (2007a). Systematic review of effects of low-moderate prenatal alcohol exposure on pregnancy outcome. *BJOG, 114*, 243-252.

Henderson, J., Kesmodel, U., & Gray, R. (2007b). Systematic review of the fetal effects of prenatal binge-drinking. *Journal of Epidemiology & Community Health, 61*(12),1069-1073.

Howell, K. K., Lynch, M. E., Platzman, K. A., Smith, G. H., & Coles, C. D. (2006). Prenatal alcohol exposure and ability, academic achievement, and school functioning in adolescence: A longitudinal follow-up. *Journal of Pediatric Psychology, 31*(1), 116-126.

Institute of Medicine. (1996). *Fetal alcohol syndrome: Diagnosis, epidemiology, prevention, and treatment.* Washington, DC: National Academic Press.

Jirikowic, T., Gelo, J., & Astley, S. (2010). Children and youth with fetal alcohol spectrum disorders: Summary of intervention recommendations after clinical diagnosis. *Intellectual and Developmental Disabilities, 48*(5), 330-344.

Jones, K. L., & Smith, D. W. (1973). Recognition of the fetal alcohol syndrome in early infancy. *Lancet, 302*(7836), 999-1001.

Jones, K. L, Smith, D. W., Ulleland, C. H., & Streissguth, A. P. (1973). Pattern of malformation in offspring of chronic alcohol mothers. *Lancet, 1,* 1267-1271.

Kable, J. A., Coles, C. D., & Taddeo, E. (2007). Sociocognitive habilitation using the math interactive learning experience program for alcohol-affected children. *Alcoholism: Clinical and Experimental Research, 22,* 313-320.

Kelly, Y., Sacker, A., Gray, R., Kelly, J., Wolke, D., & Quigley, M. A. (2009). Light drinking in pregnancy, a risk for behavioral problems and cognitive deficits at 3 years of age? *International Journal of Epidemiology, 38*(1), 129-140.

Klein, J., Chan, D., & Koren, G. (2002). Neonatal hair analysis as a biomarker for in utero alcohol exposure. *New England Journal of Medicine, 347(25),* 2086.

Kodituwakku, P. W. (2009). Neurocognitive profile in children with fetal alcohol spectrum disorders. *Developmental Disabilities Research Reviews, 15*(3), 218-224.

Kodituwakku, P. W. (2010). A neurodevelopmental framework for the development of interventions for children with fetal alcohol spectrum disorders. *Alcohol, 44*(7-8), 717-728.

Koren, G., Hutson, J., & Gareri, J. (2008). Novel methods for the detection of drug and alcohol exposure during pregnancy: Implications for maternal and child health. *Clinical Pharmacology & Therapeutics, 83*(4), 631-634.

Korkman, M., Kettunen, S., & Autti-Rämö, I. (2003). Neurocognitive impairment in early adolescence following prenatal alcohol exposure of varying duration. *Child Neuropsychology, 9*(2), 117-128.

Kulaga, V., Pragst, F., Fulga, N., & Koren, G. (2009). Hair analysis of fatty acid ethyl esters in the detection of excessive drinking in the context of fetal alcohol spectrum disorders. *Therapeutic Drug Monitoring, 31*(2), 261-266.

Lee, K. T., Mattson, S. N., & Riley, E. P. (2004). Classifying children with heavy prenatal alcohol exposure using measures of attention. *Journal of the International Neuropsychological Society, 10,* 271-277.

Lemoine, P., Harousseau, H., Borteyru, J. P., & Menuet, J. C. (1968). Les enfants des parents alcoholiques: Anomalies observes a propos de 127-cas. *Ouest Medical* (Paris), *21,* 476-482.

Loomes, C., Rasmussen, C., Pei, J., Manji, S., & Andrew, G. (2008). The effect of rehearsal training on working memory span of children with fetal alcohol spectrum disorder. *Research in Developmental Disabilities, 29,* 113-124.

Mattson, S. N., Calarco, K. E., & Lang, A. R. (2006). Focused and shifting attention in children .with heavy prenatal alcohol exposure. *Neuropsychology, 20*(3), 361-369.

Mattson, S. N., Riley, E. P., Gramling, L., Delis, D. C., & Jones, K. L. (1998). Neuropsychological comparison of alcohol-exposed children with or without physical features of fetal alcohol syndrome. *Neuropsychology, 12,* 146-153.

Mattson, S. N., & Roebuck, T. M. (2002). Acquisition and retention of verbal and nonverbal information in children with heavy prenatal alcohol exposure. *Alcoholism: Clinical and Experimental Research, 26*(6), 875-882.

May, P. A., Gossage, J. P., Kalberg, W. O., Robinson, L. K., Manning, M., & Hoyme, H. E. (2009). Prevalence and epidemiologic characteristics of FASD from various research methods with an emphasis on recent in-school studies. *Developmental Disabilities Research Reviews, 15*(3), 176-192.

Miller, M. W. (2007). Exposure to ethanol during gastrulation alters somatosensory-motor cortices and the underlying white matter in the macaque. *Cerebral Cortex, 17*(12), 2961-2971.

Mooney, S. M., & Miller, M. W. (2007). Time-specific effects of ethanol exposure on cranial nerve nuclei: Gastrulation and neuronogenesis. *Experimental Neurology, 205*(1), 56-63.

Mutsvangwa, T. E., Meintjes, E. M., Viljoen, D. L., & Douglas, T. S. (2010). Morphometric analysis and classification of the facial phenotype associated with fetal alcohol syndrome in 5- and 12-year-old children. *American Journal of Medical Genetics Part A, 152A*(1), 32-41.

Nash, K., Rovet, J., Greenbaum, R., Fantus, E., Nulman, I., & Koren, G. (2006). Identifying the behavioral phenotype in fetal alcohol spectrum disorder:

Sensitivity, specificity and screening potential. *Archives of Women's Mental Health, 9,* 181-186.

National Institute of Alcohol Abuse and Alcoholism (NIAAA). (Dec 19, 2003). *State of the science report on the effects of moderate drinking.* Retrieved from http://pubs.niaaa.nih.gov/publications/ModerateDrinking-03.htm

Nulman, I., Rovet, J., Kennedy, D., Wasson, C., Gladstone, J., Fried, S., & Koren, G. (2004). Binge alcohol consumption by non-alcohol-dependent women during pregnancy affects child behaviour, but not general intellectual functioning: A prospective controlled study. *Archives of Women's Mental Health, 7*(3), 173-181.

O'Connor, M. J., Frankel, F., Whaley, S., Schonfeld, A. M., Carpenter, E., Laugeson, E. A., et al. (2006). A controlled social skills training for children with fetal alcohol spectrum disorders. *Journal of Consulting and Clinical Psychology, 74*(4), 630-648.

O'Connor, M. J., Shah, B., Whaley, S., Cronin, P., Gunderson, B., & Graham, J. (2002). Psychiatric illness in a clinical sample of children with prenatal alcohol exposure. *The American Journal of Drug and Alcohol Abuse, 28*(4), 743-754.

O'Connor, M. H., Sigman, M., & Kasari, C. (1992). Attachment behaviour of infants exposed prenatally to alcohol: Mediating effects of infant affect and mother-infant interaction. *Development and Psychopathology, 4,* 243-256.

O'Leary, C. M., Nassar, N., Kurinczuk, J. J., & Bower, C. (2009). The effect of maternal alcohol consumption on fetal growth and preterm birth. *BJOG, 116*(3), 390-400.

O'Leary, C. M., Nassar, N., Kurinczuk, J. J., de Klerk, N., & Geelhoed, E. (2010). Prenatal alcohol exposure and risk of birth defects. *Pediatrics, 126*(4), e843-e850.

Olson, H. C., Streissguth, A. P., Sampson, P. D., Barr, H. M., Bookstein, F. L., & Thiede, K. (1997). Association of prenatal alcohol exposure with behavioral and learning problems in early adolescence. *Journal of the American Academy of Child & Adolescent Psychiatry, 36*(9), 1187-1194.

Olsen, J., Pereira, A., Da, C., & Olsen, S. F. (1991). Does maternal tobacco smoking modify the effect of alcohol on fetal growth? *American Journal of Public Health, 81,* 69-73.

Public Health Agency of Canada. (2005). *Awareness of the effects of alcohol use during pregnancy and fetal alcohol syndrome.* Results of a National Survey. Retrieved from http://www.phac-aspc.gc.ca/publicat/fas-saf-natsurv-2000/index-eng.php

Public Health Agency of Canada. (2008). *Canadian perinatal health report.* Retrieved from http://www.phac-aspc.gc.ca/rhs-ssg/pdf/survey-eng.pdf

Public Health Agency of Canada. (2009). *What mothers say: The Canadian maternity experiences survey.* Retrieved from http://www.publichealth.gc.ca/mes

Rasmussen, C. (2005). Executive functioning and working memory in fetal alcohol spectrum disorder. *Alcoholism: Clinical and Experimental Research, 29,* 1359-1367.

Rasmussen, C., Andrew, G., Zwaigenbaum, L., & Tough, S. (2008a). Neurobehavioral outcomes of children with fetal alcohol spectrum disorders: A Canadian perspective. *Paediatrics & Child Health, 13*(3), 185-191.

Rasmussen, C., Talwar, V., Loomes, C., & Andrew, G. (2008b). Brief report: Lie-telling in children with fetal alcohol spectrum disorder. *Journal of Pediatric Psychology, 33*(2), 220-225.

Roberts, G., & Nanson, J. (2000). *Best practices: Fetal alcohol syndrome/fetal alcohol effects and the effects of other substance use during pregnancy.* Canada's Drug Strategy Division, Health Canada.

Robinson, M., Oddy, W. H., McLean, N. J., Jacoby, P., Pennell, C. E., De Klerk, N. H., et al. (2010). Low-moderate prenatal alcohol exposure and risk to child behavioral development: A a prospective cohort study. *BJOG, 117*(9), 1139-1150. Epub 2010 May 28.

Rodriguez, A., Olsen, J., Kotimaa, A. J., Kaakinen, M., Moilanen, I., Henriksen. T. B., et al. (2009). Is prenatal alcohol exposure related to inattention and hyperactivity symptoms in children? Disentangling the effects of social adversity. *Evidence Based Mental Health, 10*(4), 98-100.

Rosenberg, M. J., Wolff, C. R., El-Emawy, A., Staples, M. C., Perrone-Bizzozero, N. I., & Savage, D. D. (2010). Effects of moderate drinking during pregnancy on placental gene expression. *Alcohol,*

44(7-8), 673-690.

Sampson, P. D., Streissguth, A. P., Bookstein, F. L., Little, R. E., Clarren, S. K., Dehaene, P., Hanson, J. W., & Graham, J. M. (1997). Incidence of fetal alcohol syndrome and prevalence of alcohol-related neurodevelopmental disorder. *Teratology, 56*, 317-326.

Sarkar, M., Burnett, M., Carriere, S., Cox, L., Dell, C. A., Gammon, H., et al. (2009). Screening and recording of alcohol use among women of childbearing age and pregnant women. *Canadian Journal of Clinical Pharmacology, 16*(1), e242-e263.

Sayal, K., Heron, J., & Golding, J. (2007). Prenatal alcohol exposure and gender differences in childhood mental health problems: A longitudinal population-based study. *Pediatrics, 119*(2), e426-434.

Schonfeld, A. M., Mattson, S. N., & Riley, E. P. (2005). Moral maturity and delinquency after prenatal alcohol exposure. *Journal on Studies of Alcohol & Drugs, 66*(4), 545-554.

Shor, S., Nulman, I., Kulaga, V., & Koren, G. (2010). Heavy in utero ethanol exposure is associated with the use of other drugs of abuse in a high-risk population. *Alcohol, 44*(7-8), 623-627.

Sood, B., Delaney-Black, V., Covington, C., Nordstrom-Klee, B., Ager, J., Templin, T. et al. (2001). Prenatal alcohol exposure and childhood behavior at age 6 to 7 years. A dose-response effect. *Pediatrics, 108*(2), e34.

Sowell, E. R., Jernigan, T. L., Mattson, S. N., Riley, E. P., Sobel, D. F., & Jones, K. L. (1996). Abnormal development of the cerebellar vermis in children prenatally exposed to alcohol: Size reduction in lobules I-V. *Alcoholism: Clinical and Experimental Research, 20*, 31-34.

Sowell, E. R., Leow, A. D., Bookheimer, S. Y., Smith, L. M., O'Connor, M. J., Kan, E., et al. (2010). Differentiating prenatal exposure to methamphetamine and alcohol versus alcohol and not methamphetamine using tensor-based brain morphometry and discriminant analysis. *The Journal of Neuroscience, 30*(11), 3876-3885.

Spadoni, A. D., McGee, C. L., Fryer, S. L., & Riley, E. P. (2007) Neuroimaging and fetal alcohol spectrum disorders. *Neuroscience & Biobehavioral Reviews, 31*(2), 239-245.

Spohr, H. L., Willms, J., & Steinhausen, H. C. (2007). Fetal alcohol spectrum disorders in young adulthood. *Journal of Pediatrics, 150*, 175-179.

Stade, B., Ali, A., Bennett, D., Campbell, D., Johnston, M., Lens, C., Tran, S., & Koren. G. (2009). The burden of prenatal exposure to alcohol: Revised measurement of cost. *Canadian Journal of Clinical Pharmacology, 16*(1), e91-e102.

Stade, B. C., Stevens, B., Ungar, W. J., Beyene, J., & Koren, G. (2006). Health-related quality of life of Canadian children and youth prenatally exposed to alcohol. *Health and Quality of Life Outcomes, 4*, 81.

Staroselsky, A., Fantus, E., Sussman, R., Sandor, P., Koren, G., & Nulman, I. (2009). Both parental psychopathology and prenatal maternal alcohol dependency can predict the behavioral phenotype in children. *Paediatric Drugs, 11*(1), 22-25.

Strandberg-Larsen, K., Grønboek, M., Andersen, A. M., Andersen, P. K., & Olsen, J. (2009). Alcohol drinking pattern during pregnancy and risk of infant mortality. *Epidemiology, 20*(6), 884-891.

Streissguth, A. P., Bookstein, F. L., & Barr, H. M. (1996a). A dose-response study of the enduring effects of prenatal alcohol exposure: Birth to 14 years. In H. Spohn & H. Steinhausen (Eds.), *Alcohol, pregnancy and the developing child* (pp. 141-168). Cambridge, UK: Cambridge University Press.

Streissguth, A. P., Bookstein, F. L., Barr, H. M., Sampson, P. D., O'Malley, K., & Young, J. K. (2004). Risk factors for adverse life outcomes in fetal alcohol syndrome and fetal alcohol effects. *Journal of Developmental & Behavioral Pediatrics, 25*(4), 228-238.

Streissguth, A. P., Bookstein, F. L., Sampson, P. D., & Barr, H. M. (1996b). *The enduring effects of prenatal alcohol exposure on child development.* Ann Arbor, MI: University of Michigan Press.

Streissguth, A. P., & O'Malley, K. (2000). Neuropsychiatric implications and long-term consequences of fetal alcohol spectrum disorders. *Seminars in Clinical Neuropsychology, 5*, 177-190.

Sulik, K. K. (2005). Genesis of alcohol-induced craniofacial dimorphism. *Experimental Biology & Medicine, 230*, 366-275.

Sulik, K. K., Johnston, M. C., Draft, P. A, Russel, W.

E., & Dehart, D. B. (1986). Fetal alcohol syndrome and DiGeorge DB: Critical ethanol exposure periods for craniofacial malformation as illustrated in an animal model. *American Journal of Medical Genetics, 2,* 97-112.

Suzuki, K. (2007). Neuropathology of developmental abnormalities. *Brain Development, 29,* 129-141.

Todorow, M., Moore, T. E., & Koren, G. (2010). Investigating the effects of low to moderate levels of prenatal alcohol exposure on child behavior: A critical review. *Journal of Population Therapeutics & Clinical Pharmacology, 17*(2), e323-e330.

Tough, S. C., Clarke, M., Hicks, M., & Cook. J (2006). Pre-conception practices among family physicians and obstetrician-gynaecologists: Results from a national survey. *Journal of Obstetrics & Gynaecology Canada, 28*(9), 780-788.

Tough, S. C., Ediger, K., Hicks, M., & Clarke, M. (2008). Rural-urban differences in provider practice related to preconception counselling and fetal alcohol spectrum disorders. *Canadian Journal of Rural Medicine, 13*(4), 180-188.

Williams, M. S., & Shellenberger, S. (1996). *How does the engine run? A leader's guide to the Alert Program.* Albuquerque, NM: Therapy Works, Inc.

Zieman, M. (2009). *Overview of contraception.* Retrieved from http://www.uptodate.com/home/index.html

19

Fetal Alcohol Spectrum Disorder Part II: Challenges in Adulthood

Valerie Temple, Leeping Tao, and Trudy Clifford

What you will learn:

- How FASD is diagnosed
- Intellectual abilities of people with FASD
- Mental health challenges faced by adults with FASD
- Treatment and support of adults with FASD

Children with Fetal Alcohol Spectrum Disorder (FASD) eventually grow to become adults with FASD, and adults with FASD often have very different types of challenges compared to children. This chapter will focus on issues in adulthood for individuals with FASD. It will discuss diagnosis, treatment, and the support of adult individuals with this disorder.

Diagnosis of FASD in Adults

FASD is a "categorical" term that describes a group of disorders that can occur if an individual is exposed to alcohol before birth. The Canadian Guidelines (Chudley et al., 2005) outline all of the possible

diagnoses in this category, including Fetal Alcohol Syndrome (FAS), Partial Fetal Alcohol Syndrome (pFAS), Alcohol Related Birth Defects (ARBD), and Alcohol Related Neuro-developmental Disorder (ARND).

There are currently four parameters considered when making a diagnosis within the Fetal Alcohol Spectrum. The presence and severity of the four parameters will determine if a diagnosis is given, and which one is given. The parameters are:

- *exposure* to alcohol before birth, or how much and how often the mother drank during pregnancy
- *physical growth deficits* such as low birth weight

or failure to gain weight and/or height after birth

- *specific facial features* of FAS including small eyes, a flat mid-face, a poorly developed philtrum (the two lines that run from the nose to the upper lip on the face), and a thin upper lip
- *central nervous system damage or brain dysfunction* including directly observable indicators of brain dysfunction such as seizures, microcephaly (small head circumference) or damage seen on brain imaging scans (e.g., CT scans, MRI); brain dysfunction may also be inferred through functional testing such as neurological, psychological, speech-language, and occupational therapy assessment

Individuals with exposure to alcohol, significant physical growth deficits, all the facial features, and significant CNS damage meet criteria for full FAS. Individuals with partial symptoms may receive diagnoses of pFAS, ARBD, or ARND.

At present, diagnostic criteria for adults and children are the same, but a number of substantial challenges to diagnosing adults have been encountered (Chudley, Kilgour, Cranston, & Edwards, 2007). These include changes in, or the complete disappearance of, specific FAS facial features as an individual grows up; "catch-up growth" or normalization in physical height and weight during adolescence and adulthood; and difficulties with obtaining information about alcohol exposure before birth because it is distant in time and memory for family members or because of estrangement from the family due to foster care or adoption. Spohr, Wilms, and Steinhausen (2007) found in their follow-up study of 37 individuals with FASD 20 years after diagnosis that many of the physical features of FASD documented in childhood had disappeared in the individuals they re-assessed. They noted significant gains in height, weight, and head circumference for the sample as a whole, and reported that most individuals now fell within the average range for these measurements. As well, facial features such as smaller than normal eyes had diminished across the group. This means that an individual who met criteria for full FAS in childhood, with the facial features and growth deficits, might not

meet these criteria in adulthood. The authors noted, however, that brain dysfunction and intellectual deficits remained constant throughout the lifespan.

The issue of obtaining information regarding maternal alcohol consumption during pregnancy is difficult for individuals of all ages. However, it is especially problematic in adult diagnosis. For adults, it is at least 18 years since the pregnancy took place and gaining information about alcohol consumption during a particular 9 month period that long ago is challenging at best. Mothers and other family members are often unavailable to report their activities, or even may be deceased. At times, it is possible to obtain medical or other records documenting exposure, but the information is typically limited in terms of details. This makes it very difficult to establish if there has been alcohol exposure and exactly how much exposure has occurred.

For individuals with obvious physical and facial features or substantial intellectual deficits early in life, a diagnosis of FAS in childhood is more likely. However, for those with less obvious symptoms, it could be late adolescence or adulthood before a diagnosis is reached. In some cases, FASD may be strongly suspected, but a diagnosis cannot be assigned because the maternal drinking history is not available. As is the case for many disorders, early diagnosis and intervention generally leads to better outcomes. This means that individuals with FASD who are not recognized early in life and provided with appropriate supports may have greater challenges and develop more problems relative to those with an early diagnosis. Nevertheless, adults with suspected FASD may benefit from the same treatment and supports offered to adults with a diagnosis of FASD.

Intellectual and Functional Abilities in Adults with FASD

Adults with FASD can have a wide range of abilities and deficits. Some present with a global developmental disability (DD) while others function within the borderline or even average range of intelligence, with more limited areas of disability. Level of alcohol exposure, timing of the exposure, and pre-existing genetic factors (e.g., intelligence levels of the parents) can all affect an individual's outcome in FASD (Kodituwakku, 2007). A person who is exposed to heavy alcohol consumption across the entire pregnancy, for example, may have a very different outcome than someone exposed to drinking in the early stages of pregnancy only.

The environment and experiences of an adult with FASD also work to shape his or her profile of intellectual strengths and weaknesses. As is true for everyone, life experiences influence ability and achievement. Both adverse and enriching life events can alter and impact brain development, as the vast literature on brain plasticity has documented (Doidge, 2007). Although environmental factors are also important for children with FASD, the effect is likely magnified in adults due to the greater period of time passed.

Because of the variable intellectual presentation of individuals with FASD, a set of deficits specific to FASD has been hard to identify. A common finding in the assessment of adults with FASD, however, is the existence of what is called a "scattered profile." This means a set of scores on functional testing characterized by large peaks and valleys of ability. This is different from the smaller variability in scores typically seen in other people. Adults with FASD, for example, may have arithmetic skills at the primary school level along with reading skills at the high school level; or age-appropriate (average range) ability to recognize things but severe deficits (DD range) in the ability to recall things (Kodituwakku, 2007).

Individuals with a scattered profile of abilities often present a special challenge to their families and care providers. This is because they may appear to be stubborn or oppositional if they do not perform at an age-appropriate level across different situations. For example, an individual with FASD may have average long-term memory skills but severe deficits in short-term memory. This would mean the person could recall what happened many weeks ago, but not the day before. It might therefore appear to care providers, who do not know about the deficit, that the individual chooses not to give complete or correct information about events the day before or that they are being evasive, when in fact they are simply unable to give it. This is just one possible example, but the general situation of mistaking inability for unwillingness is a common problem for this group.

Executive functioning and daily living skills

Despite the varying levels of ability and scattered profiles commonly seen in adults with FASD, there are at least two areas where deficits almost always exist. These are executive functioning and daily living skills (Chudley et al., 2007; Rasmussen, McAuley, & Andrew, 2007; Streissguth et al., 2004). Executive functioning is a group of abilities that involves managing, controlling, and organizing one's own actions and behaviour. Executive functioning skills include planning and organizing; modulating emotional reactions; initiating activities; attention and focus; and impulse control. Considering all these skills together, it is easy to see how an individual with deficits in these areas would have difficulties functioning as an adult. Because the activities of children are often controlled and managed by their parents or caregivers, executive functioning deficits may be less obvious or more easily managed in a child. An adult, however, is expected to self-direct most or all aspects of his or her own life, and individuals with executive functioning deficits are less able to do this.

Research in this area has suggested that deficits in executive functioning become more pronounced as an individual with FASD ages (Rasmussen et al., 2007). Studies of adults with FASD have shown that problems with anger management, impulse control, and social interaction are very common. This can lead to problems with the legal system, difficulties holding a job, and loss of residential placement (Streissguth et al., 1994; Tao, Temple, Clifford, & Shewfelt, 2010). Diagnoses such as Oppositional Defiant Disorder, Conduct Disorder, and Anti-Social Personality Disorder are also common in adults with FASD and are likely related to these difficulties with executive functioning skills.

Another important area of deficit for adults with FASD is daily living skills (Streissguth et al., 2010). Daily living skills refers to the ability to perform everyday tasks. It includes activities such as personal hygiene, domestic chores, using public transit, shopping for groceries, and using banking services.

Box 1: Case Study

At 20 years of age, Melissa was referred for FASD assessment by the Children's Aid Society (CAS). The CAS could only support Melissa up until 21 years of age and they were requesting services within the adult developmental sector to assist for the future. Melissa was born full term and weighed 5lbs 2oz. Her mother drank heavily throughout the pregnancy and also smoked cigarettes. Melissa was a small, frail child who had difficulty gaining weight. At 6 years of age, the CAS became involved with her family due to allegations by school personnel that she was being neglected and physically abused at home.

By 8 years of age, Melissa was removed from her mother's home and put into a series of foster home placements. Each placement began well but would break down after a short period and Melissa would attempt to run away and go back to her mother. By 15 years of age, Melissa was made a Crown Ward and had been diagnosed with Attention Deficit-Hyperactive Disorder, Depression, Oppositional Defiant Disorder, and Attachment Disorder. Teachers and caregivers believed Melissa was an intelligent but stubborn child who could do better if she would only try harder. At 16 years of age, Melissa was hospitalized for substance abuse problems and a suicide attempt. She became pregnant at 18 years of age but the child was apprehended by the CAS shortly after birth. Also around the same time, her mother died from complications related to liver disease and Melissa became profoundly depressed by these two serious losses in her life.

An FASD assessment found that Melissa met criteria for ARND. Her psychological testing found a scattered profile of skills with some abilities in the Mild range of DD, some in the Borderline range and some in the Low Average range. Following the assessment, Melissa received counselling services to address her bereavement issues, a supported housing placement, and financial assistance from the Ontario Disability Support Program. Her support workers learned that many of the problems they had previously attributed to stubbornness and oppositional behaviour were actually due to her disability. This led them to view her in a different light and provide more support, which in turn led to less problem behaviour.

Adults with FASD frequently have very low skills in this area regardless of their level of intellectual ability. Temple et al. (in press) compared overall daily living skills scores for a group of individuals with FASD to a group without FASD matched on IQ scores. They found that the FASD group had lower daily living skills scores than the non-FASD group with the same IQs. This means that the FASD group had more problems "applying" their intelligence on a daily basis than other people with DD. It is possible this is because of their greater problems with planning and organizing, which in turn influences the ability to follow through on many types of activities.

Mental Health Problems Associated with FASD

Adults with FASD are at very high risk for mental health problems. In the developmental literature, individuals with DD and a mental health problem are referred to as having a dual diagnosis. While indi-

viduals with DD as a general group have a high rate of dual diagnosis, in the range of 14%-67% (Bradley & Summers, 2003), adults with FASD have been reported to have rates in the range of 85% to 90% (Streissguth et al., 1994; Tao et al., 2010). Some common mental health challenges for adults with FASD include mood disorders such as depression, attention deficit disorders (e.g., ADHD), anxiety disorders, and personality disorders (Barr et al., 2006; Tao et al., 2010). Adults with FASD are also at high risk for problems such as abusing substances and suicide attempts (Streissguth et al., 2004; Tao et al., 2010).

Environmental stressors and adverse life events are also very common for adults with FASD, and arguably these are important in the development of later mental health problems. Streissguth (2008) reported, from her longitudinal study, that 67% of their sample of individuals with FASD had been the victims of sexual/physical abuse or domestic violence. As well, 80% were not raised by their biological parents, suggesting a high level of disrupted family experiences. As adolescents or adults, 46% had drug or alcohol problems of their own, and by adulthood 35% had spent time in jail (Streissguth et al., 2004). Interestingly, in the longitudinal study by Spohr et al. (2007), which was conducted in Germany, there were far fewer negative environmental events in childhood and adolescences reported. This suggests that cultural factors, such as access to healthcare and the availability of community supports, may be important to positive or negative outcomes for this group.

Interventions and Supports

Adults with FASD can benefit from a variety of interventions and supports. One critical area is assistance around organizing and structuring activities. Given their very poor daily living skills and executive functioning deficits, adults with FASD are generally in need of someone to organize and direct activities in their lives. For example, they may require someone to accompany them to appointments in the community, set schedules, plan events, or assist with managing their money. This may be done by a family member, a paid support worker such as an Adult Protective Services Worker, or group-home staff. In the FASD literature, this role is sometimes referred to as being the "external brain" for the person with FASD.

Another important support issue is case management. At present, there are very few community resources specifically for adults with FASD. Generic supports for individuals in the DD sector may not always be suitable for this group due to their high levels of mental health problems and unique challenges such as substance abuse. As well, many DD sector services require a diagnosis of global intellectual disability (e.g., IQ below 70) but, given the broad range of scatter common in the intellectual scores of adults with FASD, they may not qualify for DD services. Case managers can help by advocating for and finding structured and adapted work environments, residential supports, and appropriate leisure activities for adults with FASD.

Counselling services can also be helpful for this group. As adults with FASD have frequently experienced abuse, neglect and/or trauma, counselling aimed at reducing symptoms of stress, increasing self-esteem, and teaching self-regulation strategies can be very useful. Counselling techniques aimed at reducing impulsivity and behavioural problems, however, are generally less effective. Because of difficulties with managing time and organizing, it is important to make accommodations in providing counselling services to people with FASD. Ideally, appointments should be set at the same time every week or bi-weekly. Also, it may be helpful, with the permission of the individual, to involve caregivers in counselling sessions in order to gain information about problems occurring in the individual's life that they may have difficulty articulating as well as to help them to arrive at appointments on schedule.

Another intervention that has proven effective with this group is behaviour therapy. Although traditional "learning theory," which may focus on the consequences of an individual's actions, is less helpful for adults with FASD (Malbin, 2005), interventions aimed at modifying the environment to provide greater support and structure have been found useful. Role modelling, using visual cues, and using scheduling aids to improve organization, are some examples of effective supports.

Although adults with FASD have very high rates of mental health issues, at present there is very little information available regarding how well medications can help manage various mental health symptoms (Doig, McLennan, & Gibbard, 2008). Because of their unique etiology, the presentation of mental health problems in adults with FASD may be different from other individuals. At least one study, however, has reported that pharmacological interventions can provide additional support for symptom management in the very common condition of ADHD.

Summary

Adults with FASD present with a complex array of challenges. As a group, they often come from difficult family environments, and many are adopted or placed in foster care. A large number have been physically or sexually assaulted at some time in their lives, and as adults they have a very high rate of dual diagnosis, substance use, and mental health problems. Diagnosis of FASD in adulthood has many challenges, including the fact that they may "grow out" of some of the key indicators of FASD such as facial features and weight/height deficits. Functional assessment often finds these individuals have a scattered profile of intellectual abilities along with substantial deficits in executive functioning and daily living skills. These and other deficits lead to the need for a high level of support around personal care, gaining employment, managing money, and living in the community. Case management, counselling, and behaviour therapy services are some of the important interventions that can be helpful for adults with FASD. Although pharmacological interventions may help for some co-existing conditions (e.g., ADHD), research about the use of medications for adults with FASD is very limited at this time.

For Further Thought and Discussion

1. What additional challenges do you think you might encounter when treating adults with FASD as compared to children?
2. When individuals require a high degree of support and structure in their lives, ethical issues can arise for care providers (e.g., family members, professionals, and case workers). What do you think could be some of the ethical issues encountered when "managing" someone else's life? Discuss with reference to the concept of "Dignity of Risk."

More Resources

Websites:

Canadian Centre on Substance Abuse
Research and information on substance abuse issues and FASD.
www.ccsa.ca

FASD and the Justice System
Information on FASD decisions in the Canadian courts, educational materials for legal personnel, research articles on legal issues in FASD.

http://fasdjustice.on.ca

FASD Center for Excellence, Health and Human Services (U.S.A. Government)
Education material for FASD; "grab and go" fact sheets; Powerpoint training programs.
www.fasdcenter.samhsa.gov

FASD-ONE (Fetal Alcohol Spectrum Disorders-Ontario Network of Expertise)
Offers a list of diagnostic clinics across the province as well as links to agencies and resources about FASD.
www.fasdontario.ca

Public Health Agency of Canada, Canadian FASD Initiatives
Information on Canadian research, statistics, policy, across the country.
www.phac-aspc.gc.ca/fasd-etcaf/index-eng.php

Books:

Fuchs, D., McKay, S., & Brown, I. (Eds.) (2011). *Awakening the spirit: Voices from the prairies.* Regina, SK: Canadian Plains Research Centre Press. Available from *www.cecw-cepb.ca*

McKay, S., Fuchs, D., & Brown, I. (Eds.) (2009). *A Passion for action in child welfare: Voices from the Prairies.* University of Regina, Regina, SK: Canadian Plains Research Centre Press. Available from *www.cecw-cepb.ca*

References

Barr, H. M., Bookstein, F. L., O'Malley, K., 'Connor, P. D., Huggins, J. E., & Streissguth, A. P. (2006). Binge drinking during pregnancy as a predictor of psychiatric disorders on the structured Clinical Interview for DSM-IV in young adult offspring. *American Journal of Psychiatry, 163*, 1061-1065.

Bradley, E. & Summers, J. (2003). Developmental disability and behavioural, emotional, and psychiatric disturbances. In I. Brown & M. Percy (Eds.), *Developmental disabilities in Ontario* (2nd ed.) (pp. 751-771). Toronto, ON: Ontario Association on Developmental Disabilities.

Chudley, A. E., Conry, J., Cook, J. L., Loock, C., Rosales, T., & & LeBlanc, N. (2005). Fetal alcohol spectrum disorder: Canadian guidelines for diagnosis. *Canadian Medical Association Journal, 172,* S1-S21.

Chudley, A. E., Kilgour A. R., Cranston, M., & Edwards, M. (2007). Challenges of diagnosis in fetal alcohol syndrome and fetal alcohol spectrum disorder in the adult. *American Journal of Medical Genetics, Part C, 145C,* 261-272.

Doidge, N. (2007). *The brain that changes itself.* New York: Penguin Books.

Doig, J., McLennan, J. D., & Gibbard, W. B. (2008). Medication effects on symptoms of Attention-Deficit/Hyperactivity Disorder in children with Fetal Alcohol Spectrum Disorder. *Journal of Child and Adolescent Psychopharmacology, 18*(4) 365-371.

Kodituwakku, P. W. (2007). Defining the behavioral phenotype in children with fetal alcohol spectrum disorders: A review. *Neuroscience and Biobehavioral Reviews, 31,* 192-201.

Malbin, D. (2005). FASD and standard interventions: Poor fits? *British Columbia Teachers Federation-Alternative Education Association* Newsletter, Summer 2005.

Rasmussen, C., McAuley, R., & Andrew, G. (2007). Parental rating of children with Fetal Alcohol Spectrum Disorder on the Behavior Rating Inventory of Executive Functioning (BRIEF). *Journal of FAS International, 5,* e2, 1-8.

Spohr, H. L, Willms, J., & Steinhausen, H. C. (2007). Fetal alcohol spectrum disorders in young adulthood. *Journal of Pediatrics, 150,* 175-179.

Streissguth, A. P., Aase, J. M., Clarren, S. K., Randels, S. P., LaDue, R. A., & Smith, D. F. (2010). Fetal Alcohol Syndrome in adolescents and adults. *Journal of the American Medical Association, 265,* 1961-1967.

Streissguth, A. P. (2008). *FASD and secondary effects: Longitudinal study conducted.* Retrieved from www.faseout.ca/

Streissguth, A. P., Bookstein F. L., Barr, H. M., Sampson, P. D., O'Malley, K., & Kogan Young, J. (2004). Risk factors for adverse life outcomes in fetal alcohol syndrome and fetal alcohol effects. *Developmental and Behavioral Pediatrics, 25*(4), 228-237.

Streissguth, A. P., Sampson, P. D., Carmichael

Olson, H., Bookstein F. L., Barr, H. M. Scott, M., Felman, J., & Mirsky A. F. (1994). Maternal drinking during pregnancy: Attention and short-term memory in 14 year old offspring—A longitudinal study. *Alcoholism: Clinical and Experimental Research, 18*(1), 202-218.

Temple, V. K., Shewfelt, L., Tao, L. Casati, J., & Klevnick, L. (in press). Comparing daily living skills in adults with fetal alcohol spectrum disorder to an IQ matched clinical sample. *Journal of Population Therapeutics and Clinical Pharmacology.*

Tao, L., Temple, V. K., Shewfelt, L., & Clifford, T. (2010). *Ontario's first FASD diagnostic clinic for adults.* Presented at Adolescents and Adults with FASD Facing the Future together: Where Do We Go From Here? Vancouver, B.C.

20

Children with HIV and Their Families

Rebecca Renwick, Robyn Salter, Susan King, and Stanley Read

What you will learn:

- HIV as a cause of developmental delay and disabilities in children
- Some basic facts about HIV and children
- Assessment and major interventions
- Issues for families of children with HIV
- Confidentiality and disclosure issues

In this chapter you will also meet and learn more about Miriam, a child who has HIV, and about her family. Their experiences and circumstances will be used to illustrate some of the important ideas being discussed.

In 1982, the first children known to have HIV (human immunodeficiency virus) were identified (King, Lindegren, & Rogers, 2003; Oxtoby, 1994). Worldwide, there continue to be increasing numbers of children with HIV. In resource-rich countries, where HIV medications are affordable and available, programs to decrease mother-to-child transmission of HIV have successfully reduced the number of new HIV infections in children. However, for those children who have HIV infection, one of the most significant symptoms is developmental delay (Brouwers, Walters, & Civitello, 1998). Without proper treatment, between 75% and 90% of children with HIV will have some level of developmental

delay or disabilities (Belman et al., 1988) In fact, the first signs of HIV infection in children may be those that affect the development of the child's central nervous system (i.e., regression of milestones, developmental delay).

When a child has HIV, important family issues, as well as social, community, and societal issues, can dramatically affect the child's health, well-being, and quality of life. For example, families are faced with decisions about whether they should tell their child's diagnosis to anyone (e.g., the child's siblings, their own friends, their relatives, the child's school staff or daycare providers, the parent's employer). Some service providers may be fearful about working with a child who has HIV. Many people in the family's community (e.g., their landlords, their children's schoolmates), and in their society generally, may have misinformation about the causes of HIV and how it is transmitted. They may behave in ways that

Box 1: Major Symptoms of HIV Infection in Children

A child with HIV may have symptoms that include:

- *recurring diarrhea*
- *recurring fevers*
- *thrush*
- *feeding problems*
- *poor growth*
- *respiratory problems*
- *pain*
- *neurological problems (see Box 2)*
- *stunted physical growth (e.g., height, head circumference)*
- *inability to achieve normal weight for height*

Sources: American Academy of Paediatrics (2003); American Dietetic Association (2010); Health Canada (1998).

show their fear and negative attitudes towards children with HIV and their families. For these reasons, children who have HIV infection and their families could encounter some difficult and complex problems in the course of their daily lives.

Miriam, age 4 years, was diagnosed with HIV infection one year ago. She lives with her mother (Deborah), father (Michael), brother (Peter) who is 9 years old, and sister (Sarah) who is 15 months old.

HIV: The Basics

It is important to understand what HIV is and how it affects a child's health and development.

What are HIV and AIDS?

HIV (human immunodeficiency virus) causes a chronic infection that weakens and ultimately destroys the immune system. When the immune system is healthy, it can usually fight off infections and diseases. The child's immune system may deteriorate quickly or over a much longer period. As the immune system deteriorates, the child may more easily get *opportunistic infections*, that is, other infections made possible by a weakened immune system, and some forms of cancer (Kaiser & Rasminsky, 1995).

The later and final stages of HIV infection have been referred to as *AIDS (Acquired Immune Deficiency syndrome)* (Kaiser & Rasminsky, 1995). However, the term AIDS is not as commonly used among health professionals now. Instead, they distinguish between differences in the disease process mainly by referring to the CD4 levels present in the child's immune system and by measuring the amount of virus in the blood or *viral load*.

After HIV has entered the child's blood, it attaches to *CD4 cells* (cells that usually fight infection). Then the virus reproduces and starts to destroy the CD4 cells. As more CD4 cells are destroyed, the child's immune system becomes weaker. Levels of CD4 cells in the blood can be measured and these levels indicate how weak or strong the immune system is. As CD4 levels (or counts) become low, the child typically begins to have certain symptoms (American Academy of Paediatrics, 2003, 2009). The child is then said to have HIV-related *symptoms*. When a child tests positive for HIV, but does not have a very low CD4 count or any medical problems caused by HIV, he or she is said to be asymptomatic. That is, the child does not have evident HIV-related symptoms.

Symptoms and problems associated with HIV infection

The most common symptoms of HIV infection appear in Box 1. Feeding may be a problem due to swallowing difficulties, nausea, or loss of appetite. Recurring diarrhea may also lead to poor absorption of food. These feeding problems may contribute to malnutrition and poor growth. Problems with the respiratory (breathing) system can include recurring sinus and ear infections, thrush (yeast infection of the mouth), or pneumonia. Recurring fevers due to infections are common. There may also be pain (e.g., in bones or joints; due to inflammation or infection) that ranges from mild to severe (American Academy of Paediatrics, 2003; Burchett & Pizzo, 2003).

Before good *antiretroviral medications* (drugs that control HIV but cannot cure it) were available, 50% to 90% of children with HIV infection eventually developed symptoms and problems with their neurological system (i.e., brain and spinal cord) (see Box 2). Now that these medications are avail-

Box 2: Brain and Spinal Cord Symptoms of HIV in Children

Symptoms of HIV affecting the child's brain and spinal cord include:

- *delayed development*
- *loss of developmental milestones attained earlier*
- *cognitive delays*
- *memory problems*
- *problems with attention (e.g., distractibility)*
- *language impairment (i.e., producing, comprehending language)*
- *motor problems (e.g., muscle tone, walking and mobility, coordination)*
- *behavioural problems (e.g., depressed mood, irritability, impulsiveness)*
- *problems with social skills*

Source: Health Canada (1998).

able, this rate has been reduced. Still, these neurological problems can become obvious as soon as two months after birth or as late as 10 or 15 years of age (American Academy of Paediatrics, 2003; Burchett & Pizzo, 2003).

Miriam's full diagnosis is HIV with symptoms. When she was diagnosed, she was already nearly 3 years old and had been having frequent fevers and diarrhea. She was short for her age and underweight. She had just started walking and could say very few words.

How is HIV Infection Transmitted to Children?

The most common way children contract HIV infection is through mother-to-child transmission, also called vertical or perinatal transmission to prevent "blame" towards mothers. In the United States, 91% of children with HIV infection and nearly all children newly infected have acquired the disease by perinatal transmission. Perinatal means "around the time of birth." The perinatal period technically refers to the period from 28 weeks of pregnancy/gestation to the 28th day following birth (American Academy

of Paediatrics, 2003; Burchett & Pizzo, 2003; Centers for Disease Control, 2002; King et al., 2003; Public Health Agency of Canada, 2010). Children may acquire the virus during their mother's pregnancy, during delivery, or from their mother's breast milk. In adults, the most common forms of transmission are through unprotected sex with someone who has the virus, and sharing needles for intravenous drug use (Health Canada, 2003; King et al., 2003).

In the 1990s, a significant proportion of the children who were HIV-positive had been infected through transfusion. However, transfusion is no longer a source of transmission in resource-rich countries. For example, in Canada and U.S.A., the chance of transmission through transfusion is about one in a million because, since 1985, all blood products have been screened for the presence of HIV infection (King et al., 2003). Sexual abuse by a person who has HIV infection is also a possible, but much less commonly reported, form of transmission to children (Centers for Disease Control, 2002, 2010; King et al., 2003; National Institutes of Health, 2004; National Institute of Allergy and Infectious Disease, 2011; World Health Organization, 2011) (see Box 3).

All babies born to mothers with HIV will have antibodies from their mothers, which can be detected for up to 18 months. Therefore, during this time, these babies will test positive for HIV by the standard antibody tests. But most of these children will not actually have the virus itself. Without antiretroviral therapy for the HIV+ pregnant woman, about 14% to 25% of HIV-exposed babies will be infected. However, with today's therapy, this rate may be reduced to as low as 1%.

In an HIV infected baby, a clear HIV diagnosis can be made within 3 to 6 months after birth (American Academy of Paediatrics & Committee on Paediatric AIDS, 2004) by special blood tests that identify the presence of the virus itself. Therefore, HIV testing should be routinely offered during pregnancy, so that all women who test HIV-positive can have access to HIV therapy to improve their own health and reduce the risk of transmission of HIV to their babies (Tuomala et al., 2005).

During Deborah's pregnancy with Sarah, (Miriam's younger sister), the family doctor suggested HIV testing

Box 3: Ways HIV is Transmitted to Infants and Pre-Adolescent Children

Mother-to-child transmission:

- *during pregnancy*
- *during birth*
- *through breastfeeding*

Sexual abuse

Shared medical equipment (only in resource-poor countries)*

Blood and blood products (only in resource-poor countries) *

Sources: Chanock (2006); King et al. (2003).
* This information may be important with respect to recent immigrants to Canada who originate from resource-poor countries.

Box 4: Ways to Reduce Risk of HIV Transmission from Mothers to Babies

- *use antiretroviral medications during pregnancy and delivery, and for the newborn baby*
- *selectively use Caesarean section for delivering babies*
- *no breastfeeding in countries where baby formula is available*

Sources: American Academy of Paediatrics (2002); Havens et al. (2009); King et al. (2003).

for Deborah because of a new policy of recommending HIV testing for all pregnant women. (If a woman is pregnant it means she has had unprotected sex, which is a potential source of HIV infection and other sexually transmitted infections). Deborah accepted the recommendation that she be tested even though she had not previously thought that she could be HIV positive. But she did test positive. Then the family doctor arranged for all other members of the family to be tested too. Miriam and her father, Michael, also tested positive for HIV infection. The presence of HIV infection explained Miriam's physical symptoms and developmental delay.

Miriam became infected with HIV through mother-to-child transmission during pregnancy, or during delivery, or from her mother's breast milk.

Deborah's HIV diagnosis during the pregnancy with Sarah was cause for concern, not just for herself, but for her unborn baby. She accepted her doctor's recommendation to begin taking anti-HIV medications to reduce the chances of the baby getting HIV from her. The medications and other precautions (see Box 4) reduced the risk of Sarah contracting HIV infection from 25% to 1%. Sarah tested negative for HIV by the time she was 6 months old.

How could Deborah and Michael have become HIV positive? Neither had experienced any symptoms.

They had never had a blood transfusion or used street drugs requiring needles. They discussed this question and thought that Michael had probably been infected first, through sexual contact with a previous partner, and that Deborah became infected through sexual contact with Michael. Deborah did not know if she was HIV positive when she was pregnant with her oldest child, Peter. But, fortunately, Peter's HIV test results were negative.

Some people have misinformation or not enough information about how HIV infection is transmitted. Box 3 summarizes how HIV is transmitted to children, and Box 4 shows important ways to reduce the risk of mother-to-child transmission. Box 5 indicates ways some people believe it may be transmitted but, in fact, are not ways the virus is passed from the child to another person or vice versa. Box 6 summarizes major ways HIV is transmitted to adolescents and adults.

How Common is HIV Infection in Children?

Numbers of people with HIV-infection vary considerably from one country to another. For example, in Canada, up to December 2008, there have been 64,335 individuals reported to be HIV-positive, with 5,571 being children under 15 years (Health Canada, 2010. In the U.S.A., up to December 2007, it was estimated that 1,054,00 individuals were infected, with 9,590 being children under 13 years (CDC, 2010). The actual number of children with HIV infection in Canada or in Ontario is not really known. Statistics

Box 5: Dispelling Some Myths: Ways HIV is NOT Transmitted

- *hugging, touching, bathing, or kissing the child*
- *sharing household activities, facilities, and objects with the child (e.g., toilet, comb, eating utensils, bed)**
- *contact in the child's normal living, school/daycare, play activities*
- *insect and animal bites*
- *bites by humans (e.g., other children at school/daycare) if no exposure to blood results*

Sources: American Academy of Paediatrics (2003); Chanock (1999, 2006).
* Sharing of toothbrush and razor is discouraged.

Box 6: Ways HIV Can Be Transmitted to Adolescents and Adults

- *unprotected sexual intercourse (vaginal and anal)*
- *sharing sex toys*
- *sharing needles/equipment for injecting drugs or steroids*
- *blood and blood products*

Sources: Health Canada (2003, 2010); King et al. (2003); Samples, Goodman, & Woods (1998).

that are available give only numbers of children identified as having the virus. These statistics may constitute an underestimate because some women of childbearing age and children who have the virus may not have been tested for HIV infection and, thus, would not be included in such statistics.

HIV infection is a global pandemic. As of December 2008, estimates were that approximately 33.4 million people worldwide are living with HIV infection or AIDS, including 2.1 million children under 15 years of age. Most of these children are living in countries of sub-Saharan Africa and South Asia (UNAIDS, 2010). While there are effective prevention and treatment programs for pregnant women and for children in economically well-developed countries (e.g., Canada, U.S.A., and Europe), in resource-poor countries the lack of such programs is critical and HIV/AIDS continues to be a major cause of death in children (De Cock, Fowler, Mercier et al., 2000, cited in King et al., 2003).

In Canada, in the last few years, new medications have reduced illness and death for children with HIV. Consequently, Canadian families with children who have HIV now have fewer issues related to developmental delay and other symptoms of HIV than was previously the case. However, for service providers, it is important to know that there may be differences between resource-rich and resource-poor countries. In resource-rich countries, like Canada, we have medications to treat HIV but, in resource-poor countries, medications may not be available or affordable. Newcomers to Canada may not know about the hopeful treatments available here and, if they are infected with HIV, they may have more health problems. Like many Canadians, they may not have accurate information about how HIV is transmitted and they may be very fearful of the stigma and potential discrimination associated with HIV. Thus, they will likely not want to tell anyone about having HIV in their family. The example of Miriam and her family used throughout this chapter reflects these issues for families arriving from resource-poor countries.

Assessment

Assessment is particularly important because it can identify areas of difficulty, as well as strengths, related to the child and his/her family's health and quality of life. Repeated medical assessments are necessary for HIV positive children, whether or not they have symptoms, in order to detect and address any health problems as early as possible. Early treatment is most effective for treating and preventing symptoms of HIV or reducing their severity (American Academy of Paediatrics, 2003).

Regular assessment of physical growth (e.g., height and appropriate weight for height) is also important for ongoing identification of nutritional needs. In addition, nutritional assessment can address the child's specific dietary needs (e.g., particular foods, frequency and patterns of eating, and getting appropriate nutrients and enough calories) (American Dietetic Association, 2010; American Dietetic Association & Dieticians of Canada, 2000; Health Canada, 1998).

Repeated psychological assessments are also needed because of the high risk of developmental delays and disabilities for children with HIV. This kind of assessment focusses on the child's psychological functions such as intelligence, language, memory and learning, attention, concept formation, perception, and motor functions, as well as behaviour and personality (Blanchette, Smith, Fernandez-Penney, King, & Read, 2001; Brouwers et al., 1998).

Other kinds of assessments are very important for many children with HIV, especially those who have developmental delays. For example, occupational therapy assessment can identify specific daily or regular life activities (e.g., feeding/eating skills, personal care, play, learning, attending school, social activities) that are difficult for the child and his/her family or caregivers. Any difficulties identified can then be addressed to help improve both the child's ability to participate in usual daily activities and his/her enjoyment of life (Cameron et al., 2009). Physical and social aspects of the environment can also be identified and then modified to make life activities easier for the child. Physical obstacles to getting around, not enough practical help or emotional support from others are examples of aspects of the child's environment that could be improved. Physical therapy assessment can pinpoint specific needs related to muscular strength, coordination, and exercise (Cameron et al., 2009). Psychosocial assessment for the child and family is also important (Giannattasio et al., 2011; Shindler & Tangelder, 2010; Wiener, Septimus, & Grady, 1998). It can highlight the child's and the family's strengths as well as areas where supports, resources, and services could help the child and family cope better and improve their quality of life.

When Miriam was diagnosed with HIV infection, her family doctor referred her to the HIV program at a large, regional children's hospital. Miriam and her parents met with the program's paediatric specialist doctor, nurse, and social worker. They also met the other members of the team: the nutritionist, the *occupational therapist, the physical therapist, and the psychologist. The team members assessed Miriam and her family's situation so that they could recommend interventions that would be most helpful. Their focus was on Miriam's health but they also worked with both parents to make sure that infected family members had the best health care available and that the emotional and social needs of all family members were as well supported as possible. For example, they discussed Peter's (the oldest child) emotional state and how his parents could support him. They also assessed Sarah, the youngest child, and enrolled her in a program that would follow her growth and development in order to determine whether there were any effects of exposure to the anti-HIV medications Miriam took during her pregnancy with Sarah to reduce the risk of HIV being transmitted to her baby.*

Intervention

Several kinds of interventions are available for children with HIV. Some interventions are outlined here and summarized in Box 7.

Drug therapy (treatment with prescribed medications) is an area where rapid developments have taken place. Currently, most children receive a combination of medications that are effective in controlling HIV infection, but cannot cure it (Mueller, Kline, & Pizzo, 1998; Havens, Mofenson, & the Committee on Pediatric AIDS, 2009). Immunizations are also given to prevent other infections (e.g., flu vaccine to prevent influenza).

With early diagnosis and effective treatment, developmental, learning and physical problems in children related to their HIV infection are uncommon. There are still a few children who are diagnosed late and may have already developed complications (e.g., some children who have recently arrived from resource-poor countries where access to treatment is limited). Also, there are some older children who were diagnosed before optimal treatment was available.

Interventions that are carried out by therapists and other professionals include treatments and services that deal with physical and cognitive functioning and address educational, psychological, social, and

Box 7: Major Interventions for Children with HIV and Their Families

Several or all of these may be used as interventions for children with HIV and their families:

- *medications*
- *nutritional counselling/therapy*
- *nutritional supplements and/or special diet or foods*
- *feeding/swallowing strategies*
- *exercise/activities (to increase/enhance mobility, and physical strength, endurance, coordination)*
- *equipment and assistive devices*
- *facilitating activities of daily life*
- *environmental modification (physical and social aspects)*
- *education for child and family*
- *counselling (regarding adaptation to living with HIV and how it affects family relationships and mental health, as well as psychological, spiritual, legal, and financial issues)*
- *linking family and/or child to community supports/resources keeping in mind the stigma of HIV and who needs to know and does not need to know about HIV in the family*
- *future care planning for children whose parents are HIV-positive*

Sources: American Dietetic Association (2010); American Dietetic Association and Dieticians of Canada (2000); Antle, Wells, Salter Goldie, De Matteo & King (2001); Cameron, et al. (2009); Health Canada (1998).

community issues. For example, sensory stimulation strategies (e.g., use of textured materials, sounds, and moving toys for stimulating and activating the child's senses of touch, hearing, and vision) can be helpful for children who are slow to reach developmental milestones (Health Canada, 1998).

Helpful equipment and environmental modifications (e.g., ramps, wheelchair, adapted seating, bath seat, getting someone to assist the child) can also be provided so that the child can participate in daily activities. Children with muscle weakness and coordination problems can receive help to do specific exercises and use positioning to improve their motor functioning (e.g., strength, endurance, and coordination). Strategies for making swallowing food easier and/or special foods or diets are also recommended for some children (American Dietetic Association, 2010; American Dietetic Association & Dieticians of Canada, 2000; Health Canada, 1998).

Children and families often need more information and education about HIV and coping with it. They receive general information about HIV, but they also get information that is tailored to their own particular needs, including ways of coping with HIV and its impact on their lives: stressful situations related to their own HIV and to coping with their child's HIV, taking care of their child's special needs, decisions about telling others about their child's HIV, and the effects of HIV on family relationships (Margolese, 2009; Salter et al., 2007; Salter Goldie, DeMatteo, Wells, Aykroyd, & King, 2000; Wiener, Septimus, & Grady, 1998). They can also be linked with helpful community resources and supports (e.g., support groups as well as professionals and organizations that will provide practical help, information, and emotional support). Counselling is also a common intervention for these families who are struggling with a variety of serious, and often sensitive, issues (Havens et al., 2009). See the next two sections, which outline some of these issues. One or more types of counselling may be appropriate for a particular child and his/her family (e.g., psychological, family, mental health, spiritual, legal, and financial issues and issues of living with HIV).

If one or both parents also have HIV, future planning for their child's care, with the help of a professional or self-help group, can be very important. For example, parents who have HIV themselves may want to have information about how to choose a guardian who will assume responsibility for their children should the parent(s) become very ill or die (Antle et al., 2001). Although, in resource-rich countries, HIV is no longer a terminal illness and is now considered a chronic illness, parents with HIV may still think and worry about what the future holds for them and their children. Therefore, they may want some advice, assistance, and emotional support as they go through the process of selecting a guardian and making the appropriate legal arrangements. Because of advances in treatment for HIV infection, these future planning issues may be more relevant for people living in resource-poor countries than for those living in countries where there is ready access to treatment.

Based on the results of the team's assessments, Miriam began to take medications for HIV that helped her symptoms. She also started to eat special foods that her body could absorb more easily, so she began to develop and grow at a much better rate. However, she still had developmental delay.

Family Issues

Families of children with HIV are likely to be faced with some complex issues and difficulties. Parents may be experiencing extreme stress that results from several problems (e.g., health, finances, coping with their circumstances, or refugee and immigration issues). They often experience guilt, regardless of how HIV was transmitted to their child, as well as anger and depression (Shandor Miles, Gillespie, & Holditch-Davis, 2001; Wiener et al., 1998). In addition, they are trying to cope with their child's illness and the uncertainty of their future.

For parents who have HIV themselves, the ability to provide for their children in the future may be a serious concern, or they may worry that it will become a problem (see the previous section). In some families, one or both parents may be misusing drugs. These problems are often associated with employment and financial difficulties.

Parents are also faced with the difficult decisions associated with whether, how much, and when to tell their children, close relatives, friends, and others as well as reasons for such disclosures (Gerson et al., 2001; Nehring, Lashley, & Malm, 2000; Salter et al., 2007). They are often concerned about disclosure due to the stigmatization that may result for their family (Salter et al., 2007). Because they often do not do so, or delay telling for long periods of time, they may become socially isolated (Wiener et al., 1998). This lack of disclosure to those who could offer help and support often means that parents take total responsibility for the care of their child while bearing "the additional burden of keeping the truth to themselves" (Wiener et al., p. 813). Such secrecy may negatively affect their children with, and without, HIV infection who often know, at some level, that there is something worrying their parents and think that they are responsible for causing that worry. Consequently, their children may also experience heightened anxiety and depression (Shindler & Tangelder, 2010). Professional assessment of children's understanding of their illness may be useful, since such understanding may be influenced by developmental level more than age. This kind of assessment can be helpful to parents so that they can be more informed about what and when to tell their child (Salter et al., 2007; Wiener & Figueroa, 1998).

Siblings are almost always emotionally affected when their sisters, brothers, parent, or both parents are HIV-positive. Not telling others within the family or outside of it about their family member's HIV status may be stressful for children. They may be anxious about the health and/or the possible death of their affected sibling and/or parent (Wiener & Figueroa, 1998).

Miriam's parents were devastated about their own HIV diagnoses, as well as by Miriam's diagnosis. They were very worried about getting ill themselves and about what would happen to all of them, including Peter. They also felt guilty about getting HIV and about HIV being transmitted to Miriam. HIV changed their lives completely. They had to cope with strong emotional reactions as well as getting medical treatment for themselves and for Miriam. They also had to learn about how the virus and treatment work, and how to deal with all of these changes in their lives. On top of it all, they had to decide who to tell, and who not to tell, about it. At first, they decided not to tell anyone except their health care providers. Although Peter was mature enough to be told, they were not ready to tell him. But Peter knew something was wrong and often worried about his family. During counselling, the doctor, nurses, and social worker in the children's HIV clinic helped both parents to make decisions about their priorities and to learn how to cope with living with HIV.

Stigma of HIV Infection: Social and Community Issues

One of the most damaging aspects of HIV for individuals and families is the stigma that others in their community and society may associate with the illness. Stigma means that a person is seen as unworthy, disgraced, or discredited due to something about him or her that makes the person noticeably different from others (i.e., us without HIV and them with HIV) (Fielden, Chapman, & Cadell, 2010; Goffman, 1963; Letteney & Heft LaPorte, 2004). Historically, certain diseases and disorders (e.g., epilepsy, mental illness, leprosy, and syphilis), and visible physical disabilities have resulted in stigmatization of the people who have such differences. Then, and to some extent now, people tend to actively avoid, devalue, and discriminate against others who are stigmatized due to their disease, disorder, or disability. Currently, many people in our society understand HIV and accept those who have it. But others remain fearful and consider HIV to be a "punishment from God" or something a person "deserves" because of his or her own (or a parent's) behaviour or lifestyle. Such misconceptions, combined with a lack of knowledge about HIV and its transmission, may help to promote negative attitudes and behaviour towards people with HIV, including children who are especially vulnerable (Fielden et al., 2010; Letteney & Heft LaPorte, 2004).

Children with HIV and their families often fear negative consequences because of the stigma attached to the infection (Antle et al., 2001; Lee & Rotheram-Borus, 2001; Letteney & Heft LaPorte, 2004; Shindler & Tangelder, 2010). Their fear may make them want to hide the real nature of their child's illness. It may also cause them to isolate themselves from others from whom they want to hide the truth, even when those others could potentially offer help and support to the family (Burr & Emery, 1994; Salter Goldie et al., 2000; Wiener & Figueroa, 1998; Wiener et al.,1998).

At a community or societal level, public education campaigns about HIV can be a form of intervention. Information to the public is usually promoted in various ways (e.g., television, videos, newspapers, billboards, brochures, in classrooms). The purpose of such campaigns is to help prevent HIV transmission, to encourage people to be tested and receive early treatment if they test positive, and to reduce the stigma attached to HIV.

Deborah, Michael and Peter came to Canada as refugees from an endemic country when Deborah was pregnant with Miriam. During a war in their country of origin, they had been through very difficult experiences that still affected them. They had been accepted as refugees and are applying for permanent resident status, but they still worry that their HIV status could affect their immigration application. They know that if they had to return to their country of origin, HIV medications would not be available. There is also real potential for discrimination if anyone found out about their HIV. The social worker in the HIV program referred them to a special immigration lawyer who was aware of these difficult issues and will help them through the immigration process.

Deborah and Michael decided not to tell any of their family members in their country of origin about their HIV. They had two main reasons for their decision. First, they did not want to bring shame on themselves and their families. Second, they were afraid of being rejected by their families or being discriminated against because of the terrible fear associated with the disease in resource-poor countries, including their own country of origin. These are very real concerns for Deborah and Michael because of their perceptions about how society in their country of origin deals with such issues.

Box 8: Standard/Routine Practices for Preventing Transmission of Infection for Use with Children in Out-of-Home Care

Situations Requiring Precautions:

- *diapering*
- *contact with body fluids (urine, feces, vomit, exudate from wounds)*
- *contact with blood*
- *contact with body fluids containing visible blood*
- *contact with broken skin*

Practices:

- *wash Hands*
  - *before contact with any child*
  - *immediately after contact with the child*
  - *after removing latex gloves*
- *use warm, running water*
- *use soap or waterless antiseptic hand rinse*
- *selected use of gloves*
  - *use disposable latex gloves for exposures to blood and body fluids with visible blood*
  - *change gloves before and after contact with each child in this situation*
  - *use gloves to clean blood and other fluids from surfaces using a bleach solution*
  - *dispose of gloves and blood-stained materials (e.g., linens) in separate, waterproof bag (e.g., plastic)*

Sources: American Academy of Paediatrics (1999, 2003); Centers for Disease Control (2002, 2010); Chanock (1999, 2006); Health Canada (1999).

Routine/Standard Practices: Prevention of Transmission

The adoption of routine or standard practices associated with prevention of transmission of infections, including HIV, represents another approach to reducing stigma and discrimination towards people with HIV. *Standard or routine practices* are standards of practice guided by the principle that taking precautions to prevent HIV transmission only when dealing with children (or adults) who are known to have HIV or may be infected is inappropriate and discriminatory. Using these routine or standard practices is a more inclusive approach because procedures and practices to prevent any kind of communicable, infectious disease — not just HIV infection — are used with everyone in a particular setting (e.g., school, daycare facility, a community clinic, or

hospital) (American Academy of Paediatrics, 1999, 2003; Chanock, 1999, 2006; Health Canada, 1999). Communicable diseases are any infections or diseases that can be spread from one person to another. Box 8 summarizes some standard or routine prevention and infection control procedures that are commonly used.

Children with HIV must be able to attend school and daycare in regular settings and be able to participate in all activities there, as permitted by their health and treatment procedures (American Academy of Paediatrics, 1999; Chanock, 2006; King, 2004). The kinds of contact that typically take place in school and daycare settings do not result in transmission of HIV infection when there is no exposure to blood (American Academy of Paediatrics & Committee on Paediatric AIDS, 2004; Chanock, 2006). The use of routine or standard prevention and infection control practices noted in Box 8 further reduces the risk of transmission.

Deborah and Michael decided to enrol Miriam in a daycare program that accommodates children with and without developmental delay. The daycare centre Miriam attends uses standard/routine practices with all of the children who participate in its programs. All of the daycare centre staff have been thoroughly trained in these practices and the use of these practices is monitored on an ongoing basis.

Confidentiality and Disclosure

Professionals and families face some complex ethical and legal dilemmas concerning how to share or communicate information about HIV infection. Some of the major issues relevant to these dilemmas are confidentiality and disclosure, which are discussed in the two following sections.

Confidentiality issues

Confidentiality is essential for the development of trust between the child, his/her parents and their service providers. Confidentiality refers to the responsibility a professional has not to disclose information that has been obtained as a result of the client-professional relationship. However, this information is often shared with others at the same institution or agency who are providing services to the same child and family. If an agency or institution has this approach or policy with respect to confidentiality, the parents should be told during their first meeting with the service provider. In order for a service provider to be able to offer support, the parents, child, and family must perceive that their confidentiality is respected. Thus, when a service provider shares information with others outside the agency or institution who are also currently providing services to the family, the parents' permission must be obtained first.

Miriam's parents were very concerned about keeping their daughter's diagnosis confidential. As they became more familiar with the professionals providing services to Miriam and their family, they developed more trust as well as a deeper understanding of what confidentiality means. They began to realize that staff members communicated with others, such as their family doc- *tor to co-ordinate Miriam's health care. They learned that no information could be shared with their doctor or other professionals outside the hospital without their permission. This is a good time to mention that Miriam's family is not an actual family. Their story is made up from general experiences of families who a have a child with HIV. We could not use real names and details because, to preserve confidentiality, this kind of information cannot be published.*

In Ontario, there is an obligation to report occurrences of communicable diseases, including HIV infection, to public health. This procedure has been put in place to make sure that everyone in the family and other identified contacts are tested and receive education about how to prevent HIV infection from being transmitted to anyone else.

Disclosure: some guidelines

The important issue of decisions about disclosure has been referred to several times in this chapter. Whether, to whom, when, what, and how much to tell are extremely difficult decisions for families to make. Telling children with HIV infection and their siblings about the HIV diagnosis is an especially sensitive area of communication within families. These decisions are often influenced by the family's circumstances, level of acceptance of HIV, and coping styles among family members, the parents' need to protect their children with HIV infection and their uninfected siblings, and the child's age and cognitive functioning (Gerson et al., 2001; Lee & Rotheram-Borus, 2002; Letteney & Heft LaPorte, 2004; Nehring et al., 2000; Salter et al., 2007). In addition, the degree of trust shared by family members is an important factor (De Matteo et al., 2002). Parents frequently worry that if their children know about HIV in the family, they may tell someone else and bring problems (e.g., stigma, discrimination) to the family (Antle et al., 2001; Salter et al., 2007).

To assist children with HIV and their families in dealing with these issues, some service providers and facilities have developed formal policies concerning disclosure. Good policies are based on principles such as: a) disclosure is a process that unfolds over time rather than occurring as a single conversation (Nehring et al., 2000); b) professionals and parents are

Box 9: Some Important DOs and DON'Ts For Child Care Service Providers

- *DO respect the parents' right to tell or not tell others about their child's HIV.*
- *DO respect the family's values and choices about who to tell or not to tell about the child's HIV.*
- *DO show understanding and support for parents and families.*
- *DON'T tell anyone about the child's HIV without his/her parents' permission.*
- *DON'T talk to children about HIV without their parents' permission.*

partners in the children's care and can work together to assess children's needs for health information and decide the best way and time to tell children and help them understand and cope with this information; c) the parents' and child's needs may sometimes differ; and d) people from different cultures may have some differing beliefs and values that guide their behaviour and decisions (Salter et al., 2007).

If a child should learn about his/her own diagnosis in an unplanned way, it is recommended that a professional team assess the needs of the family (including the child, the parents, and siblings, as appropriate). Then they will address questions, concerns, and needs that family members may have (DeMatteo et al., 2002). Some DOs and DON'Ts for service providers concerning disclosure issues are shown in Box 9.

With the help of the HIV program staff at the hospital, Peter's parents decided to tell him and Miriam that Miriam has a problem with her blood and this is why she had to take pills and see her doctor every month. They also decided to tell Peter that they (his parents) take medications for a blood problem, too. The children had already seen them taking medications, so they felt it was important to acknowledge this and answer Peter's questions honestly, without saying HIV. They felt that if the children did not hear the HIV words, they would be less likely to worry or to tell other people.

As Peter and Miriam get older, they will need more

information about health and family issues related to HIV. Their parents will be the decision-makers about when and what they will be told. The HIV program staff members will work with them and help them with these decisions, if Michael and Deborah wish them to do so. The parents and health service providers can form a partnership based on respect and support for the family and their style of coping with this complex process of talking with their children about these very difficult issues.

Deborah and Michael are very sure that they want to prevent the stigma associated with HIV from hurting their children, so they decided not to tell any of their friends or anyone who knew the children. They knew they had the right not to tell anyone and the HIV program staff gave them support while and after they made their decisions. The staff knew that there was no risk of anyone getting HIV from Miriam at school or anywhere else.

Help for Children and Their Families

In Ontario and elsewhere in Canada,, information about HIV testing, referrals for treatment, and support services, as well as many other kinds of information are available from HIV/AIDS service organizations. Staff at these organizations are usually very knowledgeable about local medical and support services. They are also very aware of confidentiality issues.

Children and parents can be tested for HIV by their family physicians and in many other places. In Ontario, there are numerous centres for anonymous HIV testing (see the SickKids' Motherisk website at *http://www.motherisk.org/women/hivAnonymous. jsp* for a listing). The term anonymous means that only the physician who undertakes the test knows the identity of the person being tested. If children test positive, they can be referred to specialized programs that are available in many areas as well as to individual paediatricians.

There are also many other resources and organizations in Ontario, Canada, the U.S.A. and around the world that can be accessed via the Worldwide Web/ Internet. Some websites providing such lists and links appear near the end of this chapter.

Summary

This chapter has provided a broad overview of HIV in children, a very complex topic. It has discussed HIV as a potential cause of developmental delay and disabilities in children. Some basic information has been provided about HIV in children, how common it is in children, and how it is usually transmitted. Common forms of assessment and intervention have been outlined as well. The adoption of standard or routine procedures to prevent transmission of infection in settings such as schools, daycare facilities, and hospitals and the reasons for their use were emphasized.

For several reasons, a diagnosis of HIV for children also seriously affects their parents and siblings as well as their family relationships. For example, the mother is likely to be HIV-positive, and possibly the father too. In addition, the child's siblings are usually aware that their parents are very worried about health issues, even if they have not yet been told about the diagnosis. HIV can also be stigmatizing to those who have acquired it and their families, so that they often do not want to tell others anything about it. Thus, the chapter outlined some relevant family, community, and societal issues, including stigma, as well as several important issues about confidentiality and disclosure.

The chapter concludes with some general information about testing, treatment, services, and sources of help and support for children with HIV and their families. Finally, some other helpful resources, such as books for adults and children and HIV websites and organizations are listed at the end of this chapter.

Acknowledgement

Sadly, our colleague, Dr. Susan King, passed away in 2009. Dr. King was a respected and renowned clinician and researcher in the area of infectious diseases, in particular, HIV in children. She co-authored and contributed significantly to the content of the chapters on HIV, Children, and Families that appeared in the first and second editions of this book. The current chapter incorporates many of her important contributions to those earlier versions.

For Further Thought and Discussion

1. You are a service provider working with Miriam at the daycare centre she attends. You suspect that she has HIV. What would you do?
2. If you were Miriam's parents, would you tell anyone about having HIV in the family? Who would you feel comfortable to tell? How would you know, if you did tell anyone, whether they would support you and whether they would tell anyone else?
3. Have you ever tried to keep an important secret? What do you think it would be like living with the secret of HIV in the family? How would you explain why you were taking your child to the doctor so often? (Why you are so concerned about using universal precautions? Why you might be so worried or tired?)
4. How do you think the HIV diagnosis changed the lives of Deborah, Michael, Peter, Sarah, and Miriam?

More Resources

Books and Reports

Atlantic First Nations AIDS Task Force. (1996). *Healing our nations: 4th Canadian Aboriginal conference on HIV/AIDS and related issues.* Ottawa, ON, Canada: Indian and Northern Affairs Canada.

Canadian AIDS Information Treatment Exchange [CATIE]. (2009). *Managing your health: A guide for people living with HIV* (4th ed.). Toronto, ON: CATIE. (Available for downloading from www.catie.ca)

Canadian Child Care Federation. (1995). *HIV/AIDS and child care: Fact book and facilitator's guide.* Ottawa, ON: Author.

De Matteo, D., & Roberts, J. (2001). *Disclosing HIV/AIDS to children: The paths we take.* Calgary, AB, Canada: Detselig Enterprises.

Ethno-cultural Diversity Committee of the Canadian AIDS Society (ECDC-CAS). (1995). *Education and support within the context of ethno-cultural diversity.* Ottawa, ON, Canada: Canadian AIDS Society.

Pizzo, P. A., & Wilfert, C. A. (Eds.). (1998). *Paediat-

ric AIDS: The challenge of HIV infection in infants, children, and adolescents (3rd ed.). Baltimore, MD: Lippincott, Williams & Wilkins.

Internet/Websites:

Canadian AIDS Information Treatment Exchange [CATIE]
http://www.catie.ca

Canadian Child Care Federation
http://www.cccf-fcsge.ca

Centres for Disease Control and Prevention (CDC)
http://www.cdc.gov/
Diseases and conditions>HIV/AIDS>then choose topics of interest to you (e.g., basic statistics, prevention, treatment, fact sheets, frequently asked questions, and links to other related websites)

Children's Animated Television HIV/AIDS Information Site
http://www.qcfurball.com/cat/aids.html

HIV/AIDS and Disability Global Survey
http://circa.med.yale.edu/globalsurvey/

Infoseek Health Channel-AIDS & HIV
http://www.infoseek.com/health/sexual_health/ disease/AIDS_and_HIV
Health>sexual>disease>AIDS & HIV

National Institutes of Health (USA)
http://www.nih.gov/

How HIV Infection is Transmitted
http://www.niaid.nih.gov/vrc/clinitrials/ clin_transmission.htm

Mother-to-Infant HIV InfectionTransmission
http://www2.niaid.nih.gov/newsroom/simple/ perinatal.htm

The Body: An AIDS and HIV Information Resource
http://www.thebody.com/index.shmtl

The Community AIDS Treatment Information Exchange (CATIE)
http://www.catie.ca

The Integrated Network of Disability Information and Education
http://indie.ca/

SickKids' Motherisk
http://www.motherisk.org/women/hivAnonymous.jsp

The Teresa Group
http://www.teresagroup.ca

World Health Organization:
Health Topics: HIV Infections
http://www.who.int/health_topics/hiv_infections/en/

Women and Children with HIV
www.womenchildrenHIV.org

Books for Children:

Merrifield, M. (1990). *Come sit by me.* Toronto, ON, Canada: Women's Press.

The Group of Five. (2002). *Bye-bye secrets: A book about children living with HIV or AIDS in their family.* Toronto, ON: The Teresa Group and The Hospital for Sick Children.

The Teresa Group. (2005). *Hopes, wishes and dreams.* Toronto, ON: Author.

Some Groups and Organizations:

AIDS Organizations in the World
Website with list and links to AIDS/HIV organizations around the world

Children with AIDS Project (USA)
http://www.aidskids.org/

Canadian Aboriginal AIDS Network
Tel: (613) 567 1817
Fax: (613) 567 4562
The Teresa Group Child and Family Aid (Canada)

UNAIDS -The Joint United Nations Programme on HIV/AIDS
http://www.unaids.org/

References

American Academy of Paediatrics. (2003). Human immunodeficiency virus infection. In L. K. Pickering, C. J. Baker, G. D. Overturf, & C. G. Prober (Eds.), *Redbook: 2003 report of the committee on infectious diseases* (26th ed.) (pp. 360-382). Elk Grove Village, IL: Author.

American Academy of Pediatrics. (2009). *Redbook: 2009 report of the committee on infectious diseases* (28th ed.). Elk Grove Village, IL: Author.

American Academy of Paediatrics, & Committee on Paediatric AIDS. (2004). Evaluation and treatment of the human immuno deficiency virus-1-exposed infant. *American Academy of Paediatrics, 114*(2), 497-505.

American Academy of Paediatrics, & Committee on Paediatric AIDS and Committee on Infectious Diseases. (1999). Issues related to Human Immunodeficiency Virus transmission in schools, medical settings, the home, and community. *Paediatrics, 104*(2), 318-324.

American Dietetic Association. (2010). Position of the American Dietetic Association: Nutrition intervention and human immunodeficiency virus infection. *Journal of the American Dietetic Association, 110* (7), 1105-1119.

American Dietetic Association and Dieticians of Canada. (2000). Position of the American Dietetic Association and Dieticians of Canada: Nutrition intervention in the care of persons with Human Immunodeficiencency Virus infection. *American Journal of the Dietetic Association, 100,* 708-717.

Antle, B., Wells, L., Salter Goldie, R., De Matteo, D., & King, S. (2001). Challenges of parenting for families living with HIV/AIDS. *Social Work, 46*(2), 159-169.

Blanchette, N., Smith, M. L., Fernandez-Penney, A., King, S. M., & Read, S. E. (2001). Cognitive and motor development in children with vertically transmitted HIV infection. *Brain & Cognition, 46,* 50-53.

Belman, A. L., Diamond, G., Dickson, D., Horoupian, D., Llena, J., Lantos, G., et al. (1988). Pediatric acquired immunodeficiency syndrome. Neurologic syndromes. *American Journal of Diseases of Children, 142*(1), 29-35.

Brouwers, P., Walters, P., & Civitello, L. (1998). Central nervous system manifestations and assessment. In P. A. Pizzo & C. A. Wilfert (Eds.), *Paediatric AIDS: The challenge of HIV infection in infants, children, and adolescents* (3rd ed.) (pp. 293-308). Baltimore: Lippincott, Williams & Wilkins.

Burchett, S. K., & Pizzo, P. A. (2003). HIV infection in infants, children, and adolescents. *Paediatric Review, 24,* 186-194.

Burr, C. K., & Emery, L. J. (1994). Speaking with children and families about HIV infection. In P. A.

Pizzo, & C. A. Wilfert (Eds.), *Pediatric AIDS: The challenge of HIV infection in infants, children and adolescents* (2nd ed.) (pp. 923-935). Baltimore: Williams & Wilkins.

Cameron, D., McKee, E., O'Brien, K., Randall-Wood, D., Robinson, G., Wu, J., et al. (2009). HIV and rehabilitation. In Canadian AIDS Information Treatment Exchange [CATIE], *Managing your health: A guide for people living with HIV* (4th ed.) (pp. 191-206). Toronto, ON: CATIE.

Centers for Disease Control. (2002). *HIV surveillance report: 2002.* Retrieved from http://www.cdc.gov/hiv/stats/hasr/402/2002SurveillanceReport.pdf

Centers for Disease Control. (2010). *HIV surveillance report.* Retrieved from www.cdc.gov/hiv/topics/surveillance/basic.htm#hivest

Chanock, S. J. (1999). Medical issues in the home, day care, school, and community. In S. L. Zeichner & J. S. Read (Eds.), *Handbook of paediatric HIV care* (pp. 557-571). Philadelphia: Lippincott, Williams & Wilkins.

Chanock, S. J. (2006). Medical issues related to the care of HIV-infected children in the home, day-care, school, and community. In S. L. Zeichner & J. S. Read (Eds.), *Handbook of paediatric HIV care* (2nd ed.) (pp. 759-771). West Nyack, NY: Cambridge University Press.

De Matteo, D., Harrison, C., Arneson, C., Salter Goldie, R., Lefebrvre, A., Read, S. E., & King, S. M. (2002). Disclosing HIV/AIDS to children: The paths families take to truth telling. *Psychology, Health, & Medicine, 7,* 341-356.

Fielden, S. J., Chapman, G. E., & Cadell, S. (2010). Managing stigma in adolescent HIV: Silence, secrets, and sanctioned spaces. *Culture, Health, & Sexuality, 13*(3), 267-281.

Gerson, A. C., Joyner, M., Fosarelli, P., Butz, A., Wissow, L., Lee, S., et al. (2001). Disclosure of HIV diagnosis to children: When, where, why, and how. *Journal of Paediatric Health Care, 15*(4), 161-167.

Gianmnattasio, A., Officioso, A., Continisisio, G. I., Griso, G., Storace, C., Coppini, S., et al. (2011). Psychosocial issues in children and adolescents with HIV infection evaluated with a World Health Organization age-specific descriptor system. *Jour-*

nal of Developmental and Behavioral Pediatrics, 32, 52-55.

Goffman, I. (1963). *Sigma: Notes on the management of spoiled identity.* Englewood Cliffs, NJ: Prentice Hall.

Havens, P. L., Mofenson, L. M., & the Committee on Pediatric AIDS. (2009). Evaluation and management of the infant exposed to HIV-1 in the United States. *Paediatrics, 123*(1), 175-187.

Health Canada. (1998). *Rehabilitation services: A comprehensive guide for the care of persons with HIV disease.* Toronto, ON, Canada: The Wellesley Central Hospital.

Health Canada. (1999). *Routine practices and additional precautions for preventing the transmission of infection in health care.* Ottawa, ON, Canada: Author.

Health Canada. (2003). *HIV and AIDS in Canada: Surveillance report to June 30, 2003* (November). Ottawa, ON, Canada: Ministry of Health, Division of HIV/AIDS Epidemiology and Surveillance, Centre for Infectious Disease Prevention and Control.

Health Canada. (2010). *It's your health: HIV/AIDS.* (November, 2010). Ottawa, ON: Author. (ISBN: 978-1-100-15909-6)

Kaiser, B., & Rasminsky, J. S. (1995). *HIV/AIDS and child care: Fact book.* Ottawa, ON, Canada: Canadian Child Care Foundation and Health Canada.

King, S. M. (2004). Sexually transmitted diseases. In R. A. Haslam & P. J. Valletutti (Eds.), *Medical problems in the classroom: The teacher's role in diagnosis and management* (4th ed.) (pp. 609-616). Austin, TX: Pro-ed.

King, S. M., Lindegren, M. L., & Rogers, M. F. (2003). Epidemiology of paediatric HIV infection. In G. Wormser (Ed.), *AIDS and other manifestations of HIV infections* (4th ed.) (pp. 29-39). Amsterdam: Elsevier Science.

Lee, M. B., & Rotheram-Borus, M. J. (2001). Parents' disclosure of HIV to their children. *AIDS, 16*(16), 2201-2207.

Letteney, S., & Heft LaPorte, H. (2004). Deconstructing stigma: Perceptions of HIV-seropositive mothers and their disclosure to children. *Social Work in Health Care, 38*(3), 105-123.

Margolese, S. (2009). Children and HIV. In Canadian AIDS Treatment Information Exchange [CATIE]. *Managing your health: A guide for people living with HIV* (4th ed.) (pp. 227-236). Toronto, ON: CATIE.

Mueller, B. U., Kline, M. W., & Pizzo, P. A. (1998). Antiretroviral treatment. In P. A. Pizzo & C. A. Wilfert (Eds.), *Paediatric AIDS: The challenge of HIV infection in infants, children, and adolescents* (3rd ed.) (pp. 463-486). Baltimore: Williams & Wilkins.

National Institutes of Health (NIH). (2004). *Mother-to-infant HIV transmission-statistical graphs.* Retrieved from http://www2.niaid.nih.gov/newsroom/simple/perinatal.htm

National Institute of Allergy and Infections Diseases (NIAID). *HIV-AIDS.* (2011). Retrieved from http://www.niaid.nih.gov/topics/hivaids/Pages/Default.aspx

Nehring, W. M., Lashley, F. R., & Malm, K. (2000). Disclosing the diagnosis of paediatric HIV infection: Mothers' views. *Journal of the Society of Paediatric Nurses, 5*(1), 5-14.

Oxtoby, M. J. (1994). Vertically acquired HIV infection in the United States. In P. A. Pizzo, & C. A. Wilfert (Eds.), *Pediatric AIDS: The challenge of HIV infection in infants, children, and adolescents* (2nd ed.) (pp. 3-20). Baltimore: Williams & Wilkins.

Public Health Agency of Canada. (2010). *HIV in Canada: Positive HIV test reports to December 31, 2009.* Retrieved from www.phac.aspc.gc.ca/aids-sida/publications/survreport/2009

Salter, R., King, S. M., Smith, M. L., Bitnun, A., Brophy, J., Fernandes-Penney, A., et al. (2007). Disclosing HIV Diagnosis to infected children: A health care team's approach, *Vulnerable Children and Youth Studies, 2*(1), 12-16.

Salter Goldie, R. L., De Matteo, D. J., Wells, L. M., Aykroyd, G. L., & King, S. M. (2000). Social planning in Canada for children with HIV infection. *Canadian Journal of Public Health, 91,* 353-356.

Samples, C. L., Goodman, E., & Woods, E. R. (1998). Epidemiology and medical management of adolescents. In P. A. Pizzo & C. A. Wilfert (Eds.), *Paediatric AIDS: The challenge of HIV infection in infants, children, and adolescents* (3rd ed.) (pp. 615-643). Baltimore: Williams & Wilkins.

Shandor Miles, M., Gillespie, J. V., & Holditch-Davis, D. (2001). Physical and mental health in African American mothers with HIV. *Journal of the Association of Nurses in AIDS Care, 12*(4), 42-50.

Shindler, S., & Tangelder, M. (2010). Beneath the mask: A group therapy model supporting children infected with and affected by HIV/AIDS. *Social Work with Groups, 33*(4), 308-322.

Tuomala, R. E., Watts, D. H., Li, D., Vajaranant, M., Pitt, J., Hammill, H., et al. (2005). Women and Infants Transmission Study. Improved obstetric outcomes and few maternal toxicities are associated with antiretroviral therapy, including highly active antiretroviral therapy during pregnancy. *Journal of Acquired Immune Deficiency Syndromes, 38*(4), 449-473.

UNAIDS - The Joint United Nations Programme on HIV/AIDS. (2010). *Global report on HIV/AIDS*. Retrieved from www.unaids.org/Global_report.htm

Wiener, L., & Figueroa, A. (1998). Children speaking with families and children about HIV infection. In P. A. Pizzo & C. A. Wilfert (Eds.), *Paediatric AIDS: The challenge of HIV infection in infants, children, and adolescents* (3rd ed.) (pp.729-758). Baltimore: Lippincott, Williams & Wilkins.

Wiener, L., Septimus, A., & Grady, C. (1998). Psychosocial support for child and family. In P. A. Pizzo & C. A. Wilfert (Eds.), *Paediatric AIDS: The challenge of HIV infection in infants, children, and adolescents* (3rd ed.) (pp. 703-728). Baltimore: Lippincott, Williams, & Wilkins.

World Health Organization (WHO). (2011). *HIV/AIDS*. Retrieved from http://www.who.int/topics/hiv_aids/en/

21

Intractable Epilepsy: The Invisible Disability

W. McIntyre Burnham

What you will learn:

- The nature of epilepsy, and of intractable epilepsy
- Treatment options for epilepsy
- The cognitive and psychiatric problems associated with intractable epilepsy in children
- The cognitive and psychiatric problems associated with intractable epilepsy in adult
- The resources available in Ontario for people with epilepsy and intractable epilepsy

What are the Epilepsies?

The "epilepsies" are a group of neurological disorders, characterized by the occurrence of seizures. The epilepsies are also called "seizure disorders." After headaches, epilepsy is the most common condition treated by neurologists. About 4% of the population will have epilepsy some time during the course of their lives. About 1% of the population tends to have epilepsy at any particular time (Burnham, 2002; Guberman & Bruni, 1999).

"Seizures" are periods of neural hyperactivity, caused by an imbalance between excitation and inhibition in the central nervous system. During a seizure, the neurons in the brain fire in massive and synchronized bursts. After some seconds or minutes, when the inhibitory mechanisms of the brain regain control, the seizure ends. The epileptic activity in the brain during seizures can be seen as a series of "spikes" or "spikes and waves" in electroencephalic (EEG) recordings. The behaviour of the patient during the epileptic attack may or may not involve convulsions. (Many seizures are non-convulsive.) If the behavioral seizure involves tonic (rigid) or clonic (jerking) muscle spasms, it is called a "convulsion" (Burnham, 2002). Seizures are also called "attacks," which is another acceptable word. The term "fit" is acceptable in Britain, but not in Canada.

Onset of epilepsy

The onset of epilepsy may occur at any time during a person's life. In many individuals, seizure onset occurs before the age of 15. Seizure onset is less likely during young adulthood or in middle age. There is an increased incidence of seizure onset again after the age of 60. Some of these late-onset epilepsies may be the result of small strokes.

Frequency of seizures

The frequency of seizures varies with the patient. Some individuals experience only a few seizures during their whole lives, often in childhood. Other people experience many seizures every day.

Classes of epileptic seizure

There are many different types of epileptic seizures, some of which occur only in childhood. A description of all of the seizure types is beyond the scope of the present discussion, but some of the more common types are described in Table 1.

Epileptic syndromes

Recently, there has been an attempt to integrate epileptic seizures into larger entities known as "epileptic syndromes." An epileptic syndrome consists not only of a seizure type (or types), but also a prediction about the probable time of seizure onset, a possible cause, a prognosis and, in some cases, a prediction of response to medication.

Two well-known — and very serious — epileptic syndromes are West syndrome and Lennox-Gastaut syndrome. West syndrome usually has its onset during the first year of life, whereas Lennox-Gastaut syndrome usually begins between ages 1 and 8. Both syndromes involve drug-resistant seizures, an abnormal EEG between seizures and, in most cases, mild to severe developmental delay (Burnham, Carlen, & Hwang, 2002; Guberman & Bruni, 1999; Hrachovy, 2002; Niedermeyer, 2002).

Causes of epilepsy

In some individuals with seizures (about 30%), there is a clear-cut structural abnormality in the brain, such as a scar or a tumor. These people are said to have "symptomatic" epilepsy, and their seizures are thought to be caused by the brain abnormality that has occurred. In other individuals with seizures (about 70%), the brain appears to be completely normal. These people are said to have "idiopathic" epilepsy. In patients with idiopathic epilepsy,

the seizures are thought to be caused by an inherited biochemical or ionic imbalance.

In some rare types of epilepsy, the genetic factor involves a single mutation, and inheritance follows simple Mendelian rules (see chapter 9). In most cases of epilepsy, however, inheritance is "multifactorial," meaning that two or more genes are involved. In these cases, inheritance does not follow simple Mendelian rules (Burnham, 2002).

Epilepsy and other disabilities

A number of common disabilities are caused by brain damage or dysfunction. People with these disabilities often experience seizures as well. Table 2 presents a list of common disabilities, and indicates the percentage of individuals who also have epilepsy.

Can Epilepsy be Treated and Controlled?

For many people, seizures are fully controlled by medication or other treatments. For other people, however, there is no treatment that is completely effective. These people are said to have "intractable" epilepsy, which is characterized by uncontrolled seizures. Intractable epilepsy affects about 1 in 300 people in the general population (Burnham, 2007; Guberman & Bruni, 1999).

Drug therapy

The most common therapy for epilepsy is treatment with anticonvulsant medications. Anticonvulsant medications are also called "antiepileptic drugs," "AEDs" or "antiseizure drugs."

A wide variety of anticonvulsant drugs is available. Among the most commonly prescribed older drugs are ethosuximide, which is used for absence seizures, phenytoin and carbamazepine, which are used for tonic-clonic and partial seizures, and valproic acid, which is a wide-spectrum anticonvulsant, effective against many types of seizures. Phenobarbital is an older drug that is still in use, most often in children.

A number of new drugs have been introduced since 1990. These include gabapentine, lamotrigine, levetiracetam, tiagabin, topiramate, vigabatrin, and

Table 1: Common Seizure Types (old names in parentheses)

Generalized seizures (involve both cerebral hemispheres)

Absence Seizures (Petit Mal)	*Non-convulsive seizures consisting only of a few seconds of unconsciousness, blank staring and immobility. The eyelids may flutter. The EEG shows 3/second "spike and wave" activity all over the brain. The individual has no memory for the period of the attack.*
Tonic-Clonic Seizures (Grand Mal)	*Dramatic seizures involving a loss of consciousness plus whole-body convulsions which consist first of stiffening (tonus) and then of jerking (clonus). The EEG shows constant "spiking" in both hemispheres. The individual has no memory for the period of the attack.*

Partial seizures (involve only a part of the brain)

Simple Partial Seizures (Focal Cortical)	*Sensory or emotional experiences, or contralateral jerking on one side of the body. Sensory experiences relate to the part of the brain involved, and may be auditory, visual, etc. The EEG shows "spiking" limited to one part of the brain. The individual is conscious, and will remember the period of the attack.*
Complex Partial Seizures (Psychomotor)	*The individual is conscious, but is out of touch with the surrounding world. There may be automatic movements, such as lip smacking and fumbling with the clothes. The EEG shows "spiking" in the temporal lobe. The individual has no memory for the period of the attack.*

Source: Modified from Burnham (2007)

zonisamide. The new drugs are generally thought to have fewer side effects than the older drugs. It is not clear, however, that they are better at stopping seizures — and they are considerably more expensive.

The anticonvulsant medications do not cure epilepsy. They simply suppress seizures on a temporary basis. People with seizures must continue to take their medications, once, twice or three times daily, sometimes for the rest of their lives (for discussion, see Burnham, 2007; Levy et al., 2002).

Non-drug therapies

If seizures prove intractable to drug therapy, or if the side effects of the anticonvulsant drugs cannot be tolerated, several sorts of non-drug therapy are available.

If the individual experiences partial seizures — and the seizures always arise from the same area in the brain (the "focus") — he or she may be a candidate for seizure surgery. In adults, the most common type of seizure surgery involves removal of the part of the brain that contains the focus — often the anterior part of one of the temporal lobes. Surgery may stop the seizures, or make them more controllable with medication (see Luders, 1992).

Another non-drug therapy is diet therapy. The diet traditionally used is the "ketogenic" diet. This is a high-fat diet, which contains adequate protein, and very little carbohydrate. Many patients find the diet unpalatable, and it is hard to maintain since all of the food must be weighed and measured. The ketogenic diet, however, stops seizures in about a third of

Table 2: Disabilities Often Associated with Seizures (percent of affected individuals likely to have seizures indicated in parentheses)

Genetic syndromes	Non-genetic syndromes
Tuberous sclerosis (>80%)	*Cerebral palsy (frequent, varies with type)*
Sturge Weber syndrome (70-90%)	*AIDS (13%)*
Fragile X syndrome (20-40%)	*Multiple sclerosis (5-10%)*
Rett syndrome (70-80%)	*Stroke (5-10% embolic, 2.5-25%, hemorrhagic)*
Down syndrome (2-15%)	*Alzheimer's disease (15%)*
Huntington's disease (5-10%)	

Source: Modified from Guberman and Bruni (1999)

people who have failed drug therapy, and decreases seizures in another third. Traditionally, the diet has been used only in children. Some reports, however, suggest that it is effective in adults as well. Unfortunately, due to the nutritionally unbalanced nature of the diet, individuals usually stay on the diet for only two or three years (Vining, 1999). Recently, a few treatment centres have used the Atkins diet with some success. It is far easier to maintain than the traditional ketogenic diet, and appears to be beneficial in some patients (Kossoff et al., 2007).

A further treatment for drug-resistant seizures is vagus nerve stimulation. A device similar to a cardiac pacemaker is implanted into the chest muscle, and a wire is connected to the vagus nerve — a nerve that originates in the brain. Intermittent stimulation of the vagus nerve is used to control seizures. Vagus nerve stimulation is not as effective as surgery or the ketogenic diet, but it can be considered when the other therapies fail. Vagus nerve stimulation, or "VNS," is now the second most common type of non-drug therapy in the United States (see McLachlan, 1997). Unfortunately, many people with intractable seizures fail non-drug therapy as well as drug therapy. These individuals face a life of uncontrolled seizures, despite the best attempts at therapeutic intervention.

Intractable Epilepsy as a Disability

If seizures are responsive to medication — as they are in about 70% of cases — the patients may never have another seizure. They will have to take their medications regularly, but epilepsy will not interfere unduly with a full, productive life. If the seizures are partially or fully resistant to the best anticonvulsant drugs or other treatments, however, the patients will continue to have epileptic attacks. Drug-resistant seizures of this sort are called "refractory" or "intractable," and patients with seizures of this sort are said to have "intractable epilepsy."

Epilepsy is sometimes called the "invisible disability." If one thinks of people with drug-responsive seizures, the term "disability" is probably too strong. People with controlled seizures can lead normal lives, and reach their full potential for accomplishment. Intractable epilepsy, on the other hand, is clearly a disability. People with intractable epilepsy face both social and economic discrimination, and must surmount significant barriers in their struggles to live a normal life. Some of these barriers relate to seizures per se, while others relate to the "comorbidities" of epilepsy (conditions that exist at the same time and sometimes exist because of it).

The role of seizures in intractable epilepsy as a disability

In part, the problems of intractable epilepsy relate to the seizures themselves. Seizure-related problems include aspects of personal safety, driving, being able to hold a job, and economic and social discrimination.

First, there is the risk of injury during seizures. The falls that occur during some seizures may lead to head injury if they occur on pavement or near furniture with hard edges. Even more serious injuries may occur if falls happen on stairs, on ladders, or at the edges of subway platforms. Furthermore, people with uncontrolled seizures are warned against swimming alone, and may be told to take showers rather than baths. Life is circumscribed not by physical incapacity but by fears related to personal safety.

In addition, people with seizures cannot legally drive. Drivers' licences are typically suspended with the first seizure, and are re-issued only if the person is totally seizure-free for a period of time — often one year. Thus, a person with even one seizure a year will not be able to drive legally or to participate in work or social activities that require driving.

Finally, there are social and economic problems related to society's response to seizures. People who seize at public events are often not invited to future events, and people who seize at work are frequently fired. Thus, people with uncontrolled seizures are at risk of social isolation and, because they are often unemployed or underemployed, of financial stress

and poverty. Their annual incomes are certainly lower than those of the general public (Wiebe et al., 1999).

The role of co-morbidities in intractable epilepsy as a disability

Both parents and educators agree that the co-morbidities of intractable childhood epilepsy are often more serious than the seizures themselves. The co-morbidities are summarized in Table 3. If seizures cannot be stopped by drug or non-drug therapy, the co-morbidities must be addressed, and strategies for dealing with them must be evolved.

The Co-Morbities of Intractable Epilepsy: Children

Cognitive impairment

Intractable epilepsy is often associated with cognitive impairment. Studies of children with and without seizures have found that children with uncontrolled seizures may have lower IQs, often in the low-normal range of 80-85. These studies have also found a significant correlation between low IQ and the duration of the child's seizure disorder.

In some rare epileptic syndromes, IQs are often very low. West syndrome and Lennox-Gastaut syndrome are well known examples of these syndromes. If the seizures cannot be stopped in these syndromes, the children begin to regress mentally. Four out of five will eventually display developmental delay. Some of the children will later outgrow their seizures, but the developmental delay will remain. Fortunately, these syndromes are rare.

Even when IQs are in the normal range, children with uncontrolled seizures do less well in school than non-epileptic children with similar IQs. A number of factors may contribute to this:

- One cause of learning problems is frequent absence seizures. These mild, non-convulsive attacks consist only of brief lapses of consciousness. Some children have hundreds every day, however, and clusters of dozens may occur within a few minutes. During these periods, the child cannot follow what is going on around him or her. Children with absence epilepsy, therefore,

Table 3: Co-Morbidities of Intractable Epilepsy*

Cognitive
  Lowered IQ
  Developmental delay (West and Lennox-Gastaut syndromes)
  Selective deficits (related to partial seizures)
  Global memory problems due to seizures
  Global memory problems due to the sedative side-effects of anticonvulsant drugs

Psychosocial
  Low self-esteem
  Psychiatric disturbances (found in at least 30%)
  AD/HD (20-30% of children)
  Personality changes due to the side-effects of anticonvulsant drugs

Reproductive (adults)
  Lowered fertility
  Lessened desire and responsiveness

* All of these vary from individual to individual. They are sometimes present and sometimes absent.

may give the appearance of being "slow learners." In fact, their intelligence is usually normal. It is important to recognize these children, so that they can receive proper therapy.

- Severe seizures, such as tonic-clonic attacks, cause a major perturbation in the brain's signaling systems. The after-effects of such seizures may last for hours or days. If a child has had one or more seizures during the night, he or she may show excessive fatigue during the following day, may have trouble concentrating, and may appear to have forgotten things he or she knew perfectly well the day before.

- Some children, and particularly those with complex partial epilepsy, have a series of brief, single epileptic "spikes" called "interictal spikes" between their seizures. These "spikes" produce no outward manifestation, but, if they are frequent, they may slow down the child's ability to process and retrieve information, causing transient cognitive impairment.

- Children with an epileptic focus in a particular part of the brain may show selective deficits related to that area. Children with a focus in the hemisphere dominant for language, for instance, often have trouble with finding or remembering words.

- One of the most common complaints in people with intractable epilepsy is a general defect in memory. Children complain that they need their lessons to be repeated over and over again before they can remember them. They know that their classmates do not have this problem. The reasons for memory impairment are not completely clear. In some cases, it may relate to the side-effects of anticonvulsant drugs (see below). In others, it may relate to changes in the brain. Individuals with long-standing intractable epilepsy arising in the temporal lobes begin to lose neurons in the hippocampus, a sub-cortical forebrain structure. This loss of neurons is called "hippocampal sclerosis" or "mesial temporal sclerosis." The hippocampus is involved in memory formation and, if severe, is associated with memory problems.

- In addition to the cognitive impairments

associated with intractable seizures per se, there also exist impairments that are associated with the sedative (sleep inducing) side-effects of the anticonvulsant drugs. These side-effects are most serious at the start of therapy. They improve as tolerance develops, but they never entirely disappear. They are worse with the older drugs such as phenobarbital and primidone, but they may occur (in susceptible individuals) with almost any of the anticonvulsants. They are seen in many children with seizures, but are more of a problem in children with intractable seizures, since these children are often taking multiple drugs. Table 4 presents some commonly used anticonvulsants, and indicates whether they are more or less likely to significantly impair cognition.

Psychosocial impairment

Emotional and behavioural difficulties are disproportionately high in children with uncontrolled epilepsy. Psychologists working with epileptic children report that they are some of the most disturbed children they have treated.

In some children, negative emotions are a normal response to living with seizures. Children with uncontrolled seizures experience a repeated and unpredictable loss of control. They never know when the next one will occur. They may respond with anxiety, shame, and anger. There is frequently a loss of self-confidence. There is also social rejection and bullying by classmates. It is normal that negative emotions should occur in this context.

Unfortunately, in some cases, these problems progress out of the normal range. In one large-scale study, about 50% of children with intractable epilepsy were identified as having serious psychosocial problems. In another study, psychiatric disorders were identified in 33% of children with epilepsy, as compared to 7% in the general population and 12% in children with other chronic illnesses. Some of the more common problems associated with intractable epilepsy include anxiety, depression, irritability, aggression, and irrational periods of rage (Johannessen et al., 1995; Sahlholdt, 1995). These emotional problems are often responsive to therapy, including therapy

Table 4: Anticonvulsant Drugs that are More and Less Likely to Cause Cognitive Impairment (have "sedative" side-effects)

More likely*

> *Phenytoin (high doses)*
> *Phenobarbital*
> *Primidone*
> *Clonazepam*
> *Topiramate*

Less likely*

> *Carbamazepine*
> *Valproate*
> *Clobazam*
> *Vigabatrin*
> *Gabapentin*
> *Lamotrigine*

*Effects vary from individual to individual.
Source: Modified from Guberman and Bruni (1999)

with psychotrophic medications, but, unfortunately, they are seldom diagnosed or treated. Therapy often focuses on seizure control, and emotional problems are neglected.

In addition to emotional problems, children with uncontrolled seizures may have problems with hyperactivity. It is estimated that 20-30% of children with epilepsy experience concurrent attention deficit/hyperactivity disorder (ADHD). A still larger number of children with seizures show deficits in attention or in impulse control without showing the full ADHD syndrome.

The emotional and behavioural problems noted above are often compounded by the effects of the anticonvulsant drugs. Children may show a change of personality after being started on the anticonvulsants; they may become impulsive, hyperactive, and irritable, and they may exhibit both verbal and physical aggression. These problems usually disappear when the drug is stopped.

Anecdotally, neurologists report that most of the anticonvulsants can produce these emotional or behavioural side-effects. The most severe problems are probably associated with clonazepam (Rivotril). A related drug, clobazam (Frisium), causes fewer problems. In young children, phenobarbital also sometimes causes a hyperactive syndrome. One of the new drugs, vigabatrin (Sabril), is associated with depression or outright psychosis in a small number (2-4%) of the children who take it. Vigabatrin is prescribed infrequently now, however, since it tends to cause visual field defects.

The connection between anticonvulsants and emotional or behavioural problems is often overlooked. It should not be. If a child demonstrates a change in emotional or behavioural state after starting a new drug, the parents should discuss the situation with the child's neurologist. Children who show severe behaviour problems while taking one drug may not do so when taking another.

Intractable epilepsy and the family unit

Intractable seizures and the emotional, cognitive, and behaviour problems that accompany them are a burden, not just for the child, but also for the entire family. Psychologists working with the families of children with uncontrolled epilepsy report that these families are some of the most disturbed families they have treated. It seems to be the episodic, unpredictable nature of epilepsy that makes it harder to live with than other chronic childhood disabilities. Both mothers and fathers live in fear of the next attack. It is common in newly diagnosed cases that one parent will stay up all night for fear that the child will die during sleep. Many parents go through the stages of denial, anger, and depression usually seen when a child dies. Some develop psychosomatic reactions, such as sleep disturbances, headaches, and loss of appetite.

Parents, and particularly mothers, also often blame themselves for their child's epilepsy. In some cases, shame is added to guilt as other family members blame the parents for their child's condition. Eventually, most parents come to terms with their child's epilepsy. Some, however, remain "stuck" in a state of constant crisis. Many parents of children with chronic epilepsy would benefit from short-term psychotherapy. They seldom seek it or receive it, however.

Support groups, consisting of other parents with similar problems, are of considerable help to parents. These are usually organized by the regional epilepsy associations (see below). In the absence of therapy or support, there is unfortunately a very real possibility of divorce.

Siblings of epileptic children may also develop both emotional complaints (fear of becoming sick or dying, nightmares) and physical complaints (headache, vomiting). There may be sibling rivalry, as parents are often perceived as "favouring" the child with seizures. A large study found that about 25% of the siblings of children with chronic epilepsy were perceived as "disturbed" by their teachers (Johannessen et al., 1995). Not only do epileptic children and their parents require therapy, but also siblings often require therapy as well (Sahlholdt, 1995).

Intractable epilepsy and the school system

Children with intractable epilepsy often have major problems at school. This may be partially due to the cognitive problems associated with seizures. Because the children often have selective learning difficulties, it is important that epileptic children undergo psychological or psychoeducational assessments to identify their areas of weakness and strength. Once it has been established that the child has specific learning difficulties, an education plan can be identified to improve his or her academic performance.

From the school's point of view, however, most difficulties relate not to cognitive problems, but to behaviour problems. Teachers typically have little training in epilepsy, and often do not understand the connection between uncontrolled seizures and behaviour problems. When behaviour problems occur, the child is simply perceived as a "bad apple." Children with epilepsy are frequently sent to the principal, and are often suspended from school. The children themselves sometimes express hatred of their teachers, and their families often end up "at war" with the school system.

The stigma of epilepsy and the insensitivity of other children — and sometimes teachers — negatively affect the emotional and behavioural status of epileptic children. Many children with seizures are excluded from school and recreational activities by teachers, and are teased and bullied by their peers.

The school situation would be much improved if both schools and parents understood the gravity of the co-morbidities associated with intractable epilepsy. What is needed is a partnership between health care providers, the parents and the schools. It is important that:

1. Parents and health care providers inform the school about the child's seizures, and about how they are to be managed.
2. The co-morbidities of intractable epilepsy are explained and dealt with.
3. An education plan to improve academic success is evolved.
4. Appropriate supports, such as an educational assistant, are put in place.
5. The importance of the child's participation in recreational and class activities is accepted.
6. Social interactions with peers are encouraged.

The Co-Morbidities of Intractable Epilepsy: Adults

Adults with uncontrolled seizures encounter as many hardships and difficulties as children with uncontrolled seizures. The seizures themselves, with the chance of embarrassment, injury, and rejection, are a large and obvious part of the problem. Less obvious, but equally important are the unrecognized co-morbidities of uncontrolled epilepsy.

Cognitive impairment

As children grow, the co-morbidities of intractable epilepsy grow with them. Cognitive deficits, once acquired, are likely to remain. The after-effects of seizures continue to occur, as do the sedative side-effects of the anticonvulsant medications.

Psychosocial impairment

A healthy psychosocial outcome is most often associated with seizure remission before mid-adolescence. For those who continue to experience seizures as adults, the outlook is bleaker. Emotional disturbances, especially anxiety and depression, are common in adults with intractable epilepsy. Such adults experience low self-confidence. Often there is social isolation and withdrawal. Adult children may continue to live with their parents (Jahnukainen, 1995). The suicide rate is five times higher than in the general adult population. People with seizures are also over-represented in the jail population.

As with children, to a certain extent these negative feelings are the natural outcome of coping with a difficult life situation. Some individuals, however, develop psychiatric problems that are outside the normal range. In addition to serious anxiety and depression, some adults with intractable seizures develop a schizophreniform psychosis. This occurs in about 5-10% of people with intractable epilepsy. Usually the patient has complex partial seizures with a focus in one of the temporal lobes. Often, he or she has had uncontrolled epilepsy for at least 10 years. In a few patients, the psychosis will clear after a seizure, and then gradually reappear (Guberman & Bruni, 1997).

A study of adults with both uncontrolled seizures and normal IQs reported that about 30% had psychiatric disorders, including psychosis, antisocial personality disorders, anxiety, and depression (Blumer, 2002; Johannessen et al., 1995). Unfortunately, as in children, adult therapy for epilepsy tends to focus only on seizure control. The accompanying psychiatric problems are often neglected.

Intractable epilepsy and reproductive problems

Reproductive and hormonal disorders are common in both men and women with intractable epilepsy. This is particularly true if the epilepsy is of temporal lobe origin. In women, menstrual disorders are seen, such as irregular or missed menstrual cycles, or cycles in which there is no ovulation. Fertility is reduced to 70-80% of normal. Possible hormonal disorders include hypogonadism (too little estrogen) and polycystic ovaries (too much estrogen). Anticonvulsant drugs, in particular valproate, may contribute to these disorders. In men with intractable epilepsy, there is an increased risk of erectile dysfunction. Over 90% of men with epilepsy have abnormal semen analyses, including decreased sperm count and impaired sperm mobility. In both

sexes, diminished sexual desire and responsiveness have been described.

Intractable epilepsy, work and driving

Perhaps the biggest problems for adults with seizures center around work. The majority of adults with uncontrolled seizures are unemployed or underemployed (employed in unskilled jobs that are well below their level of competence).

Part of the problem relates to driving. In most countries, driver's licences are revoked after the first seizure. They can be reinstated if the driver is seizure-free for a period of time — often a year. People with intractable epilepsy, however, are seldom seizure free for as long as a year. Most of them will never legally drive again. Therefore, they cannot take any job that requires driving, or that can only be reached by car. A second problem is public seizures. People are often fired if they experience seizures at work. Even though the law in Canada forbids firing an employee because of epilepsy, employers often eliminate people with public seizures, usually using some other pretext. A third problem is disclosure. People with seizures fear that they will not be hired if they disclose their epilepsy to potential employers. They also fear that they will be fired later if they do not disclose. There are no simple solutions to these problems. Work and a stable income are major concerns for adults with intractable epilepsy.

Help for Individuals with Epilepsy and Their Families

Ontario has a number of types of resources available for people with intractable seizures and their families.

Medical resources

All of the larger cities in Ontario have hospitals with specialized programs for the treatment of epilepsy. Every person with uncontrolled seizures should be referred to such a program.

Some of the larger urban hospitals also have programs for treating the cognitive and psychosocial problems related to epilepsy. Of special note is the Epilepsy Classroom at the Hospital for Sick Children in Toronto. In this experimental program, an epileptic child attends classes at the hospital for approximately 12 weeks. During this time, psychologists and teachers assess the child's cognitive/learning status, and evolve strategies designed to meet the child's particular needs. The strategies are then communicated to the child's parents and the child's school.

Epilepsy associations

Ontario has the largest network of regional epilepsy associations in Canada. These non-profit organizations offer brochures and information about epilepsy. Larger urban associations also have epilepsy libraries open to the public. In addition, they offer support groups for people with seizures and their families. Some associations also offer job and personal counselling. Upon request, they make presentations at schools and at work places.

These regional associations are linked by Epilepsy Ontario, which is a provincial organization. Epilepsy Ontario can be reached toll free at 1-800-463-1119. It will refer interested clients to their regional associations. Epilepsy Ontario also sponsors a camp for children with seizures, called the "Spike and Wave" camp, as well as retreats for adolescents and young adults.

Summary

In addition to experiencing seizures, children with intractable (uncontrolled) epilepsy may have a lowered IQ and/or encounter problems with learning and memory. They may also have significant psychosocial problems, some of which result from the use of anti-convulsant drugs. People who work with these children must be patient, and must develop new strategies to promote learning.

Adults with uncontrollable seizures also have cognitive and psychosocial problems. They cannot legally drive, and they may develop reproductive disorders. They face discrimination in the workplace, and are frequently either unemployed or underemployed. Work and a stable income are major concerns. Their emotional problems are frequently untreated, even though they are in considerable need of treatment. Intractable epilepsy is a true — if invisible — disability.

Acknowledgements

The author would like to thank Dr. Paul Hwang MD, CMFRCPC, Irene Elliott RN, MHSc, Mr. Trevor Lee and the staffs of Epilepsy Ontario and Epilepsy Toronto for their help in preparing this chapter.

For Further Thought and Discussion

1. Much of the stigma associated with epilepsy arises from the fact that seizures can be frightening to watch. Should the public be made aware of what seizures look like? Should they become accustomed to seizures? Should they be taught first aid for seizures?

2. People with seizures who continue to drive have more accidents than those in the general population. However, they do not have more accidents than drivers who have diabetes or heart disease. People with diabetes or heart disease are allowed to drive. Neither people with seizures nor those with diabetes and heart disease have as many accidents as disease-free young adult males. Should people with seizures be allowed to drive?

3. What are the economic and social costs of intractable epilepsy? This disorder often starts in childhood, lasts through life, and is found in 1 in every 300 people.

4. Teachers receive little or no training related to the epilepsies they will meet in the classroom. Should education in the epilepsies be a part of teacher training?

More Resources

Further reading:

Aicardi, J. (1994). *Epilepsy in children*. New York: Raven Press.

American Journal of Medical Genetics, 106. (2001). (This whole volume is devoted to the genetics of epilepsy).

Burnham, W. M. (2007). Antiseizure drugs. In H. Kalant & W. Roschlau (Eds.), *Principles of medical pharmacology*. New York: Oxford University Press.

Burnham, W. M., Carlen, P. L., & Hwang, P. A. (Eds.). (2002). *Intractable seizures: Diagnosis, treatment and prevention.* New York: Plenum Press.

Dodson, W. E., & Pellock, J. M. (Eds.). (1993). *Pediatric epilepsy diagnosis and therapy.* New York: Demos Publications.

Engel, J., & Pedley, T. A. (Eds.). (1997). *Epilepsy: A comprehensive textbook.* New York: Lippincott-Raven.

Guberman, A., & Bruni, J. (1999). *Essentials of clinical epilepsy.* Woburn, MA: Butterworth-Heinemann.

Johannessen, S., Gram, L., Sillanpaa, M., & Tomson, T. (Eds.). (1995). *Intractable epilepsy.* Bristol, PA: Wrughtson Biomedical Publishing Ltd.

Levy, R. H., Mattson, R. H., Meldrum, B. J., & Perucca, E. (Eds.). (2002). *Antiepileptic drugs.* Philadelphia: Maple Press.

Luders, H. O. (Ed.). (2001). *Epilepsy surgery.* New York: Raven Press.

McLachlan, R. (1997). Vagus nerve stimulation for intractable epilepsy: A review. *Journal of Clinical Neurophysiology, 14,* 358-368.

Rowan, A. J., & Ramsay, E. E. (1997). *Seizures and epilepsy in the elderly.* Boston: Butterworth- Heineman.

Wallace, S. (Ed.). (1996). *Epilepsy in children.* New York: Chapman and Hall Medical.

Internet information

The following websites provide useful information on the subject of epilepsy:

Epilepsy Ontario: *http://epilepsyontario.org*

Epilepsy Toronto: *http://epilepsytoronto.org*

Epilepsy Canada: *http://www.epilepsy.ca*

Canadian Epilepsy Alliance: *http://www.epilepsy-matters.com*

Epilepsy Foundation of America: *http://www.efa.org*

References

Blumer, D. (2002). Psychiatric aspects of intractable epilepsy. In W. Burnham, P. L. Carlen, & P. A. Hwang, (Eds.), *Intractable seizures: Diagnosis, treatment and prevention* (pp. 133-147). New York: Plenum Press.

Burnham, W. M. (2002). Epilepsy. In L. Nadel, (Ed.), *The encyclopedia of cognitive neuroscience* (Vol. 2; pp. 1-7). London: Nature Publishing Group.

Burnham, W. M. (2007). Antiseizure drugs. In H. Kaland, D. Grant, J. Mitchell (Eds.), *Principles of medical pharmacology* (pp. 223-235). Toronto, ON: Elsevier Canada.

Burnham, W. M., Carlen, P. L., & Hwang, P. A. (Eds.). (2002). *Intractable seizures: Diagnosis, treatment and prevention.* New York: Plenum Press.

Guberman, A., & Bruni, J. (1999). *Essentials of clinical epilepsy.* Woburn, MA: Butterworth-Heinemann.

Hrachovy, R. A. (2002). West's syndrome: Clinical description and diagnosis. In W. Burnham, P. L. Carlen, & P. A. Hwang, (Eds.), *Intractable seizures: Diagnosis, treatment and prevention* (pp. 33-50). New York: Plenum Press.

Jahnukainen, H. (1995). Psychosocial consequences of intractable epilepsy in adults. In S. Johannessen, L. Gram, M. Sillanpaa, & T. Tomson, (Eds.), *Intractable epilepsy* (pp. 165-169). Bristol, PA: Wrightson Biomedical Publishing Ltd.

Johannessen, S., Gram, L., Sillanpaa, M., & Tomson, T. (Eds.). (1995). *Intractable epilepsy.* Bristol, PA: Wrughtson Biomedical Publishing Ltd.

Kossoff, E. H., Rowley, H., Sinha, S. R., & Vining, E. P. G. (2007). A prospective study of the modified Atkins Diet for intractable epilepsy in adults. *Epilepsia, 49,* 316-319.

Niedermeyer, E. (2002). Lennnox-Gastaut syndrome: Clinical description and diagnosis. In W. Burnham, P. L. Carlen, & P. A. Hwang, (Eds.), *Intractable seizures: Diagnosis, treatment and prevention* (pp. 61-75). New York: Plenum Press.

Sahlholdt, L. (1995). Psychosocial consequences of intractable epilepsy in children. In S. Johannessen, L. Gram, M. Sillanpaa, & T. Tomson (Eds.), *Intractable epilepsy* (pp. 153-163). Bristol, PA: Wrightson Biomedical Publishing Ltd.

Vining, E. P. G. (1999). Clinical efficacy of the ketogenic diet. *Epilepsy Research, 37,* 181-290.

Wiebe, S., Bellhouse, D. R., Fallahay, C., & Eliasziw, M. (1999). Burden of epilepsy: The Ontario Health Survey. *Canadian Journal of Neurological Science, 26,* 263-270.

Part III

Support and Intervention

22

An Introduction to Assessment, Diagnosis, Interventions, and Services

Ivan Brown and Maire Percy

What you will learn:

- Why assessment and diagnosis are important for intervention and services
- Types of assessments and reasons for assessments
- Pros and cons of giving a diagnosis, and best practices for doing so
- What interventions are and guidelines for effective interventions

To introduce this book's Support and Intervention section, this chapter presents four topics that are very much interrelated in practice: assessment, diagnosis, intervention, and services. The term *assessment* refers to the process of investigating and documenting knowledge, skills, capabilities, attitudes, and beliefs. In the field of developmental disabilities, assessment is used primarily to help determine the strengths and support needs of children or adults, and to suggest the most appropriate types of interventions and services. Assessment is also sometimes used to determine whether a person has a developmental disability or other condition and, if so, to describe its nature or type on the basis of its signs, symptoms, and the results of various tests. The conclusion reached from this process is called a *diagnosis*. Making a diagnosis in the developmental disabilities field can be complex and sometimes requires ongoing assessment over a number of months or years as well as input from various types of professionals.

The word *intervention* refers, in a literal sense, to the act or an instance of interfering or intruding. In the field of developmental disabilities, intervention means something slightly different. It refers to a group of methods for taking intentional action to help people improve their lives in a variety of positive ways, and it should be based on sound assessment procedures that are ongoing in nature. The term *service* (also sometimes called *support*) refers to the potential for helping others, or to the act of helping others or of doing work that provides assistance or benefits to someone. Service for people with developmental disabilities is multidisciplinary, and it includes direct care, health, education, and support in a variety of special areas. Some service is designed to be specifically for people with disabilities and other service is for broader populations but is also available to people with disabilities. Overall, though, service means the presence of formal and informal resources that are available to people with disabilities that can directly help to improve their lives. Interventions, to be effective, very much depend on the availability of services. Services are referred to throughout this chapter, but are not described in detail here. Instead, a summary of common service types and of services available in Ontario is described in Chapter 23.

This chapter provides an introduction to assessment, diagnosis, intervention, and services because it is critical to stress their importance to the overall support provided to children and adults with developmental disabilities. These topics have been addressed through a vast number of books, articles, and practical materials. It is not possible to represent or summarize all of the information that is available in these resources; thus, this chapter serves as an introduction to a much larger area of study. Readers are encouraged to explore, through more specific reading and study, specific diagnostic criteria and guidelines, as well as the large number of specific methods of assessment and intervention strategies for a broad array of purposes that are available in the disability literature. For example, see the recent American Association on Intellectual and Developmental Disabilities (AAIDD) publication *Intellectual disability: Definition, classification, and systems of supports* (11th ed.) (Schalock, Borthwick-Duffy, Buntinx, Coulter, & Craig, 2010). Also to note are two manuals that deal with the diagnosis of mental disorders in persons with developmental disability (Fletcher, Loschen, Stavrakaki, & First, 2009a; 2009b). Readers are encouraged to become fully familiar with services that are available in their local areas.

Assessment

The field of developmental disabilities — like the fields of education, social work, psychotherapy, psychiatry, and medicine — has a well-developed literature on assessment for both individuals and populations (groups of individuals). This literature places a strong emphasis on individual assessment to identify and address the specific needs of individuals with disabilities and, to a lesser degree, on population assessment to identify and address the needs of groups of people with disabilities. This literature continues to evolve. Yet, its basic premise has remained stable over time — namely, that assessment is crucial to providing information for identifying needs and difficulties that can be addressed through interventions or services, for the specific purpose of helping to maintain or improve people's lives.

Ongoing need for intervention and services is the most important reason for assessment, but it also has become important to deliver intervention and services in the most cost-effective and efficient manner that benefits individuals. In Ontario, services and the funds to support them have expanded quite dramatically since the mid-20th century. Along with this expansion, there has been a shift toward attempting to ensure that these services are cost effective and efficient (see Chapter 4 for a fuller discussion). This trend has increased the need to assess as accurately as possible the requirements of individuals and groups of individuals so that they can be more directly addressed.

At the same time, broad concepts such as inclusion, quality of life, and self-determination have gained tremendous attention since about 1990, especially because they emphasize the importance of maximizing independence, abilities, and the quality within each person's life. Service has incorporated many of the core ideas and values related to these concepts into the daily work of frontline workers and placed a stronger emphasis on person-centred approaches to service (see Chapters 4 and 23). The emphasis on these ideals has further increased the need for individual assessment that can accurately identify aspects of life that currently provide quality and thus need to be maintained and enhanced, as well as those aspects of life that are problematic and need to be improved or removed from the person's life (Brown & Brown, 2003).

OVERALL APPROACH TO ASSESSMENT FOR SERVICE NEEDS

There is a large amount of literature on assessment for people with developmental disabilities. Numerous texts, detailing assessment methods and strategies that are useful for many purposes and over the life span, are readily available in such places as university and professional libraries. Here, in keeping with the objectives of this chapter, an overall approach to assessment is outlined.

Individual and population assessment

Assessment involves gathering information about something and drawing conclusions based on that information. In the field of developmental disabilities, that "something" for an individual is most typically the person's health and social history, characteristics, skills, knowledge, or behaviour; the environment in which the person lives; and the interaction between the person and that environment or the interaction between the person and other people. Assessment may occur for a variety of reasons, including teaching and learning, physical and mental health, support in everyday activities, and identifying needed services and supports. Whatever the reason for carrying out a specific individual assessment, its overall purpose is to suggest strategies or interventions that help improve the way an individual does things, the support in an individual's life, or the environment in which an individual lives.

Assessment for populations, or a focus on a group of individuals, is also important in the field of developmental disabilities. For example, by gathering data on a large number of individuals in a region it may become apparent that a significant number of youth with disabilities do not have major daily activities immediately on leaving school and that this situation is problematic for both the youth and their families. Such information, once gathered, can lead to recommendations for resources so that interventions, supports, and services that address these needs can be put in place.

Assessment for specific reasons and ongoing assessment

Often, assessment is carried out for a very specific reason. Frontline support personnel, family members, or others may refer an individual for a formal assessment because they would like opinions or answers to questions that they have identified. For example, educators may want information on the learning strengths and preferred learning styles of an 8-year-old girl to help determine the most appropriate class setting and teaching strategies for her. In this case, they may refer her to a school psychologist for assessment. In another example, parents may want to understand why their 40-year-old son is showing symptoms of depression and is having mood swings. They may seek a referral to a psychiatrist for their son.

Not all individual assessment is carried out for a specific reason, at a specific time, or in such a formal way. At times, professionals or frontline workers may carry out an assessment themselves to address a specific question or problem that has arisen. In these types of cases, assessment may — and should — be conducted in an ongoing way by those who support people with developmental disabilities. A simple example is a 5-year-old boy who is crying. His caregiver will probably wonder if he is hurt, frightened, hungry, or tired, or if there is another problem. She will, in all likelihood, try to find out why he is crying and attempt to do something about it. If she determines that he is crying because he is frightened, she will probably try to separate him from the source of his fear and offer him physical and emotional comfort. In doing these things, the caregiver has gathered information about a problem situation, made a decision about the cause of the problem, and taken steps to improve it. Using the same basic approach, effective caregivers, support personnel, and professionals notice numerous small and not-so-small things during the course of a day that they assess for the purpose of improving or maximizing their support or the environment. For example, if a caregiver notices that a child is having trouble tying her shoe, he may observe and perform a series of small tests to determine if the child does not have the manual

Table 1: Steps for Blending Quality-Of-Life Concepts Into Assessment and Intervention

Look at the person and his or her environment

- *Person's own life experiences*
- *Personal domains common to most people (e.g., family, friends, accommodations, work, leisure)*
- *Environmental, social, and historical conditions in which the person lives*
- *Environmental domains common to most people (e.g., community resources, public safety)*

Set priorities for action

- *First: Basic necessities*
- *Second: Satisfaction with what is important*
- *Third: Achieving high levels of fulfillment and meaning in life*

Carry out initial appraisal

- *Determine individual strengths and needs*
- *Determine the individual's wishes*
- *Determine if short term or long term and if immediate or distant*

Determine how to assess

- *Use objective indicators and standardized instruments*
- *Gather personal perceptions of the individual and others*
- *Take into account the importance and value to the person of the needs being assessed*
- *Shape information toward stated personal goals*

Consider two key aspects

- *Holism/domains: Life is often thought of in parts but works as an integrated whole*
- *Changing nature of life over time*

From Brown, I., & Brown, R. I. (2003). Quality of life and disability: An approach for community practitioners (pp. 117–118). London: Jessica Kingsley Publishers; adapted by permission.

dexterity to tie the shoe, needs step by step instruction for how to do it, needs to be allocated time and space for the task, or if there is another reason. Once the reason has been determined, a plan of action can be generated for improving the situation. In this way, individual assessment is integrated into the ongoing daily care, education, and support that are provided to individuals.

Five basic assessment actions

Assessments are described and organized in many different ways. They differ quite markedly because the purposes of assessments are different. For example, one would use different methods to assess hearing, vision, speech and language ability, communication,

motor skills, level of intelligence, daily living skills, need for physical and occupational therapy, ability to be responsible for a pet, capacity for traveling independently on a bus, or friend-making skills. Regardless of the specific assessment methods, they share some basic, overall components. Five actions that describe such common components are to:

1. Attend to a situation or problem that has come to one's attention for a specific reason or simply because it is occurring in an individual's life
2. Gather as much information as possible about the situation or problem
3. Analyze which aspects of the situation are working well (strengths) and which aspects are not working well (needs)

Focus on what to assess and apply
- *What is valued, relevant, and important to the person*
- *What the individual perceives as leading to satisfaction and happiness*
- *What offers opportunities for improvement*
- *What reflects personal choice*
- *What enhances self-image*
- *What contributes to personal empowerment*

Consider other practice factors
- *Effect on families and close others*
- *Professional considerations*
- *Ethical issues*
- *Policy and management issues*

Look to goals (end points) in five key areas of improvement
- *Well-being*
- *Enjoyment/satisfaction*
- *Personal meaning*
- *Positive self-image*
- *Social inclusion*

---

4. Understand the factors that help improve the situation, as well as factors that hinder its improvement
5. Decide on plans to maintain or enhance factors that help improve the situation and to decrease or eliminate factors that hinder improvement; such plans, once put into action, are often referred to as intervention (Brown & Brown, 2003)

Theoretical frameworks for assessment

It is often helpful to conceptualize and conduct assessment within a set of procedures that reflect both a theoretical stance and sound professional-ethical practice. Many such sets of procedures are available in assessment texts. One example (see Table 1) was put forward by Brown and Brown (2003) who advocated from the theoretical perspective that effective quality of life is an inherent right for all people with disabilities.

FORMAL ASSESSMENT

Assessment can, and should, be carried out by all disability professionals on an ongoing basis. At times, however, it is advisable to have an assessment carried out in a more formal way by a qualified professional. Formal assessments are usually carried out when there is a need to explain an individual's achievment levels or behaviour, when there is a need to understand more clearly what learning strategies or behaviour strategies might be best suited to the individual's abilities, when a health or life course problem arises and needs to be addressed, or when there is a need to ascertain if an individual is eligible for a specific service (such as special education or vocational support).

Table 2 summarizes the most common target areas of formal assessment in developmental disability. Formal tests are very often included in an assessment battery (a group of tools that use a variety of methods — e.g., intelligence tests, tests of adaptive behaviour, tests of motor skills, hearing and vision tests). Typically, formal tests are characterized as either objective or subjective, and both are often used in testing to provide balance. Objective tests include fixed and well-defined scoring procedures. Often, these tests are referred to as "standardized" tests. Being standardized means that the test has been applied to a group of individuals of defined age and sex; thus, test results of a person being tested for a disability are compared with the test results of others of similar age and sex. Subjective tests typically seek the perception or perspective of the person being assessed and other people, and they are often designed to be interpreted by the assessor (e.g., ink blot tests, tests of apperception — perception as modified and enhanced by one's own emotions, memories, and biases).

Should formal testing be required for eligibility to services? Due to fiscal restraints and a perceived need for greater accountability since the 1990s, it has become more common in Ontario to require formal testing of individuals to confirm that they have a developmental disability before some types of services are offered. There are a number of advantages to requiring formal testing to determine eligibility for services. The most important of these are ensuring that services are available to the individuals for whom they were intended, ensuring that people are not given inappropriate or unnecessary services, and being accountable to administrators (and indirectly to taxpayers) for monies spent on services (see also discussion in Chapter 1).

On the other hand, there is considerable literature available on the difficulties of obtaining reliable test results from some individuals. For example,

difficulties with hearing, vision, mobility, speech and language, mood, anxiety, concentrating, distractibility, and hypersensitivity to bright light interfere with formal testing. Another problem is that formal assessment is not always widely available and it is expensive. Thus, not everyone who is considered to need testing is able to access it in a timely manner or sometimes at all. One of the problems with requiring a formal diagnosis of developmental disability as part of eligibility is that many people who have IQ scores between 70 and 85 (approximately one seventh of the general population in North America) have social and emotional problems that are not addressed well by generic services. These individuals, however, are usually ineligible for developmental disability services because they do not have a formal diagnosis or meet other eligibility criteria set by service providers (Tymchuk, Lakin, & Luckasson, 2001; Zetlin & Murtaugh, 1990).

Trend toward multifaceted formal assessment

Multifaceted (or multidisciplinary) assessment involves professionals with different areas of expertise (e.g., pediatrics, family medicine, neurology, psychiatry, clinical genetics, education, psychology, social work), and the compilation of information from these different sources. It often involves observing adaptive and maladaptive behaviours in more than one environment. This type of assessment is considered especially useful in developing individualized plans for supports and services. Multifaceted assessment is typically carried out in environments that reveal needs for early childhood services, educational services and, in some cases, social services for adults or families that have children with disabilities.

The purposes of multifaceted assessment often differ according to the age-related needs of the individual. For example, a pediatric clinic conducts assessments of young children for diagnostic purposes or health care needs, an educational team assesses individuals to pinpoint educational strengths and weaknesses during the school years, and community agencies assess adult support needs for skill development and care management in relation to community living and/or special care.

Table 2: Common Target Areas of Formal Assessment in Developmental Disability

Formal assessment typically identifies needs and strengths in these areas:
- *Intellectual functioning (an essential component of most formal assessments)*
- *Adaptive skills (an essential component of most formal assessments)*
- *Learning abilities and learning styles*
- *Neurosensory functions (i.e., hearing, vision, and motor skills)*
- *Speech and language function*
- *Health and medical conditions*
- *Dental health*
- *Nutrition*
- *Neuropsychological issues*
- *Life skills*
- *Activities of daily living*
- *Living environment*
- *Available supports*

Diagnosis

A diagnosis of developmental disability, or a specific type of developmental disability, is a formal statement of the presence of a condition affecting personal characteristics, intellect, development, and/or behaviour. It is made as a conclusion of assessment, which is sometimes carried out over extended periods of time. A diagnosis need not be more specific than identifying a descriptive term such as intellectual disability, developmental disability, developmental delay, or learning disability. In Ontario, as elsewhere, a diagnosis is almost always made in accordance with widely recognized criteria, typically provided by professional organizations or legislation (e.g., American Association on Intellectual and Developmental Disabilities and others as described in Chapter 1 of the AAIDD publication by Schalock et al. (2010), or on the website of the Royal College of Psychiatrists, 2004).

For many people, a more specific diagnosis can be made, sometimes in addition to the more general diagnosis of developmental disability. Again, this is made in accordance with widely recognized criteria such as those contained within the *Diagnostic and Statistical Manual of Mental Disorders, Fourth Edition, Text Revision* (DSM-IV-TR; American Psychiatric Association [APA], 2000), and is also made based on known reasons for the disability. (See also Fletcher et al., 2009a; 2009b.) There are two main types of such diagnoses: 1) classification diagnosis (e.g., autism, Asperger syndrome, schizophrenia, dementia, behaviour problem), which classifies disabilities according to characteristics or behaviours common to groups of people, and 2) primary diagnosis, also sometimes called etiological diagnosis (e.g., Down syndrome, fragile X syndrome, fetal alcohol syndrome), which addresses the cause(s) of the disability (see also Chapters 12 and 13).

An aspect of diagnosis that sometimes seems confusing is that these more specific diagnoses may be made for people who have a diagnosis of developmental disability, as well as for people who do not have such a diagnosis. For example, it may be helpful to understand in more detail the diagnosis of a person with intellectual disability by having a further diagnosis of cerebral palsy, but not all people with cerebral palsy have lower intellectual functioning and thus these people would not have a diagnosis of intellectual disability. Similarly, some people with autism, Tourette syndrome, and many other syndromes or conditions may or may not have an intellectual disability.

ISSUES IN MAKING A DIAGNOSIS

A diagnosis of development disability needs to be made after careful consideration by a qualified professional, in accordance with established diagnostic criteria, and with an understanding of the effects the diagnosis may have on the individual and his or her family.

Responsibility for making a diagnosis

A diagnosis needs to be made and communicated in a serious and responsible manner. Often, such responsibility is set out in legal documents or formal policy by government bodies, service or educational organizations, or professional organizations. Such is the case in Ontario (see Box 1).

Understanding the reason for the diagnosis

A diagnosis is a formal designation that identifies a specific term describing a condition in a person. Thus, when an individual is diagnosed with a developmental disability, he or she is formally identified as a person who has the characteristics of that disability.

A diagnosis that determines the primary reason(s) for the disability is often very helpful. It helps others understand the person's characteristics and behaviours, and it helps others identify services and interventions that will help the person develop and enjoy life. It can also be helpful because many of the support needs in diagnosed conditions are already known from studies of populations with the particular condition. Practitioners, family members, and people with disabilities themselves can use this information to plan the most appropriate support resources and activities. In spite of this beneficial intent, some individuals, family members, and service providers are somewhat cautious about seeking or making a diagnosis because of the possibility of stigma associated with being labelled, over-identification with specific characteristics, or assumptions that are made both by practitioners and others based on the diagnosis. Another reason for caution is that professionals at times provide a diagnosis without making provision for support services (e.g., counselling or information for parents), which distresses some families. Thus, professionals should make, or not make, a diagnosis following careful thought, and they should be certain that the benefits of making a diagnosis outweigh the drawbacks. Professionals should also bear in mind the possibility of dual diagnosis (see Chapter 36).

Typically, professionals exercise some flexibility in whether or not to make a diagnosis of developmental disability, except where the cause is clearly genetic (such as in Down syndrome or fragile X syndrome). For some parents, having a diagnosis is a relief because it explains behaviour and delayed development. For others, it is a source of stress and worry, and it might be best to postpone a diagnosis. Access or lack of access to services is another reason for flexibility in diagnosing. For example, a child may be diagnosed if the diagnosis is required for a needed and helpful service, but he may not be diagnosed if those services are not required or are not available in the area where the person lives.

When a diagnosis is made, it is often permanent, and becomes part of the way that individual is seen by others and how she sees herself throughout her life. For this reason, a diagnosis should be made with care. This is especially important because conditions and skills change over the life span. For example, in order to be eligible for early intensive behavioural intervention services in some jurisdictions, a child must be diagnosed as having "severe autism." Nonetheless, this program is so successful in some instances that the child is able to participate successfully in the general education classroom and enjoy most aspects of family and community life without undue negative effects (Jacobson, Mulick, & Green, 1998; Mudford Martin, Eikeseth, & Bibby, 2001). In these cases, the label is still relevant, but the support needs are considerably reduced. Thus, it is essential to think of a diagnosis in terms of the present need of the person with a disability and the supports that are indicated.

It is sometimes important, as well, to exercise flexibility in interpreting the results of formal assessment instruments when making a diagnosis, as results for people with developmental disabilities

Box 1: Ontario Professionals Designated to Communicate Diagnoses

In Ontario, the Regulated Health Professions Act (1991 S.O. 1991, c. 18) sets out guidelines for specific health professions and professionals regarding scope of practice, qualifications, job titles that can be used only according to specific rules and regulations (e.g., psychologist, massage therapist), and procedures that only members are permitted to perform (e.g., need to be a member of the Ontario College of Physicians and Surgeons to perform surgery).

For diagnosing developmental (and intellectual) disabilities, the Regulated Health Professions Act stipulates that either a psychologist or a physician should communicate a diagnosis to a patient or client. This is to prevent the harm that might come to the patient or client if the explanation is not communicated correctly. There is a possibility that those who are not entitled to communicate a diagnosis might be prosecuted under the Regulated Health Professions Act; therefore, it is their responsibility not to communicate information that might be construed to be a diagnosis.

(see Government of Ontario, 1991)

are not always accurate, may change over time, and may reflect a different set of values or needs (e.g., results may be low because mathematics or expressive language skills are low, but the person may not actually need mathematics skills in daily life, or may have a useful alternative expressive language system). The main purpose of a diagnosis must remain clarifying personal characteristics and needed supports that are helpful in improving skills and enjoyment of life.

The challenge of determining if people have disabilities

Determining whether a person has a developmental disability can be a challenge at times because it is not an exact science (see Chapter 1). It is sometimes difficult to conduct an accurate assessment, meanings and definitions of developmental disabilities vary somewhat over time and place, and policies or regulations that set out diagnostic requirements for

services are not always consistent.

A diagnosis needs to be based on a set of criteria, as mentioned above. Around the world, and even throughout Ontario, regions and services use a variety of available sets of criteria for determining if a diagnosis should be made. For example, psychologists within a school system may use one set of criteria for diagnoses and those in an adult living services agency may use another. There are many similarilities among the common sets of criteria, but there are also some significant differences (see Chapter 1). In addition, some services have their own sets of criteria and if those services are to be accessed, the diagnosis has to be in accordance with them. Even when one set of criteria is used, it may be interpreted in different ways. Moreover, there are rigorous and less formal ways of assigning a diagnosis (e.g., autism; see Chapter 16).

Certain aspects of diagnostic criteria are sometimes stressed more than others for particular reasons. Different services — such as residential services, vocational services, mental health services, recreational programs, life-skills development, and schools — may require demonstration of need in a particular area, resulting in its being overstressed for the purpose of getting the needed support. Unfortunately, there are wait lists for many services, and to compete for eligibility for those services, family members and professionals sometimes present the needs (diagnosis) of the person with the disability in ways that minimize ability and maximize disability.

Perhaps the most important limitation to any one set of diagnostic criteria is that it is impossible to design a set of criteria that works well for every individual in every circumstance. There are people who match diagnostic criteria well but do not need services, and people who very much need services but do not quite match the diagnostic criteria. Moreover, matching criteria and individual needs change over time with developing skills, maturation, and different environmental demands. There has been considerable debate in the disability literature about how strictly criteria should be interpreted, and there have been many calls for allowing for a degree of flexibility, especially to reflect clinical opinion that people are in need of services.

Box 2: Issues in Interventions for Behaviour Problems and Mental Health

At least four issues should be considered regarding interventions for behaviour problems and mental health:

1. *It is crucial to distinguish clinical symptoms of problem behaviour and/or psychiatric illness from symptoms that might be characteristic of an underlying disability. Although both may be treatable, they may require different intervention techniques.*

2. *Psychotropic drugs appear to still be considerably overused among people with developmental disability, especially those with challenging behaviour (see Chapter 34 for a full discussion).*

3. *It is important to ask what standards professionals should use for making decisions about interventions for behaviour problems and mental health. Some special consensus statements have been developed to guide professionals. For example, AAMR (Rush & Frances, 2000) published a special volume of its journal American Journal on Mental Retardation (since 2010 the American Journal on Intellectual and Developmental Disability), and the American Academy of Child and Adolescent Psychiatry also published guidelines (1999).*

4. *Attempts have been made to educate and empower individuals with developmental disabilities regarding use of their medication. For example, the Ohio State University's PROJECT MED group published a set of seven booklets intended for individuals with such disabilities. These booklets explain the uses of psychotropic medications and their side effects in an easy to understand manner (Aman et al., 1999).*

Intervention

The term intervention in disability support work refers to action intentionally taken by others to positively affect the life of a person with developmental disabilities. It is essential for disability workers to understand clearly that the only intent of intervention is to maintain or improve the person's life in some way. In this section, numerous interventions are identified or briefly described. Those mentioned are not intended to represent all that are practised throughout Ontario. Rather, they are intended to illustrate the richness of interventions that are available in some areas and that might be developed in others.

Interventions are carried out by a wide variety of professional frontline workers and specialists of various kinds. It is what these professionals "do" in their working time when they are supporting, advising, or treating people with disabilties. Family members or other nonprofessionals may also carry out interventions at times, especially when working as part of a team with professionals.

General guidelines for effective intervention

Numerous sets of guidelines for effective intervention are available from a wide variety of sources,

and readers are encouraged to seek out some of these (see More Resources). Some general guidelines are highlighted here to provide an overall context to understanding and using such guidelines. Intervention should:

- Address a specific assessed need
- Set clear and achievable objectives that are designed to improve the life of the person with disabilities
- Be based on a sound theoretical or practical rationale
- Use methods that 1) are the choice of the person with disabilities, 2) are agreeable to the person with disabilities, and/or 3) do not cause the person with disabilities harm
- Use ongoing evaluation to assess the degree to which progress is being made, and, using this information, adjust the methods to move toward the objectives in an more effective way
- Ensure a smooth transition away from the intervention
- Provide for follow-up intervention, if required

Types of interventions

Many interventions are described in other chapters of this book, and readers are encouraged to seek additional information by consulting the many comprehensive texts on intervention that are available in academic and professional libraries. Interventions can take a wide variety of forms and are practised in numerous services areas such as social services, education, health, and others. Intervention may be carried out in specialized settings (e.g., school classrooms, psychotherapy, medical intervention, special behavioural intervention), in the home or workplace, or in other settings. The specific types of interventions used in developmental disability are extremely varied, because they need to respond — sometimes in creative ways — to the assessed needs of individuals, and to promote benefits to individuals within their unique life circumstances. Among these, a variety of general types of interventions and therapies have been particularly important to people with developmental disabilities. Some examples are:

- *Activity-focused therapies*: art therapy, aquatic therapy, music therapy and music participation, pet therapy, play therapy, recreation therapies, sand play therapy. For a discussion of complications associated with Internet use, see Katz (2001).
- *Age-related therapies*: intensive early childhood behavioural intervention, transition counselling, grief and loss counselling.
- *Communication*: audiology, speech-language therapy.
- *Education and training*: academic upgrading (e.g., completion of school or courses; improvement of specific skills such as reading, writing, or working with numbers), special educational programs, vocational programs.
- *Health and medicine*: alternative medicine, correction of hearing and vision problems, gene therapy, hormone replacement, nutritional therapy (general and for specific problems such as phenylketonuria), physiotherapy, pharmacotherapy, surgery for heart and gastrointestinal defects, correction of physical deformities.
- *Lifestyle and personal support*: personal support, assistance animals, assistive technology, helpful specialized techniques (e.g., special feeding methods, hygiene and toileting assistance, community involvement, training

to travel independently, bathing assistance, medicine schedule monitoring, enhancement of social skills).
- *Personal and skills development*: assertiveness training, behaviour therapy (see Box 2 for issues in behaviour problems and mental health), counselling, family therapy, individual therapy, group therapy, life skills training, money management training, occupational therapy, psychotherapy, promoting friendships for people with developmental disability, sex education, social skills training, and travel training.

It should be noted that in practice not all interventions are helpful, and some might even be harmful to a particular person. For example, the administration of psychotropic medications is common for behaviour disorders because it helps many people, yet not all people with developmental disabilities respond to these drugs as expected and, at the same time, they may experience serious side effects (see Chapters 33 and 34 for more details). Children and adolescents with developmental disabilities may experience functional impairment and akathisia (involuntary changes in posture), tics (pointless rapid movements or repeated sounds), and other dyskinesias (movement disorders) when administered traditional neuroleptic medications (Brasić, Barnett, Kowalik, Tsaltas, & Ahmad, 2004). Another example is the response to phenytoin for treatment of epileptic seizures. Although this drug has beneficial effects for many people, it may have life-threatening adverse effects in people with Down syndrome who have developed late onset seizures, especially in those who have dementia of the Alzheimer type (Tsiouris et al., 2002; see also Chapters 14, 31, and 37.)

New Interventions

New interventions, sometimes for particular developmental disabilities, are continually being developed and evaluated. Some of these may prove to be effective in the future, and others may not. For this reason, expert opinion should be sought and care should be taken if these are undertaken.

At the time of publication, some examples of such interventions that are being investigated in clinical research studies are:

- Avoidance of milk and milk products, as well as gluten, for autism (Whitely et al., 2010).
- Minocycline and mGluR5 antagonists for fragile X syndrome (Wang, Berry-Kravis, & Hagerman, 2010).
- Cholesterol supplementation and other strategies for Smith-Lemli-Opitz syndrome (Irons, 2007).
- Deep brain stimulation for Alzheimer's, depression, and Parkinson's disease (No Authors Listed, 2010).
- Fetal surgery for spina bifida (Adzick et al., 2011).
- In utero blood transfusions for severe haemolytic disease of the newborn (Illanes & Soothill, 2009).
- Intramuscular botulinus toxin injection for cerebral palsy (O'Flaherty, Janakan, Morrow, Scheinberg, & Saugh, 2011).
- Stem cell therapy for spinal cord injury (Ruff, Wilcox, & Fehlings, 2011)
- The Atkins diet for epilepsies resistant to pharmacological intervention (Tonekaboni et al., 2010).
- Transcranial magnetic stimulation for refractory epilepsy (Bae et al., 2011).

Summary

Assessment, diagnosis, intervention, and services are closely linked. They must go hand in hand if improvements are to be made to the support for people with developmental disabilities, their families, and their care providers. Some people with developmental disabilities receive formal assessment and diagnosis, but others do not. Assessment should identify needed supports, and diagnosis should identify causes or classification of an individual's disability with the goal of helping provide needed supports. Numerous types of interventions are applicable to improving the lives of people with developmental disabilities. Although assessment and specific interventions are essential for support to people with developmental disabilities, more general interventions in the form of services must also be available.

For Further Thought and Discussion

1. Think of a person you know who has a developmental disability. What types of assessment would be best to ascertain what his or her support needs are? Who would be best suited to carrying out this assessment?
2. When a diagnosis is made, when should it be thought of as long-term, and when should it be thought of as short-term? Illustrate your view by giving examples from people with disabilities. When, if ever, is it appropriate not to give a diagnosis? What diagnostic criteria are used in the main service you work (or plan to work) in?
3. Working in a small group with others, identify the services that are available locally for a teenager with developmental disability and for a 40-year-old woman with developmental disability. What diagnosis, if any, is required for these services? What are the main interventions these services offer for each person?
4. Think of one person with a developmental disability who has a specific need or problem. Describe that need or problem, then set out a plan for how you would assess it in the short term and over a one-year period.

More Resources

Online Resources:

Ontario Ministry of Community and Social Services
http://www.mcss.gov.on.ca/en/mcss/index.aspx/

American Association on Intellectual and Developmental Disabilities (AAIDD)
(2011). Definition of intellectual disability. Retrieved from *http://aaidd.org/content_100.cfm?navID=21*

American National Centre on Birth Defects and Developmental Disabilities
www.cdc.gov/ncbddd/

American Psychiatric Association
http://www.psych.org/

American Psychological Association
http://www.apa.org/

DSM-IV-TR (Diagnostic and Statistical Manual of Mental Disorders (APA Diagnostic Manual Electronic DSM -IV-Text Revision 2000)
www.mhc.com

Disabilities weblinks
www.disabilityweblinks.ca

MIT Encyclopedia of the Cognitive Sciences (Electronic MITES, 1999)
http//cognet.mit.edu/MITES/Front/au

New York Online Access to Health
Ask NOAH about genetic disorders
www.noah-health.org/english/illness/genetic_diseases/geneticdis.html

On-line Mendelian Inheritance in Man
Catalog of all known genetic disabilities and their causes
http://www.ncbi.nlm.nih.gov/entrez/query.fcgi?db=OMIM

Quality of Life for People with Developmental Disabilities
utoronto.ca/qol/pwdd.htm

Regulated Health Professionals Act (1994)
List of professionals regulated under the Act. Copies also available at tel: 416-326-5300
www.gov.on.ca

Diagnosis:

AAIDD. (2010). *Intellectual disability: Definition, classification, and systems of support* (11th ed.). Washington, DC: American Association on Intellectual and Developmental Disabilities.

intellectualdisability.info. (2011). *Understanding intellectual disability and health: Diagnosis.* Retrieved from http://www.intellectualdisability.info/diagnosis

Harris, J. C. (2005). *Intellectual disability: Understanding its development, causes, classification, evaluation, and treatment* (Developmental Perspectives in Psychiatry). New York: Oxford University Press.

Other:

Centers for Disease Control and Prevention (CDC)
4770 Buford Highway NE, Mail Stop F-45, Atlanta, GA 30341-3724, USA tel: 770-488-7035
http://www.cdc.gov/health/nfantsmenu.htm

National Easter Seal Society
230 West Monroe St., Suite 1800, Chicago, IL 60606-4802. tel: 1-800-221-6827
http://www.charitywire.com/charity59/

References

Adzick, N. S., Thom, E. A., Spong, C. Y., Brock, J. W., Burrows, P. K., Johnson, M. P. et al.; the MOMS Investigators. (2011). A randomized trial of trenatal versus postnatal repair of myelomeningocele. *New England Journal of Medicine,* Feb 9. [Epub ahead of print]

American Academy of Child and Adolescent Psychiatry. (1999). Practice parameters for the assessment and treatment of children, adolescents, and adults with mental retardation and co-morbid mental disorders. *Journal of Child and Adolescent Psychiatry, 38*(12, Suppl.).

American Psychiatric Association. (2000). *Diagnostic and statistical manual of mental disorders* (4th ed., text rev.). Washington, DC: Author.

Aman, M. G., Benson, B. A., & Campbell, K. M., et al. (1999). *Project Med Booklet series.* Columbus, OH: The Ohio State University.

Bae, E. H., Theodore, W. H., Fregni, F., Cantello, R., Pascual-Leone, A., & Rotenberg, A. (2011). An estimate of placebo effect of repetitive transcranial magnetic stimulation in epilepsy. *Epilepsy & Behavior, 20*(2), 355-359. Epub 2011 Jan 7.

Brasić, J. R., Barnett, J. Y., Kowalik, S., Tsaltas, M. O., & Ahmad, R. (2004). Neurobehavioral assessment of children and adolescents attending a developmental disabilities clinic. *Psychological Reports, 95*(3, Pt. 2), 1079-1086.

Brown, I., & Brown, R. I. (2003). *Quality of life and disability: An approach for community practitioners.* London: Jessica Kingsley Publishers.

Fletcher, R., Loschen, E., Stavrakaki, C., & First, M. (Eds.) (2009a). *Diagnostic manual-Intellectual disability (DM-ID): A textbook of diagnosis of men-*

tal disorders in persons with intellectual disability. Kingston, NY: NADD Press.

Fletcher, R., Loschen, E., Stavrakaki, C., & First, M. (2009b). *Diagnostic manual-Intellectual disability (DM-ID): A clinical guide for diagnosis of mental disorders in persons with intellectual disability.* Kingston, NY: NADD Press.

Government of Ontario. (1991). Regulated Health Professions Act, (1991 S.O. 1991, c. 18).

Illanes, S., & Soothill, P. (2009). Noninvasive approach for the management of hemolytic disease of the fetus. *Expert Reviews in Hematology, 2*(5), 577-582.

Irons, M. (1998; updated 2007 Oct 24). Smith-Lemli-Opitz syndrome. In R. A. Pagon, T. D. Bird, C. R.,Dolan, & K. Stephens (Eds.), *GeneReviews* [Internet]. Seattle, WA: University of Washington, Seattle. Retrieved from http://www.ncbi.nlm.nih.gov/bookshelf/br.fcgi?book=gene&part=slo

Jacobson, J. W., Mulick, J. A., & Green, G. (1998). Cost-benefit estimates for early intensive behavioral intervention for young children with autism – general model and single state case. *Behavioral Interventions, 13*, 201-226.

Katz, G. (2001). Adolescents and young adults with developmental disabilities interface the Internet: Six case reports of dangerous liaisons. Mental Health *Aspects of Developmental Disabilities, 4*(2), 77-84.

Mudford, O. C., Martin, N. T., Eikeseth, S., & Bibby, P. (2001). Parent-managed behavioral treatment for preschool children with autism: Some characteristics of UK programs. *Research in Developmental Disabilities, 22*, 173-182.

No Authors Listed. (2010). Deep brain stimulation shows promise for Alzheimer's, depression treatment. Doctors also now have more options in how DBS is used to treat Parkinson's disease. *Duke Medicine Health News, 16*(11), 1-2.

O'Flaherty, S. J., Janakan, V., Morrow, A. M., Scheinberg, A. M., & Waugh, M. C. (2011). Adverse events and health status following botulinum toxin type A injections in children with cerebral palsy. *Developmental Medicine & Child Neurology, 53*(2), 125-130. doi: 10.1111/j.1469-8749.2010.03814.x

Royal College of Psychiatrists. (2004). *OP48. DC-LD: Diagnostic criteria for psychiatric disorders for use with adults with learning disabilities/mental retardation.* Retrieved from http://64.233.167.104/search?q=cache:rT-gNxTX5NQJ:www.rcpsych.ac.uk/publications/gaskell/op48.htm+diagnostic+criteria+learning+disabilities+United+Kingdom&hl=en

Ruff, C .A., Wilcox, J. T., & Fehlings, M. G. (2011). Cell-based transplantation strategies to promote plasticity following spinal cord injury. *Experimental Neurology*, Feb 17. [Epub ahead of print]

Rush, A. J., & Frances, A. (Eds.). (2000). Expert consensus guideline series: Treatment of psychiatric and behavioural problems in mental retardation [Special issue]. *American Journal on Mental Retardation, 105*(3).

Schalock, R. L., Borthwick-Duffy, S. A., Buntinx, W. H. E., Coulter, D. L., & Craig, E. M. (2010). *Intellectual disability: Definition, classification, and systems of supports* (11th ed.). Washington, DC: AAIDD.

Tonekaboni, S. H., Mostaghimi, P., Mirmiran, P., Abbaskhanian, A., Abdollah Gorji, F., Ghofrani, M., et al. (2010). Efficacy of the Atkins diet as therapy for intractable epilepsy in children. *Archives of Iranian Medicine, 13*(6), 492-497.

Tsiouris, J. A., Patti, P. J., Tipu, O., et al. (2002). Adverse effects of phenytoin given for late-onset seizures in adults with Down syndrome. *Neurology, 59*, 779-780.

Tymchuk, A. J., Lakin, K. C., & Luckasson, R. (2001). *The forgotten generation: The status and challenges of adults with mild cognitive limitations.* Baltimore: Paul H. Brookes Publishing.

Wang, L. W., Berry-Kravis, E., & Hagerman, R. J. (2010). Fragile X: Leading the way for targeted treatments in autism. *Neurotherapeutics, 7*(3), 264-274.

Whiteley, P., Haracopos, D., Knivsberg, A. M., Reichelt, K. L., Parlar, S., Jacobsen, J., et al. (2010). The ScanBrit randomised, controlled, single-blind study of a gluten- and casein-free dietary intervention for children with autism spectrum disorders. *Nutritional Neuroscience, 13*(2), 87-100.

Zetlin, A., & Murtaugh, M. (1990). Whatever happened to those with borderline IQs? American *Journal on Mental Retardation, 94*, 463-469.

23

Introduction to Services and to Ontario's Developmental Disability Service System

Ivan Brown and Diane Galambos

What you will learn:

- The importance of informal and formal supports
- How and why supports and services keep changing
- Person-directed and family-directed approach to services and planning
- What is meant by Ontario's developmental disability service system
- Types of supports and services currently available in Ontario
- Dealing with Ontario's developmental disability service system
- Current service / system issues

In the previous chapter, we learned the important relationship between assessment and intervention. It was also noted that formal assessment and intervention occur primarily within the structure of a service system. This chapter provides an introduction to services in general and to Ontario's service system for children and adults with developmental disabilities and their families.

The Importance of Informal and Formal Supports

All people, both with and without disabilities, need support from others. For people with disabilities, we use the word *support* in another sense as well: to refer to the additional actions, routines, structures, and resources that others provide because of the disability to help make life better. Supports are available in Ontario for children and adults with developmental disabilities and their families to help with the particular needs that arise because of disability. These supports are both informal and formal.

Informal supports are offered within the natural settings of home and community. They include the countless ways that family members, friends, neighbours, co-workers, community people, and others help those who need it. All of us contribute to informal supports when we hold a door open for someone who uses a wheelchair or offer to look after a neighbour's child while the parents go shopping. Others give much more substantial informal support. Many parents and other family members make very large commitments to children and adults with developmental disabilities. Relatives, friends, and neighbours often give a great deal of their time and other resources. Volunteers contribute time, energy, and expertise in any number of areas of life. On the whole, the contribution of informal supports to people with developmental disabilities in Ontario is enormous, and without such supports a large number of people would be experiencing a very poor quality of life.

Formal supports are those that are set up purposely to address the needs of groups of people, although there is usually latitude for them to be tailored to individuals' needs. Because formal supports require planning, organization, legislation or policy, and resources, they have a structure and are usually called services. Services in Ontario for children and adults with developmental disabilities are funded primarily by the Ontario government, but other services are funded and provided by private groups, not-for-profit organizations, charitable groups and organizations, municipal governments, and others. Services have expanded considerably in Ontario over the past few decades, and they have become increasingly diverse.

Approaches to Service in Ontario

Services for people with developmental disabilities follow philosophical trends, and these have resulted in differing approaches to service. At one time in Ontario, almost all services took the form of institutional care. In the mid-1900s, parent groups organized across Ontario and started schools and day programs that provided alternate opportunities for both children and adults. Increasingly, because of changing attitudes and values, community agencies funded by the Ontario government took on these responsibilities, and the philosophy of community living replaced that of institutional care (see chapter 2 in particular for more information). Such changes briefly illustrate how there have been different approaches to service over the past 100 years, and how they have changed dramatically during that time.

There is almost always some push-and-pull be-

tween and among approaches to services, especially in times of service change. For example, consider the tensions that we have experienced — and are still experiencing — between:

- Institutional care vs. Community living
- Independent living vs. Supported care
- Family responsibility vs. Public responsibility

Over time, such tensions tend to work themselves out, but are usually replaced by other new ones.

Today, approaches to service are still changing in keeping with current philosophical, social, and economic changes. The mission statements of organizations and agencies across Ontario speak to the value placed on independence, community participation and inclusion, quality of life, and self-determination, yet it is up to the service system to put ideals into practice in the best way it can within the context of social and economic realities. This results in smaller but ongoing changes in approach to the service system. Four of the most important of these changes in approach that have begun too occur in recent years are:

- Providing funding, and control over that funding, directly to individuals and families in accordance with their specific support needs.
- Reframing the role of community agencies to reflect the support needs of individuals and families, rather than to generate programs for groups of people with developmental disabilities.
- Allocating financial and other resources in accordance with the assessed support needs of individuals and families.
- Coordinating services from various Ontario ministries, such as Children and Youth Services, Community and Social Services, Education, and Health.

Some changes in approaches to services occur in "small" ways such as response to new or altered policies or practices, while others emerge in larger and more formal ways, such as the introduction of the *Services and Supports to Promote the Social Inclusion of Persons with Developmental Disabilities Act, 2008* (Service Ontario, 2011). At other times, a group of changes may be initiated under program names such as Passport (Ontario Ministry of Community and Social Services, 2011), or under a change strategy such as Transformation, which is an MCSS plan to change the way that services and supports are provided to individuals and families.

Person-Directed and Family-Directed Support

Underlying a great many of the changes in services in recent years has been the gradual adoption of person-centred and family-centred support. The term person-centred, which is widely used in the disability literature, is referred to as person-directed in the *Services and Supports to Promote the Social Inclusion of Persons with Developmental Disabilities Act, 2008*, and thus the terms person-directed and family-directed are used as synonyms in this section. This approach to support is described in some detail here.

Developmental disability services in Ontario have experienced a change in terminology since about the mid-1990s. In daily practice, we have moved away from using "providing services to people with disabilities" and toward using "supporting people with disabilities." We also speak of "supporting families of children or adults with development disabilities." This may appear to be a small change in terminology, but the change in meaning is significant. It infers that we are not so much providing for a person or family as we are helping that person or family to strengthen their abilities and strengthen their environment so that they will be able to function in a better way.

Person-directed support for people with developmental disabilities means focussing attention and resources on the wants and needs of the person with disabilities when planning, delivering, or reviewing services and supports. Simply put, it means respecting the person's opinions and choices. Person-directed support is a way of delivering services and providing supports that place the person — rather than the service, organization, or system — at the centre. A number of useful resources have been developed to help professionals take person-directed approaches (e.g., Hagner, Helm, & Butterworth, 1996; Holburn

& Vietze, 2002; King, King, Rosenbaum, & Goffin, 1999; Strock-Lynskey & Keller, 2007; also see More Resources).

Family-directed support is very similar. Here, however, the whole family of the individual with a disability is the focus of the support, most often in cases where the child or adult with a disability lives with his or her family. It is recognized that the family is the immediate environment for the person, and that the functioning of the family unit in this environment very much affects the life of the person with a disability. In addition, family members (and parents in particular) have a responsibility for providing care and a positive living environment for their family member with a disability, and many family members require some support to do this effectively.

Person-directed and family-directed supports encompass four of the most important aspects of good services and supports:

1. Respect each person with a disability and family member as an individual human being with unique and valued characteristics.
2. Consider the rights and privileges of individual people with disabilities and individual families over the rights and privileges of groups of people or service providers, except when there is harm to oneself or others.
3. Develop and provide services and supports that are tailored to the needs and wants of individual people with disabilities and individual families, and that enhance the quality of their lives.
4. Determine the cost of services and supports, and the responsibility for administering funds, for each individual or each family rather than for groups or programs.

Person-directed and family-directed supports often incorporate other trends. It is often assumed, for example, that for people with developmental disabilities to have a high quality of life, they should do so in ways that are close to the way the general population lives. This involves living in communities and taking part in the resources and activities that communities have to offer in ways that are best suited to the individual person. Thus, the trend toward person-directed and family-directed support builds on other trends in the fields of developmental disabilities and on existing values held by most members of society. At the same time, it represents a shift in values toward people with disabilities as individuals and their families by addressing their unique needs, working toward effective choice and self-determination (Brown & Brown, 2009; Wehmeyer, 2002, 2007), and improving individual and family quality of life (Turnbull, Brown, & Turnbull, 2004).

PERSON-DIRECTED AND FAMILY-DIRECTED PLANNING

Planning is a normal everyday activity in which all people engage — some with more or less skill and success than others. One's everyday plans focus on how one wants things to be, what one would like to happen next, and how it should happen. Planning may take place at home, at work, at school, or during leisure activities. Although some plans may be quite comprehensive and might even be thought of as life plans, others are very specific — focussing on only one aspect of a person's life. There is no one way to formulate a plan that will work with all people in every setting, but planning of some kind does help to give a compass on our daily lives as well as our longer life journeys.

Most planning is informal and does not have accompanying documentation. From time to time, however, people engage in more formal planning activities such as career planning, education planning, financial planning, or retirement planning. For people with developmental disabilities and their families, and especially for those who are supported by other people, planning can be essential to:

- Identify the goals everyone is working toward
- Clarify each person's role
- Specify what each person is expected to do
- Tie funding to specific activities and expected outcomes
- Set some timelines for getting things done
- Mark accomplishments

Some key times to engage in planning

Planning may be carried out at any point in life — whenever there is a perceived need for it. Some formal services (such as schools or disability services through a community agency) may require plans as part of the service they provide, either at the beginning of the service or at specific times during the service. In addition, planning may be particularly important for:

- Deciding what jobs to train for and what employment to seek
- Selecting where and with whom to live
- How to pay for daily living expenses
- Learning about relationships and sexuality
- Making improvements in life in areas such as health, lifestyle, or leisure activities
- Making any major change in one's life
- Making any major change in the structure or circumstances of the family

What the planning process involves

One service provider described the person-directed planning process in this way: "An individual, along with his or her support network, develops a tailor-made support plan that identifies specific goals, expected outcomes, and natural and/or specialized support services required to actualize community living, participation, and quality of life" (Galambos, 2003, p. 394). Another description of person-directed planning is that the individual selects others to assist in a process of developing the plan that is the basis of support arrangements, whether they involve informal supports or more formal services. Family-directed planning is similar, except that family members, acting together, sets the agenda.

Whatever description is used, person-directed and family-directed planning is a shift away from planning by others and toward supporting people with disabilities and families in planning for themselves. Such planning is no longer based on what a service organization has to offer; rather, it is based on the person's or a family's wants and needs, as well as on their dreams and hopes for life — whatever those may be.

When engaging in person-directed and family-directed planning, it is essential to:

- *Remember who is in charge.* The person at the centre of planning should ideally "own" and direct his or her plan as well as the process for developing and implementing it. Optimal involvement in and control of planning may, at times, be best achieved with help from unpaid members of a support circle and/or an advocate. All those involved have a responsibility to help ensure that plans developed are personal and individual.

- *Focus on people, not on disabilities.* Being acknowledged as people first involves affirmation as a unique individual who happens to have a disability that may require some form of additional support. Consequently, the wants and needs of the person should govern what supports are required and how supports will be provided.
- *Connect people to natural supports, not just to programs.* Connecting people who have disabilities with natural supports — both people and community resources — is especially important for some individuals.
- *Avoid mindlessness.* In paid service provision, attempts to reduce the complexities of the workplace have at times resulted in planning processes and documents that are used like recipes. Interactions can become routine, hampering positive mindsets and creativity. Mindful staff remain alert to new ideas, especially those that emerge from natural interaction, and they participate in planning in ways that are both innovative and focussed on the individual.
- *Plan for today, not just tomorrow.* It is important to remember that most people make plans for the next hour, day, and week. Planning for the longer term can be very helpful too and should be done, but remember the thrill of spontaneity that comes from choosing to alter one's own plans and decide to willingly embrace something different.
- *Make plans for broad human needs.* Plans should reflect the fact that all people share the same universal needs for security, belonging, recognition, achievement, and control over one's life.

Who should participate in planning?

The individual with a disability, and the family members, should be involved as much as possible in developing the plan. The level of involvement may depend on his or her age, ability, and preferences. Anyone who knows and is committed to the individual and/or the family might also be involved. Thus, other members of the support network or planning team may include:

- Parents/guardians
- Other family members (e.g., brothers, sisters, grandparents, aunts, uncles, cousins)
- Friends and neighbours
- People from school, work, place of worship, or other community group
- An individual who specializes in planning and who has been asked (or hired) to facilitate the planning process
- Service providers
- Government or funding representative
- Medical personnel

The general principle for involving others is that the person himself or herself has the last word in who helps to construct the plan.

The plan can be written by the individual, family members, a facilitator, a friend, an advocate, or an experienced consultant. Plans can be simple or elaborate, of varying lengths, and in formats other than that of a formal report. They can include stories, journals, portfolios, photos, drawings, and diagrams — any form of representation or communication favoured by the individual.

Style and content

The written plan is a compilation of materials reflecting endeavours to understand who the person is and how his or her quality of life can be established, maintained, and enhanced. The plan usually includes the following information:

- An outline, or "map," of the person's support network
- Relevant information about the person's background and present circumstances
- A vision for the future
- A description of the person's likes and dislikes, wants and needs, and desires and hopes
- A statement of objectives to be attained
- A description of the support that is required to

attain the objectives

- A list of specific ways the objectives will be attained
- A list of the people who will help to attain the objectives
- A description of how the planning team will know when the objectives have been attained

All of the preceding items are often put together and formalized into a document that contains personal and private information. It is always important to remember that not everyone needs to know everything about a person with a disability. Involvement in planning begins with people with disabilities being in control over who knows what about their lives and circumstances. People with disabilities and their written plans become the focal point of a planning process that involves understanding, deciding, doing, and reviewing.

Moving from planning to implementation

Once a person-directed or family-directed plan has been developed, it is essential to put it into action and to monitor progress. In doing so, it is typically the case that those involved in the planning discuss and agree upon who will do what to make sure the plan comes to life. It is also an excellent idea to discuss and agree upon how, and at what points in time, progress will be monitored, and how it will be recognized (i.e., how will we know if the expected results or outcomes have been achieved?). Finally, no plans work out fully as anticipated and there are always some changes along the way. This is not a bad thing, because there are usually very good reasons why some changes need to be made. For example, life circumstances can change, or members of the planning team may realize that another course of action would lead to better results. Because there are always some changes, it is important to document what these are, why they have occurred, and what the revised outcomes are expected to be. A record of the implementation process needs to be kept, and kept up to date. There are many ways to record such information and each team should devise a way that best suits its needs, but Table 1 provides one simple way.

Ontario's Developmental Disability Service System

A major factor that influences how services and supports are provided to individuals with disabilities and their families is how Ontario's developmental disability service system functions.

WHAT IS A DEVELOPMENTAL DISABILITY SERVICE SYSTEM?

A number of service systems exist in Ontario, and all of us have used many of these over the course of our lives. Almost all of us have attended one or more parts of Ontario's education system (preschools, elementary schools, secondary schools, colleges, and universities), and all of us have accessed at least some part of Ontario's health care system (e.g., family doctors, hospitals, nursing homes, emergency care, dental care, and a broad array of health specialists). Some of us have used financial support systems, and a few of us have been involved in Ontario's legal system. The social service system is another of the many more examples of service systems in Ontario that many of us have used in various ways.

For people with developmental disabilities, the trend in Ontario for the past number of years has been to use, where possible, the services that are available to the general population. This trend has resulted in large numbers of people with developmental disabilities, like people with other disabilities, becoming involved in generic social services, health services, education services, income support, and many other services. In other words, they use the same services that are available to all of us wherever possible.

At times, though, some additional services are required to address the special needs of people with developmental disabilities and their families. Together, these special services can be thought of as *Ontario's developmental disability service system.*

ONTARIO MINISTRIES AND ONTARIO'S DEVELOPMENTAL DISABILITY SERVICE SYSTEM

A great many of the supports and services that constitute Ontario's developmental disability service system for people with developmental disabilities and their families originate from various Ministries of the

Table 1

Planned activity	What will be done?	Who will do it?	What are the expected results?	How and when will we know it has been accomplished?	Changes and reasons for changes
1.					
2.					
3.					
4.					

Ontario government. The Ontario government ministries are structured according to function, rather than according to populations. Thus, we have ministries in education, health, social services, and many others that are each designed to encompass the needs of all Ontarians within their area of function. Often, however, there is a need to focus within ministries on sub-populations that have specific needs, such as people with developmental disabilities. Thus, several ministries, but primarily the Ministry of Community and Social Services, have programs or special services that, together, comprise Ontario's developmental disability service system. The main services offered by four key ministries at the time of this book's publication (summer 2011) are described below.

Ministry of Community and Social Services

MCSS offers a wide array of services for adults with developmental disabilities. Six important areas of services are:

1. *Services provided by community agencies:* Approximately 380 community agencies in Ontario provide a large number of supports. These include supports to help people stay and be included in their communities, improve their activities of daily living, and participate in: work, volunteer, leisure, and recreation activities; residential supports (e.g., group homes); respite services; dual diagnosis support; assessment and counselling services; adult protective services; family support services, vocational training, specialized thera-

pies (e.g., speech and language, sex education, psychometric testing, autism programs); and many others.

2. *Residential supports:* These include group homes (called supported group living residences and intensive support residences under the new legislation); specialized residences; shared family homes.

3. *Passport:* This is a program to help with the transition from school to adult life, which promotes learning independence, building community living skills, and encouraging continued personal development.

4. *Special Services at Home:* SSAH provides funding for the special services that children with physical disabilities and children and adults with developmental disabilities need to continue living at home, including teaching new parenting skills. It also provides respite for family members.

5. *Ontario Disability Support Program.* ODSP provides income support to people with developmental disabilities who are in financial need to cover the cost of basic living expenses. It can also be used for vocational training or setting up self-employment. ODSP also provides numerous benefits, including health (drugs, dental, vision, medical supplies, and extended health benefits); disability-related (assistive devices, hearing aids, mobility devices, and guide dog benefits); employment (training, childcare costs, work-related benefits, transition benefits); and housing (start up and maintenance, and home repairs).

6. *Ontario Works.* This program is not specifically for people with developmental disabilities, but those who do not qualify for ODSP are sometimes covered by it. OW provides temporary financial assistance and employment assistance to those in need (including some additional costs such as childcare, counselling, etc.). It can also provide drug, dental, and vision care; assistive devices; extended health benefits; start up coverage; guide dog costs; child benefits for some people; and other special benefits.

Ministry of Children and Youth Services

MCYS offers an array of supports and services for special needs children. These supports cover children and youth with atypical developmental, physical and mental health problems, and behaviour difficulties. For children with developmental disabilities, services offered include:

- Special services at home
- Behaviour management
- Infant development
- Rehabilitation of various types (e.g., physiotherapy, occupational therapy, speech and language therapy)
- Specialized community supports to help children and youth live in their communities
- Respite care
- Residential services
- Autism Spectrum Disorder supports (e.g., intensive behaviour intervention, or IBI)

Ministry of Education

Since 1980, all children with disabilities, like non-disabled children in Ontario, have been entitled to free public education. There is also some limited support for continuing education for youth and adults. Education services for people with developmental disabilities in Ontario include:

- Preschool programs
- Support for exceptional students in elementary and secondary schools
- Some support within community colleges
- Some adult learning opportunities

(see chapter 41 for additional details)

Ministry of Health and Long-Term Care

The broad range of services offered by the Ministry of Health and Long-Term Care to the general population of Ontario is also available for people with developmental disabilities. These include:

- Physical health services
- Mental health services
- Dental care and drug coverage (for those who are eligible for Ontario Disability Support Program and Ontario Works benefits)
- Various types of rehabilitation
- Residential care, especially for older people with developmental disabilities
- Other specialized services, such as the Assistive Devices Program (see More Resources section for more information)

DEALING WITH ONTARIO'S SERVICE SYSTEM

Families in Ontario who have a child or adult with a developmental disability can find it very frustrating to understand, access, and navigate Ontario's developmental disability service system. There are some strategies, however, that can make it easier.

How do you know you need services?

Disability services are needed if a child or adult with a developmental disability is experiencing problems that are difficult or troublesome, and if dealing with those problems extends beyond the capabilities of usual family and community supports. Family members, in particular, should gather information from professionals (family doctors, pediatricians, teachers, social workers, etc.) about what services are available for their child, even if they think those services are not needed at the present time.

Can I get all services?

As mentioned, Ontario has numerous services available for children and adults with developmental disabilities. Most have eligibility criteria, and these are not necessarily the same from one service to another. Family members and disability support workers need to inquire and be knowledgeable about eligibility criteria for specific services. For some services, including adult developmental services and supports, a formal diagnosis of developmental disability will be necessary from a physician or psychologist. Many services cannot be accessed immediately, but rather applicants must "wait their turn" until an opening becomes available. Applicants should follow the progress of waiting lists, and remain open to alternatives that might provide similar service.

Applying for services

A new method was put in place, effective July 1, 2011, to apply for adult developmental disability services in Ontario. Regional contact points for developmental services, called Developmental Services Ontario, are designed to act as initial contact points for providing information, confirming eligibility, determining service and support needs, and recommending people to services and supports for which they are eligible (Ontario, 2011). Many services can be applied to directly as well. For example, application forms for Passport, ODSP, and Ontario Works are posted on the MCSS website and can be submitted online. Other services have different application procedures, including in-person and paper applications, or being referred by a disability support professional, physician, or other practitioner. Family members or professionals can make inquiries and initial contact for services through the intake departments of local community agencies.

Hints for keeping on top

Keeping up with what services are available, and how and when to apply for them takes time and effort. For family members who are busy with their own lives and have a son or daughter with a disability, keeping on top of changing services in Ontario may not be something they cherish doing. Still, most people find it helpful to be knowledgeable about services and to have some involvement in ongoing advocacy for better services. Some of the ways family members and disability professionals find useful to keep on top of service changes are to:

- Keep up with new developments in services (e.g., through Ontario ministry websites, information from local community agencies).
- Know local service providers such as community agencies, people who work for MCYS or

MCSS, and consult with them when needed.
- Visit reputable websites, or subscribe to one or more of the many excellent magazines in developmental disability.
- Explore ways to keep abreast of new research findings and new ideas of disability scholars.
- Read books, blogs, and other accounts written by people with disabilities and family members.
- Join social media discussions, and exchange views and new discoveries.
- Become involved in community leisure and recreational activities for children and adults with disabilities.
- Become involved in fund raising for specific causes.
- Join parent and family advocacy groups.
- Become familiar with politicians who exercise influence over disability policy and funding.

Ongoing Issues and Challenges for Our Field

In spite of the numerous services that are available in Ontario for people with developmental disabilities, some important challenges remain. The questions of what services should be available and who should receive these services has been debated for many years. These questions are particularly important because the pressing need for services has been apparent for several decades but, from the numbers of people currently on waiting for services, this need appears to be as great now as it ever was.

Seven key challenges that need to be more fully addressed, and that should be useful at the policy, service, and advocacy levels, are:

1. To what degree is the well-being of people with developmental disabilities in Ontario the responsibility of the Ontario public? To what degree is it the responsibility of families of individuals with developmental disabilities and other people in their support networks?

2. How can we promote a person-directed and family-directed approach to services when there are long waiting lists for many services, and people often have to settle for what they can get?

3. How can families who do not currently receive

services, but who need them, be made aware of the services that are available?

4. How can the services that are in place for families and people with developmental disabilities best be offered?

5. How can we know how many children and adults in Ontario have developmental disabilities (currently we get information from PALS, the Paricipation and Acitivity Limitations Survey (Statistics Canada, 2007), although this information has limitations)? How can we know how many of these really need services? For those who do not receive services, how can we know if and when they will need services in the future?

6. How can such services be available in an equitable way to those across Ontario who need them?

7. How can we ensure that such services respect high standards of quality of care, and that they promote better quality of life for people with developmental disabilities?

Summary

Ontario, like other jurisdictions, relies on both formal and informal support for people with developmental disabilities. Formal supports, usually referred to as services, come in many forms, and the services from several Ministries of the Ontario government and other organizations comprise Ontario's developmental disability service system. The service system is somewhat complicated, but there are numerous types of services available for children, adults, and families. Specific services have different eligibility criteria, and many have their own application process. Providing services presents some challenges that emerge from the central question of how to adequate address the needs of people with developmental disabilities and their families and how to ensure that people are able to lead quality lives.

Acknowledgements

The authors are very grateful to Allan Devlin and Maria Gitta for their helpful comments on the content of this chapter. The contributions of Denise Poston and Ann Turnbull to the discussion of person-directed and family-directed approaches are also greatly appreciated.

For Further Thought and Discussion

1. Considering your own usual daily activities and those of your family members and friends, list ways that you provide informal support to people with disabilities. Give a specific example where applicable.

2. Debate with your classmates how a person-directed and family-directed approach might guide the development of new services (what new serives, how they are structured, etc.).

3. In a group, design a person-directed plan for an individual you know, or a family-directed plan for a family you know. Include a method for implementing and tracking to progress of the plan.

4. Ontario's developmental disability service system is currently an amalgam of programs and services from several Ontario ministries. List reasons why this works well, and list reasons why a more coordinated approach might work better.

5. Write a short case study on how an individual or family accesses a new service. Share case studies with your classmates, and discuss challenges to individuals and families. Identify, where possible, solutions to these challenges.

6. Select one of the ongoing issues and challenges from the final section of this chapter's text. Discuss why this is an ongoing issue, and what might be done to work toward a resolution.

More Resources

Ontario Government Ministries:

Ministry of Children and Youth Services
http://www.children.gov.on.ca/

Ministry of Community and Social Services — Developmental Services
http://www.mcss.gov.on.ca/en/mcss/programs/developmental/index.aspx

Ontario Disability Support Program
http://www.mcss.gov.on.ca/en/mcss/programs/social/odsp/

Ontario Works

http://www.mcss.gov.on.ca/en/mcss/programs/social/ow/index.aspx

Ministry of Education — Special Education

http://www.edu.gov.on.ca/eng/parents/speced.html

Ministry of Health and Long-Term Care

http://www.health.gov.on.ca/en/

Assistive Devices Program

http://www.health.gov.on.ca/english/public/program/adp/adp_mn.html

Web resources:

Allen, Shea, and Associates. A resource list on person-centered planning

http://www.allenshea.com/resource.html

British Institute of Learning Disabilities. Factsheet — person centred planning.

http://www.bild.org.uk/pdfs/05faqs/pcp.pdf

Centre for Community Child Health. Family-centred practice readings and resources

http://www.rch.org.au/emplibrary/ccch/EY_Ref_mod2.pdf

Cornell University ILR School, Employment and Disability Institute. What is person-centered planning?

http://www.ilr.cornell.edu/edi/pcp/

Mencap. Person-centred approaches

http://www.mencap.org.uk/page.asp?id=608

NADD. Elements of family-centered care.

http://www.thenadd.org/cgi-bin/checkmember.pl?page=pages/membership/bulletins/v1n4a3

References

Brown, I., & Brown, R. I. (2009). Choice as an aspect of quality of life for people with intellectual disabilities. *Journal of Policy and Practice in Intellectual Disabilities, 6*(1), 11-18.

Hagner, D., Helm, D. T., & Butterworth, J. (1996). "This is your meeting": A qualitative study of person-centered planning. *Mental Retardation, 34,* 159–171.

Holburn, S., & Vietze, P. M. (Eds.) (2002). *Person-centered planning: Research, practice, and future directions.* Baltimore: Paul H. Brookes Publishing Co.

Galambos, D. (2003). Individual approaches to support. In I. Brown & M. Percy (Eds.), *Developmental disabilities in Ontario* (2nd ed.) (pp. 391-406). Toronto, ON: Ontario Association on Developmental Disabilities.

King, G., King, S., Rosenbaum, P., & Goffin, R. (1999). Family-centered caregiving and well-being of parents of children with disabilities: Linking process with outcome. *Journal of Pediatric Psychology, 24*(1), 41-53.

Ontario. (2011). *One-window access for developmental services.* Retrieved from http://www.news.ontario.ca/mcss/en/2010/11/one-window-to-access-to-information-and-services.html

Ontario Ministry of Community and Social Services. (2011). *Services and supports for people with a developmental disability: Passport.* Retrieved from http://www.mcss.gov.on.ca/en/mcss/programs/developmental/servicesAndSupport/passport.aspx

Service Ontario. (2011). *Services and Supports to Promote the Social Inclusion of Persons with Developmental Disabilities Act, 2008.* Retrieved from http://www.e-laws.gov.on.ca/html/statutes/english/elaws_statutes_08s14_e.htm

Statistics Canada. (2007). *Participation and Activity Limitations Survey.* Retrieved from http://www.statcan.gc.ca/cgi-bin/imdb/p2SV.pl?Function=getSurvey&SDDS=3251&lang=en&db=imdb&adm=8&dis=2

Strock-Lynskey, D., & Keller, D. W. (2007). Integrating a family-centered approach into social work practice with families with children and adolescents with disabilities. *Journal of Social Work in Disability & Rehabilitation, 6*(1&2), 111-134. Also available from http://www.informaworld.com/smpp/content~content=a902816690~db=all~jumptype=rss

Turnbull, A., Brown, I., & Turnbull, R. (Eds.) (2004). *Families and persons with mental retardation and quality of life: International perspectives.* Washington, DC: American Association on Mental Retardation.

Wehmeyer, M. L. (2002). The confluence of person-centered planning and self-determination. In S.

Holburn & P. M. Vietze (Eds.), *Person-centered planning: Research, practice, and future directions* (pp. 51–69). Baltimore: Paul H.Brookes Publishing Co.

Wehmeyer, M. L. (2007). *Promoting self-determination in students with developmental disabilities.* New York: Guilford Press.

Behavioural Intervention and Developmental Disabilities

Rosemary A. Condillac

What you will learn:

- Why many people with developmental disabilities need behavioural intervention
- How to decide which behaviours need intervention
- What behavioural intervention is
- Why behavioural intervention is usually the best choice for individuals with developmental disabilities
- What types of behavioural intervention are used in the treatment of people with developmental disabilities
- What the current model of best practice for assessing and treating the problematic behaviour of individuals with developmental disabilities is

Why Do Many People with Developmental Disabilities Need Behavioural Intervention?

North American reports of the prevalence of problematic behaviour suggest that between one-third and one-half of individuals with developmental disabilities exhibit some form of problematic behaviour. A province-wide study conducted in Ontario, Canada found that, of 948 individuals with developmental disabilities, problematic behaviour was exhibited by over 50% of children from 4 to 11 years of age, and over 45% of adolescents and adults aged 12 years and older. The most frequently exhibited behaviours were physical aggression, inappropriate verbal behaviour, self-injury, and non-compliance (Atkinson et al., 1994). A recent study from Scotland reported that 22.5% of their sample of adults with DD exhibited problematic behaviours (Cooper, Smiley, Morrison, Williamson, & Allan, 2006). Problematic behaviours can increase the risk of social isolation, and decrease the quality of life experienced by individuals with developmental disabilities.

People with developmental disabilities may be more

Box 1: Questions to Ask about the Topography of Behaviour

Topography refers to a precise and detailed description of a landscape. Behaviour analysts borrow this term in an effort to provide specific, observable, and measurable descriptions of behaviours that are considered to be problematic. Four key questions to ask that help to put together a topography are listed below. Behaviours that cross boundaries suggested by each of the four question areas — how often, how intense, how long, and wrong situation — may warrant behavioural intervention.

> *Frequency: Does the behaviour occur too often (e.g., hitting others) or not often enough (e.g., initiating social interaction)?*
>
> *Intensity: Is the behaviour too intense (e.g., causing bleeding or broken bones) or not intense enough (e.g., speaking too quietly for others to hear)?*
>
> *Duration: Does the behaviour last too long (e.g., rocking repeatedly) or is it too brief (e.g., sitting and attending for only very short periods)?*
>
> *Discrimination: Does the behaviour occur in the wrong place (e.g., masturbating in public), at the wrong time (e.g., laughing at a funeral), with the wrong people (e.g., hugging strangers)?*

Sources: Martin and Pear (1999) and York Behaviour Management Services (1997).

likely to exhibit problematic behaviours when they have limited development of communicative, cognitive, social, emotional, and adaptive skills (Feldman & Griffiths, 1997). Those with limited communication skills may exhibit problematic behaviour as a result of their inability to make their needs and wants known in more appropriate ways. Others with compromised cognitive skills might demonstrate problem behaviour if task demands or curricula are beyond their current skill levels. Some have learned over time that problematic behaviour can be an effective way to elicit change in an environment where they may otherwise lack power and freedom of choice. Thus, it is important that behavioural assessment and intervention practices take into account both the individual's developmental ability and the environmental events that might affect their problematic behaviour.

Finally, many individuals with developmental disabilities who do not exhibit problematic behaviour require additional supports to learn new skills. Behavioural teaching methods have been demonstrated to be effective methods for increasing communication skills, social skills, activities of daily living, and academic skills in community settings (Repp, Favell, & Munk, 1996). These methods for skill development can be used to develop target skills that have been identified by the individual, or by professionals such as speech and language pathologists, occupational therapists, and teachers.

Which Behaviours Need Intervention?

People with developmental disabilities can exhibit a wide range of problematic behaviours. Before attempting to change a behaviour, it is important to determine why it is problematic (Griffiths, 1989; Martin & Pear, 1999). Some behaviours, such as hitting, spitting, or head banging can be considered problematic if they cause physical harm, and/or limit opportunities for learning and community integration. Other behaviours, such as screaming, having tantrums, or throwing items can be problematic if they are disruptive to routines, or limit opportunities for social interaction. (See Box 1 for more information.) Another important reason for targeting a specific behaviour for change is because the individual him/herself has expressed a desire to change. In other situations, care-providers may have to assist the individual in understanding why a particular behaviour is problematic, and why it needs to be changed. It is not considered ethical to target a behaviour for change simply because it is "annoying." If this were acceptable, virtually everyone with or without developmental disabilities would have at least one behaviour program. It is important to note that in addition to behavioural excesses (e.g., hitting, screaming), deficits in behaviour can also require intervention. Some typical areas of skill deficits for people with developmental disabilities include communication skills, social skills, dressing skills, eating skills, and leisure skills. Similar to behavioural excesses, skill deficits can have limiting effects on an individual's quality of life.

What Is Behavioural Intervention?

Behavioural intervention is the name used to describe a wide range of techniques that are based on learning theories. These theories focus on observable environmental events that prompt, increase, maintain, and decrease the occurrence of both appropriate and inappropriate behaviours. Another term used to describe behavioural intervention is applied behaviour analysis (ABA; Baer, Wolf, & Risley, 1968).

There are several key tenets in ABA. Conditions that are known to prompt a particular behaviour are called antecedents. Antecedents precede a behaviour and set the stage for it to occur. For example, the smell of freshly baked bread might be an antecedent for entering a bakery. Conditions that increase, decrease, or maintain behaviours are called consequences. Consequences are the responses (or lack of response) that immediately follow an individual's behaviour. A consequence that results in an increase in a particular behaviour is called reinforcement. Reinforcement literally means strengthening. For example, a student who stays up all night to cram for a mid-term exam might be reinforced for her behaviour if she receives a good grade. We will be able to say this with more certainty if the student crams again for her next exam. Reinforcement is a process that results in an increased likelihood that the behaviour will re-occur.

A consequence that decreases the likelihood that specific behaviour will re-occur is called punishment. The consequence only counts as a punisher if the behaviour in question decreases. For example,

Box 2: Is This an Example of Reinforcement or Punishment?

Zack is a 10-year-old with limited communication and motor skills. During art class, he is asked to cut out shapes and glue them together. After approximately 1 minute, Zack throws the glue on the floor. The teacher, wanting to punish him for this behaviour, sends Zach out to the hallway for 5 minutes. When 5 minutes are up, Zach is returned to his table in the classroom and given his project back. He immediately throws the glue again and is sent back to the hallway for 5 minutes. This scenario is repeated three more times in the next 20 minutes.

Did the consequence of being removed from the task have a reinforcing or a punishing effect on Zack's behaviour? Because Zack threw glue often, it had a reinforcing effect. Zack's teacher intended the consequence of sending him into the hallway to be a punishment. However, it was not an effective punisher because throwing did not decrease. Instead, Zack's throwing increased as a result of being sent out of the classroom. This is what is known as inadvertent reinforcement of problematic behaviour. In other words, Zack was taught to throw the glue to get out of art class, although this was certainly not the teacher's intention.

Source: Condillac (2003).

if a person who regularly leaves a car in a no parking zone returns to the car to find a sizeable parking ticket, and consequently stops parking in such zones, an effective punishment has occurred. What is important to note is that it is not our intention, but rather the effect of the consequence upon the individual's behaviour, that determines if an event is reinforcing or punishing (see Box 2). These are some of the basic tenets of applied behaviour analysis — tenets that are essential to a clear understanding of behavioural intervention.

Types of Behavioural Intervention Used

For decades, behavioural interventions have been used in the education and treatment of individuals with developmental disabilities. One of the great

Box 3: Positive Behaviour Support (PBS)

A group of researchers (Carr, Horner, & Turnbull, 1999) completed a research synthesis of PBS in 1999 in response to a request from the U.S. Department of Education. They did a comprehensive review of articles published between 1985 and 1996 that evaluated the use of PBS to treat individuals with intellectual disabilities and problem behaviour. The major findings of this research included the following:

- *PBS is widely applicable for individuals with intellectual disabilities living in community settings and can be implemented by direct care staff and families.*
- *The major growth in the field is in the area of changing deficient environments and emphasizing antecedent strategies.*
- *PBS is effective for between one-half and two-thirds of reported cases of challenging behaviour.*

There is an almost two-fold improvement in outcome when intervention is based on the results of a functional analysis and implemented by care providers in natural environments.

Source: Condillac (2003).

debates in the treatment of problematic behaviours for individuals with developmental disabilities has been the use of intrusive versus non-intrusive procedures (Repp & Singh, 1990). Intrusive procedures include such procedures as contingent electric shock, seclusionary time out, contingent use of facial screening, physical or mechanical restraint, and various other techniques that emphasize punishment. There are concerns that these intrusive punishment procedures adversely affect the relationship between the participant and the punisher, and that they bring about decreases in the problematic behaviour only in the presence of the punisher or in the environment where it was used (LaVigna & Donnellan, 1986). There is a further concern with the use of such techniques in community settings (e.g., at a restaurant or shopping mall), as they may have a negative impact on community acceptance of individuals with developmental disabilities. There is also concern that more intrusive procedures impact on the dignity and personal freedoms of individuals with developmental disabilities.

Over the past 20 years, there has been extensive research into and development of less intrusive techniques, which have come to be known as positive behavioural supports (Koegel, Koegel, & Dunlap, 1996; Jackson & Veeneman Panyan, 2002; see also Box 3). Positive behavioural supports have been demonstrated to be effective in treating self-injuri-

ous, aggressive, and severely disruptive behaviour exhibited by children and adults with developmental disabilities in community settings (Feldman, Condillac, Tough, Hunt, & Griffiths, 2002). An additional aspect of positive behavioural supports is that they endeavour to affect behaviour change in ways that avoid pain and loss of dignity (Jackson & Veeneman Panyan, 2002). These include environmental changes, increased positive reinforcement, skill building, and planned natural consequences. Many of these approaches attempt to decrease problematic behaviour by changing antecedents. When successful, these techniques result in reduced rates of problematic behaviour through prevention, thus avoiding the need for more intrusive punitive consequences. The emphasis has shifted from "cookbook" style applications of behavioural procedures (e.g., if aggression, use time out) to the current idea of focussing on the comprehensive assessment of medical and environmental patterns, and determining the function of the problem behaviour for the individual (Feldman & Griffiths, 1997).

Why Behavioural Intervention Is a Good Treatment

A large North American study that examined treatment effectiveness found that those behavioural interventions that were functionally related

Box 4: Case Example of Biomedical Assessment

Lisa, a 7-year-old with severely limited verbal skills, had been banging her head with increasing frequency over the course of a few weeks. Her behaviour increased in the evening, and it was highest when she was lying down on her bed or in the living room.

Given the sudden onset of this behaviour, a medical check-up would be recommended to confirm or rule out a possible medical condition. This was done, and Lisa was found to have otitis media, a painful ear infection. Self-injurious behaviour, such as head banging, may have served to decrease or distract from the pain brought on by Lisa's medical condition.

Once Lisa's ear infection was successfully treated by her physician, head-banging decreased significantly. It did not go away completely, however, as it was still being maintained by environmental factors.

Source: Condillac (2003).

to the cause of severely problematic behaviours had the most demonstrated effectiveness for individuals with developmental disabilities (National Institute of Health (NIH), 1991). In this study, experts developed a consensus report based upon existing scientific evidence. They found that there was scientific evidence to support the use of behavioural interventions that included behaviour enhancement strategies (aimed at increasing desirable behaviour), behaviour reduction strategies (aimed at decreasing undesirable behaviour), educational strategies (aimed at teaching adaptive replacement skills), and eco-behavioural strategies (aimed at preventing problem behaviour by changing the environment).

The researchers in this study also found that an alarming number of individuals with developmental disabilities who engaged in serious problematic behaviour were treated only with psychotropic medication, despite the absence of scientific evidence for this approach (in isolation) as a treatment for behaviour problems. Medication should be used, when appropriate, to treat medical and psychiatric issues that are diagnosed by a qualified practitioner and that can potentially underlie the individual's

problematic behaviour. As a treatment for problematic behaviour, medication should be used: a) as a last resort when less intrusive methods have been unsuccessful, b) as a temporary crisis intervention measure, c) only when monitored closely by a physician, and d) in conjunction with a behavioural intervention program.

The final recommendation of this panel was to endorse the use of multi-elemental behavioural interventions as the treatment of choice for individuals with developmental disabilities who exhibit severe problematic behaviours. Psychopharmacological intervention (use of medication) should usually be prescribed only to treat a psychiatric or medical condition. In some serious cases, short-term use of behaviour control medication might be warranted to assist in the implementation of behavioural interventions and as a crisis intervention. Finally, the panel's findings remind us that regardless of the type of intervention used, valid, informed, legal, and voluntary consent must be obtained from the individual and/or the legal guardian (National Institute of Health (NIH), 1991).

Current Model of Best Practice For Treating Problematic Behaviour

Behavioural intervention can be seen as consisting of two complementary parts: a comprehensive functional behavioural assessment, and a treatment plan. A treatment plan should be guided by the information gleaned from the assessment, and should be developed using positive behavioural supports (Sugai et al., 2000). The treatment plan should flow naturally from the results of the assessment, and should include recommendations that stem from a working hypothesis. More intrusive approaches should only be considered for those cases where careful and systematic attempts at using less intrusive approaches have been unsuccessful (Feldman, 1990).

WHAT IS A COMPREHENSIVE BEHAVIOURAL ASSESSMENT?

A comprehensive behavioural assessment should be undertaken by a trained professional, such as a

Box 5: Case Example of Environmental Assessment

Jerome is a 53-year-old who lives in a community-group home. Staff are concerned about his aggressive behaviour. After keeping track of his hitting for 2 weeks, it became evident that the majority of problems occurred just before, or on the way to, evening outings with the other residents.

What possible antecedent change might you suggest? Simply offering Jerome more control over his environment by allowing him to choose between two desirable activities might prevent many incidents of aggression. Of course, it would be important to know other information as well. With whom does he sit in the van? Does he like the places they go? Is there something he would rather be doing at home?

Source: Condillac (2003).

psychologist with training in applied behaviour analysis, or a behaviour therapist who has received relevant training. The assessment must consider biomedical, environmental/interactional, and functional explanations for the problematic behaviour. Any combination of these factors may influence the emergence and maintenance of problematic behaviour (NIH, 1991; Ontario Association for Behaviour Analysis, 1998).

Biomedical assessment

Biomedical issues often underlie problematic behaviour in people with developmental disabilities (Feldman & Griffiths, 1997). This can be magnified by the individual's inability to communicate his or her symptoms. Medical questions can also arise if the individual is taking medication with potentially adverse side-effects. It is essential to uncover any potential biomedical or psychiatric explanations for problematic behaviour and to ensure that they are treated or that medical causes are ruled out before treating the problem using a behavioural approach. If the onset of the problematic behaviour was recent, or if there has been a sudden increase in problematic behaviour, there may be an underlying medical issue. It would be unethical to provide behavioural intervention without ruling out an un-

derlying medical cause.

Many individuals with developmental disabilities may lack the communication skills necessary to make their basic needs known, and may lack the daily living skills to meet these needs for themselves (Singh, Oswald, & Ellis, 1998). With this in mind, we must consider issues such as hunger, thirst, fatigue, and illness, including earaches, toothaches, headaches, and other forms of pain as potential underlying influences for problematic behaviour. It is important to note that even if physical or medical issues have been the initial cause of problematic behaviour, environmental factors may be maintaining the behaviour even after these issues have been properly addressed. See Box 4 for an example.

Environmental/interactional assessment

Routines and interactions in the individual's natural environment may also influence problematic behaviour. Sometimes activities are too difficult, while at other times activities are not adequately challenging. Some activities involve participation with a group, and others require independence. Unfortunately, many people with developmental disabilities are not given the choice of participating in activities that they prefer. Many are taught to comply with requests from staff or family members at the expense of personal preference. As a result, some activities may be associated with more problematic behaviour because they lack appeal to the individual with developmental disabilities (Brown, Shirage, York, Zanella, & Rogan, 1984). Therefore, it is important to determine the activities and situations that are associated with the highest rates of problematic behaviour, and the situations that are associated with the lowest rates or absence of the problematic behaviour (Touchette, MacDonald, & Langer, 1985). With this information, routines can be altered to create a better match between the individual and his or her environment. Wherever possible, it is essential to involve individuals with developmental disabilities in any treatment plan, and to consider their personal preferences when suggesting alternate activities.

Some potential antecedent events that may prompt problematic behaviour can include: 1) ending a pre-

Table 1: The Functions of Problem Behaviour

- *Behaviour might serve to provide escape from tasks or people. Time-out (an intended punisher) often provides students with escape from difficult demands or demanding individuals. As a result, it serves to strengthen behaviour instead of decreasing it.*
- *Behaviour may serve to gain access to increased attention from caregivers. Even seemingly unpleasant interactions, such as reprimands, may positively reinforce (increase) problematic behaviours.*
- *Behaviour may result in increased access to tangibles (e.g., activities, items). An individual might be given an item (e.g., a Popsicle) when a care provider notices the individual biting her fingers.*
- *Behaviour that serves a sensory function serves to gain access to internal reinforcement, independent of environmental factors (e.g., rocking back and forth for hours when alone).*

Source: Iwata, Dorsey, Slifer, et al. (1982).

ferred activity; 2) task demands that are too difficult or that are incompatible with the person's developmental level; 3) interaction (or lack thereof) with people in the environment; or 4) being denied access to something that the person has requested. This information is used to develop environmental change procedures that can prevent or reduce problematic behaviour by reducing or eliminating the occurrence of antecedent events. For example, if a behaviour occurred every time an individual were asked to wash the dishes, a prevention strategy might include not asking him to wash the dishes, asking him to wash only one dish or a few dishes, or asking him to choose one of three times when he will begin to wash the dishes. See Box 5 for another example.

Functional assessment

All behaviour serves a purpose for an individual. It may serve to increase attention, or to end an unpleasant situation. In order to determine the purpose that problematic behaviour serves, a functional behavioural assessment (FBA) should be completed (FBA; Sugai, et al., 2000). An FBA is an assessment technique used to determine the sources and types of reinforcement that an individual receives in response to his/her behaviour.

Research regarding the effectiveness of treatment has demonstrated that functional assessment is a better predictor of the success of behavioural intervention than the specific type of treatment used. That is, treatments that are guided by the results of

functional assessment have proven to be more effective than those that do not use this method (Carr et al., 1999; Freeman, 1993).

There are two categories of functional assessment techniques used by experts: experimental and descriptive (Cooper, Heron, & Heward, 2007). Experimental approaches, which are considered to be the gold standard, include a series of sessions designed to demonstrate the influence of different consequences on the problem behaviour (Iwata et al., 1982). Descriptive approaches include both indirect and direct assessment of the function of problem behaviour. Indirect assessment includes such tools as interviews (e.g., O'Neill, Horner, Albin, Storey, & Sprague, 1990) or informant rating scales (e.g., Durand & Crimmins, 1988). Direct assessment approaches typically involve observations in the person's natural environment (O'Neill et al., 1990). Irrespective of the approach used, the four functional categories that are most commonly used by clinicians include access to escape, attention, tangibles, and sensory stimulation (see Table 1). Once the function(s) of the behaviour is (are) determined, the individual can be taught to use an appropriate behaviour to serve the same purpose(s) as the problematic behaviour (Carr & Durand, 1985). It is not unusual for one behaviour to serve multiple functions or for two behaviours to serve the same function (see Box 6 for an example).

Behavioural assessment is typically based on the collection of relevant information from interview

Box 6: Case Example of Functional Assessment

Kevin is a 23-year-old with severe multiple physical and intellectual disabilities. His problematic behaviour consists of screaming for periods ranging from 10 to 30 minutes. Staff try to calm him down by talking to him, but the only thing that appears to calm him down is when staff (as a last resort) make him a cup of tea. In fact, he has been getting so much tea to calm him that staff have stopped making Kevin tea at other times.

Because functional analysis focusses on the consequences of an individual's behaviour, in this case it was necessary for staff members to ask, "What happens when Kevin screams?" They realize that the answer is that staff talk to him for awhile, then make him a cup of tea. The next question they asked was, "When else do staff give Kevin their undivided attention and a cup of tea?" Unfortunately, the answer is only when he screams. His screaming serves to gain him both increased attention (staff talk to him) and increased access to tangibles (tea).

Kevin needs to learn a way to ask for these things without having to scream. One approach might be for staff to teach Kevin to raise his hand or blow a whistle when he wants their attention. Another option would be to permanently attach a travel mug to Kevin's chair so Kevin could touch the mug to show staff that he would like tea. Once learned, these new skills may serve the same purpose for Kevin as his screaming and thus make screaming unnecessary.

Source: Condillac (2003).

and observational methods. Several data collection techniques may be required to carry out a single comprehensive assessment. These can include interviewing the individual and the care providers, keeping track of the specific problem behaviour and the context (antecedents and consequences) in which it occurs, and monitoring the frequency, intensity, and duration of a problematic behaviour.

WHAT IS A TREATMENT PLAN, AND HOW IS IT DEVELOPED?

After the comprehensive behavioural assessment is completed, a treatment plan specific to the individual's needs should be developed. A treatment plan needs to be: a) developed in consultation with a trained professional; b) documented; and c) monitored (Feldman, Atkinson, Fotis-Gervais, & Condillac, 2004; see Box 7 for more details). The treatment plan flows directly from the findings of the behavioural assessment and is based on the data that has been collected.

The goal of the plan is to prevent or decrease problematic behaviour using the least intrusive procedures while teaching the individual adaptive replacement skills. Regardless of the level of intrusiveness of the interventions being used, the treatment plan must be clearly and thoroughly reviewed by the individual with developmental disabilities and/or his/her parent or guardian. Informed and voluntary consent must be obtained before the plan can be implemented.

Prevention

Prevention strategies are developed from the findings of the environmental assessment. The goal of this phase of treatment is to prevent problematic behaviours from occurring by making appropriate changes to the antecedents (e.g., routines and interactions) in the environment that prompt the individual's problematic behaviour. Another objective is to create the best match possible between the individual with developmental disabilities and the living and learning environments. Prevention strategies create an environment in which the antecedents that pose the highest risk of prompting the problematic behaviour are avoided whenever possible. These high-risk activities are replaced by activities that are not typically associated with the problematic behaviour. A careful look at the antecedents might suggest, for example, that an individual exhibits more problematic behaviour when watching television alone, and rarely acts out

Box 7: Formal versus Informal Behavioural Interventions

A study examining the use of behavioural interventions to treat individuals with intellectual disabilities found that more than 50% of the interventions being implemented were informal, undocumented, and not monitored (Feldman et al., 2004). Formal treatment plans that were: 1) designed (or supervised) by a qualified professional, 2) written (documented), and 3) evaluated (data is collected and monitored) were found to be more effective and less intrusive than informal strategies that were implemented by caregivers. Informal interventions tend to evolve from dealing with behaviour on an incident-by-incident basis. The following example of an informal approach is NOT recommended as a treatment approach:

Terry threw a plate, so the staff members did not allow him to watch television after dinner on Monday. He threw a plate again on Tuesday and was sent to his room to keep him from watching television with his housemates. On Wednesday he threw his plate and was sent to his room to think about what he had done. On Thursday, he threw the plate and was sent to his room. He started screaming, so staff members shut the door. It took two staff members to keep Terry from opening the door and exiting the room.

This type of informal intervention is problematic in several ways. First, it is not based on an assessment, and there is no consideration of the function of Terry's behaviour. Second, the removal of television evolved into being sent to his room, then to having the door closed and held shut. In many jurisdictions, it is against the law for paid caregivers to implement this type of procedure without proper documentation and supervision. Third, the behavioural issue became worse, and the informal intervention escalated in intrusiveness, yet Terry (or his consent source) had not agreed to the intervention plan.

Unfortunately, such situations are quite common. Whenever possible, caregivers implementing behavioural interventions should: 1) enlist the help of a qualified professional in developing and monitoring the intervention, 2) write down the plan so that all involved are using the same strategies, and 3) have regular reviews of the progress (or lack thereof).

Source: Condillac (2007).

when helping a staff person make dinner. In this case, watching television alone should be avoided, while opportunities to assist staff should be maximized (Touchette, MacDonald, & Langer, 1985). Antecedent changes can result in rapid decreases in problematic behaviour without the use of more aversive techniques.

Skill promotion

Once problematic behaviours are successfully being prevented, the stage is set to teach new adaptive behaviours. The goal of the second phase of treatment, skill promotion, is to teach the individual skills that will serve the function that was originally served by the problematic behaviour. Naturally, this phase of treatment is dependent upon the results of the functional analysis.

If, for example, the functional analysis reveals that the individual's self-injury and aggression serves to gain escape from difficult tasks, he or she will be taught to access escape from task demands by requesting a break. There are several ways to request a break. A few possibilities include: a verbal request such as "break please," signed words such as "break" or "finished," picture communication such as touching a picture of a "stop sign" or giving a "break" card, or even a gesture such as pointing to the chair used when taking a break. This approach is called functional communication training (see Carr et al., 1994 and Durand, 1990 for comprehensive coverage of this topic). Box 8 provides an example.

It is essential to consider the person's developmental level when selecting an appropriate replacement skill. If a person lacks verbal skills, then perhaps they could be taught to use a sign. If the person cannot gesture or identify pictures, then perhaps using actual objects would be a better way to start.

Once the replacement skill has been selected,

Box 8: Sample Skill Promotion Program

At present, Jeanine exhibits aggressive behaviour, in the form of pinching, during difficult tasks. To functionally replace this behaviour, her caregivers will teach her to sign BREAK to request breaks from difficult tasks. So that Jeanine can learn the meaning of the sign, they will give her: 1) increased opportunities to request breaks, and 2) brief breaks (even just 1-minute breaks) each time she approximates the sign. Once Jeanine has learned to use the sign to request breaks, her caregivers will teach her to tolerate waiting for her break by systematically increasing the time Jeanine must work before her break is given and by offering social praise for waiting.

Jeanine's caregivers recognize that prior to implanting the program, the reinforcer (i.e., breaks from task) was being delivered in response to problematic behaviour. This program will have the same desired consequences delivered in response to a new socially appropriate behaviour.

Source: Condillac (2003).

a systematic teaching program should be implemented. The teaching program should include the methods for prompting and reinforcing the new desired behaviour. Another aspect of the teaching program must include strategies for generalization. Generalization refers to a person's ability to apply or transfer skills across people, settings, materials, and responses (Stokes & Bear, 1977). For example, when teaching individuals to gain attention more appropriately, they would need to know a variety of responses that would achieve that outcome, such as raising a hand, calling a person's name, or tapping someone on the shoulder. This would allow them to gain attention in many situations with many different people.

Intervention

During the implementation of the program, the identified problematic behaviour is typically ignored (no eye contact or verbal response), and if necessary, physically blocked (to prevent injury to the teacher or the other students). The individual is redirected to task using a simple monotone cue (e.g., "shoe on"). This phase of treatment will result in the extinction

(or a gradual elimination) of the problematic behaviour. If the behaviour is of a serious nature, and the individual and/or others are at increased risk, a crisis plan should be developed by a trained professional. This plan should detail the steps in handling problematic behaviour if it does occur.

Evaluation and training

The final component of the treatment plan should include clear guidelines for monitoring progress and fine-tuning the program (Martin & Pear, 1999). Data should be collected on both the problematic behaviour targeted for change, and the skill(s) being taught to replace the problematic behaviour. Criteria for success should be identified (e.g., 80% increase in the replacement skill, and 80% decrease in the problematic behaviour). It is essential to monitor both the desired effects and the potential side-effects of the behavioural intervention (Griffiths, 1989). Regularly scheduled reviews by the trained professional can offer opportunities for discussing progress, dealing with set-backs, and troubleshooting for potential difficulties.

It is important to note that, unlike other treatment approaches, behavioural interventions typically rely on consistent implementation by care providers in the individual's natural environment. Families, direct-care staff, and teachers often require hands-on training in behavioural techniques. Training can include topics such as data collection, effective use of reinforcement, teaching skills, and crisis intervention techniques. Training improves the quality of the behavioural intervention and has been demonstrated as essential to the success of treatment.

Summary

Behavioural interventions are important for individuals with developmental disabilities because they can help increase desirable behaviours, and decrease less desirable behaviours. Many individuals with DD develop serious problem behaviours, that if left untreated can have a detrimental influence on life quality (Wachtel & Hagopian, 2006). It is essential that care providers seek out trained professionals to provide comprehensive assessment and treatment plans. Assessment procedures should consider biomedical, environmental/inter-actional, and functional explanations for the problem behaviour. The assessment should lead to the development of a formal, documented behavioural intervention program that uses positive behaviour supports. Once problematic behaviours are being successfully prevented, the individual can be taught adaptive skills that functionally replace the previously problematic behaviour. Since behavioural interventions are typically implemented by natural care providers with minimal training in applied behaviour analysis, providing additional training in behavioural methods is often essential to the success of the intervention. Training must convey an understanding of behaviour principles, strategies, and techniques for on-going evaluation. Effective training should also include opportunities to demonstrate the skills being taught, and receive performance feedback.

For Further Thought and Discussion

1. Why do you think the incidence of problematic behaviour is so high in the population of people with developmental disabilities?
2. Behavioural interventions can increase the control that an individual with developmental disabilities has on her/his environment. Why is this statement true?
3. Since behavioural intervention focuses on information that can be seen, heard, and counted, why is the biomedical assessment so important?
4. Why would using prevention strategies as a first course of treatment be a better choice than simply punishing the behaviour until it disappears?
5. Research has found that functional analysis is critical to the effectiveness of behavioural intervention. Why do you think this is the case?

More Resources

If you require assistance with respect to the problematic behaviour of an individual with developmental disabilities you should contact your local association for community living or social services office to find out about agencies who provide applied behaviour analysis and other adjunctive supports. You can find a Board Certified Behaviour Analyst at *www.bacb.com/*

Books:

Cooper, J. O., Heron, T. E., & Heward, W. (2007). *Applied behavior analysis* (2nd ed.). Upper Saddle River, NJ: Pearson.

Cuvo, A. J. (1997). Review of behavior analysis in developmental disabilities 1968–1995 (3rd ed.), edited by Iwata et al. *Journal of Applied Behavior Analysis, 30*, 595-598.

Demchak, M., & Bossert, K. (1996). *Assessing problem behaviors*. American Association on Mental Retardation Research to Practice Series Innovations, Number 4.

Jackson, L., & Veeneman Panyan, M., (2002). *Positive behavioral support in the classroom: Principles and practice*. Toronto, ON: Paul H. Brookes.

Luiselli, J. K., & Cameron, M. J. (1998). *Antecedent control, innovative approaches to behavioural support*. Baltimore: Paul H. Brookes.

Singh, N. (1997). *Prevention & treatment of severe behaviour problems: Models and methods in developmental disabilities*. Pacific Grove, CA: Brooks/Cole.

Witt, J. C., Daly, E. M., & Noell, G. (2000). *Functional assessments: A step-by-step guide to solving academic and behavior problems*. Longmont, CO: Sopris West.

Web:

Behaviour Analysis, University of South Florida
http://www.coedu.usf.edu/behavior/behavior.html
The behaviour analysis home page at the University of South Florida has resources for those interested in learning and teaching about applied behaviour analysis.

Consensus Report on the Treatment of Destructive Behaviours
http://text.nlm.nih.gov/nih/cdc/www/75.html
Text version of the 1991 National Institute of Health (NIH) Consensus report on the Treatment of Destructive Behaviours in Persons with Developmental Disabilities.

Positive Behavioural Supports

http://www.pbis.org/english/default.htm
The Office of Special Education Programs, US Department of Education, offers the Technical Assistance Center on Positive Behavioral Interventions and Supports (PBIS). The goals of the webpage are to disseminate information about positive behavioural supports to schools, families, and communities.

Professional Associations:

The Association for Behavior Analysis International (ABAI):
ABAI is dedicated to promoting and disseminating professional and public information relating to applied behaviour analysis. www.abainternational.org Contact: The Association for Behavior Analysis International, 550 West Centre Avenue, Suite 1, Portage, MI 49024 Telephone: (269) 492-9310; Fax: (269) 492-9316, E-mail: *mail@abainternational.org*

The Association for Behavioral and Cognitive Therapies:
(ABCT). AABT is a professional organization concerned with the role of behavioural and cognitive sciences in understanding human behaviour, the development of interventions that enhance the human condition, and the promotion of systematic use of these interventions. *http://www.aabt.org* Contact: 305 7th Avenue, 16th Floor, New York, NY 10001-60008, Tel. (212) 647-1890, Fax (212) 647-1865

The Ontario Association for Behaviour Analysis (ONTABA):
ONTABA is a professional organization with the goals of promoting and supporting an interest in behaviour analysis through public education, student and professional development, networking, advocacy, and consultation. *www.ontaba.org* Contact: ONTABA, 283 Danforth Ave., Suite 413 Toronto, ON, M4K 1N2; E-mail: *contact@ontaba.org*

Contact the Author

Rosemary A. Condillac, Ph.D., C.Psych.
Centre for Applied Disability Studies
Brock University, 500 Glenridge Ave
St. Catharines, ON Canada L2S 3A1
Tel (905) 688-5550 ext 5671 Fax 905 378 5719
rcondillac@brocku.ca

References

Atkinson, L., Feldman, M., McNamara, A., Uhlin, L., Niccols, A., Leiserson, V., Paglia, A., Cheung, A., Christian, R., & Lucas, H. (1994). *Survey of aberrant behaviour and its treatment in persons with developmental disabilities in Ontario.* Final Report to Ontario Mental Health Foundation, Toronto, ON.

Baer, D. M., Wolf, M. M., & Risley, T. R. (1968). Some current dimensions of applied behavior analysis. *Journal of Applied Behavior Analysis (JABA)*, 1, 91-97.

Brown, L., Shirage, B., York, J., Zanella, K., & Rogan, P. (1984). *A life-space analysis strategy for students with severe handicaps.* Madison, WI: University of Wisconsin and Madison Metropolitan School District.

Carr, E. G., & Durand, M. V. (1985). Reducing behavior problems through functional communication training. *Journal of Applied Behavior Analysis, 18,* 111-126.

Carr, E. G., Horner, R. H., & Turnbull, A. P. (1999). *Positive behavior support for people with developmental disabilities: A research synthesis.* Washington, DC: American Association on Mental Retardation.

Carr, E. G., Levin, L., McConnachie, G., Carlson, J. I., Kemp, D. C., & Smith, C. E. (1994). *Communication-based intervention for problem behavior.* Baltimore: Paul H. Brookes.

Condillac, R. A. (2003). Behavioural intervention and developmental disabilities. In I. Brown & M. Percy (Eds.), *Developmental disabilities in Ontario* (2nd ed.) (pp. 407-419). Toronto, ON: Ontario Association on Developmental Disabilities.

Condillac, R. A. (2007). Behavioral interventions and intellectual disabilities. In I. Brown & M. Percy (Eds.), *A comprehensive guide to intellectual & developmental disabilities* (pp. 363-272). Baltimore: Paul H. Brookes Publishing Co.

Cooper, J. O., Heron, T. E., & Heward, W. L. (2007). *Applied behavior analysis* (2nd ed.). Upper Saddle River, NJ: Pearson.

Cooper, S., Smiley, E., Morrison, J., Williamson, A., & Allan, L. (2007). Mental ill-health in adults with intellectual disabilities: Prevalence and associated factors. *British Journal of Psychiatry, 190*(1), 27-35.

Durand, V. M. (1990). *Severe behavior problems: A functional communication training approach.* New York: Guilford Press.

Durand, V. M., & Crimmins, D. B. (1988). Identifying the variables maintaining self-injurious behavior. *Journal of Autism and Developmental Disorders, 18*, 99-117.

Feldman, M. A. (1990). Balancing freedom from harm and right to treatment for persons with developmental disabilities. In A. C. Repp & N. N. Singh (Eds.), *Perspectives on the use of nonaversive and aversive interventions for persons with developmental disabilities* (pp. 261-272). Sycamore, IL: Sycamore Publishing Co.

Feldman, M. A., Condillac, R. A., Tough, S. E., Hunt, S., & Griffiths, D. (2002). Effectiveness of community positive behavioral intervention for persons with developmental disabilities and severe behavioral challenges. *Behavior Therapy, 33*, 377-398.

Feldman, M. A., & Griffiths, D. (1997). Comprehensive assessment of severe behaviour disorders. In N. N. Singh (Ed.), *Prevention & treatment of severe behaviour problems: Models and methods in developmental disabilities* (pp. 23-48). Pacific Grove, CA: Brooks/Cole.

Freeman, N. L. (1993). *Treatment strategies for aberrant behaviour in people with developmental disabilities.* Toronto, ON: Ontario Mental Health Foundation.

Griffiths, D. (1989). Quality assurance for behaviour interventions. *Habilitative Mental Healthcare Newsletter, 8*, 74-79.

Iwata, B. A., Dorsey, M. F., Slifer, K. J., Bauman, K. E., & Richman, G. S. (1982). Toward a functional analysis of self-injury. *Analysis and Intervention in Developmental Disabilities, 2*, 1-20.

LaVigna, G. W., & Donnellan, A. M. (1986). *Alternatives to punishment: Solving behaviour problems with non-aversive strategies.* New York: Irvington.

Jackson, L., & Veeneman Panyan, M. (2002) *Positive behavioral support in the classroom: Principles and practice.* Baltimore: Paul H. Brookes Publishing Co.

Koegel, L. K., Koegel, R. L., & Dunlap, G. (Eds.).

(1996). *Positive behavioral support: Including people with difficult behavior in the community.* Baltimore: Paul H. Brookes Publishing Co.

Martin, G., & Pear, J. (1999). *Behavior modification: What it is and how to do it.* Upper Saddle River, NJ: Prentice Hall.

National Institute of Health [NIH]. (1991). *Treatment of destructive behaviours in persons with developmental disabilities.* Consensus Development Conference, September 11-13, 1989, Bethesda, MD: Author.

Ontario Association for Behaviour Analysis. (1998). *Draft standards of practice of the Ontario Association for Behaviour Analysis.* Toronto, ON: Author.

O'Neill, R. E., Horner, R. H., Albin, R. W., Storey, K., & Sprague, J. R. (1990). *Functional analysis of problem behavior: A practical assessment guide.* Pacific Grove, CA: Brooks/Cole.

Repp, A. C., Favell, J., & Munk, D. (1996). Cognitive and vocational interventions for school-age children and adolescents with mental retardation. In J. W. Jacobson & J. A. Mulick (Eds.), *Manual of diagnosis and professional practice in mental retardation* (pp. 265-276). Washington, DC: American Psychological Association.

Repp, A. C., & Singh, N. N. (Eds.). (1990). *Perspectives on the use of nonaversive and aversive interventions for persons with developmental disabilities.* Sycamore, IL: Sycamore Publishing Co.

Singh, N. N., Oswald, D. P., & Ellis, C. R. (1998). Mental retardation. In T. M. Ollendick & M. Hersen (Eds.), *Handbook of child psychopathology* (3rd ed.) (pp. 91-116). New York: Plenum.

Stokes, T. F., & Baer, D. M. (1977). An implicit technology of generalization. *Journal of Applied Behavior Analysis, 10*, 349-367.

Sugai, G., Horner, R. H., Dunlap, G., Hieneman, M., Lewis, T. J., Nelson, Nelson, C.M., et al. (2000). Applying positive behavioral support and functional behavioral assessment in schools. *Journal of Positive Behavioral Interventions, 2*, 131-143.

Touchette, P. E., MacDonald, R. F., & Langer, S. N. (1985). A scatterplot for identifying stimulus control of problem behaviour. *Journal of Applied Behavior Analysis, 18*, 343-351.

Wachtel, L. E., & Hagopian, L. P. (2006). Psycho-pharmacology and applied behavioral analysis: Tandem treatment of severe problem behaviors in intellectual disability and a case series. *Israel Journal Psychiatry Related Science, 43,* 265–274.

York Behaviour Management Services. (1997). *The options manual: A community based behavioural approach for teachers with students with developmental disabilities.* Richmond Hill, ON: York Central Hospital Behaviour Management Services.

Challenging Families: Mending Broken Spirits through Support and Therapy

J. Dale Munro

What you will learn:

- Why professionals find some families of people with disabilities so challenging
- Some behavioural patterns of challenging families
- What front-line professionals and managers can do to help families
- How trained family therapists can help
- The Positive Intervention-Family Support Model

Families are the emotional shock absorbers of society that, ideally, help people cope with and face the struggles of life. When specifically discussing families of people with developmental disabilities, most are supportive of their family members with a disability and the professionals and organizations working with them. Yet, in every community agency or school setting, there are a few families that might be described as *challenging*. In this chapter, the term *challenging family* is described as *a group of two or more blood or adopted relatives, at least one of whom has a developmental disability, that repeatedly and chronically behaves in a manner that seems extremely self-destructive, intimidating, unpredictable, aggres-* *sive or resistant.* As much as we might hate to admit it, some of the most challenging behaviour that front-line professionals and managers ever face may not be from people with disabilities, but from their families!

Challenging families pose one of the greatest dangers to the emotional well-being of the person with a developmental disability, and are a constant source of frustration for front-line professionals and agency or school administrators (hereafter referred to as professionals). These families tend to draw attention to themselves and their own needs, inadvertently obstructing service delivery to the person who has the disability. Professionals need to become familiar

Box 1: Family Coping/Grieving Process*

In mourning the loss of the dream of the normal or perfect child, family grieving is multi-layered and the pain is experienced on many levels – emotionally, intellectually, physically & spiritually. This is not a simple straight-line, cause and effect process, with clear-cut stopping and starting points. Instead, it involves dynamic and evolving phases that vary by person and situation. Predicting how long this process will take to work through is highly personal, and it may happen relatively quickly. Yet, clinical experience suggests that healthier families probably will need somewhere between 18 months to about 6 years.

*Challenging families, however, because of unresolved or complicated grief, seem permanently stuck in the first three **nonacceptance** phases. Coming to terms with the inescapable reality of the disability is necessary if family members are to escape an emotional prison of self-doubt, deep sadness, guilt, shame, anger and a need to punish themselves or others. Challenging families need increased social support and/or specialized counselling, if they hope to work through and accept complex feelings, and move towards greater acceptance, psychological wholeness and general happiness.*

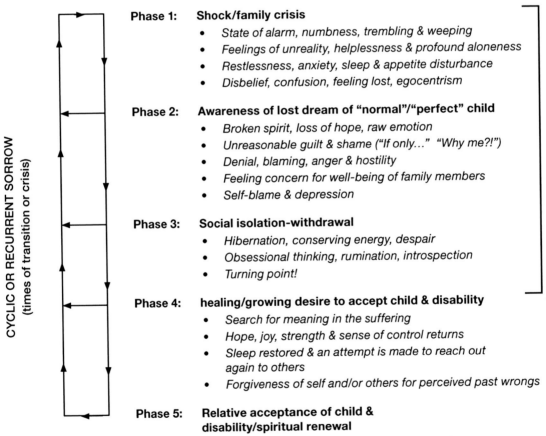

CYCLIC OR RECURRENT SORROW (times of transition or crisis)

CHALLENGING FAMILIES STUCK AT NONACCEPTANCE (chronic sorrow)

Phase 1: **Shock/family crisis**
- *State of alarm, numbness, trembling & weeping*
- *Feelings of unreality, helplessness & profound aloneness*
- *Restlessness, anxiety, sleep & appetite disturbance*
- *Disbelief, confusion, feeling lost, egocentrism*

Phase 2: **Awareness of lost dream of "normal"/"perfect" child**
- *Broken spirit, loss of hope, raw emotion*
- *Unreasonable guilt & shame ("If only..." "Why me?!")*
- *Denial, blaming, anger & hostility*
- *Feeling concern for well-being of family members*
- *Self-blame & depression*

Phase 3: **Social isolation-withdrawal**
- *Hibernation, conserving energy, despair*
- *Obsessional thinking, rumination, introspection*
- *Turning point!*

Phase 4: **healing/growing desire to accept child & disability**
- *Search for meaning in the suffering*
- *Hope, joy, strength & sense of control returns*
- *Sleep restored & an attempt is made to reach out again to others*
- *Forgiveness of self and/or others for perceived past wrongs*

Phase 5: **Relative acceptance of child & disability/spiritual renewal**
- *Feeling wiser from the experience, more at peace*
- *Changed identity (e.g., proud parent of a child with a disability)*

Appreciation is expressed to Keith Anderson and Susan Hutton for their consultation.

with strategies for diffusing the frustrations, anger and tension that challenging families are experiencing, not only to assist these families, but also to promote good mental health in the person with the disability. This chapter was written to provide direction to front-line professionals and managers. It examines probable causes of challenging family behaviour, describes some specific behavioural patterns exhibited by these families, and presents a positive intervention model for helping these needy and complicated families.

Why Do Some Families Seem So Challenging?

Most parents suffer almost unbearable pain and trauma, when they first learn that their child has a developmental disability. The entire family is confronted with new demands that tax relationships both inside and outside the family. Most parents and other family members go through *a coping (grieving) process* that is life-changing. As illustrated in Box 1, normally this grieving process is thought to comprise five phases, starting with initial shock and family crisis, when the child is first found to have a permanent disability. The process proceeds slowly through several phases to, eventually, spiritual renewal and relative acceptance of the child and the disability. Years later, even healthy families may periodically experience short periods of *cyclic or recurrent grief*, around transition or crisis times in the life of the person who is disabled (e.g., starting school or graduating, birthdays, changes in teaching or support staff, leaving home, major illness, anniversary date when disability identified). But most parents and other family members gradually learn to accept the person and the disability, and are often positively transformed and psychologically stronger for doing so (Munro, 2007).

In contrast, *challenging families seem permanently stuck in the three earliest phases in this grieving and coping process.* Their intense reaction and non-acceptance of the child and the disability is chronic and does not diminish with time — resulting in what has been called *chronic sorrow* (Olshansky 1961; Sanders 1999). Siblings and grandparents of the family

member who is disabled also can become trapped in the parents' cycle of grief, denial, guilt and anger (Ashton & Ashton 1996; Davis 1987; Moses 1988; Parks 1983; Sieffert 1978; Singer & Powers 1993).

The self-destructive, extremely aggressive or resistant behaviour exhibited by challenging families results from what has been referred to as "complicated grief." Sanders (1999) suggested that complicated grief occurs when the typical family grieving process is confounded by extenuating factors. In the case of families of people with developmental disabilities, seven extenuating factors contribute to complicated grief reactions and ultimately challenging behaviour:

1. *Personality variables or the basic thinking style* of individual family members can impede the family coping process. For example, parents or siblings who typically blame someone or something else about life problems, or persist in blaming themselves, frequently will respond in a similar manner when confronted with the reality of a family member with a permanent disability.

2. *Other unresolved grief or situational factors* may negatively influence personality factors. For instance, the family may experience a serious family crisis (e.g., financial, critical illness or injury, marital discord or separation, or a recent death); needed services may be unavailable, or service cutbacks may leave parents fearful regarding what the future may hold for their (young or adult) child.

3. *The large, bureaucratic and somewhat impersonal nature of "the system"* of educational, health, social service, or correctional organizations can frustrate otherwise reasonable family members. Complicating this situation is the fact that some overworked professionals experience burnout, or they behave in a defensive, insensitive or unsophisticated manner when confronted by frustrated or hostile family members.

4. Some challenging family members may have intellectual or communication deficits, making it difficult to work cooperatively with them.

5. *Language, cultural, religious or other differences between families and professionals* can contrib-

ute to tension, misunderstanding and conflict. As highlighted in Box 2, agency and school representatives have to overcome prejudice, and become sophisticated in overcoming barriers to communication, acceptance, and collaboration.

6. *Power imbalances* may disproportionately favour family members (e.g., those sitting on agency boards) or service system representatives, creating unhealthy and mean-spirited interactions between the family and the service system.

7. *Untreated psychiatric difficulties*, such as clinical depression, severe anxiety or obsessional thinking, alcohol or drug abuse, post-traumatic stress (e.g., past abuse), schizophrenia, autism spectrum disorders, or personality disorders can cause family members to behave in a manner that makes them appear to be totally unreasonable.

Recognizing Challenging Family Patterns

Challenging families often seem overwhelmed with guilt, ambivalence, hostility and loneliness. They may deny these feelings when confronted directly, but show their emotional pain in a variety of overt or passive-aggressive ways. They sometimes try to present an image that "everything is OK" in their families, or they may mistakenly believe that most of their problems result from having a family member with a disability. In response to tremendous family tension, individuals with developmental disabilities often begin to exhibit disturbed behaviour, inadvertently making them a spokesperson for the underlying dysfunction in the entire family.

As professionals become involved to try to help the family with their "problem" relative, they sometimes encounter tremendous resistance. The homeostasis (balance) in the family may depend on maintaining the relative with the disability in the scapegoat or problem role, in order that tension is not refocused on the real source of conflict — the parental and family dysfunction. Challenging families of people with developmental disabilities frequently show one or more of the following behavioural patterns (Munro, 2007), any one of which signifies that seri-

ous needs are being expressed that require a professional response.

1. *Mental exhaustion and a broken spirit* may be prevalent, when family members have spent years trying to support a relative or child with significant behavioural, psychiatric and/or physical needs. Many of these family members have quit jobs, lost contact with friends, and unsuccessfully tried advocacy to obtain additional and needed support for their relative. They frequently show symptoms of clinical depression, bitterness, and disillusionment with the service system; they often express a sense of hopelessness, thinking that their home situation, and that of their disabled relative, will never improve.

2. *Loud chronic complaining* is a common pattern. These families literally scream and create crises out of minor concerns, even when special and repeated efforts have been made to meet their needs ("It's never enough!"). They seem preoccupied with the way agencies, professionals and school systems "should" and "must" provide quality and expanded services, with little appreciation for large caseloads or limited service resources. Some of these families complicate situations by turning to lawyers, agency or school executives, or the mass media before first trying to resolve concerns with front-line professionals or managers.

3. *Program (person) sabotage* is shown by some families who seem to perceive professionals and service providers as adversaries. These families may block attempts to provide treatment interventions, such as psychotropic medication or behavioural approaches, which are needed to assist relatives exhibiting extreme self-injury, suicidal or aggressive behaviour. They may insist on their family member being "discharged against advice" from specialized treatment settings, just as the person is beginning to show progress. They may not show up for scheduled appointments with professionals. Or they may have unrealistically high or overly pessimistic expectations for their family member who is disabled that impede the person's potential for

Box 2: Family Diversity in the 21st Century

Society's definition of what constitutes a family has changed greatly over the past fifty years. Professionals and managers in the developmental disability field today need to remain open-minded and accepting of various family constellations. For instance, the traditional nuclear family with father as the breadwinner and mother at home, or dual wage earners with a couple of children still exists. But many other family structures have emerged as well. Options may include blended families with parents remarried and forming new families with existing or new children. Common-law arrangements, single parent families and extended families with three generations living under one roof, sometimes are found. As well, openly gay, lesbian, bisexual and transgender parents with disabled children are now frequently seeking support.

At the same time, Canada is a country that values and depends on immigration from every corner of the world. Our citizens now represent every race, religion and culture. The first language of families may be English, French, or a huge array of other languages, making it necessary for agencies and schools to have interpreters available when needed or to employ professionals and managers who are multi-lingual and representing many diverse populations. Complicating matters is the fact that poverty and limited education may make it difficult for some disadvantaged families to access services and seek assistance – and they may need extra support to do so. Professionals and managers are encouraged to celebrate the wonderful range of family diversity found in modern-day Canada!

positive change and emotional growth.

4. *Extreme overprotectiveness* is demonstrated by some families who seem overwhelmed by guilt, anxiety and obsessional thinking. These over-involved families tend to infantilize their relative (e.g., providing child-like haircuts and clothing, bathing otherwise capable individuals) and want the person protected at all times (e.g., refusing to allow dating or independent use of public transportation). They may be unwilling to go away on vacations without their relative, for fear that something awful might happen when they are gone; or they may tolerate seemingly intolerable behaviour on the part of the person who is disabled (e.g., repeated physical violence or property destruction). Parents may become family "martyrs" who, on one hand, seem totally devoted to their child, but who, on the other hand, secretly resent the life-long cost (e.g., friends, a career) of constantly caring for the person.

5. *False hope/jumping on treatment bandwagons* is a pattern shown when long-term denial and unrealistically-high expectations are a potent underlying dynamic in the family. Every new treatment "advance" is met with near-religious fervour by these family members. "Shopping

around" from one specialist to another to find a miracle (often expensive) cure for their relative's disability is not uncommon. Some families may discontinue helpful anticonvulsant or psychotropic medication, falsely thinking it is no longer necessary. These families may even demand that physicians perform unnecessary surgery, use improperly tested drugs, or change the person's treatment to some "medical breakthrough" described in sensationalized popular news publications. Though rare, a few families may sincerely believe that their religion, prayer or the right faith healer will cure the disability. Unfortunately, the ongoing zeal of these families to try the latest panacea, often gets in the way of initiating more helpful approaches.

6. *Symbiotic (enmeshed) relationships* are found where there is a pathologically close relationship between the person who is disabled and at least one parent; each feels uncanny sensitivity for the other's pain. These relationships stifle independent thought and action on the part of the person who is disabled; and healthy parent-child emotional boundaries are continually violated. More troubled families may have shared delusions of grandeur in which the person who is disabled is idolized beyond any realistic

dimensions, and may become the recipient of too much family attention and concern.

7. *Open warfare and abuse* is observed in some families. Overt hostility, so-called mind-games, sarcastic exchanges, backbiting, and violent arguments seem to be their hallmark. Intense sibling rivalry may last into adulthood. Brothers and sisters vacillate between displacing enormous anger onto their disabled sibling, to competing to prove who loves the person more (e.g., overindulgent gift-giving). Shared family secrets create ongoing tension (e.g., incest, physical violence, alcohol and drug problems, or past mental illness). The person who is disabled can be an easy target for the ever-present hostility, as can school or community agency personnel and other professionals who try to get involved.

8. *Paranoia and pervasive evasiveness* are manifested by some families who, because of social isolation or delusions of persecution, begin to believe that professionals, agencies, school systems, neighbours, family or associates are conspiring against them. These families may leave cryptic or hostile messages on agency or school phone systems; refuse to meet or fail to show up for scheduled appointments; show hypervigilance to criticism or bear grudges; be preoccupied with unjustified doubts about the loyalty of others; fabricate stories or communicate in a confused manner; or physically threaten outsiders. Serious psychiatric disturbance and avoidance are the distinguishing characteristics of these exceedingly suspicious families and, as a consequence, communication and support planning with them concerning their relative with a disability can be particularly difficult.

9. *Avoidance of the person* is a pattern shown by families who completely terminate contact with the individual who is disabled. They may never visit, write, or even acknowledge their relative's existence. Such total rejection can destroy the person's self-worth, precipitate severe depression, and leave the individual fantasizing about the family that never comes. Other family members may maintain contact only until money

from an inheritance runs out; make promises that are never kept (e.g., visits, gifts); or one parent may withdraw totally into work, volunteer or leisure activities, leaving the other parent to deal almost single-handedly with the person with the disability.

10. *Psychosocial deprivation* characterizes families frequently found in isolated rural or urban slum areas. Neglect and harsh discipline may be common, and often little attention is paid to the special needs of the person who is disabled, since all family members face day-to-day struggles meeting basic needs. The disability may never even be diagnosed, unless it is severe or a major crisis occurs. These families tend to distrust professionals, schools and agencies, since many are frustrated after long-term contact (sometimes involving more than one generation) with services and government programs.

Positive Intervention-Family Support Model

When professionals in the field of developmental disabilities perceive challenging families, they are usually encountering families with complicated backgrounds and problems that are coming into conflict with rigid, overextended or unresponsive human service systems. In fact, *problems with communication and cooperation within formal support systems (health, education, corrections and social services) can make family problems appear much more serious than they really are!*

Because of these difficulties — and based on four decades of work in the developmentally disability field — the chapter author has developed a family support and intervention model that combines the best elements of traditional family assessment and counselling approaches with interventions that recognize the complexity of human service systems. *The author calls this model of treatment Positive Intervention-Family Support (PIFS Model), and it is particularly helpful in situations where family and service system cooperation must be high. This is a highly effective and positive model that reduces family-sys-*

tem distress; improves communication and interpersonal relationships among key people; clarifies roles; and improves planning, case management, advocacy, and support for people with disabilities.

Necessity of being positive: mending broken spirits

There is a unique type of pain, grief and trauma found in most families of people with developmental disabilities that psychotherapists in the general counselling community seldom understand. Many therapists and other professionals working from a traditional biopsychosocial model may not recognize the fact that many of these families have broken spirits and effective intervention must also focus on *spiritual healing*. Spiritual (not necessarily religious) approaches include showing compassion and kindness, helping families discover meaning in suffering, offering hope and developing faith that current painful circumstances can improve, and striving to find some degree of peace, joy, harmony, fellowship and untapped sources of energy, even in seemingly hopeless situations (Munro, 2009). The PIFS Model suggests that frequently there are viable approaches that can be helpful, if the professional is really motivated to assist such troubled people. To a large extent, success depends on the professional's persistence, high energy, unflappable optimism, flexibility, knowledge of community resources, persuasiveness, charisma, patience and ability to be satisfied with small gains.

The PIFS Model emphasizes that a positive or unconditionally constructive attitude on the part of front-line professionals and managers, often leads to beneficial results when working with challenging families (Munro, 1997). In fact, professionals working in the developmental disabilities field seldom meet people who could accurately be described as "bad" parents or family members. But they do meet family members with broken spirits who are exhausted, disillusioned, burned-out and frightened about the future. Most families are trying too hard to do the right things for their relatives who are disabled — almost to the point of making themselves sick. In this sort of emotional climate, negativity on the part of professionals can breed a

self-perpetuating cycle of frustration and hopelessness in family members.

The PIFS Model incorporates many elements of the *strengths-based perspective* to social work practice and positive psychology (Early & GlenMaye, 2000; Harris, Thorensen, & Lopez, 2007; Russo, 1999; Saleeby, 1992). This perspective, along with strategies suggested in Box 3 which can help professionals deal with their own burnout, distress and spiritual pain, provides a positive foundation for building effective working relationships with challenging families. The strengths-based approach is antithetical to the historical family pathology model, on which many professionals relied in the past. The professional's sense of humour, insight and loyalty are often viewed as important ingredients for successful family work. Real problems are not ignored, but *this perspective focuses on what is right, rather than wrong with families*. Family empowerment and resilience — and the possibility of positive transformation and rebound from personal trauma, abuse, oppression, sickness and tragedy — are emphasized. This perspective liberates family members to pursue their own personal dreams, and accepts that people are more motivated for positive change when they have genuine decision-making power, and when their strengths and worldviews are respected (King, et al., 2009).

Essential family-work skills for front-line professionals and managers

Agency and school professionals often find themselves in situations where they are confronted by frustrated and angry challenging families (Munro, 2007). The PIFS Model insists that professionals should ask themselves this question: *"When a family is really struggling, or upset with you or your agency or school, what tools do you have in your tool-kit?"* With this in mind, Munro (2009) recommended that all agency and school personnel should learn some essential family-work skills, such as:

1. *Understanding history.* As a starting point, it is vitally important to help professionals who themselves may be overly critical of families, to gain some level of historical perspective. They need to be informed that almost every significant service advance for people with developmental dis-

Box 3: Broken Spirits in Professionals: Managing Expectations, Stress and Burnout

Agency and school personnel often find working with challenging families emotionally demanding and at times discouraging. Self-destructive or intimidating family behaviour can raise self-doubt and unconscious emotional reactions in professionals, causing them to question their own helping abilities. One manager reported that her staff members sometimes become so "rattled" by the behaviour of some family members that their job performance suffers: "Staff [managers] operating out of fear, make mistakes!" This can result in professionals themselves experiencing broken spirits (their original dream of helping others seems crushed) and exhibiting "burnout" symptoms.

Professionals must prepare themselves for family antagonism without being provoked into defensiveness, angry outbursts or power struggles. In order to cope, survive and thrive in their work with families, the PIFS Model suggests that agency and school personnel should:

- *Simplify their thinking, and abandon perfectionism and unrealistic rescue fantasies when dealing with highly complex families and emotionally-charged situations. Keep professional expectations realistic and achievable!*

- *Remind families that their situation is very complex. Let them know that there are no quick fixes for the family's difficulties. Slow and careful planning and collaboration usually results in the best long-term outcome for everyone involved. This is a Marathon, not a sprint!*

- *Insist that discussion in family-system meetings focus on the here and now problems and solutions. This avoids the tendency of some families to dwell on past problems and perceived injustices against them.*

- *Use (appropriate and well-timed) humour if possible, to reduce tension and defuse potentially hurtful interactions.*

- *Carefully document agency and school involvement as a safety precaution, just in case the family considers a lawsuit or creates bad publicity, which does occur on occasion.*

- *Hold regular professional meetings to privately air frustrations and discuss positive approaches for helping and coping with disturbing family behaviour.*

- *Practise good stress management every day (e.g., meditation, time management, healthy diet and physical exercise); encourage service organizations to hold wellness and self-care seminars for their personnel.*

- *Consider personal psychotherapy, family counselling or psychiatric consultation if a professional is not coping well with an "impossible" family.*

---

abilities has come about because of hard-fought advocacy by dedicated family members. It is also worth noting that there have been tragic times in human service history, when professionals recklessly blamed parents for their children's disabilities (e.g., the outrageous belief that "refrigerator mothers" caused autism (Bettelheim, 1967). We, as professionals, must never allow ourselves to return to this sad historical tendency to blame parents; and we must vigorously guard against viewing families as "the enemy."

2. *Recognizing "healthy" families.* Professionals are often too quick to criticize the relatives of peo-

ple with disabilities, and may tend to pathologize family behaviour that is essentially normal (e.g., appropriate assertive expression of concerns). Professionals must recognize that even healthy families can become negative at times, if they are exhausted or not comfortable with how services are provided. They can have a rough day; or they can be argumentative on occasion, if frustrated. As well, professionals can be taught that healthy behaviour is manifested by those families who project a sense of pride, safety, mutual support, affection, and fun; who are protective of each other; and who regularly involve the person with a disability in family and community activities.

3. *Building positive relationships.* Professionals sometimes need to be reminded that collaborative relationships with families frequently begin in the simplest of ways, by initially engaging in casual small talk, practising empathic listening and sharing a coffee. Rapport with families can be enhanced by professionals who focus on "here and now" issues; avoid jargon; celebrate (even small) successes with the family; and strategically use well-timed (appropriate) humour, frankness, cheerleading, and brief inspirational and motivational speeches. When dealing with particularly disturbed people with disabilities, families often are desperate for, and appreciate receiving, staff suggestions about calming activities that allow visits with the individual to go better (e.g., going for walks in nearby parks, car rides, trips to the beach, or preparing a favourite food together). Such advice can contribute to a growing sense of family-agency teamwork and cooperation. As well, family-professional relationships can improve through the use of regular planning or support circle meetings that may include the individual, family members, friends, volunteers and key professionals. These meetings help to reduce family isolation, improve planning and create strong family-service system networks (Munro, 1997; VanDenBerg & Grealish, 1998).

4. *Becoming aware of unspoken family questions.* To ensure family-system cooperation, agency and school representatives need to become more skilled at reassuring families. This reassurance (requiring examples from the individual's typical week) must address questions that are seldom stated openly. Family members often continuously "test" professionals and organizations to reassuringly answer four unspoken (but vitally important) questions:
   - Do you really care [about my relative/me]?
   - Is my child/relative really safe?
   - Is my child/relative happy?
   - Am I a good parent/sibling/grandparent?

5. *Learning "the name of the game is reframe."* In the author's clinical experience (and from conducting presentations with a variety of professional audiences), it is not unusual for some professionals who work in agency or school programs, when speaking privately, to talk about families in an extremely pejorative manner. Reframing is an extremely positive and powerful strategy that professionals need to learn to help counteract this tendency. Reframing involves teaching professionals to re-think, in a more constructive, less emotional and more rational manner, their negative descriptions, perceptions, or thoughts about a family member or situation. To be effective, professionals must learn to purge negative and degrading words not only from their everyday speech; but also from their beliefs and thoughts! For example, a professional's angry statement ("That mother is a control freak, a manipulator and a real bitch!") might be much more accurately and sensitively reframed as ("She is a concerned, courageous and passionate advocate!"). When professionals begin to utilize reframing in their thoughts and verbal interactions, their relationships with families tend to immediately improve. When professionals teach family members to reframe their perceptions of professionals, agencies and events around them, families ultimately become healthier, cope better, and become more cooperative (Lustig, 2002; Minnes & Woodford, 2005).

6. *Clarifying roles.* One of the greatest sources of acrimony and confusion between service providers and families is unclear roles and expectations. Families and professionals can improve their relationships and reduce distress by deciding who does what, how, and when. To illustrate, in particularly complicated situations, *a written service agreement* is often useful in outlining the responsibilities of service organizations, professionals, families and the individual, to enhance the possibility of treatment success. As well, it is often wise to *designate only one contact person* (usually a supervisor or middle manager) through whom families can raise serious concerns with an agency or school. Some families prefer to approach many different (often part-time or less experienced) staff with complaints

Box 4: What Role Can Family Therapists Play?

Front-line professionals and managers in agencies and school systems need to know when, and how, to involve registered social workers or other clinicians with specialized family therapy skills. The PIFS Model suggests there are four possible roles for family therapists in our field:

1. *The family therapist may play a consultant role offering advice regarding family support strategies to agency or school representatives with the therapist having little or no actual face-to-face involvement with the family.*

2. *The professional might act as an outside mediator who is brought in as an impartial third party, to meet with key people and to help resolve complicated family-system disputes (Munro, 1997).*

3. *The professional may feel a necessity to work directly with the challenging family — playing a role similar to that of a traditional family therapist. This might involve several private therapy sessions focusing on clearly agreed clinical goals. If the professional does provide direct family therapy, a key feature of the PIFS Model is that a service system representative (e.g., from a local agency) who knows the individual with the disability well should act as a co-therapist. This provides an excellent learning opportunity for the co-therapist in effective family work. It also helps to monitor whether any real and positive change is occurring in terms of family functioning, family-system collaboration; and it helps to provide a reliable check-in, as to how the individual with the disability is coping.*

4. *On occasion, the family therapist may provide individual psychotherapy to the person with a disability without getting directly involved with the family. This counselling can provide emotional support, and develop assertive and coping skills in individuals who are being rejected, abused or treated as scapegoat by their family members. Again, it is sometimes advantageous to include a service system representative who knows the individual well to act as a co-therapist.*

or deep concerns, but this usually results in miscommunication and emotional upset. One contact person should be identified; and *a brief written script* can be created and rehearsed by staff, to be used if family members approach them with complaints, such as: "I know you're concerned and I will ask Joe, the contact person, to get back to you about it!" Likewise, staff should feel empowered to suggest positive ideas or raise concerns about the family's behaviour with the designated contact person. Staff ideas or concerns can then be addressed with the family at regularly scheduled planning or support circle meetings.

7. *Learning to cope with "difficult" people.* Strategies have been developed that can help professionals maintain confidence, assertiveness, and power balance when facing families who seem intimidating, explosive or manipulative. These coping techniques often utilize role-play, and focus on maintaining politeness and finding one's centre of calm. These approaches emphasize the need

to stand up without fighting, since families will never respect people whom they feel they can push around (Bramson, 1981; Glass, 1995). As well, staff can be taught to respond effectively with angry or anxious family members by calmly speaking more quietly, firmly, slowly, succinctly and gently maintaining eye contact; and by systematically ignoring outrageously negative family comments and personal attacks.

8. *Setting proper boundaries.* Boundaries are the physical, psychological and spiritual space that professionals create around themselves that define how they will relate to individuals and their families, and how they are willing to let others treat them (Black & Enns, 1997). Front-line professionals and managers who learn to set appropriate work-related boundaries (e.g., reducing excessive overtime, politely ending acrimonious meetings, demonstrating team solidarity in not disclosing certain personal information with families, showing caution about receiving gifts or giving hugs, and not giv-

Box 5: Siblings

Our longest lifetime relationships are with our siblings. Siegel and Silverstein (1994) provide a revealing look at the issues and needs of siblings of individuals with developmental disabilities. They state that sibling relationships act as a "prototype" for later adult relationships (who is chosen as a friend or life partner, relationships with employers, and so on). Growing up with a disabled brother or sister who is self-centred, or who shows serious behavioural or health problems, can sometimes be a stressful or even psychologically damaging to the non-disabled sibling. Siblings frequently attempt to cope in one of four ways:

- *Becoming "parentified" (taking on parental or caregiving roles).*
- *"Withdrawing" and developing separate interests from the rest of the family.*
- *Exhibiting "acting out" behaviours (e.g., hostile outbursts, serious adolescent rebellion, alcohol or drug abuse, school failure, or trouble with the law).*
- *"Superachieving" or showing perfectionism.*

Fortunately, most siblings of people with disabilities are highly resilient and typically live happy, productive lives. Most grow up to be wonderful contributing citizens who truly love their disabled brother or sister (and the feeling is mutual). Many feel that they have been positively transformed and benefitted from having a close relative with a disability (Findler & Vardi, 2009). In fact, they usually are psychologically stronger and more flexible in dealing with life challenges; and they quite often choose life and career paths (e.g., developmental service workers, social worker, psychologists, teachers, physicians, nurses) that reflect the sensitivity that they developed by growing up with a family member with special needs.

ing out home phone numbers) tend to manage stress better — and families inadvertently benefit from dealing with healthier, more confident agency and school personnel.

9. *Teaching families how to advocate.* Many families of people with disabilities seem hesitant or unsure about how to gain access to human service systems. However, professionals (with their knowledge of services) can teach family members how to successfully navigate service systems. Families are empowered and strengthened by the knowledge that they have had the courage to stand up for their family member with a disability. The "Step Approach Model" for effective family advocacy is recommended (Munro, 1991).

Family therapy strategies

It is not realistic to expect most community agency and school professionals to be sophisticated family therapists. In our field, registered social workers tend to be the primary designated profession systematically trained in family therapy and support methods.

Trained family therapists can play many useful roles in helping challenging families, as illustrated in Box 4. Commonly, there is a need for private therapy sessions with families to help them deal with unresolved social, emotional, trauma, sexuality and grief issues. In some cases, longer-term therapy is required.

In many ways, challenging families seem caught in a bind. They desperately need clinical help, but simultaneously push away potentially helpful outsiders with abusive or socially unacceptable behaviour. Nevertheless, the PIFS Model emphasizes that therapists must persist with the objective of building a positive "therapeutic alliance" or relationship with the family. Counselling support usually is gradually accepted, after the family has had time to test out the therapist's degree of commitment and concern. With this in mind, the following therapeutic family approaches can be particularly helpful.

1. *Family therapy sessions usually should be held in the privacy of a counsellor's office. Occasionally, it may be useful to meet at the family's home in order to obtain a greater understanding of*

the family's everyday living environment, or in cases where family members may be wheelchairs or have mobility problems. However, it is often better to meet in a more neutral site, such as a professional office, especially in particularly tense situations. During interviews, professionals must ensure that people adhere to basic rules of etiquette (e.g., no interrupting the person speaking). Sometimes it is helpful to meet the entire family together. Other times, it is better to meet alone with parents (i.e., couple sessions), siblings (often an untapped resource), or the person who is disabled, to permit free expression of troubling feelings and concerns, and discussion of possible solutions.

2. *All promises or commitments therapists and co-therapists make to the family must be faithfully kept,* and any constructive ideas presented by family members should be supported and carried out, in order gradually to encourage desired behaviour and to gain trust.

3. *Therapists must make use of (and teach agency and school personnel) listening approaches that promote assertiveness* to counteract aggressiveness or passivity in families. Professionals must be cautioned against treating the problems raised by chronically complaining families too lightly. Usually, even the most "dysfunctional" families have some legitimate concerns hidden behind their perceived "bitching." Professionals are encouraged to use *active* or *empathic listening* which involves putting oneself emotionally in the family's shoes, paraphrasing briefly the family member's words and message, and acknowledging how she/he is feeling. *Being really listened to, as simple as it might seem, is a powerful therapeutic tool,* with even the most demanding family. Challenging families often have a history of being ignored, put off, or not taken seriously by others, which can lead them to treating others in a passive-aggressive manner. They may have to tell stories about the pain and grief in their lives over and over again, until they feel truly understood. Only then, do many families begin to let go of guilt and hostility, begin to exhibit assertiveness rather than "manipulation," accept the reality of their family member's disability and the need for outside help.

4. Use *negative inquiry.* This is another powerful technique that can be used in conjunction with active listening to encourage assertiveness in families. Therapists should actively use this approach in their practice and, as clinical consultants, they should teach it to agency and school personnel. Negative inquiry involves calmly and rather paradoxically prompting family members to criticize existing services even more than they might want to (e.g., "Are there any other concerns that you have?" "Are you sure there isn't anything else?") This brings information to the surface that might be helpful, or exhausts criticism if it is manipulative. This process usually guides family members and professionals toward becoming more assertive, less critical, and feeling really understood. This process works even better if the professional takes a pen and takes written notes and carefully records family concerns, with the understanding that each concern will be taken seriously and addressed in turn (sometimes at a pre-arranged later date when further information has been gathered).

5. Therapists can *give permission* to family members to do positive things that they would typically never allow themselves, and to establish more healthy physical and emotional boundaries. For instance, parents may be encouraged to plan vacations, evenings, or weekends away without their children; continue their education; return to work outside the family; join support groups; attend physical exercise programs, wellness and stress management seminars; use parent respite services; spend more time with their non-disabled children; or, for divorced or widowed parents, consider dating again.

6. If needed, therapists can arrange *individual or family sessions with the siblings* of people with developmental disabilities who may feel extreme rejection, depression, even envy, because of the excessive attention that is sometimes directed at the person with the disability. Some siblings may worry about genetic disorders and whether having children is even a viable option for them.

Others may feel violated or traumatized by physical assaults from a brother or sister with a disability. Working with siblings can be a significant part of family therapy in the field of developmental disabilities (see Box 5).

7. *Psycho-education* can be an important part of family therapy. Often families need accurate information regarding their relative's specific disability, such as a syndrome (e.g., Prader-Willi), autism spectrum disorder, or mental health disorder. They may also need information about helpful websites and books, and about family stress management (e.g., Baskin & Fawcett, 2006).

8. When appropriate, therapists can suggest to family members that they might benefit from a psychiatric assessment, *psychotropic medication or specialized counselling*. Many family members who at first seem challenging are much less so after receiving proper professional help.

Summary

Families play a tremendously important and influential role in the lives of people with developmental disabilities. Yet challenging families can cause significant difficulties for frontline and management professionals; and ultimately can affect the emotional well-being of their relatives with disabilities who receive support. It is essential that frontline professionals and managers familiarize themselves with methods for successfully reducing the frustrations, anger, grief and tension that challenging families present, while attempting to mend the broken spirits of everyone involved. Effectively dealing with these problems using positive approaches can bring out the strengths in these families, contribute to the overall functioning of agencies and schools, and promote good mental health in the person with a disability.

For Further Thought and Discussion

1. Why is the adjective challenging used in quotation marks throughout this chapter to describe families?

2. What are some specific family behaviours that might be associated with each of the ten behavioural patterns of challenging families that are described in this chapter? Can you think of any other patterns not listed?

3. Why might professionals find challenging families very frustrating to deal with?

4. What can professionals do, both as individuals and as part of the service system, to improve relations with challenging families?

5. How can trained family therapists help community agency or school programs? What strategies might these therapists use to help challenging families?

More Resources

Books:

Baskin, A, & Fawcett, H. (2006). *More than a mom: Living a full and balanced life when your child has special Needs.* Bethesda, MD: Woodbine House.

Marshak, L.E., & Prezant, F.P. (2007). *Married with special needs children: A couples' guide to keeping connected.* Bethesda, MD: Woodbine House.

Nichols, M.P. (2009). *Family therapy: Concepts and methods* (9th Edition). Boston: Allyn & Bacon.

Internet/Websites:
(Locating Family-work Specialists)

Adult Protective Service Assocation of Ontario (Ask your local APSW)
www.apsao.org

Family Service Ontario (Ask for the Family Service Agency in your local community)
www.familyserviceontario.com

Ontario College of Social Workers & Social Service Workers (Ask for Registered Social Workers designated with "RSW" in your community)
www.ocswssw.org

Ontario Association of Marriage & Family Therapists (Ask for registered members of this association in your community with the designation "RMFT")
www.oamft.on.ca

References

Ashton, J., & Ashton, D. (1996). *Loss and grief recovery: Helping caring for children with disabilities, chronic or terminal illness.* Amityville, NY: Baywood.

Baskin & Fawcett (2006). *More than a mom: Living a full and balanced life when your child has special needs.* Bethesda, MD: WoodbineHouse.

Bettelheim, B. (1967). *The empty fortress: Infantile autism and the birth of welf.* New York: Collier-Macmillan.

Black, J., & Enns, G. (1997). *Better boundaries: Owning and treasuring your life.* Oakland, CA: New Harbinger.

Bramson, R. M. (1981). *Coping with difficult people.* New York: Ballantine.

Davis, H. D. (1987). *Disability and grief. Social Casework, 6,* 352-358.

Early, T. J., & GlenMaye, L. F. (2000). Valuing families: Social work practice with families from a strengths perspective. *Social Work, 45,* 118-130.

Findler, L., & Vardi, A. (2009). Psychological growth among siblings of children with and without intellectual disabilities. *Intellectual and Developmental Disabilities, 47,* 1-12.

Glass, L. (1995). *Toxic people: 10 ways of dealing with people who make your life miserable.* New York: St. Martin's Griffin.

Harris, A. H. S., Thorensen, C. E., & Lopez, S. J. (2007). Integrating positive psychology into counseling: Why and (when appropriate) how. *Journal of Counseling & Development, 85,* 3-13.

King, G., Baxter, D., Rosenbaum, P., Zwaigenbaum, L., & Bates, A. (2009). Belief systems of families of children with autism spectrum disorders or Down syndrome. *Focus on Autism and Developmental Disabilities, 24,* 50-64.

Lustig, D. C. (2002). Family coping in families with a child with a disability. *Education and Training in Mental Retardation and Developmental Disabilities, 37,* 14-22.

Minnes, P., & Woodford, L. (2005). Well-being in aging parents caring for an adult with a developmental disability. *Journal on Developmental Disabilities, 11,* 47-66.

Moses, K. (1988). [video, 72 minutes]. *Lost dreams & growth: Parents' concerns.* Evansville, IN: Resource Networks Inc.

Munro, J. D. (1991). Training families in the 'Step Approach Model' for effective advocacy. *Canada's Mental Health, 39,* 1, 1-6.

Munro, J. D. (1997). Using unconditionally constructive mediation to resolve family-system disputes related to persons with disabilities. *Families in Society, 78,* 609-616.

Munro, J. D. (2007). A positive intervention model for understanding, helping and coping with challenging families. In I. Brown, & M. Percy (Eds.), *A comprehensive guide to intellectual & developmental disabilities* (pp. 373-382). Baltimore: Paul H. Brookes Publishing.

Munro, J. D. (2009). Working with families: Essential skills every professional and manager should know! *The NADD Bulletin, 12*(3), 45-49.

Olshansky, S. (1961). Chronic sorrow: A response to having a mentally defective child. *Social Casework, 43,* 190-193.

Parks, R. M. (1983). Parental reactions to the birth of a handicapped child. In L. Wikler, & M. P. Keenan (Eds.), *Developmental disabilities: No longer a private tragedy* (pp. 96-101). Silver Spring, MD: National Association of Social Workers, and Washington, DC: American Association on Mental Deficiency.

Russo, R. J. (1999). Applying a strengths-based practice approach in working with people with developmental disabilities and their families. *Families in Society, 80,* 25-33.

Sanders, C. M. (1999). *Grief: The mourning after: Dealing with adult bereavement.* New York: Wiley.

Saleeby, D. (1992). *The strength perspective in social work practice.* New York: Basic Books.

Sieffert, A. (1978). Parents initial reactions to having a mentally retarded child: A concept and model for social workers. *Clinical Social Work Journal, 6*(1), 33-43.

Siegel, B., & Silverstein, S. (1994). *What about me? Growing up with a developmentally disabled sibling.* New York: Insight Books.

Singer, H. S., & Powers, L. E. (1993). *Families, disability and empowerment: Active coping skills and strategies for family interventions.* Baltimore: Paul H. Brookes Publishing.

VanDenBerg, J., & Grealish, E. M. (1998). *The wrap-around process training manual.* Pittsburgh, PA: The Community Partners Group.

26

Augmentative and Alternative Communication

Nora Rothschild and Ralf Schlosser

What you will learn:

- Communication and developmental disability
- What augmentative and alternative communication (AAC) is
- AAC services in Ontario
- Funding sources in Ontario for AAC equipment

Communication and Developmental Disability

What is communication?

Communication refers to the act or process involved in the mutual sharing of information between at least two people, whereby one person assumes the role of a sender and the other that of a receiver. The National Joint Committee for the Communication Needs of Persons with Severe Disabilities (2003) defined communication as:

> *Any act by which one person gives to or receives from another person information about that person's needs, desires, perceptions, knowledge or affective states. Communication may be intentional or unintentional, may involve conventional or unconventional signals, may take linguistic or nonlinguistic forms, and may occur through spoken or other modes. (p. 2)*

The essence of this definition is the concept of shared meaning. Communication is effective to the extent that there is shared meaning between the sender and receiver. Another important aspect of this definition is the recognition that communication can occur through a variety of behaviours and modes (e.g., gesture mode, graphic mode) other than speech. Another view of communication comes from the work of B. F. Skinnner (1957). Skinner described a class of verbal behaviour that is communicative in the sense that it is effective only indirectly through the mediation of a listener. For example, a person might request a cup of coffee from a waiter, rather than getting a cup directly from the coffee machine. Whether the request works depends on whether there was another person present who heard and understood the request and was willing and able to deliver the requested object.

Because communication allows us to feel a sense of belonging and to participate in social activities, it is often regarded as representing the essence of life. Communication impairment can negatively impact a person's quality of life. Indeed, Ferguson (1994) noted that communication is the most important means by which individuals obtain membership in society.

Communication results from a complicated interplay of many sensory and cognitive processes. It includes not only mastery of the verbal component but also mastery of visual, social, and behaviour skills (Grizzle & Simms, 2005). In broad terms, there is a distinction between linguistic (verbal) and nonlinguistic (nonverbal) modalities of communication. Linguistic modalities include spoken and written words, certain graphic symbol systems, and sign languages. Nonlinguistic or pre-linguistic modalities include facial expressions, body language, use of certain pictures, and gestures.

Prevalence studies indicate that as much as 16% of the U.S. population has some type of communication disorder. This topic is very important because there is considerable evidence that children who have impairments in speech and language can make substantial and lasting gains if identification of the problem and intervention occur early. Severe speech and language disorders pose a particular challenge. People with severe communication impairments may benefit from a form of treatment known as augmentative and alternative communication (AAC).

What is language?

Language refers to the code with which one communicates. It is an arbitrary system of symbols used by groups of people to communicate their thoughts and feelings, and it involves thought processes, symbols, grammar, meaning, memory, and words. The reason this system of symbols is called "arbitrary" is because the symbols usually bear no resemblance to their referents. For example, the word *chair* does not look like the object chair. Symbols may be communicated through speech, writing, graphic representation, gestures and body movements. In spoken language, the skills of articulation are used; in written language, spelling is substituted for articulation. Both auditory and visual skills are important for understanding language and for using it to communicate.

In spoken language, a set of complex, interacting rules governs the ways that individual words are organized and used. Because cognition is the foundation upon which language is built, this area of communication is likely to be affected by cognitive impairments.

Language consists of three components: form, content, and use (Bloom & Lahey, 1978).

Form: Form refers to the coding of words into meaningful sentences — that is, the grammar or syntax of language. As an individual develops greater language competence, form refers to the way the sentences are sequenced and organized to form narratives or discourse production.

Content: Content refers to the content, or the semantic of language. The development of semantics takes place throughout an individual's life. In a larger sense, this component of language relates to word meanings and more abstract, logical word relationships.

Use: Use refers to the pragmatic use of language — that is, the way in which language is used for different social and communicative functions. It takes conversational rules into account. It is the component of language that most strongly influences how adaptive an individual is or how well a person functions in his or her environment.

Interaction of the three components: Form, content, and use are all important for the production of language. However, impairments may occur within one of the three components with little influence on the other two components. For example, people with autism may have good language structure and a well-developed vocabulary, but they may use language in an inappropriate or inadequate manner, resulting in a significant impairment in social functioning. Frequently, however, language disorder results from more than one component being affected.

Speech and language are not mutually dependent on one another. It is possible to have fully intact language in the absence of speech, as demonstrated by sign language. It is equally possible to have completely intact speech development with major impairments in all components of language (e.g., specific language impairment).

How speech and language disorders are related to developmental disabilities

Because communication and cognition are highly related, a developmental disability often involves some communication disorder. McQueen et al. (1987) noted that speech disorders were commonly associated with intellectual disability. They estimated that up to 65.5% of children with intellectual disability had speech disorders of varying types and degrees. Approximately 30% to 50% of individuals with autism do not have speech (Mirenda & Iacono, 2009; National Research Council, 2001). Some syndromes associated with developmental disability are associated with speech or language problems characteristic of the particular syndrome (e.g., Down syndrome, fragile X syndrome, Velocardiofacial syndrome) or with unusual speech or language characteristics (e.g., Williams syndrome). Given these high prevalence rates, it is understandable that communication intervention is a priority for individuals with developmental disabilities. However, the severity of the disability does not always act as a predictor of the extent or type of communication difficulty. Some people with developmental disabilities experience voice and fluency disorders that are unrelated to their disability and are no more common in this population than in the general population (e.g., stuttering; McQueen et al., 1987).

Individuals with mild to moderate speech and language disorders may continue to rely on their natural residual speech, which can include delays in the emergence of speech and aspects of language use, such as multiword utterances, syntax, and conversational skills. It is unclear whether the language development of individuals with mild to moderate disabilities is best described as different or delayed (Zigler & Balla, 1982).

A significant percentage of individuals with de-velopmental disabilities other than autism also have little or no functional speech, resulting in severe communication impairment. Individuals with such severe communication impairment often acquire a prelinguistic level of communication development characterized by the use of vocalizations, informal gestures, and facial expression. For these people, intervention most likely will need to focus on the use of some AAC strategies and systems in addition to, or instead of, their prelinguistic behaviours.

How speech and language disorders are related to challenging behaviours

People with speech and language disorders have long been described as a group at risk for social, emotional, and behavioural difficulties. The most logical and simple explanation for this is that speech and language impairments affect an individual's ability to understand and/or be understood by others. The greater the communication difficulty, the greater the risk of negative consequences. The range of negative consequences is as great as the range of impairments themselves (Burke-Brassem & Palace, 2003).

Some people may react to communication difficulties by demonstrating externalizing behaviours such as impatience, tantrums, impulsiveness, and aggression. Others may display internalizing behaviours such as withdrawal, avoidance, depression, and dependence. Speech and language impairments also are associated with self-injury and stereotypical behaviours. Individuals with intellectual and developmental disabilities may have learned to use these challenging behaviours to communicate basic wants and needs. For instance, challenging behaviours may allow individuals to communicate that they wish to escape from difficult tasks; for example, an individual who bangs his head against the wall when work demands are placed on him may be granted a break from work. Others may seek to obtain or keep their favourite tangible objects. The behaviour of some individuals may be maintained by social attention from communication partners. For instance, each time a student engages in self-injurious behaviour, the teacher pays attention to her. Finally, some individuals are motivated by sensory consequences.

Sensory factors that contribute to speech and language difficulties

Sensory impairments such as those related to hearing and vision may contribute to the previously discussed speech and language difficulties. In fact, these sensory issues are so important that "the presence of sensory impairments should always be ruled in or out as contributing factors in cases of communication disability" (Blischak & Wasson, 1997, p. 254). All people with developmental disabilities should have a hearing assessment and a vision assessment, as well as a speech and language assessment.

Similar to hearing impairment, many types and degrees of visual impairment exist, including loss of visual acuity and visual field loss. Also similar to hearing impairment, it is important that visual impairments be detected or ruled out through an adequate visual assessment. If undetected or uncorrected, a visual impairment may seriously thwart social, communication, educational, and vocational opportunities of individuals with developmental disabilities. As with the assessment of hearing impairment, visual assessments may require adaptations in order to be functional. Interventions vary from those that are primarily medical (e.g., surgery) to those that are more "low-tech" (e.g., using appropriate font size, display style, spacing, contrast, and distance between symbols for someone using AAC; using magnifying glasses or eye-glasses). Regardless of the intervention, with adequate support many vision impairments can be successfully treated and their negative impact on functioning, including communication, minimized.

Who may benefit from speech and language intervention

Determining whether an individual requires intervention and, if applicable, determining the specific types of intervention needed are complex tasks. These decisions also depend on a number of variables: age, personality, history of adjustments, supports, awareness of difficulties and when to use compensatory strategies, the degree to which a person can be stimulated, and family or living situation. There are many varied communication assessments and treatments available, sometimes commercially marketed, that may serve as treatment options for people with disabilities including autism, pervasive developmental disorder, behaviour disorder, attention-deficit / hyperactivity disorder, dyslexia, and auditory processing disorder. Sometimes the intervention serves as a solution for a variety of problems associated with the full spectrum of developmental disabilities.

The overall goal of intervention, whether through direct therapy (i.e., working with the client directly) or indirect therapy (i.e., working with communication partners of the client), should recognize, encourage, and respond to appropriate communicative attempts and the underlying function of those attempts. For example, an individual pointing to something outside may be simply trying to join another person, get someone's attention, or engage in some common commentary (verbal or nonverbal) on the identified object.

The approach to intervention that may allow the individual to become a more effective, empowered communicator may not always involve individual, direct, structured therapy. A more appropriate approach to intervention may recognize the individual's social, familial, and work or school milieu; the individual's expectations and functioning within these environments; and ways to facilitate understanding, development, and success within them. Once the proper focus of intervention has been determined, the order, timetable, and type of therapy need to be considered. For example, perhaps a child's specific impairments have not been identified but it turns out that the child has apraxia. Encouraging him or her to speak may be detrimental to further development. In such cases, it may be more appropriate to explore alternative means (e.g., AAC) by which the child can communicate with others. The child's parents and teachers can work together with professionals to foster the child's desire and ability to use another system to augment speech.

Communication goals will likely vary considerably depending on the nature and severity of a person's communication impairment. Individuals with mild and moderate speech impairments may benefit from early intervention to accelerate the acquisition of vocabulary and the transition from single to multiword utterances. Because delays in expressive speech are typically more obvious than delays in receptive language, it is important to intervene to increase the understanding of speech. In terms of expressive speech intervention, it may be necessary to establish communicative functions such as requesting or commenting that are absent or underdeveloped, and this may vary across different disability conditions (Duker, van Driel, & van de Bercken, 2002). Articulation training may be indicated for individuals with hearing impairment and oral-motor problems.

For individuals with severe communication impairment due to developmental disability, there is often the need to teach functional communication skills that will enable them to communicate basic wants and needs in an efficient manner. To be efficient, others must be able to readily interpret their communication responses. This often means trying to replace existing prelinguistic behaviours with more conventional forms, such as manual signs or the use of a picture-based communication system.

It is important to note that individuals who may benefit from speech and language intervention do not constitute a homogeneous group, even when they share the same diagnosis. The nature and severity of the communication impairment determines the type of intervention that would be most appropriate. The type of intervention that may benefit an individual also depends on his or her age and lifestyle.

For individuals who exhibit challenging behaviours that have been determined to be communicative, functional communication training may be an effective intervention strategy (Bopp, Brown, & Mirenda, 2004). Functional communication training involves the teaching of a replacement behaviour that serves the same communicative function as the challenging behaviour. In other words, an individual whose behaviour is motivated by escape from tasks needs to be shown how to escape through more socially acceptable means, such as asking for a break. The communication status of the individual, as well as the needs of his or her environment should be taken into account for selecting an appropriate communicative response modality. A person with sufficient verbal repertoire may be taught to use words to request a break. Individuals with little or no functional speech may need to learn how to use AAC.

Augmentative and Alternative Communication

Individuals with developmental disabilities who have severe communication impairments may be candidates for AAC. As noted, *AAC* refers to approaches that add to (hence, the term *augmentative*) or replace (hence, the word *alternative*) a person's natural speech and/or writing abilities to communicate. Some individuals who cannot make any sounds use AAC to replace natural speech. Others who have some functional speech use AAC to augment their speech attempts. In addition, individuals who use AAC often use a variety of modes to communicate. These may consist of vocalizations, gestures, picture or alphabet displays, or others. It is not uncommon for an individual to use many different ways of communicating, either together in the same setting or separately in different settings and with different partners. This is often referred to as multimodal communication.

AAC can be used to share ideas and thoughts using a variety of strategies involving symbols. For example, a child may point to a photograph of a *playground* in a book or may use a specialized "talking computer" to indicate the message "I want to play." These kinds of strategies are called aided approaches. They include different modes or ways of signalling messages (e.g., communication display, device), as well as various strategies for doing so (Lloyd, Fuller, & Arvidson, 1997).

Other approaches may rely solely on the body. For example, a child may use a manual sign or may use vocalizations and gestures for playground to communicate the desire to play. Such communications do not involve any external aids and thus are referred to as unaided approaches. An individual's AAC system may include both aided and unaided approaches. Aided approaches include low-tech and high-tech aids. Low-tech refers to a range of non-technical but potentially powerful communication systems such as pictures, symbols, alphabets, or word displays. High-tech generally refers to specialized electronic or computer-based equipment. High-tech equipment includes various "talking devices," which are called voice output communication aids (VOCAs) or speech generating devices (SGDs); standard or specialized computers; software; and computer components.

In a review of the literature, Mirenda (2003) considered issues related to the use of manual signs versus graphic-based communication systems for individuals with disabilities. Mirenda concluded that both types of systems can be taught and can be functional for the person, provided the communicative partners are familiar with and can interpret the system. Furthermore, there is no reason why only one type of AAC mode needs to be selected. In many cases, it is necessary for an individual to be able to use a variety of forms and modes for communication. AAC intervention can and should include procedures to teach gesture and graphic mode communication.

AAC is often confused with assistive technology. Assistive technology refers to devices or services used to help individuals with functions and activities. Although AAC may include assistive technology (e.g., use of a device such as a SGD), this would be only one part of an AAC system. AAC also involves the use of many methods of communication, such as gestures, manual signs, and vocalizations, which are not considered to be assistive technology.

Components of an AAC assessment

Decision making in assessment and intervention should be based on the principles of evidence-based practice (EBP). Schlosser (2003) defined EBP as "the integration of best and current research evidence with clinical/educational expertise and relevant stakeholder perspectives in order to facilitate decisions about assessment and intervention that are deemed effective and efficient for a given direct stakeholder" (p. 3).

In carrying out an assessment for AAC, it is important to keep in mind that any person with developmental disabilities who is nonspeaking, regardless of his or her diagnosis or developmental level, can benefit from AAC strategies. AAC assessment should provide a clear picture of the individual's

skills and abilities by addressing a number of questions, including the following:

- What is the individual able to communicate?
- What purposes does the individual's communication serve?
- How competent is the individual in communicating for various purposes?
- What barriers prevent the individual from participating?
- What are the individual's receptive and expressive language skills?
- What are the individual's cognitive abilities?
- What are the individual's physical/motor abilities?
- What types of symbols will meet the individual's needs both now and in the future?
- What are the individual's literacy abilities?
- What are the individual's sensory/perceptual abilities, including vision, hearing, and tactile senses?

Observation: The first step in an AAC assessment is typically to observe the individual who has complex communication needs with familiar communication partners. This is ideally carried out in the individual's usual and familiar environments. These observations indicate what the individual is capable of communicating and suggest what his or her future communication needs may be.

Communicative competence involves looking at the individual's linguistic, social, operational, and strategic abilities (Light & Binger, 1998), as well as the individual's developmental level. Although some individuals who are nonspeaking may not use speech to communicate, they may still be considered competent communicators if they use AAC strategies to communicate their needs, wants, and ideas functionally and adequately (Blischak, Loncke, & Waller, 1997). In this way, the communication strengths as well as communication needs will be documented. Standardized tests are generally not a salient part of the assessment, as each individual with complex communication needs has a unique set of skills and abilities.

Observations also show the general attitudes, abilities and kinds of strategies that different communication partners have and use. Observations of familiar communication partners should take into account their existing strategies and how effective they appear to be. Observation and inventory of the various environments in which the person carries out life activities is also an important part of the assessment. This should include the opportunities available for participating in environments and the barriers to such participation (Beukelman & Mirenda, 2005). As part of this inventory, it is important to include the various activities or tasks the individual is doing on a regular basis and to ask whether the individual's communication needs to be further optimized in those activities.

Determining needs and skills: From the information gathered through observation and the information shared by the individual and relevant communication partners, it is possible to project the ideal potential requirements of feature options of the AAC system(s) and AAC strategies. It is also important to identify the preferences of the AAC user, as well as his or her family and other communication partners. A trial, including trial teaching, should occur to see whether the match is effective or whether changes are required, especially when communicating with different partners.

In determining which one of the many available approaches or modes fits best, it is also important to match the AAC system with the individual's environments. Different needs and expectations arise in various settings, with different partners, and from the demands of various tasks. As a result, different strategies and priorities for communication need to be considered with these in mind. For example, unaided approaches (e.g., signs, specific gestures) may not be understood in the larger community. Thus, if goals include inclusion, independent communication, and participation in the community at large, manual signs may not be appropriate. In other situations, aided approaches may not be appropriate. For example, the action of a child who is pointing to a graphic symbol to request the teacher's attention only works when the teacher is in close proximity. The research on AAC and social networks reflects that individuals who use AAC often use very different modes of communication depending on the type of communication partners (Blackstone & Hunt Berg, 2003).

Setting goals: The information gathered from the observations, reports by the individual and the team, and an analysis of the individual's skills and needs are helpful in developing meaningful and functional communication goals and an intervention (action) plan that will ensure that goals are implemented. It is essential for the entire team to set measurable goals so that everyone on the team knows when the goals have been reached. An individual support plan has been found to be a useful tool for setting goals and action plans, as well as monitoring the attainment of goals (Rothschild, McGinnis, & Norris, 1996). In Ontario and many other areas of North America, clinicians working with AAC often include the use of SMART goals. These goals are documented as being Specific, Measurable, Achievable, Realistic and Time-bound. These goals are reviewed and analyzed by the individual and his or her team at designated times. Because AAC assessment usually does not include standardized tests — and thus outcome measures are not standardized — these clinicians may also include the use of Goal Attainment Scaling (GAS). GAS is a technique for evaluating individual progress toward goals. GAS also allows comparability across goals and clients through aggregation, and provides a focal point for team energies (Schlosser, 2004).

Ongoing assessment: As communication skills change and new situations arise, there is a continuing need for assessment. This is a process that interweaves assessment and intervention in an ongoing way. That is, as an intervention is being implemented, the clinician and team assess how the intervention has been working, modify as necessary, and continue with the intervention. This occurs more formally when the team reviews the goals that were set during the time specified by the team.

When AAC should be considered

As mentioned earlier, it has been said that communication is the "essence of human life" (Article II, Section 1, United States Society for Augmentative and Alternative Communication Bylaws; for further information see *http://www.ussaac.org*). To the extent that this is true, successful AAC intervention has the potential to improve an individual's quality of life in very substantial ways. AAC may help to create important life possibilities by removing communication barriers.

Numerous anecdotes and personal accounts from AAC users describe the potential for AAC to improve quality of life. Without a doubt, AAC should be used for this purpose. Justin Clark's legal struggles illustrate how AAC can be used effectively to improve a basic human right of people with speech and language difficulties. On November 26, 1982, Judge John Matheson of the Lanark County Court in Perth, Ontario stated, "In a spirit of liberty, the necessity to understand the minds of other men and the remembrance that 'not even a sparrow falls to earth unheeded,' I find and declare Matthew Justin Clark to be mentally competent" (McNaughton, 1982, p. 3). So ended what has been called a landmark case for the rights of people with disabilities — and the first court case in Canadian history in which Blissymbols were used by a witness to give testimony.

Protection from abuse is another area where AAC should be used, and has been used with some success. Whether or not individuals with developmental disabilities use AAC, they are highly over-represented in cases of physical, sexual, and emotional abuse (Ahlgrim-Delzell & Dudley, 2001; Vig & Kaminer, 2002). Often, they are considered unreliable witnesses by the legal system (Valenti-Hein & Schwartz, 1993). The Speak Up project, which describes itself as safeguarding people who use AAC from sexual abuse and victimization (Augmentative Communication Community Partnerships Canada; ACCPC, 2010), reported that people with physical disabilities combined with severe speech disorders are 2 to 6 times more likely to experience physical, mental, and sexual abuse as a result of their inability to communicate effectively (Sobsey, 1994). Victims who cannot communicate are less able to prevent or report abuse. Without access to the words they need to communicate, people who use augmentative and alternative communication (AAC) cannot discuss, learn about, disclose or report issues, let alone take legal action relating to victimization (Farrar, 1996).

Many people with developmental disabilities, however, may be regarded as competent witnesses if they are carefully questioned and if minor adjustments are made in legal proceedings (Perlman, Ericson, Esses, & Isaacs, 1994). Ericson, Isaacs, and Perlman (2003) and Collier et al. (2007) have provided useful strategies to enhance communication with people in the justice system who have developmental disabilities and who use AAC tools and strategies.

For everyday life activities, AAC may be helpful for people with a variety of developmental disabilities, including autism, cerebral palsy, developmental apraxia of speech, developmental delay, specific language disorders, and others (Mirenda & Mathy Laikko, 1989). The need for AAC support may vary in degree and focus across the life span. Often a child is 2 to 3 years old when his or her parents first seek professional help because the child is not speaking. During early childhood, parents often wish to bring the child's communication skills up to the appropriate age level. The focus of AAC intervention at this time often includes increasing participation in daily routines, expanding the child's communication range, and developing symbolic communication.

During the school-age years, concerns frequently centre around friendships, the school curriculum, and literacy. Current trends for school and community inclusion make it necessary for a child to have a way of communicating that is effective with all peers, including those with and without disabilities. Providing opportunities to participate in the curriculum is essential, whether the curriculum is standard or adapted in some way. Participation in early literacy experiences is particularly important if students are to learn the skills necessary for communication, as well as to succeed in school and in the workplace. During adulthood, AAC needs often focus on supporting individuals in managing independent living, attendant care, employment, community participation, leisure, and friendships (Collier, 2000). The primary goal of AAC use and intervention is for the individual to become a better or more competent communicator.

Zangari and Kangas (1997) provided a list of criteria for establishing AAC goals. Rothschild and Hunt (2008) suggested that goals should be prioritized by individuals and their teams and that goals should be balanced, based on the four domains suggested by Light and Binger (1998):

1. Linguistic (language, literacy, comprehension and expression, etc.)
2. Social (interpersonal dynamics, relationships, interacting with various partners, pragmatics, etc.)
3. Operational (knowledge and skills to technically operate the AAC system)
4. Strategic (compensatory strategies to overcome limitations in linguistic, operational and/or social skills)

Relationship between AAC and natural speech production

Parents, teachers, and therapists often wonder if AAC use will interfere with the acquisition of natural speech. During early childhood years, parents may find it difficult to accept AAC because they fear that using such approaches will delay their child's speech production. However, AAC involves using a variety of modes or ways of communicating, including speech. Thus, children who use AAC to communicate are encouraged not only to use pictures or manual signs but also to do so in conjunction with their speech, if possible. Communication partners are also encouraged to model both speech (by speaking to the individual) and other methods of communication. In addition, auditory feedback from SGDs can function as speech models. These models can be elicited by the user herself. AAC always encourages the use of whatever vocalizations the individual is capable of using, despite other modes of communication that are available to the individual. Children whose vocalizations are understood by partners would not be asked to repeat themselves using their communication systems. Rather, the partners would acknowledge the messages conveyed through the vocalization.

There is no evidence that AAC intervention hinders speech production; to the contrary, there is some preliminary evidence that suggests AAC intervention may actually increase natural speech production in children with developmental disabilities in general (Millar, Light, & Schlosser, 2006) and children with autism in particular (Schlosser & Wendt, 2008). That being said, the resulting in-

creases tend to be of a modest nature and ought to be viewed as a bonus to AAC interventions rather than a primary aim. To reiterate, the primary aim of intervention is to facilitate communication through whatever means, rather than to focus solely on increased speech production.

Components of successive intervention with AAC

The issue of timing often comes up when discussing the need for AAC intervention. Specifically, families ask, "My child doesn't seem ready. Should we wait to use AAC?" In the past, some authors considered that there were certain cognitive "prerequisites" that the child needed to master prior to introducing AAC. For example, it was believed that a child needed to understand a cause-and-effect relationship before moving to AAC as a communication method. The difficulty with applying this prerequisite theory is that some people might be kept waiting indefinitely for prerequisites to be learned. Moreover, sufficient research data to support this point of view have not emerged. For these reasons, professionals in the field of AAC have generally accepted that many of these skills may actually be developed by using basic AAC strategies themselves (Kangas & Lloyd, 1988; National Joint Committee for the Communication Needs of Persons with Severe Disabilities, 2003). For instance, if a child who activates a switch that says, "Give me juice please" is given juice each time, he or she may learn that the action of switch activation results in getting a drink of juice. In general, it is advisable to begin AAC intervention early in life.

AAC interventions should be needs based, documented by goals, and accompanied by appropriate measurement of progress to ensure accountability of everyone involved. One way of ensuring accountability is to monitor when goals are attained. The perspectives of the person receiving service, the family, and other team members — such as the speech-language pathologist, the special educator, and the occupational therapist (teams are formed based on the client's needs) — are usually used to determine when goals have been attained. Although it is important to know whether these stakeholders perceive changes in the desired direction, more objective measures of

Table 1: Commonly Used Intervention Strategies That Have Proven To Be Effective

AAC Strategy	Partner Strategies	Description	References
Linguistic			
Increase requesting for:	*Provide opportunities by using the missing-item strategy.*	*Give a person all but one item of the items needed to complete or engage in a preferred activity.*	*Reichle, York, & Sigafoos (1991)*
1. objects	*Provide opportunities by using inadequate portions.*	*Use small or inadequate amounts or portions of food during snack time or lunch.*	
2. action	*Provide opportunities by using the interrupted chain strategy.*	*Momentarily interrupt the person from completing or continuing an on-going activity.*	
3. assistance	*Provide opportunities by using delayed assistance.*	*Use materials that require assistance. After observing that the person needs help, walk over and wait for him or her to request assistance before providing the help needed.*	
Increase commenting	*Provide opportunities by creating absurd situations.*	*Present absurd or silly situations and wait for the person to comment.*	*Zangari & Kangas (1997)*
	Provide opportunities through interesting materials/tasks.	*Use interesting materials and activities and wait for the person to comment.*	
Increase rejecting	*Provide opportunities by using disliked objects.*	*Use something the person does not like and wait for him or her to reject it*	*Reichle et al. (1991)*
Social			
Communicate as spontaneously as possible	*Invite communicative responses using least-to-most prompting.*	*Use in a hierarchical fashion according to the degree of intrusiveness of prompts. "Least-to-most" starts with a pause and may end with a full model. Use of pauses between prompt levels is essential.*	*Reichle et al. (1991)*
Increase interaction	*Increase interaction by teaching use of:*		*Light & Binger (1998)*
	a. introductory statements	*Teach the person to introduce himself or herself to the partner using least-to-most prompting.*	
	b. partner-focussed questions	*Teach the person to ask questions that are oriented to the interests of the partner using least-to-most prompting.*	
	c. unforced turns	*Teach the person to take turns even though the situation may not necessarily force a turn using least-to-most prompting.*	

AAC Strategy	Partner Strategies	Description	References
Operational			
Learn to associate symbols with words	*Provide models of AAC use and tell learner that AAC is accept–able through augmented input.*	The partner provides models with the AAC user's system (e.g., points to the symbols while speaking or signs while speaking).	*Goossens, Crain, & Elder (1992); Romski & Sevcik (1996)*
Ensure that gestures are read correctly	*Be consistent in interpreting gestures across situations by relying on a Gesture Dictionary for interpretation.*	Important in the early stages of gesture development or for someone with highly idiosyncratic gestures (includes all elements that are part of the person's gesture, including facial expressions, eye gaze, and vocalizations).	*Beukelman & Mirenda (2005)*
Strategic			
Respond with the least amount of prompting	*Encourage appropriate communicative behaviour by using most-to-least prompting.*	"Most-to-least" provides the most intrusive prompt first and then gradually reduces intrusiveness. Often used when teaching a person to use AAC instead of challenging behaviour. The use of pauses between prompt levels is essential.	*Mirenda (1997); Schlosser (1997)*
Communicate appropriately rather than with challenging behaviour	*Encourage appropriate communicative behaviour using Functional Communication Training.*	Train the individual to express the function served by the challenging behaviour through appropriate means (e.g., request favourite objects).	*Mirenda (1997); Schlosser (1997)*
Use partner feedback to modify message if necessary	*Avoid communication breakdown by providing descriptive feedback.*	Provide feedback in the form of expanded repetition of the augmented communicator's message.	*Beukelman & Mirenda (1992)*
Communicate functionally within routine activities	*Elicit communication by using activity-based intervention.*	A comprehensive approach that aims at the development of functional and generative skills within the context of child-initiated, planned, or routine transactions using logically occurring events that occasion the behaviour and consequences that follow the behaviour.	*Bricker & Cripe (1991)*

accountability are also useful, as perspectives sometimes get influenced by wanting to see the desired effects. Observation in natural settings and recording data observed of behaviour provide more objective measures. For example, clinicians and parents may want to record such progress data as the number of symbols used in functional contexts, the number of choices communicated successfully in a given time period, or the number of words or phrases expressed through AAC modes during specified activities. Children with developmental delay require intense, consistent, and systematic intervention during natural activities, especially for the acquisition of the first functional symbols. Individuals with developmental disabilities in general (Rispoli, Franco, van der Meer, Lang, & Camargo, 2010) and individuals with autism in particular (van der Meer & Rispoli, 2010) have learned to use SGDs for a variety of communicative functions. Table 1 lists some commonly used intervention strategies that have proven to be effective.

How to help make communication more effective for AAC users

As with any form of communication, AAC is not carried out by one person; it always requires a partner. For this reason, AAC interventions often include changing the partner's behaviours in order to elicit desired communication from the augmented communicator. In other words, communication partners can often offer the most effective intervention strategies to assist individuals who have complex communication needs to communicate more effectively. Information in Table 1 illustrates that communication goals for these individuals are most easily reached when appropriate partner strategies to facilitate the attainment of goals are used.

It is important to ensure that all partners in the individual's world understand the strategies they can use during their interactions. Partners should include parents, siblings, other family members, friends, nannies, teachers, educational assistants, other students, co-workers, attendants, nurses, and others involved with the individual. Communication does not happen in a vacuum. It is driven by the activities and settings in which people participate. In addition

to partner strategies, the environment (e.g., classroom curriculum) often has a strong impact on the degree of success of AAC intervention. Depending on the particular goals targeted, different intervention strategies may be appropriate.

To assist a person in communicating more effectively, partners can create opportunities for communication. Increased opportunities for communication assist the person in learning and maintaining communication skills. As suggested in Table 1, the need for communication can be created in several ways, such as the following:

- Temporarily withhold a wanted or needed object until the person communicates a desire for the object.
- Give the person a small amount of a preferred object, thereby creating a need for the person to request more.
- Temporarily block the person from completing an activity, thereby creating a need for the person to communicate.
- Wait a short period of time (e.g., 10 seconds) before giving the person help with a difficult task. This increases the person's motivation to request help.
- Give the person a wrong item, thereby creating a need for the person to offer a correction.

Augmentative and Alternative Communication (AAC) Services in Ontario

In Ontario, the Ministry of Health and Long-Term Care is the major player in providing health and health-related services. It funds the health care system in general, and oversees operations of many hospitals, chronic care, long term care, Community Care Access Centres (CCACs), and other service agencies. Some of these organizations provide various AAC services such as assessment, intervention and consultation, training for using low-tech and high-tech communication systems, partner strategies, sign language training, and others.

In addition, the Assistive Devices Branch of this Ministry, also known as the Assistive Devices

Program (ADP) provides one source of funding for communication aids for eligible Ontario residents. This funding includes a variety of AAC devices listed in the ADP Product Manual. These speech generating devices are sometimes called *face-to-face communication systems* because they help individuals who cannot speak to communicate in conversations. Also included are devices that help persons who cannot use pens and pencils to write and those who may benefit from various *writing aids* such as computers.

ADP has a process for evaluating these devices that helps determine which devices will be listed in the ADP Product Manual and if the devices can be purchased or leased. Equipment for leasing is available through the *Centralized Equipment Pool (CEP)*. CEP is set up as a recycling program so clients lease equipment and return it to CEP when the equipment no longer meets the client's needs. Leasing through CEP is helpful, if the equipment is no longer required, if the needs of the person with disabilities change, or if repair or replacement is needed. CEP serves people with changing medical conditions and individuals who use high-tech SGDs. It is a resource for those who are eligible for ADP and is only available to eligible individuals through the ADP-Designated AAC Clinics listed in Table 2. CEP also provides educational opportunities for Ontario professionals interested in AAC (see CEP website).

There are numerous vendors who represent and distribute AAC products on behalf of various manufacturers. The vendors demonstrate, sell, and support their products to any interested clinicians, agencies, or CEP, and directly to people with disabilities and their families.

ADP has put a process in place to authorize individuals and ADP-Designated AAC Clinics in Ontario to ensure standards are met to help individuals who use AAC. Some clinicians and some agencies that provide AAC services have chosen to become involved with the ADP service delivery system. The system has three levels: Individual Authorizers, General Level ADP-Designated AAC Clinics, and Expanded Level ADP-Designated AAC Clinics.

Speech-language pathologists (S-LPs) can become ADP Individual Authorizers (IA). As an IA, S-LPs can prescribe a variety of relatively simple face-to-face SGDs for clients who can access the device directly as well as software needed to create low-tech AAC displays. If the item is ADP approved, then the S-LP can authorize the device and ADP will pay approximately 75% of the purchase cost, with the client paying the rest. As Individual Authorizers, S-LPs may access CEP for short term loans of these simple devices.

Similarly, Occupational Therapists (OTs) can become ADP IAs. As an ADP IA, OTs can prescribe relatively simple "off-the-shelf," unmodified *writing aids* if the client does not need any hardware or software modifications. Simple switches and commercial mounting systems are also covered.

In Ontario, there are ADP-Designated AAC Clinics (see Table 2) who meet specific standards. One of these standards is having a dedicated inter-professional AAC team (S-LPs, OTs, special educators, technologists) to address the needs of clients with more complex clinical issues that may require an inter-professional team. The ADP-Designated AAC Clinics' mandate includes addressing clients in need of more complex face-to-face communication SGDs and writing aids listed in the ADP Product Manual. They may customize low-tech communication displays and obtain ADP funding. They can authorize more complex mounting systems that require customization. As ADP-Designated AAC Clinics, they may authorize devices for purchase with 75% ADP funding. They can also access the CEP pool of devices purchased by ADP for the recycling/leasing program. Eligible clients may lease the devices, if authorized by an ADP-Designated AAC Clinic, for an annual fee of approximately 10% of the device cost to a maximum of $800 per year. General Level ADP-Designated AAC Clinics may authorize devices for purchase or lease for clients who can access the device directly. Expanded Level ADP-Designated AAC Clinics may authorize devices for clients who access the devices directly or indirectly by using various means of alternate access.

The Ontario Ministry of Community and Social Services (MCSS) is also involved in providing funding for some agencies such as children's rehabilitation centres and programs that support people who need AAC. For eligible clients, MCSS also provides

Table 2: ADP-Designated AAC Centres in Ontario (as at July 2010)

Types of Clinics/Location	Name of AAC Clinic	Telephone
General Level AAC Clinics		
Youth Clinics:		
Chatham-Kent - Children's Treatment Centre of Chatham-Kent	Augmentative and Alternative Communication Clinic	519-354-0520
North Bay - Nipissing, Muskoka, Parry Sound - One Kids Place Children's Treatment Centre	Augmentative and Alternative Communication Clinic	705-476 5437
York & Simcoe - Children's Treatment Network of Simcoe York	Augmentative Communication Consultation Service	1-866-377-0286
Youth and Adult Clinics:		
Toronto - Surrey Place Centre	Augmentative Communication and Writing Aids	416-925-5141
Expanded Level AAC Clinics		
Youth Clinics:		
Kingston - Hotel Dieu Hospital	Augmentative Communication Service	613-544-3310
Kitchener-Waterloo - KidsAbility	Augmentative Communication Services	519-886-8886
London - Thames Valley Children's Centre	Augmentative Communication Services	519-685-8680
Mississauga - Erinoak	Assistive Devices Resource Service	905-820-7111 x 2316
Ottawa - Ottawa Children's Treatment Centre	Clinic for Augmentative Communication	613-688-2126
Peterborough - Five Counties Children's Centre	Augmentative Communication Service	705-748-2221 x 320
St. Catherines - Niagara Peninsula Children's Treatment Centre	Communication Assessment & Support Team	905-688-3550 x 130
Sudbury - Sudbury Regional Hospital, Pediatrics	Children's Treatment Centre, Assistive Communication Clinic	705-560-8000
Toronto - Holland Bloorview Kids Rehabilitation Hospital (formerly Bloorview MacMillan Children's Centre)	Communication & Writing Aids Service	416-424-3805

The ADP-Designated AAC Clinic information listed above reflects the changes and the dynamism of the health care service delivery system in Ontario and are regularly in flux. The information printed here is current only as at July 2010.

Types of Clinics/Location	Name of AAC Clinic	Telephone
Youth and Adult Clinics:		
Hamilton - Hamilton Health Sciences, Chedoke Division	Technology Access Clinic	905-521-2100 x 77833
Sarnia - Pathways Health Centre for Children	Augmentative Communication Service	519-542-3471
Thunder Bay - George Jeffrey Children's Treatment Centre	Augmentative Communication Program	807-623-4381
Windsor - John McGivney Children's Centre	Augmentative Communication Clinic	519-252-7281
Adult Clinics:		
Kitchener - Grand River Hospital, Freeport Health Centre	Communication Technology Service	519-749-4300 x 7278
Ottawa - The Rehabilitation Centre	Augmentative Communication & Writing Service	613-737-7350 x 75302
Ottawa - Saint Vincent Hospital	Augmentative & Alternative Communication Clinic	613-233-4041
Sudbury - Sudbury Regional Hospital Adult Laurentian Site	Assistive Communication Clinic	705-522-2200 x 3550
Toronto - Baycrest Brain Health Centre	Assistive Technology Clinic & Elkie Adler, MS Clinic	416-784-3600
Toronto - Bridgepoint Health	Augmentative Communication & Writing Clinic	416-461-8251 x 2334
Toronto - Toronto Rehabilitation Institute	Queen Elizabeth Centre, AAC Clinic	416-597-3028
Toronto - Toronto Rehabilitation Institute, Lyndhurst Centre	Assistive Technology Clinic	416-597-3422
Toronto - Sunnybrook Health Sciences Centre CIL	Assistive Technology Clinic	416-480-5756
Toronto - West Park Hospital Healthcare Centre	AAC Clinic	416-243-3600 x 4679

the family's portion of the device costs for devices that are prescribed by ADP authorized IAs or ADP-Designated AAC Clinics. Thus, clients who are eligible for both ADP and MCSS funding may obtain these devices with full government assistance — whether purchased or leased, as long as the devices are authorized by an ADP authorized professional.

The Ontario Ministry of Education and Training is also involved in providing supports, as well as funding to students who require equipment for face-to-face or written communication. Students need to be identified by their schools as having special needs in order to access special supports and services. An Individual Education Plan documents the student's special communication and other needs as well as individual goals and action plans. The Individual Education Plan determines the level of funding, including related AAC equipment and resources. Most school boards have access to S-LPs and OTs to support these students and classroom staff. Their roles differ depending on their experience, student needs, school board philosophy and availability of resources. Some of these staff may also be accredited as IAs by the Ministry of Health and Long-Term Care's ADP.

Since September 1998, each student in Ontario identified as having special needs has been funded by using a province-wide formula based on the level and type of support required. All special needs students are eligible for a Special Education Per Pupil Allotment grant to access special education services. Some students may, in addition, qualify for a Special Equipment Amount (SEA) grant for specialized support or equipment. School-based equipment funded by a SEA grant is intended to move with the student throughout the school system and from school to school within the province. The Ontario Ministry of Education's Special Education Funding Guidelines (2010) states that the SEA:

> ...provides funding to school boards to assist with the costs of equipment essential to support students with special education needs where the need for specific equipment is recommended by a qualified professional. This equipment is to provide students with accommodations that are directly required and essential to access the Ontario curriculum and/or a board-determined alternative program and/or course and/or to attend school. (p.1)

Beginning in September 2010, the SEA guidelines for accessing funding were altered and a finalized system is planned to be in place by 2014-15.

What AAC services are available in Ontario?

Service delivery and philosophy among the three Ministries and the community agencies they support often differs to some extent. Most services are still program-centred, but are beginning to become more family-centred by including people with disabilities and their families as part of service delivery teams. Individuals with AAC needs may access any service that includes them in their mandate. Mandates may be selective based on such things as geography, age, diagnosis, need, or enrolment, or they may be all-inclusive and provincial. To find out what AAC services are available in your region, contact a local speech-language pathologist, and/or various contacts listed in Table 2.

Who provides these services and what are their roles?

In Ontario, AAC services are usually provided by S-LPs, OTs, and/or special educators. These professionals may have various levels of training or experience in AAC. Currently, there is no generally accepted certification needed to provide AAC services in Ontario, although there is an on-line course offered through CEP that is required by all clinicians in ADP-Designated AAC Clinics. Areas of AAC expertise commonly acknowledged for these three professional groups include the following:

- *S-LPs* focus on speech or other means of communication, strategies used for communication, and functions or use of literacy and language including vocabulary and AAC symbols.
- *OTs* focus on physical and functional skills, access to communication systems, physical and writing modifications, environmental modifications, and sensory issues.
- *Special educators* focus on literacy and curriculum modification to integrate students, using AAC, smoothly into the curriculum.

Many ADP-Designated AAC Clinics encourage

staff to cross these traditional professional boundaries while working together as a team. Depending on needs, resources, mandates and philosophies, an individual who uses AAC may be seen by any one, or a combination, of these local providers. ADP encourages individuals with limited technical and/or straightforward clinical needs to see individual authorizers in their local communities. Individual authorizers can be employed by any agency or they can be in private practice.

As of July 2010, there were 23 ADP-Designated AAC Clinics in Ontario (see Table 2). They each serve a specific geographic area and sometimes specific age groups, and they have somewhat different mandates and services. If the person with a disability is eligible for ADP funding and if the ADP-Designated AAC Clinic recommends approved equipment, part or all of the communication system may be funded by ADP, as described above. If ADP funding is not an issue, the consumer may go to any service provider or purchase desired equipment directly from a vendor. In this case, they are not limited to the devices listed in the ADP Product Manual.

How Do I Find Funding for AAC Equipment?

To summarize information presented above, in Ontario, the best known source of funding for personal communication systems continues to be ADP. ADP provides partial funding support for different kinds of basic, personalized assistive devices (including communication aids) to meet basic communication needs essential for independent living. ADP may pay up to 75% of the total cost (to a maximum set by ADP). The ADP Policy and Administration Manual documents specific eligibility criteria for funding, and the ADP Product Manual includes device listings. Additional funding may be available from other Ontario government programs.

It is possible for individuals to purchase equipment directly from vendors (see More Resources below for Canadian distributors of AAC related products). In order to access ADP funding, however, it is necessary to have an authorizer sign an ADP form before purchasing the product. In fact, most other funding sources also require notice from a "recognized professional" before receiving an invoice. To ensure reimbursement, check the exact procedures with ADP or the specific funding agency prior to purchase.

In addition to the above, there are numerous other supports and services, as well as funding sources for AAC equipment in Ontario. These include:

1. Various benefits within MCSS: Ontario Disability Support Program (ODSP); Ontario Works (OW) and Assistance to Children with Severe Disabilities (ACSD).
2. Not-for-profit organizations (e.g., Ontario March of Dimes).
3. Service clubs (e.g., Rotary clubs);
4. Charitable foundations (e.g., Jennifer Ashleigh Foundation).
5. Insurance companies (check with the specific insurance company).

For access to funding, services, or suggestions for regional access, consumers are encouraged to contact local Easter Seal Society offices for children and youth, and local Ontario March of Dimes offices for adults 19 years of age and older (see More Resources below for additional AAC support and service resources in Ontario).

Summary

Communication — commonly carried out between and among people by the use of speech and language — has been described as the essence of human life. Speech and language difficulties are common in populations of people with developmental disabilities, and sometimes lead to behaviour challenges. Fortunately, there are effective interventions, one group of which is known as augmentative and alternative communication (AAC).

AAC provides approaches that help people communicate by augmenting or replacing their natural speech and/or handwriting. AAC approaches may be grouped into those that are aided or unaided. AAC should be considered for individuals with a variety of developmental disabilities. It is best to start AAC use as early as possible, rather than waiting until an individual may or may not meet what some authors have called "cognitive prerequisites." Possible outcomes of AAC use are: increased communicative competence, improved speech production, replacement of challenging behaviours, and an overall enhancement of the individual's quality of life. Basic components of an AAC assessment and commonly used intervention strategies have been developed. AAC intervention should be goal-driven, needs-based, and accompanied by a way of measuring progress to ensure accountability. The Ontario AAC services system includes a number of funding sources and various sources of support.

For Further Thought and Discussion

1. Given that there are no cognitive prerequisites for introducing AAC, provide a rationale for why it is, nonetheless, important to conduct an assessment.
2. This chapter suggests a strong relationship between individuals' challenging behaviours and their ability to communicate. Discuss whether this means that all challenging behaviours exhibited by individuals with little or no functional speech are communicative in nature.
3. Given that communication involves the AAC user and at least one communication partner, what do you see as the implications for assessment and intervention?
4. Discuss what role, if any, you see for self-advocacy in navigating the Ontario service delivery system.

More Resources

Ontario AAC Supports and/or Services:

Assistive Devices Branch (ADP)
Tel: (416) 327-8804
http://www.health.gov.on.ca/english/public/program/adp/adp_mn.html

Breaking the ICE for people who use AAC
www.breakingtheiceconference.ca

Centralized Equipment Pool (CEP)
Tel: (416) 698-3793 / 1-800-804-7188

http://www.cepp.org

Children's Treatment Centres of Ontario (OACRS)
http://www.oacrs.com/treatment.php

Easter Seal Society (ESS)
Tel: (416) 421-8377; 1-888-ESS-KIDS h
ttp://www.easterseals.org/default.asp

Ontario Federation for Cerebral Palsy
Tel: (416) 244-9686
http://www.ofcp.on.ca/index.html

Ontario March of Dimes (OMOD)
Tel: (416) 425-3463/ 1-800-263-3463
http://www.marchofdimes.ca/dimes

Ontario Ministry of Community and Social Services
Tel: (416) 325-5666
http://www.mcss.gov.on.ca/en/mcss/index.aspx

Ontario Ministry of Education and Training
Tel: (416) 325-6847 / 1-800-268-5755
http://www.edu.gov.on.ca/eng

Ontario Ministry of Health
Tel: (416) 327-4327 / 1-800-387-5559
http://www.health.gov.on.ca/en

Canadian Distributors of AAC Equipment & Books:

Aroga Technologies Ltd.
Tel: 1-800-871-2521
http://www.aroga.com

Bridges Canada
Tel: 1-800 353 1107
http://www.bridges-canada.com/

DynaVox Mayer-Johnson
Tel: (416) 568-3342
http://ca.dynavoxtech.com/products/sales/canada.aspx

MicroComputer Science Centre, Inc.
Tel: 1-800-290-6563
http://www.microscience.on.ca

Parentbooks
Tel: (416) 537-8334; 1-800-209-9182
http://www.parentbooks.ca

Quillsoft Ltd.
Tel: 1-866-629-6737
http://www.wordq.com

VocaLinks
Tel: 1-877-410-0342
http://www.vocalinks.com

References

Augmentative Communication Community Partnerships Canada (ACCPC). (2010). *Access to justice for people with communication disabilities.* Retrieved from http://www.accpc.ca/equaljustice.htm

Ahlgrim-Delzell, L., & Dudley, J. R. (2001). Confirmed, unconfirmed, and false allegations of abuse made by adults with mental retardation who are members of a class action lawsuit. *Child Abuse and Neglect, 25,* 1121-1132.

Beukelman, D. R., & Mirenda, P. (2005). *Augmentative and alternative communication: Supporting children and adults with complex communication needs* (3rd ed.). Baltimore: Paul H. Brookes Publishing Co.

Blackstone, S. W., & Hunt Berg, M. (2003) *Social networks: A communication inventory for individuals with complex communication needs and their communication partners.* Berkley, CA: Augmentative Communication Inc.

Blischak, D., Loncke, F., & Waller, A. (1997). Intervention for persons with developmental disabilities. In L. L. Lloyd, D. Fuller, & H. Arvidson (Eds.), *Augmentative and alternative communication: A handbook of principles and practices* (pp. 299-339). Boston: Allyn & Bacon.

Blischak, D. M., & Wasson, C. A. (1997). Sensory impairments. In L. L. Lloyd, D. Fuller, & H. Arvidson (Eds.), *Augmentative and alternative communication: A handbook of principles and practices* (pp. 255-279). Boston: Allyn & Bacon.

Bloom, L., & Lahey, M. (1978). *Language development and language disorders.* New York: Wiley.

Bopp, K. D., Brown, K. E., & Mirenda, P. (2004). Speech-language pathologists' role in the delivery of positive behavior support of individuals with developmental disabilities. *American Journal of Speech-Language Pathology, 13,* 5-19.

Burke-Brassem, M., & Palace, L. (2003). Communication considerations associated with developmental disabilities. In I. Brown & M. Percy (Eds.), *Developmental disabilities in Ontario* (2nd ed.; pp. 453-464). Toronto, ON: Ontario Association on Developmental Disabilities.

Collier, B. (Producer). (2000). *Communicating matters: A training guide for personal attendants working with consumers who have enhanced communication needs* [Videotape]. Baltimore: Paul H. Brookes Publishing Co.

Duker, P. C., van Driel, S., & van de Bercken, J. (2002). Communication profiles of individuals with Down's syndrome, Angelman syndrome and pervasive developmental disorder. *Journal of Intellectual Disability Research, 46,* 35-40.

Ericson, K., Isaacs, B., & Perlman, N. (2003). Enhancing communication with persons with developmental disabilities: The special case of interviewing victim-witnesses of sexual abuse. In I. Brown & M. Percy (Eds.), *Developmental disabilities in Ontario* (pp. 465-474). Toronto, ON: Front Porch Publishing.

Farrar, P. (1996). *End the silence: Preventing the sexual assault of women with communication disorders.* Calgary, AB: Technical Resource Centre, University of Calgary.

Ferguson, D. L. (1994). Is communication really the point? Some thoughts on interventions and membership. *Mental Retardation, 32,* 7-18.

Grizzle, K. L., & Simms, M. D. (2005). Early language development and language learning disabilities. *Pediatrics in Review, 26*(8), 274-283.

Kangas, K., & Lloyd, L. (1988). Early cognitive skills as prerequisites to augmentative and alternative communication use: What are we waiting for? *Augmentative and Alternative Communication, 4,* 211-221.

Light, J. C., & Binger, C. (1998). *Building communicative competence with individuals who use augmentative and alternative communication.* Baltimore: Paul H. Brookes Publishing Co.

Lloyd, L., Fuller, D., & Arvidson, H. (1997). *Augmentative and alternative communication: A handbook of principles and practices.* Boston: Allyn & Bacon.

McNaughton, S. (1982). Justin gives to us all. *Communicating Together, 1,* 3-4.

McQueen, P. C., Spence, M. W., Garner, J. B., Pereira, L. H., & Winsor, E. J. (1987). Prevalence of major mental retardation and associated disabilities in the Canadian Maritime provinces. *American Journal of Mental Deficiency, 91*, 460-466.

Millar, D., Light, J., & Schlosser, R. W. (2006). The impact of augmentative and alternative communication intervention on the speech production of individuals with developmental disabilities: A research review. *Journal of Speech, Language, and Hearing Research, 49*, 248-264.

Mirenda, P. (2003). Toward functional augmentative and alternative communication for students with autism: Manual signs, graphic symbols, and voice output communication aids. *Language, Speech, and Hearing Services in Schools, 34*, 203-216.

Mirenda, P., & Iacono, T. (2009). *Autism spectrum disorders and AAC.* Baltimore: Paul H. Brookes Publishing Co.

Mirenda, P., & Mathy Laikko, P. (1989). Augmentative and alternative communication applications for persons with severe congenital communication disorders. *Augmentative and Alternative Communication, 5*, 3-13.

National Joint Committee for the Communication Needs of Persons with Severe Disabilities. (2003). Position statement on access to communication services and supports: Concerns regarding the application of restrictive "eligibility" policies. *ASHA Supplement, 23*, 19-20.

National Research Council. (2001). *Educating children with autism.* Washington, DC: National Academies Press.

Ontario Ministry of Education. *Special education funding guidelines: Special equipment amount (SEA), 2010-11.* Retrieved from http://www.edu.gov.on.ca/eng/funding/1011/2010-11_SEA_Guidelines.pdf

Perlman, N., Ericson, K., Esses, V., & Isaacs, B. (1994). Developmentally handicapped witnesses: Competency as a function of question format. *Law and Human Behaviour, 18*, 171-187.

Rispoli, M., Franco, J., van der Meer, L., Lang, R., & Camargo, S. P. H. (2010). The use of speech-generating devices in communication interventions for individuals with developmental disabilities: A review of the literature. *Developmental Neurorehabilitation, 13*(4), 276-293.

Rothschild, N., McGinnis, J., & Norris, L. (1996). Outcome measures—tools and processes in AAC: What's driving us? *Journal of Speech-Language Pathology and Audiology, 19*, 257-267.

Rothschild, N., & Hunt, T. (2008). *AAC basics based on the SETT framework.* Richmond Hill, ON: Children's Treatment Network of Simcoe York.

Schlosser, R. W. (2003). *The efficacy of augmentative and alternative communication: Towards evidence-based practice.* San Diego: Academic Press.

Schlosser, R. W. (2004). Goal attainment scaling as a clinical measurement technique in communication disorders: A critical review. *Journal of Communication Disorders, 37*, 217-239.

Schlosser, R. W., & Wendt, O. (2008). Effects of augmentative and alternative communication intervention on speech production in children with autism: A systematic review. *American Journal of Speech-Language Pathology, 17*, 212-230.

Skinner, B. F. (1957). *Verbal behavior.* Upper Saddle River, NJ: Prentice-Hall.

Sobsey, D. (1994). *Violence and abuse in the lives of people with disabilities: The end of silent acceptance.* Baltimore: Paul H. Brookes Publishing Co.

Valenti-Hein, D. C., & Schwartz, L. D. (1993). Witness competency in people with mental retardation: Implications for prosecution of sexual abuse. *Sexuality and Disability, 11*, 287-294.

van der Meer, L., & Rispoli, M. (2010). Communication interventions involving speech-generating devices for children with autism: A review of the literature. *Developmental Neurorehabilitation, 13*(4), 294-306.

Vig, S., & Kaminer, R. (2002). Maltreatment and developmental disabilities in children. *Journal of Developmental and Physical Disabilities, 14*, 371-386.

Zangari, C., & Kangas, K. (1997). Intervention principles and procedures. In L. Lloyd, D. Fuller, & H. Arvidson (Eds.), *Augmentative and alternative communication: A handbook of principles and practices* (pp. 235-253). Boston: Allyn & Bacon.

Zigler, E., & Balla, D. (Eds.). (1982). *Mental retardation: The developmental-difference controversy.* Mahwah, NJ: Erlbaum.

27

Communication Considerations Associated with Developmental Disabilities

Jill Taylor, Maureen Burke, and Leora Palace

What you will learn:

- How we hear
- The importance of hearing assessments and interventions
- Communication difficulties and developmental disabilities
- Speech and language difficulties and their treatment

*Note: Words in **bold italics** are explained in the Special Terms section following the Summary.*

Audiological (Hearing) Considerations

The ear and hearing

The human auditory system is a very complex sensory system (see Figure 1). Sound waves are produced by pressure changes and vibrations in the air. The process of hearing begins when vibrating air molecules come into contact with the eardrum, causing it to vibrate. The vibrations of the eardrum are relayed to a lever-pulley system of the three middle ear bones, which amplifies and re-codes these incoming signals and transmits them to the inner ear, or cochlea. The actual detection of sound occurs when the ear's auditory receptors generate neural signals.

Actual hearing occurs in the cochlea. The third middle ear bone is connected to the cochlea. Movement of this bone causes the fluid in the cochlea to move with incoming sound. The cochlea's internal structures, the inner and outer hair cells, respond to movements in the fluid produced by the incoming sound in different and complementary ways. This results in the firing of neural impulses that are relayed to the brain by the ***auditory nerve***, the ***cochlear nucleus***, and the ***brainstem*** that connects with many other levels of the brain's cortex.

The development of hearing in children

Our sense of hearing gives us pleasure and connection with our environment, and enables us to participate in verbal communication. The sense of hearing is fully functional in the second trimester of pregnancy, so that a new-born is able to recognize its mother's voice at birth.

The detection of *puretones* at intensities of less than 15 *decibel hea ring level (dB HL)* — a unit used to measure sound — is considered to be normal hearing for children. Yet the detection of puretones within normal limits does not encompass the entire process of hearing. There are millions of rapid acoustic events that occur during a typical conversation. They require extremely rapid and efficient auditory processing in order for a listener to obtain the full message intended by a speaker. These skills develop by adolescence in a person with normal hearing.

The presence of hearing deficits in children acts as an invisible acoustic filter that has an impact on their auditory processing capacity, their verbal language competency, their behaviour, their reading and writing capacity, their academic options, and even their independent functioning. The impact of hearing loss can be exacerbated ten-fold for a child with a developmental disability if left undetected or unaddressed. Thus, early detection and treatment of hearing disorders is critical.

Types of hearing loss

Sensorineural hearing loss: This condition refers to hearing loss resulting from damage to inner ear structures (i.e., outer and inner hair cells of the cochlea) or to auditory nerve (VIII) dysfunction. Impairment is permanent.

Conductive hearing loss: This disorder refers to hearing loss resulting from problems in the outer or middle ear (i.e., wax build up in the ear canal, middle ear infections). The resulting hearing loss is usually temporary and medically treatable, but may be permanent.

Mixed hearing loss: As the name implies, mixed hearing loss has both a sensorineural and conductive component. The conductive component will make the permanent hearing loss worse by decreasing hearing further.

Auditory neuropathy: In this disorder, the fibres in the auditory nerve do not work in unison (together) and affect transmission of sound from the cochlea to the brain. Symptoms of this type of hearing loss include fluctuations in hearing sensitivity, reduced awareness of sound, poor localization, and poor understanding of speech in quiet and noisy listening environments.

(Central) auditory processing disorder: This type of disorder results from a deficit in neural processing of auditory stimuli that is not related to higher order language, cognitive ability, or related factors. Peripheral hearing is typically normal.

Risk factors for hearing loss and developmental disabilities

Children with developmental disabilities are often at high risk of hearing loss (see Table 1). Highlighting the risk factors prematurity and low birth weight, a study performed in Edmonton, Alberta found that from a group of 40 three-year-old children identified in the study with permanent hearing loss, 28 (63%) presented with a developmental disability (Robertson, Howarth, Bork, & Dinu, 2009). Research performed at Surrey Place Centre, an interdisciplinary service centre in Toronto for persons with developmental disabilities, suggests many adults with developmental disabilities present with some type of hearing loss (Lowe & Temple, 2002). In addition, research shows hearing loss may go undiagnosed because a problem is not suspected by the caregiver(s) of the adult with the developmental disability (Lowe & Temple, 2002), or because testing services are not in place for this population (Meuwese-Jongejeudg et al., 2006). For these reasons, it is recommended that all people with developmental disabilities be seen for regular audiology (hearing) services throughout their lives.

Hearing assessment

Many people with developmental disabilities come to audiology appointments with special needs. These needs are delineated by their developmental level, their communication ability, their higher than average frequency of hearing loss and middle ear disease and, at times, their uncooperative behaviour during testing. Although these factors need to be taken into account, a low developmental level does not prevent people with developmental disabilities from undergoing a successful hearing assessment. Procedures that might be used with people with developmental disabilities are listed below (College

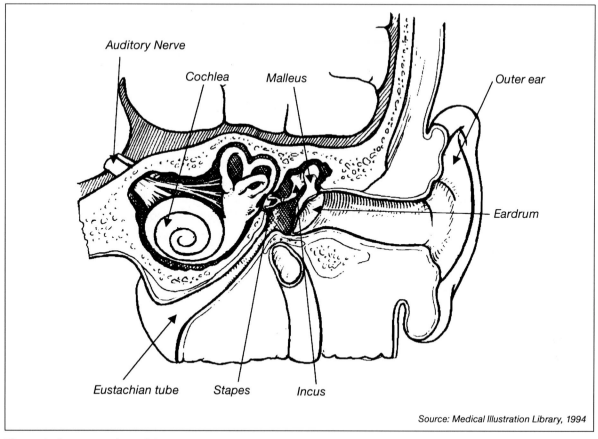

Source: Medical Illustration Library, 1994

Figure 1. Cross-section of the ear.

of Audiologists and Speech Language Pathologists of Ontario (CASLPO), 2008).

- If unable to participate in conventional audiometry, with practice an audiogram can be obtained with behavioural test methods such as ***Visual Reinforcement Audiometry (VRA)*** or ***Conditioned Play Audiometry (CPA)***. Testing may be performed with insert earphones for ear specific results, or in the soundfield, with results reflecting hearing ability for at least one ear. For insert phones the preferred stimulus is pure tone, and warble tone stimuli are preferred for soundfield assessment. ***Bone Conduction Audiometry (BCA)*** is also performed to identify the etiology (cause) of the hearing loss.

- When testing is not possible using behavioural test methods, objective test procedures such as ***Otoacoustic Emissions (OAE)*** testing and ***Auditory Brainstem Response (ABR)*** audiometry must be included in the test battery. OAE testing is not a hearing test — it is a physiological measure of the peripheral or preneural auditory function. When normal OAEs are measured, grossly normal peripheral hearing is supported for the frequencies tested. ABR audiometry is a test of synchronous neural firings in the cochlear nerve (VIII). Tone burst stimuli are used with the ABR procedure to estimate hearing sensitivity at select frequencies. Click ABR stimuli are used to assess neural integrity, and in combination with other hearing test results (i.e., OAE/Acoustic Reflex), can determine the likelihood of auditory neuropathy.

- ***Impedance Audiometry (IA)*** and ***Acoustic Reflex*** measurements are included in the test battery to assess middle ear function. Results from both tests are used to identify the etiology of the hearing loss.

An Infant Hearing Program (IHP) was implemented in Ontario in 2002 to identify permanent hearing loss in all children by three months of age, and have them fitted with hearing aids and obtain support services, like speech and language therapy, by six-months of age. As babies with developmental disabilities are at risk for hearing impairment, when a pass result is obtained for both ears on the initial hearing screening, hearing status still needs to be closely monitored. All children identified with a permanent hearing loss (conductive or sensorineural) receive audiological care through IHP up to six years of age. For more information on the Infant Hearing Program, please refer to resource material on the Ontario Ministry of Children and Youth Services (2010) website.

People with different types of developmental disabilities may require different audiological considerations. For example, a person with Down syndrome should undergo regular hearing tests in order to monitor recurrent conductive hearing loss (common in early childhood), mixed hearing loss in early adolescence, and progressive sensorineural hearing loss in early adulthood. These repeated assessments also give the person more experience with audiology procedures, eventually resulting in more reliable and accurate hearing thresholds, and usually a complete audiogram.

Children with developmental disabilities may present with normal hearing, but demonstrate difficulty processing auditory information. The evaluation of a child's (Central) Auditory Processing [(C)AP] abilities is complex. The auditory processing test battery requires thoughtful planning designed around the child's primary complaint, based on observations of what processing problems the child is having. Although the tests themselves may be reliable, the children's behaviour and responses may not be reliable and consistent, and need to be interpreted with great caution. Furthermore, many computerized assisted remediation programs often recommended following positive findings of (C)AP difficulties, are not supported by evidence that they are effective. Parents need to be careful about what they read, and should question and seek accurate information from the Audiologist before pre-

maturely spending large sums of money and raising their hopes.

Hearing loss and vision

When a hearing loss is identified in any child or adult with a developmental disability, it is important to check their vision. A dual sensory impairment (vision plus hearing) would be expected to have a greater impact on communication abilities, and on quality of life. As a group, children with developmental disability are at risk of hearing and vision problems (Bhasin, Brocksen, Avchen, & Braun, 2006). Children with Down syndrome have a number of vision issues, and a large percentage (48%) have been shown to require corrective lenses by preschool age (Stephen, Dickson, Kindley, Schott, & Charleton, 2007). For this reason, health care guidelines for children with Down syndrome recommend early and appropriate monitoring of vision (Forster-Gibson & Berg, 2011).

Ontario implemented a Blind and Low Vision Program in 2007 and services are available for children from birth to Grade 1. To learn more about this program, please refer to the Ontario Ministry of Children and Youth Services website.

Recent studies have identified high rates of undiagnosed dual sensory impairment among adults with developmental delay (Fellinger, Holzinger, Dirmhirm, Dijik, & Goldberg, 2009; Meuwese-Jongejeudg et al., 2008). Canadian guidelines for the primary care of adults with developmental disabilities provide testing protocols and time frames for hearing and vision assessment (Sullivan et al., 2011). Implementation of these guidelines would be expected to identify problems sooner, and in turn make available intervention strategies to foster an improved quality of life.

Audiological intervention suggestions

When a permanent hearing loss is identified, or a conductive hearing loss does not resolve with medical intervention, a hearing aid should be considered for the affected ear(s). Paediatric amplification protocols (College of Audiologists and Speech Language Pathologists of Ontario (CASLPO), 2002) recommend behind-the-ear (BTE) style hearing

Table 1: Risk Factors for Hearing Loss and Developmental Disability

Risk Factor	Critical Facts
Family history of hearing loss	*One-half of the cases of congenital hearing loss are inherited and may span any degree or configuration of hearing loss.*
Congenital perinatal (around birth) infections	*These include: toxoplasmosis, rubella, cytomegalovirus, herpes virus hominus, and syphilis. Hearing loss is typically sensorineural, occurs immediately or progressively gets worse.*
Any malformation of the head or neck	*Assume that anyone with a cranio-facial anomaly has a hearing loss until audiological assessment demonstrates otherwise.*
Neonatal intensive care of more than 5 days or any of the following regardless of length of stay	*Prematurity (less than 28 weeks), low birth weight (under 1500 grams), assisted ventilation, exposure to ototoxic medications or loop diuretics. Hearing loss is typically sensorineural and can be progressive.*
Interference in fetal development	*These include: chromosomal abnormalities, fetal infection, maternal substance abuse, multiple pregnancy, placenta anomalies, maternal renal disease, maternal malnutrition, placental infection, maternal hypoxemia, and excessive maternal smoking.*
Hyperbilirubinemia*	*If the level requiring exchange transfusion is reached, the child is at risk for hearing loss.*
Meningitis*	*This is the cause for the majority of acquired sensorineural hearing loss, which can range from mild to extremely profound. The hearing loss is not always immediate, and clients should be followed for up to two years post meningitis.*
Severe asphyxia*	*If seizures occur following asphyxia, up to 80% will show CNS impairment including bilateral high frequency sensorineural hearing loss at long term follow-up.*
Head injury	*Conductive hearing loss results from injury of the middle ear structures, and sensorineural hearing loss due to cochlear trauma or rupture of the inner hair cells. Sometimes there is some improvement in hearing post insult.*

* See Special Terms section

aids for infants and school aged children, and that bone conduction hearing aids and cochlear implants be reviewed with families when a BTE is not appropriate. The style of hearing aid and amplification characteristics chosen for an adult will depend on the hearing loss and the person's lifestyle (CASLPO, 2000). The audiologist should use evidence-based practices when prescribing amplification for an individual with developmental disability, and should frequently review the operation and care of the recommended hearing aid(s) with the recipient of the hearing aid(s), family members (i.e., when fitting a child), and alternate caretakers (CASLPO, 2000, 2002).

Assistive listening devices represent another amplification option for this population. Use of personal *FM systems* with light-weight headsets provides amplification for recurrent, fluctuating hearing loss. When an individual needs a hearing aid and refuses to wear amplification, information can be delivered to the listener through a small, portable speaker (i.e., totable soundfield FM system).

Amplification may not necessarily have an overt and immediate impact on communication ability, but often dramatically impacts people's observable behaviour and the pleasure they get from life. After receiving bone conduction hearing aids, children with Down syndrome reported they were making better progress with their education and learning, had better concentration and listening skills, and were less easily distracted. In addition the children reported their overall life was much better after receiving the hearing aid (McDermott, Williams, Kuo, Reid, & Proops, 2008). Adults with a mild to moderate developmental disability have reported hearing aid use reduced their level of fatigue, improved detection of sound, and improved comprehension of speakers and radio and television programs (Meuwese-Jongejeudg, Verschuure, & Evenhuis, 2007).

A hearing aid checklist for caregivers is provided in Table 2. For additional information on hearing, hearing tests and hearing aid prescription, please consult the references for this chapter and the More Resources section.

Communication and Developmental Disabilities

All people with developmental disabilities should have a hearing assessment and a speech and language assessment. A hearing difficulty can result in an impairment of speech and language and an impairment of communication. Furthermore, because communication and cognition are highly related, a developmental disability invariably involves some communication difficulty. However, the severity of the developmental disability does not always act as a predictor of the extent or type of communication difficulty.

Consequences of communication difficulties

People with communication difficulties have long been described as a group at risk for social, emotional, and behavioural difficulties. The most logical and simple explanation for this is that deficits in speech and language clearly affect the individual's ability to understand and/or be understood by others. The greater the communicative difficulty, the greater the risk of negative consequences is.

The range of negative consequences is as great as the range of deficits themselves. Some people may react to communication difficulties by demonstrating externalizing behaviours such as impatience, tantrums, impulsivity and aggressive symptoms. Others may display internalizing behaviours such as withdrawal, avoidance, depression, and dependence.

The degree to which living environments are able to adapt to communication difficulties very often influences the outcome and consequences more than the communication difficulties themselves. An individual with very limited output (single and two word utterances) may be well contained and empowered in an environment that understands and responds to the intent, as opposed to the structure, of the communication. On the other hand, the deficits of an individual who has more complex language, but who has difficulty in recognizing and taking another person's expression of perspective into account, may not be understood by others in his environment. Such lack of understanding may result in any number of negative emotions and behaviours.

Communication difficulties that may be encountered

Communication refers to the act or process involved in the mutual sharing of information between two people. This is a highly complex process that involves much more than the simple words or signals (signs, pictures, etc.) used in the exchange. It may be achieved through either verbal (spoken) or nonverbal means (sign language, written language, etc.). Here, we focus primarily on verbal communi-

Table 2: A Hearing Checklist

Checklist item	Notes
1. *Be certain to have the person's hearing assessed as often as is necessary. Ask an audiologist.*	
2. *Be certain to obtain the recommended medical follow-up.*	
3. *Understand the person's hearing levels and the listening ramifications.*	
4. *Modify your speech and language as recommended, to assist with the person's comprehension.*	
5. *Ascertain if the person could benefit from amplification devices — even for the short-term. Such devices include: hearing aids, personal FM systems, and soundfield FM systems.*	
6. *When speaking to a hearing impaired person, minimize competing backround noise, and provide adequate lighting.*	
7. *Encourage the use of amplification technology for today's classrooms, homes, workplaces, and community venues.*	
8. *Be aware that a person's hearing levels may change — even day to day.*	

cation, with information on augmentative communication discussed elsewhere in this book. The main factors affecting verbal communication are:

- Voice
- Fluency
- Speech
- Language

Voice and fluency disorders (stuttering) are no more common in people with developmental disabilities than in the general population. They are easily identified, and do not usually detract seriously from the overall intelligibility of communication. For these reasons, they are often not seen as pressing problems. Speech and language, however, greatly influence the individual's ability to understand and to be understood by others.

Speech and Language Difficulties

Difficulties in speech production

A large number of factors affect adequate production of speech. The main ones include:

- *Sensory deficit (hearing loss):* The inability to hear, or inconsistent hearing, leads to a distortion in the individual's ability to perceive individual sounds and sound groups needed for adequate speech production.
- *Structural abnormalities:* Differences in any of the physiological structures that are needed to support speech production (e.g., cleft palate, oral-facial deformities) can result in abnormalities of speech production. In addition, differences in muscle tone may result in speech being dysarthric (i.e., characterized by an

imprecise production of sounds together with distortions in voice quality, nasality, and timing). People with Down syndrome frequently have low muscle tone. This results in their tongues and lips lacking adequate mobility and strength to produce clear, precise sounds. Consequently, their speech may sometimes sound sloppy and unclear. Individuals with Cerebral Palsy may have a strained, strangled voice quality, hypernasality, a slow rate of speech and consonant imprecision due to high muscle tone.

- *Oral-motor and verbal apraxias:* The term apraxia refers to the inability to program muscle movements needed for the voluntary production of speech. This occurs in spite of normal musculature, and is thought to be controlled within the cortex of the brain.
- *Developmental delays in speech acquisition:* Delays of this kind generally fall into two categories: articulation and phonology. Articulation refers to the manner and place in which individual sounds are produced. For example, an "s" sound is always produced by placing the tongue tip on the palatal ridges immediately behind the upper teeth. A typical articulatory distortion of the "s" sound may involve sticking the tongue out between the teeth to produce a "th" sound in place of the "s". A phonological delay affects whole sound groups, as opposed to individual sound production. In this instance, there will be a delay and arrest of some of the normal processes that children go through in suppressing error patterns and acquiring accurate speech patterns. For example, the phonological process of "backing" is one in which the individual changes a sound that is made with the front of the tongue to a sound made with the back of the tongue (e.g., guck/duck, gog/dog).

Language difficulties

Language refers to the code with which one communicates. A set of complex, interacting rules governs the ways that individual words are organized and used. Since cognition is the foundation upon which language is built, the area of communication is likely to be affected by cognitive deficit. Language may be thought of as consisting of three components (see Figure 2).

Form: This refers to the coding of words into meaningful sentences, that is, the grammar or syntax of language. As the individual develops greater language competence, the form refers to the way in which the sentences are sequenced and organized to form narratives or discourse production (e.g., instructions on how to get from one place to another). The acquisition of this component of language is usually a function of age. It follows typical developmental patterns, and is not highly dependent upon personality or stimulation influences.

Content: This refers to the content, or the semantics of language. The development of semantics takes place throughout the individual's life. In a larger sense, this component of language relates to word meanings and more abstract, logical word relationships. Although this component is closely allied to cognition, it may be significantly influenced by stimulation and experience.

Use: This refers to the pragmatic use of language, or the way in which language is used for different social and communicative functions. It takes conversational rules into account (e.g., turn taking, being able to maintain topics introduced by others, being able to introduce topics of interest to others). It is the component of language that is often least examined or addressed, but that most strongly influences how adaptive the individual is, or how well a person functions in his or her environment.

Interaction of the three components: Deficits may occur within one of the three components with little influence on the other two components. For example, people with autism may have good language structure, and well-developed vocabulary, but may use language in an inappropriate or inadequate manner, resulting in a significant impairment in social functioning. A splintering of language components is also common in Williams syndrome. Here, individuals develop relatively intact language structure and are seen as highly sociable and interactive (i.e., they have an adequate use of language). However, their word choices (semantics) are frequently peculiar, and they are often described

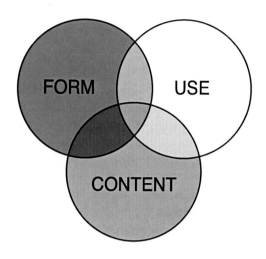

Figure 2. Interacting components of language.

as having cocktail party speech.

Frequently, however, a language disorder results from more than one component being affected. In these cases, there is an interaction of the three language components. This occurs, for example, in fragile X syndrome, where individuals frequently have difficulties with all three components.

Speech and language are not mutually dependent upon one another. It is highly possible to have a fully intact language in the absence of speech as, for example, in sign language. Moreover, it is equally possible to have completely intact speech development with major deficits in all components of language (e.g., specific language impairment).

Speech and language treatment

As in the general population, determining whether an individual requires treatment and the specific types of treatment needed is complex and dependent upon a number of variables. These include:

- Age
- Personality and history of adjustments
- Supports
- Awareness of difficulties and when to use compensatory strategies
- Stimulability
- Family or living situation, and focus of that situation

The overall goal of treatment, whether through direct or indirect therapy, should recognize, encourage, and respond to all communicative attempts and the underlying function of those attempts. For example, an individual pointing to something outside may be simply trying to join with another person, get their attention, and engage in some common commentary (verbal or nonverbal) on the identified object.

The approach to treatment that may lead to the individual becoming a more effective, empowered communicator and with the least consequences, may not always involve individual, direct, structured therapy. A more appropriate approach to treatment may recognize the individual's social, family and work or school milieu, the individual's expectations and functioning within these environments, and how to facilitate understanding, development, and success within them.

Once the proper focus of intervention has been determined, the order, timetable, and type of therapy need to be considered. For example, encouraging an apraxic child or deaf child whose impairments have not been identified to speak may be detrimental to further development. In these cases, it may be more appropriate to explore alternative means by which the child can communicate with others. Parents, teachers and professionals must then work together, exploring ways to foster the individual's desire and ability to use such a communication system.

Techniques to facilitate early language development

Some of the common techniques include:

- *Expansion:* The child's utterance is expanded into the correct grammatical form
- *Simple expatiation:* The adult expands on the child's utterance, keeping it relevant
- *Alternative model:* Inquiring about the meaning or logic of an utterance, thereby encouraging the child to think of alternative ways to express ideas
- *Imitation:* Immediate, corrected imitation of the child's utterance
- *Completion:* The child completes something presented by the adult
- *Forced alternative:* Presenting the child with a

choice of possibilities

- *Verbal absurdity*: Incorrect statements or ridiculous questions are used to encourage the child to recall lexical items or to correct grammatical structures

Other treatment options

There are many varied communication assessment and treatments available, sometimes commercially marketed, that may serve as treatment options for persons with developmental disabilities, including those with autism, pervasive developmental disorder, behaviour disorder, attention deficit disorder, dyslexia, and auditory processing disorder. Sometimes the treatment serves as a solution for a variety of problems associated with the full spectrum of developmental disabilities. It is highly recommended that the consumer investigate clinical and commercial treatments fully, and examine their empirical-based evidence, before consenting to treatment.

Services in Ontario

Audiology and speech-language services are available to all persons with a medical referral and a valid Ontario health card. Services are offered in many different settings, such as hospitals, community health centres, schools, specialized treatment centres, and private practice clinics. Speech-language services in private practice clinics are not covered by the Ontario Health Insurance Plan (OHIP). Funding for amplification and augmentative communication devices may be accessed through programs covered by the *new Social Assistance Reform Act, 1997* (SARA). SARA governs the Assistive Devices Program (ADP), the Ontario Disability Support Program (formerly Vocational Rehabilitation), and Assistance to Children with Severe Disabilities (formerly Handicapped Children's Benefits). The current financial rules are intended to be more generous for people with disabilities (Ontario Ministry of Community and Social Services, 1997). Services available in the pre-school sector are much better funded and more easily accessible. For more information about alternative and augmentative communication see Chapter 26. For more information

about speech and language disorders, see Schlosser, Sigafoos, Rothschild, Burke, and Palace (2007).

Summary

People with developmental disabilities tend to have a variety of communication difficulties. These difficulties differ widely among individuals, however. They contribute to emotional, behavioural, social and academic difficulties. Ongoing audiology and speech-language assessments, accompanied by prudent and interdisciplinary clinical interventions, will support the overall development and the quality of life of persons with developmental disabilities.

Special Terms

Acoustic Reflex: Contraction of the stapedius and tensor tympani muscles, in response to intense sound. Limits movement of the middle ear ossicles and attenuates incoming sound.

Asphyxia: A condition in which an extreme decrease in the concentration of oxygen in the body accompanied by an increase in the concentration of carbon dioxide leads to loss of consciousness or death (e.g., by choking, drowning, electric shock, injury, or the inhalation of toxic gases.

Audiogram: A graph which depicts thresholds of hearing sensitivity, determined behaviorally, as a function of pure-tone frequency.

Auditory Brainstem Response testing (ABR): An advanced, computer-assisted method of interpolating hearing from the electrical activity generated by the various cell bodies found in the brainstem upon auditory stimulation.

Auditory nerve: A bundle of fibres that connect the cochlea (organ of hearing) to the human central auditory system.

Bone Conduction Audiometry: A form of audiometry that is sometimes used to evaluate loss of hearing. This procedure involves vibration of the skull by direct contact with a stimulator (e.g., a tuning fork). The vibration passes through the bone, bypasses the external and middle ears, but affects the cochlear liquid.

Brainstem: A small part of the brain that contains

many cell bodies and fibre tracts for many functions of the body such as hearing, vision, sensation of touch and autonomic functions such as regulating breathing. There are many cell bodies of the auditory system found in the brainstem.

Cochlear nucleus: The first stop that the auditory fibres make on their passage through the central auditory system.

Conditioned Play Audiometry (CPA): Employs the use of a play response, such as placing pegs into a board, upon the detection of test tones. Usually, this is demonstrated for the child, and then modelled hand-over-hand until the child initiates a response on their own. Responses obtained are considered to be near or at threshold.

Decibel Hearing Level (dB HL): These are standardized (i.e., ISO-1964, ANSI-1969) sound pressure levels (SPL) that represent 0 reference levels on the audiogram. For example, 0 dB HL at 250 Hz is 25.5 dB SPL for a particular earphone (TDH-39), whereas 0 dB HL at 2000 Hz is 9.0 dB SPL. These different SPL values reflect the differences in sensitivity by the human ear that is affected by the ear canal, pinna, and human evolution.

FM: This is a method of transmitting signals (speech, music, data etc) on carrier frequencies. FM is Frequency Modulation where the carrier frequency is modified by the signal frequency.

FM System: A two-part amplification system. Part one is the microphone-transmitter that broadcasts on a dedicated FM frequency to a receiver or some type of amplifier.

Hyperbilirubinemia: Abnormally high levels of bile pigment (bilirubin) in the blood. This is a common condition in newborns usually due to immaturity of the liver; it usually resolves spontaneously. When bilirubin levels are very high, treatment can include phototherapy and hydration.

Impedance Audiometry (IA): A form of testing the function of the ear in which measurements of sound reflected from the tympanic membrane are made with varying air pressures in the sealed external auditory canal. It is also known as Immitance Audiometry.

Meningitis: An infection of the membranes covering the brain and spinal cord.

Otoacoustic Emissions (OAE): Another advanced, computer-assisted method of interpolating hearing from the electrical activity generated in the cochlea by the hair cells upon auditory stimulation.

Personal FM System: A two-part portable amplification system. Part one is the microphone-transmitter that transmits on an FM frequency to the listener. Part two is the FM receiver unit that amplifies the speaker's voice, without background noise or the effects of room distortion, for the listener. Personal FM systems may be connected directly to hearing aids or to lightweight earphones.

Puretones: Soundwaves containing a simple sinusoid. In Conventional Pure Tone Audiometry, a hand is raised or button pushed upon the detection of test tones.

Soundfield FM System: Employs the same two-part transmitter-receiver principle as the Personal FM System. Part one is the portable microphone-transmitter that transmits to a receiver unit in the room. The receiver unit is hard-wired to speakers in the room to provide an even amount of mild amplification with reduced background noise and reverberation (room echo).

Visual Reinforcement Audiometry (VRA): Involves the use of visually animated toys to reinforce a child's overt and repeatable auditory responses (usually a localization of the test stimuli). A VRA test paradigm may take place in the soundfield or with earphones in place. Responses are close to threshold.

Warble tones: Test stimuli that oscillate or change around the centre frequency by + 3 Hz. They were designed for soundfield usage, in order to prevent standing waves or areas of peaks and valleys of sound during testing.

For Further Thought and Discussion

1. Should assessment of communication (speech-language and hearing) be a mandatory part of assessment of a person's capacity and potential?
2. If a person has an undetected communication difficulty (hearing or speech-language), what parts of their lives could be affected?
3. List and explain ways to minimize the developmental effects of a communication difficulty.

More Resources

Organizations/Services:

Assistive Devices Program
http://health.gov.on.ca/english/public/program/adp/adp_mn.html

Canadian Association of Speech Language Pathologists and Audiologists (CASLPA)
http://caslpa.ca

Ontario Association of Speech Language Pathologists and Audiologists (OSLA)
http://osla.ca

Preschool Speech and Language Programs
http://health.gov.on.ca/english/public/program/child/speech/speech_mn.html

The Hearing Foundation of Canada
http://thfc.ca/Default.aspx

Additional Reading:

Bagatto, M., Moodie, S., Scollie, S., Seewald, R., Moodie, S., Pumford, J., & Liu, K. P. R. (2005). Clinical protocols for hearing instrument fitting in the desired sensation level method. *Trends in Amplification, 9*(4), 199-226.

Berlin, C. I., Hood, L. J., Morlet, T., Wilensky, D., Li, L., Mattingly, K. R., Taylor-Jeanfreau, J., Keats, B. J., John, P. S., Montgomery, E., Shallop, J. K., Russell, B. A., & Frisch, S. A. (2010). Multi-site diagnosis and management of 260 patients with auditory neuropathy/dys-synchrony (auditory neuropathy spectrum disorder). *International Journal of Audiology, 49* (1), 30-43.

Buchanan, L. H. (1990). Early onset of presbycusis in Down syndrome. *Scandinavian Audiology, 19*, m, 103-110.

Early Hearing and Communication Development. Canadian Working Group on Childhood Hearing (CWGCH) Resource Document. Ottawa, ON. Minister of Public Works & Government Services Canada (2005). Retrieved from *http://www.phac-aspc.gc.ca/rhs-ssg/index.html*

Gerber, S. E. (2002). *The handbook of pediatric audiology.* Washington, DC: Gallaudet University Press.

Marcell, M. M., & Cohen, S. (1992). Hearing abilities of Down syndrome and other mentally handicapped adolescents. *Research in Developmental Disabilities, 13*, 533-551.

Mudford, O. C., Cross, B. A., Breen, S., Cullen, C., Reeves, D., Gould, J., & Douglas, J. (2000). Auditory integration training for children with autism: No behavioral benefits detected. *American Journal on Mental Retardation, 105*(2), 118-129.

Musiek, F., & Chermak, G. (2006). *Handbook of (central) auditory processing disorder: Vol. 1: Auditory neuroscience and diagnosis.* San Diego, CA: Plural Publishing Inc.

Pober, B., & Dykens, E. (1996). Williams syndrome: An overview of medical, cognitive, and behavioural features. *Mental Retardation, 5*, 929-942.

Scollie, S., Seewald, R., Cornelisse, L., Moodie, S., Bagatto, M., Laurnagaray, D., Beaulac, S., & Pumford, J. (2005). The desired sensation level multistage input/output algorithm. *Trends in Amplification, 9*(4), 159-197.

Shott, S. R. (2006). Down syndrome: Common otolaryngologic manifestations. *American Journal of Medical Genetics Part C (Seminars in Medical Genetics), 142*C, 131-140.

References

Bhasin, T. K., Brocksen, S., Avchen, R. N., & Braun, K. N. (2006). Prevalence of four developmental disabilities among children aged 8 years — Metropolitan Atlanta developmental disabilities surveillance program, 1996 and 2000. *MMWR (Surveillance Summaries), 55*(SS01), 1-9. Retrieved from http://www.cdc.gov/mmwr/preview/mmwrhtml/ss5501a1.html

College of Audiologists and Speech Language Pathologists of Ontario (CASLPO). (2000). *Preferred practice guidelines for the prescription of hearing aids to adults.* Retrieved from http://www.caslpo.com/Portals/0/ppg/preshearingaidsadults.pdf

College of Audiologists and Speech Language Pathologists of Ontario (CASLPO). (2002). *Preferred practice guidelines for the prescription of hearing aids to children.* Retrieved from http://www.caslpo.com/Portals/0/ppg/preshearingaidschild.pdf

College of Audiologists and Speech Language Pathologists of Ontario (CASLPO). (2008). *Practice* standards and guidelines for hearing assessment of children by audiologists. Retrieved from http://www.caslpo.com/PracticeStandards/Preferred-PracticeGuidelines/tabid/162/Default.aspx

Fellinger, J., Holzinger, D., Dirmhirn, A., Van Dinik, J., & Goldberg, D. (2009). Failure to detect deaf-blindness in a population of people with intellectual disability. *Journal of Intellectual Disability Research.*, *53*(10), 874-881.

Forster-Gibson, C., & Berg, J. M. (2011). Healthwatch table — Down syndrome. In *Developmental disabilities primary care initiative. Tools for the primary care of people with developmental disabilities.* Toronto, ON: MUMS Guideline Clearinghouse.

Lowe, C., & Temple, V. (2002). Identifying hearing loss in adults with developmental disabilities. *Journal of Speech Language Pathology and Audioloy, 26*(1), 20-26.

McDermott, A-M., Williams, J., Kuo, M. J., Reid, A. P., & Proops, D. W. (2008). The role of bone anchored hearing aids in children with Down syndrome. *International Journal of Pediatric Otorhinolaryngology*, *72*, 751-757.

Medical Illustration Library. (1994). Baltimore: Williams & Williams.

Meuwese-Jongejeugd, A., Vink, M., Van Zanten, B., Verschurre, H., Eichorn, E., Koopman, D., Bersen, R., & Evenhuis, H. (2006). Prevalence of hearing loss in 1598 adults with an intellectual disability: Cross-sectional population based study. *International Journal of Audiology*, *45*, 660-669.

Meuwese-Jongejeudg, A., Verschuure, H., & Evenhuis, H. M. (2007). Hearing aids: Expectations and satisfaction of people with an intellectual disability, a descriptive pilot study. *Journal of Intellectual Disability Research, 55*(11), 913-922.

Meuwese-Jongejeugd, A., Van Splunder, J., Vink, M., Stilma, J. S., Van Zanten, B, Verschuure, H., Bernsen, R., & Evenhuis, H. (2008). Combined sensory impairment (deaf-blindness) in five percent of adults with intellectually disabilities. *American Journal of Mental Retardation, 113*(4), 254-262.

Ontario Ministry of Community and Social Services. (1997). *Social Assistance Reform Act, 1997.* Retrieved from http://ontla.on.ca/bills/bills-files/36_Parliament/Session1/B142rp.pdf

Ontario Ministry of Children and Youth Services. (2010). *Notice from Early Childhood Programs, April 27, 2010.* Retrieved from http://www.children.gov.on.ca/htdocs/English/topics/earlychildhood/index.aspx

Robertson, C. M. T., Lowarth, T. M., Bork, D. L. R., & Dinu, I. A. (2009). Permanent bilateral sensory and neural hearing loss of children after neonatal intensive care because of extreme prematurity: A thirty-year study. *Pediatrics, 123*(5), 797-808.

Schlosser R. W., Sigafoos, J., Rothschild, N., Burke, M., & Palace, L. M. (2007). Speech and language disorders. In I. Brown & M. Percy, *A comprehensive guide to intellectual and developmental disabilities* (pp. 383-402). Baltimore: Paul H. Brookes Publishing Co.

Stephen, E., Dickson, J., Kindley, A. D., Scott, C. C., & Charleton, P. M. (2007). Surveillance of vision and ocular disorders in children with Down syndrome. *Developmental Medicine & Child Neurology, 49*, 513-515.

Sullivan, W. F., Berg, J. M., Bradley, E., Cheetham, T., Denton, R., et al. (2011). Primary care of adults with developmental disabilites. Canadian consensus guidelines. *Canadian Family Physician, 57*(5), 541-553. Retrieved from http://www.cfp.ca/content/57/5/541.full.pdf+html

Role of Diversity in Psychological Assessment and Intervention

Farrokh Sedighdeilami and Shahar Gindi

What you will learn:

- Definitions of concepts used with reference to diversity
- Multicultural issues in the assessment of individuals with developmental disabilities
- The importance of culturally sensitive intervention
- Diversity and multiculturalism are important issues in the work of any practitioner in the helping professions

This chapter outlines a number of key issues that should assist professionals working with individuals of culturally and ethnically diverse individuals with developmental disabilities, both with regard to assessment and intervention.

Definitions

Diversity is a broad term that includes a wide range of attributes including race, culture, ethnicity, age, gender, language, social and economic status, and so on (Geva, Barsky, & Westernoff, 2000). Culture is a more specific term and a key aspect of diversity. People of the same culture often share common attitudes, behaviour patterns, beliefs, values, and customs of which the professional needs to be aware.

Two extremely important aspects of diversity that go hand in hand with culture are race and language.

Race refers to "a subgroup of people who possess certain physical characteristics, that are genetically determined and that are more or less distinct from other subgroups" (Sue, Kuraski, & Srinivasan, 1999, p. 57). Language refers to the verbal communication exchanged among people who may or may not be of a certain ethnic background. Moreover, language often carries with it considerable cultural influence and inherent points of view.

Race has been emphasized as a dominant feature of diversity in North America because of the large populations of African-, Asian- and Hispanic-Americans in the United States. However, diversity may be manifested differently in different countries around the world. In some countries, diversity involves ethnic groups that speak different languages. In other areas of the world, religious affiliation is dominant in determining differences. In other societies, tribal affiliation requires the clinician's sensitivity most. For the sake of simplicity, we will refer to clients of diverse cultural backgrounds, or to clients of ethnic/minority backgrounds; however, the reader will keep the complexity of diversity in mind, and note how language limits us even in referring to this issue.

Multicultural Issues In Assessment

CULTURAL COMPETENCE SKILL

The assessment of any child requires the examiner to be culturally competent. For professionals dealing with the assessment of clients with developmental disabilities, the importance of understanding their cultural background is critical.

Cultural competence means that the professional is perceived as credible and giving (Sue & Zane, 1987). This means that the professional is perceived by the client both as trustworthy and as delivering a valuable service. Cultural competence includes having a comprehensive base of information regarding cultural background (Rodriguez, 2000). Such information includes familiarity with the culture, its history, traditions, and customs. The professional should also be familiar with ethnographic data, including socio-economic status, structure, socialization, employment and literacy.

In addition to these informational aspects of cultural competence, cultural competence should include an understanding of the culture based on personal experiences (experiential understanding) (Copeland, 1983; Dana, 1993). Experiential understanding does not necessarily require that the professional needs to be of the same cultural background as the client. Experiential understanding can be gained by role-playing, visiting, taking part in cultural activities, and by being attuned and empathic to the culture's narratives.

A third aspect of cultural competence is a mastery of skills that are compatible with clients from different cultures. As will be discussed later, assessing culturally diverse clients for the possibility of developmental disability requires much more than basic skills in the administration of standardized tests.

INTERPROFESSIONAL TEAMWORK

Geva et al. (2000) stressed the importance of working in an interprofessional team to provide a culturally sensitive assessment. In an interprofessional team, practitioners from different professional backgrounds work together throughout the assessment process. Geva et al. (2000) argued that an interprofessional team is a good fit for a culturally competent practice because this framework encourages professionals to consider other people's perspectives, brings a consortium of knowledge (professional and general education) to the assessment, and may bring professionals from diverse personal backgrounds together. An interprofessional assessment team working in the field of developmental disabilities strongly benefits from the participation of psychologists, speech-language pathologists, psychiatrists, pediatricians, occupational therapists, clinical audiologists, behavioural geneticists, and others.

THE ASSESSMENT PROCESS

In addition to discussing steps such as referral and culturally based behavioural observations, this section explains how assessing individuals from diverse ethic backgrounds must involve distinguishing cultural difference from developmental disability and accounting for second language and translation issues. In addition, the section covers the related topics of measurement, social and emotional functioning, and communicating diagnoses to clients and their families.

Referral

The importance of considering cultural issues starts when the referral is made. The assessment team needs to consider the purpose of the assessment in relation to the cultural context. For example, many referrals are made in order to establish that the person's cognitive functioning is in the deficient range in order to obtain funding. However, aspects of diagnoses may be sensitive and complex for clients of diverse cultural backgrounds with developmental disabilities. When considering whether the reason for a referral is appropriate, the assessment team should always strive for a meaningful assessment that is functional and focused on the person's strengths rather than only on weaknesses, and provides useful recommendations. Case study 1 provides an example of cultural sensitivity in the stage of the referral.

Culturally-based behavioural observations

Another important step in the assessment process is making behavioural observations. Behavioural observations provide a distinctive opportunity to assess behaviour within a context relevant to the person being assessed. Here, the examiner needs to take into account different sources of bias when observing a client of a different cultural background, and be aware of the cultural context involved in the observed behaviour. For example, if a child does not make eye contact with adults, the examiner may conclude that the child lacks social pragmatics. However, a child from India may feel that making eye contact with his elders is impolite. The examiner also needs to be aware of his or her own biases and values in order to avoid judgments without understanding the other individual's perspective.

Distinguishing cultural difference from developmental disability

Different cultures understand disability in different ways. Smitsky and Greenspan (2006) provided an insightful collection of essays from experts on issues ranging from whether intellectual disability really is a slowing of mental development to how cultural norms affect the definition of the condition worldwide. Rao (2006) described how Bengali mothers of children with disabilities construct disability and normality. He argued that family members did indeed use very different approaches for understanding disability and that the norms they used and their perceptions of intelligence were much broader than those used by professionals.

When a family asks that their child be assessed for the possibility of a developmental disability, the clinician needs to separate the influence of the ethnic/cultural background from the influences of a developmental disability on the child's achievement in language and cognitive assessments. The first step in assessing the impact of a second language is to

Case study 1

Chung is a 10-year-old boy who was referred for an assessment to evaluate his functioning in academic areas. Chung and his family emigrated from China when Chung was 3 years old, and he was diagnosed with autism when he was 6. Chung's parents are hard working and caring, spending long hours with him and his siblings and helping them with their homework. Like many immigrants from Asia, his parents felt that their children have been given a chance for a life better than theirs and that the children should use this opportunity by studying hard, going to university, and finding lucrative jobs. When the assessment team received the referral, there was a need to clarify with the parents what the purpose of the assessment would be. The members of the assessment team told the parents that, given Chung's diagnosis, it was highly probable that the preferable intervention for him would not be academic but rather one that would address social skills. The parents were loving and caring people. Although they understood that Chung would not progress academically as far as his siblings, working with Chung on his homework was the only way they knew to help him. When these issues were clarified, the assessment team was able to establish a clear understanding of the purpose of the assessment, which was to provide a profile of Chung's strengths and weaknesses and find effective social skills interventions for his parents to use with him.

obtain information from the family about language development and the preferred language at home. It is extremely important to know to which languages the child has been exposed, the child's preferred language, and the language spoken at home by other family members. Siblings may provide a "control group" to examine the differential impact of the child's first language. For example, finding that only one child has difficulties while the other(s) do not provides important evidence that language development and cognitive capacity are influenced by a developmental disability rather than second language issues. Remember, however, that it is important to compare the sibling's progression at an equivalent age, and that development among siblings differs.

This information needs to be obtained sensitively. Families who have immigrated to a new country may strongly believe that exposing a child to their native language will hinder the child's acquisition of the spoken language where they now live. This belief has little empirical research support (Geva, 2000), yet parents may feel defensive because of such beliefs. It is important for clinicians to inform the parents about the research in the field that shows the benefits of preserving the first language (e.g., Cummins, 1984), and to reassure them that they have "done their child good rather than bad" by promoting their heritage and their language. Furthermore, retaining their heritage may contribute to the family's cohesiveness, decrease identity confusion, and contribute to other emotional aspects important to coping with being in a new country and coping with developmental disabilities.

Second language and translation issues

Sometimes, information gathered about language development and comparison to siblings is insufficient to determine whether the cause for the child's difficulties is related to a developmental disability or to acquiring a second language. In such cases, the assessment team should directly address this issue. It is a good practice to conduct some assessment in the child's first language, if that is possible.

However, it may be quite difficult to conduct a first language assessment that would be valid. First, it may be difficult to find psychologists, psychometrists or other professionals who know the language in question. There may be a need to search for translators — not always easy to find — and even with their help, some qualitative information may be lost in translation. Second, it may be quite difficult to find materials for a language or psychological assessment in the client's language, and impossible to find materials that were normed on a comparable population.

There are certain rules about how assessment instruments should be translated. These rules are also helpful to bear in mind when using a translator. Some of these rules are:

- The use of metaphors and idioms should be avoided as much as possible.
- The issue of construct validation should be considered. That is to say, the examiner needs

to be alert at all times to the possibility that the construct to which he or she is referring does not exist in the examinee's culture/language or assumes a different function. For example, when administering a measure of receptive language to a child who has recently immigrated from a desert country like Sudan, asking about an umbrella may be problematic because in Sudan umbrellas are used mainly to protect from the sun, rather than from rain.

When second language seems to be an important issue in impeding the client's achievement, the assessment team may choose to use a dynamic assessment paradigm (see below). This involves a training session to provide the client with information necessary to solve the specific task.

Measurement issues

When faced with a person of a different cultural background thought to have a developmental disability, the assessment team is inevitably faced with issues of measurement. In North America, assessment typically uses measurement tools that have been administered in a standardized way to a representative sample of the population. These tests are administered individually to the child by a skilled professional. Intelligence tests require clinically trained examiners, preferably a psychologist holding a Master's or a Doctoral degree. Tests of language competence are best administered and interpreted by a speech-language pathologist. The results are analyzed according to the assumption that the scores will follow a normal (bell-shaped) distribution. Norms are then set according to the analyses so that the raw scores will be converted to standard scores, placing the examinee in relation to the larger population.

Many problems arise when using standardized tests with clients of diverse cultural backgrounds and with developmental disabilities. First, people with developmental disabilities have been excluded from the population used in developing many of the test norms. Second, people of diverse cultural backgrounds may not have been tested in the norming process of the test. Thus, the possibility that people of diverse cultural backgrounds with developmental disabilities have been tested for the norming is very unlikely. For example, in their research Li and his colleagues (Li, D'Angiulli, & Kendall, 2007) described the limitations of the Early Development Index (EDI) (a teacher completed checklist intended to be a measure of children's readiness for school and an alert for developmental problems) as a universal rating tool, particularly with regard to children from culturally and linguistically diverse backgrounds. Third, diversity is defined differently in different countries (e.g., White, African-American, Hispanic, and Asian-American in the U.S.). Finally, the development of norms for a specific culture may be criticized for classifying minorities as static entities (Jones & Thorne, 1987), that is, by not taking into account the fact that various cultural groups are dynamic entities that evolve constantly (e.g., acculturation, the process of adjustment to a new culture).

Issues of measurement are especially critical when measuring intelligence. Racial/cultural minority spokespersons in the United States have argued fervently against the use of intelligence tests for school placement, even resorting to litigation. The main argument has been that the norms applied in intelligence tests reflect a Western/Eurocentric worldview. As a result, the use of intelligence testing may well represent a bias against minority groups.

Standardized tests: The assessment team is faced with several options when faced with intelligence testing of a person of diverse cultural background with a possible developmental disability. One option is to use the "traditional" norm-referenced intelligence tests, such as the Wechsler or the Stanford Binet, without any modifications. This approach is useful since it assists in delivering a diagnosis for developmental disability where one is needed. In addition, using the tests in the way they were standardized is a condition for the scores to be considered meaningful. Unfortunately, this may be necessary, but it does not seem to be sufficient for people of diverse cultural backgrounds. Unless the test is also administered to individuals with developmental disabilities and to people of diverse cultural backgrounds, the scores will lack validity.

The assessment team may tackle the potential bias in traditional norm-referenced intellectual tests by using nonverbal intelligence tests. Nonverbal testing has been defined as using assessment procedures to provide more accurate estimates of abilities in populations where language demands decrease the validity of the assessment results. The assessment team needs to distinguish three aspects of nonverbal testing: nonverbal contents of the test, nonverbal responses by the examinee, and nonverbal administration by the examiner. For example, the Raven Progressive Matrices is nonverbal in content, but its administration is verbal. By comparison, the Leiter International Performance Scale (Brown, Sherbenou, & Johnsen, 1997) and its revised edition (Leiter-R) are nonverbal in administration as well as in content.

Nonverbal tests have the advantage of being normed on relevant populations, thus decreasing the influence of language. For example, the Mental Measurements Yearbook reported that the Test of Nonverbal Intelligence – Third Edition (TONI-3) was developed to assess aptitude, intelligence, abstract reasoning, and problem solving in a completely language-free format. Other researchers have claimed certain psychological tests to be culture-free.

Although the cultural bias is decreased in nonverbal tests, it is important for professionals to be aware of the impacts of cultural preference and language in any test. For example, matching geometric figures, a task used in the Raven Progressive Matrices, is a skill that is valued and taught in Eurocentric/Western culture, but not necessarily in other cultures. In addition, the examiner cannot be expected to be a "blank slate" in the assessment. The examiner is always influenced by his or her values and beliefs, and should be mindful of this potential bias at all times.

Dynamic assessment: Another paradigm the assessment team may use involves dynamic assessment (Cole, 1996). Dynamic assessment is an approach within the domains of psychology, speech/language, or education that focuses on the ability of the learner to respond to intervention. In this paradigm, the information needed to solve a task is taught to the child and the child's ability to maintain and generalize the knowledge is assessed. Dynamic assessment usually involves using pretest, teaching, and posttest measures. Teaching can be done in many ways depending on the area that is assessed. For example, if the assessment question concerns the child's readiness for literacy, the examiner may use a phonetic approach and a "whole word" approach to actually teach the child some reading in the assessment session. Based on the success of these interventions, the examiner will assess the child's readiness and recommend the appropriate interventions. The extent to which the examinee requires coaching is a measure of his or her ability to perform independently. Dynamic assessment is the method of choice in cases where second language is impeding the examinee's performance on standardized measures.

Social and emotional functioning

Another important aspect of a psychological assessment is assessing the examinee's social and emotional functioning. In general, the assessment of emotional functioning has not always been given the attention it deserves in assessments of developmentally disabled children and adults. This has been largely due to the false idea that the cognitive impairment is an overarching attribute that explains all different aspects of the personality.

One of the commonly used ways to assess social and emotional functioning is by using projective measures such as the Thematic Apperception Test (TAT), the Rorschach Inkblot Test, the Roberts Apperception Test for Children (RATC), and others. Although such projective techniques can be useful, several cautions should be taken when applying them. First, it is extremely important when using projective techniques that the stimuli be culturally relevant (Dana, 1993). For example, almost all the human figures included in the TAT picture-cards appear Caucasian, while the RACT includes pictorial representations of visible minority children. The TAT provides stimuli that are more relevant to dominant Western white culture, while the RATC provides more culturally diverse pictures throughout the test. Culturally relevant pictures can be added, however, to elicit stories in order to validate the qualitative analysis. The Rorschach is another choice that has relatively little cultural loading. In fact, Rorschach's original studies included individuals with developmental disabilities. He argued that

the inkblot test would be useful for assessing individuals with lower intelligence because the results are far less influenced by educational background.

When using such projective techniques to assess social-emotional functioning, it is recommended that examiners rely on qualitative information and analysis of themes, rather than on standardized scoring (e.g., the Rorschach Workbook; Exner, 1990). First, there is a dearth of measures that were standardized on developmentally disabled populations. Second, finding a measure that has been standardized on children with developmental disabilities of a specific cultural background is practically impossible. Third, people with developmental disabilities have fewer resources to cope with stress. Thus, coping strategies or reactions to stress that are appropriate to the individual's developmental level can be misinterpreted in the projective techniques as representing psychotic processes.

Communicating diagnoses to clients and their families

Diagnosis is an issue of great concern. People of different cultures may have different world-views of this issue. As explained above, world-view is a set of assumptions about the world shared by people from a common culture. One important aspect of world-view is the understanding of health/illness. In some cultures, a diagnosis may be a source of shame for the family, or even a threat to its identity. Before delivering a diagnosis, the assessment team should assess the client's and his or her family's beliefs surrounding the diagnosis, and the medical model that is implicit in diagnoses. It is important to consult the literature and experts in the field in order to make informal judgements here.

Once the team has obtained an understanding of the client's/family's world-view, it is important to try as much as possible to convey the diagnosis from within their world-view, and not from one that contradicts it. It is important to consider not only the effects of traditional cultural world-view, but the effects of acculturation as well. For example, Gajjar (2001) found that many clients hold their traditional cultural beliefs and Western medical perspectives concurrently.

Case study 2

Teresa's mother called a university clinic to seek an assessment for her daughter. She told the intake worker that 11-year-old Teresa had been identified with a learning disability two years ago. However, Teresa's mother found Teresa to be progressing slowly and wanted to find out why. At the parent interview it was apparent to the assessment team comprised of a psychometrist and a psychologist that the family was from a diverse cultural background. The mother's appearance was visibly of Filipino-Canadian origin and the father was of South American background. In the parent interview, the father spoke little and obviously had acquired English as a foreign language recently. Often, when the father asked for clarification the mother would translate to Spanish. The first hurdle the assessment team needed to avoid was to misclassify the cultural background based on appearance only. While the mother's racial genealogy did originate from the Philippines her cultural background was unique to a cultural group that immigrated from the Philippines to South America and she herself was born in South America.

When the assessment team started to compile past reports, it became apparent that Teresa had not been diagnosed with a learning disability in the prior assessment; rather, she had been diagnosed with a mild intellectual disability. The assessment process, which was also complicated by family issues that needed to be addressed, needed to take into account the parents' world-view. Specifically, beliefs about developmental disabilities needed to be examined. In consultation with a university psychology professor whose field of research is Latino culture, the assessment team learned that in this culture, developmental disabilities are sometimes seen as a source of shame for the family. The team had to walk a tight rope during the feedback in delivering a diagnosis with integrity, while not offending the family in a manner that would alienate them.

First, the team avoided the use of terms with derogatory connotations such as mental retardation. The team explained that the term learning disability, which the mother used with the intake worker, was inaccurate in describing Teresa's condition. The team explained the phenomenology of Teresa's diagnosis and talked about realistic expectations for the future. The team explained that this is called a developmental disability.

Epilepsy is a good example of a disorder that has been investigated in different cultures (Gajjar, 2001). Epilepsy is important and relevant to the field of developmental disabilities because they are often co-morbid (existing at the same time; Kawasaki, 1989). It is remarkable to observe the ways in which epilepsy is perceived by different cultures. For example, in Tanzania, epilepsy is attributed to spirits possessing the body (Jilek-Aall, 1999). In China, the entire family of a person with epilepsy is affected negatively (World Health Organization, 1997). In India, epilepsy is frequently treated using traditional spiritual techniques (Desai, Padma, Jain, & Maheshwari, 1998). In a study of a large sample (n=1500) in Denmark (Jensen & Dam, 1992), 70% of the respondents were opposed to allowing their children to be in contact with a person with epilepsy. Results from the World Health Organization survey (1997) indicated that 20% of the respondents in Germany believed that epilepsy is a form of mental illness.

In the field of developmental disabilities, psychologists are sometimes faced with the awkward situation of whether or not to deliver a diagnosis of developmental disability (see chapters 1 and 22 for more information). There is also some question of how to do so. Some family members are still most familiar with the now well-outdated and stigmatizing term mental retardation and, because of this, some clinicians might use that term in conjunction with more acceptable terms today such as developmental delay, developmental disability, or intellectual disability. When delivering a diagnosis to people with diverse cultural backgrounds, it is important to have an understanding of which terms are probably most acceptable to them, and which ones have negative connotations, and might be considered degrading and shameful. On the other hand, using ambiguous terms may lead the family to develop an inaccurate understanding of their child's functioning and needs. For example, it has been the experience of these authors that the

Case study 3

Mustafa is a 20-year-old young man with spinal-cord injury and mild cognitive impairment. He was reared in a traditional and rural community in Nigeria. Mustafa and his family were living on a farm during the first 12 years of his life, but when he was injured in an accident, his family moved to Toronto to seek medical services for him. He is the only black student in his class and one of a very few African students in his school. Mustafa felt mismatched and misunderstood. He felt alienated by his classmates. While he likes to socialize with other students, he perceived his classmates as being highly competitive, analytical, and aggressive.

term "delay" is often interpreted to mean something transient and that the person would eventually catch up. Thus, the assessment team should try to deliver the diagnosis in a sensitive, but clear manner. Case study 2 illustrates the complexities that are sometimes involved with delivering the diagnosis.

Culturally Sensitive Intervention

Working with culturally diverse clients with developmental disabilities should be considered an exciting challenge to professionals. Professionals should be prepared, though, to engage in a time-consuming task. In order to provide meaningful and culturally sensitive intervention, the treatment should be designed to include clients' cultural background, level of acculturation, and both past and present personal experiences within the majority culture. These factors have great and direct impact on the way that environment is experienced, on how the information received is processed, and on what kind of behaviour is produced by clients from visible minority groups.

Service providers should be open to various aspects of different cultures, should be intellectually flexible, and should be emotionally capable of dealing with the psychological challenges of clients from different cultures. They must also be aware that different variables from the client's culture may enter the therapeutic relationship. According to guidelines for providers of psychological services to ethnically,

Case study 4

Amir, a 16-year-old adolescent with mild cognitive disability who attends a special education class was referred by his school for psychological intervention because of his high levels of anxiety and anger problems. Amir's parents emigrated to Canada from Egypt when he was 10 years old. During the initial screening and consultation interview, Amir's parents told the interviewer: "Amir has difficulty in learning various subjects, especially math and spelling. According to Amir, he also does not fit in with his Canadian classmates. He told us that other kids do not like him because he is from Egypt and because he likes Arabic music and food. Sometimes, Amir would come home from school in a very bad mood because his classmates have made some jokes about Arab people and their culture."

linguistically, and culturally diverse populations developed by American Psychological Association (APA, 1990), psychological service providers need a socio-cultural framework to consider diversity of values, interactional styles, and cultural expectations in a systematic fashion. These guidelines also suggest that the psychologist should have appropriate knowledge and skills required for multicultural assessment and intervention including: 1) recognize cultural diversity; 2) understand the role that culture and ethnicity/race play in sociopsychological and economic development of ethnic and culturally diverse populations; 3) understand that socio-economic and political factors significantly impact the psychosocial, political and economic development of ethnic and culturally diverse groups; and 4) help clients to understand/maintain/resolve their own sociocultural identification; and understand the interaction of culture, gender, and sexual orientation on behaviour and needs (APA 98th Annual Convention, 1990). Unfortunately, some therapists, because of incomplete training, are unaware or find it difficult to consider cultural issues and apply only values and beliefs based on their own psychology and psychiatry training to the treatment.

Clients from diverse cultural/ethnic backgrounds may bring an entirely different set of values and beliefs

Case study 5

Alhandra was born and reared in a traditional family in Peru. Alhandra and her family moved to Ontario when she was 4 years old. She was diagnosed as having Williams syndrome, a condition that is now recognized to be caused by a microdeletion of chromosome 7. Williams syndrome is characterized by a recognizable pattern of dysmorphic facial features, connective tissue abnormalities, cardiovascular disease, delayed development, a specific cognitive profile, and a unique personality. Although she attends a special education program with other adolescents with developmental disabilities, Alhandra still feels alone and alienated because of her family's background. For example, in one of the therapy sessions, she told the therapist that nobody in her cooking class likes to learn how to make a meal from Peru, and she felt that she was forced to conform and to learn things that were different from what is related to her family situation and what she likes to learn.

to the therapy sessions. According to Pinderhughes (1989), the feelings aroused in professionals who work with clients whose culture differs from their own "are more frequently than not negative and driven by anxiety, [and] they can interfere with successful therapeutic outcome" (p. 21). Of course, service providers are not expected to know every aspect of every different culture, or to be absolutely free of cultural biases. However, awareness and consideration of cultural issues is an essential variable that will have an important impact on the effectiveness of the treatment.

ACCULTURATION

The classical definition of acculturation was provided by Redfield and his colleagues in 1936. They defined acculturation as a process that "comprehends those phenomena which result when groups of individuals having different cultures come into continuous first-hand contact with subsequent changes in the original culture patterns of either or both groups" (Redfield & Herskovits, 1936, p. 149). According to Berry (1997), acculturation is a strategy that is overtly or inadvertently adopted by individuals when they come into contact with people of different cultures. Acculturation is a neutral term in principle and the change may occur in either or both groups. However, from a practical point of view, acculturation induces more changes in one of the majority groups than in the other. While working with clients from different cultures, it is important for clinicians to be aware that acculturation is not an isolated phenomenon. It is affected by the social, political, and economic environment in the host society and by the experiences and attitudes of clients.

Acculturation can be highly stressful for an individual, especially for those who try hard to retain their original culture and reject the culture of the host country. It may also be stressful for those who do not hang onto their minority culture and do not adjust to majority culture either. A client who is highly acculturated may not be as influenced by cultural factors as a non-acculturated client. For instance, a psychologist working with an Ontario-born and raised minority client needs to address different issues than one working with a client from a minority culture who has recently immigrated to Ontario. It is important to note that the level of acculturation may vary greatly among different members of a particular ethnic minority, and within members of the same family.

DIFFERENTNESS AND THE MISMATCH SYNDROME

Research on children and adolescents with developmental disabilities indicates that the feeling of being different is typical among those who have developmental disabilities. Culturally diverse children and youth may face a double challenge in this regard. Not only are they confronted with the challenges of disabilities, but they must also deal with the difficulties of adapting to a new and different culture. The feeling of being culturally different may add to their feelings of alienation and loneliness. They may also feel misunderstood. Cultural differences may make children feel mismatched with other people and with the environment. According to Ramirez (1991), the common dynamic in the "differentness syndrome" is mismatch, which may cause loneliness, hopelessness, depression, self-rejection, and rigidity of thinking. Case studies 3–5 illustrate how cultural differences may relate to the mismatch syndrome in children and adolescents with developmental disabilities, and case study 3 does this explicitly.

CULTURAL FACTORS AFFECTING ASSESSMENT AND INTERVENTION

There are several cultural factors that may affect intervention and its effectiveness. In the following sections, some of the most important of these are discussed.

Communication

According to Storti (1994), communication is central to multicultural encounters. Communication may be defined as the sending of a message from a source to a receiver with the least possible loss of meaning. Hall (1963) argued that culture itself is communication because culture can be viewed as a continuous process of sending and receiving messages and reinforcing different norms. He emphasized that some aspects of our activities, of which we may or may not be aware, transmit messages that are easily misunderstood cross-culturally. For example, Asian, African, and Hispanic people apply restricted codes in which sentences are shortened without a loss of meaning and non-verbal messages delivered simultaneously. For instance, among some Asian and Middle Eastern individuals, a hesitant "yes" is a way of politely expressing "no," and gestures and body postures sometimes substitute for words and sentences. Some people from Middle East look away from the person to whom they are talking when expressing "no" politely. In contrast, Anglo-Americans emphasize verbal messages and elaborate codes in which many words are applied to convey a message. Therefore, it is essential for a psychologist working with clients from minority cultures to be aware of and familiar with their communication styles during the process of treatment.

Cultural norms

Norms are a set of unwritten rules about what is usually "done." Cultural norms are those norms that refer to what is usually done and accepted within a specific culture that are unique to that culture. Norms and cultural norms are more than simply non-verbal communications, such as gestures, body language, and manners. Our understanding of them makes human interactions meaningful. For example, in some Native cultures, silence is meaningful, while in Western culture it is typically considered awkward. Similarly, in some Middle East and Far East cultures, looking into the eyes of an older person during a conversation is considered impolite. Another example of nonverbal behaviour in different cultures is crossing legs while sitting in front of another person. Although acceptable in Western culture, this would be considered rude in Middle Eastern cultures. Unfamiliarity with such cultural norms and not taking cultural differences into account during intervention may result in an unsuccessful treatment without positive gain for the client.

Attention to the environment

Aspects of a new environment and culture provide constant sensory information that an individual must filter and categorize. A culturally diverse child with a developmental disability who has cognitive deficiencies may feel overwhelmed by an unfamiliar and sometimes completely different environment and culture. He or she may not be able to absorb all the new aspects of the new culture easily and automatically because his or her cognitive capacity may not be at the level needed to deal with it. Therefore, absorbing the type of information that occurs quite easily within the home culture may become a major and sometimes exhausting task.

Culturally diverse children and youth with developmental disabilities who do not hear their own language and see little or nothing familiar to their home culture in the new environment, who use body language and gestures differently from the majority, who verbalize in unexpected and different ways, and who may expect authority to be exercised differently, may experience differentness that may in turn cause isolation and loneliness.

This experience of differentness sometimes makes it harder for professionals to establish a rapport with those clients and to have children's cooperation during the process of intervention. This is particularly true for service providers who are not familiar enough with cultural issues, and who do not consider cultural differences as an important aspect in their practice. Nonetheless, considering cultural differences in providing services is an absolute necessity.

Behavioural norms

Each culture has different behavioural norms. In addition to the examples provided above, in most Eastern cultures, children are typically expected to be quiet and defer to adults, while in Western cultures, children and youth are typically encouraged to express themselves and to be independent. Some cultures place great emphasis on family, interdependence, and collectivism (e.g., Middle Eastern or Far East cultures); others emphasize independence from family, self-reliance, and individualism (e.g., North American culture).

All of these cultural norms affect the client's behaviour and influence how an individual behaves toward the therapist or service worker during an intervention. For instance, in a society where individualism is encouraged, a therapist may tend to view a child's difficulty as residing within the client, rather than in the family or society in large. The therapist may, as a result, use a client-focused strategy to address the problem, with the goal of the intervention focused on changing the child.

The client's family may see the importance of the child's contribution to the problem, but they may also put great emphasis on systemic and social factors. If the therapist shares and works with, or at the very least understands, their views and perceptions, the treatment will be both more constructive and more successful.

One important non-verbal behaviour is eye contact. In a psychologically-based intervention, eye contact or the avoidance of eye contact has diagnostic significance. Service providers who do not consider cultural issues in their practices may interpret the lack of eye contact as a sign of shyness, unassertiveness, or even depression. This may lead to misunderstandings when dealing with culturally diverse children and adolescents with developmental disabilities. As mentioned above, it is not necessary

for many people from the Middle and Far East to look at one another in the eyes when communicating — in fact, direct eye contact may be considered a rude and impolite behaviour, especially for children and young adults. An adolescent may be involved in doing other things when engaged in a conversation. Thus, some professionals may view a client from the Middle East as being resistant or uncooperative, when they are actually trying to be polite.

Cultural values and beliefs

Behind human behaviours are the values and beliefs that cultures hold. Cultural values about personal relationships affect client-worker interaction (Canino & Spurlock, 2000). A factor that may potentially contaminate the process of a professional's intervention is the failure to recognize clients' cultural differences. Pinderhughes (1989) argued that service providers can have a blind spot, and may perceive clients from their own culture as being like themselves.

Not distinguishing between their own culture and that of their clients can interfere with treatment and can have a negative impact on the therapeutic environment, as those professionals fail to explore the meaning of particular events for their clients and assume that the clients' issues are similar to their own. As a result, educating culturally diverse clients and their families about the intervention and its process is usually considered necessary. Culturally diverse clients and their families may have had little or no exposure to these types of intervention, and may view them as irrelevant and disconnected from their problems. As a consequence, they may simply not return. Professionals should therefore avoid making interpretations and giving meaning only to communication and behaviours that fit into their own value systems.

Patterns of thinking

It is important for professionals to be aware of the fact that cognitive and thinking patterns vary from client to client, especially when the client is from a different culture. For example, it is helpful to know if clients usually think deductively or inductively. Does the child or adolescent consider his or her environment when he or she thinks, or does he or she ignore it?

Some clients typically begin a conversation with concrete facts, and then build their ideas based on those facts. On the other hand, others may be accustomed to starting with abstract ideas, moving on to concrete facts. Such patterns of thinking may be developed within individuals because of cultural influences. Information of this kind can be very helpful to the interaction between the professional and the client.

Styles of communication

Different cultures have their own communicative styles. A gesture, a smile, a tone of voice, or a way of shaking hands may add to a message or give special meaning to the reciprocal communication. It is important to note that the addition of an emphasis or meaning to a message varies from one culture to the next. For example, in some cultures, low tone (pitch) of voice is encouraged, while other cultural groups may encourage high tone and loud speech. Gesture and body language also differ greatly from culture to culture. For example, people from the Middle East tend to show more emotion, speak slowly, and touch (e.g., touch on the arm) more than people from the West.

Another factor to be considered is personal space, the distance at which people from different cultures are comfortable when conversing or interacting. This also varies from one culture to another and may have a marked effect on elicited responses.

Summary

Professionals who work with individuals with developmental disabilities are often confronted with various challenges (e.g., determining situations specific to the client's behaviour problem). When the clients come from diverse cultural backgrounds, the challenge is often compounded. Professionals should move beyond the traditional assessment and intervention approaches, should be familiar with multicultural issues related to both assessment and intervention, and should be able to design a treatment protocol that includes the client's cultural background and personal experiences. They should also be open to various aspects of different cultures, be intellectually flexible, and be able to determine the impact of cultural differences and acculturation issues. On the other hand, clinicians should be cautious of over-focusing on the client's cultural/ ethnic background.

Challenges clients experience may be related to issues other than their ethnicity. Inability to consider clients' cultural background may contaminate the process and the results of both assessment and intervention, and may cause frustration for both client and clinician. It is not possible for professionals to know every aspect of different cultures.

However, consideration and awareness of cultural issues is essential, and will have a considerable effect on the outcomes associated with treating individuals with developmental disabilities from various cultures. One way to provide such an awareness is adding a mandatory course to the university and college curricula for psychology major students and especially for those who are attending graduate programs in psychology about the effects of culture and ethnicity on the processes of psychological assessment and intervention. Cultural awareness can also be achieved, in part, through attending seminars and workshops focused on cultural issues and their impact on the process of psychological works.

For Further Thought and Discussion

1. Why is it important for professionals to be aware of cultural issues in working with culturally diverse individuals with developmental disabilities?
2. Define the "mismatch or differentness syndrome" and explain how it can affect an individual you know from a minority group.
3. There are various cultural variables that may affect the process of intervention and its effectiveness. Explain how these variables affect one intervention that you select.
4. Illustrate, by presenting a case example in a creative way, how a client's first language can affect the assessment process and its results.

More Resources

General:

British Institute of Learning Disabilities
Green Street, Kidderminster, Worcestershire, UK
http://www.bild.org.uk

Canadian Ethnocultural Council (CEC)
176 rue Gloucester St, Suite 400,
Ottawa, Ontario
K2P 0A6.
Phone: (613) 230-3867.

EU Monitoring and Advocacy Program of the Open Society Institute
H-1051, Budapest, Nador 11, 4th floor
Tel: 0036 1 327 3100
http://www.eumap.org

National Center for Latinos with Disabilities, Inc
http://homepage.interaccess.com/

National Multicultural Institute
3000 Connecticut Avenue NW, Suite 438
Washington DC 20008-2556
(202) 483-0700
(202) 483-5233 (FAX)
www.nmci.org

Ontario Specific:

Afghan Association of Ontario
(416) 744-9289

African Community Service of Peel
(905) 206-9497

Arab Community Centre of Toronto
(416) 231-7746

Association of Women of India in Canada
(416) 499-4144
www.awic.org

Bangladeshi Canadian Community Services
(416) 699 2323
www.bangladeshi.ca

Bathurst Jewish Community Centre
(416) 636-1880
www.bjcc.ca

Canadian Arab Federation
(416) 493-8635

Canadian Tamil Women's Community Services
(416) 289-2099

Chinese Cultural Centre of Greater Toronto
(416) 292-9293
www.cccgt.org

Federation of Muslim Women
www.fmw.org

Iranian Community Association of Ontario
(416) 441-2656
www.iranianassociation.ca

Iranian Women's Organization of Ontario
www.irontario.com

Japanese Canadian Cultural Centre
(426) 441-2345
www.jccc.on.ca

Nepalese Canadian Community Services
(416) 363 6610
www.nccs.ca

Pakistani Canada Association
(519) 579-3800

South Asian Family Support Services
(416) 431-4847
www.safss.com

South Asian Couple Counselling
(416) 736-2100 ext 33224
www.southasianfamilies.com

South Asian Women's Centre
(416) 537-2276

Thunder Bay Multicultural Association
(807) 345-0531

Toronto Council Fire Native Cultural Centre
(416) 360-4330
www.councilfire.ca

Ukrainian Culture Centre Toronto
(416) 531-3610

References

American Psychiatric Association. (2000). *Diagnostic and statistical manual of mental disorders* (4th ed., text rev.). Washington, DC: Author.

American Psychological Association. (1990). *The guideline for providers of psychological services to ethnically, linguistically, and culturally diverse populations.* Paper presented at at the annual convention of the American Psychiatric Association, Boston, MA.

Berry, J. W. (1997). Immigration, acculturation, and adaptation. *Applied Psychology: An International Review, 46*(1), 5-68.

Brown, L., Sherbenou, R. J., & Johnsen, S. K. (1997). *Test of nonverbal intelligence.* Austin, TX: Pro-Ed.

Canino, I. A., & Spurlock, J. (2000). Diagnostic categories. In I. A. Canino & J. Spurlock (Eds.), *Culturally diverse children and adolescents: Assessment, diagnosis, and treatment* (2nd ed.) (pp. 103-147). New York: Guilford.

Cole, E. (1996). Immigrant and refugee children and families: Supporting a new road travelled. In M. Luther (Ed.), *Dynamic assessment for instruction: From theory to application* (pp. 35-42). Toronto, ON: Captus Press.

Copeland, E. J. (1983). Cross-cultural counseling and psychotherapy: A historical perspective, implications for research and training. *Personnel Guidance Journal, 62*(1), 10-15.

Cummins, J. (1984). Four misconceptions about language proficiency in bilingual education. *The Journal of the National Association for Bilingual Education, 5*(3), 31-45.

Dana, R. H. (1993). *Multicultural assessment perspectives for professional psychology.* Needham Heights, MA: Allyn & Bacon.

Desai, P., Padma, M. V., Jain, S., & Maheshwari, M. C. (1998). Knowledge, attitudes and practice of epilepsy: Experience at a comprehensive rural health services project. *Seizure, 7,* 133-138.

Exner, J. E. J. (1990). *The Rorschach workbook for the comprehensive system.* Bayville, NJ: The Rorschach Workshops.

Gajjar, M. M. (2001). Developing a rating scale for assessing culture-specific beliefs and attitudes about epilepsy. *Disseration Abstracts International, 62*(4), 2056.

Geva, E. (2000). Issues in the assessment of reading disabilities in L2 children — beliefs and research evidence. *Dyslexia, 6,* 13-28.

Geva, E., Barsky, A., & Westernoff, F. (2000). Inter-professional and diversity informed practice. In E. Geva, A. Barsky, & F. Westernoff (Eds.), *Interpro-*

fessional practice with diverse populations: Cases in point (pp. 1-28). Westport, CN: Auburn House.

Hall, T. (1963). *The silent language.* New York: Anchor Press.

Jensen, R., & Dam, M. (1992). Public attitudes toward epilepsy in Denmark. *Epilepsia, 27,* 316-322.

Jilek-Aall, L. (1999). Morbus sacer in Africa: Some religious aspects of epilepsy in traditional cultures. *Epilepsia, 40,* 382-386.

Jones, E. E., & Thorne, A. (1987). Rediscovery of the subject: Intercultural approaches to clinical assessment. *Journal of Consulting & Clinical Psychology, 55,* 488-495.

Kawasaki, Y. (1989). Developmental disorders and epilepsy. *Journal of Mental Health, 35,* 15-23.

Li, J., D'Angiulli, A., & Kendall, G. E. (2007). The Early Development Index and children from culturally and linguistically diverse backgrounds. *Early Years: An International Journal of Research and Development, 27*(3), 221-235.

Pinderhughes, E. (1989). *Understanding race, ethnicity and power: The key to efficacy in clinical practice.* New York: Free Press.

Rao, S. (2006). Parameters of normality and cultural constructions of "mental retardation": Perspectives of Bengali families. *Disability & Society, 21*(2), 152-178.

Ramirez, M. (1991). *Psychotherapy and counseling with minorities: A cognitive approach to individual and cultural differences.* New York: Pergamon Press.

Redfield, R. L., & Herskovits, M. (1936). Memorandum on the study of acculturation. *American Antropologist, 38,* 149-152.

Rodriguez, C. (2000). Culturally sensitive psychological assessment. In I. A. Canino (Ed.), *Culturally diverse children and adolescents: Assessment, diagnosis, and treatment* (2nd ed.) (pp.84-102). Spurlock, NY: Guilford.

Smitsky, H. N., & Greenspan, S. (Eds.). (2006). *What is mental retardation: Ideas for an evolving disability in the 21st century* (p. 358). Washington, DC: American Association on Mental Retardation.

Storti, C. (1994). *Cross-cultural dialogues: 74 brief encounters with cultural difference.* Yarmouth, ME: Intercultural Press.

Sue, S., & Zane, N. (1987). The role of culture and cultural techniques in psychotherapy: A critique and reformulation. *American Psychologist, 42*(1), 37-45.

Sue, S., Kuraski, K. S., & Srinivasan, S. (1999). Ethnicity, gender, and cross-cultural issues in clinical research. In P. C. Kendall, J. N. Butcher, & G. N. Holmbeck (Eds.), *Handbook of research methods in clinical psychology* (2nd ed.) (pp. 54-71). New York: John Wiley & Sons.

World Health Organization. (1997). *Epilepsy: Social consequences and economic aspects.* Retrieved from http://www.who.int/mediacentre/factsheets/fs166/en/

29

Roles, Education, Training, and Professional Values of Disability Personnel

Roy I. Brown

What you will learn:

- Setting the scene: context for disability personnel and their roles
- Education and training of disability personnel
- Philosophy and values of disability personnel
- Ethical issues and challenges

Working with people who have developmental disabilities can lead to occupations and life experiences that are challenging, rewarding, and rich with opportunities for personal fulfillment. This is the case for the many different types of paid and unpaid support people who actively work with individuals who have disabilities. In this chapter, the wide range of people whose work involves supporting people with developmental disabilities is referred to as disability personnel (see Box 1).

The work of all disability personnel is essential for people with disabilities to enable them to live in communities in ways that include their lifestyles with others and promote their quality of life. As noted in Box 1, many such personnel work in com-munity settings; others work directly within a wide variety of structures, systems, and processes that are usually referred to, collectively, as service organizations. Service organizations typically employ disability personnel in the form of managers and supervisors, policy makers, frontline practitioners of various types, and support staff.

Frontline practitioners — those who work most closely with people with developmental disabilities — are especially important to ensuring that effective support is provided. The main reasons for this are that frontline practitioners:

- Are most knowledgeable about the characteristics and behaviour of people with disabilities
- Are key to helping other professionals and

Box 1: Disability Personnel

Disability personnel are professionals and nonprofessionals who have a direct role in the day-to-day care, support, and rehabilitation of people with developmental disabilities. These include family members, friends, volunteers, and community members, as well as people who work in residential and group homes, day centres, homes of people with disabilities who live independently with assistance, family homes, places of employment, community service organizations, and care settings of various kinds. This group also includes personnel whose day-to-day work provides support by visiting families in their homes and in the local community and bringing together the necessary resources for the individuals and families they support. Such individuals work under a variety of names: outreach workers, community and rehabilitation practitioners, community counsellors, child-care workers, early childhood workers, developmental educators, and so forth.

People with developmental disabilities, especially those who live in the community, obtain considerable amounts of support from a wide variety of professionals and nonprofessionals. The importance of informal support (see Chapter 23 for more information) — from such people as store employees, bus drivers, neighbours, schoolmates, children in the playground, and even strangers — cannot be overstated. Such support is invaluable to the inclusion of people with disabilities into community life.

More formal support is provided by professionals who assist people with disabilities as a part of their work. Such is the case for a teacher who has one child with Down syndrome in his classroom, a family physician who has three patients who have intellectual disabilities, or a lawyer who dedicates 5% of her practice to assisting people with disabilities. Other examples include, but are not limited to, medical doctors including pediatricians, psychiatrists and neurologists, psychologists, dentists, general nurses, physiotherapists, homecare workers, occupational therapists, speech-language pathologists, audiologists, behaviour therapists, and drama and music therapists. Some of these professionals may have little formal knowledge of disability, and others may have considerable knowledge.

policy makers understand the person with disabilities and any difficulties he or she faces

- Are central figures in the multidisciplinary teams needed to support most people with disabilities
- Carry out most informal (and sometimes formal) assessment and intervention, and provide needed care and help
- Are in positions of trust, with direct responsibility for supporting personal well-being of those with disabilities

Frontline practitioners do work that is highly varied and personal because, of necessity, they must respond to the support needs of specific individuals. Some frontline practitioners are family members, and others are paid workers who are trained and educated at a variety of levels. The latter are described by terms that vary by region and by job function, but include names such as disability counsellors, aides, rehabilitation counsellors or practitioners, disability support workers, and residential and

community support personnel. A great many frontline practitioners work in or for a wide variety of community-based organizations, both publicly and privately funded, and some work in family homes. Others carry out their roles in institutions and hospitals. They are the people who have the closest ongoing contact with the people they support.

This chapter focuses on issues that concern all disability personnel, especially frontline practitioners. Yet, disability personnel carry out their work within a sometimes complex system of disability legislation, funding, and services that involves many other professionals and nonprofessionals and operate within broader social environments that have their own values and manifest their own attitudes toward disability. For this reason, the information presented is highly relevant to a broad spectrum of people across the disability field: policy makers whose decisions create the environment within which disability personnel work to provide effective support; professionals and nonprofessionals whose daily work sometimes includes people with disabilities; and society at large, which is ultimately responsible for how people with disabilities are treated as they carry out their lives in their communities. It also underscores why personnel have to collaborate with a wide range of people.

Setting the Scene: Context for Disability Personnel

Before addressing the specific issues for disability personnel, it is important to describe the context — or "set the scene" — for these issues. Three broad issues, discussed below, are increasing knowledge of disability, changes in support methods, and family challenges.

Increasing knowledge of disability

The last half of the 20th century and the beginning years of the 21st century has been a time of massive increase in knowledge about developmental disabilities. The unraveling of the genetic code and the subsequent development of the human genome (see Chapter 9) has led not only to an increasing ability to identify genetic deficiencies but also to an ability to provide, through genetic counselling, advice to prospective parents. Identification of genetic causes of developmental disability has and will lead to new treatments and possibly even cures.

These advances have been paralleled by extraordinary changes in understanding of other aspects of life, such as physical health, psychology and behaviour. There also have been advances in knowledge about health and gender differences, and these have been tied to advances in technological skills (Prasher & Janicki, 2002; Walsh & Heller, 2002),

There has been immense growth in understanding of environmental causes of disabilities (e.g., fetal alcohol spectrum disorder, the leading non-genetic cause of fetal malformations and intellectual disability worldwide). It is increasingly recognized that, in many countries, environmental damage related to inadequate food and health services, isolation, and social living conditions cause environmentally induced developmental disabilities. For example, children who are born into adverse family and social environments are at risk of developing not only physical diseases and deformity but also mild to severe intellectual disability. To prevent these kinds of disabilities, it is critical for people (particularly infants and children) to receive the basic elements of a healthy life, including clean water, food, and a safe and supportive family environment. Yet, as such improvements occur, countries will see a rise in the number of people with disabilities surviving to greater ages.

Aging, in fact, has become an important area of this increasing knowledge. Many people with severe and profound disabilities now survive and require support, care, and training over an increasingly longer life span. Those with more mild disabilities are likely to have even longer lifespans and require both generic and specialized services to an advanced age. For example, people with developmental disabilities may eventually move to homes for people who are aging, although they also require specialized support because of social and possibly behavioural issues (Janicki & Ansello, 2000). One of the most remarkable changes in lifespan has occurred in people with Down syndrome. At the beginning of the 20th century, they lived on average to approximately 11 years, but they now live on average to more than 55 years in most affluent countries (Brown, 2004). People with Prader-Willi syndrome are beginning to show similar changes (James & Brown, 1993).

As a consequence of such factors, disability personnel in the early 21st century work with a wider range of people with developmental disabilities about whom increasingly more is known. Adding to this challenge is the fact that this increased knowledge has been accompanied by enormous changes in support methods (Bigby, 2004; Brown & Brown, 2003), including approaches within developing countries and various cultural groups (see Keith & Schalock, 2000; McConkey, O'Toole, & Mariga, 1999).

Changes in support methods

The years since the mid-20th century have been a time of fundamental changes in how people with disabilities are perceived and how services are delivered. Despite some changing economic conditions over these years, there were ongoing efforts to change the lives of people with disabilities for the bet-

Table 1: Generally Accepted Priorities for Supports and Services

Support and services should be based on:

- *Broad knowledge of disability's causes and contributing factors*
- *Broad-based knowledge across key domains of life experience*
- *Collaboration between generic and specialized services and resources*
- *Collaboration among all levels of professional personnel and families*
- *Community based delivery, rather than institutionally based care*

Support and services should be:

- *Enabling and enhancing to quality of life*
  - *Complete, timely, and efficient*
  - *Ethical and respectful*
  - *Improving in response to evidence-based research*
  - *Proven to be the best way of helping people with their specific problems and concerns (i.e., in accord with best practice standards)*
- *Integrated*
- *For the life span*
- *Multidisciplinary*
- *Multilayered*
- *Sensitive to culture, religion, family structure, and social circumstances*

ter — although these efforts took different forms in different countries. Such efforts have occurred, and are still occurring, within a world context associated with a move from a disablement-based model to one of participation and activity by people with disabilities (see World Health Organization, 1997). The trend is toward supporting and enabling individuals to become more responsible for their own development and to be key participants in decision-making.

The philosophical foundation for many of these changes was the principle of normalization (Wolfensberger, 1972), later referred to by the same author as social role valorization. This perspective sought to persuade individuals, families, communities, and governments that regular lifestyles in normal circumstances with valued roles for people with developmental disabilities are not only important and possible, but also critically necessary and ethically required. This, and complementary, perspectives have made it apparent that despite a growing awareness of the genetic influence on behaviour and the extent of physical impairment, the degree to which people see themselves as "disabled" and the degree to which other members of society see them as "disabled" are strongly influenced by social attitudes and values, most commonly demonstrated by the absence or presence of discrimination and oppression (Schalock et al., 2002; see also Chapter 3).

These changes have taken many forms. In Ontario, as in other provinces and affluent countries, institutional care has been replaced by a wide variety of rehabilitation and support systems based in the community. As a result, most people with developmental disabilities remain in their home communities — often with their families — or live in communities of their choice. Even those with severe medical and psychiatric conditions, who were once thought to be extremely difficult to move from institutions successfully, are being provided for in community settings. The thrust for inclusive education, supported by legislation, brought about a dramatic decrease in the number of special (segregated) classrooms and schools and an increase in the number of supports within general education classrooms for children with disabilities. Various forms of individualized funding are being tried out in many countries. Indeed, individuals, families, and people within service organizations who support those with disabilities are developing and implementing an array of new methods of support for all aspects of life, some of which will prove to be highly beneficial and widely used in the future. These methods not only are typically based on generally accepted priorities for supports and services, as outlined in Table 1, but also represent some unique and innovative ways of putting ideas into practice.

Service variation among regions: The services and supports provided by disability personnel in

Box 2: Case study of Sanjeev, a 5 year old with cerebral palsy

Sanjeev is 5-year-old boy with cerebral palsy. He lives in Bhaktapur, Nepal, with his family. His mother, Adity, stays at home and takes care of him and her 10-year-old daughter, Pranisha. Sanjeev's father, Padam, works as a waiter in a local family restaurant. Several times per week, Adity, Sanjeev, and Pranisha ride the local bus for 2 hours in order to get to Kanti Children's Hospital, where Sanjeev receives treatment. Kanti is the only hospital of its kind in Nepal. There are no other special facilities or homes for people with developmental disabilities such as Sanjeev's, so Kanti is the only place that provides care for children with cerebral palsy. Adity pays 120 Nepalese rupees for six treatments of physiotherapy at the hospital.

As a result of his disability, Sanjeev is unable to attend school or any other special programming. He enjoys playing with toys and with his older sister. Pranisha treats him like any one of her friends and tries to help him improve his dexterity and movement. Adity works with the occupational therapist and assists in stretching Sanjeev's limbs in order to expand his range of motion.

Source: Rebecca Zener, University of Toronto.

different regions have somewhat different accents. Priorities for services and service development differ, partly because need for services can vary markedly from region to region and also within regions. There are many factors that can influence how priorities for services are put into place. These factors also vary among regions and within regions but include: population size and demographics, availability of government and other funding, laws, policies, social customs and traditions, availability of community resources, and education and training of professionals both inside and outside the disability field.

Services can also be influenced by geography (see Box 2 for an interesting example from Nepal). For example, in Australia's "outback," services are widespread, far apart, and situated over difficult terrain, whereas in larger cities like Adelaide or Sydney services are closer at hand. Similarly, in Ontario, providing services in Northern Ontario is considerably more difficult (and expensive) than doing so in Ottawa or Toronto. It is often easier to administer and monitor services in urban areas because of proximity and ease of travel, but the complexity of urban life and the larger number of people who need services in cities can make the work more challenging and sometimes less accessible. Services for Indigenous peoples in Ontario — as is the case in other provinces and countries of the world such as Australia, the United States (and many other countries of the world such as India, Mexico, Japan, the Philippines) — sometimes differ considerably from services for non–Indigenous peoples, especially those in urban and socially well-developed areas (Timmons, 1999). The challenges for workers in the rural areas are often much more acute and long-term for they often do not have colleagues who can provide close support. Importantly, video conferencing (VC) technology has the potential to increase accessibility to certain healthcare services for those living in rural or underserved communities (Temple, Drummond, Valiquette, & Jozsvai, 2010).

These types of challenges are particularly evident in rural areas, but may arise in all communities. This raises the more general question of how disability planners can ensure that there is reasonable professional and experienced support and help for professional and ethical issues. This question needs to be addressed at the policy level, but also within university and college education, and this includes follow-up once a person is placed in employment.

In general, improved living standards in any country seem to accompany greater attention to disability services by governments, communities, and service organizations. Lessening of wealth, recession, and a perceived need for economic strengthening tend to accompany the withholding of services from people and families where disability occurs. For example, in the late 1990s in Ontario there was some withdrawal of funding for all social services and, as a consequence, many needed supports for people with developmental disabilities and their families were not funded or were underfunded. How do such situations affect ethical and professional practice? Experience and research tell us that the impact can be quite striking, especially since the lack of needed personnel and other supports comes at a time when poverty is more likely to occur for people with disabilities and their families. Poverty and disability are already linked with poor nutrition, single-parent families, maltreatment, and behaviour challenges (e.g., see Emerson, Robertson, & Wood, 2005; Fudge Shormans & Brown, 2002), and this creates a very challenging situation for disability professionals.

Importance of social values: The availability of support and services is not simply a matter of adequate funding for many basic social and community needs. It is also a matter of social values and local attitudes toward people with disabilities, as well as long-term planning that sets government priorities for policy and action. Priorities and values/attitudes work in combination, and results in these areas can be seen, for example, in the following areas: how services address inclusion for people with disabilities once they have completed inclusive schooling, how issues of pregnancy and child care are addressed for mothers who themselves have a disability, and how services provide care and support for individuals with disabilities who are becoming elderly. Where attitudes toward children and adults with disabilities remain negative and where government disability priorities are not strong, as is the case especially in economically developing countries, people with disabilities are often still regarded as a source of individual and personal shame.

Family challenges

The needs of families over the lifespan of individuals with developmental disabilities are becoming increasingly important. One response to this is the development of a quality of life approach, which now clearly involves family needs and support — where there is a son or daughter with a developmental disability — from childhood into adulthood and old age. This means that parental needs and responsibilities continue, often with the relative who has a

disability living with them or with siblings. But here lie new challenges for parents, who now look after and support children often with severe and multiple disabilities, and who are themselves often facing extreme stresses.

New challenges are also resulting from inclusion. For example, many children with disabilities attend inclusive schools at least to the age of 18 years, but then have no employment in their early adult years, and live lifestyles that are different from their non-disabled peers. This can result in further exclusion as a person ages and this raises major ethical and practical challenges, both for family members and for other professionals.

Because of the increased life expectancy of people with developmental disabilities, a number of new challenges arise in terms of support. First, there are a number of broad professional and ethical questions such as: To achieve a set objective, is a change in policy and practice required that will enable more funding and service support within and for the family home? What are the responsibilities of support personnel in terms of integrating services so that elderly parents can be supported along with the person with a developmental disability? Second, aging parents are often ambivalent about obtaining outside support for their sons and daughters. For example, children with mild and moderate disabilities are often a comfort to them and provide support and help with practical issues such as making beds or carrying shopping. Third, disability services and services for people who are aging are not always coordinated, causing gaps in service. In many instances, this poses economical hardship on families and additional expenses for the departments concerned (Brown, Hong, Shearer, Wang, & Wang, 2010; Jokinen & Brown, 2010).

Points to remember

The preceding discussion focused on setting the scene or context for the work carried out by disability personnel. It is within this complex picture that the chapter discusses disability personnel and their roles, the education and training that are required to support these roles, and the philosophy and values of disability personnel.

Box 3: Challenges Facing Caregivers of Aging Adults with Disabilities

John worked as a frontline service provider for individuals who were aging and had developmental disabilities. In this role, he was expected to arrange for support for individuals who lived in their own homes and who had a range of disabilities — physical, behavioural, and mental disturbance. He worked with a couple whose adult son had an intellectual disability and required support.

After discussions with the family members, it was agreed that John would set out to arrange coordinated support services for all members of the family. However, the local services for aging did not provide services for people with developmental disabilities, so their funds and resources could not be used for the couple's son. Funding problems also arose regarding services for people with disabilities. The frontline community workers funded from each of these services could establish liaisons, but they could not make the best economic use of funds or services because of the separate policy and financial jurisdictions of the services involved.

Disability Personnel and Their Roles

In one sense, disability personnel all do the same thing: they support people with disabilities. They do so, however, in an enormous variety of ways. Many disability personnel still work in specialized units or within services that provide specific disability care. Increasingly, though, disability personnel work in community settings, where the support required for people living with their families, with others, or on their own in the community can cover a wide range of activities. Each of these employment environments has its own knowledge base and methods for obtaining the required support. In addition, disability personnel who work with families and others who support people with disabilities directly must understand the stresses and needs of those people in order to help them provide the best possible support.

The complexity of the roles of disability personnel can seem rather daunting for someone just coming into the field. There are approximately 300 known causes of intellectual and developmental disabilities and knowledge about these, although still quite sparse in some areas, is growing very quickly. Specialized knowledge and skills are increasing rapidly, and support to people with disabilities has extended into areas that were not provided in past decades (e.g., mental health and abnormal behaviour). In addition, there has been a strong emphasis since approximately 1990 on personal development, quality of life, and living a full, holistic lifestyle (see

Brown & Brown, 2003; Schalock et al., 2002). For example, drama, art, and music (Warren, 1988), leisure and recreation (Fidler & Velde, 1999), and spiritual activities (Crompton & Jackson, 2004) are seen to play a role in holistic development, enabling people to be more effective in employment and daily living. Thus, it is increasingly necessary, for disability personnel to know about, and demonstrate competence in, the spectrum of disciplines that address community living, home living, recreation, and employment.

Disability personnel as members of multidisciplinary teams

As a result of this growing complexity, disability personnel often specialize in a particular aspect of disability to respond to the ever-increasing knowledge of disabilities and to meet the wide variety of needs that emerge (see Box 3 for one example). Specialization allows disability personnel to become experts in specific areas (e.g., autism, HIV infection in children, mobility needs) or interventions (e.g., teaching methods, behavioural strategies, psychotherapy), and such expertise is extremely beneficial to a great many people. It also increases the need for multidisciplinary consultation, because teams of specialists often need to be drawn together to provide a full assessment and develop an intervention strategy that is useful to all. Organizations that provide full or partial services to people with disabilities need to facilitate multidisciplinary consultation by including it as part of the role of disability personnel.

Disability personnel and growing independence

The need for multidisciplinary consultation is particularly important because many disability personnel in the early 21st century work largely on their own — they often do not work in the same environment as their manager or other personnel. Their days may be spent visiting and supporting individuals within the individuals' homes, places of employment, or recreation venues. Some disability personnel work in generic services where they are the only "expert" on disability. Increasingly, individuals with disabilities have a part in decisions concerning what work should be carried out, where it is carried out, and the people who are involved. A frontline worker is there to provide support and arrange for services to meet individual needs, through his or her own resources or through available specialized and generic services.

The change in function from traditional institutional settings, such as sheltered workshops and rehabilitation centres, results in some new challenges that, if not met, can result in increased stress for personnel. First, there is a reduced ability to monitor services in traditional ways; thus, new methods of assessing the performance of disability personnel have to be created. Second, community interventions and support also reduce the opportunity of managers to literally see what is happening, and this affects how changes are made to the overall service system. Third, there are frequently reduced opportunities for multidisciplinary consultation. Working on one's own in the community means that disability personnel often must be able to assess and address unexpected situations independently. This increases their need to have broad personal knowledge about disabilities and services that are available. Finally, professional and ethical behaviour of personnel who work in communities needs to be adapted to fit the nature and context of the work that is being done (see Brown & Brown, 2003).

Disability personnel as links to generic services

Increasingly, people with disabilities use generic services, augmented by specialized services, to meet their needs. Disability personnel have an important role to play in connecting people with disabilities to community services that are available to the general population. Part of this role involves identifying the needs of the people with disabilities whom they support, matching those needs with available generic services, assisting people with disabilities to obtain those services, and sharing information and strategies with professionals in generic services so that the work they do will have a stronger likelihood of success.

The use of generic services has advanced in many countries to the point where disability personnel now work within many services that are available to the general population. This is seen especially in some places of employment, many recreation centres, the educational and medical care systems, and increasingly within the mental health systems. Nonetheless, there are many gaps where generic services are not particularly adapted or available to people with developmental disabilities. For example, the links between generic services and disability services for older adults is often poor. Such gaps place stress on disability personnel and, more particularly, on older adults with disabilities and those who care for them. Box 3 gives an example of challenges that arise in the field of geriatric care.

Integrating disability and generic services to address the needs of people with developmental disabilities continues to be a strong aspect of the role of many disability personnel. One aspect of this is to integrate, or at least to coordinate, services for people with various types of disabilities and disadvantages. For example, in South Australia, disability personnel work for various units representing different disability groups, such as people with brain injury, intellectual disability, physical disability, and sensory disability. Many of the services required by these groups are similar, because individuals may have multiple disabilities and because different disabilities may give rise to similar challenges (e.g., adapted housing and home appliances, supported employment, personal and family recreation, social and behaviour support). Integration and coordination of specialized and generic services is being carried out in many developed countries and takes a wide variety of forms.

Box 4: Behavioural Challenges and Residential Placement

Bev has autism and is seven years old. She has been considered to be unmanageable at school, even though she is in a special class. She seems to become calmer when she hears quiet and soothing music. In other situations, she frequently rushes around late at night knocking down or breaking household articles. She also shows uncontrolled behaviour in local shopping centres, often running away then sitting in the middle of a main road. Behavioural intervention has not worked. The family's relatives and friends have suggested full-time residential care where they can visit and have her at home weekends if she stabilizes. The parents need support, for one of them has to stay with Bev all of the time. No family occasions or outings are possible as a family group. Many professionals, whom the family has seen, have indicated that the child should ideally remain at home as this is the most inclusive environment. Others have indicated that living in the community can represent exclusion if neighbours and others become concerned about involvement with the family, an experience reported by many families with children who have severe and multiple disabilities involving behavioural concerns (Brown et al., 2010). What are the issues and what steps would you suggest to rectify the situation in support of the family and Bev and why? What ethical and professional issues are involved?

Disability personnel as support to families

Increasingly, the role of disability personnel is to support people with disabilities living in family homes. In this situation, family members, most often parents, are the main caregivers and thus take on the function as frontline worker. For a number of reasons (see Chapter 4), disability personnel often find themselves working with families and giving support to family members to help them better provide for their family member with the disability.

This trend has led to a realization in the disability field that professionals must understand and recognize the impact of family members on the person with disabilities and the impact of disability on the family (see Turnbull, Brown, & Turnbull, 2004). As reported at a 2005 Roundtable in Quality of Life and Intellectual Disability (an Internal Association for the Scientific Study of Intellectual Disabilities special interest research group) in Vancouver, Canada, one mother stated, "Our family is necessary for our son, as we influence his quality of life. But the opposite is [also] true — our child and his disability affect our family's quality of life." Frequently, the child with a disability is a primary focus of family activities, particularly regarding use of the mother's resources (Renwick & Brown, 1998; Todd et al., 2004). This can frequently result in stresses and strains for all members of the family. This suggests that family quality of life needs to be taken into account when

providing support in order to enhance family well-being and thus the family's ability to support the individual with the disability.

To enhance family well-being effectively, it is necessary for disability personnel to have a clear understanding of a family's needs and to be in a position to deploy funds and provide resources, including counselling and practical support, to foster family capacity. Families' needs have been made abundantly clear in numerous accounts (e.g., see Brown, 2000). Many require a skilled frontline person with whom they can discuss ideas, funds need to be at least partially controlled by family members, and — if families are asked to take the main responsibility for individuals with disabilities — it is necessary for agencies to use financial and personnel resources to support families as a whole. This is particularly important in single-parent families and families facing multiple disabilities or poverty. Reports of family quality of life research from various countries underscore these issues (Brown, 2010; Brown et al., 2010; Brown, Mac Adam-Crisp, Wang, & Iarocci, 2006).

One of the challenges in terms of family support is the devastating effect the birth of a child with severe behavioural and multiple disabilities can have on family life. In extreme cases, it may be important to remove such a child from the family for a period of time in order to stabilize the family situation, although this gives rise to issues over the perception of institutionalization (see Box 4). There

Box 5: Experiences of a Rural Frontline Field Coordinator

My frontline experience was wonderful and I enjoyed it. The experience with clients was amazing. However, the workload was enormous, and I did not feel qualified to deal with some of the situations. I had a lot of clients with intellectual disabilities who had high needs, and in some families the parents were aging. I had a few clients who were very difficult. I had to deal with the issues concerning a woman who committed suicide and another person who gave up eating because she did not wish to continue living. I was sometimes phoned late at night with serious issues and I was 75 kilometers away. I found it all very interesting, but there were just too many crises.

The number of crises seemed to reduce somewhat over time, although crisis relief does not make problems go away. The families still had to face enormous stress and challenge, and many of the families were exhausted.

I found the training I had was extremely important. I had to make a lot of use of it, but I also learned a lot, particularly from my clients. I have now left my position, but understand from the person who has taken over from me that work is still hectic, although the crisis situations are not as numerous. In rural areas, disability personnel do not go to the city very often, and they really have to rely on their own resources. They work together supporting one another and helping one another with particular needs that arise.

Overall, there are too many crises. The workload is enormous. Respite opportunities have improved and they are wonderful, but they are not the whole answer.

Source: This abbreviated commentary is reproduced with permission of Disability Family Services, South Australia, originally recorded in full in the Brown Report (Brown, 2000, pp. 7-8).

are now many examples of such families. If the child is extremely disabled and the family can no longer cope effectively, the existing authorities may indicate that the child must remain in the home so inclusion and normalization can take place, as this is the current policy. In such situations even a casual observer can see that inclusion is not possible. Frequently the child is disruptive at home and in the community and, further, siblings cannot study at home or have their friends visit, and neighbours often withdraw from the family. This is exclusion in an inclusive setting and has to be resolved. The professional and ethical issues are challenging and have to be dealt with at a policy level with input from parents and service organizations. It is inappropriate to expect frontline personnel to deal with these situations on the grounds of inadequate resources (see Brown, 2011).

At a different level, an increasing number of women with developmental disabilities are becoming partners or wives and become pregnant, raising further ethical and professional issues relating to custody and support. Llewellyn, Traustadottir, McConnell, & Bjorg Sigurjonsdottir (2010) have looked at these issues through research and practice, and it is suggested that conventional practices and approaches

need to be revised. The work of these editors and their colleagues indicates that with support such parents can often be effective in child rearing (see Chapter 48 for more information on people with developmental disabilities as parents). It is important to be sure that students and practising professionals are up to date in their knowledge about this area, and that there is a policy framework developed that provides evidence-based guidelines for all relevant service and government departments.

The application of resources in ways that meet the family's perceived needs and enhance family well-being will require greater individualization of services and supports. This may seem to add to the role of disability personnel considerably in the short term but, in the longer term, it may reduce family stresses and benefit family adaptation, thereby leading to a better life for both people with disabilities and their families.

Disability personnel in urban and rural areas

Many disability personnel work in urban areas where the number of needs of the people they support, and types of services and resources that these people require, are very broad. Others work in isolated conditions, where they essentially have to carry out all needed work themselves. Box 5, which describes the experiences of a rural worker in Australia but is highly applicable to work in rural Ontario, provides an excellent example of this.

Disability personnel as advocates for policy change

Disability personnel have always had — and continue to have — important roles in informing policy makers of needed changes and to holding them accountable to the decisions that are made. This need appears to be more important now than ever, because of the increasing number of facets to the roles of disability personnel and the growing complexity of systems of services and supports. There is a need to recognize which services are not available, not accessible, or not appropriate to the specific needs of people with disabilities and their families, and then to make this known. Such vigilance should be carried out with knowledge of individuals' rights and entitlements (see Chapters 5 and 6). The overall goal of this aspect of the role of disability personnel is to ensure that policy makers are able to set a context in which effective supports are possible and, as a consequence, that those with developmental disabilities are able to lead the best life possible.

Education and Training of Disability Personnel

As we have learned in the preceding sections, disability personnel require a sound professional knowledge of disability, an understanding of the ways in which the needs of people with disabilities are changing, familiarity with the available and needed resources associated with these changes, and a practical knowledge of "what to do" that is learned in training and on the job. Education at a higher educational institution, blended with ongoing training and supervised experience, provides this knowledge.

Higher education

In Ontario, specific training in developmental disabilities is provided through a number of commu-nity colleges. The Developmental Services Worker program is the most direct form of specialized college education, but people in programs in related fields, such as early childhood education, education support, child and youth support, community services, social services, social work, nursing, and others also sometimes become disability professionals. For a complete list of Ontario community colleges and their programs see the More Resources section at the end of this chapter.

Some disability personnel have university education that relates directly to their field. In Ontario, Ryerson Polytechnic University, Brock University, and York University have programs specific to disability and disability studies, while others (e.g., McMaster University, Queen's University, and University of Western Ontario) have a focus on disability within related departments. Special Education is included in all university education programs. Virtually all Ontario universities have faculty within various departments who teach and do research in disability, while numerous other faculty include aspects of disability in their courses. Many professionals who become full-time disability personnel, or who include disability in their work, have received higher education in disability in this way through disciplines such as medicine, sociology, psychology, social work, nursing, education, physiotherapy, occupational therapy, audiology, counselling, and psychotherapy. Having received a first degree or diploma in these fields, however, does not guarantee expertise for the field of developmental disabilities. In one Australian study (Brown, 2000), the frontline personnel (options coordinators who worked in all areas of disability and were responsible for providing support and integrating services for the individual with a disability) had among them more than 50 different qualifications. In these cases, additional training in developmental disability is required. Such situations can and do arise in Ontario.

Regarding personnel recruitment, there is not always coordination between organizations that provide support to people with disabilities and universities and colleges that prepare people for such careers. As a consequence, there are often not enough front-line workers available for service agencies to employ,

Box 6: Employers Need to Understand Skills and Knowledge of Disability Personnel

It is essential that employers are well aware of the skill and knowledge requirements for frontline positions. This may seem obvious, but experience shows that directors of services may have little knowledge or understanding of the demands and skills required of individual disability personnel at the frontline level. For example, there are sometimes directors of services who have little idea of the stresses and challenges faced by such personnel, although other directors recognize this gap in knowledge and make it their job to track and work alongside frontline personnel on a daily basis for a period of time to gain a practical knowledge of the challenges involved.

and incentives to specialize in developmental disability are not always provided to potential professionals (e.g., physicians, dentists, lawyers, psychologists, psychotherapists) who might develop special knowledge and training. Challenges for the field include developing effective methods for engaging institutions of higher learning in planning for the future needs of people with disabilities and engaging a variety of professions in helping to train new specialists who will be able to meet the needs.

Ongoing training

There is a strong need for ongoing training of disability personnel because of the wide variation in education, the need for broad-based education to meet new developments in the disabilities field, and the increase in individualized and community-based supports and services. There is no guarantee, even in Ontario where opportunities to receive education in developmental disabilities are readily available, that new entrants to the field will have special knowledge about disabilities. There is also no guarantee that disability personnel who already work in the field will receive ongoing training, although it is needed. The needs of disability personnel, whatever they are, should be clearly recognized by those who employ them (see Box 6).

There are many ways to provide and receive ongoing training. Some of these are formal (e.g., courses that earn credits) and others are less formal. The most common forms of training, all available in Ontario, are listed below.

- In-service training is often provided by service organizations, especially for their own employees, volunteers, and family members of people they support. These may take many forms, such as workshops, visits, lectures, various presentations, specific skill learning, or involvement in day-to-day work. In-service training often is not mandatory or related to accreditation for practice, but it is sometimes required by service organizations to improve the skill and knowledge levels of disability personnel.
- Enrichment courses and workshops of various types are run by disability consultants or disability-related organizations.
- Training events are offered periodically by the Ontario Ministry of Community and Social Services, the Ontario Ministry of Education, and the Ontario Ministry of Children and Youth Services.
- Ontario colleges and universities periodically offer special training workshops and lectures on topics in developmental disabilities.
- Developmental disability conferences are offered in Ontario every year. Of particular note is the annual conference of the Ontario Association on Developmental Disabilities, which includes its popular Research Special Interest Group day.
- Numerous national and international conferences, usually sponsored by professional organizations, are held each year. Many of these provide those attending with official letters of attendance, which may be recognized as training credits, and are offered in a number of cities in Ontario on a regular basis (e.g., Hamilton: Stages of Autism Conference).
- Certificate and degree-level part-time programs are available at many local colleges and universities. Some of these are available as extension or electronic courses, and video–communication workshops have become increasingly used since the 1990s. In particular, distance and distributed education is providing oppor-

tunities at all levels from interest courses in disabilities through undergraduate and graduate programs. A number of these courses are online and can be taken through the Internet. An advantage of these courses is that they can involve students from a variety of regions and from a variety of academic backgrounds, who can share their experiences and ideas. One challenge in distance learning is the requirement for supervision in a practicum setting. Supervision remains an important challenge and needs consideration in terms of policy at government, university and college levels not least because the development of distance learning sometimes diminishes the opportunities for appropriate supervision in the field, giving rise to major professional and ethical challenges. For example, supervision in the field should reflect the learning that has taken place through on-line courses. Typically, such courses provide a clear understanding of the role of disability personnel. They are embedded in a clearly stated ethical paradigm and cover a wide range of practical issues such as home care, signs of health and illness, and abuse and neglect. They usually also stress the need for professional standards, effective practice, and advocacy.

- Disability texts and journals are widely available in university and college libraries and from publishers that specialize in disability.
- Various societies for intellectual disabilities, some of which focus on a disability type, also provide formal training packages. For example, in the United Kingdom, the Down Syndrome Educational Trust continues to prepare books for professionals and parents. These books are 25–60 pages in length and address state-of-the-art practice, opportunities and experiences, and the application of research to practice (see http://www.downsed.org). Other groups provide detailed information on line and also include some published articles that can be downloaded from their web sites.
- Less formally, most workplaces provide computers with Internet access for looking up needed information. The Internet contains a wealth of information about a variety of disability-related topics. In fact, one of the simplest and most cost effective methods of training is to make computers available and to provide workshops on how to retrieve information from the Internet. However, sites vary in standard, accuracy, and breadth of information.

Supervised experience

As the preceding sections demonstrate, professional training needs to take place at different levels and at different times. Furthermore, because of ongoing changes in the field of developmental disabilities, the need for ongoing training of disability personnel never ceases. Yet, neither of these can take the place of on-the-job experience. All disability personnel, no matter what their formal education and ongoing training, grow enormously in their professional capacity by learning on the job. This is especially the case when practical work is supervised in a way that focuses on building the skills and knowledge of disability personnel. The importance of learning the numerous "tricks of the trade" cannot be overstated. The following areas of practical learning are among the most important for working with people who have developmental disabilities:

- Understanding of current trends and philosophies in disability, as well as ability to apply these to relationships involving people with disabilities
- Knowledge about the causes and characteristics of disabilities
- Facility in communicating effectively with people with disabilities
- Familiarity with resources and other sources of support (professional and nonprofessional)
- Ability to effectively form liaisons with family members
- Expertise in managing relationships with people with disabilities in ways that respect their choices and points of view
- Capacity to foster, and work within, a multidisciplinary team

For students who are required to gain practical experience as part of their course work, and for volunteers who do practical work for personal development, it is essential to select a disability organization that supports their training needs well. Characteristics of such organizations are that they:

- Allocate sufficient time to pass on information
- Demonstrate numerous practical ways of supporting people with disabilities
- Have the capacity to demonstrate effective programs
- Illustrate, through their practices, professional values and ethics
- Provide meaningful opportunities to develop skills and knowledge
- Represent current thinking and philosophy, without being overly dogmatic
- Respect people with disabilities and allow for their reasonable self-determination

Challenges for education and training

Providing education and training to current and future disability personnel is not without challenges. Six critical challenges are outlined below.

1. *How should disability personnel be educated and trained?* There is a wide variety of educational programs for students and ongoing training courses for professionals. Yet, in Ontario, as is the case elsewhere, poor salary levels relative to other segments of society result in shortages of both frontline practitioners and other disability professionals who have specific training, at the very time when it is becoming all the more important to have well-trained practitioners. There often are crises in finding qualified staff to provide support for persons with developmental disabilities. In many regions, the response to this need has been to hire frontline practitioners who have little formal training. This has led to community service providers coining the phrase "two feet and a heartbeat" to refer to the fact that they may have to take anyone "standing and breathing" off the street to work in the field (Crocker & Cran, 2010). The dilemma for service provider organizations is whether to provide personnel who do not have as much training as desired to meet their need for sup-

port, or to provide too few trained personnel who cannot meet all the support needs of the people with disabilities.

2. *What is the best way to provide support?* Approaches to, and beliefs about, how to support people with developmental disabilities differ somewhat among disability personnel and sometimes across regions of Ontario. An ongoing challenge to our field is how to understand current philosophical trends and exemplary evidence-based practice, and to communicate these effectively through education and training. In Ontario, the Ontario Association on Developmental Disabilities (OADD) is addressing this challenge by hosting an annual conference, by publishing the *Journal on Developmental Disabilities* and the textbook *Developmental Disabilities in Ontario*, and by the sponsoring of three special interest groups — the Research Special Interest Group (RSIG), the Developmental Services Special Interest Group (DSSIG), and the Great Lakes Society (GLS), which promotes the interests of people with developmental disabilities and their families. The OADD also has an awards and scholarship program for recognizing committed professionals and students. For more information about the OADD and its activities, see the OADD website (OADD, n.d.).

3. *What is the relationship between knowledge and effective support?* Even if disability personnel are trained adequately, having knowledge of disability does not guarantee effective support. Perhaps the key is to recognize that increased understanding has forced the field to view disabilities in a complex of interacting and changing dynamics, and it is this knowledge — put into practice by frontline professionals and recognized and supported by policy makers — that can ensure effective and comprehensive delivery of optimum services. Thus, the word multidisciplinary necessarily takes on wider meaning, since these changes tend to increase the variability of service delivery and support. It is necessary to make support services more versatile and wider reaching.

4. *What is the role of disability personnel and other professionals in advocacy?* Some people have questioned whether professionals can be advocates, given that they work for particular organizations and represent specific knowledge and views (Jackson, 2004). The defense counsel in a trial relating to sterilization of people with intellectual disabilities asked the chapter author if he was essentially an advocate (rather than an unbiased professional). The author's reply was that all effective professionals needed to be advocates for their clients. The important point is not to assume that what one knows and practises is necessarily the best that can be provided. Advocates who represent the views of a client need to be respected whether or not they come from a professional base. All knowledge and concern should emerge from listening respectively to advocates' ideas. However, it is equally essential to recognize that one is serving the individual, the family, or one's service agency. There are occasions where one has to decide where loyalties and interests lie. In such circumstances, it may be necessary to ensure that there are others who represent the views and concerns of interested parties who have a legitimate stake in proceedings. Basic knowledge about advocacy procedures is therefore critical (see Gray & Jackson, 2001).

5. *How can those in the field plan adequately for the future?* Any forecast for service development must recognize ongoing changes in the field of developmental disability and predict those that are likely to occur in the future. It is the lack of forward planning that causes concern and worry in many communities — for example, as older parents wonder what will happen to their children with disabilities (see Jokinen & Brown, 2005). This is a challenge for policy and service development, but the lack of adequately trained frontline personnel puts pressure on the disability system as well as on families, which then taxes the resources of the practitioners who are currently involved.

6. *The web: what are the ethical challenges arising?* The web is able to provide a wide range of information on developmental disabilities ranging from incidence of particular conditions, genetics, environmental issues, challenging behaviours and many more. The issues relate in part to the accuracy of information and the way students and practitioners use the information. Many web sites are set up by reliable sources. These include many disability associations, universities and government departments. However, it is important when using research information that individuals check the sources and cite them in any presentation or written material. It is important that those quoting from web sites do their best to ensure the validity of the information. Three reliable examples are provided. All three provide information about disabilities and provide access to downloading in many instances.

- Down Syndrome Education International
  http://www.downsed.org/en/gb/default.aspx
- The Allan Roeher Centre library listing
  http://orlabs.oclc.org/identities/lccn–n96–9038
- International Encyclopedia of Rehabilitation, CIRRIE International Research Information University of Buffalo
  http://cirrie.buffalo.edu/encyclopedia/index.php

Philosophy and Values of Disability Personnel

A critical aspect of working in the field of disabilities is the development of each employee's professional values. These underlie the nature of the relationships that disability personnel have with individuals with disabilities; in turn, they determine the nature of the work that is done. Professional philosophy changes somewhat over time, but it needs to be laid on solid value foundations that should be discussed during education and training and when disability personnel are interviewed for potential employment. Professional values are closely tied to ethics and professional judgment; thus, in the discussion that follows, readers will note a definite overlap.

Vignettes of challenging situations

A clear professional value system is especially important when disability personnel are up against crises or find situations that challenge their own personal values and philosophy (Brown, 1997). The following five vignettes, taken from the work of disability personnel, illustrate some of the issues and concerns personnel face involving their professional values (see Brown & Brown, 2003, for additional examples). These vignettes demonstrate that there are not always simple answers. Readers are invited to think what they might do in each of the cases described and to discuss their ideas with colleagues or classmates. Sometimes individual client choices conflict with service rules and regulations. Other times, a professional's response may not support current laws and policies, although it may support strongly-held personal views.

Often, disability personnel face the dilemmas described in the vignettes below when they work in relative isolation, and they need to make the best judgments possible with little direct supervision. The foundation for making such judgments should be the development of an effective professional values system and professional philosophy, with clear demarcation between professional and private views. This may involve many parties — disability personnel; other professionals; people with disabilities; and advocates, including, as necessary, the public advocate (a formal, paid position within a province). In addition, policy makers and those who develop the regulations and rules that guide services must be included. For this reason, ongoing training in professional values and ethics needs to be part of the work of all disability personnel, particularly frontline practitioners, and needs to be updated on a regular basis.

Vicky and Dan: Vicky was a support worker in a centre-based day program that encouraged people to obtain work in the community. One person she supported, Dan, wanted to get what he described as "a real man's job." He was 25 years old and had sound social skills. Dan's mother made it clear that she did not wish Dan to be placed in employment. She said that she did not think he could hold down

a job and that if he had a full time job, he would lose his disability pension. If he failed at work, he would then have to start applying for disability pension all over again. Vicky believed that Dan had a right to choose, but was not sure how to deal with his mother's forceful views.

The questions arising from this story are numerous. Where do Vicky's loyalties lie? Should she accept the mother's views or Dan's wishes? Dan is an adult, and according to Ontario law, Dan's mother does not have legal responsibility for him. She has a mother's interests and concern and fears that if things go wrong, she may be left to deal with the resulting financial situation. Now imagine that the manager of the day program says the agency must support the mother at all costs, as the family has given a major donation to the centre. What should Vicky do?

Arthur and George: Arthur is a community support worker. He has strong religious views about marriage and the need for a wedding before people live together. A young man he supports, George, wants to live with his girlfriend, who also has a disability. George has requested help from Arthur to help to bring this about, as he knows cooperation will be needed between the two agencies from which he and his girlfriend get support. Arthur feels, on religious grounds, that he cannot agree with this partnership.

Arthur has various options. He could decline to assist George, discuss his situation and beliefs with George, consult his manager, or request another support worker to take over. What would you advise Arthur do in this situation?

Ann and Eva: Eva, a young woman with a developmental disability, is pregnant. Ann, a doctor at a medical clinic, does not tell Eva that her unborn child has Down syndrome. Ann believes Eva would request an abortion. Ann is strongly opposed to abortion, which she believes is highly immoral. She wishes to protect Eva from facing a decision involving abortion.

The issues identified in this story, and similar issues, raise the potential difference between personal and professional value systems and personal and professional philosophy. Ann may be breaking policies set by her employer and her profession, but she believes that her religious views should take precedence. In other countries or regions, Ann may not be breaking laws or policies and may, in fact, be supporting them. Nonetheless, the question of the right to withhold information is still problematic. The question is how disability personnel can comfortably separate their personal and professional philosophy and value systems, should there be a conflict between the two.

Sometimes, the personal views of a professional may be consistent with those of an organization and the individual with a disability. For example, if Eva herself had strong views against abortion, and the organization where she lived and was supported held similar values, everyone's views may well have been consistent. Thus, there would be no dilemma, although withholding information would at least remain a concern on both social and behavioural grounds. Suppose, however, that despite prevailing beliefs, Eva did not want to continue the pregnancy. Whose views should prevail?

Disability personnel need to separate personal and professional value systems, and this often takes place on the job. Such separation is becoming even more challenging because field workers do not always have other professionals working closely with them who understand, or are knowledgeable about, the exact circumstances. This is another reason why new personnel need internship periods under the supervision of professionals, as these senior and more experienced colleagues can offer modelling.

Two other issues presented by this vignette are: 1) the potential for development of self–image through decision making and exercising personal choice based on impartial information, and 2) the need for independent advocacy. Apparently, Ann did not consider the possibility of asking for outside assistance through an advocate. In turn, Eva loses an opportunity to learn from her experience, understand that actions have consequences, and further develop her problem-solving skills. How might Ann have handled this situation differently? Remember to consider that people with developmental disabilities have different and various skill levels for making and following through on their own decisions.

John and Tyler: John has a severe physical disability and a mild intellectual disability. He does not want to work and prefers to wander the streets downtown in his city. He often leaves his group home at night, and in the past has become involved with drugs through the people he meets on the street, where he sometimes sleeps. There have been suggestions that he has been asked to carry drugs, and police have warned him on several occasions. John says it is his right to choose how he lives. The agency says that for John to stay in the group home where he lives, he must abide by the group home rules relating to permission to sleep away from the home and to keep within the law. Yet, John's care worker, Tyler, believes John has the right to choose for himself.

In this situation, John's views and needs, society's requirements, and agency requirements are in conflict. Yet, Tyler is left to try to sort out the conflict. Clearly, Tyler has his own point of view, but he has to answer to other people and agencies. What are Tyler's options? How much time will he have to spend resolving the conflict rather than simply helping John? The answers to such questions are neither simple nor clear at first glance.

Staff Attending a Workshop: At a workshop on sexual and personal development of people with developmental disabilities, disability personnel were provided with examples of employment experiences and jobs for people with disabilities. They were also provided with examples of personal activities in relation to partnership and marriage. Disability personnel appeared able to accept people with disabilities working in a wide range of skilled and unskilled jobs. When it came to personal and sexual matters, though, they sometimes made remarks such as, "I would not want my son or daughter doing that."

Why did disability personnel accept employment options for people with developmental disabilities but not options for family and sexual development? One explanation is that because these disability personnel were well trained in employment activities, they used a professional base for their judgement. When it came to more personal activities, they referred to a personal base because they lacked professional-level experience and knowledge in this area. Emotional and personal experience dominated their thinking.

Table 2: Operationalizing and Sorting Values and Philosophy

How do you feel and think as 1) a private citizen, and 2) a professional, in relation to the following:

- *People with developmental disabilities in general*
- *The right of people with any disability to be included in society*
- *Discrimination against people with disabilities*
- *Euthanasia for people who are getting very old and who have developmental disabilities*
- *Sterilizing a person with a developmental disability, without his or her consent, 1) when there is no previous aberrant sexual behaviour, or 2) when there is a record of previous and serious aberrant sexual behaviour*
- *Working with people who have developmental disabilities*
- *The language used to describe persons with disabilities*
- *Being in the company of an individual with profound physical and intellectual disabilities at a party*
- *Having a person with a disability as a friend*
- *Having a person with a disability as a relative*
- *Having your child in a class with someone who has a severe developmental disability*
- *Having your child in a class with someone who has both an emotional and intellectual disability*
- *Having an adolescent or adult child becoming serious about a partnership with someone who has a disability*
- *Having an adult child with or without a developmental disability using an escort service*

There is also a possibility that even disability personnel hold long-held prejudices about what people with disabilities should and should not do. Moreover, there are parallel issues that exist in many societies, such as sterilization of people with disabilities, ease of obtaining an abortion, and euthanasia for people with disabilities. New issues are also on the horizon, such as the impact of genetic engineering and the right to give birth to individuals with disabilities. Moreover, there are other issues that are beyond the day-to-day concerns of advocates, such as the judicial court rulings in relation to doubtful confessions from individuals with developmental disabilities who are accused of crimes. Thinking more broadly, many of the issues make it necessary to re-evaluate the definition of disability and how an ever-changing society should respond to it (see Brown & Brown, 2003). When living in multi-racial and multi-religious communities, as many people in Ontario do, these issues become much more challenging and sometimes more confusing (Keith & Schalock, 2000).

Self-analysis of personal and professional values

The preceding vignettes illustrate several instances in which ethical dilemmas arise for disability personnel. It is clearly important that personal and professional value systems must be in place for making judgements in such cases. Yet, it is also clear that personal and professional value systems do not always fit together. It is helpful for disability personnel to undertake self-analysis of their personal and professional views and to determine strategies to follow when there is a conflict or when there is not a perfect match. Considering the topics presented in Table 2 is one method of undertaking such self-analysis to sort out these values.

Characteristics of disability personnel who have effective values systems

Professional values are put into practice through the behaviour of disability personnel. Putting such values into practice is easier for some people than it is for others because of their personal and professional characteristics. Disability service organizations might look for favourable characteristics as criteria in hiring new employees. Perhaps more importantly, however, they should provide ongoing training to help employees develop the characteristics of effective disability personnel.

The personal characteristics that are frequently considered helpful, if not necessary, include (Brown & Brown, 2003, p. 214):

- Ability to differentiate personal values and needs from client values and needs
- Creativity
- Emotional energy to change the environment
- Flexibility
- Innovation
- Patience
- Sense of humor
- Stamina
- Strong and positive values related to people in need
- Understanding of own values, attitudes, and beliefs
- Warm and supportive personality

The professional characteristics that are typically considered important include the ability to do the following (Brown & Brown, 2003, pp. 214–215):

- Accept a variety of lifestyles and different options
- Advocate effectively for those they support
- Assess their own professional and personal strengths and abilities and determine when they need to seek outside assistance
- Assume some risks
- Discuss challenges and problems impartially
- Feel comfortable letting others, especially people with disabilities, assume control
- Make decisions regarding difficult ethical issues
- Separate personal choice (i.e., the choices they would make for themselves or within their family) from the choices made by the people they support
- Solve problems in a constructive way
- Work well as a member of a team

Need for sound professional skills

Personal and professional values cannot be operationalized effectively unless an individual has a sound knowledge base and sound professional skills to put the values into place. Table 3 outlines some of these knowledge and skill requirements; it should be recognized that new knowledge constantly emerges and expands the list. Such skills are often incorporated into formal education courses and into both formal and informal training, although many may need to be expanded. The disability field is evolving, and it seems likely that both knowledge about disabilities and the ways of effectively supporting people with disabilities will continue to expand quickly. Disability personnel need not only to develop sound professional skills but also to recognize that such skills need to be upgraded continuously. This is important for policy makers, directors of services, professionals who only do part of their work with people who have disabilities, and many others. Yet, it is most important for frontline disability personnel who daily support people with disabilities, for their roles hold an immense amount of influence — and thus responsibility — at the personal level.

Summary

People who work in the field of developmental disabilities do a wide variety of work. Some directly support people with disabilities while others are in professions that support people with disabilities as part of their work. This chapter collectively refers to such people as *disability personnel*. Of all disability personnel, frontline practitioners have an especially important role, because they work most closely with people who have disabilities.

The work of disability personnel has become more complex since approximately the 1990s, because knowledge of disability is expanding at a fast rate, and because the approach to services and supports has changed a great deal. For these and other reasons, formal education, ongoing training, and on-the-job training are all important. Disability personnel may have formal education in their specific field or in any one of numerous related disciplines.

Table 3: Knowledge and Skills Base

Knowledge base includes, but is not limited to

- *Clinical knowledge of disabilities*
- *Knowledge about family systems, dynamics, and issues*
- *Knowledge about the development of services*
- *Knowledge of community and environmental factors that contribute to disabling conditions*
- *Knowledge of community services and supports available*
- *Knowledge of language development and common problems associated with language and speech*
- *Knowledge of learning principles*
- *Knowledge of legislation related to disability*
- *Knowledge of life-span development, including early life, transitions, and aging*
- *Knowledge of multicultural concerns*
- *Knowledge of quality of life principles*
- *Knowledge of social and emotional development*
- *Knowledge of the main approaches to treatment and intervention*
- *Understanding of the long-term nature of working with people with disabilities*

Skills that relate to professional practice strategies include

- *Ability to judge issues for the best results*
- *Appropriate interviewing skills*
- *Basic knowledge and understanding of policy and management processes*
- *Effective counselling skills based on eclectic counselling theory and practice*
- *Effective interpersonal communication and collaboration skills*
- *Effective observation skills*
- *Effective verbal and writing skills*
- *Effective teaching strategies*
- *Effective time-management skills*
- *Organizational and coordination skills*
- *Skills in understanding the perspective of others*

Skills that are supplementary, and in some situations critical, include

- *Knowledge about local community access and challenges*
- *Knowledge about when to make referrals and suggest alternative methods*
- *Knowledge of possibilities associated with adaptive and technical aids*
- *Specialized knowledge in specific disability areas*

Source: Brown, I., & Brown, R. I. (2003, pp. 212-213).

Because of shortages of trained personnel, frontline practitioners are sometimes hired without formal education in disability. As a result, specific disability training is usually required for new employees.

When carrying out their work, disability personnel encounter a number of challenges, which they sometimes have to face and solve on their own or with little direct supervision. To help guide disability personnel in making wise judgments, professional values and ethics should be part of their education and ongoing training. Clear guidelines for what to do in cases where professional values and personal values conflict, or when professional values and employer policies conflict, need to be in place for disability personnel to function effectively. Professional values are manifested through particular characteristics, which disability service organizations might look for when hiring employees and might provide training for to develop desired skills in existing employees.

For Further Thought and Discussion

1. Critically examine your personal values about people with disabilities, then examine how they might contrast or support your developing professional values and philosophy.

2. Examine your knowledge base and consider what additional knowledge and skills you require to become effective within the disability services field. List the courses and specific training that you require, and see which colleges and universities best respond to your perceived needs.

3. Given your knowledge and experience, consider how you will ensure you maintain up-to-date knowledge and expertise in your chosen field?

4. What strategies and tactics do you need to develop to act as a change agent, encouraging the services with which you have contact to develop and take on board new ideas and systems?

5. Some people do not believe that restricted financial resources alone are the major barriers to advances in support for people with disabilities. Consider which issues are most important when funding is limited. What strategies could

be used to advance support for people with disabilities when funding is limited?

6. Consider some critical ethical issues in the field of developmental disabilities, and examine how they might be resolved.

More Resources

Community Colleges in Ontario
http://www.canadian–universities.net/Community-Colleges/Ontario.html

Disability Studies Programs, Courses, Schools and Degrees in Ontario Universities
http://www.canadian–universities.net/Universities/Programs/Disability_Studies–Ontario.html

Ontario Ministry of Community and Social Services
http://www.mcss.gov.on.ca/en/mcss/index.aspx

Special Needs Ontario Window (University of Toronto)
http://snow.utoronto.ca/

Ontario Association on Developmental Disabilities
http://www.oadd.org/

Community and Rehabilitation Studies, University of Calgary
http://www.ucalgary.ca/pubs/calendar/current/md–3.html

Down Syndrome Education International
downsed.org/en/gb/default.aspx

References

Bigby, C. (Ed.). (2004). *Ageing with a lifelong disability: A guide to practice, program and policy issues for human services professionals.* London: Jessica Kingsley Publishers.

Brown, I. (2010). Family quality of life: A comparison of trends in eights countries. In. V. Prasher (Ed.), *Contemporary issues in intellectual disabilities* (pp. 255-264). New York: Nova Publishers.

Brown, I., & Brown, R. I. (2003). *Quality of life and disability: An approach for community practitioners.* London: Jessica Kingsley Publishers.

Brown, R. I. (1997). Quality of life and professional

education. In R. I. Brown (Ed.), *Quality of life for people with disabilities* (pp. 310–326). Cheltenham, United Kingdom: Stanley Thornes.

Brown, R. I. (2000). *Evaluation of options co-ordination: Report to the Minister for Disability Services from the Committee on the Evaluation of Quality Services for People with Disabilities.* Adelaide, Australia: Government of South Australia.

Brown, R. I. (2004). Life for adults with Down syndrome: An overview. In R. I. Brown (Series Ed.), *Down Syndrome Issues and Information (DSii) Adult Living series.* Portsmouth, United Kingdom: Down Syndrome Educational Trust.

Brown, R. I., (2011). Quality of life: Dimensions, perceptions and practice. In R. Jackson (Ed.), *Camphill: Changes & challenges.* Edinburgh: Floris Book.

Brown, R. I., Hong, K., Shearer, J., Wang, M., & Wang, S. (2010). Family quality of life in several countries: Results and discussion of satisfaction in families where there is a child with a disability. In R. Kober (Ed.), *Enhancing the quality of life of people with intellectual disability: From theory to practice* (pp. 377-400). Dordrecht, The Netherlands: Springer.

Brown, R. I., Macadam Crisp, J., Wang, M., & Iarocci, G. (2006). Family quality of life where there is a child with a developmental disability? *Journal of Policy and Practice in Intellectual Disabilities,* 3(4), 238–245.

Crocker, C., & Cran, S. (2010). Two feet and a heart beat: The Canadian professional identity crisis in community disability services. *Journal on Developmental Disabilities,* change to 16(3), 60-67.

Crompton, M., & Jackson, R. (2004). Spiritual well-being of adults with Down syndrome. *Adult Series: Down Syndrome issues and information.* Portsmouth, United Kingdom: Down Syndrome Educational Trust.

Emerson, E., Robertson, J., & Wood, J. (2005). Emotional and behavioural needs of children and adolescents with intellectual disabilities in an urban conurbation. *Journal of Intellectual Disability Research,* 49, 16–24.

Fidler, G. S., & Velde, B. P. (Eds.). (1999). A*ctivities: Reality and symbol.* Thorofare, NJ: Slack.

Fudge Shormans, A., & Brown, I. (2002). An investigation into the characteristics of the maltreatment of children with developmental disabilities and the alleged perpetrators of this maltreatment. *Journal on Developmental Disabilities,* 9(1), 1–19.

Gray, B., & Jackson, R. (Eds.). (2001). *Advocacy and learning disability.* London: Jessica Kingsley Publishers.

Jackson, R. (2004). Advocacy and adults with Down syndrome. *Downs Syndrome Issues and Information.* Portsmouth, United Kingdom: Down Syndrome Education International.

James, T. N., & Brown, R. I. (1993). *Prader–Willi syndrome: Quality of life issues in home, school and community.* London: Chapman & Hall.

Janicki, M. T., & Ansello, E. F. (Eds.). (2000). *Community supports for aging adults with   lifelong disabilities.* Baltimore: Paul H. Brookes Publishing Co.

Jokinen, N., & Brown, R. I. (2005). Family quality of life from the perspective of older parents. *Journal of Intellectual Disability Research,* 49(10), 789–793.

Keith, K. D., & Schalock, R. L. (Eds.). (2000). *Cross cultural perspectives on quality of life.* Washington, DC: American Association on Mental Retardation.

Llewellyn, G., Traustadottir, R., McConnell, D., & Bjorg Sigurjonsdottir, H. B., (Eds.). (2010). *Parents with intellectual disabilities: Past, present and future.* Oxford: Wiley–Blackwell.

McConkey, R., O'Toole, B., & Mariga, L. (1999). Educating teachers in developing countries about disabilities. *Exceptionality Education Canada,* 9(1&2), 15–38.

Ontario Association on Developmental Disabilities (OADD). (n.d.). Retrieved from *http://oadd. org/index.php?page=17*

Prasher, V. P., & Janicki, M. P. (Eds.). (2002). *Physical health of adults with intellectual disabilities.* Oxford: Blackwell Publishing.

Renwick, R., & Brown, I. (1998). *The Family Quality of Life Project. Report to Developmental Services Branch, Ontario Ministry of Community and Social Services.* Toronto, ON: University of Toronto, Faculty of Social Work.

Roundtable in Quality of Life and Intellectual Disability. (2005, April). IASSID–SIRG roundtable on quality of life. Vancouver, BC, Canada.

Schalock, R. L., Brown, I., Brown, R. I., Cummins, R. A., Felce, D., Matikka, L., Keith, K., & Parmenter, T. (2002). Conceptualization, measurement and application. Of quality of life for persons with intellectual disabilities. Results of an international panel of experts. *Mental Retardation*, 40, 457–470.

Temple, V., Drummond, C., Valiquette, S., & Jozsvai, E. (2010). A comparison of intellectual assessments over video conferencing and in-person for individuals with ID: Preliminary data. *Journal of Intellectual Disability Research*, 54(6), 573–577.

Timmons, V. (1999). Quality of life of teenagers from Mi'kmaq descent. *Exceptionality Education Canada*, 9(1&2), 5–14.

Todd, S., Young, P., Shearn, J., & Jones, S. (2004). Family quality of life in Wales. In A. Turnbull, I. Brown, & H.R. Turnbull (Eds.), *Families and people with mental retardation and quality of life: International perspectives* (pp. 103–150). Washington, DC: American Association on Mental Retardation.

Turnbull, A., Brown, I., & Turnbull, H. R. (Eds.). (2004). *Families and people with mental retardation and quality of life: International perspectives.* Washington, DC: American Association on Mental Retardation.

Walsh, P. N., & Heller, T. (Eds.). (2002). *Health of women with intellectual disabilities.* Oxford, United Kingdom: Blackwell Publishing.

Warren, B. (1988). *Disability and social performance: Using drama to achieve successful 'acts of being.'* Cambridge, MA: Brookline Books.

Wolfensberger, W. (1972). N*ormalization: The principle of normalization in human services.* Toronto, ON: National Institute on Mental Retardation.

World Health Organization. (1997). ICIDH-2: International Classification of Impairments, Activities, and Participation: A manual of dimensions of disablement and functioning. Geneva: Author.

Part IV

Health and Developmental Disabilities

30

Ethical Issues Relating to Consent in Providing Treatment and Care

John Heng and William F. Sullivan

What you will learn:

- Similarities and differences between legal and ethical approaches to consent
- Why consent is important
- What informed and voluntary consent means in ethics
- Why some people with developmental disabilities have difficulty giving or withholding consent in particular situations
- What supported decision making means and when it is appropriate
- Skills needed by care providers to address ethical issues surrounding consent

Understanding the Term Consent in Ethics

This chapter discusses consent in the health care of people with developmental disabilities. Although the basic legal requirements for consent to treatment and care in Ontario are reviewed, the chapter's focus is on ethical issues, particularly those that arise from applying the law to people with developmental disabilities. In Ontario, the *Mental Health Act* (1990), *Powers of Attorney Act* (1990), *Substitute Decisions Act* (1992), *Health Care Consent Act* (1996), *Personal Health Information Protection Act* (2004), together with their amendments and regulations, are the principal legislation relating to health care consent

(McKelvey, 2011). (For additional details on consent to health care in Ontario, see Chapter 6.)

Distinguishing legal and ethical approaches to consent

The focus of care providers in obtaining consent from people with developmental disabilities or their authorized substitute decision maker is very often placed only on fulfilling legal requirements and documenting implied or expressed consent. In these cases, ethical issues tend to be overlooked.

There are significant areas of overlap between a legal and an ethical approach to health care consent, but there also are differences. First, the legislation mentioned above mainly focuses on consent to treatment and care, or the disclosure and use of health information. However, ethical issues arise in many other areas requiring consent that might have an impact on a person with a developmental disability's health status, such as living and employment conditions, relationships, and sexuality (Eastgate, 2005; Evans, 1997; Robertson et al., 2001). Second, laws on consent are general rules that apply to a broad class of circumstances. Ethics concerns the basis of our judgments about what is the best thing to do in particular circumstances. It might happen that what generally meets a legal standard might be in conflict with an ethical duty in a particular circumstance, such as the avoidance of a harm in that situation. Third, laws on consent typically emphasize the capacity of people to understand and judge factual information before making choices. Ethics goes beyond the law to consider what it means for persons to choose based on personal preferences and values, including those shared with their community, such as cultural or religious beliefs. Fourth, the laws and regulations in Ontario apply an all-or-none criterion for determining capacity to consent: either a person is capable of consenting to a particular treatment or not. Thus, a strictly legal approach might obscure the obligation to consult and seek the assent of persons with developmental disabilities, and to support them in some areas of decision making, even though they might not meet the overall legal standard for capacity to consent.

Why consent is important

People with developmental disabilities have dignity because of their intrinsic value as human beings. This dignity does not depend on the person's level of cognitive and adaptive functioning. In health care, people generally are in a vulnerable condition relative to their care provider, and people with developmental disabilities especially so. At the heart of the relationship between a care provider and the person whom he or she supports is a specific obligation to respect that person's dignity. Respecting dignity includes obtaining voluntary and informed consent for treatment and care whenever possible, but entails more than just this. It involves supporting the person's participation in decision making to the extent

of his or her capabilities, while being mindful of particular vulnerabilities. This cannot be done well without getting to know the person involved, his or her history, living conditions, and support network.

Because of their knowledge of the person with a developmental disability and their familiarity with how best to communicate with that person, family members and support workers can contribute to the process of decision making and obtaining informed consent, and might sometimes need to act as advocates. Only the person with developmental disabilities whose treatment or care is being considered, however, is legally entitled to provide consent for it, if he or she is assessed to be capable of consenting. If not, an authorized substitute decision maker, usually a family member, is required to provide consent. Neither the health care provider nor any of the person's paid or volunteer support workers are authorized to act as substitute decision makers under the law except in very rare cases when they have been specifically appointed to act as a guardian or a representative with the power of attorney for personal care (Sullivan et al., 2011).

Although much of the above seems straightforward and self-evident to professionals in health care and in community and social services, a recent review of research published in English between 1990 to 2007 on informed consent to health care interventions provided to people with a developmental disability's found a wide range of reported attitudes and behaviours among health care professionals regarding what consent means and when it is required (Goldsmith, Skirton, & Webb, 2008). The authors concluded that, besides the person with developmental disabilities' capacity to consent, the attitudes and behaviour of care providers were also a crucial factor for obtaining voluntary and informed consent to treatment and care. The ability of care providers to communicate appropriately has also been found to be an important variable (Truffrey-Wijne & McEnhill, 2008).

What informed and voluntary consent means in ethics

The Ontario *Health Care Consent Act* (1996) stipulates four conditions for valid consent: it must relate to the particular treatment, be informed, be voluntary, and not have been obtained through fraud or misrepresentation. What, however, does informed and voluntary consent mean in ethics? There is a broad consensus among ethicists that the following ought to be considered (Grisso, 1986; Morris, Niederbuhl, & Mahr, 1993, Wong, Clare, Gunn, & Holland, 1999; Wong et al., 2000). The person must:

- Be free from any impediment to giving or withholding consent
- Have sufficient factual information relating to the nature of his or her health issue and the proposed treatment
- Understand this information and retain it
- Be able to weigh the risks and benefits of the proposed treatment against possible alternative treatments or non-treatment
- Communicate a decision

An additional criterion that is not as often cited is the person's ability to form intentions or goals for his or her life, as shown by the presence of some sense of his or her own character, history, preferences and values, and to decide in accordance with these factors (Koppelman, 2002).

Capacity to consent depends on the complexity of the information and decision making skills involved and might also vary over time and with changing circumstances. Thus a person with a developmental disability's capacity to consent must be considered before each decision that is required for a treatment or other procedure, assessed if there are any signs that the person lacks this capacity, and re-assessed during the course of treatment whenever necessary (e.g., when it appears that the person's level of cognitive and/or adaptive functioning has changed). A person who capably consents to a particular treatment or treatment plan may withdraw that consent at a later time if he or she is assessed to be still capable of doing so.

Presumption of capacity to consent, developmental issues, and family-centred care

The Ontario *Health Care Consent Act* (1996) presumes that a person is capable of providing voluntary and informed consent to treatment and care unless it can be demonstrated otherwise. (See Chapter 6 for details on capacity and substitute decision making in Ontario). There is also no minimum age for capacity to consent in Ontario. However, the focus of Ontario's *Health Care Consent Act* on capacity to consent rather than on age does raise some significant ethical issues regarding its application to persons with developmental disabilities.

Although there is a legal presumption of capacity to consent, developmental issues are obviously important to consider in relation to people with developmental disabilities. Many health professionals in Ontario who adhere to a family-centred model of pediatric and adolescent care consider it their ethical obligation to go beyond the requirements of the *Health Care Consent Act* to seek the consent of both a youth under 16 who is assessed to be capable of consenting to treatment and his or her parents or other primary caregiver, especially if the youth still lives at home and is dependent on parental support and care for his or her medical condition. On the other hand, when such a child or youth is assessed to be incapable of consent, and a parent or other substitute decision maker is authorized to give or refuse consent, the child's or youth's assent or agreement to treatment or care is nonetheless usually solicited. There is a legitimate but perplexing ethical question, therefore, whether these practices ought to be extended to people with developmental disabilities who are 16 years of age or older, and who are dependent on family or other primary caregivers for support and care.

Cea and Fisher (2003) and Fisher et al. (2006) showed that, for people with developmental disabilities, there is a positive correlation between scores on assessments of intelligence and adaptive functioning, and their capacity to give consent. People with severe or profound developmental disabilities have been found generally to lack the capacity for considering and weighing the risks and benefits of a proposed treatment in relation to alternatives. Even among people with moderate developmental disabilities, few (around 20% in the Cea and Fisher study) have these decision making skills, as compared to about 50% of those functioning in the mild range of developmental disabilities. An implication of these research findings is that health care providers should always take as much time and effort as is needed to assess the capacity to consent of any person with a developmental disability, even those in the mild range.

Difficulty giving or withholding consent

Health care providers should be aware that people with developmental disabilities experience particular challenges and vulnerabilities that may affect their capacity to give or withhold consent. Some are unable to communicate well or at all, and some use alternative means of communication with which care providers might be unfamiliar. In these situations, the standard interview process for obtaining consent needs to be modified. Communicating effectively with people with developmental disabilities is necessary in order to assess their capacity to consent and obtain consent (Sullivan et al., 2011). Often it is helpful to involve caregivers who know the person well and can help with communication and interpretation (Morris et al., 1993). The successful use of illustrations and/or story vignettes showing different options and outcomes of similar procedures or treatments to those being proposed has also been described in the literature (Arscott, Dagnan, & Kroese, 1999). The Ontario Developmental Disabilities Primary Care Initiative (DDPCI) has developed a tool on informed consent for adults with developmental disabilities that contains a checklist and sample questions for assessing capacity to consent (Sullivan & Kelly, 2011). Another DDPCI tool gives guidance on how to communicate effectively with people with developmental disabilities with various levels of severity (Sullivan & Kelly, 2011).

Psychiatric disorders and/or emotional disturbances are common among persons with developmental disabilities, but their manifestations might mistakenly be regarded as typical for them (Deb, Matthews, Holt, & Buras, 2001; Rush & Allen, 2000). It is important that care providers obtain an adequate psycho-social history and recognize mental health factors that might affect an individual's capacity to give or withhold consent.

The limited range of life experiences that many people with developmental disabilities have had, such as living in a protective family or a highly-structured institution, might reduce their ability to understand and appreciate options that are described in obtaining consent. A negative experience of some past treatment, whether of oneself or others, could also unduly influence a person's willingness to consent to similar treatments.

Finally, acquiescence and learned helplessness can make a person with a developmental disability overly compliant with the requests of care providers and unaware or doubtful that they may choose an alternative treatment or discontinue it (Morris et al., 1993; Dunn, Kroese, Thomas, McGarry, & Drew, 2006).

Many of these challenges are illustrated in the true story of a man in Ontario with a developmental disability. We have changed his name to "Jack." This case resulted in a coroner's report in Ontario, which is part of the public record.

The Story of Jack

At age 28 years, Jack had a developmental disability in the mild-to-moderate range. He attended a supported school setting, found work in a hamburger restaurant as a teenager, and lived with his parents until he was 23 years old. He then moved into a group home while continuing to work at the restaurant.

Jack's transition to the independence and responsibilities of adulthood was complicated by limitations that were part of his developmental disability. Two such limitations were a tendency to constipation due to his inability to monitor and care for himself, and a long-standing fear of medical procedures, especially if they involved needles.

Although Jack was typically in excellent health, his first major encounter with the medical system occurred at age 26, when he developed abdominal pain and persistent diarrhea. His family physician referred him to a nearby teaching hospital for further assessment and management. The hospital's emergency department staff determined that Jack's diarrhea was due to severe constipation. They soon became aware of Jack's opposition to any of the proposed medical investigations and treatments for his constipation.

Concerned that Jack's fear of medical procedures was affecting his ability to make decisions in this instance, the emergency department staff asked a psychiatrist who had experience in this area to assess Jack's capacity to give or withhold consent. The consulting psychiatrist concluded that Jack was not capable of withholding consent because he was not able adequately to understand his health condition and the consequences of declining the proposed investigation and treatment. A family member became Jack's substitute decision-maker. This person consented on Jack's behalf to the emergency department staff's proposed treatment. Jack's constipation improved following treatment, and he was released from the hospital.

Eighteen months later, Jack again developed symptoms of constipation. After Jack's family physician referred him to the hospital, Jack refused the same treatment that he had received before. This time, however, the emergency department staff presumed that Jack was capable of refusing. They decided that it would be best to honour his refusal and just to monitor his condition.

Over the next five days, Jack continued to refuse the recommended treatment. Jack's refusal caused escalating tensions between his family and the health care providers. Jack's family wanted him to be treated and argued that Jack had been assessed before as being incapable of refusing the same treatment.

The health care providers were hesitant to override Jack's refusal to consent. They argued that even though Jack had previously been assessed to be incapable of refusing the proposed treatment, each situation is different. Since Jack had undergone the treatment before, he could be presumed to understand what is involved. Since he now stated clearly that he did not want the treatment, he seemed to meet the criteria for capacity to consent under the law. To treat Jack despite his refusal to be treated would be to impose their own, and Jack's family's, decision on him. This could constitute an assault.

For thought and discussion

Before relating the conclusion of Jack's story, the reader should consider the following questions:
1. Do you think that the physicians at the hospital emergency department needed to ask for Jack's consent to carry out the proposed treatments?
2. Would it make any difference to your answers if the situation did not involve what you perceive to be an emergency? For example, if Jack had refused to go to his family doctor to check out diarrhea that he had been having for the last few days, would you, as a residential counsellor or teacher, have taken him there anyway?
3. Would you agree with Jack's family that he did not have the capacity to provide consent? What signs in Jack's background and behaviour would you look for to support your opinion?
4. What do you think constitutes a capacity to give voluntary and informed consent, and who should assess this for a person with a developmental disability?

The Process of Decision Making

Jack's story highlights problems that might arise when care providers consider legal issues in isolation from medical and ethical ones. This might in part be driven by a fear of litigation or because care providers have certain mistaken beliefs regarding what is involved in giving consent. Before returning to Jack's story, we want to identify and examine some of these beliefs.

Values and choices

Care providers sometimes confuse medical and ethical decision making, which is a process, with a choice, which may or may not have involved any deliberation. They might think that a person's communication of consent or refusal is sufficient for legal purposes, even if the person does not understand the significance of the choice and what it entails. A choice can also be driven by fear, depression, learned helplessness, habit or other factors.

Sometimes a choice can turn out to be contrary to what a person ultimately wants and considers to be good. For example, someone with a developmental disability and a swallowing disorder might want to maintain his or her nutrition and health while avoiding choking but might refuse the insertion of a gastrostomy-tube. With respect to decisions about treatment and care, therefore, it is important for care providers not to take a person's choice simply at face value. Instead, care providers need to take the time and make the effort to discover, through appropriate means of communication, whether a given choice truly reflects what the person ultimately desires. Is the choice reflective of and compatible with the person's values or life goals? Does the person realize that in consenting to or refusing treatment, what he or she holds to be ultimately good might be compromised? In Jack's case, it is possible that, in choosing to avoid short-term discomfort and pain out of fear, and understandably so, he might not be capable of appreciating the possible risks in the long run to his health and life, which he deeply values.

Supported decision making

To exercise autonomy in a morally responsible way in a given situation requires more than just the capacity to understand one's health issue and the treatment or care that is being proposed and its possible risks and benefits. Giving, refusing, or withdrawing consent involves many different cognitive skills: an individual must be able to ask questions not only about the proposed treatment or care but also the availability of other options, understand this information, weigh the relative risks and benefits of each alternative, and judge when there is sufficient evidence for a decision.

Care providers who are aware of these skills in themselves can prompt and help the people whom they support to complete the process of decision making to the best of their ability. From an ethical standpoint, this assistance is not interfering with the self-determination of people with developmental disabilities or taking over their decision making; rather, it is supporting their ability to make responsible decisions about their treatment and care.

An objection may be raised as to whether, as a society, we hold people with developmental disabilities to a higher standard of responsibility in their decision making than others. Such an objection overlooks the reality that people generally desire what they regard as ultimately good for themselves and try to avoid what they regard as ultimately harmful. As a result of various causes and for various reasons,

however, not everyone chooses to strive for this in every situation. In people with a developmental disability, irresponsible decisions (decisions that do not contribute to the ultimate good that an individual truly desires) are often not the result of a choice but of intellectual, affective, psychological, and social challenges or limitations they have.

Substitute decision makers

In most situations, an assessment of the capacity of a person with a developmental disability to give informed consent may be conducted by any health professional (e.g., family physician, nurse, psychologist or psychiatrist) but it should involve family members or regular caregivers who know the person being assessed well. Care providers should not presume a person's capacity or incapacity to consent based on a single assessment in the past. It is also important for health professionals to be aware of the issues surrounding consent-giving in people with developmental disabilities, such as those outlined in this chapter. Tools have been developed for this purpose (Sullivan & Kelly, 2011). In some instances, when a care provider is unsure of the abilities and challenges of a person with a developmental disability, referral to a psychologist or psychiatrist or some other professional trained to conduct capacity assessments is necessary. The decision to seek a formal capacity assessment should not be based merely on a care provider's or family's disagreement with someone's decision or the reasons for that decision. Rather it should be based on a perceived lack of the person with a developmental disability's capacity to perform the sorts of cognitive skills described above.

When a person with a developmental disability is found to be incapable of consenting to treatment and care, it will be necessary for a substitute decision maker, usually a family member, to step in. Substitute decision makers should consider what is in that person's best interests, including the person's values or life goals, if known.

Advance care planning

Advance care planning can often make a positive difference to the outcome of difficult life transitions and crises that require treatment, and for end-of-life care. All adults with developmental disabilities and their main caregiver(s) should discuss advance care plans with a primary care provider, such as a family physician. What is most important to determine is the preference of the person with a developmental disability regarding who should be his or her substitute decision maker in the event that he or she is assessed to be incapable of giving or withholding consent to treatment. Advance care plans should be recorded, and discussed and reviewed periodically (Sullivan et al., 2011).

The Story of Jack: Conclusion

Let us return to Jack's story to reveal what actually occurred and reflect on how clarity on some of the issues just highlighted might have changed the outcome.

Jack's abdomen became increasingly distended due to his ongoing constipation over the course of his admission to hospital. In the early morning hours of the fifth day of his hospital admission, Jack's condition worsened suddenly and his primary care provider summoned a member of the surgical staff to assess him. The surgeon removed a large amount of stool from Jack's rectum by manual disimpaction, and this appeared to improve his distress. This apparent improvement was temporary, however, and three hours later Jack suffered a cardio-respiratory arrest and died. The cause of death was recorded as "respiratory arrest and electro-mechanical dissociation as a consequence of aspiration of mineral oil, due to bowel obstruction."

For thought and discussion

Knowing this outcome, would you now change any of your answers to the previous questions? If so, why?

Skills Needed by Care Providers

Personal decision-making skills

In this case, did Jack have the capacity to weigh the evidence and assess the implications of refusing the proposed treatment? Arguably, he was unable to appreciate the seriousness of the symptoms that were distressing him, and to understand that certain interventions were necessary to avoid further life-threatening complications such as those he experienced (e.g., aspiration and dehydration). His fear of receiving a needle might have been sufficient to compromise his freedom to consider his medical options responsibly.

On the other hand, Jack's health care providers appeared overly hesitant in recognizing Jack's inability to make a capable decision about treatment under these circumstances. They disagreed with his choice but went along with it without considering Jack's specific challenges, which his family had identified.

They might not have had an adequate understanding of what is involved in a responsible decision. It is important for care providers to have some personal familiarity with the range and sequence of skills that are required for responsible decision making and to recognize in themselves, situations when they made decisions that they later regretted as a result of not performing these skills well. Unless they recognize adequate and inadequate decision making skills in themselves, they might not recognize them in others.

Mediation skills

Jack's story suggests that care providers might also need to have skills in counselling and mediation. When a person with a developmental disability is capable of making an informed and valued-based decision, but their freedom to do so is impeded by factors such as anxiety, fear or hasty acquiescence, a skillful mediator can help to put the person at ease and support the person through the decision making process.

Ethical difficulties sometimes also arise when there are disagreements among family members, between family members and health professionals, or among members of a health care team, as to what ultimately is good for people who do not have the capacity to consent to treatment. To resolve these disagreements practically, the involvement of an outside but trusted mediator, such as a clinical ethicist or member of the clergy, can be helpful in addition to legal measures, such as appealing to the Ontario Consent and Capacity Board or to the Office of the Public Guardian and Trustee.

Resource management skills

Another set of skills that care providers should cultivate relates to the area of resource management. This involves having some knowledge of, and capacity to engage and manage, various community resources that are available to assist the people whom they wish to support. For instance, in this case, Jack's health care providers needed to recognize their own limitations in assessing Jack's capacity to consent and to engage colleagues with such expertise.

In addition, Jack's problem with self-management placed him in the situation of being constipated repeatedly and requiring to give consent for invasive emergency treatments. Jack's care providers should have identified and offered health resources and support strategies that could have helped him to prevent recurrent constipation.

Summary

There are legal requirements to consent but, beyond that, there are ethical considerations. Ethics guides our decisions regarding what to do in particular circumstances. It involves a range of skills that the law recognizes as necessary for being capable of consenting to treatment and care, such as the ability to grasp why a decision has to be made, to form and communicate questions, to understand and retain factual information, to weigh benefits and risks of harm for oneself, and to communicate a decision. However, ethics also entails being capable of deciding based on one's values or beliefs regarding what is good.

People with developmental disabilities might have challenges with respect to any or all of these skills in a given situation, even those whose level of cognitive and adaptive functioning is in the borderline or mild range of developmental disabilities. Since capacity to consent is decision- and time-specific, health care providers should consider a person with a developmental disability's capacity to consent to each treatment or treatment plan and, if appropriate, assess or refer him or her for an assessment of this capacity.

When the person with a developmental disability does not to meet the legal standard for capacity under the *Health Care Consent Act*, an appropriate substitute decision maker should be found to give or withhold consent, after having considered the person's best interests. Even if the person with a developmental disability is assessed to be not legally capable of consent, he or she might be capable still of participating to some extent in the decision making process, if approached with an appropriate level and means of communication and provided with the support of others who know them well. For instance, it might be possible, through observation, a thorough history, discussion and asking for the imput of those who know the person well, to determine the person's values and beliefs regarding what is good, even if he or she is incapable of applying them to the concrete decision that needs to be made.

Although there is a presumption in the law that people are capable of consent unless proven otherwise, in the case of people with developmental disabilities, it would be prudent to be aware of their particular challenges and vulnerabilities, and to make appropriate adaptations in communication and in the process of obtaining consent. We conclude that an important goal in obtaining consent from persons with a developmental disability is supported decision making.

Just as people with developmental disabilities receive resources, support, and training with skills in other areas of their lives, it is also crucial that they have assistance in augmenting their skills related to health care decision making.

More Resources

Books:

Dinerstein, R. D., Herr, S. S., & O'Sullivan, J. L. (1999). *A guide to consent*. Washington, DC: American Association on Mental Retardation.

U.K. Department of Health. (2001). *Seeking consent: Working with people with learning disabilities*. London: Department of Health Publications.

Internet websites and documents:

Consent and people with intellectual disabilities: The basics

*http://www.intellectualdisability.info/how-to../
consent-and-people-with-intellectual-disabilities-the-
basics*

**Informed consent in adults with developmental
disabilities**

*http://www.surreyplace.on.ca/Documents/
Informed%20Consent%20in%20Adults%20
with%20DD.pdf*

Contacts:

Developmental Disabilities Primary Care Initiative
(Director: Dr. William Sullivan)
2 Surrey Place
Toronto, Ontario M5S 2C2
Telephone: 416-925-5141
email: bill.sullivan@surreyplace.on.ca

**Office of the Public Guardian and Trustee,
Treatment Decisions Consultant**

595 Bay Street, Suite 800, Toronto, ON, M5G 2M6
Tel.: (416) 314-2788
Toll-free: 1-800-387-2127
Fax: (416) 314-2637

Ontario Consent and Capacity Review Board
151 Bloor Street West, 10th Floor
Toronto, Ontario M5S 2T5
Phone: (416) 327-4142
TTY/TDD: (416) 326-7TTY or (416) 326-7889
Fax: (416) 924-8873

References

Arscott, K., Dagnan, D., & Kroese, B. A. (1999). Assessing the ability of people with a learning disability to give informed consent to treatment. *Psychological Medicine, 29,* 1367-1375.

Cea, C. D., & Fisher, C. B. (2003). Health care decision-making by adults with mental retardation. *Mental Retardation, 41,* 78-87.

Deb, S., Matthews, T., Holt, G., & Bouras, N. (2001). *Practice guidelines for the assessment and diagnosis of mental health problems in adults with intellectual disability.* Brighton, U.K.: Pavilion.

Dunn, A., Kroese, B. S., Thomas, G., McGarry, A., & Drew, P. (2006). 'Are you allowed to say that?':

Using video materials to provide accessible information about psychology services. *British Journal of Learning Disabilities, 34,* 215-219.

Eastgate, G. (2005). Sex, consent and intellectual disability. *Australian Family Physician, 34,* 163-166.

Evans, D. R. (1997). *The law, standards of practice, and ethics in the practice of psychology.* Toronto, ON: Edmond Montgomery Publications.

Goldsmith, L., Skirton, H., & Webb, C. (2008). Informed consent to healthcare interventions in people with learning disabilities: An integrative review. *Journal of Advanced Nursing, 64,* 549-563.

Fisher, C. B., Cea, C. D., Davidson, P. W., & Fried, A. L. (2006). Capacity of persons with mental retardation to consent to participate in randomized clinical trials. *American Journal of Psychiatry, 163,* 1813-1820.

Grisso, T. (1986). *Evaluating competencies: Forensic assessments and instruments.* New York: Plenum Press.

Health Care Consent Act, 1996, S.O. 1996, c. 2, Sched. A.

Koppelman, E. R. (2002). Dementia and dignity: Towards a new method of surrogate decision making. *Journal of Medicine and Philosophy, 27,* 65-85.

McKelvey, M. C. (Ed.). (2011). *Ontario consent and capacity legislation.* Toronto, ON: Canada Law Book.

Mental Health Act, 1990, R.S.O. 1990, c. M.7.

Morris, C. D., Niederbuhl, J. M., & Mahr, J. M. (1993). Determining the capability of individuals with mental retardation to give informed consent. *American Journal on Mental Retardation, 98,* 263-272.

Personal Health Information Protection Act, 2004, S.O. 2004, c. 3, Sched. A.

Powers of Attorney Act, 1990, R.S.O. 1990, c. P.20.

Robertson, J., Emerson, E., Hatton, C., Gregory, N., et al. (2001). Environmental opportunities and supports for exercising self-determination in community-based residential settings. *Research in Developmental Disabilities, 22,* 487-502.

Rush, A., & Allen, J. F. (Eds.). (2000). Treatment of psychiatric and behavioral problems in mental retardation. *American Journal on Mental Retardation, 105,* 169-170.

Substitute Decisions Act, 1992, S.O. 1992, c. 30.

Sullivan, W. F., Berg, J. M., Bradley, E., Cheetham, J., Denton, R., Heng, J., et al. (2011), Primary care of adults with developmental disabilities: Canadian consensus guidelines. *Canadian Family Physician, 57,* 541-553.

Sullivan, W. F., & Kelly, M. (Eds.). (2011). *Tools for the primary care of people with developmental disabilities.* Available from http://www.surreyplace. on.ca/Clinical-Programs/Medical-Services/Pages/ PrimaryCare.aspx

Tuffrey-Wijne, I., & McEnhill, L. (2008). Communication difficulties and intellectual disabilities in end-of-life care. *International Journal of Palliative Nursing, 14,* 189-194.

Wong, J. G., Clare, I. C. H., Gunn, M. J., & Holland, A. J. (1999). Capacity to make health care decisions: its importance in clinical practice. *Psychological Medicine, 29,* 437-446.

Wong, J. G., Clare, I. C. H., Holland, A. J., Watson, P. C., & Gunn, M. (2000). The capacity of people with a 'mental disability' to make a health care decision. *Psychological Medicine, 30,* 295-306.

Physical Health and People with Developmental Disabilities

Tom Cheetham and Shirley McMillan

What you will learn:

- Crucial role of caregivers
- Some important medical issues for people with developmental disabilities
- Barriers to effective health care
- The medical database required by the health care provider
- Strategies to enhance the role of health care advocate

The decade since the first edition of *Developmental Disabilities in Ontario* was published has witnessed an explosion of information on health care for people with developmental disabilities. However, the fundamental process of the health care encounter is unchanged. The focus of this chapter is on primary care, the point of first contact with the health care system, and the role of caregivers, both families and paid workers. Increasingly, health care is provided by interdisciplinary teams that better serve the complex needs of individuals with developmental disabilities.

The emphasis here is on care of adults with developmental disabilities since paediatric services include infants and children with developmental disabilities. General paediatricians and family physicians call on developmental paediatricians and child and adolescent psychiatrists for more specialized care as needed. It is adults, no longer age appropriate for paediatric care, who may face challenges finding a family physician, nurse practitioner, or family health team with training and experience in developmental disabilities. Many of the issues presented in this chapter apply equally to medical specialists and other health care professionals who need to collaborate to provide optimal care. These include: nurses, dentists, occupational therapists, speech language therapists, psychologists, behaviour therapists, physiotherapists, social workers, dietitians, pharmacists, chiropodists, kinesiologists, and recreation therapists. In Ontario, family physicians generally complete four years of medical school, followed by a two year postgraduate residency in family medicine. Medical specialists complete four to six years of postgraduate training after medical school graduation; psychiatrists, for example, have five years specialty training. Advanced practice nurses (nurse practitioners and clinical nurse specialists) have a minimum of two years at a Masters level beyond a four year undergraduate nursing degree, although some nurse practitioners have a Bachelor of Science in Nursing. The United Kingdom (UK) has unique training for nurses and psychiatrists; developmental disabilities (called learning disabilities in the UK) is a specialty in each field. Sadly, at present there is little requirement for specific developmental disability education for most health professionals in Ontario.

Crucial Role of Caregivers

Persons with perhaps the most crucial role in ensuring high quality health care for individuals with developmental disabilities are often unrecognized as key professionals. They are care providers and family members. Here, both will be referred to as caregivers. These individuals are knowledgeable, caring, and involved, and they have an advantage possessed by no other professional. Caregivers who are with the person with disabilities day in and day out know that person best. A caregiver is ideally positioned to detect a change from the person's usual functioning and to best interpret idiosyncratic forms of communicating states, wants and needs, or vital elements in accurate assessment. In Ontario, one route to training as a paid caregiver is a two year college diploma program as a Developmental Services Worker (DSW). Another route is to train as a personal support worker (Personal Support Worker Canada, 2011). Other training may be through university programs, mentorships, and other methods. However professional support roles are attained, they are key to supporting individuals with developmental disabilities in effective ways.

With increased awareness of the central role of the caregiver has come more attention from researchers to explore relevant issues. Recent publications have included such diverse topics as the important role in implementing treatment of visual impairment (Evenhuis, Sjoukes, Kooijman, & Koot, 2009); the accuracy in recognizing a decline in everyday functioning heralding dementia (Jamieson-Craig, Scior, Chan, Fenton, & Strydom, 2010); health promotion and support for women through menopause (Willis, Wishart, & Muir, 2010); and, recognizing signs of depression (Munden & Perry, 2002). The caregiver literature also has explored job stress and burnout (e.g., Skirrow & Hatton, 2007), character-

istics of effective training (van Oorsouw, Embregts, Bosman, & Jahoda, 2009) and the increased rate of injury among direct care staff (Manning, 2005). An Australian study comparing carers' and primary care physicians' concerns in meeting the health care needs of people with developmental disabilities found the two groups agreed that more health care provider training in developmental disabilities was required (Iacono, Davis, Humphries, & Chandler, 2003).

Exceedingly important functions performed by caregivers include: identifying health issues that require attention because of a change in functioning of a person who may not recognize the need to see a health care provider, or being able to express discomfort or pain; providing information for diagnosis; assisting with the medical encounter; and carrying out and monitoring subsequent treatment. In addition, the caregiver can advocate for health screening and prevention strategies to maintain health. One paid caregiver stated it best when describing her frustration of having her observations ignored by the clinician as she tried to have a client's problem with constipation addressed, "We are in the business of observation." She also understood constipation potentially was a life threatening problem for her client, something the provider failed to appreciate based on training and experience with patients who did not have developmental disabilities. On the other hand, observation by caregivers sometimes requires clarification and an additional source of information. For example, Kerr et al. (2003) found that they sometimes under-reported vision and hearing problems (Kerr et al., 2003).

Even after 30 years experience with people with developmental disabilities in health care settings, the present authors continue to be surprised at how apparently trivial and nonspecific observations can herald significant health problems. In many instances it has been the caregiver's concern that has led to discovery of important medical problems. The following vignette of one of our patients is a powerful illustration.

Case Vignette

Mr. R.W. (pseudonym) was a 27 year old man who had a profound developmental disability due to congenital rubella. He was blind and deaf, and did not like to be touched. One day he developed a fever that lasted four hours and went away without treatment. He had no other signs of illness. The next day the caregiver had him seen by his primary care practitioner because she said, "There is something wrong," and "He is not right." She could not be more specific about what she thought was wrong. There had been no further fever and he had no cough, no congestion, no vomiting, no diarrhea, no apparent urinary problem, and no rash. Eating and sleeping were unchanged from his usual. It always was difficult to determine if he was experiencing pain, but she did not think so. While he was fed his favourite snack, the health care provider attempted a physical examination, including ears, throat, chest and abdomen. The examination was challenging but no obvious abnormalities were evident.

The next day the caregiver returned because, as she said, "There's something wrong with him." There had been no further fever and no new signs of illness. The provider thought Mr. R.W. should just be monitored for any new indications of ill health over the next few days. When the caregiver returned again the following day, the health care provider ordered blood tests and urine sample to investigate further, mainly because the caregiver continued to be so insistent that "He still is not right." He felt vindicated when the tests all were normal, including no elevation in leucocytes, which would have indicated some infection. This did not convince the caregiver. She continued to indicate to the health care provider that "He's not himself," and that "Something's wrong." This was in spite of no recurrence of fever, and no new signs of illness. The exasperated physician finally ordered a large amount of sedation and sent the patient for a chest X-ray to prove to the caregiver that her concerns were groundless. He was concerned about the possible serious side effects from the sedation but knew it was the only way the X-ray would be possible. The chest X-ray showed bilateral pneumonia.

There are important lessons from this case for clinicians and caregivers. To health care providers, even those experienced in developmental disabilities medicine, some complex individuals with developmental disabilities present very atypically and your

training, experience and common sense can mislead you, to the detriment of the patient. Remember caregivers may detect changes in the person without knowing anything more than "Something is not right," and can report only a vague feeling that there is a problem.

And to caregivers: when you think something is not right, do not give up in your role as advocate even when the health care practitioner does not understand — you may save your family member or client's life. This caregiver did.

High quality medical care for persons with developmental disabilities is a collaborative effort between the person with disabilities, the caregiver(s), and the health care providers. Having considered the people involved in providing care, next we will look at primary care in general terms.

Important Medical Issues for People with Developmental Disabilities

Since Beange, McElduff, and Baker (1995) conducted a landmark study of 202 individuals with intellectual disability, and found a mean of 5.4 medical diagnoses per person (half previously unrecognized), a substantial literature on primary care for individuals with developmental disabilities has developed. Disparities in health care have received considerable attention in Canada (Ouelette-Kuntz, 2005), the United States (Krahn, Hammond, & Turner, 2006), and internationally (Scheepers et al., 2005). From these and other reports (Charlot et al., 2010; Cooper, Smiley, Morrison, Williamson, & Allan, 2007; de Kuijper et al., 2010; Hollins, Attard, Fraunhofer, McGuigan, & Sedgwick, 1998; Straetmans, van Schrojenstein Lantman-De Valk, Schellevis, & Dinant, 2007; van Schrojenstein Lantman-De Valk, 2005; van Schrojenstein Lantman-De Valk, Metsemakers, Haveman, & Crebolder, 2000; van Schrojenstein Lantman-De Valk & Walsh, 2008; Tyrer et al., 2008), it has been found that people with developmental disabilities differ from the general population with respect to their health in four key ways. They have:

1. *Increased mortality (death rate).* Life expectancy for people with developmental disabilities has

increased in recent decades but remains below that of the general population. Risk factors associated with higher mortality include: mobility impairments, epilepsy, vision and hearing impairments, and inability to feed oneself.

2. *Increased morbidity (disease state).* People with developmental disabilities experience more than twice the health problems compared to the general population, particularly vision and hearing impairments, epilepsy, dental problems, gastrointestinal problems (e.g., constipation, dysphagia, gastroesophageal reflux), and obesity. Psychiatric disorders are also common (see Chapters 34 and 36 for more details).

3. *Increased number of medications.* Compared to the general population, individuals with developmental disabilities receive four times the number of prescriptions. There is also considerable evidence of overuse of psychotropic medications, often without psychiatric diagnoses to justify the medication use, and in spite of the fact that there is not strong evidence that psychotropic medications are effective with this population (see Chapter 34 for a full discussion). Medications have side effects of various kinds, and these might easily be missed if the person receiving the medication cannot describe them. Recent international guidelines have called attention to the overuse of psychotropic medications (Deb et al., 2010). Why does overuse occur? A criti-

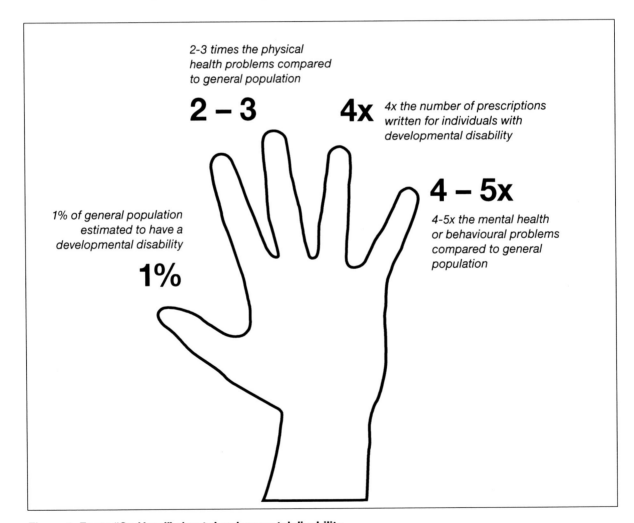

Figure 1. Facts "On Hand" about developmental disability.

cal aspect of physical health is the intertwining of physical and behavioural/psychiatric issues. It is both challenging and interesting to work through a behavioural problem to determine what physical health issues may be contributing. However, if the provider has no framework to approach presenting problems, and has had little opportunity for learning under a more experienced clinician, it can feel overwhelming.

4. *Barriers to health care.* Numerous barriers to health care exist, especially access to health care providers who have knowledge and experience in developmental disability. A more detailed list of barriers is provided in the section below.

Barriers To Effective Health Care

Barriers to effective health care are numerous, but can be thought of under three broad categories:

1. *Health care provider issues.* These include:
   - Lack of training and experience with patients with developmental disabilities.
   - Negative attitudes towards people with developmental disabilities.
   - Diagnostic overshadowing, which refers to overlooking a health issue and attributing behaviour solely to the developmental disability (Reiss, 1994). This leads to missing treatable conditions.
   - Lack of suitable environment (e.g., physical access to the building, examination room or exam table for a client who uses a wheelchair or who has spasticity).
   - Insufficient time (a typical family physician appointment is about 10 minutes and there is evidence more time is required).
   - Challenges in obtaining a history and performing a physical examination.
   - Feelings of uncertainty about diagnosis that may make the provider anxious. Even detected problems may be untreated or inadequately treated.
   - Lack of knowledge of community services and resources.
   - Problems obtaining informed consent.
2. *Health care system issues.* These include:
   - Failure to consistently pay for medications.

For example, some are paid by the Ontario Drug Benefit Plan (ODB) for limited defined diagnoses only if certain criteria are met. With gastroesophageal reflux disease (GERD), twice as common in people with developmental disabilities, treatment with an effective class of drugs requires re-evaluation after 6 months for continuation of ODB payment. The criteria fail to recognize the difficulty in obtaining the client's self-report of improvement.
   - Long wait lists.
   - Lack of available community services and resources.
   - Inadequate payment for providers relative to the time required.
   - Increased need for tests (because of often inadequate history and physical examination), perhaps with sedation or anaesthetic (e.g., computed tomography (CT) scan or magnetic resonance imaging (MRI)).
3. *Patients with developmental disabilities themselves.* They may:
   - Have difficulty recognizing a health issue requiring attention.
   - Have difficulty reporting past medical history and describing current problems.
   - Not complain, so health problems go undetected. For example, the client who dutifully accompanied a caregiver on a one km walk, but became agitated afterwards, was found to have a rectal abscess the size of the physician's fist — the source of unimaginable pain.
   - Have different patterns of illness. For example, gastroesophagal reflux disease (GERD) is twice as common in people with developmental disabilities as in the general population, and epilepsy is twenty or more times more frequent.
   - Have different presentation of illness. Even serious medical problems may present in atypical ways such as as irritability, inactivity, aggression, or changes in appetite or sleep; pneumonia can occur without usual signs as in the case vignette above; people

may walk on fractures, and so on.

- Have sensory problems. Vision and hearing impairments are prevalent. As well, people with autism spectrum disorders may have sensory sensitivities and sensory integration problems that can present as behavioural problems. The underlying annoying, uncomfortable or even painful sound, smell, or touch not experienced by a caregiver or clinician can be completely overlooked (e.g., the humming of fluorescent lights).

- Not exhibit typical pain behaviour so this can be unappreciated or neglected completely.

- Have communication challenges, or may not use verbal communication. There may be a discrepancy between expressive and receptive language abilities. It is easy to overestimate the receptive language skills, and hence comprehension, in someone who has good expressive language. Similarly, a person may have poor expressive verbal skills yet understand more than their expressive language would suggest.

- Be unwilling or unable to cooperate with the examination because of previous unpleasant experiences, lack of understanding of what is being asked, or physical limitations.

- Have lack of understanding of the need to adhere to a treatment plan.

- Not have good continuity of care if visited by a caregiver (or different caregivers) with variable knowledge of the person.

Additional factors complicating good health care include the following:

1. *Poor health promotion and disease prevention activities.* There is evidence that persons with developmental disability are less physically active, brush their teeth less frequently, and are vaccinated less often than persons in the general population. Furthermore, women are screened for cervical and breast cancer, and men for testicular cancer, at lower than average rates. A recent curriculum designed for people with developmental disabilities and their caregivers

to address some of these issues gives optimism for future improvement in health promotion activities (Marks, Sisirak, & Heller, 2010).

2. *Negative determinants of health.* Health has been understood for more than half a century by the World Health Organization to refer to a state of complete physical, mental and social well-being and not merely the absence of disease (WHO, 1946). The determinants of health include genetic, social circumstances, environmental exposures, individual behaviour and health care access. The individual with a developmental disability may have a genetic syndrome and, although this cannot yet be modified, knowledge of associated health risks should lead to focussed screening. For example, people with Down syndrome should be screened at regular intervals for thyroid function. However, for the remaining determinants, caregivers have an important role. Supporting the family member/client to establish and maintain friendships, obtain employment, have safe and healthy living arrangements, and advocate for good health care are within the scope of the caregiver.

3. *Aging population.* With increasing life expectancy, people with developmental disabilities are facing issues of aging that are similar to those in the general population. Since this is rather recent, however, clinicians are only beginning to focus on how aging plays out against a background of lifelong developmental disability. Goals of healthy aging have been presented in an international context in conjunction with the World Health Organization (Evenhuis, Henderson, Beange, Lennox, & Chicoine, 2001).

Next, we shall consider the information the caregiver can help provide for the clinician.

The Health Record

The health record, which also may be called the medical record, is the summary of all the health information, past and current, on a patient that forms the basis for health care diagnosis and treatment planning. The health record lists a patient's medical history, findings from physical examinations, and further investigations conducted by the health care provider. A first visit to the health care provider typically involves gathering details of the new patient's history and current health issues, and subsequent visits focus more on updates to this information and current presenting problems.

Any visit to a health care provider adds information to the health record. It updates the history, physical examination findings (often focussing on the presenting problem), and sometimes results in additional tests or examinations. Following this, a diagnosis is made and a corresponding treatment plan is formulated. In most cases, description of the current problem, together with information of what has occurred in the past, contributes about 75% of the information used to make a diagnosis. The examination and any further investigations — such as a blood test, urine test, a CT scan, or MRI — contribute only about 25% of the diagnostic information (Cutler, 1985). For this reason, health care providers are critically dependent upon the history provided by the patient or others who know the person well.

Caregivers can provide details that are crucial to an effective visit with a health care provider. Even someone with good verbal communication can have difficulty providing an accurate history. The person who indicates that "Everything hurts," or "Nothing hurts," is difficult to assess. In addition, it is often important to know when something began to be wrong or began to hurt, and it may be challenging for some individuals with developmental disabilities to recall or report such times. Without accurate information, the provider cannot play an effective part in the person's health care.

Clearly, the more efficiently the patient and caregiver can present the required information, the more accurate the diagnosis will be, and the more effective the visit. However, if the scheduled visit time is focussed on obtaining the history, there is less chance to discuss other relevant issues, such as various treatment options. A satisfying encounter for the health care provider can go a long way in having him or her recognize the challenges and the rewards of caring for people with developmental disabilities.

History

A patient's history has several components. The provider wants to know about the present problem, what has brought the person here today, what has happened in the past, any medications the person is taking, and if there are any other things that may be important and might have been overlooked in the discussion between patient and clinician. The structure for this information takes the following form:

1. Presentation of the problem/chief complaint
2. History of the present illness
3. Past medical history
   a. past illnesses
   b. immunizations
   c. developmental history
   d. behavioural/psychiatric history
   e. operations/surgery
   f. hospitalizations
7. Allergies
8. Medications
9. Family history
10. Psychosocial history/patient profile
11. Review of systems

The *presenting problem,* also called the *chief complaint,* is a few words to indicate why the person is seeing the provider and why the visit is occurring at this time. This is followed by a detailed description of the problem, including: when it started, any associated symptoms, things that make it better or worse and, if there is pain, where it starts and if it travels. If the client has limited verbal communication, what are the behaviours that suggest the symptoms? The detailed description comprises the *history of the present illness.*

The *past history* is divided into sections for clarity, including serious illnesses, operations, and any hospital admissions for medical or psychiatric / behavioural problems. All of these should include the reason or diagnosis, and dates. Immunizations are recorded under past history. Developmental history includes information about the pregnancy and delivery, followed by developmental milestones such as age of sitting alone, standing, walking, babbling, and so on. A brief summary of school progress is also part of the developmental history.

True *allergies* are distinguished from side effects, if possible. All drugs have the potential for side effects, such as nausea or vomiting from an antibiotic. A rash, hives, or swelling are more likely to result from an allergy. The more detailed the description, the more helpful it is to the clinician. For example, allergy to sulpha conveys less information than knowing the person had a whole body red rash 10 days after starting a sulpha drug for a urinary tract infection. The medications list should include all current medications, their start dates, and the strengths and frequencies of the doses. Previous medications should include dates and doses as well as effectiveness. For example, the drug history that a particular antidepressant "did not work" might be misleading. This would be the case if more detailed information revealed a small dose was given for two weeks and stopped because it was not thought to be effective, when it takes up to 6 weeks to see an effect from an adequate dose of an antidepressant. Over the counter medications, vitamins, herbal preparations, and any other natural products (e.g., items from the health food store) are important to include on the medication history, as there can be interactions with prescription drugs.

Family history can be extremely helpful as some conditions tend to run in families. Knowing that there is a positive family history may make the difference when diagnosis in the person with developmental disabilities is difficult to make. What health issue, in which relative, and at what age? If a relative is deceased, knowing the age and cause of death can assist in screening the person for that condition at an earlier age.

Psychosocial history/patient profile for the general population encompasses smoking, alcohol and substance use and abuse, as well as marital status, children, and employment. However, for the individual with a developmental disability, in addition to these elements, the patient profile provides an opportunity for the caregiver to educate the clinician by presenting a brief picture of the person. Therefore, it should include living arrangements, day programs, and leisure activities. Communication skills, both expressive and receptive, should be noted, and self care skills such as eating, toileting, dressing and grooming should be commented upon. Sexual history tends to be overlooked but should be included with the patient profile. Is there any history of abuse? A more complete understanding of the patient can result from a brief description of a "day in the life" but should be no longer than two or three sentences.

The last element of the history is the *review of systems,* a series of questions usually starting at the head and working down the body to ensure no signs or symptoms have been missed. (Signs are observable by the health care provider; symptoms are the things that the patient states.) As with all parts of the patient history, if the person cannot answer the questions, the information must come from someone who knows the person well. With individuals who have communication challenges, there is more attention to those elements of the history that are observable. These include changes in: appetite, weight, sleep pattern, bowel function, urinary function, energy level, preferred activities, seizures, menstrual cycle, and sexual functioning.

Physical examination

It is important to conduct a physical examination. Experienced providers have pointed to the lack of physical findings on examination in some people with developmental disabilities, but touching the patient is another way the clinician communicates and begins to develop a relationship with the client. The examination may be even more important in someone who does not use verbal communication. In addition, since there can be challenges to obtaining the history, there may be findings that were not suspected before examining the person. With practice, the provider will discover techniques to elicit more information from the physical examination. For example, blowing on a pinwheel or blowing bubbles encourages deep breathing in order to examine a person's chest. Of course, skills that enhance examination of the person with developmental disabilities can be useful in others who have difficulty cooperating, such as a patient with dementia or a child.

Vital signs include temperature, pulse (heart rate), blood pressure, and respiratory rate; these are key elements of an examination as with any patient. But, here too, there may be differences compared to the general population; for example, hypothermia (low temperature), rather than fever, may be present with acute infections. Sweaty palms may indicate sympathetic nervous system hyperarousal, indicative of anxiety or thyroid dysfunction. Positive physical findings are helpful, but unimpressive findings on examination should not be trusted to rule out significant health problems, particularly pain.

Pain is problematic because it is so important in diagnosis. In a patient with abdominal pain, mild pain on examination suggests different diagnostic possibilities from the patient with severe pain. In this way, the clinician may be dangerously misled in the diagnostic possibilities. Behaviour in the person with a developmental disability that is not typical of showing pain, such as walking on a hip fracture, sometimes erroneously is thought to indicate the person doesn't feel pain. If the clinician believes the person feels no pain, pain likely will not be treated. In fact, pain is a complex experience influenced by many factors, including a component that is learned. The person with a developmental disability may never have had the opportunity to learn typical pain behaviour, or past expression of pain may have resulted in negative consequences and so be suppressed (see, for example, Symons, Shinde, & Gilles, 2008). In addition to acute pain, it may not be surprising that chronic pain is under-recognized and under-treated (McGuire, Daly, & Smyth, 2010). Tools are available to aid health care clinicians in pain assessment (Regnard et al., 2007). The approach of the present authors is to treat the person as one would treat any patient; a painful condition should be treated as it would in a patient without a developmental disability.

Investigations

More laboratory tests, X-rays, and other diagnostic tests are often required for a person with developmental disability due to limited information from the history and physical examination. However, these investigations can be equally challenging. More than one attempt may be necessary before a test can be completed, or a period of desensitization to the procedure may be required. Creative solutions can work — for example, being accompa-

nied by a favourite person and receiving a preferred food during the test. Another strategy includes visiting the local laboratory where blood tests or other investigations will be performed beforehand to convey to the technologists who will be doing the procedure, what the world is like for the person with the developmental disability, as well as his/her individual preferences and fears. Developing rapport and a trusting relationship can go a long way to making the experience better for all. Obviously, the preliminary visit is the opportunity to educate the patient, as well as to reduce anxiety from a change in routine or fear of the unknown. A topical anaesthetic cream or patch applied a minimum of an hour prior to bloodwork can be effective. At times, sedation may be necessary; rarely, only after carefully weighing the risks and benefits, and with informed consent, would a general anaesthetic be necessary. If investigations are avoided because of the difficulty in performing them, serious conditions may be missed.

Diagnosis and treatment plan

From the three components of history, physical examination, and investigations, the health care provider develops a list of possible diagnoses; this is the *differential diagnosis*. The most likely diagnosis from which the provider proceeds is the *working diagnosis*. Again, the caregiver is important in the process; for example, reminding the provider that a particular antibiotic has not been effective in the past could enhance better treatment with a working diagnosis of pneumonia. Knowledge of current trends in chest infections at that time of year, or in the local region, is information the provider contributes to the treatment plan. Another role for the caregiver is to make the clinician aware of practical issues in implementing the recommended treatment, such as a client who will not leave a dressing on a wound.

Now, armed with the knowledge of the critical role of the caregiver in a health care encounter, and with some general aspects of primary health care and information on the structure and content of the database required for medical diagnoses, we consider guidelines and tools to assist the health care provider.

Strategies to Assist the Health Care Provider

In 2005, an experienced group of Ontario clinicians, researchers, and academics, together with international experts, met to develop consensus guidelines for primary care of adults with developmental disabilities to assist health care providers with care in the community. These were first published in November 2006 in *Canadian Family Physician*, which is distributed to family physicians across Canada (Sullivan et al., 2006). The revised edition of the guidelines, published in 2011, is accompanied by a set of tools to enhance their practical implementation (Sullivan et al., 2011).

The guidelines are designed to highlight considerations for primary care practitioners that are in addition to, or different from, what would be done for the general population but in the absence of a known cause of the developmental disability. However, when the etiology is a known syndrome, the relevant Health Watch Table (discussed below) is to be consulted. This information assists clinicians who may have had little training and experience, but also can empower people with developmental disabilities and their caregivers to advocate for optimum health care.

The 2011 guidelines are divided into three sections: nine guidelines describe general issues, twelve discuss physical health, and ten address behaviour and mental health. General issues note that disparities exist for individuals with developmental disabilities, and that specific attention to health care needs can improve their primary care. These speak to the importance of establishing the etiology (cause) of the disability as it informs health screening and preventive care, and considering current adaptive functioning in order to determine required supports. Pain is highlighted as often unrecognized and may present as non-specific behaviour changes. Further, the use of medications is discussed, with a caution of the harm that can result from multiple or long-term use of some drugs. The remaining general considerations present abuse and neglect, the issue of capacity for informed consent, and the need for advanced care planning for transitions, crisis, and

end-of-life care. The final general guideline notes the need for an interdisciplinary team to provide effective care for individuals with complex developmental disabilities.

The twelve physical health guidelines of the second section describe: physical inactivity and obesity, vision and hearing impairments, dental disease, cardiac disorders, respiratory disorders, gastrointestinal and feeding problems, sexuality, musculoskeletal disorders, epilepsy, endocrine disorders, immunization, and cancer screening. In addition to obesity and physical inactivity being prevalent, underweight is a health issue in some individuals with developmental disabilities. The vision and hearing guideline draws attention to under-diagnosis of both impairments and includes specific screening frequencies. Dental disease is one of the most common health problems; discomfort from dental disease often may present as behavioural changes. Other physical health guidelines call attention to cardiac disorders being prevalent, and respiratory disorders such as aspiration and pneumonia are among the most common causes of death. Also under respiratory conditions, sleep apnea may be missed because of unusual presentation. Similarly, gastrointestinal (GI) and feeding problems are common and may present atypically, with unexplained symptoms or weight or behavioural changes. Investigations for GERD, constipation, H. pylori (a prevalent GI organism that causes ulcers), and other conditions should be conducted. The seventh physical health guideline discusses sexuality, an often neglected topic. The remaining five guidelines turn the reader's attention to: musculoskeletal problems such as scoliosis, contractures, spasticity, and osteoporosis; epilepsy; endocrine disorders such as thyroid and hypogonadism; immunizations; and cancer screening.

The third section, behavioural and mental health guidelines, is beyond the scope of the present chapter but is discussed in other chapters of this book.

Guidelines can help clinicians, yet working in an unfamiliar area like developmental disability can still be challenging. To operationalize the principles set forth in the guidelines and to provide practical advice to clinicians and caregivers, a collection of about 20 tools has been developed. A directory of these tools is located on the Surrey Place Centre website under Medical Services in the Clinical Programs menu (*http://www.surreyplace. on.ca/Clinical-Programs/Medical-Services/Pages/ PrimaryCare.aspx*). These tools are organized into general tools, physical health tools, and behavioural and mental health tools. Examples include: information regarding referral for a genetics assessment and psychological assessment, preventive care checklist for females and males, levels of adaptive functioning, tips for communicating effectively, office organizational issues, informed consent, and forms to aid caregivers with information collection prior to an appointment.

Health Watch Tables provide specific recommendations tailored to a syndrome and highlight health issues organized by body system for children and adults. Examples include Down, fragile X, Prader-Willi, Smith-Magenis, Williams, 22q11.2 deletion (velocardiofacial) syndromes and autism, with 13 more planned (see the Surrey Place Centre website for links to these tables).

This chapter has introduced the reader to the critical role of caregivers in ensuring optimum health care for people with developmental disabilities, provided a brief overview of a number of principles of primary care, and described the information required by the health care practitioner. The *Primary Care of Adults with Developmental Disabilities: Canadian Consensus Guidelines* and the accompanying Toolkit will assist clinicians and caregivers alike in providing care to end the longstanding disparities experienced by this vulnerable group of patients.

Summary

To offer effective health care for people with developmental disabilities, a health care provider must have knowledge of the disability the patient has and be aware of particular medical conditions that may occur in that condition, have an understanding of the atypical presentation of signs and symptoms, and conduct regular routine screenings for people with developmental disabilities. The most crucial component in providing medical care, however, is the careful observations of support people who know the person well. Such caregivers have knowledge of health issues related to the person's particular developmental disability, and provide strong advocacy on the person's behalf.

For Further Thought and Discussion

1. Select one person with developmental disability. What barriers to physical health care have you encountered for this person? How were they overcome, or how could they be handled in the future?
2. Think of another person with a developmental disability whom you know well. Practise summarizing the person's history succinctly — perhaps in five or six sentences — to present to a health care provider.
3. Consider ways to deal with a health care provider who does not seem to recognize the importance of the information provided by a support person.
4. Review the special problems and easily overlooked issues section while thinking of a person you support or might support in the future. Can you identify any previously unrecognized medical issues within the different areas discussed?

More Resources

Websites:

Community Networks of Specialized Care
http://www.community-networks.ca/uploads/ Common/Eastern%20CNSC%20Builidng%20 Health%20Care%20Capacity%20Launch%20 Event%20-%20March%203%202011.pdf

Organizing Health Care Services for People with an Intellectual Disability
http://www2.cochrane.org/reviews/en/ab007492. html

Surrey Place Centre
http://www.surreyplace.on.ca/Pages/Home.aspx

Understanding Intellectual Disability and Health
http://www.intellectualdisability.info/

Books and Articles:

Cheetham, T., Lovering, J. S., Telch, J., Telch, F., & Percy, M. (2007). Physical health. In I. Brown & M. Percy (Eds.), *A comprehensive guide to intellectual and developmental disabilities* (pp. 629-643). Baltimore: Paul H. Brookes Publishing Co.

O'Hara, J., McCarthy, J., & Bouras, N. (2010). *Intellectual disability and ill health: A review of the evidence.* Cambridge: Cambridge University Press.

Sullivan, W. F., Berg, J. M., Bradley, E., Cheetham, T., Denton, R., Heng, J., Hennen, B., Joyce, D., Kelly, M., Korossy, M., Lunsky, Y., & McMillan, S. (2011). Primary care of adults with developmental disabilities: Canadian consensus guidelines. *Canadian Family Physician, 57*(5), 541-553.

References

Beange, H., McElduff, A., & Baker, W. (1995). Medical disorders in adults with intellectual disability: A population study. *American Journal of Mental Retardation, 99*(7), 595-604.

Charlot, L., Abend, S., Ravin, P., Mastis, K., Hunt, A., & Deutstch, C. (2010). Non-psychiatric health problems among psychiatric inpatients with intellectual disabilities. *Journal of Intellectual Disability Research, 54*, 1-11.

Cooper, S.-A., Smiley, E., Morrison, J., Williamson, A., & Allan, L. (2007). An epidemiological investigation of affective disorders with a population cohort of 1023 adults with intellectual disabilities. *Psychological Medicine, 37*(6), 873-882.

Cutler, P. (1985). *Problem solving in clinical medicine: From data to diagnosis* (2nd ed.). Baltimore: Williams & Wilkins.

Deb, S., Kwok, H., Bertelli, M., Salvador-Carulla, L. Bradley, E., Torr, J., et al. (2010). International guide to prescribing psychotropic medication for the management of problem behaviours in adults with intellectual disabilities. *World Psychiatry Association, 8*, 181-186.

de Kuijper, G., Hoekstra, P., Visser, F., Scholte, F. A., Penning, C., & Evenhuis, H. (2010). *Journal of Intellectual Disability Research, 54*(7), 659-667.

Evenhuis, H., Henderson, C. M., Beange, H., Lennox, N., & Chicoine, B. (2001). Healthy ageing – Adults with intellectual disabilities: Physical health issues. *Journal of Applied Research in Intellectual Disabilities, 14*(3), 175-194.

Evenhuis, H. M., Sjoukes, L., Koot, H. M., & Kooijman, A. C. (2009). Does visual impairment lead to additional disability in adults with intellectual disabilities? *Journal of Intellectual Disability Research, 53*(1), 19-28.

Hollins, S., Attard, M. T., von Fraunhofer, N., McGuigan, S., & Sedgwick, P. (1998). Mortality in people with learning disability: Risks, causes and death certification findings in London. *Developmental Medicine & Child Neurology, 40*(1), 50-56.

Iacono, T., Davis, R., Humphreys, J., & Chandler, N. (2003). GP and support people's concerns and priorities for meeting the health care needs of individuals with developmental disabilities: A metropolitan and non-metropolitan comparison. *Journal of Intellectual and Developmental Disabilities, 28*(4), 353-368.

Jamieson-Craig, R., Scior, K., Chan, T., Fenton, C., & Strydom, A. (2010). Reliance on carer reports of early symptoms of dementia among adults with intellectual disabilities. *Journal of Policy and Practice in Intellectual Disabilities, 7*(1), 34-41.

Kerr, M., McCulloch, D., Oliver, K., McLean, B., Coleman, E., Law, T., et al. (2003). Medical needs of people with intellectual disability require regular reassessment, and provision of client and carer-held reports. *Journal of Intellectual Disabilities Research, 4*(2), 134-145.

Krahn, G. L., Hammond, L., & Turner, A. (2006). A cascade of disparities: Health and health care access for people with intellectual disabilities. *Mental Retardation and Developmental Disabilities Research Reviews, 12*(1), 70-82.

Manning, S. M. (2005, Winter). Injury among direct health care staff in public immediate care facilities. *The Digest* (Association of Public Developmental Disabilities Administrators), 6-7. Retrieved from http://apdda.org/pdf/APDDA%20Newsletter%20Winter%202005.pdf

Marks, B., Sisirak, J., & Heller, T. (2010). *Health matters.* Baltimore: Paul H. Brookes Publishing Co.

McGuire, B. E., Daly, P., & Smyth, F. (2010). Chronic

pain among people with an intellectual disability: Under-recognised and under-treated? *Journal of Intellectual Disability Research, 54,* 240-245.

Munden, A. C., & Perry, D. W. (2002). Symptoms of depression in people with learning disabilities: Knowledge of various members of the multidisciplinary team involved in the care and assessment of challenging behaviour. *Journal of Learning Disabilities, 6*(1), 13-22.

Ouellette-Kuntz, H. (2005). Understanding health disparities and inequalities faced by individuals with intellectual disabilities. *Journal of Applied Research in Intellectual Disabilities, 18*(2), 113-121.

Personal Support Worker Canada. (2011). *Personal support worker PSW.* Retrieved from http://personalsupportworker.ca/psw_jobs.html

Regnard, C., Reynolds, J., Watson, B., Matthews, D., Gibson, L., & Clarke, C. (2007). Understanding distress in people with severe communication difficulties: Developing and assessing the Disability Distress Assessment Tool (DisDAT). *Journal of Intellectual Disability Research, 51*(4), 277-292.

Reiss, S. (1994). Psychopathology in mental retardation. In N. Bouras (Ed.), *Mental health in mental retardation: Recent advances and practices* (pp. 67-78). Cambridge: Cambridge University Press.

Scheepers, M., Kerr, M., O'Hara, D., Bainbridge, D., Cooper, S. A., Davis, R., et al. (2005). Reducing health disparity in people with intellectual disabilities: A report from health issues special interest research group of the international association for the scientific study of intellectual disabilities. *Journal of Policy and Practice in Intellectual Disabilities, 2*(3-4), 249-255.

Skirrow, P., & Hatton, C. (2007). 'Burnout' amongst direct care workers in services for adults with intellectual disabilities: A systematic review of research findings and initial normative data. *Journal of Applied Research in Intellectual Disabilities, 20*(1), 131-44.

Straetmans, J. M., van Schrojenstein Lantman-De Valk, H. M., Schellevis, F. G., & Dinant, G. J. (2007). Health problems of people with intellectual disabilities: The impact for general practice. *British Journal of General Practice, 57*(534), 64-66.

Sullivan, W. F., Berg, J. M., Bradley, E., Cheetham, T., Denton, R., Heng, J., Hennen, B., Joyce, D., Kelly, M., Korossy, M., Lunsky, Y., & McMillan, S. (2011). Primary care of adults with developmental disabilities: Canadian consensus guidelines. *Canadian Family Physician, 57*(5), 541-553.

Sullivan, W. F., Heng, J., Cameron, D., Lunsky, Y., Cheetham, T., Hennen, B., Bradley, E. A., Berg, J. M., Korossy, M., Forster-Gibson, C., Gitta, M., Stavrakaki, C., McCreary, B., Swift, I. (2006). Consensus guidelines for primary health care of adults with developmental disabilities. *Canadian Family Physician, 52*(11), 1410-1418.

Symons, F. J., Shinde, S. K., & Gilles, E. (2008). Perspectives on pain and intellectual disability. *Journal of Intellectual Disability Research, 52*(4), 275-286.

Tyrer, P., Oliver-Africano, P. C., Ahmed, Z., Bouras, N., Cooray, S., Deb, S., et al. (2008). Risperidone, haloperidol, and placebo in the treatment of aggressive challenging behaviour in patients with intellectual disability: A randomized controlled trial. *Lancet, 371*(9606), 57-63.

van Oorsouw, W. M., Embregts, P. J., Bosman, A. M., & Jahoda, A. (2009). Training staff serving client with intellectual disabilities: a meta-analysis of aspects determining effectiveness. *Research in Developmental Disabilities, 30*(3), 503-511.

van Schrojenstein Lantman-De Valk, H., Metsemakers, F. M., Haveman, J., & Crebolder, H. (2000). Health problems in people with intellectual disability in general practice: A comparative study. *Family Practice, 17*(5), 405-407.

van Schrojenstein Lantman-de Valk, H. (2005). Health in people with intellectual disabilities: Current knowledge and gaps in knowledge. *Journal of Applied Research in Intellectual Disabilities, 18,* 325-333.

van Schrojenstein Lantman-de Valk, H., & Walsh, P. (2008). Managing health problems in people with intellectual disabilities. *British Medical Journal, 337,* 1408-1412.

World Health Organization (WHO). (1946). *WHO definition of health.* Retrieved from http://www.who.int/about/definition/en/print.html

Willis, D. S., Wishart, J. G., & Muir, W. J. (2010). Carer knowledge and experiences with menopause in women with intellectual disabilities. *Jour-*

nal of Policy and Practice in Intellectual Disabilities,
7(1), 42-48.

32

Nutritional Considerations in Children with Developmental Disabilities

Diana Mager and Paul Pencharz

What you will learn:

- Nutrition concerns in children with developmental disabilities
- Common causes of malnutrition and obesity in children with developmental disabilities
- How nutritional and feeding problems are identified and managed

*Note: Words in **bold italics** are explained in the Special Terms section following the Summary.*

The most common nutritional concern in children with developmental disability is growth failure caused by feeding difficulties. Thirty to thirty-five percent of children with neurodevelopmental disabilities have feeding problems that result in slow growth, inadequate weight gain, developmental delay, psychosocial problems, *anemia*, and vitamin/mineral deficiencies (Palmer, Thompson, & Linscheid, 1975; Telch & Telch, 2003). Overnutrition leading to obesity is also common in this population. This usually results from dietary intake in excess of energy requirements, and diminished physical activity/mobility. Proper nutrition is an important issue for children with developmental disabilities. A comprehensive approach to nutrition support in this population can result in improved rates of growth, improvement in development, and enhanced quality of life.

Assessment of feeding difficulties should include an interdisciplinary approach involving at least a physician, nurse, and registered dietitian. The team also could include a speech language pathologist, occupational therapist, physiotherapist, radiologist/interventional radiologist, dentist and dental hygienist, psychiatrist, social worker, teacher, and pharmacist. Some countries have laws mandating that infants and children at risk for developmental disability are entitled to nutritional assessment and treatment within the context of a family-centred approach (see Telch & Telch, 2003).

Common Causes of Malnutrition

Malnutrition in children with developmental disabilities may be caused by several factors. These include the presence of significant swallowing and gastrointestinal dysfunction, medication, development, and behavioural issues. Swallowing problems, or dysphagia, is very common in children with developmental delay (Palmer, Thompson, & Linscheid, 1975; Reilly, Skuse, & Pobete, 1996; Zemel & Stallings, 1997). The most common causes of dysphagia in this population include neurological impairment, and structural abnormalities (e.g., cleft palate) of the oral and pharyngeal cavities (Rudolph, 1994). Dysphagia can lead to poor food intake, impaired feeding efficiency (length of time to finish a meal), choking, regurgitation, and aspiration of food contents into the lung. Severity and duration of swallowing impairment has also been linked to a lag in the developmental progress in children with neurological impairment (Cloud, 1993; Zemel & Stallings, 1997). Significant improvement in nutritional status in children with developmental disabilities can occur following assessment of nutritional requirements, dietary intake, type and severity of swallowing dysfunction, and functional capacity to self-feed (Reilly et al., 1996; Rudolph, 1994; Zemel & Stallings, 1997).

Common causes of gastrointestinal dysfunction in children with developmental disabilities may include delayed gastric emptying, impaired intestinal motility (movement through the intestine) and *gastroesophageal reflux disease (GERD)*. Severe and persistent GERD can cause esophagitis (inflamed mucosa of the esophagus), vomiting, failure to thrive, or lung disease from aspiration (Sondheimer & Morris, 1979). GERD and delayed gastric and/or intestinal motility are usually treated with medications that promote motility and block acid production in the gut. Treatment of GERD and delayed gastric emptying with these medications can promote increased dietary intake and improved weight gain (DiLorenzo, Piepz, Ham, & Cadrane, 1991). Impaired intestinal motility can also cause constipation leading to vomiting, decreased food intake and weight loss. Improvement in the frequency of bowel motions can lead to significant improvement in dietary intake (DiLorenzo et al., 1991; Sullivan, 1997). Treatment of constipation in children includes the use of motility agents, stool softening agents, suppository or fleet enema, and assessment of fluid and fibre intake to ensure that adequate amounts are present in the diet.

Patients with persistent GERD and delayed gastric emptying may develop feeding aversions (DiLorenzo et al., 1991). Feeding aversions may include partial or total food refusal, selectivity of food choices (picky eating) and food texture (e.g., a child may refuse to eat solids, or liquids) (Cloud, 1993; Rodas-Arts & Benoit, 1998). Behaviours such as tantrums associated with eating or changes in food texture and delay in self-feeding may also result in impairment of feeding efficiency. These problems can be exacerbated by swallowing problems. Treatment and management of behavioural problems associated with feeding is complex (Cloud, 1993; Rodas-Arts & Benoit, 1998). Assessment of behavioural feeding problems should include a review of functional (e.g., posture) and physiological (e.g., swallowing function, gastrointestinal function) aspects of feeding.

The use of medications in children with developmental disabilities may have a significant impact on nutritional status. These include potential drug-nutrient interactions or such side effects as nausea, vomiting, diarrhea, or poor appetite. For example, anticonvulsant medications (e.g., phenytoin) used in children with seizure disorders may interfere with the absorption and utilization of vitamin D and calcium, leading to increased risk for bone fracture (Lifschitz & Maclaren, 1975). Use of antibiotics may produce gastrointestinal symptoms (e.g., diarrhea), and psychotropics may cause depressed appetite (Roe, 1982). In addition, many children with developmental disabilities take multiple medications (prescribed and non-prescribed) that potentially may interact and cause adverse reactions (Roe, 1982).

Nutrition Assessment of Children

Nutrition assessment in children includes the assessment of growth, body composition, dietary intake (past & present), and current health status. Assessment of growth includes examining weight and height growth to determine the adequacy of nutritional status. Deficits in growth and reductions in fat and lean body mass are the most common indicators of malnutrition (Cloud, 1993; Zemel & Stallings, 1997). Assessment of body composition is also necessary to establish severity of obesity in over-nutrition. Assessment of dietary intake (past & present) is important for identifying causative factors in over- and under-nutrition. This assessment includes a review of current and past intake, preferences, food frequency, use of caloric, vitamin and mineral supplementation, food availability and a review of feeding patterns (Cloud, 1993; Rudolph, 1994; Zemel & Stallings, 1997). The review of feeding patterns can include timing of meals, behavioural patterns associated with feeding, and difficulties with feeding. A review of current health status may include a review of medical history (acute and chronic) and current medications (drug-nutrient interactions) in order to identify potential factors affecting current nutritional status. The history includes a review of body systems, with emphasis on the child's ability to chew, swallow, and digest food to identify potential causes for under- or over-nutrition (nausea, vomiting, malabsorption, reflux, diarrhea, etc.) (Cloud, 1993; Reilly et al., 1995; Rudolph, 1994; Zemel & Stallings, 1997).

Blood tests are also done in a nutritional assessment to screen for vitamin and mineral deficiency. These blood values should be assessed along with the medical, growth, and nutritional history to ensure completeness of assessment. The most common blood parameters used in nutrition assessment are measurements of *serum albumin* and a CBC (complete blood count). Serum albumin is a good indicator of adequacy of *visceral protein status* over the previous month in the absence of kidney and liver disease (half-life is 18-20 days) (Hopkins, 1993). Other markers of visceral protein status include *transferrin*, thyroxine-binding pre-albumin (transthyretin) and retinol-binding protein. Evaluation of the CBC (hemoglobin, hematocrit, and red cell indices) is a useful screening tool for the detection of nutrition-related anemias (Hopkins, 1993). A more complete analysis of iron status includes assessment of *ferritin* (iron stores), serum iron, *transferrin*, and iron binding capacity (Cloud, 1993; Zemel & Stallings, 1997).

Assessment of Growth in Children

Assessment of growth in children is an important part of nutritional assessment. A complete assessment here includes measurement of height (lying or standing), weight, and skinfolds (Cloud, 1993; Zemel & Stallings, 1997). Height and weight of a child should be plotted using standard growth curves (Hamil et al., 1979). Children grow at different rates over time. The highest rates of growth occur in utero, during early infancy and around puberty. Differences in growth may occur annually, with faster rates during the spring and summer and slower rates in the fall and winter months in some countries (Goldbloom, 1997). Growth measurements should be recorded at regular intervals to account for these changes in growth patterns. Assessment of growth can be done by comparing height and weight percentiles, channel differences (one channel is representative of the distance between two percentile curves), or velocity curves. Children usually maintain their heights and weights in the same channels during the preschool and early childhood years (Guo et al., 1991). However, growth in any particular channel may not be defined until after two years of age (Guo et al., 1991; Roche & Himes, 1980). Genetic inheritance also plays a large role in growth in infancy and early childhood. Adjustment of stature of length measurements using mid-parental stature charts is a technique that may be used to correct for differences in genetic potential for linear growth (Himes, Roche, Thissen, & Moore, 1985).

For children with neurological impairment, growth may be impeded by dysphagia, chronic illness and the presence of skeletal disorders. Weight loss or lack of weight gain, in particular, may place these children at significant risk for malnutrition. Obesity can also be a problem in these children. This can hamper their mobility and can result in additional complications, including increased risk for cardiovascular disease.

Assessment of Growth Indicators

Specific indicators of growth include height, height velocity, and weight. Each is discussed next.

Height

Measurement of height is an important tool in the assessment of a child's nutritional status. Linear growth is an excellent marker of a child's nutritional

Table 1: Nutritional Considerations at a Glance

A. Feeding Issues

Factors that affect food intake
- *Acute and chronic illness (gastrointestinal dysfunction, neurological impairment, etc.)*
- *Psychosocial variables (depression, poverty, drug abuse)*
- *Drug therapy (anorexia, nausea, vomiting, diarrhea)*
- *Functional capacity*
- *Dysphagia (inability to swallow or dysfunctional swallow*

There is a need to differentiate between a normal versus abnormal swallow (dysphagia), and to define issues regarding functional capacity. Impairment of fine and gross motor skills and the presence of dysphagia can affect functional capacity or the ability to self-feed.

Signs of oral/pharyngeal dysphagia
- *Drooling*
- *Slow eating (low feeding efficiency, or time to finish one meal)*
- *Altered posturing of head and neck during swallow*
- *Large food residual in mouth following a swallow*
- *Coughing during and after the swallow*
- *Choking with significant shortness of breath*
- *Voice quality changes*
- *Expectoration of food and/or saliva*

Signs of impairment of fine and gross motor skills
- *Causes may be neurological or structural as outlined below:*
- *Ataxia (failure of muscle co-ordination resulting in poorly judged movements)*
- *Dysarthria (imperfect articulation of speech due to disturbances in muscle control)*
- *Abnormal reflexes (such as tongue thrusting in the infant)*
- *Apraxia (inability to plan and execute a skilled movement in the absence of sensory and motor deficits)*

Compensatory feeding strategies
- *Changes in Food Bolus Consistency (e.g., puree textures vs. soft, thin vs. thickened liquids)*
- *Postural change (head should be in upright position, not over on one side)*
- *Verbal cues (gentle reminders or cues to redirect attention to eating)*
- *Controlled intake (pacing of intake, portion size, outside distracters such as noise)*
- *Adaptive equipment (adaptive utensils, wrist or hand splints)*
- *Other therapies (effortful swallow, supraglottic swallow* vs. supersupraglottic* swallow)*

Food intake assessment techniques

- *Food frequency*
- *Intake records or diary*
- *24 hour recall*
- *Food preferences (likes vs. dislikes)*
- *Direct observation*
- *Diet history. This includes a review of current and past food intake and food preferences. It also usually includes a review of issues related to food intake (dental health, psychosocial factors such as depression, socio-economic status, occupation, physical health, age, allergies, medication, etc.) and functional capacity (i.e., ability to self-feed, prepare food, have access to food, etc.).*

Food frequency assessment techniques

- *Determination of food portion size*
- *Determination of food type/food group*
- *Determination of food frequency and number of servings per day vs. per week vs. per month*
- *Single food type vs. multiple food types (e.g., cheese slice vs. cheese casserole re: estimation of portion size/nutrient composition)*

Strategies to aid with food identification and estimation of food portion size

- *Pictures of foods, food labels*
- *Food models (especially plastic food models)*
- *Commercial product containers and labels to identify food types, food products, and food ingredients (especially important in cases of food allergy/intolerance)*
- *Food utensils (commercial product containers, measuring cups, cups, bowls, plates, cutlery, etc.) to approximately measure food portion size*
- *Handmeasures or rulers to identify thickness or dimensions of foods*
- *Kitchen scales to precisely measure food portions*

Factors affecting accuracy of food intake assessment

- *Recollection or memory of the interviewee about issues regarding duration or length of time of particular food intake (i.e., is this the usual intake, vs. the most recent intake vs. seasonal intake vs. holiday or special occasion (e.g., birthday) intake)*
- *Seasonal variations in food intake*
- *Food preparation techniques (e.g., baking vs. frying to estimate fat content)*
- *Methods used to estimate portion sizes*
- *Method or type of interview*
- *Order of presentation of food groups (bias may be introduced)*
- *Socio-economic factors*

Table 1: Nutritional Considerations at a Glance (cont'd)

B. Screening Issues

Purpose of nutrition screening

- *Identification of individuals with inadequate nutritional status*
- *Identification of risk factors for malnutrition*
- *Prevention of inadequate/sub-optimal nutritional status*

Nutritional risk factors

- *Inadequate oral intake*
- *Significant or Recent Weight Loss (i.e., Ideal Body Weight, % Recent Weight Change)*
- *Psychosocial variables (depression, poverty, drug abuse, etc.)*
- *Chronic or acute illness*
- *Drug therapy (drug-nutrient interactions, anorexia, nausea etc.)*
- *Altered functional capacity (due to changes in mobility, muscle strength)*

Anthropometrics

- *BMI (Body Mass Index)*
- *% IBW (Ideal Body Weight), % UBW (Usual Body Weight)*
- *% Recent Weight Change =* $\dfrac{\text{usual weight - current weight* 100\%}}{\text{usual weight}}$
- *Significant weight loss:*
  >1-2% over 1 week
  >5% over 1 month
  >7.5% over 3 months
  >10% over 6 months

Biochemical measurements of blood samples

- *Hemoglobin – to detect iron deficiency anemia*
- *Triglyceride/cholesterol –to detect hyperlipidemia*
- *Albumin –to estimate visceral protein status when hepatic, renal, gastrointestinal functions and hydration status are normal*

Diet history

- *Sub-optimal intake for more than three days*
- *Abnormal eating pattern*
- *Nutrition-related problems present (dentition, gastrointestinal upset (acute and chronic), dysphagia, food intolerance, anorexia)*

---

* See special terms

history and helps in distinguishing between short and long-term nutritional problems (i.e., height reflects longer-term nutritional issues). Recumbant lengths (lying down) are used for infants and children less than two years of age or for children over three years of age who are unable to stand. Recumbant length is not identical to standing height and must be measured using a device called a length board (Goldbloom, 1997; Roche & Davila, 1974). Plotting of height on reference growth curves

Screening tools

- *Canada's Guide to Healthy Eating*
- *Computer Nutrient Data Base (e.g., Food Smart)*
- *Food Frequency Questionnaires*
- *Nutrition Screening Checklists (include information about past medical history, food consumption patterns, socio-economic status, multiple medications, weight history, mobility, etc.)*

C. Labs at Admission*

This section explains the various tests that are usually ordered at admission to a hospital for nutrional assessment.

- *Albumin (serum): normal, 33-58 g/L; 31g/L is indicative of decreased visceral protein stores or inflammation in gut*
- *Erythrocyte Sedimentation Rate (ESR): normal, 1-10; elevated in collagen vascular disease, inflammatory states, acute phase reactions*
- *Electrolytes (serum): measures of ions such as sodium, potassium, calcium and magnesium*
- *Platelets*: normal, 150-450; 617 or above is a non-specific gut inflammatory marker (e.g., of Crohn's disease*)*
- *Hemoglobin: normal, 120-160; 76 or below is indicative of blood loss, microcytic anemia**
- *MCV, mean corpuscular (red cell) volume: normal, 80-94; 63 or below is indicative of microcytic, hypochromic anemia*
- *MCH, mean corpuscular (red cell) hemoglobin: normal, 24-31; 20 or below is indicative of microcytic anemia*
- *Serum iron: normal, 9-27 m moles/L; 8 or below is abnormal*
- *Ferritin (serum): normal, 18-300 ng/mL*
- *Transferrin (serum): normal, 24-48 m moles/L; 14.6 or below is abnormal*
- *Transferrin saturation: normal, 20%; 6% or below is abnormal.*
- *Transferrin saturation = serum iron/2 x serum transferrin*
- *Transferrin saturation is a marker of iron supply to the tissues. Low values are indicative that iron stores are inadequate for erythropoiesis**

should be done at sequential intervals for assessment of growth (Dietitions of Canada, 2004; Hamil et al., 1979; Himes & Roche, 1985).

The Centers for Disease Control and Prevention (CDC) (2009) provides useful growth charts that can be used for comparative purposes (*http://www.cdc.gov/growthcharts/clinical_charts.htm#Set1*).

The CDC charts consist of charts for infants from birth to age three for weight, recumbent length, head circumference, and weight-for-recumbent length,

Table 2: Classification of the Risk for Protein-Energy Malnutrition (PEM)

Ratio of actual weight to ideal body weight	Risk of PEM
90-110%	normal
85-90%	mild PEM
75-85%	moderate PEM
<75%	severe PEM

McLaren, D.S, & Read, W.C. (1972). Classification of nutritional status in early childhood. The Lancet, 2, 146; reprinted with permission from Elsevier.

and a set for children and adolescents from ages 2 to 20 for weight, height, and body mass index. The charts are available in two forms: individual charts, and clinical charts. The clinical charts were designed for use by health care providers (Dietitians of Canada, 2004). The World Health Organization (WHO) in collaboration with the United Nations Children Fund has developed new growth standards for children that are more representative of an ethnically diverse population (WHO, 2011; see also de Onis et al., 2007; Garza & de Onis, 1999; Grummer-Strawn, Garza, & Johnson, 2002). Use of these curves to evaluate growth in children with developmental disabilities needs to be evaluated.

Measurement of recumbent or standing height may be inappropriate for children with spinal curvature or contractures because proper positioning for these measurements may not be possible (Goldbloom, 1997). The use of arm span, or upper, lower and segmental arm length measures may be more appropriate. Comparison to reference standard tables should be used to compare growth when using these measures (Schenker & Ward, 1999; Spender, Cronk, Charney, & Stallings, 1989). Sometimes severe physical disabilities make even these measurements difficult. For example, the

presence of severe contracture or spinal curvature may make it difficult to measure arm span or upper and lower arm lengths accurately. Assessment of height using arm span lengths is also not appropriate in children with bony skeletal disorders, such as ***achrondroplasia***, as lower bone growth may be significantly different from upper bone growth, leading to over-estimates of stature (Goldbloom, 1997; Zemel & Stallings, 1997). The use of upper and lower arm lengths for assessment of linear stature is the most appropriate method to use when recumbent and when standing lengths are not possible (Schenker & Ward, 1999; Zemel & Stallings, 1997). Repeated measures on the same side of the body with the least involvement and comparison of both upper and lower measure should be done to minimize error and to ensure accuracy of height estimates (Goldbloom, 1997; Zemel & Stallings, 1997).

Height velocity

Assessment of height velocity (how height changes over time) should be used to assess rates of linear growth. Calculation of height velocity over time should be done at one-year intervals to account for seasonal variations in growth. Comparison to reference curves may be done to assess rates of linear growth (Roche & Himes, 1980). The use of these curves for the assessment of linear growth in children with skeletal impairment may be of limited value because growth patterns may be significantly different due to impairment of bone growth.

Weight

Infants and children should be weighed wearing little or no outer clothing on the same scale to ensure accuracy in measurements. Weight should be measured to the nearest 0.1 kg for older children and to the nearest 0.01 kg in infants (Goldbloom, 1997; Zemel & Stallings, 1997). The scale should be zeroed between measurements to ensure precision of the weight measurement. Factors that affect accuracy of weight measurements in children include the presence of ***edema***, ***organomegaly***, and measurement technique. It is important to distinguish between these variables when assessing weight in terms of a child's nutritional status. Plotting of weight on reference growth curves should be done at sequential intervals for assessment of growth (Guo et al., 1991; Hamil et al., 1979).

Head circumference

Below-normal head circumference in children and infants is often associated with developmental delay (Goldbloom, 1997). Hence, head circumference is not a useful marker of nutritional status in children with central nervous system impairment. Another cause of poor cranial growth includes premature fusion of cranial sutures (***premature synostosis***). Premature synostosis can lead to increased intracranial pressure, and abnormal cranial skeletal development (Goldbloom, 1997). Head circumference that is larger than normal is usually familial (known as *familial megalencephaly*). Head circumference should be serially monitored on clinical charts as an integral part of assessment of neurological development in children (see CDC growth charts).

Nutritional status using weight as a percentage of ideal body weight

Evaluation of the nutritional status of children includes assessment of growth parameters. Plotting the height and weight of a child on standard growth curves over time is critical when assessing height and weight growth failure. Growth failure may include lack of height or weight growth or both. Lack of weight gain or loss of weight over several months may be indicative of the presence of severe under-nutrition, disease, or psychosocial disturbance (Goldbloom, 1997). Excessive weight gain may be indicative of excessive energy intake, edema, or organomegaly. Disturbances of linear growth may also be due to the presence of chronic under- or over-nutrition, chronic disease and/or endocrine abnormalities (Goldbloom, 1997; Zemel & Stallings, 1997).

Assessment of weight as a percentage of ***ideal body weight*** assists the clinician in identifying the risk and severity of either under- or over-nutrition (Table 2) (McLaren & Read, 1972). Calculation of ideal body weight should be done using the 50th percentile weight for chronological age, or determining the child's height percentile and finding the corresponding weight for that percentile. Calculation of the ratio between the child's actual weight and ideal body weight is used to identify the risk for ***protein-energy malnutrition (PEM)***. The way in which such ratios are used to classify the risk for PEM is given in Table 2.

Plotting growth (height and weight) patterns of children on standard growth curves (CDC clinical curves; WHO growth curves) may not be appropriate in children with quadriplegia, as linear growth retardation is common in this population (Tanner, Whitehouse, & Takaishi, 1966). Growth studies in children with cerebral palsy indicate that growth is severely depressed (Krick, Murphy-Miller, Zeger, & Wright, 1996). Growth retardation has been attributed to nutritional and non-nutritional factors in this population. One reason for this is a lack of weight bearing, which plays a direct role in the growth of long bones (Krick et al., 1996). Depressed weight gain is likely due to the prevalence of oral-motor dysfunction, decreased feeding efficiency, dysphagia, and/or gastroesophageal reflux.

Skinfold measures

Skin fold measures may be used to assess subcutaneous fat and lean body mass stores in the body. Tricep and subscapular skinfold measures are good indicators of whole body fat stores (Goldbloom, 1997; Zemel & Stallings, 1997). Calculation of ***mid-arm muscle circumference (MAMC)*** using ***mid-arm circumference (MAC)*** and ***tricep skinfold measures*** may be used to assess lean body stores. Decreased MAMC measures reflect skeletal muscle wasting due to denervation and/or malnutrition, while decreased tricep skin fold measures reflect wasting secondary to malnutrition only (Nutrition Committee, 1994). Comparison of MAMC and tricep skin fold measures with reference standards may be done to assess the adequacy of lean body mass and fat stores (Canadian Bureau of Nutritional Sciences, 1983; Cronk & Roche, 1982; Spender, Hediger, Cronk, & Stallings, 1988). Assessment of body composition using these measures is most useful with sequential measurements.

There are limitations to the use of these measures (Spender et al., 1988). Use of single site skin

Box 1: Case Study: Mary

The following case study demonstrates how a nutritional assessment resulted in improved growth and quality of life for Mary, an eight-year-old girl with spastic quadriplegia.

Clinical history

Mary was admitted to the hospital because of frequent recent admissions to the hospital with pneumonia. It was thought that this was related to the aspiration of food in her lungs. This child had had a gastrostomy tube inserted at the age of three years because she was malnourished. Her current feeds through the gastrostomy tube were overnight feeds that provided 500 kcal per day, including 15 grams of protein.

Height and weight

- *Current height (estimated): 110 cm (3%ile)*
- *Current weight: 15 kg (3%ile)*

Current issues

- *Failure to thrive.*
- *Intolerance to overnight gastrostomy feeds. Mary was experiencing vomiting with these feeds. This was thought to be due to gastroesophageal reflux.*
- *Diet history indicated an energy intake of 200-300 kcal per day, and a difficulty with chewing meats and raw vegetables. There was no history of choking on liquids. Mary was now vomiting after each meal. Mealtimes were associated with a lot of stress associated with feeding. Her caregivers were very anxious about her food intake.*
- *Diagnostic tests such as a gastric emptying study and a pH probe indicated delayed gastric emptying and gastroesophageal reflux. A feeding study indicated feeding difficulty with solids. Soft foods were tolerated.*

---

fold measurements may lead to inaccurate assessments of body composition because fat deposition in the body may be site-dependent. Measurement technique may also affect the accuracy and precision of information derived from use of this technique. Individuals responsible for measurement of skinfolds should be trained in this method and measurements should be done in triplicate to minimize errors due to technique. A repeat measure by the same individual over time also ensures that the values obtained from these measurements are consistent over time. Measurement of skinfolds should also be done using the same calipers to reduce the potential for instrument error. Hence, standardizing the method of measurement of skinfolds and mid-arm circumference is important to reduce the potential for error in assessment of body composition.

Assessment of Energy Requirements

Assessment of energy requirements is an essential component of nutrition assessment. Under- and over-nutrition in children with developmental disabilities may be caused by deficits or surpluses of dietary intake over current energy requirements. Total energy requirements (total amount of energy expenditure in 24 hours) may be divided into the following components: basal requirements (energy expended at rest, shortly after awakening, after a 12-14 hour fast), energy requirements secondary to activity, thermic effect of food (energy required to digest and store food eaten), and disease-related losses (fever, burns etc.) (Zemel & Stallings, 1997). *Resting energy expenditure (REE)* refers to the amount of energy expended under conditions of rest, two hours after feeding.

Assessment

- *Ideal body weight: 19.5 kg.*
- *Current percent ideal body weight: 77%. This indicated a moderate protein energy malnutrition or that Mary needed more nutrition.*
- *Total energy requirements (based on WHO formula: REE x 1.1) = 950 kcal per day. Mary's total energy intake (by gastrostomy tube + oral intake) was not sufficient to meet these needs. Her current intake was providing only 75% of total energy requirements.*

Interventions that were recommended

- *Provide increased energy diet with soft textures that are more easily tolerated.*
- *Document intake with goal of meeting total energy intake via oral intake and gastrostomy feeds. Gastrostomy tube feeds should be kept at present level with goal to adjust regimen in accordance with her tolerance and rate of weight gain. The goal should be to promote oral intake and supplement with feeds via the gastrostomy tube. Weight to be monitored monthly in an out-patient setting.*
- *Focus on normalizing the feeding environment by promoting self-feeding. Initiate occupational therapy referral regarding positioning and feeding utensils to facilitate self-feeding. Meal times to be limited to 20-30 minutes.*
- *Start on gastric motility agents and/or proton pump inhibitors for treatment of delayed gastric emptying and gastroesophageal reflux.*

Outcome

Mary started to gain weight. She gained 1 kg (2.2 pounds) over the next 8 weeks. Her oral food intake started to increase. Her mother felt that this was due to the medications, as her vomiting had stopped. Mary still did not want to feed herself, but was more willing to take food from her mother.

There are several methods that may be used to determine energy requirements in children with developmental disabilities. These include measurement of resting energy requirements using such techniques as indirect calorimetry, doubly-labelled water techniques, reference equations, or recommended nutrient intake data (Spender et al., 1988). The use of recommended nutrient data is not appropriate in this population, as it does not reflect the differences in activity, body composition, and body size that are characteristic of people with developmental disabilities (Canadian Bureau of Nutritional Sciences, 1983). The use of the doubly-labelled water technique is most appropriate in research settings due to its high costs and demands for technical support. Use of indirect calorimetry is appropriate for assessment of resting energy requirements in this population, but requires the availability of a skilled technician for use in a clinical setting.

The most convenient tool to assess energy requirements of children with developmental disabilities in the clinical setting are the WHO formulas (WHO, 1985). These formulas allow individualized assessment of resting energy requirements based upon the age and weight of the child. Assessment of total energy requirements may be accomplished by adjustment for activity and disease factors. For healthy children, this translates into total energy requirements. Total energy requirements is equal to resting energy expenditure or REE (based on WHO standards) multiplied by a factor of 1.5-1.7. However, for children with spastic quadriplegic cerebral palsy, estimates of total energy requirements should be based on REE (based on WHO standards) multiplied by a factor of 1.1 (Azcue, Zello, Levy, & Pencharz, 1996; Bandini, Scholler,

Gukagawa, Wykes, & Dietz, 1991; Fried & Pencharz, 1991; Johnson, Goran, Ferrara, & Poehlman, 1995). Adjustment of REE (based on WHO standards), should be done to account for estimations of total energy requirements that also consider current neuromuscular function. For example, children with cerebral palsy with significant athetosis (continuous, involuntary motion) or who are ambulatory have increased energy needs that may also require adjustment of the REE values (Johnson et al., 1995). Hence, adjustments to estimates of resting energy requirements based on the WHO standards should consider neuromuscular status in children with spastic quadriplegic cerebral palsy to ensure that accurate assessments of total energy requirements are made (Azcue et al., 1996; Bandini et al., 1991; Johnson et al., 1995).

Nutritional Management

Feeding difficulties that result from dysphagia can be managed as follows (Cloud, 1993; Palmer et al., 1975; Reilly et al., 1996; Telch & Telch, 2003; Zemel & Stallings, 1997):

- Altering food textures to ensure safety of swallowing
- Increasing the energy density of the diet
- Proper positioning during feeding
- Selecting appropriate feeding utensils
- Assessing the route of feeding

Alteration in food texture to minimize the risk of aspiration of food contents into the lungs is the most common compensatory strategy for children with dysphagia. Food texture alterations may include the use of minced, pureed, or thickened textures. Choice of food texture(s) is based on feeding efficiency and on the ability to swallow a food texture safely. Limitations in food texture choices and selections may result in decreased food intake and weight loss. Energy intake may be enhanced by the addition of protein, carbohydrate, and/or fat modules to foods, or by the addition of high-energy/high protein oral supplements to the diet.

Persistent under-nutrition can lead to the necessity of enteral (intestinal) support to meet nutritional and hydration requirements (Cloud, 1993; Zemel & Stallings, 1993). Enteral support involves the insertion of **enterostomy devices** such as nasogastric (short term) or gastrostomy (long term) feeding tubes (Grunow, Chait, Savoie, Mullan, & Pencharz, 1994; Nutrition Committee, 1994; Telch & Telch, 2003). These tubes are used to deliver nutrition and hydration to children unable to meet their requirements orally. Feeding with these devices is usually supplemental. However, when the risk of aspiration from oral feeding is significant or when oral intake is severely limited, the insertion of enterostomy devices may be necessary to meet total nutritional and hydration needs of the child (Reilly et al., 1996). Careful monitoring of tolerance to tube feeding regimens, oral intake, and enterostomy devices can make this mode of nutrition support successful. Transition from tube to oral feeding should be a primary goal in supplemental tube feeding. The weaning process should be directed toward supporting optimal nutrition, growth, and development during transition to oral feeding, with feeding interventions directed towards the developmental stage of the child (Grunow et al., 1994; Nutrition Committee, 1994). Assessment of nutritional status, swallowing function, and feeding behaviours (willingness to eat) should be done throughout this process to ensure a successful transition to oral feeding. Tube feeding should be discontinued when more than 75% of total energy needs can be met through oral intake (Nutrition Committee, 1994; Schauster & Dwyer, 1996). Removal of gastrostomy devices should occur after 8-12 weeks of discontinuing nutrition support through these devices and when oral intake and rate of weight gain has become consistent (Nutrition Committee, 1994; Schauster & Dwyer, 1996).

Functional Capacity

Assessment of the functional capacity to self-feed is also very important in children with neurological impairment (Cloud, 1993; Reilly et al., 1996). Significant impairment in gross and fine motor skills may lead to a loss of independence to self-feed by limitations of food access, inability to participate in food preparation, and loss of fine motor skills that are required to self-feed. Adaptive feeding devices and assistance with positioning may be useful in increasing independence and safety in feeding. Functional impairments may include ataxia (failure of muscle coordination resulting in poorly judged movements), apraxia (inability to plan and execute a skilled movement in the absence of sensory and motor defects), and skeletal-muscular limitations (e.g., upper limb contracture). When possible, patients should be comfortably positioned in an upright position during a meal to facilitate ease and safety of feeding. Assistance with feeding by caregivers should promote independence with feeding. Pace of feeding, volume of the food bolus (how much food is being chewed at one time), and alterations in food textures can promote a self-feeding environment for the child with neurological impairment. Length of meal times should be limited to approximately 30 minutes to ensure optimal feeding efficiency (Cloud, 1993; Reilly et al., 1996).

Intervention by a behavioural feeding specialist can also assist in identifying and treating feeding problems in children with developmental disabilities. Focus is placed on the child-feeder interaction in addition to oral-motor skills and functional capacity to assist in normalizing the feeding environment (Rodas-Arts & Benoit, 1998). This usually includes mealtime observation for assessment of caregiver responses to adaptive and maladaptive feeding behaviours and intervention to promote appropriate eating behaviours (Rodas-Arts & Benoit, 1998).

Nutrition Related Medical Problems

Numerous medical problems can arise from improper nutrition. Two of these, obesity and celiac disease, are described here because they are commonly encountered.

Obesity

The most common causes of obesity in children with developmental delay include dietary intake in excess of energy requirements and lack of mobility. A few children with spastic quadriplegic cerebral palsy have been shown to have decreased resting energy

expenditure (Azcue et al., 1996; Fried & Pencharz, 1991). Caregiver overestimation of energy requirements can lead to overfeeding and excessive weight gain in this population. Obesity is also common in children and adults with Prader-Willi syndrome, where a much smaller than average number of calories is required to maintain normal body weight, and in children and adults with Down syndrome. Special growth charts are available for use in Down syndrome (Cronk et al., 1988; see also Chumlea & Cronk, 1981).

Assessment of obesity in children with developmental disabilities may be difficult due to limitations in the ability to measure height, weight, and skinfold measures. This limits the use of the Body Mass Index (BMI) to quantify or serial track the onset and severity obesity in this population. Waist circumference measures have been used to provide information regarding the severity of obesity in children (Rudolf et al., 2004). Measurement of waist circumference is a simple and easy tool that can be used to provide additional information regarding the severity of obesity in this population.

Dietary treatment of obesity in children with developmental disabilities involves modification of energy intake. Dietary intake should include all food groups to prevent macro- and micro-nutrient deficiency with energy restriction. Pediatric enteral formulas should be used in children fed via enterostomy devices. These formulas contain higher nutrient/energy ratios, which decrease the risk of micro-nutrient deficiency with energy restriction (Azcue et al., 1996; Fried & Pencharz, 1991). Dietary counselling of caregivers by a registered dietitian regarding food portion size and food selection is an essential component to the successful dietary treatment of obesity in this population. A weight management program that has been used with considerable success by many people with Prader-Willi syndrome is called the Red-Yellow-Green Weight Control Program. This is based on the traffic light color system. Green means "go!" Yellow means "caution — be careful, go slow" and Red means "stop!" (Balko, 2006). The program requires a dietitian skilled in its application to support its application.

Celiac disease

Celiac disease (CD) is an autoimmune disease that is commonly found in individuals in the more affluent countries of the world. Children and adults with this disorder have an autoimmune intolerance to gluten/gliadin, a common protein found in wheat, rye, and barley. Recent evidence suggests that the prevalence is approximately 1 in 100 (Rajani, Huynh, & Turner, 2010; Turner, Pellerin, & Mager, 2009). Individuals with CD may have a variety of symptoms at time of presentation that include gastrointestinal (GI) symptomology (nausea, *anorexia*, constipation, and irritability), iron deficiency anemia, fatigue, and poor growth and bone health. However, it is not uncommon for children and adults to be diagnosed with CD without any apparent GI symptomology at all; and in fact many children present with only fatigue and poor bone health as the major symptomology. Poor bone health can be of considerable concern, particularly in adolescence, due to the increased risk for osteoporosis later in life.

Although serological markers to screen for CD have been developed (anti-tissue transglutaminase and endomysial IgA antibodies), the only way to definitively diagnose CD is through jejunal (the middle portion of the small intestine) biopsy. The hallmark feature of intestinal biopsy is the presence of a flattened jejuna mucos, which is associated with macronutrient and micronutrient malabsorption (absorbing too few or too many nutrients). The potential for micronutrient deficiency of nutrients is particularly high for iron, zinc, magnesium and the fat soluble vitamins fats (A, D, E, and K) if CD is left untreated. Vitamins D and K in particular are important for healthy bone development and growth, and hence children and adolescents with chronic undiagnosed CD are at increased risk for poor bone health.

For children with developmental disabilities, poor bone health can be further exacerbated by issues related to immobility. Treatment for children and adolescents requires life-long restriction of dietary gluten/gliadin. Complete exclusion of gluten/gliadin from the diet can bring about full GI recovery for individuals with CD and can quickly contribute to improved overall well-being. Although controversial, exclusion of dietary avenin, a common protein found in oats, is still recommended.

Vitamin supplementation may be required in the period following diagnosis of CD, but it should not be routinely needed if compliance to the gluten free diet is achieved. For the child with developmental disabilities and CD, following the gluten free diet carefully can result in significant overall improvements in quality of life. Education regarding the diet by a registered dietitian is imperative to ensure that the child or adult with CD is following a gluten free diet (Rajani et al., 2010; Turner et al., 2009). For information regarding the gluten free diet, consult: *http://www.celiac.ca/*

Summary

Under- and over-nutrition are common concerns of children with developmental delay. Under- and over-nutrition are the deficit or surplus of dietary intake over total nutritional needs. The common causes of malnutrition in children with developmental delay include poor dietary intake and diminished feeding efficiency that result from swallowing and gastrointestinal dysfunction. Feeding problems and functional impairments to self-feeding may compound this. Assessment of nutritional status should include assessment of growth parameters, body composition, diet and medical history, and energy requirements to identify risk for under- and over-nutrition. Management of nutritional disorders in children with developmental disabilities is complex and should include a multidisciplinary approach.

For Further Thought and Discussion

1. Consider both the children and adults with developmental disabilities that you have known. How common do you think malnutrition might be in this population?
2. Think of a child you know who might benefit from a nutrition assessment. What steps would you take to ensure that a full multidisciplinary assessment occurs?

3. In a group with three others, identify four children with developmental disabilities who have feeding difficulties of various kinds. What are some practical ways that each could be helped in ways that promote their independence?

Special Terms

Achondroplasia: An autosomal dominant disorder characterized by short stature and a distinctive and identifiable phenotype at birth.

Anemia: A reduction below normal in the number of red cells per unit of blood, the quantity of hemoglobin, or the volume of packed red cells per unit of blood, when the equilibrium between blood loss and blood production is disturbed.

Anorexia: Lack or loss of the appetite for food.

Crohn's disease: A disease in which the small intestine and/or the large intestine becomes scarred following a chronic inflammation; it frequently leads to intestinal obstruction.

Edema: The condition characterized by an excess of watery fluid collecting in the cavities or tissues of the body.

Enterostomy devices: An enterostomy device is a tube or feeding device that is placed in the gastrointestinal tract. This tube may be inserted via a stoma (hole) through the skin or via the mouth or nasal passages. This may include tubes placed in the stomach (gastrostomy) or small intestine (jejununostomy or gastrojejunal tubes) via an outside opening on the skin, or through the mouth or nose. Examples of feeding tubes are nasogastric tubes or nasojejunal feeding tubes.

Erythropoiesis: The production of erythrocytes (red blood cells).

Ferritin: A protein that helps to compartmentalize iron inside the cells. Serum ferritin is the biochemical marker used to assess total body iron.

Gastroesophageal reflux disease (GERD): Refluxing of the contents of the stomach into the esophagus (the musculomembranous passage extending from the back of the mouth to the stomach).

Hypochromic anemia: Abnormal decrease in the hemoglobin content of the red cells.

Ideal body weight: This is located on standard Weight for Height Measures. The ideal body weight is located on the same percentile curve as the height percentile, or it can be considered to be the weight at the 50%ile for age (there are tables for this). However, comparison for 50 percentile weight for age does not take into consideration genetic, race, or other factors that might be relevant for assessment of Ideal Body Weight.

Microcytic anemia: Anemia characterized by smaller than normal red blood cells, decreased mean red cell volume, and less circulating hemoglobin.

Mid-arm circumference (MAC): Composite measure of muscle, fat and bone on the arm. It is sensitive to current nutritional status and can be used in combination with the triceps skinfold thickness measure to estimate muscle area and arm fat area. MAC is measured by measuring the diameter of the arm. The measurement should be taken at the halfway point between the acrominion process (shoulder) and the elbow.

Mid-arm muscle mass (MAMC): Reflects the muscle mass. It can be calculated using the following equation: MAC - 3.14 x (tricep skin fold) / 10

Organomegaly: Enlarged organ.

Platelets: Cells in the blood that agglutinate or clot together in response to local tissue injury in the blood system.

Premature synostosis: Premature joining of the bony plates in the skull.

Protein energy malnutrition (PEM): Condition in which the ratio of actual body weight to ideal body weight is 90% or less.

Resting energy expenditure (REE): Amount of energy expended under conditions of rest two hours after feeding. REE is measured using indirect or direct calorimetry methods. Indirect calorimetry involves the use of equipment that measures and collects inspired and expired air of an individual. Indirect calorimetry bases estimates of energy expenditure on oxygen consumption and carbon dioxide production.

Serum: The clear liquid part of blood that remains after blood cells and clotting proteins have been removed.

Serum albumin: The main protein in blood plasma. Low levels occur in people with malnutrition, inflammation and serious liver and kidney diseases.

Transferrin: A protein used to assess iron binding capacity. Serum transferrin receptor, in conjunction with serum iron, is used to assess total iron binding capacity.

Tricep skinfold measure: Skinfold measure taken at the midway point between the acrominion process and the elbow. The measure is done on the tricep skin fold. Tricep skin fold measures reflect the fat composition in the body.

Supersupraglottic swallow: Swallow that is done when a person is holding their breath and putting strain on their rectal sphincter (as when having a bowel movement, but they don't actually have one). These manoeuvers can result in closing of the epiglottis over the open airway, closure of the vocal cords, and velopharyngeal closure.

Supraglottic swallow: Individual takes a deep breath, holds their breath and then initiates a strong, purposeful swallow. The idea is to initiate vocal cord closure, for airway protection.

Velopharyngeal: This term refers to the area on the back of the velum to the posterior pharyngeal wall. The velum is part of the soft palate, and is a small flap that presses against the back of the posterior pharyngeal wall when a swallow is triggered. This prevents passage of food into the nasal passages.

Visceral protein status: Reflects lean body mass stores (primarily skeletal muscle mass).

More Resources

A health professional's guide for using growth charts
http://www.ncbi.nlm.nih.gov/pmc/articles/ PMC2720489/

Health Canada: Food and Nutrition. Canada's Food Guide: *http://www.hc-sc.gc.ca/fn-an/food-guide-aliment/index-eng.php*

National Health and Nutrition Examination Survey at CDC's National Center for Health Statistics
http://www.cdc.gov/nchs/nhanes.htm

Nutrition for individuals with intellectual or developmental disabilities: Nutrition standards of care. *http://mtdh.ruralinstitute.umt.edu/Publications/ StandardsStaff.htm*

Public Health Agency of Canada:
Childhood and Adolescence
http://www.phac-aspc.gc.ca/hp-ps/dca-dea/index-eng.php

The Red-Yellow-Green Weight Control System (The Stoplight or Traffic Light Diet)
For information about this program in Canada contact Dr. Glenn Berall or Karen Balko, Gastroenterology/Nutrition, North York General Hospital, 4001 Leslie Street, Toronto, Ontario, Canada M2K 1E1;
Tel.: (416) 756-6222;
E-mail: kbalko@nygh.on.ca.
http://www.pwsnetwork.ca/pws/docs/abcs_nutrition_2.pdf

References

Azcue, M. P., Zello, G. A., Levy, L. D., & Pencharz, P. B. (1996). Energy expenditure and body composition in children with spastic quadriplegic cerebral palsy. *Journal of Pediatics, 129*, 870-876.

Balko, K. A. (2006). *The ABCs of nutrition. Implementation of the Red, Yellow, Green, system (RYG) of weight management.* Retrieved from http://www.pwsnetwork.ca/pws/docs/abcs_nutrition_2.pdf

Bandini, L. G., Scholler, D. A., Gukagawa, N. K., Wykes, L. J., & Dietz, W. H. (1991). Body composition and energy expenditure in adolescents with cerebral palsy or myelodysplasia. *Pediatric Research, 29*, 70-77.

Canadian Bureau of Nutritional Sciences. (1983). *Recommended nutrient intakes for Canadians.* Health & Welfare Canada, Canadian Government Publication Centre, Ottawa, ON, Canada.

Centers for Disease Control and Prevention, National Center for Health Statistics. (2009). *CDC growth charts: United States.* Retrieved from http://www.cdc.gov/growthcharts/

Chumlea, W. C., & Cronk, C. E. (1981). Overweight among children with trisomy 21. *Journal of Mental Deficiency Research, 25*, 275-280.

Cloud, H. (1993). Feeding problems of the child with special health care needs. In S. W. Ekvall (Ed.), *Pediatric nutrition in chronic diseases & de-*

velopmental disorder (pp. 203-217). New York: Oxford University Press.

Cronk, C. E., & Roche, A. E. (1982). Race- and sex-specific reference data for triceps and subscapular skinfolds and weight/stature. *American Journal of Clinical Nutrition, 35*(2), 347-354.

Cronk, C., Crocker, A. C., Pueschel, S. M., Shea, A. M., Zackai, E., Pickens, G., & Reed R. B. (1988). Growth charts for children with Down syndrome: 1 month to 18 years of age. *Pediatrics, 81*, 102-110.

de Onis, M., Onyango, A. W., Borghi, E., Siyam, A., Nishida, C., & Siekmann, J. (2007). Development of a WHO growth reference for school-aged children and adolescents. *Bulletin of the World Health Organization, 85*, 660-667.

Dietitians of Canada. (2004). A health professionals guide to using growth charts. *Paediatrics & Child Health, 9*(3), 174–176. Retrieved from http://www.ncbi.nlm.nih.gov/pmc/articles/PMC2720489/

DiLorenzo, C., Piepz, A., Ham, H., & Cadrane, S. (1991). Gastric emptying with gastroesophageal reflux. *Archives Disabled Children, 62*, 499-453.

Fried, M. D., & Pencharz, P. B. (1991). Energy and nutrient intakes of children with spastic quadriplegia. *Journal of Pediatrics, 119*, 947-949.

Garza, C., & de Onis, M. (1999). A new international growth reference for young children. American *Journal of Clinical Nutrition, 70*(Suppl. 1), 169-172.

Goldbloom, R. B. (1997). Assessment of physical growth and nutrition. In R. B. Goldbloom, *Pediatric clinical skills* (2nd ed.) (pp. 23-48). New York: Churchill Livingston.

Grummer-Strawn, L. M., Garza, C., & Johnson, C. L. (2002). Childhood growth charts. *Pediatrics, 109*, 141-142.

Grunow, J., Chait, P., Savoie, S., Mullan, C., & Pencharz, P. B. (1994). Recent advances in gastrostomy feeding. In T. J. David (Ed.), *Recent advances in Paediatrics* (12th ed.) (pp.23-29). London: Churchill Livingston.

Guo, S., Roche, A.F., Fomon, S.F., Nelson, S.E., Chumlea, W.C., Rogers, R. R., et al. (1991). Reference data on gains in weight and length during the first two years of life. *Journal of Pediatrics, 119*, 355-362.

Hamil, P. V., Drizd, T. A., Johnson, C. L., Reed, R. B., Roche, A. F., & Moore, W. M. (1979). Physical growth: National Center for Health Statistics (NCHS) percentiles. *American Journal Clinical Nutrition, 36*, 607-629.

Himes, J. G., Roche, A. F., Thissen, D., & Moore, W. M. (1985). Parent-specific adjustments for evaluation of recumbent length and stature of children. *Pediatrics, 75*, 304-313.

Hopkins, B. (1993). Assessment of nutritional status. In M. M. Gottschlich, L. E. Matarese, & E. P. Shronts (Eds.), *Nutrition support dietetics core curriculum* (2nd ed.) (pp. 15-63). Silver Spring, MD: American Society of Parenteral & Enteral Nutrition.

Johnson, R. K., Goran, M. I., Ferrara, M. S., & Poehlman, E. T. (1995). Athetosis increases resting metabolic rate in adults with cerebral palsy. *Journal of the American Dietetic Association, 95*, 145-148.

Krick, J., Murphy-Miller, P., Zeger, S., & Wright, E. (1996). Pattern of growth in children with cerebral palsy. *Journal of the American Dietetic Association, 96*, 680-685.

Lifschitz, F., & Maclaren, N. K. (1975). Vitamin D-dependent rickets in institutionalized, mentally retarded children receiving long-term anticonvulsant therapy: A survey of 288 patients. *Journal of Pediatrics, 56*, 52-57.

McLaren, D. S., & Read, W. C. (1972). Classification of nutritional status in early childhood. *Lancet, 2*, 146.

Nutrition Committee, Canadian Paediatric Society. (1994). Clinical practice guidelines: Undernutrition in children with a neurodevelopmental disability. *Canadian Medical Association Journal, 151*, 759.

Palmer, S., Thompson, R. J., & Linscheid, T. R. (1975). Applied behavior analysis in the treatment of childhood feeding problems. *Developmental Medicine and Child Neurology, 17*, 333-339.

Rajani, S., Huynh, H. Q., & Turner, J. (2010). The changing frequency of celiac disease diagnosed at the Stollery Children's Hospital. *Canadian Journal of Gastroenterology, 24*(2), 109-112.

Reilly, S., Skuse, D., & Poblete, X. (1996). Prevalence of feeding problems and oral motor dysfunction in children with cerebral palsy: A community survey. *Journal of Pediatrics, 129,* 877-882.

Roche, A. F., & Davila, G. H. (1974). Differences between recumbant length and stature within individuals. *Growth, 38,* 313.

Roche, A. F., & Himes, J. H.(1980). Incremental growth charts. *American Journal of Clinical Nutrition, 33,* 2041-2052.

Rodas-Arts, D., & Benoit, D. (1998). Feeding problems in infancy and early childhood: Identification and management. *Paediatric Child Health, 3,* 21-27.

Roe, A. (1982). *Handbook: Interactions of selected drugs and nutrients in patients* (3rd ed.). Chicago: American Dietetic Association.

Rudolph, C. D. (1994). Feeding disorders in infants and children. *Journal of Pediatrics, 125,* S116-S124.

Rudolph, M. C. J., Greenwood, D. C., Cole, T. J., Levine, R., Sahot, P., Walker, J., et al. (2004). *Archives of Diseases of Childhood, 89,* 235-237.

Schauster, H., & Dwyer, J. (1996). Transition from tube feedings to feedings by mouth in children: Preventing eating dysfunction. *Journal of the American Dietetic Association, 96,* 277-281.

Schenker, J., & Ward, R. (1999). Development and application of a pediatric anthropometric evaluation system. *Canadian Journal of Dietetic Practice and Research, 60,* 20-26.

Sondheimer, J. M., & Morris, B. A. (1979). Gastroesophageal reflux among severely retarded children. *Journal of Pediatrics, 94,* 710-714.

Spender, Q. W., Cronk, C. E., Charney, E. B., & Stallings, V. A. (1989). Assessment of linear growth of children with cerebral palsy: Use of alternative measures to height or length. *Developmental Medicine and Child Neurology, 31,* 206-214.

Spender, Q. W., Hediger, M. L., Cronk, C. E., & Stallings, V. A. (1988). Fat distribution in children with cerebral palsy. *Annals of Human Biology, 15,* 191-196.

Sullivan, P. B. (1997). Gastrointestinal problems in the neurologically impaired child. *Baillieres Clinical Gastroenterology, 11,* 529-556.

Tanner, J. M., Whitehouse, R. H., & Takaishi, M. (1966). Standards from birth to maturity for height, weight, height velocity and weight velocity: British children 1965, I and II. *Archives Disabled Children, 41,* 454-471, 613-615.

Telch, J., & Telch, F. E. (2003). Practical aspects of nutrition in the disabled pediatric patient. *Clinical Nutrition, 3,* 1-6.

Turner, J., Pellerin, G., & Mager, D. (2009). Prevalence of metabolic bone disease in children with celiac disease is independent of symptoms at diagnosis. *Journal of Pediatric Gastroenterology and Nutrition, 49*(5), 589-593.

World Health Organization (WHO). (1985). *Energy and protein requirements. Technical report series #724.* Geneva, Switzerland: World Health Organization.

World Health Organization (WHO). (2011). *The WHO Child Growth Standards.* Retrieved from http://www.who.int/childgrowth/standards/en/

Zemel, B., & Stallings, V. A. (1997). Energy requirements and nutritional assessment in developmental disabilities. In W. A. Walker & J. B. Watkins (Eds.), *Nutrition in Pediatrics* (pp. 169-177). London: Decker Inc.

33

Safe Medication Practice and Front Line Professional Practice

Andrea Rutherford

What you will learn:

- Front line professionals need to be knowledgeable about medications
- Skill is required for front line professionals to administer medications effectively
- Front line professionals must exercise judgement when administering medications

Medication is an essential component of the health and well-being of many individuals with developmental disabilities. Currently, in Canada, there are no standards of practice for administering medications in developmental services, yet it is very often front line staff — unregulated professionals — who are responsible for doing so. This responsibility can be onerous, especially because following medication protocols, documenting administration and responses to medications, and meeting the needs of each individual supported can be challenging.

Two additional factors add to the challenges of front line professionals administering medications to people with developmental disabilities. First, it is difficult to bring such people together, as they are employed across many different areas of practice. In Ontario, they may work in hospitals and long term care settings, community settings (residential, sup-

ported independent living, and respite programs), day programs and work support, and many other settings. Many administer medications themselves, while others are involved in the medication support plans from other places. Second, there is considerable turnover of staff and there are frequently staff vacancies in developmental services, which results in qualified and trained staff not always being in place. Front line professionals are in short supply, especially in some geographic areas of Ontario, and the resulting high vacancy rates increase demand for qualified staff, which, in turn, results in a shrinking supply of qualified people (Hewitt & Larson, 2007).

Within this context in Ontario, it seems essential that we make every effort to ensure that front line professionals in developmental services are identified and trained, so that responsible administration of medications can occur. This requires high levels of communication, coordination, and interaction (CIHI, 2005). Woodrow, Colbert, & Smith (2011) suggested that care staff (in any field) must possess three vital responsibilities in the safe and accurate administration of medications: sound knowledge, well-developed skill, and informed judgement. These three responsibilities appear to be central components of the role of any staff who administers medication in our field. They also appear to provide a more general basis for considering safe administration of medications.

Front Line Professionals Need Knowledge

Knowledge about medications and their administration is required of professionals employed in developmental services. It is crucial that front line professionals know relevant and up-to-date information about each medication prescribed and administered to all individuals they support, and what its effects might be. Such knowledge comes from study, education, and training, but also from experience and practice.

It is generally assumed that any front line professional has considerable knowledge of this kind. However, many lack basic, current information about the medications they administer on a daily basis. Research suggests that front line professionals wish to know more about the medications they administer, but do not receive adequate training through their employment (Chapman, Gledhill, Jones, Burton, & Soni, 2006). Although training is frequently provided shortly after hiring, many front line professionals feel they need ongoing training. When this is not the case, they may lack current information and, as a consequence, lack confidence in their ability to safely administer and monitor medications prescribed by the health care providers (family doctor or psychiatrist). On the other hand, there are many skilled and experienced front line professionals who practise and role model exceptional skills in administering medications, and work in close partnership with other professionals in doing so.

Having knowledge specific to the actual drugs pre-scribed is essential in practice. Drug specific information in terms of drug side effects, contraindications, interactions, and adverse effects are part of the knowledge required (Woodrow, Colbert, & Smith, 2011). In addition to this, front line professionals administering medications must be fully aware of all storage procedures, health teaching and special instructions necessary prior to any administration. This also means that front line professionals need to share this information with the individuals they support, members of their families, and with any other members of the multidisciplinary support team.

Front line professionals required to administer medication must obtain relevant information prior to first administration of the medication, and they may do so from a number of sources. The most common sources are: instructions from the prescribing physician, the pharmacist (or what is provided in print), drug reference guides, reliable internet sites, or other reputable sources. With the acquisition of basic drug knowledge, front line professionals have the basis for providing the best care and medication administration practice possible.

The essential need for knowledge in safe medication practice must also pair with site specific policies and procedures in the workplace. In every practice setting where medication is administered, there should be a unique set of policies and procedures guiding medication practice. For front line professionals, policies and procedures must be clear in their explanation, current and updated on a regular basis, and reviewed with every front line professional. The materials should be available and stored in accessible areas the site where medication is administered. Front line professionals responsible for medication administration are encouraged to ask questions and learn from observing other staff in the site who safely (and knowledgeably) administer medications. Just as practice changes and evolves over time, the needs of all individuals being supported change as well.

Building upon the development of knowledge, front line professionals should have the ability to engage in a comprehensive assessment, well planned intervention, and intensive evaluation related to medication practice. Beyond using skills to determine whether or not the medication is actually managing and treating the symptoms or illness and evaluating the effectiveness of the drugs administered, front line professionals are required to be fully aware of the additional responsibilities that are required with administering some medications to individuals with developmental disabilities. There could possibly be a need for ongoing lab work, additional documentation and tracking, and communication with professionals and colleagues about symptoms and behaviours, or planning for an unexpected situation or medication related emergency that could arise. Front line professionals must have knowledge of an individual's health history and allergies in order to be prepared for all unexpected events.

One particular reason for needing a high degree of knowledge in front line practice is that, in reality, there is always the potential for medication errors. Much of the literature available in Canada indicated that complex health issues and ongoing disparities continue to exist across all areas of health care for individuals with developmental disabilities (CIHI, 2005). Medication practice has also shifted focus to a culture that holds safety and improved individual outcomes as priorities (CIHI, 2005). With this shift in focus, there is even more scrutiny placed upon front line professionals who are directly involved with providing health care.

Reporting critical incidents and errors in practice is mandatory (CIHI, 2005). CIHI (2005) noted that many of the challenging adverse events that occur in health care are not necessarily the result of negligence, carelessness or incompetence on the part of the front line professionals involved in care, and that the system of "incident reporting is experiencing a shift from a culture of 'blame and shame' to one focused on safety and learning" (p. 4). Many of the errors that occur and the lack of reporting are the consequence of staff lacking knowledge and not fully knowing the impact of their actions on the care provided. With an increased responsibility on front line professionals to report all medication errors, Jenkins and Vaida (2007) noted that injuries due to errors in medication are preventable. In preventing errors as part of safe medication administration practice, front line professionals need to again con-

sider providing the best education available to individuals supported, adequately communicate with colleagues, consider safe storage and labeling for all medications, and foster a culture based upon safety (Jenkins & Vaida, 2007). Providing safe medication administration requires knowledge.

Skill in Administering Medications is Essential

Skill in the safe delivery of medications must be timely and accurately performed, and carried out in accordance with individual rights and adherence to prescription guidelines. According to Woodrow et al. (2011), skill in responsible delivery comes with the best interest of the individual in mind, and fully supported by correct, well detailed, and adequate documentation. Again, much like knowledge, skill comes with practice.

Skill is acquired through exposure to a variety of individuals, practice scenarios, training, and education. It should be noted that skill is not something that every front line professional possesses instantly. Skill grows and evolves with practice over time. Front line professionals in developmental services should access opportunities to develop their skills and enhance their knowledge through collaborative practice. Role playing scenarios, demonstrations, and hands on practice should be engaged in continuously over time. Skills can always be enhanced. Safe and skilled medication practice is not only beneficial to the individuals who directly receive care, but also builds confidence and adds to knowledge in front line professional practice.

Skilled medication practice involves a check of RIGHTs throughout the actual administration process. According to Woodrow et al. (2011), the six RIGHTs of medication practice consist of the right documentation, the right route, the right medication/drug, the right time, the right amount/dosage and, lastly, administration of medication to the right person. A good way for frontline professionals to remember these six RIGHTs as they approach individual medication administration is by using the easy acronym 'DR M TAP' (Figure 1). By using the "DR M TAP" acronym, medication administration

Figure 1. "DR M TAP"

Documentation

Route

Medication

Time

Amount/dosage

Person

© Andrea Rutherford, 2006.

practice, costly errors, oversights, and unnecessary untherapeutic care can be avoided.

Managing time and the countless responsibilities that front line professionals have are also important aspects of practice to be considered. Front line professionals are required to perform a variety of functions in their daily work that demand additional skills. It is imperative that front line professionals arrive at the work site and plan their shifts or work day structure. In terms of maximizing safe medication practice and using skills appropriately, a well-established work plan incorporates what medication tasks are required, and allows time for careful thought, assessment, planning, and evaluation of therapeutic treatment.

Front Line Professionals Must Use Judgement

For safe medication practice, and in addition to knowledge and skill, all front line professions need to exercise *wisdom* and *judgement* (Woodrow et al., 2011). Much like common sense, wisdom and judgement are vitally important. It might be suggested that common sense develops out of wisdom and decision making. An additional aspect of wisdom and judgement is that front line professionals must possess the ability to be able to respond appropriately and in a timely way in the event of an emergency or accident with medication and medication administration practice (Woodrow et al., 2011).

In order to make good decisions and judgements in practice, front line professionals need to know and understand all required policies and procedures regarding medication and health care. Front line professionals need access to up to date health history and information about the individual receiving support. Professionals working in the field must also have access to other professionals through attending conferences, taking part in external training, and networking with peers (Hewitt & Larson, 2007). Knowing full information (or as much as possible) about every individual receiving support provides that basis for ongoing safe medication administration practices. Ultimately, applying knowledge and skills enhances decision making abilities and the use of judgement in front line practice.

Safe Medication Administration in Practice

In considering the Woodrow et al. (2011) responsibilities for safe medication practice, it is easy to see that knowledge, skill, and judgement's form the most basic foundation of safe medication practice. Front line professionals must collaborate and communicate with professionals and other service providers as part of this. Individuals who require ongoing, daily medication rely on front line professionals to communicate with their primary physicians and other health professionals involved in their care. Service providers (including physicians) must share knowledge and promote the concept of the equal team member (Jenkins & Vaida, 2007). Making use of the equal team member perspective supports communication in order to work to avoid serious medication errors or harm to the individual receiving medication as part of treatment (Jenkins & Vaida, 2007).

Summary

In order to best support any individual with a developmental disability who requires medication, front line professionals must possess knowledge, skill and judgement. These three key responsibilities do not promise best practice, but certainly help front line professionals to administer medications to individuals with developmental disabilities in the safest way possible.

Case Scenario

Jack is a 48 year old man with a developmental disability and multiple health challenges. Jack lives in a residential home with three other men. Jack is nonverbal and requires a lengthy list of medications to be administered three times per day. Jack requires total support and depends on the front line professionals that staff his home. Among the medications that Jack requires are those related to gastrointestinal, respiratory, and cardiovascular problems, but several of the other medications are from those psychotropic classifications. There are at least two or three shift changes per day in Jack's home. The residential home often uses agency staff during times of high staff turnover.

If front line practice uses knowledge, skill, and judgement, what would front line professionals do to support Jack?

Knowledge: Front line professionals need to know Jack's health history (knowledge of the specific developmental challenge and all relevant facts about problem behaviours and psychiatric diagnoses), allergies, and full medication profile. All information about each and every medication administered to Jack (including drug uses, side effects, interactions, and contraindications) should be available on site for all front line professionals to access. All medication specific information, including dosage, times to be administered, special instructions, storage, and accurate documentation and tracking records are necessary too.

Skill: Front line professionals working with Jack in this setting should have the opportunity for training (both site specific and agency) with regular audits or testing to ensure that safe medication administration practices are followed and understood. Accessibility of supervisory staff and other relevant health professionals involved in care should be provided in case of discrepancies in practice or questions arise.

Judgement: Regular team meetings, follow up appointments with medical and health care professionals and ongoing communication among front line professionals will enhance the care that Jack receives. Front line professionals need to make informed decisions and act instantly in situations as the need or situation arises. Therefore, access to on site policies and procedures, medication information, and all required documentation will support the decisions made by front line professionals in this process. As Jack's needs change, the decisions made by front line professionals involved in his care will also change. Change will influence safe medication practice.

For Further Thought and Discussion

1. What training do you think a newly-hired staff should receive before he or she is entrusted to administer medications alone?
2. Pretend that you are a front line professional who has responsibility for administering medications, but you consider that you do not have enough knowledge or skill to do so without some risk of error. What would you do to acquire more knowledge and skill?
3. Discuss with your classmates how you would demonstrate good judgement if you are working alone in a support situation, and someone to whom you have administered medication has an adverse reaction.
4. Debate with your classmates whether or not Ontario needs standards of practice for administering medications to people with developmental disabilities. When arguing pro or con, consider Woodrow's three components of good medication administration practice — knowledge, skill, and judgement.

More Resources

Children's Hospital of Eastern Ontario (CHEO)
What you need to know about financial coverage for medications in Ontario. Fact sheet for parents and caregivers.
http://www.cheo.on.ca/uploads/Financial%20supports/Financial%20help%20for%20medications.pdf

The Institute for Safe Medical Practices Canada (ISMP Canada)
http://www.ismp-canada.org/

MedsCheck. Ontario Ministry of Health and Long-Term Care
http://health.gov.on.ca/en/public/programs/drugs/medscheck/

PSWLaw.ca
Can't afford your medication? The Ontario Trillium Drug Program may be able to help.
http://pswlaw.ca/2010/05/cant-afford-your-medi-cation-the-ontario-trillium-drug-program-may-be-able-to-help/

Patients for Patient Safety Canada
http://patientsforpatientsafety.ca/

Seniors Info. Medications and Drugs
http://www.seniorsinfo.ca/en/categories/560

King, R., Wilson, J., & Atchison, J.-A. (2008). *PRN protocols: Applying pharmacokinetic principles to practice; supporting individuals with developmental disabilities and mental health concerns in community settings.* Retrieved from *http://findarticles.com/p/articles/mi_6883/is_3_11/ai_n31344585/*

References

CIHI. (2005). *Canadian adverse events drug study, medication incident reporting and prevention systems environmental scan.* Statistics Canada, Health Statistics Division, Health Reports, 19, 2. Published by authority of the Minister responsible for Statistics Canada. Minister of Industry, 2008.

Chapman, M., Gledhill, P., Jones, P., Burton, M., & Soni, S. (2006). The use of psychotropic medication with adults with learning disabilities: Survey findings and implications for services. *British Journal of Learning Disabilities, 34,* 28–35.

Hewitt, A., & Larson, S. (2007). The direct support workforce in community supports to individuals with developmental disabilities: Issues, implications, and promising practices. *Mental Retardation and Developmental Disabilities Research Reviews, 13,* 178–187.

Jenkins, R. H., & Vaida, A. J. (2007). Simple strategies to avoid medication errors. *Family Practice Management, 14*(2), 41–47.

Woodrow, R., Colbert, B., & Smith, C. (2011). *Essentials of pharmacology for health occupations* (6th ed.). Toronto, ON: Delmar Publishing (Delmar Cengage Learning).

34

Psychopharmacology of People with Developmental Disabilities

Kenneth Boss

What you will learn:

- History of psychoactive drugs
- Some common psychiatric medications and their modes of action
- Problems in treating people with intellectual and disability with psychoactive drugs
- Evidence based intervention
- Influence of the pharmaceutical industry

Psychoactive drugs have been used by humans since prehistoric times. Various psychoactive mushrooms have been used as intoxicants in tribal rituals for millennia. Alcohol has been produced and consumed by humans since the Neolithic period. St. John's wort, a common medicinal herb used for mild to moderate depression, was recommended by physicians in ancient Greece. The systematic use of chemical compounds for the treatment of psychiatric disorders, however, did not exist prior to the middle of the 20th century.

The principal therapeutic tools available to psychiatrists prior to 1950 were convulsive therapies, which involve the induction of a seizure (as in electroconvulsive therapy), and psychosurgery, which consists of severing selected white matter connections within the brain (as in the prefrontal leucotomy or

lobotomy). Although forms of these procedures are still in use today, they are generally considered treatments of last resort and are regarded by the general public with skepticism or even disgust.

Today, medication therapy is the primary focus of psychiatric treatment and the psychopharmaceutical industry has become a multi-billion dollar business. The burgeoning field of psychopharmacology is seen by many as a testament to progress in the neurosciences as well as heightened public and professional awareness of psychiatric disorders as medical illnesses, leading to a decrease in stigma and an increase in recognition and treatment. Others regard psychopharmacology as a dangerous means of social control and an unethical collusion between psychiatry and the pharmaceutical industry that assures continued growth for both (Illich,

Box 1: The Birth of Psychopharmacology

The birth of modern psychopharmacology coincides with the introduction of chlorpromazine (CPZ) in France in the early 1950s, although psychoactive compounds such as opiates and barbiturates were used for their calming properties prior to that time. CPZ was originally used to inhibit the physiological stress reaction of the central nervous system during surgery. The effects on anxiety and emotional stress were so marked that Henri-Marie Laborit, who conducted the first clinical trials of CPZ in surgery in 1951, suggested its use in psychiatry. The following year, Pierre Deniker and Jean Delay, working at Sainte-Anne Hospital in Paris, conducted the first pivotal studies of CPZ treatment in psychiatric patients. They described a "neuroleptic syndrome" in which CPZ slowed motor activity and induced affective indifference and emotional neutrality, and proposed the name "neuroleptic" to designate a class of medications that produced this syndrome (López-Muñoz, Alamo, Rubio, & Cuenca, 2003). The eventual discovery that antipsychotic medications tended to share the feature of blocking dopamine type 2 (D2) receptors led to the dopamine hypothesis of schizophrenia. This posits that too much dopaminergic activity in certain areas of the brain causes the so-called "positive symptoms" (hallucinations, delusions, and disorganized behaviour and speech).

Zola, McKnight, Caplan, & Shaiken, 1977). These issues have become particularly contentious for children and adults with intellectual and developmental disabilities (IDD), because they are dependent upon others to make treatment decisions for them. In the absence of resources such as effective behavioural interventions, appropriate housing, and meaningful recreational and social activities, even the most well-meaning physician will often prescribe psychiatric medications to individuals with IDD for risk of significant harm to self or others.

Medications and Psychiatric Diagnoses in Intellectual and Developmental Disabilities

Between 20% and 45% of all people with IDD are taking psychotropic medication (Deb & Fraser, 1994), making them the most medicated group in society (Nøttestad & Linaker, 2003). This percentage is rising, especially among children and adolescents with intellectual disability (ID) (Kaperanovic & Simpson, 2006), despite the fact that only about 14% of these individuals meet DSM-IV criteria for a psychiatric disorder once diagnoses of autism spectrum disorders are excluded (Cooper, Smiley, Morrison, Williamson, & Allan, 2007). As many as two-thirds of medications prescribed are antipsychotics (Spreat, Conroy, & Jones, 1997) even though schizophrenia

and other psychotic disorders affect only about 3-4% of people with ID. On the other hand, "problem behaviours" (also sometimes referred to as "challenging behaviours") occur in over 20% of people with IDD (Cooper et al., 2007).

This situation runs counter to the paradigm of contemporary psychiatry, which dictates that a medication be prescribed to treat a specific diagnosis for which that medication has proven to be effective.

When antipsychotic medications were first discovered, it was their sedating and tranquilizing effects that were appreciated rather than their ability to decrease hallucinations, delusional thinking, and disorganized speech and behaviour, the hallmark symptoms of psychosis. As psychiatry has sought to become an increasingly refined discipline, psychopharmacological specificity (targeting specific and well-defined symptoms of an illness with a medication that is proven to reduce these symptoms with a minimum of side effects) has become an important goal. In fact, sedation is now considered a negative side effect of an antipsychotic, one that should ideally be achieved only with sedative medications specifically designed for that purpose. In this modern context, the use of an antipsychotic medication to reduce behaviours rather than to treat a diagnosed condition whose symptoms have been proven to respond to this class of medications harkens back to the days of the "neuroleptic syndrome" (see Box 1).

Box 2: Factors Affecting the Use of Psychoactive Drugs

Unusual and challenging behaviour in people with IDD can result from a number of different factors. These include: difficulties with adaptation due to the intellectual disability (e.g., lack of developmental maturity, limited self-expression skills), mental illness (e.g., schizophrenia, bipolar disorder, generalized anxiety disorder) or learning history (e.g., banging one's head because of the attention received when one does so). Any of these factors can obscure the contribution of the others in certain settings.

Attributing all problem behaviours in people with IDD to their disability is referred to as diagnostic overshadowing. In the original experiment designed to explore this phenomenon, a scenario describing an individual with a severe phobia was presented to a number of psychologists. In some cases, the individual was presented as having normal intelligence and in others as having an intellectual disability. The psychologists were less likely to diagnose this phobia in the individual with an intellectual disability, suggesting that they regarded such symptoms as normal for someone with an intellectual disability (Reiss, Levitan, & Szyszko, 1982). Diagnostic overshadowing presents a barrier to the delivery of proper medical diagnosis and treatment, and can hinder the identification not only of psychiatric diagnoses, but of physical causes of challenging behaviours as well (dental pain, esophagitis, gall stones, etc.).

The opposite occurs when behaviours tend to be attributed to psychiatric illness without other causes being considered. This is especially problematic when the psychiatric diagnosis is made on the basis of behaviours, as is often the case. Once an individual receives a psychiatric diagnosis, mental health workers often come to regard various behaviours as indicative of mental illness. This tendency is referred to as diagnostic overemphasis. Someone who is demonstrating moodiness for whatever reason may be told that their "bipolar is acting up." An individual who is particular about details may be described as "OCD." Someone who engages in a lot of psychomotor activity may be described as "anxious." Attributing all difficult or unusual behaviours to a psychiatric diagnosis is a hallmark of diagnostic overemphasis.

It also frequently occurs that behaviours are over-attributed to the individual's learning history. For example, a certain behaviour may be described as attention-seeking because of the presumption that previous emissions of that behaviour led to attention, resulting in the individual learning to emit the behaviour when attention is sought. This sort of over-attribution is referred to as behavioural overshadowing.

Thus, a physician who sees a person with an ID who is engaging in behaviours that are clearly harmful (such as those which endanger self or others), but that are not readily categorized as any DSM-IV diagnosis, can: a) provide a diagnosis that seems to approximate his or her overall impression of the situation (risking diagnostic invalidity) and give medications whose use is supported by this diagnosis; b) give medications without a psychiatric diagnosis at all (risking accusations of inappropriate use of psychiatric medications); or, c) give no medications at all (risking ongoing harm due to the behaviours). Social factors including diagnostic overshadowing and the medicalization of disability, as well as the occurrence of behaviour phenotypes (see Box 2) may also play a role in the approach chosen.

Rationale for pharmacotherapeutic interventions

In spite of problems associated with using medications as intervention for people with IDD, there are times when doing so is the best option. The two principal scenarios are the presence of a dual diagnosis and the occurrence of very challenging behaviours.

Dual diagnosis

Bona fide psychiatric diagnoses do occur in people with IDD and at a higher rate than in the general population, although they are noted in only a fraction of those who end up accessing mental health services. These diagnoses include psychotic disorders (e.g., schizophrenia), mood disorders (e.g., major depressive disorder and bipolar disorder), and anxiety disorders (e.g., obsessive-compulsive disorder, generalized anxiety disorder, and post-traumatic stress disorder). There is no evidence to prove that the pharmacological treatments used for these disorders in the general population are effective for those with IDD, or to refute their efficacy either. Hence, psychiatric medications are used for people with IDD as in the general population, although some special considerations do exist (see section on "General Principles" below).

Challenging behaviours

The majority of individuals with ID who come to mental health services have no clear psychiatric diagnosis, but have a behaviour that warrants intervention. These challenging behaviours may take the form of aggression towards others, self-injurious behaviour (SIB), inappropriate sexual behaviours, or non-physical forms of agitation and aggression such as shouting or threatening others. Behaviours related to control and stubbornness are also common, such as needing to have objects placed in certain order, demanding to always having to have a certain place at the table or in automobiles, seeking to be the centre of attention, and insistence on helping to the point of intrusiveness.

Although non-pharmacological interventions are the preferred treatment for challenging behaviours, some factors limit our ability to implement these as the sole intervention, and others prevent us from implementing them at all. Sometimes behaviours are so harmful, frequent and/or severe that medications are initiated immediately because of the clear need to intervene as quickly as possible. In other cases, the degree of agitation present makes it impossible to initiate non-pharmacological interventions. Frequently individuals' behaviours overwhelm caregivers, resulting in potential loss of community placement if something is not done immediately.

In many cases, however, non-pharmacological approaches simply fail or are not an option. For example, although the identification of triggering environmental factors or undiagnosed medical conditions can lead to dramatic improvements in behaviour problems, these can be difficult to iden-

tify, especially when the person with an ID cannot communicate what it is that is disturbing him or her. When challenging behaviours have a function and are reinforced through caregivers' responses (e.g., an individual who hits himself gets attention; therefore, someone who wants more attention may learn to hit himself), behavioural interventions to extinguish these maladaptive forms of communication require patient and consistent application of behavioural techniques (e.g., not providing attention when the individual hits himself, and providing attention when he does not). This can be difficult for caregivers to do consistently, even when the behavioural principles are explained to them. Further compounding the problem, there is a critical shortage of community behaviour therapists to do this sort of work.

An Introduction to Psychiatric Medications

In this section, we will first review the special considerations regarding the administration of psychiatric medications to persons with IDD. This will be followed by a brief review of the relevant physiology underpinning the mechanism of action of psychiatric medications, which should help to understand the final section, in which the main psychiatric medications in use today will be introduced.

GENERAL PRINCIPLES FOR ADMINISTERING MEDICATIONS

Psychiatric medications, regardless of the population being treated, should be started slowly to minimize and monitor side effects, and they should be discontinued gradually to avoid discontinuation syndromes. This is particularly relevant to the treatment of individuals with IDD, who have more "fragile" brains due to proven or presumed damage or dysfunction or because of particular genetic mutations, making them particularly susceptible to adverse medication side effects. As a general rule, prescriptions for this group should start with even lower dosages, the increases in dosages should be smaller and less frequent, and special caution should be exercised with regard to potential side effects. For example, certain medications have known side effects that could be expected to impact negatively on functions that are already compromised, the most obviously example being those that can cause cognitive impairment. In addition, many medications have side effects that can impair balance and coordination, such as those that cause joint rigidity or dizziness secondary to decreased blood pressure. Furthermore, side effects that cause discomfort of any sort may be difficult for someone with an ID to express and, as such, may progress to a medical emergency without caregivers being aware. Finally, medications can cause unusual side effects in those with ID that do not follow recognized patterns, and the possibility that unusual behaviour is due to a medication must always remain present in the minds of those caring for these individuals. One example of a drug used commonly to control seizures in the general population, but that has serious adverse effects in older persons with Down syndrome, is phenytoin (Tsiouris, Patti, Tipu, & Raguthu, 2002).

NEUROTRANSMITTERS AND RECEPTORS

A key to understanding the actions of psychiatric medications in the brain is the concept of neurotransmitter-receptor interactions. As explained in chapter 7, neurotransmitters are chemicals that transmit electrical impulses from one neuron to another. Receptors on the second neuron are specifically configured to recognize neurotransmitters released at the end of the transmitting neuron; once the neurotransmitter binds to the receptor, a series of events is initiated that allows the electrical impulse to proceed or to stop. The specific manner in which a neurotransmitter binds to a specific receptor is likened to a "lock and key" mechanism. Neurotransmitter molecules in the space between the two neurons (the synapse) that are not bound to receptors may be recycled through the process of *reuptake* back into the terminal of the first neuron through special reuptake channels (refer to chapter 7 for figures of a neuron and a synapse).

REVIEW OF PSYCHIATRIC MEDICATIONS

Psychiatric medications are often grouped into five major classes: antipsychotics, antidepressants, mood stabilizers, sedative-hypnotics, and psycho-

stimulants. In this section we review the mechanism of action, indications, and major side effects of the medications that make up these classes, as well as a few examples that do not fit into any of these classes. This review is not intended to be exhaustive, and will be limited to the most commonly used medications. (See Table 1 for a list of some medications and typical dose ranges in adults).

Antipsychotic medications

The antipsychotics are probably the most studied and most prescribed class of medications for the management of mental health problems in people with IDD. Their uses include schizophrenia, mania, attention-deficit hyperactivity disorder (ADHD), psychotic depression and treatment-resistant depression, in addition to challenging behaviours. The antipsychotics are separated into two major groups: *typical* and *atypical* antipsychotics.

Typical antipsychotics: These are the older group, and also are referred to as neuroleptics or major tranquilizers due to their ability to decrease agitation and anxiety. Their principle pharmacological mechanism of action is blockade of brain dopamine type 2 (D2) receptors. This prevents dopamine from exerting effects at this receptor type. Although it is not clear why this blockade results in antipsychotic action, it has led to the "dopamine hypothesis" of schizophrenia (see Box 1).

Dopamine blockade is also responsible for one of the major side effects caused by typical antipsychotics, namely *neurolepetic-induced parkinsonism*. This refers to the tendency of typical antipsychotics, at sufficient doses, to cause symptoms that resemble those seen in Parkinson's disease. These include the triad of resting tremor, rigidity, and bradykinesia (or akinesia). The tremor has a typical appearance often referred to as "pill-rolling" because of its resemblance to the movement performed by pharmacists in the days when pills were prepared by hand. Rigidity refers to stiffness at the joints that results from increased muscle tone. It can usually be detected when an examiner flexes the joints of a person with neuroleptic-induced rigidity while he or she is at rest. This rigidity is often "cogwheel" in type, which refers to the tendency of superimposed

Table 1: Selected Psychiatric Medications and Typical Adult Dose Ranges

Generic Name	Trade Name	Dose Range (mg/day)*
Antipsychotics		
Typical		
Chlorpromazine	Largactil	50-1000
Flupenthixol	Fluanxol	1-12
Haloperidol	Haldol	0.5-10
Loxapine	Loxapac	10-250
Methotrimeprazine	Nozinan	25-500
Thioridazine	Mellaril	30-800
Trifluoperazine	Stelazine	2-40
Zuclopenthixol	Clopixol	10-100
Atypical		
Risperidone	Risperdal	0.5-6
Olanzapine	Zyprexa	5-40
Clozapine	Clozaril	12.5-900
Aripiprazole	Abilify	10-30
Ziprasidone	Zeldox	20-200
Depot		
(long-acting injectable)		
Risperidone	Risperdal Consta	25-50 q2wks
Flupenthixol	Fluanxol Depot	5-100 q2-3wks
Fluphenzaine	Modecate	2.5-100 q2wks
Haloperidol	Haldol LA	50-300 q4wks
Zuclopenthixol	Clopixol Depot	100-400 q2wks
Zuclopenthixol acetate	Clopixol Acuphase	25-150 q2-3days

Generic Name	Trade Name	Dose Range (mg/day)*
Antidepressants		
Serotonin-Specific Reuptake Inhibitors		
Citalopram	Celexa	10-60
Escitalopram	Cipralex	5-20
Fluvoxamine	Luvox	50-300
Fluoxetine	Prozac	10-80
Paroxetine	Paxil	10-60
Sertraline	Zoloft	25-200
Novel		
Bupropion	Welbutrin	150-300
Venlafaxine	Effexor	37.5-375
Mirtazapine	Remeron	15-60
Tricyclic Antidepressants		
Desipramine	Norpramin	50-300
Nortryptiline	Aventyl	25-150
Amitriptyline	Elavil	25-300
Clomipramine	Anafranil	25-300
Doxepin	Sinequan	25-300
Imipramine	Tofranil	25-300
Monoamine Oxidase Inhibitors		
Phenelzine	Nardil	15-90
Tranylcypromine	Parnate	20-40

Table 1: Selected Psychiatric Medications and Typical Adult Dose Ranges (Cont'd)

Generic Name	Trade Name	Dose Range (mg/day)*
Mood Stabilizers		
Lithium	Carbolith, Duralith	based on drug levels
Carbamazepine	Tegretol	200-1600
Oxcarbazepine	Trileptal	300-2400
Valproate	Epival	250-3000
Topiramate	Topamax	25-800
Lamotrigine	Lamictal	25-250
Sedative-Hypnotics		
Benzodiazepines		
Alprazolam	Xanax	0.5*
Clonazepam	Rivotril	0.25*
Diazepam	Valium	5*
Lorazepam	Ativan	1*
Oxazepam	Serax	15*

* *Typical starting doses; maximum dose depends on tolerance.*

Non-Benzodiazepines		
Zopiclone	Imovane	7.5
Buspirone	BuSpar	5-60
Trazodone	Desyrel	25-500
Melatonin	-	0.3-12
Phenelzine	Nardil	15-90
Tranylcypromine	Parnate	20-40
Psychostimulants		
Methylphenidate	Ritalin	5-60
Methylphenidate SR	Ritalin SR	20-60
Methylphenidate ER	Concerta	18-54
Atomoxetine	Strattera	40-100

Generic Name	Trade Name	Dose Range (mg/day)*
Opioid Receptor Antagonists		
Naltrexone	*Revia*	*12.5-200*
α₂ – Adrenergic Receptor Agonists		
Clonidine	*Catapres*	*0.1-0.6*

α_2 – Adrenergic Receptor Agonists

* unless otherwise indicated

rigidity and tremor to create a rhythmic, ratchetlike resistance when the joint is manipulated, particularly rotation of the wrist. Bradykinesia and akinesia refer to a decrease in spontaneous movements, resulting in a lack of facial expression ("masklike"), decreased use of gestures, reduced armswing, and slowness in initiating speech and gait.

Other movement disorders are frequently caused by typical neuroleptics. *Akathisia* is a common side effect consisting of subjective feelings of restlessness and/or an inability to remain still. *Acute dystonia*, which typically occurs in young males given a neuroleptic for the first time, consists of a severe contraction of muscles that result in abnormal sustained postures such as oculogyric crisis (affecting the eyes) and torticollis (affecting the neck). Acute dystonia is a medical emergency that responds very well to the administration of antiparkinsonian medications such as benztropine. *Tardive dyskinesia* usually occurs after long-term treatment with typical antipsychotics and involves involuntary writhing movements, most commonly seen in the mouth, but which can occur in various parts of the body, particularly the upper body.

Atypical antipsychotics: Typical antipsychotics have been largely supplanted by the advent of the atypical antipsychotics due to the latter being marketed as having a better side effect profile. However,

it has been frequently remarked that the side effects of typical antipsychotics are simply different than those of atypical antipsychotics and that calling one set of side effects better than the other involves a value judgment. Although atypical antipsychotics have a much lower risk of causing movement disorders than do typical antipsychotics, they are much worse when it comes to causing metabolic side effects such as weight gain, elevations in serum lipid levels (e.g., LDL cholesterol), and increases in fasting blood glucose levels (associated with an increased risk of diabetes). Atypicals are also distinct from the typicals in that they cause much less D2 blockade (which may be partly responsible for the reduced incidence of movement disorders) and tend to block serotonin type 2A (5-HT2A) receptors. Thus, they are sometimes referred to as serotonin-dopamine antagonist medications.

The first serotonin-dopamine antagonist drug developed was clozapine, which remains the gold standard for antipsychotics due to its being the most effective drug for treating psychosis. Clozapine causes negligible movement disorder symptoms, but has a number of other side effects, including seizures, cardiac disorders, weight gain, and *agranulocytosis*. Agranulocytosis is a life threatening disorder of the body's production of white blood cells, which are necessary to prevent and to fight infections. This rare but potentially deadly side effect prevents it from being used as a drug of first choice and necessitates careful monitoring of the blood count when it is used.

Of the atypical antipsychotics, risperidone is the most likely to cause movement disorders, although risk of weight gain is less than with olanzapine and clozapine. Quetiapine causes almost no movement disorders at all. The newer medications in this group, paliperidone, ziprasidone and aripiprazole, are marketed as causing less weight gain and movement disorders than prior medications, but more time may be required to get a true sense of their effectiveness.

Depot antipsychotics: Depot antipsychotics are special preparations of antipsychotic medications that are given by intramuscular injection every 2 to 4 weeks, depending on the drug. All currently available depot antipsychotics are typical antipsychotics with the exception of risperidone Consta, which is an atypical agent. Depot antipsychotics have the same side effects as their oral counterparts, but it is felt that these side effects may be less severe due to a lower fluctuation in blood levels than is seen with oral administration. Depot antipsychotics are often used in individuals living independently in the community for whom compliance with oral medications is questionable. The regular administration of a depot antipsychotic leaves no doubt as to whether an individual is receiving their medication or not.

Antidepressant medications

Antidepressants are also divided up into subclasses. The newest and by far the most commonly used today are the serotonin-specific reuptake inhibitors (SSRIs) and the novel antidepressants bupropion, venlafaxine and mirtazapine. Antidepressants are used for a number of mental health issues, including major depressive disorder, bipolar depression, anxiety disorders, eating disorders, attention deficit hyperactivity disorder (ADHD), and some personality disorders, in addition to their use in challenging behaviours in IDD. Generally, their pharmacological action is to prevent the reuptake of certain neurotransmitters from the synaptic cleft by presynaptic neurons.

Serotonin-specific reuptake inhibitors (SSRIs): SSRIs, as their name implies, specifically block the reuptake of serotonin, which results in an increase in serotonin concentration in the synapse. How this translates into antidepressant activity is unknown, especially given the fact that antidepressants have a delayed onset of action of about 2-4 weeks. It is hypothesized that the antidepressant effect coincides with changes in receptors on the presynaptic neuron that occur secondary to the increased availability of serotonin, which would explain the delay.

Although SSRIs are widely used for depression, there is significant evidence that their actual effectiveness in treating depression is minimal. On the other hand, their ability to treat anxiety (particularly panic disorder) is much more impressive. One particular type of anxiety disorder, obsessive-compulsive disorder (OCD), is treated exclusively with SSRIs, as well as with the most serotonin-specific of the older antidepressants, clomipramine.

Typical side effects of SSRIs are not life threatening, especially when they are not mixed with the older antidepressants. Certain combinations of SSRIs with these older antidepressants can lead to a fairly severe condition called serotonin syndrome, a form of toxicity the symptoms of which include increased heart rate and blood pressure, fever with shivering and sweating, nausea and diarrhea, hypervigilance, agitation, and confusion. In severe cases, high fever can lead to life-threatening complications. Perhaps the most troublesome side effect of SSRIs and other serotonergic medications (e.g., venlafaxine) is sexual dysfunction, which occurs to varying degrees in a significant number of people taking these medications. This can include lack of desire as well as difficulties with performance, including inability to achieve erections (in men) or orgasm (in both men and women). However, this side effect has also been used to advantage in the treatment of premature ejaculation.

Non-SSRI (novel) antidepressants: Most of the non-SSRI antidepressants also cause varying degrees of serotonin reuptake inhibition, but they tend to block the reuptake of other neurotransmitters associated with depression, known as the catecholamines, as well. This chemical group includes norepinephrine (also known as noradrenaline), epinephrine (adrenaline), and dopamine. The catecholamines are much more highly associated with antidepressant effects (and less so with antianxiety effects) than is serotonin. Dopamine, for example, is the neurotransmitter that is responsible for the effects of amphetamines (which cause dopamine release), and cocaine (which blocks dopamine reuptake). Both of these drugs are recognized for their tendency to enhance well-being and mood in the short term (although they are also known for causing paranoia and other psychotic symptoms, lending further support to the dopamine hypothesis of schizophenia). Norepinephrine and epinephrine are associated with the increased energy, alertness and arousal of the "fight or flight" syndrome of the sympathetic nervous system.

Venlafaxine is a drug that blocks reuptake of serotonin, norepinephrine and dopamine; the norepinephrine and dopamine effects are seen at higher dose ranges. Although venlafaxine is marketed for use as an antianxiety agent, many people find that at higher doses (i.e., above 150 mg/day), or even at lower doses, it can cause unpleasant physical anxiety symptoms. As well, at higher doses it is associated with occasional mild to moderate increases in blood pressure. Despite these potential side effects, venlafaxine may have a faster onset of action, greater effectiveness in severe depression, and a more "activating" effect than the SSRIs.

Bupropion has no effect on serotonin, and in fact its mechanism is not clear, although norepinephrine seem to be implicated in its mechanism of action. It is notable for not causing sexual dysfunction, a common rationale for its use. It is also regarded as an activating antidepressant in that it generally does not cause fatigue and often causes increases in energy. It has also been used as an anti-smoking drug under the trade name of Zyban.

Mirtazapine potentiates serotonin and norepinephrine transmission by blocking receptors (α2-adrenergic type) that decrease their activity. Mirtazapine tends to be sedating and has negligible gastrointestinal side effects (e.g., nausea), properties that theoretically make it a good choice for those with depressive symptoms associated with loss of appetite and insomnia. However, its relative effectiveness as an antidepressant is not clear.

TCAs and MAOIs: Prior to the advent of the SSRIs and the novel antidepressants, the two classes of antidepressants available were the tricyclic antidepressants (TCAs) and the monoamine oxidase inhibitors (MAOIs). TCAs take their name from their molecular structure, which contains three rings of atoms, and their mechanism of action is to block the reuptake of the neurotransmitters serotonin and norepinephrine. MAOIs work by deactivating monoamine oxidase, the enzyme that degrades serotonin, norepinephrine and dopamine, resulting in greater amounts of all three in the brain. Despite being possibly superior in efficacy to the newer antidepressants, both of these classes of drugs have fairly significant side effects, and thus are currently seldom used.

Mood stabilizers

Mood stabilizers are generally used for the treatment and prevention of mood episodes in bipolar disorder, particularly the prevention of manic episodes. One notable exception is lamotrigine, which is used exclusively for the treatment and prevention of bipolar depression. All except lithium are also anticonvulsants, meaning that they are used in the treatment of epilepsy to prevent seizures. Mood stabilizers are particularly dangerous to the fetus and their use should be avoided during pregnancy.

Lithium is perhaps one of the most controversial psychiatric medications, with supporters and detractors within the psychiatric community. It is an element, which alone sets it apart from all other psychiatric medications, and its reckless and misguided use as a cure-all in the late-19th and early-20th centuries delayed its acceptance for many years. However, it has remained the drug of first choice in the treatment of acute episodes of bipolar mania and depression; it also is used on an ongoing basis to prevent episodes of both types. It has also consistently been shown to decrease suicidality, and is used as an add-on treatment to antidepressants in treatment-resistant depression.

On the other hand, lithium is a drug with many risks. It has a narrow therapeutic range, which means that the difference between an effective and a toxic dose is fairly small, necessitating regular monitoring of blood levels. Lithium toxicity is characterized by marked tremor, ataxia (severe lack of coordination, especially of gait) and confusion or, in more severe cases, stupor and coma. This is a life-threatening condition which can be brought on by dehydration, interactions with other medications (including several diuretics, anti-inflammatory agents, and ACE inhibitors) or impaired kidney function.

The side effects of lithium are many, and include thirst, skin problems (acne and psoriasis), cognitive dysfunction (lack of spontaneity and memory problems), tremor, thyroid dysfunction, and kidney impairments. Although actual kidney failure caused by lithium is quite rare, nephrogenic diabetes insipidus, an impairment of the ability of the kidneys to concentrate urine resulting in loss of body water due to a large output of dilute urine, is very common. In my experience, the side effects of lithium can be particularly devastating to individuals with intellectual disabilities, who are particularly impacted by diabetes insipidus and cognitive deficits. Although increased urine output and memory problems may be annoying to a non-disabled individual, for a person with ID, these side effects can mean the difference between continence and incontinence in the former case, and between relative independence and dependence in the latter. It is crucially important to remain aware of lithium's potential side effects in this population.

Valproate and carbamazepine are anticonvulsant medications that both show evidence of effectiveness in bipolar disorder. Both are used to prevent episodes of mania and depression and in the treatment of manic episodes. Carbamazepine is also used to control impulsive and aggressive behaviours in non-psychotic individuals, and because of this its use in IDD is quite common. Carbamazepine has somewhat more serious side effects than valproate, such as aplastic anemia (loss of red blood cell production) and agranulocytosis (loss of white blood cell production), as well as an allergic type of hepatitis. Valproate has resulted in severe hepatitis in children under the age of 10, but is quite safe for adults. The most common side effects related to its use are hair loss, benign increases in blood levels of liver enzymes, nausea, and tremor.

Lamotrigine is an anticonvulsant that is used for treatment and prevention of depression in bipolar disorder. Bipolar depression has long been a very difficult condition to treat because of the propensity of antidepressant medications to cause mania or dangerous "mixed states," in which depressive symptoms such as suicidal ideation co-occur with manic symptoms such as racing thoughts and increased activity. Lamotrigine has been shown to have an antidepressant effect in individuals with bipolar disorder without causing a switch into mania or mixed states. Most side effects are mild, but in vary rare cases a life-threatening skin condition can develop known as Stevens-Johnson Syndrome or Toxic Epidermal Necrolysis. Any rash, especially in the first few weeks of treatment, should be closely monitored.

Sedative-hypnotics

A sedative is a drug that tends to produce a calming, sedating effect, whereas a hypnotic is a drug that is used to promote sleep. Sedative-hypnotics are a very commonly used class of medications, given the fact that sleep complaints, anxiety, and agitation are such common therapeutic targets. Some of these medications are primarily hypnotics (e.g., trazodone, melatonin) and others are principally sedatives (e.g., buspirone), whereas benzodiazepines are used for both purposes.

Benzodiazepines: The benzodiazepine class contains a number of medications that have in common their actions on γ-aminobutyric acid type A ($GABA_A$) receptors in the brain. GABA is an inhibitory neurotransmitter that causes a decrease in the activity of neurons through its activity on GABA receptors that are located throughout the brain. Benzodiazepines, which bind to the $GABA_A$ receptor at a site adjacent to the site where GABA binds, enhance the activity of the receptor resulting in greater inhibition and, as a result, produce a calming and sedating effect. Benzodiazepines are also very effective at stopping and preventing seizures.

The most commonly used benzodiazepines are probably lorazepam (Ativan) and clonazepam (Rivotril). Lorazepam is a short-acting benzodiazepine (half life of 15 hours) that is often used for occasional difficulty falling asleep or for treatment "as needed" of anxiety or agitation. Clonazepam, a long-acting benzodiazepine (half life of 34 hours) is often given in regular doses to prevent frequent anxiety states and agitation that occurs regularly.

Long-term regular use of any benzodiazepine can result in tolerance and dependence. The implications of this are that an individual who uses benzodiazepines regularly for longer than a few weeks may find that if they stop taking the medication very suddenly they will experience greater anxiety than they did before they started taking it (withdrawal) and will need to keep taking it (dependence). As well, they may find that the effect begins to wear off and that they need higher doses to fall asleep or manage their anxiety than they did initially (tolerance). Finally, the sudden discontinuation of high dose long-term use of benzodiazepines can lead to withdrawal seizures. Because of these qualities, benzodiazepines are recommended only for short-term use. As well, they should not be stopped "cold turkey" unless already at the lowest possible dose. Rather, they should be slowly decreased until discontinuation. Even with slow tapering, when the lowest dose is discontinued, many individuals experience an emergence of anxiety and insomnia. Another potential side effect of benzodiazepines is the effect of "paradoxical disinhibition." Although the typical response to benzodiazepines is a decrease in activity and placidity, some people become aggressive, impulsive or silly after ingesting a benzodiazepine. Although this effect is reported as being rare, it may be more common amongst those with brain injury, making it a phenomenon to be aware of in people with IDD.

Despite these limitations, benzodiazepines are probably the most effective medications in all of psychiatry for short-term relief of distress. It is unfortunate that concerns regarding dependence have led to a backlash against their use. Many people take benzodiazepines for years and continue to benefit without ever needing to increase the dose until they encounter a well-meaning physician who weans them off. When successful, a merely theoretical benefit has been achieved; when unsuccessful, quite remarkably bad outcomes can occur.

Non-Benzodiazepines: More recently, so-called "non-benzodiazepine" drugs (sometimes called "the Z drugs" because their names all begin with the letter Z) that act at the same site on the GABA receptor as benzodiazepines, such as zopiclone, have become available. Despite being touted as lacking the dependency potential of benzodiazepines, clinical experience has proven this to be untrue, and they are also now recommended for occasional use only.

Trazodone was originally developed as an antidepressant, and has a structure similar to that of some of the older antidepressants. Although it is seldom used for depression, it has impressive effects on sleep quality that have made it a very popular and effective medication for chronic sleep disturbances. Trazodone is highly sedating, increases total sleep time, and decreases the amount of REM sleep relative to the much more restorative stage 4 sleep. It also lacks serious side effects and has no concerns related to issues of dependence and tolerance.

Psychostimulants

Psychostimulants are used in the treatment of attention-deficit hyperactivity disorder (ADHD) and as add-on treatments to antidepressants in treatment-resistant depression. The most well known is methylphenidate, better known as Ritalin.

Methylphenidate blocks the reuptake of dopamine from pre-synaptic axon terminals. You may recall that this is the same mechanism of action of cocaine, although the euphoria that one gets from cocaine does not occur with methylphenidate when it is taken orally (rather than injected or snorted) and at therapeutic doses. However, the high potential abuse has been a major concern and has led to the production of formulations that are more difficult to abuse, such as the slow-release form known as Concerta.

Although it seems counterintuitive to give a stimulant for hyperactivity, the overall effect generally is an increased ability to focus on tasks and a decrease in impulsive behaviours. Common side effects of methylphenidate include loss of appetite, nervousness and insomnia, and it is usually recommended that Ritalin not be taken in the evening to avoid sleep disturbance.

Atomoxetine is not officially a psychostimulant, but is a stimulating medication used in the treatment of ADHD. Also known as Strattera, atomoxetine is a norepinephrine reuptake inhibitor that was originally developed as an antidepressant. Recall that the antidepressant venlafaxine also blocks the reuptake of norepinephrine, and this is believed to be responsible for its more activating tendencies. Venlafaxine, as well as the other stimulating antidepressant bupropion, is commonly used in the treatment of ADHD. Atomoxetine has important safety concerns, including the potential for inducing psychosis and mania or worsening suicidal thoughts. These side effects have also been reported to occur in young people prescribed antidepressants, and have brought criticism to the medication treatment of young people and adolescents.

Opioid receptor antagonists

Naltrexone, a drug that blocks opioid receptors, merits mention due to its use in treating self-injurious behaviour (SIB). It is chemically very similar to naloxone, also an opioid receptor blocker, used as a treatment for opioid overdose. Opioids are chemicals that tend to decrease pain and include morphine and the endogenous (i.e., produced by the human body) opioids, which include the endorphins. Opioid receptor antagonists block opioid receptors and prevent these chemicals from exerting their effects. Their use in self-injurious behaviour is based on the hypothesis that individuals who engage in SIB do so to cause the release of endorphins, which occurs as a natural physiological response to pain stimuli. Several studies have shown that naltrexone is often very effective at reducing SIB in individuals with intellectual disabilities.

α_2 – adrenergic receptor agonists

Originally produced as a medication for the treatment of high blood pressure, clonidine stimulates α_2 – adrenergic receptors on presynaptic terminals, which results in a decrease in the amount of norepinephrine released into the synaptic cleft. This results in lower blood pressure and lower levels of arousal. Clonidine is often used in the treatment of ADHD to try to decrease hyperactivity and aggression. Although it can be quite effective, it may simply cause sedation. Rapid discontinuation of Clonidine can cause an increase in blood pressure, and thus it must be stopped gradually.

Evidence Base for Pharmacological Interventions

Evidence based medicine

Evidence based medicine (EBM) is a term that refers to the implementation of health research into medical practice (Haynes, Devereaux, & Guyatt, 2002) and could be said to represent an organized attempt to transform the "art" of medicine to the "science" of medicine. The primary goal of EBM is to ensure that physicians are making decisions based on research that is of the highest scientific standard. Although there are many types of research study designs, the highest standard of scientific research with respect to the evaluation of the effectiveness of pharmacological interventions is the randomized controlled trial (RCT).

Randomized controlled trials and their limitations

A pharmacological randomized controlled trial is a study in which two or more drug treatments are compared. The subjects of the study, to whom the treatments will be administered, are randomized, meaning they are randomly assigned to different treatment groups, rather than being assigned to a treatment group by non-random means. Non-random treatment allocation can lead to what is known as *selection bias* or *sampling bias*, in which the groups selected differ in ways that influence outcome. Ideally, the randomization procedure also includes *matching*, a process that ensures that important demographic factors such as age, gender, and other factors are equally represented in both groups. The trial is *controlled* by the presence of a placebo group to prevent factors other than the treatment itself causing the outcome being studied. A placebo is a treatment that contains no active ingredient, but is identical in appearance to the active treatment. If, for example, we wish to study the effect of a certain vitamin on its ability to cure the common cold, and we have no placebo group, the vitamin will appear to cure the cold due to the fact that colds usually resolve on their own. If we compare the group receiving the vitamin to a comparison group that does not receive anything — vitamin or placebo — that group may recover more slowly than the vitamin group because the psychological effect of receiving treatment in the vitamin group may lead to a quicker recovery. If, however, we provide the control group with a pill that looks exactly the same as the vitamin but contains only inert ingredients, then both groups should have equal expectations of benefit due to receiving treatment. We will likely find that both groups recover from the cold within the same time period equally well, given that vitamins tend to have no effect on recovery from the common cold. The expectation of improvement due to receiving a treatment is called the placebo effect, and is particularly important in psychiatry, as 1) we still do not understand exactly how psychiatric medications cause improvements in psychiatric disorders, 2) RCTs of psychiatric medications often show only small differences in improvements between placebo groups and active treatment groups (e.g., Kirsch & Sapirstein, 1998), and 3) brain activity studies have shown that similar changes in the brain occur in placebo and active treatment groups (Mayberg et al., 2002), suggesting that the placebo effect has a physiological effect similar to that of active treatments.

Whether the groups being compared include a placebo group or not, the study should be blinded. Blinding refers to a state of ignorance in participants and evaluators with regards to which treatment group subjects belong to. If only the subjects are unaware of their treatment allocation, the trial is considered to be a single-blind trial, which is problematic because researchers, like study subjects, may believe that one of the treatments is superior and as a result be inclined to rate improvement as greater in that group. If both the subjects and the investigators responsible for evaluating response to treatment are unaware of who belongs to which group (preferable), the study is considered to be double-blinded. However, there are limitations to blinding procedures. For example, in the case of a placebo-controlled trial in which the active treatment causes side effects (a common scenario), subjects may become "unblinded" by either experi-

encing or not experiencing side effects and the study becomes uncontrolled. Worse, there exist numerous examples of trials whose outcome was influenced by *subversion bias*, in which researchers surreptitiously unblind themselves by looking through sealed allocation envelopes or breaking into filing cabinets to obtain randomization codes (Schulz, 1995).

Statistical versus clinical significance

Even in a properly conducted trial it is possible to draw misleading conclusions. One of the most common of these relates to the difference between statistical significance and clinical significance. Statistical significance refers to the likelihood that a result did not occur due to chance. For example, if we want to know which of two sports teams is better, we could ask them to play a game against each other. If the final score is 20-0, we might conclude that the team that won is the better team. If the final score is 3-2, we might be less convinced that the winning team is the better team, but consider that the win may have been due to a "fluke" (i.e., chance) and ask for a best 4 out of 7 series. If the result of each of the games in this series was a score of 3-2, we might still not be convinced. If these two teams went on to play a thousand games, all with a close result, we might still not be convinced which team was better. Statistically, however, the greater the number of games played, the greater the chance of finding a statistical difference favouring one of the teams, even if the difference in the average scores is so small that we might not consider it significant.

In the same way, if a study comparing two treatments enrolls enough subjects, statistical analysis may reveal superiority of one treatment that statistically is not due to chance. However, if the difference is of a very small magnitude, it is likely *clinically insignificant* or of negligible real benefit. Alternatively, if we enroll too few subjects, we may fail to find a statistically significant difference when in fact there is a clinically significant difference.

The general public, physicians, and researchers also need to be aware that statistics is not always correctly applied in the medical and other literature, and that the conclusions of a study do not always reflect what the data indicate. Furthermore, reporting by journalists is not always accurate. These issues indicate that, while the results of research that uses sound methodology need to be closely heeded when deciding whether or not to use medications, qualified medical practitioners also need to interpret how such results are best applied to individuals in their clinical practices. This process brings us back to the "art" of medicine.

The influence of the pharmaceutical industry

Because pharmaceutical companies have such vast financial resources compared to government-funded research agencies, the majority of data available regarding the efficacy and safety of psychiatric medications comes from research projects that are funded by the pharmaceutical companies themselves. Because it is in the financial interest of the pharmaceutical industry to portray their products in the most positive light possible, commercial interests often supplant research interests in how these studies are conducted and reported. With regard to study design, the sources of bias outlined above can be exploited to enhance the outcome of a clinical trial. Once the studies are completed, however, there are further means of inflating the apparent significance of research.

One quite simple method involves neglecting to publish negative trials (i.e., those in which the treatment in question demonstrates no apparent benefit). For example, there is an emerging body of evidence that antidepressant medications have little efficacy when compared to placebo. A recent meta-analysis examining the efficacy of antidepressants in published clinical trials found that 75% of the effect is duplicated by placebo (Kirsch & Sapirstein, 1998). In a subsequent study by the same group of authors that included non-published studies, the placebo effect increased to about 80% (Kirsch, Moore, Scoboria, & Nicholls, 2002). It may be that antidepressants are effective in more severe types of depression, whereas they are relatively ineffective in mild to moderate cases. In fact, pharmaceutical companies often need to fund several large-scale studies of a medication before one yields positive results while withholding the results of the negative studies.

In the past few years, an even more disturbing trend in pharmaceutical research has come to light — that of academic ghostwriting. Numerous allegations have been made that research papers were written by medical writing firms hired by pharmaceutical companies to create research that exaggerated the benefits or minimized the risks of the drug in question. These papers were then sent out to various medical experts requesting that they agree to have their name listed as author in return for substantial financial compensation. Once a physician's name is attached as author, the article has the appearance of scientific neutrality (despite the various biases contained within) and as such appears acceptable for publication by reputable scientific journals. Currently there is much debate about the pros and cons of this practice (e.g., Gotzsche et al., 2009; Lacasse & Leo, 2010).

Evidence base for psychopharmacological treatments in intellectual disabilities

Matson and Neal (2009) reviewed the evidence for the use of psychotropic medications for challenging behaviours in IDD. In their review, the authors included only those studies that had, in their design, placebo control, randomization, double-blind subjects, standardized doses, standardized evaluations of symptoms, and appropriate statistical procedures. They identified 12 studies that met all of these criteria. Of these 12 studies, 3 studied typical antipsychotics, seven studied the atypical antipsychotic risperidone, 1 studied the antidepressant imipramine, and 1 studied both a typical (haloperidol) and an atypical (risperidone) antipsychotic. Of the 12 studies, 8 found a significant benefit associated with medication use, and 4 found no benefit. The 8 that found a benefit included all of the 7 that studied risperidone alone, whereas of the 4 that failed to demonstrate medication advantage 1 examined imipramine, 2 focussed on the typical antipsychotic thioridiazine, and 1 studied both risperidone and the typical antipsychotic haloperidol. Interestingly, the 4 that found no benefit were the only ones that utilized both objective observation and standardized rating scales, whereas the 8 that found a significant benefit relied only on the use of rating scales. The largest and highest-quality study (Tyrer et al., 2008) was judged to be the one that found no advantage to risperidone or haloperidol compared to placebo.

In summary, the majority of studies of psychotropic medications for challenging behaviours in developmental disabilities that have employed a rigorous methodology have focussed on risperidone. This makes it difficult to conclude that risperidone is superior to other medications for this purpose, as we have little evidence supporting or refuting the use of other medications. Furthermore, despite the number of RCTs showing benefit from risperidone compared to placebo, the fact that a high quality study using a more rigorous methodology failed to replicate this finding does cast some doubt on the relevance of these results.

Consensus guidelines and surveys

Despite the lack of research evidence to support their use, it is still generally accepted that pharmacological interventions play an important role in the treatment of challenging behaviours in individuals with intellectual disabilities. As outlined above, there are many situations in which the risk of harm due to behaviour is so great that the failure to administer psychiatric medications would be unethical. Most psychiatrists working with people with IDD have many examples from their own practice of situations in which the initiation of psychiatric medications appeared to provide significant, and sometimes dramatic, benefits. It may be that the dearth of research evidence to support these benefits is due to inadequacies in study design or in our current ability to predict which individuals will benefit from medications. Although considered a low level of evidence in an evidence-based framework, the opinion of those with experience in the field is our best, and often only, guide in how to proceed.

When high-level evidence for interventions is lacking, or if evidence is conflicting, experts will often convene to create consensus guidelines. Expert consensus is considered a level of evidence, though not a very strong one, as it is based on clinical experience and opinion, which are vulnerable to various types of bias. There have been a number of consensus guidelines created to help guide the use of psychotropic medications in those with IDD (e.g.,

Reiss & Aman, 1997). However, the recent consensus guidelines published by Deb et al. (2009) concluded that there was insufficient evidence to make any recommendations regarding specific medication treatments for challenging behaviours, and that non-pharmacological interventions should be tried first when no medical or psychiatric disorder is found to explain the behaviours.

In the absence of expert consensus, consensus surveys can be conducted to determine the practices of a broad sample of clinicians working in the field. Although this type of information is subject to major biases and nonscientific trends, it can at least provide a framework to make treatment decisions that would be considered reasonable by a majority of colleagues. In one recent consensus survey, the opinions of 108 British psychiatrists were compiled regarding the treatment of aggression towards others and self-injurious behaviour (SIB) in IDD. For the treatment of aggression, 80.6% chose antipsychotics as their first choice of medication class, followed by anti-anxiety drugs (e.g., benzodiazepines), which were the first choice for 12.0%, and antidepressants, which were chosen by 6.5%. When given the choice of which antipsychotic they would choose for the treatment of aggression, 78.8% chose risperidone and 13.0% chose olanzapine. For SIB, 49.1% chose antipsychotics as their class of first choice, 25.9% chose antidepressants, and 11.1% chose anti-anxiety drugs. The choice of antipsychotic agent was very similar for the treatment of SIB as for aggression, with 74.1% of respondents selecting risperidone as their first choice, compared to 12.0% who chose olanzapine first.

The overwhelming choice of antipsychotics, and risperidone in particular, likely reflects the greater evidence base supporting this medication in aggression in developmental disabilities. However, many psychiatrists try to avoid antipsychotics if at all possible when there is no evidence of psychosis, and for this reason antianxiety drugs for many are the drug of first choice for aggression not due to psychosis. Finally, the relatively greater preference of antidepressants for SIB than for aggression likely reflects fears that aggression may be due to an underlying bipolar disorder that could be exacerbated by the administration of antidepressant medications (resulting in manic or mixed features), whereas SIB may be regarded as resulting from anxious or depressive symptoms. Among the antidepressants, SSRIs were the overwhelming choice for both the treatment of aggression and SIB, with 81.6% choosing one of the SSRIs as their first choice of antidepressant for aggression and 81.5% choosing an SSRI as their preferred antidepressant for SIB. Citalopram and fluoxetine were the top two first choices for both aggression and SIB.

Although no respondents chose mood stabilizers as their first choice for the treatment of aggression, it was the most popular second choice, selected by 40.7% for this ranking. This likely indicates that many psychiatrists would first choose an antipsychotic for the treatment of aggression, and would then add a mood stabilizer if the antipsychotic was incompletely effective, or would switch to a mood stabilizer if the antipsychotic had to be stopped because of unacceptable side effects. The preferred mood stabilizers for both aggression and SIB were carbamazepine, chosen first amongst mood stabilizers by 44.4% for aggression and 40.7% for SIB respectively, and valproate, ranked first by 37.0% for aggression and 31.5% for SIB. They were also the top ranked second choices, indicating that most psychiatrists see these two medications as the mood stabilizers of choice. Lithium was relatively unpopular, chosen by only about 10% as the mood stabilizer of first choice for both aggression and SIB. Interestingly, naltrexone for the treatment of SIB was not mentioned in the study.

Summary

Although psychiatric disorders seem to occur at a higher rate in individuals with intellectual and developmental disabilities than in the general population, the most common mental health problem that brings individuals with these disabilities to mental health and psychiatric services is a poorly defined group of disruptive and dangerous behaviours commonly referred to as "problem behaviours" or "challenging behaviours." The most commonly examined of these are aggression towards others and self-injurious

behaviours. These behaviours are responsible for the majority of psychiatric medications prescribed to people with developmental disabilities, who are the group of people in society that receive these medications at the highest rate. Although most physicians would agree that non-pharmacological interventions are preferable to pharmacological interventions, issues regarding the degree of risk posed by the behaviours and the unavailability of appropriate behavioural interventions, as well as other factors, frequently lead to medication administration.

Psychiatric medication is a huge industry, and much of the medical research that is available to support their use is produced and controlled by the pharmaceutical companies themselves. There are very few high quality studies looking at medication treatment of challenging behaviours in intellectual disabilities, and the majority of them focus on the use of risperidone for aggression. Although these studies generally indicate that risperidone is superior to placebo, some data have cast some doubt on the generalizability of these results. Despite the lack of empirical data, psychiatrists continue to use a variety of psychiatric medications to try to deal with behaviours that often are beyond our understanding, especially in situations where the risk of doing nothing seems to significantly outweigh the risk of providing medications.

For Further Thought and Discussion

1. Individuals with an intellectual disability generally have communication deficits, making it difficult for psychiatrists to evaluate the effects of medications using traditional interviewing methods. What can primary caregivers do to support psychiatrists in the evaluation of the effects of medications?

2. Debate with your classmates: To what degree do front line workers need to be knowledgeable about the effects (including side effects) of medications that they administer?

3. What would you do, as a front line worker or supervisor, if you suspected that a medication prescribed was not having the intended effect?

4. Consider ways that we can get research results

about medications that are sound, scientific, and above all unbiased.

5. Sometimes psychiatric medications are given regularly (i.e., the same time every day) for behaviour problems, whereas sometimes they are given as "prn"s (as-needed). What are the potential advantages and disadvantages to each approach?

6. Although we often give medications to the individuals we support for their behaviours, giving a medication is also a behaviour. What factors (e.g., behavioural factors such as reinforcement and punishment; emotional factors such as guilt, anger, etc.) inherent to the mental health worker (rather than inherent to the client) might make that worker more or less likely to give a medication to an individual with a developmental disability?

More Resources

Websites:

Dalhousie University, College of Pharmacy
Drug information resources.
http://dir.pharmacy.dal.ca/canadianresources.php

Department of Justice Canada
Food and Drugs Act.
http://laws.justice.gc.ca/PDF/Statute/F/F-27.pdf

Health Canada
Drugs and health products.
http://www.hc-sc.gc.ca/dhp-mps/index-eng.php

NADD Ontario
Dual Diagnosis Links
http://www.naddontario.org/links.html

USA. Department of Health & Human Services
Medication guides.
http://www.fda.gov/Drugs/DrugSafety/ucm085729.htm

Review Articles:

Bramble, D. (2007). Psychotropic drug prescribing in child and adolescent learning disability psychiatry. *Journal of Psychopharmacology, 21*(5), 486-491.

Bramble, D. (2011). Psychopharmacology in children with intellectual disabilities. *Advances in Psychiatric Treatment, 17,* 32-40. doi: 10.1192/apt.bp.108.005587

Handen, B. L., & Gilchrist, R. (2006). Practitioner review: Psychopharmacology in children and adolescents with mental retardation. *Journal of Child Psychology & Psychiatry, 47*(9), 871-882.

van den Anker, J. N. (2010). Developmental pharmacology. *Developmental Disabilities Research Reviews, 16*(3), 233-238.

Resource Text:

Stahl, S. (2008). *Stahl's essential psychopharmacology.* Cambridge: Cambridge University Press.

References

Cooper, S., Smiley, E., Morrison, J., Williamson, A., & Allan, L. (2007). Mental ill-health in adults with intellectual disabilities: Prevalence and associated factors. *British Journal of Psychiatry, 190,* 27-35.

Davis, L. (2002). *Bending over backwards: Disability, dismodernism & other difficult positions.* New York: New York University Press.

Deb, S., & Fraser, W. (1994). The use of psychotropic medication in people with learning disability: Towards rational prescribing. *Human Psychopharmacology, 9,* 259-272.

Deb, S., Kwok, H., Bertelli, M., Salvador-Carulla, L., Bradley, E., Torr, J., & Barnhill, J. (2009). International guide to prescribing psychotropic medication for the management of problem behaviours in adults with intellectual disabilities. *World Psychiatry, 8,* 181-186.

Gøtzsche, P. C., Kassirer, J. P., Woolley, K. L., Wager, E., Jacobs, A., Gertel, A., & Hamilton, C. (2009). What should be done to tackle ghostwriting in the medical literature? *PLoS Medicine, 6*(2), e23.

Haynes, R. B., Devereaux, P. J., & Guyatt, G. H. (2002). Physicians' and patients' choices in evidence based practice. *British Medical Journal, 324,* 1350.

Illich, I., Zola, I. K., McKnight, J., Caplan, J., & Shaiken, H. (1977). *Disabling professions.* London: Marion Boyars.

Kaperanovic, S., & Simpson, G. M. (2006). Review of antipsychotics in children and adolescents. *Ex-*

pert Opinion on Pharmacotherapy, 7, 1871-1885.

Kirsch, I., & Sapirstein, G. (1998). Listening to Prozac but hearing placebo: A meta analysis of antidepressant medication. *Prevention & Treatment, 1,* Article 0002a. Available from http://www.journals.apa.org/prevention/volume1/pre0010002a.html

Kirsch, I., Moore, T. J., Scoboria, A., & Nicholls, S. S. (2002). The emperor's new drugs: An analysis of antidepressant medication data submitted to the U.S. Food and Drug Administration. *Prevention & Treatment, 5,* Article 0023. Available from http://alphachoices.com/repository/assets/pdf/EmperorsNewDrugs.pdf

Lacasse, J. R., & Leo, J. (2010). Ghostwriting at elite academic medical centers in the United States. *PLoS Medicine, 7*(2), e1000230.

López-Muñoz, F., Alamo, C., Rubio, G., & Cuenca, E. (2004). Half a century since the clinical introduction of chlorpromazine and the birth of modern psychopharmacology. *Progress in Neuro-Psychopharmacology & Biological Psychiatry, 28,* 205-208.

Matson, J. L., & Neal, D. (2009). Psychotropic medication use for challenging behaviors in persons with intellectual disabilities: An overview. *Research in Developmental Disabilities, 30,* 572-586.

Mayberg, H. S., Silva, J.A., Brannan, S. K., Tekell, J. L., Mahurin, R. K., McGinnis, S., & Jerabek, P. A. (2002). The functional anatomy of the placebo effect. *American Journal of Psychiatry, 159,* 728-737.

Nøttestad, J. A., & Linaker, O. M. (2003). Psychotropic drug use among people with intellectual disability before and after deinstitutionalization. *Journal of Intellectual Disability Research, 47,* 464-471.

Reiss, S., & Aman, M. G. (Eds.). (1997). *Psychotropic medications & developmental disabilities: The international consensus handbook.* Columbus, OH: Ohio State University Nisonger Center.

Reiss, S., Levitan, G. W., & Szyszko, J. (1982). Emotional disturbance and mental retardation: Diagnostic overshadowing. *American Journal of Mental Deficiency, 86*(6), 567-574.

Schulz, K. F. (1995). Subverting randomization in clinical trials. *JAMA, 274,* 1456-1458.

Spreat, S., Conroy, J., & Jones, J. (1997). Use of psychotropic medication in Oklahoma: A statewide survey. *American Journal of Mental Retardation, 102,* 80-85.

Tsiouris, J. A, Patti, P. J., Tipu, O., Raguthu, S. (2002). Adverse effects of phenytoin given for late-onset seizures in adults with Down syndrome. *Neurology, 59*(5), 779-780.

Tyrer, S. P., Oliver-Africano, P. C., Ahmed, Z., Bouras, N., Cooray, S., Deb, S., et al. (2008). Risperidone, haloperidol, and placebo in the treatment of aggressive, challenging behavior in patients with intellectual disability: A randomized, controlled trial. *The Lancet, 371,* 57-63.

35

Introduction to Abnormal Behaviour and Associated Conditions

Wai Lun Alan Fung, Maire Percy, and Ivan Brown

What you will learn:

- What are normal and abnormal behaviours
- Relationship between abnormal behaviours, mental disorders, mental ill health and other terms
- Classification systems for disorders associated with abnormal behaviours
- Major diagnostic categories in the DSM-IV
- Suicidal behaviour and suicide
- Brain injury and other causes of abnormal behaviour
- Behavioural phenotypes, stereotypic and self-injurious behaviours
- Future directions

This chapter is intended to be an introduction to the topic of abnormal behaviour. As the reader will see, this is a complex field that is addressed differently by different disciplines. The chapter begins with a description of what normal and abnormal behaviours are from a "lay" point of view. The relationship between the term *abnormal behaviours* and other related terms (*mental disorders, mental ill-health, dual diagnosis*) used in the field of developmental disability is then described, with a view to understanding that some aspects of developmental disability contribute to some abnormal behaviours and that abnormal behaviours arising from mental health conditions sometimes contribute to disability. Next, the reader is introduced to systems currently used to classify abnormal behaviour associated with different mental disorders in persons with or without disability, with a focus on the DSM-IV-TR Multiaxial Diagnostic System (American Psychiatric Association (APA), 2000). Some special topics in the abnormal behaviour field — suicide, brain injury and other causes of abnormal behaviour, as well as "behavioural phenotypes," stereotypic and self-injurious behaviours — are covered. Although considerable detail is given, readers should focus on obtaining an overview. The reader should also clearly understand that abnormal behaviour occurs in both people with developmental disabilities and people without physical or intellectual disabilities. A better understanding of abnormal behaviour should lead to more effective treatments and interventions and help to improve the quality of life for individuals affected by conditions that affect behaviour and/or personality.

What Is Behaviour?

We all do hundreds of things every day, from the moment we wake up to the time we go to sleep, and even while we are sleeping. All these things we do constitute our behaviour. Behaviour is what other people see us doing; thus, it is a principal way others form their understanding of us and their views on who we are as people.

Behaviour can take many forms and can be described in many ways. For example, it can be described as actions or reactions, conscious or unconscious, intentional or unintentional, or overt (obvious) or covert (secretive). Behaviour occurs on the "outside" but is a result of internal functions — the body's endocrine system (the network of tissues and organs that secrete hormones) and the nervous systems (see Chapter 11). The complexity of human behaviour is related to the complexity of the human nervous systems. For many years, there has been a debate over whether behaviour is the consequence of nature or nurture. At the beginning of the 21st century, it is accepted that both factors are involved. One's behaviours, both normal and abnormal, are produced and controlled by the brain. Different brain regions are responsible for different behaviours. To note, however, is that the brain is affected by genetics, nutrition, the immune system, by many different environmental factors, and by learning experiences that occur throughout life. Such learning results from a person's unique life experiences, abilities and disabilities, and interactions with the numerous aspects of changing environments.

Normal And Abnormal Behaviours

Normal behaviour

Behaviour is expected to conform to certain patterns that are acceptable to most people. In the sociology field, acceptable patterns of behaviour are called *behavioural norms*, although society in general usually thinks of these patterns as "*normal*"

behaviour. Behavioural norms differ from one culture to another and from one time period to another, but they serve an important purpose. When almost everybody conforms to them, behaviour is largely predictable. Predictable behaviour exhibited by others alleviates stress and encourages trust.

At the same time, there is considerable variation in normal behaviour at the personal level. Each person, while behaving generally in accordance with behavioural norms, also does things that are unique. In fact, people are often described in terms of the unique aspects of their behaviour because that is what distinguishes them as individuals. One of the things most intriguing about other people is how their behaviour is different from one's own, even if both people follow the same general behavioural norms.

Having some degree of unique behaviour is also beneficial to humans as a species, because it allows people to explore and experiment with new ideas independently. The human race would not have developed to where it is today had each person held fast to the same behavioural norms. Still, the unique behaviours of individuals need to be acceptable to others and to fit into the broader rules set for behavioural norms. Thus, it is considered "normal" for humans to show a range of individual behaviours while conforming to a general set of behaviour rules.

Abnormal behaviour

Abnormal behaviour in a literal sense, means "away from" normal behaviour. It is behaviour that seems too far from the behavioural norm, too odd, or too unusual to be acceptable. It usually means rare in the statistical sense. For example, a person walking down the street shouting angrily at unseen people is exhibiting a behaviour that is usually considered to be abnormal because it seems too unusual and is not commonly seen.

It is important to distinguish between *abnormal behaviours* and *mental illness*. While mental disorders are typically characterized by abnormal behaviours, not all abnormal behaviours would constitute mental illness. For instance, someone walking naked in a public area, which would be considered as an abnormal behaviour in most societies, may have done so for a reason other than mental ill health.

Indeed, any person may exhibit some abnormal behaviours at certain point. A few less serious abnormal behaviours in any one person are typically acceptable, especially if they are counterbalanced by many more normal behaviours. If a person has a number of abnormal behaviours, however, these may outweigh the normal behaviours such that the behaviour pattern as a whole deviates too far from acceptable norms.

Abnormal behaviour may be troublesome — either to the people who exhibit the behaviour or to others who experience it. It is unpredictable and creates stress and uncertainty. It can lead to great personal distress and interfere with daily functioning. It can result in the breakdown of relationships with other people, and sometimes it even leads to the need for institutional care. In a broader sense, abnormal behaviour can threaten the well-being of family and community. The troublesome aspects of abnormal behaviour can take many forms. It might, for example, be amoral, dangerous, compulsive, counterproductive to well-being, distressful, incomprehensible, irrational, maladaptive, uncomfortable or painful, unconventional, or unwanted. Because of the difficulties it creates, abnormal behaviour is considered undesirable and, if possible, something to be improved through intervention. The goal of intervention is to reduce the number or degree of abnormal behaviours so that day-to-day life can be more enjoyable and less troublesome for people who are affected and others who interact with them. One should note that behaviours that are not normal are sometimes called atypical, challenging, and/or difficult. Also, intervention that results in a cure is sometimes referred to as a treatment rather than an intervention.

Relationship Between Abnormal Behaviours, Mental Disorders, And Mental Ill-Health

Abnormal behaviour and mental disorders

Abnormal behaviour is often an outward indication of a mental disorder. The mental disorder is the underlying condition — the dysfunctional way the mind works — and the disorder results in behaviour that appears to others as abnormal. For this reason, to gain an understanding of abnormal behaviour, it is important to understand the mental disorders from which they result.

The term *mental disorder* is frequently used in the psychiatric and psychological literature. Mental disorders are accompanied by abnormal behaviours. However it is acknowledged in the mental health field that there is no definition that adequately specifies precise boundaries for the concept of *mental disorder*, and the term lacks a consistent operational definition that covers all situations. A variety of concepts, such as distress, dysfunction, dyscontrol, disadvantage, disability, inflexibility, irrationality, syndromal pattern, etiology, and statistical deviation, have been used to define mental disorders. Each is a useful indicator for a mental disorder, but none is equivalent to the concept.

Abnormal behaviour, mental ill-health and other terms

Other terms such as *psychiatric disorders* and *psychological disorders* are also used to describe abnormal behaviours, but like the term mental disorders, these also lack precise definitions. One may define these disorders as those treated by psychiatrists and psychologists, respectively, although there is still no consensus on which disorders or behaviours would fall into each group. In addition, the treatment of psychiatric and psychological disorders often involves a multidisciplinary team consisting of mental health professionals other than psychiatrists and psychologists. Broadly speaking, the core elements of mental disorders, psychiatric and psychological disorders, are cognitive, behavioural, and affective perturbations resulting in distress or disabilities. Recently, the term *mental ill-health* has been proposed as an all-encompassing term describing such behavioural, emotional, and psychiatric disturbances in people with or without developmental disability. As such, this is the term of choice throughout this book (e.g., see Chapter 36). Of note, the term *dual diagnosis* is being used to describe the co-occurrence of mental ill-health and developmental disability in the same individual.

Abnormal behaviours may be the result of many differen factors, including a wide variety of so-called mental disorders that are classified in manuals of mental disorders (see below). Such disorders can occur in any person in the general population, regardless of any co-existing condition, including intellectual and/or developmental disability. Abnormal behaviours may also result from traumatic brain injury, from physical conditions resulting in pain, from other medical conditions, recreational drug use or withdrawal, and as side effects from medication use or withdrawal. As well, certain developmental disabilities are associated with characteristic patterns of behaviour (called *behavioural phenotypes*) that result from the underlying genetic problem causing the disorder.

Classification Systems for Disorders Associated with Abnormal Behaviour

Classification is the process by which the complexity of phenomena is reduced by arranging them into categories according to some established criteria for one or more purposes (Zimmerman & Spitzer, 2009). A common misconception is that a classification of abnormal behaviours classifies people, when actually what are being classified are disorders that people have. The ultimate purpose of classification is to improve treatment and prevention efforts. A classification of mental disorders enhances communication, control, and comprehension of such conditions.

The major classification system used by the majority of clinicians to classify disorders associated with abnormal behaviour is contained in the *DSM-IV-TR* (APA, 2000). This manual classifies abnormal behaviours as mental disorders. The latter encompass clinically significant behavioural or psychological syndromes or patterns that occur in individuals, and that are associated with present distress (e.g., painful symptom) or disability (i.e., impairment in one or more important areas of functioning) or with a significantly increased risk of suffering death, pain, disability, or an important loss of freedom. The syndrome or pattern must not be merely an expectable and culturally sanctioned response to a par-

ticular event (e.g., death of a loved one). Whatever its original cause, a mental disorder must currently be considered a manifestation of a behavioural, psychological or biological dysfunction in the individual. Neither deviant behaviour (e.g., political, religious, or sexual) nor conflicts that are primarily between the individual and society are considered to be mental disorders unless the deviance or conflict is a symptom of a dysfunction in the individual, as described above. A similar system for classification of abnormal behaviour is described in *Chapter V: Mental and Behavioural Disorders*, part of the *International Statistical Classification of Diseases and Related Health Problems, Tenth Revision* (ICD-10; World Health Organization [WHO], 1992). This manual tends to be used in Europe, whereas the DSM is used in North America. (See also Hassiotis, Barron, & Hall, 2009.)

Mental disorders are formally classified in the DSM-IV-TR into five categories called Axes. Conditions comprising Axes I and II are grouped into 17 sections as indicated in Table 1. For approximately half of the diagnostic categories in Axes I and II, sets of diagnostic criteria are provided that must be met in order to establish a diagnosis. This is because individual symptoms may not be problematic on their own (Zimmerman & Spitzer, 2009).

Individuals with developmental disabilities may experience any mental disorder as classified under the DSM-IV and/or ICD-10. Nonetheless, it has been noted that these classification systems may be difficult to apply to this population, due to deficits in emotional regulation, and cognitive and adaptive functioning skills in these individuals. Adaptations of the DSM-IV (DM-ID: Diagnostic Manual-Intellectual Disabilities) and ICD-10 (DM-LC: Diagnostic Criteria for Psychiatric disorders for use with Adults with Learning Disabilities/ Mental Retardation) have been developed specifically for use in this population. Further details on the development of DM-ID are available from the website *www.dmid.org*. See also Fletcher, Loschen, Stavrakaki, & First (2009a; 2009b).

A new edition of the DSM — the DSM-5 — is in preparation. This was begun in 1999 and has been conducted over the past decade. The draft criteria for the new edition were published in early 2010 for public feedback. The DSM-5 taskforce is now revising the draft criteria, and the revised criteria are being tested in field trials. The final DSM-5 is set to be published in May, 2013. Proposed criteria and updates are available from *www.dsm5.org*. Among the major changes are the classification of personality disorders — with a push towards dimensional rating of personality traits instead of categorical classification into distinct personality disorders.

Major Diagnostic Categories Of The DSM-IV

Many mental ill-health symptoms may result from an underlying medical condition and/or substance use. However, with the exception of substance-related disorders, the text in this section assumes that underlying medical conditions or substance use have been excluded as etiology for the mental ill-health syndromes.

1. Disorders usually first diagnosed in infancy, childhood and adolescence

This section lists conditions based on the age that they are usually first diagnosed. These include intellectual disability (referred to as mental retardation in the DSM-IV-TR), learning disorders, motor skills disorder, communication disorders, pervasive developmental disorders (PDD), attention-deficit/hyperactivity disorder (ADHD), conduct disorder, oppositional defiant disorder, feeding and eating disorders (such as pica, rumination disorder), tic disorder, elimination disorders, several affective disorders in childhood (separation anxiety disorder, selective mutism, reactive attachment disorder), stereotypic movement disorder. The DSM-IV-TR notes that this grouping is only for convenience, and does not indicate a clear distinction between these disorders and others in the manual.

Attention Deficit / Hyperactivity Disorder: ADHD typically emerges in early childhood, but its origin remains unclear. The features of ADHD present along a continuum of degree of expression; at a certain point, the degree of expression may warrant clinical diagnosis in keeping with conventional

Table 1: Major Diagnostic Groupings of Axes I and II Disorders in DSM-IV-TR

- *Disorders Usually First Diagnosed in Infancy, Childhood, or Adolescence*
- *Delirium, Dementia, and Amnestic and Other Cognitive Disorders*
- *Mental Disorders Due to a General Medical Condition*
- *Substance-Related Disorders*
- *Schizophrenia and Other Psychotic Disorders*
- *Mood Disorders*
- *Anxiety Disorders*
- *Somatoform Disorders*
- *Factitious Disorders*
- *Dissociative Disorders*
- *Sexual and Gender Identity Disorders*
- *Eating Disorders*
- *Sleep Disorders*
- *Impulse-Control Disorders Not Elsewhere Classified*
- *Adjustment Disorders*
- *Personality Disorders*
- *Other Conditions That May Be a Focus of Clinical Attention*

guidelines. The DSM-IV-TR, which sets out the guidelines primarily used for diagnosing this disorder, presents a subtype conceptualization as follows:

1. Attention-Deficit/Hyperactivity Disorder, Combined Type;
2. Attention-Deficit/Hyperactivity Disorder, Predominantly Inattentive Type; and
3. Attention-Deficit/Hyperactivity Disorder, Predominantly Hyperactive-Impulsive Type (APA, 2000, p. 87).

Features associated with ADHD include:

- Poor sustained attention
- Distractibility and inadequate persistence with tasks
- A tendency to talk out of turn, with a blurting-out quality

- General social impulsiveness
- Poorly sustained motivation and initiative for activities
- Poor follow-through on instructions
- Impulsivity and seeking immediate gratification
- Poor organizational and planning skills
- Poor regulation of adaptive level of mental arousal
- Daily forgetfulness
- Compromise in working memory
- Compromise in verbal self-mediation (strategic self-talk that helps to control impulsivity)
- Poor metacognition (awareness and reflection on the quality of one's own learning and thinking style)

In individuals for whom hyperactivity is the predominant feature, there is obvious difficulty with sitting still. These individuals often are fidgety, restless, and excessively physically active with a driven quality; they may also be excessively talkative.

Problems associated with ADHD are quite variable, tending to some degree to be affected by the subjective interest or boredom level that an individual experiences in a given situation and whether the situation provides immediate reward. The symptoms associated with ADHD show some resemblance to mild frontal lobe injury. ADHD is also associated with elevated rates of socio-emotional problems in some individuals. Problems are typically expressed most pronouncedly in the context of school. Typically, unaddressed ADHD has a significant negative impact on school performance. ADHD tends to be over-diagnosed in young boys.

Intervention for ADHD requires a multifaceted approach and might include school accommodations, family therapy, behavioural intervention, medications such as stimulants (e.g., methylphenidate) or atomoxetine, and parental self-care strategies (e.g., strategies to prevent discipline problems). Evaluating individuals for sensitivities to particular foods (e.g., food additives, refined sugars), allergies, and fatty acid deficiencies are other strategies (though not evidence-based) that might be pursued. (General sources: APA, 2000; Humphries, 2007; Stevens, Kuczek, Burgess, Hurt, & Arnold, 2010;

WHO, 1992; Wilens & Spencer, 2010.)

Pica: Pica is an eating disorder that may have benign or life-threatening consequences. The word pica comes from the Latin word meaning "magpie," a bird of indiscriminate appetite. Pica is typically defined as the persistent eating of non-nutritive substances for a period of at least 1 month at an age in which this behaviour is developmentally inappropriate (e.g., beyond the age of 18–24 months). The definition of the disorder sometimes includes the mouthing of non-nutritive substances. People with pica ingest substances ranging from clay, dirt, and pebbles to paint chips, vinyl gloves, light bulbs, needles and thread, and burnt matches. Eating such items sometimes results in serious health problems such as lead poisoning, constipation, intestinal obstruction or perforation, damage to teeth and gums, and infections.

Pica is the most common eating disorder in people with intellectual and/or developmental disabilities, especially autism. Pica also can be a problem in some pregnant women and in some people with epilepsy. It can occur as the result of brain injury. It also can be associated with deficiencies of specific nutrients, such as iron or zinc (although pica does not usually correct these deficiencies), malnutrition, dieting, parental neglect, and mental health conditions such as obsessive compulsive disorder and schizophrenia. Pica can be managed by a number of different approaches, including education about what is acceptable or not acceptable to eat, behavioural intervention to teach a person how to eat more appropriately, prevention of access to nonfood items (e.g., by using safety-locks and high shelving and keeping household chemicals and medications out of reach), medication, as well as screening for and treatment of life-threatening complications of pica. (See Ashworth, Hirdes, & Martin, 2009, and McAdam, Sherman, Sheldon, & Napolitano, 2004, for additional information.)

2. Substance-related disorders

These disorders can be broadly divided into *substance-use* and *substance-induced* disorders. The former include *substance abuse* and *substance dependence*. The latter include emotional, behavioural and/or cognitive disturbances resulted from substance use (e.g., depression).

Use of alcohol and other drugs, both legal and illegal, brings about effects that many people consider to be positive. These include such feelings as freedom from stress and anxiety, mood elevation, euphoria, enhanced sensory perception, and sense of increased capacity. However, excessive use of alcohol and drugs can affect people's lives negatively in many ways. When people become dependent on habitual or excessive use, their overall behaviour pattern very often becomes more destructive than constructive; when this occurs, the term *substance abuse* is typically used to describe their over-reliance on alcohol or other drugs. Dependence is associated with tolerance, whereby the individual must increase the amount of a drug to maintain its original effect and/or whereby the body begins to rely on the substance to the point where symptoms of withdrawal result if it is absent.

There are many harmful effects on individuals resulting from the overuse of alcohol and other drugs. Over time, alcohol can damage the liver and other organs. Chronic use of some street drugs may cause brain damage or permanent changes that affect emotion and cognition. Single use of powerful hallucinogenic drugs, such as lysergic acid diethylamide (LSD) or psilocybin, has the potential to cause emotional and/or cognitive alterations that are permanent and harmful.

Substance abuse is difficult to treat not only because of the dependence but also because its effects are self-reinforcing for many people. Withdrawal from alcohol or drugs, especially in cases of serious dependence, should be treated by an expert because it can result in strong physical and emotional reactions such as loss of appetite, difficulty sleeping, mental confusion, hallucinations, fear, anxiety, body tremors, fever, increased heart rate, perspiration, stomach pain, and chest pain. Referrals for treatment at a substance abuse facility or a doctor with appropriate experience should be made through one's family physician or by another appropriate means, such as the Substance Abuse Facility Locator (Substance Abuse and Mental Health Services Administration, 2006). The literature is sparse about the topic of substance abuse in people with intellectual and dis-

abilities, but a recent survey suggests that this issue, unfortunately, is alarmingly prevalent (Joszvai, Gajdos, Lean, & Hewitt, 2007). (See also the website of the Canadian Network of Substance Abuse and Allied Professionals, 2010).

3. Schizophrenia and other psychotic disorders

Psychotic disorders are characterized by *delusion* (a false belief based on erroneous inference about external reality that is firmly sustained despite incontrovertible proof or evidence to the contrary, that is not shared by the person's cultural or religious groups) and/or *hallucination* (a sensory perception with compelling sense of reality of a true perception that occurs without external stimulation of the relevant sensory organ).

To better understand schizophrenia and other psychotic disorders, the concept of clusters of symptoms is often used. Symptom patterns, or syndromes, include *positive symptoms*, in which something has been added to the typical pattern of behaviour (can be psychotic or disorganized symptoms such as delusions, heightened perceptions, excessive or unusual movements, hallucinations, emotional turmoil, angry speech), and *negative symptoms*, in which something is lacking from the typical pattern of behaviour (e.g., poverty of speech, blunted or flat emotional expression, unresponsiveness to the environment). An individual with psychotic disorder may have either or both clusters of symptoms.

Schizophrenia: Schizophrenia is characterized by a mixture of positive and negative symptoms with marked social or occupational dysfunction sustained over at least 6 months. The DSM IV-TR (APA, 2000) and ICD-10 (WHO, 1992) specify criteria that need to be met for its diagnosis. According to the DSM IV-TR, there are several subtypes of schizophrenia:

- Paranoid schizophrenia: Characterized by suspicion and grand schemes of persecution; hallucinations; and delusions (which are more common and prominent)
- Disorganized schizophrenia (DSM-IV-TR) or Hebephrenic schizophrenia (ICD-10): Characterized by verbal incoherence and moods and emotions that are not appropriate

to the situation; hallucinations are not usually present

- Catatonic schizophrenia: Characterized by withdrawal, negative affect, isolation, and psychomotor disturbance
- Residual schizophrenia: Characterized by lack of motivation and interest in day-to-day living
- Undifferentiated schizophrenia: Meeting the general diagnostic criteria for schizophrenia

Schizoaffective disorder: Related but not a subtype of schizophrenia, schizoaffective disorder is characterized by symptoms of schizophrenia as well as mood disorder (e.g., major depression, bipolar mania, mixed mania; to be discussed in the next section).

Schizophrenia is among the top 10 of disabilities worldwide in terms of prevalence. It affects approximately 1 in 100 people worldwide, and is more common than Alzheimer's disease or multiple sclerosis worldwide (Beers, Porter, & Jones, 2006). The prevalence of schizophrenia appears similar between the genders, though the incidence appears higher in males than females (Abel, Drake, & Goldstein, 2010). Generally speaking, women have a later onset of schizophrenia and a better course of illness than men, while both genders show a peak incidence in their early twenties and a second (lower) peak around middle age, women show a lower peak in their twenties and more pronounced peak in middle age than men (Abel et al., 2010). Onset in childhood, early adolescence, or late life is not uncommon, though. Schizophrenia is increasingly being conceptualized as a neurodevelopmental disorder (Insel, 2010). At one time, it was also thought to be progressive, but there is no compelling evidence that this is the case. It is often a lifelong condition, however, and poses enormous emotional, social, and financial burdens to individuals and their families.

Trying to understand the causes of schizophrenia continues to be the subject of considerable study (Kirkbride & Jones, 2010). Genetic factors are known to be involved in many cases. A developmental disorder known as 22q11.2 deletion syndrome resulting from abnormalities of chromosome 22, is associated with symptoms of schizophrenia

and other psychiatric conditions (Fung, McEvilly, Fong, Chow, & Bassett, 2010; see Chapter **13** for more information about this syndrome). In fact, 22q11.2 deletion syndrome is the highest known risk factor for schizophrenia, and approximately 1% of people with schizophrenia have been found to have this disease (Bassett & Chow, 2008). Maternal exposure to famine, influenza in the second trimester of pregnancy, and Rh incompatibility in a second or subsequent pregnancy also are associated with an increased risk of schizophrenia in offspring. Increased incidence rates of schizophrenia of up to 10-fold have also been reported in various ethnic minority migrant groups (especially African-Caribbeans) in Europe (reviewed in Fung, Bhugra, & Jones, 2009). Overall, however, schizophrenia is thought to be a complex and multifactorial disorder (Verdoux & Cougnard, 2006). The onset, remission, and recurrence of symptoms of this disorder are thought to result from interaction between vulnerabilities and environmental stressors. Environmental stressors include stressful life events such as ending a relationship. With schizophrenia, the risk of violent behaviour is relatively modest; the level of risk is much less than with substance abuse, for example. At times, people with schizophrenia go to shelters or hospital emergency departments and show somewhat violent behaviour when they actually want food, shelter, or medical or psychiatric care.

Schizophrenia is associated with an approximate 10% risk of suicide. Individuals who have paranoid forms with late onset and good functioning before being diagnosed — the very people with the best prognosis for recovery — are also at the greatest risk for suicide (Fenton, 2000; Roy & Pompili, 2009). The reason for this association is not known, but this information helps clinicians to identify affected individuals who are at the highest risk for suicide. (General sources: APA, 2000; Beers, Porter, & Jones, 2006.)

4. Mood disorders

Unipolar (depressive) and bipolar (manic-depressive) disorders: Unipolar (depressive) and bipolar (manic-depressive) disorders are the most common of a heterogeneous group of illnesses known as mood disorders or affective disorders. Sadness and joy are part of everyday life, but they can be distinguished from clinical depression and unusual elation. Transient depression ("the blues") may result from things such as getting a bad mark at school, or it may occur at certain times such as during the premenstrual phase.

People are diagnosed with *major depression* when they have a sustained period (more than 2 weeks) of depressed mood and/or loss of interest or pleasure in almost all activities, together with a number of bodily symptoms (e.g., change in appetite, sleep, energy level, concentration, psychomotor activities); feelings of worthlessness or guilt; and/or recurrent suicidal thoughts/plan/attempt. There may or may not be an identifiable trigger/stressor. *Dysthymic disorder* refers to a milder but more chronic (at least 2 years) form of depression. People are diagnosed with *mania* when they are considerably more elated than seems appropriate for the situation and to a degree that causes problems. Unipolar major depressive disorder is almost twice as common in women as it is in men; approximately 20% of women and 12% of men, at some point in their lives, experience the effects of this disorder to a degree that may require treatment (Beers, Porter, & Jones, 2006). Unipolar disorders typically, but not always, begin when people are in their 20s, 30s, or 40s.

Bipolar disorder, in which episodes of depression alternate with periods of mania, affects 4%–5% of the general population (Beers, Porter, & Jones, 2006). This affects the sexes equally, but depressive forms predominate in women whereas manic forms predominate in men. Four different subtypes of bipolar disorder are recognized: *bipolar I, bipolar II, cyclothymia,* and *rapid cycling*. Bipolar I is characterized by extreme high periods (*manic episodes*) that may or may not be associated with periods of major depression. Bipolar II is characterized by episodes of relatively modest mania (*hypomanic episodes*) associated with periods of major depression. In cyclothymia, there are relatively moderate episodes of mania and depression. In rapid cycling disorder, there may be up to four periods of great energy and periods of depression within a year. Bipolar disorder used to be diagnosed when people

were in their 20s or 30s, but now it is being diagnosed in teens and even in younger children (Kluger & Song, 2002). The diagnosis of bipolar disorder is often confused with ADHD, although up to 15% of children thought to have ADHD may have bipolar disorder. Genetic factors are thought to play a strong role in bipolar disorder. A child with one parent who has the disorder has a 10%–30% risk of developing the condition. Family, twin, and adoption studies indicate that bipolar disorder has a strong genetic basis, but the involvement of specific genes is not clear (Bondy, 2011). Approximately 70% of those with bipolar disorder respond favourably to lithium therapy (Young & Newham, 2006).

Bipolar disorder, if not treated, has an approximately 15% risk of death by suicide. The risk of suicide attempts are substantially higher in bipolar II disorder than in any other psychiatric disorder (Cassidy, 2010). (General sources: APA, 2000; Beers, Porter, & Jones, 2006; Kluger & Song, 2002; MedlinePlus — Health Information, 2006.)

5. Anxiety disorders

The term *stress* is common in everyday language, and everyone experiences it at some time or another. Stress is an internal process that occurs when a person is faced with a demand that is perceived to exceed the resources available to effectively respond to it and where failure to effectively deal with the demand has important and undesirable consequences. In other words, stress causes the effects that individuals feel when people or events in their environment are too demanding for them to cope with easily. These factors are called *stressors*.

Stress can result from many different things (e.g., infection, childbirth, life events, psychological factors), and it may be temporary or long lasting. Individuals vary greatly in the degree to which they can tolerate stress, and most people tolerate one kind of stress more than other kinds. Some stress in life is usually seen as a good thing, because it motivates people to do new things and to adapt their behaviour to the conditions that exist around them. The process of stress leads to arousal and selection of a coping response. If the coping response is effective, the coping response leads to relaxation.

However, too much stress at once or a great deal of stress that lasts over a long period of time can be harmful. If ineffective coping responses are used, arousal increases, resulting in strain. If stress is unresolved, it leads to burnout. Burnout, in turn, contributes to diagnosable conditions such as depression, anxiety disorders, and substance abuse (Franke, 1999). Harmful effects of stress include increased heart rate and blood pressure and other body changes associated with alarm reaction that can lead to exhaustion and suppression of the immune system. Mental health harm occurs when there is too much emotional arousal and too much demand to cope, such that behaviour becomes irrational or unpredictable. In severe cases of stress, psychological and physiological resources are exhausted, and psychological disorganization (e.g., delusion, hallucinations) or personality disintegration can occur. Furthermore, ineffective coping may be a factor in a wide range of mental and physical illnesses with many different causes. See Chapter 11 for details about the changes that occur in the body when a person is subjected to stress.

Sometimes stress occurs suddenly and affects a person's life strongly. For example, the death of someone close, an accident, a divorce, a rape, war, or a natural disaster can have an enormous and sudden impact on a person. *Acute stress disorder* is a term used to describe the numb, detached feeling people have for a few days or a few weeks after the event. If these symptoms persist, and especially if the person continues to mentally re-experience the traumatic event, the term *post traumatic stress disorder* is typically used.

Anxiety: Anxiety is defined as a feeling of apprehension characterized by physical symptoms such as heart palpitations, sweating, and other unpleasant feelings that often are experienced in a stressful situation. It is a particular type of reaction to a stressor. All humans experience anxiety. Under normal circumstances, certain amounts of anxiety are adaptive. They create emotional, physiological, and behavioural responses to recognized external threats (e.g., an intruder, a runaway car) that make people evaluate situations and mobilize their resources to escape or to protect their loved ones or themselves. Without this response, people would not be able to free themselves from danger. However, too much anxiety or anxiety that lasts too long can result in an unpleasant emotional state in which a person evaluates a situation incorrectly and is unable to mobilize his or her resources. Most people have experienced this situation at one time or another — for example, when they are unable to move when scared suddenly or feel the dreadful feelings that arise in times of panic.

Anxiety can have both physical and psychological effects, especially if people are overwhelmed by events. People exhibit different degrees of anxiety; they also differ in their ability to cope with anxiety in general and with specific types of anxiety. Whatever the causes and despite individual differences, when the effects of anxiety are strong and/or prolonged, a person may experience irrational, unrealistic, and disabling fear. This can be characterized as an anxiety disorder. Anxiety disorders are serious medical illnesses that are very common. They affect approximately 19 million U.S. adults, but the prevalence of specific anxiety disorders varies considerably among countries and across cultures. These disorders fill people's lives with overwhelming fear. Unlike the relatively mild, brief anxiety caused by a stressful event such as a job interview, making one's first public presentation, or a first date, anxiety disorders can progressively worsen if not treated.

Anxiety disorders occur when the anxiety system is operating improperly. Numerous physiological and psychological factors contribute to this. For example, research with animals suggests that some anxiety disorders may be associated with the *amygdala*, a small part of the brain that controls the emotions of fear and anxiety and the development of emotional memories, which may function differently among individuals. Anxiety-related behaviour might be influenced by a variation in a gene for a protein involved in transporting the neurotransmitter serotonin around the brain (the serotonin transporter gene) (Lin & Madras, 2006).

It is also possible that maternal-infant misatunement in infancy is a cause of, or contributes to, anxiety disorders. This results in permanent dysregulation of the autonomic nervous system, which may contribute to anxiety disorders.

Anxiety may be elevated as a result of physical disorders, such as neurological disorders (e.g., brain trauma), infections, inner ear disorders, cardiovascular disorders (e.g., heart failure, arrhythmias), endocrine disorders (e.g., overactive adrenal or thyroid glands), low blood sugar, middle-ear problems, certain types of tumors, and respiratory disorders (e.g., asthma, chronic obstructive pulmonary disease). Anxiety may be caused by use of drugs, such as alcohol, stimulants, caffeine, cocaine, and many prescription drugs. Also, drug withdrawal is commonly associated with anxiety.

A careful history and physical examination are needed to accurately distinguish anxiety disorders from disorders with purely physical causes. The physical examination should involve a chest X-ray, an electrocardiogram (ECG), and a full battery of blood tests — including tests of blood chemistry and thyroid function.

Anxiety disorders also must be distinguished from anxiety that occurs in certain other psychiatric disorders, because they respond to different specific treatments. Treatment should be directed at the primary causes rather than the secondary anxiety symptoms. If anxiety remains after a physical disorder is treated as effectively as possible, or after a causative substance is discontinued long enough for withdrawal symptoms to abate, treatment of anxiety symptoms with appropriate drugs, behaviour therapy, and/or psychotherapy is indicated. (General sources: APA, 2000; Beers, Porter, & Jones, 2006.)

Other than the acute stress disorder and posttraumatic stress disorder, the other major anxiety disorders described in the DSM-IV-TR include:

Phobias: Phobias are fears that are persistent and disproportionate to the actual threat. Specific phobias include fear of things such as snakes, spiders, open water, heights, or being enclosed. Social phobias involve excessive fear of social situations such as feeling embarrassed or fearful in the presence of others. Agoraphobia describes the behaviour of people who are fearful of leaving their safe environments. It literally means "fear of open spaces." Phobias differ between genders and age groups and are affected by genetic and environmental factors as well.

Panic disorder: Panic disorder is characterized by recurring attacks of sudden, unexpected panic. These are commonly accompanied by feelings of losing control, losing one's mind, fear of dying, increased heart rate, sweating, shortness of breath, dizziness, expecting something terrible to happen, disorientation, or detachment from one's environment. Panic attacks differ from other types of anxiety in that they are of short duration and are very intense. Panic disorders stem primarily from emotional and cognitive factors, but are also partly related to aspects of biological functioning, including genetics. Agoraphobia, which may or may not be associated with panic disorder, is anxiety about, or avoidance of, places or situations from which escape might be difficult (or embarrassing) or in which help may not be available in the event of having a panic attack.

Generalized anxiety disorder: Generalized anxiety disorder is an ongoing state of excessive worry or fear about numerous things. In some cases, this is related to another fear or anxiety, but in other cases it is not. It is characterized by chronic symptoms of physical and emotional arousal. People with generalized anxiety disorder are typically in a state of anxious apprehension, and they try to foresee and deal with future problems but feel unable to do so because they are highly anxious and feel out of control. Such apprehension overtakes logic, even logic that seems quite obvious, and leaves them feeling tense, upset, and discouraged. It sometimes leads to physical and emotional exhaustion.

Obsessive compulsive disorder: Obsessive compulsive disorder has two aspects that are very often related. First, obsessions are characterized by ideas, worries, and fears that are recurrent and unwanted. These are often accompanied by behaviours that the person feels compelled to do, even if he or she does not want to. Often, these behaviours are repetitive and ritualized. To other people, they may seem silly, weird, nasty, or even horrible, but to the person doing them they often allow an easing of mental tension and anxiety, even if it is only temporary. For example, some people have the obsession that their hands should always be clean and fears that there may be germs on their hands. As a consequence, they wash their hands hundreds of times each day. Obsessive-compulsive disorder affects men, women, and children. In Canada, the prevalence is listed as 1.8% in persons 18-64 years of age (Public Health Agency of Canada, 2002).

6. Somatoform disorders

Somatoform disorder: Somatoform disorder is a relatively new term for what was often called psychosomatic disorder. Somatoform disorder is actually a group of psychiatric disorders characterized by physical symptoms that suggest — but are not fully explained by — a physical disorder, and that cause significant distress or interfere with social, occupational, or other functioning. To be considered as a somatoform disorder, neither the physical symptoms nor their severity and duration are obviously explained by an underlying physical condition. Disorders listed in the DSM-IV-TR under this group include somatization disorder, undifferentiated somatoform disorder, conversion disorder, hypochondriasis, pain disorder and body dysmorphic disorder. (General sources: APA, 2000; Beers, Porter, & Berkow, 2005.)

7. Sexual and gender identity disorders

There is tremendous variation in sexual practices, and attitudes toward those practices, among different cultures of the world. In addition, norms change over time. For example, at the beginning of the 21st century, it seems almost curious to think that masturbation (practised by approximately 92% of males and 67% of females) was once perceived by Western society as a perversion and something that might cause mental illness. Today, masturbation is considered a normal sexual practice unless it is done publicly, impairs partner relations, or is done compulsively to the point of distress. Sexual orientation (including same-sex marriage and family rights) is protected by Canadian and Ontario laws and thus is no longer a "disorder" in the legal or social sense. Gender identity differences and practices are also increasingly accepted as falling within the normal range of behaviours.

The DSM-IV-TR lists three groups of disorders under "sexual and gender identity disorders." The most common form of these disorders observed by practitioners is *sexual dysfunction* — divided into sexual *desire, arousal, orgasmic* and *pain* disorders. The *gender identity disorders* are characterized by identification with the opposite sex and discomfort with one's biological sex. *Paraphilias* are characterized by recurrent, intense sexual urges, fantasies or behaviours involving unusual objects, activities, or situations, such as *fetishism, transvestic fetishism, voyeurism, exhibitionism, sexual sadism, sexual masochism, pedophilia,* and *frotteurism* (rubbing against a nonconsenting person). Among these, the behaviours that are associated with forms of sexual abuse are most troublesome. Pedophilia (adult preference for a child as a sexual partner), incest (sexual relations between family members), and rape (sexual activity that occurs under threat of coercion or force) are all considered very serious and highly undesirable psychosexual behaviours. Treatments for paraphilias — both serious and less serious — that combine cognitive and behavioural techniques (e.g., aversion therapy, social skills training, and cognitive restructuring) have met with some success. Success has been limited, however, because the reasons for the behaviours in the first place are frequently deeply rooted in the person's personality, because a desire for change is often reluctant or only in response to having been arrested or convicted of a crime, and because the degree to which such methods should be used has been the subject of some controversy. A great deal of work still needs to be done to balance effective treatment methods, public protection, moral and ethical practice, and individual rights. (General sources: APA, 2000; Beers, Porter, & Berkow, 2006.)

8. Eating disorders

Eating disorders are characterized by severe disturbances in eating behaviour, and many cases typically first appear in mid-adolescence. *Anorexia nervosa, bulimia nervosa,* and *binge-eating disorder* (the latter fall under the DSM-IV-TR diagnostic category of 'eating disorder not otherwise specified'; EDNOS) are the most commonly known eating disorders. *Pica* (discussed above) and certain other conditions related to eating disturbances are lesser known.

Anorexia nervosa, bulimia nervosa, and binge-eating disorder: Anorexia nervosa, bulimia nervosa, and binge-eating disorder are the three most common types of eating disorders. Approximately 90% of individuals affected by these eating disorders are females.

Anorexia nervosa can be a severe, life-threatening disorder in which an individual refuses to maintain a normal weight, is intensely afraid of gaining weight, and exhibits a significant distortion of the perception of the shape or size of the body as well as dissatisfaction with body shape and size. It affects 0.5%–2% of the general population (Beers, Porter, & Jones, 2006).

Bulimia nervosa can also be a life-threatening disorder. It is characterized by recurrent episodes of binge eating following by self-induced vomiting and other purging methods such as excessive use of laxatives and/or diuretics, excessive exercise, and fasting in an attempt to avoid weight gain. The lifetime prevalence is 3%, and the ratio of female to male patients ranges from 10:1 to 20:1.

Binge-eating disorder is characterized by recurrent episodes of compulsive overeating or binge eating. It affects approximately 2% of the population and occurs in approximately 30% of people participating in medically supervised weight loss programs. The purging in an attempt to prevent weight gain characteristic of bulimia nervosa is absent. Binge-eating leads to obesity, a cause of premature death in many people, and predisposes individuals to anorexia and bulimia.

A host of medical complications can accompany anorexia and bulimia nervosa. If untreated, they can become life threatening. Approximately 10% of affected individuals succumb to death as the result of starvation, cardiac arrest, or suicide. Individuals who experience an eating disorder may be unaware that they have a problem. If a serious eating disorder is suspected, friends or loved ones should ask for advice about how to help. Treatment for an eating disorder should involve a variety of approaches and experts, including a paediatrician or internist, a nutritionist, an individual psychotherapist, and a family therapist. Much research is being done in the field of eating disorders. It presently is not known what factors are causal and what are consequences in the different eating disorders (General sources: APA, 2000; Beers, Porter, & Jones, 2006.)

Conditions associated with eating disturbances: Prader-Willi syndrome is a genetic developmental disability in which an eating disorder is part of the syndrome. In this syndrome, the hypothalamus of the brain is affected, resulting in a constant feeling of hunger that can lead to excessive eating and morbid obesity. A high rate of diabetes is associated with this disorder (see Chapter 13 for further details). *Psychosocial dwarfism* (sometimes called *Psychosocial Short Stature*, or PSS) is an eating disorder that is considered to be a reactive attachment disorder, a consequence of child abuse and neglect. This disorder involves food hoarding, binge eating, and bizarre behaviour such as eating out of garbage cans. Many other conditions, such as depression and anxiety disorders, may be associated with less striking eating problems. (General sources: APA, 2000; Beers, Porter, & Jones, 2006.)

9. Sleep disorders

Sleep is a normal, essential behaviour, although the functions of sleeping remain largely mysterious. Sleep disorders, therefore, are considered to be forms of abnormal behaviour. Sleep disorders include *sleep apnea* (an interruption or cessation of breathing during sleep), *insomnia* (inability to fall and/or stay asleep), *narcolepsy* (a disorder with bouts of sleepiness and drowsiness), *restless leg syndrome* (a disorder characterized by an irresistible urge to move the legs especially when lying down), and *circadian rhythm disorder* (shifted and/or irregular sleep-wake cycles), among others. These disorders can vary considerably in both frequency of occurrence and intensity. They interfere with daily functioning and with the enjoyment of life, although such interference varies from very mild to severe. Sleep deprivation studies repeatedly show a variable (negative) impact on mood, cognitive performance, learning, behaviour, and motor function. Sleep disorders in young people affect not only their functions and behaviours but also those of their families and particularly their mothers, who may already suffer from increased levels of stress and poorer mental health.

Because people with special needs, particularly those with autism spectrum disorder, are reported to have more frequent and persistent sleep problems than their unaffected peers, it is particularly important that they receive appropriate intervention for their sleep problems. (General sources: APA, 2000; Beers, Porter, & Jones, 2006.)

10. Impulse-control disorders

The essential feature of these disorders is the failure to resist an impulse, drive or temptation to perform an act that is harmful to the person or to others. Listed in the DSM-IV-TR, these include *intermittent explosive disorder* (discrete episodes of failure to resist aggressive impulses, resulting in serious assaults or destruction of property), *kleptomania* (impulses to steal objects not needed for personal use or monetary value), *pyromania* (fire setting for pleasure or relief of tension), *pathological gambling* (persistent maladaptive gambling behaviour), and *trichotillomania* (recurrent hair-pulling for pleasure or relief of tension) (APA, 2000).

11. Personality disorders

Personality is a unique pattern of traits and behaviours that each person develops to interpret and respond to his or her surroundings. Well-functioning people have personalities that allow them to adapt to and cope with the ever-changing conditions, limitations, and opportunities of life.

People who are said to have personality disorders have some inflexible, maladaptive personality traits and behaviours that prevent adequate functioning in some aspects of their lives. Personality disorders are usually evident from adolescence. People with personality disorder are often unaware of the social and personal problems they have created, even when they contribute to the deterioration of relationships with others. Personality disorders may affect as many as 13%–14% of the population, including people with intellectual and developmental disabilities. Research findings and clinical descriptions are available that describe in detail the relationship between specific personality disorders and disability (APA, 2000; Beers, Porter, & Jones, 2006). Individuals with personality disorders

may show symptoms such as depression or anxiety, or they may show maladaptive behaviour such as paranoia, hypochondria, violence, vengefulness, self-defeating or self-destructive behaviours (e.g., alcohol or drug abuse), erratic mood, or rigidness. Behaviours of this type, if carried over into parenthood, can contribute to severe mental health and emotional problems for children. Psychotherapy for personality disorders meets with some success. Selective serotonin reuptake inhibitors (SSRIs) and mood stabilizers can also be effective in the treatment of personality disorders.

According to the DSM-IV-TR (APA, 2000), there are three broad categories of personality disorders — *odd/eccentric*, *dramatic/erratic*, and *anxious/inhibited* — which are further broken into distinct types.

i. Odd/eccentric: One disorder in the odd/eccentric personality category is *paranoid personality disorder*. Individuals with this disorder are suspicious of the intentions of others. They tend to be hypervigilant and easily come to believe that others do not like them, or mean to exploit or manipulate them. They are mistrusting and reluctant to confide in others. They often work independently and are generally focused and driven.

Individuals with *schizoid personality disorder* are introverted, self-absorbed, and emotionally distant or blunted. They prefer to be alone and do not mix well with others socially. They often seek work that allows them to be isolated. Close relationships are not sought. Generally, they show little interest in any form of interpersonal intimacy. They may be anxious or fearful around others.

Individuals with *schizotypal personality disorder* appear similar in many ways to individuals who have schizophrenia. They may display very odd beliefs, peculiar ways of thinking that are not logical or rational, and mild delusional or paranoid tendencies. It is not unusual for individuals with this personality disorder to dress very peculiarly. They tend to be socially isolated and lacking in close relationships. People with schizotypal personalities may have a mild variant of schizophrenia (Beers, Porter, & Jones, 2006).

ii. Dramatic/erratic: One variant of the dramatic/

erratic category is *antisocial personality disorder* (previously psychopathic or sociopathic disorder). In developed countries, this condition mostly occurs in males. People with this personality disorder are intentionally insensitive and tend to exploit others. They do not anticipate the repercussions of their actions and often believe that they are justified in their destructive behaviour. This disorder is associated with: lack of empathy and interpersonal insensitivity; violent and other forms of antisocial behaviour; impulsiveness; attention problems; excessive self-interest and self-serving goals; and lack of insight, remorse, and guilt. Their harmful actions may be obviously criminal or may be "white collar" crimes.

Individuals with *borderline personality disorder* are unstable in their self-image, mood, behaviour, and relationships. In severe cases, they may experience psychotic episodes of paranoia and hallucination. Individuals with borderline personality disorder experience depression, misery, regular failure in their pursuits, self-destructive behaviour, feelings of emptiness, fear of abandonment, feelings of entitlement, severe lack of insight, poor reality checking, and easily elicited rage responses. These individuals have low tolerance for constructive criticism. As in all personality disorders, there is also a particular cognitive style associated with borderline personality disorder.

Individuals with *histrionic personality disorder* (formerly called hysterical personality disorder) are vain, melodramatic attention seekers. Their behaviours often stem from a desire for caring and support. They express emotions superficially and immaturely, which often results in sympathetic or erotic attention from others and fleeting superficial relationships. Affected individuals are often seductive while being sexually unfulfilled or inhibited.

Individuals with *narcissistic personality disorder* have exaggerated feelings of superiority and entitlement. They are often under the impression that others are envious and can be exploited. They require admiration and are intolerant of criticism. Failure or disappointment results in anger and bouts of depression. Their relationships tend to be shallow and exploitive. They tend to feel empty, unfulfilled, and somewhat lacking in empathy. Often their

behaviours are ultimately self-defeating. They have minimal tolerance for criticism and are quick to disassociate themselves from others for minor shortcomings. Their insight into these problems is limited.

iii. Anxious/inhibited: Individuals with *avoidant personality disorder* are desperate to avoid rejection and are reluctant to embark on new relationships or experiences for fear that they may fail or be disappointed. Any sign of rejection leads to further withdrawal. People with avoidant personality recognize their desire for care and understanding and are therefore distraught by their difficulties in social interactions and relationships.

Individuals with *dependent personality disorder* relinquish control in major areas of their lives, then give priority to the needs of those whom they have come to depend upon. They are insecure and feel incapable of caring for themselves and making decisions. Their behaviour stems both from a belief that others are more competent, as well as from a fear of offending others with their opinions or perceived demands. Dependency may be masked by other more blatant behaviour problems such as histrionic or borderline behaviours.

Individuals with *obsessive-compulsive personality disorder* develop and abide by structured routines, which they are averse to changing. Their personalities tend to have excessive rigidity. They are self-reliant and have difficulty relinquishing control of their environment and their emotions; this makes spontaneity and relationships a challenge. They are diligent and determined but may lose focus on a task or become anxious and indecisive as they analyze all aspects and consequences of their decisions. Some people who have obsessive-compulsive personalities can apply their perfectionism to advantage, in ways such as excelling at academic study (Beers, Porter, & Jones, 2006).

Suicidal Behaviour and Suicide

Suicidal behaviour includes *attempts, completed suicide,* and *suicide gestures,* which are actions that could be interpreted as suicidal even if they are unlikely to lead to completion. While they are not classified as a separate mental disorder, they are often associated with chronic mental, neurological and other medical disorders. It has recently been proposed that suicidal behaviour be included as a separate diagnosis in a separate axis in the DSM-5 (Oquendo, Baca-García, Mann, & Giner, 2008).

In the United States, drug overdose is the most common method of attempted suicide, and firearm use is the most common in completed suicide. Alcohol use, addiction, and intoxication are implicated in many suicides and suicide attempts.

Risk for suicidal behaviour is affected by age and sex, and also by sociocultural factors, both within a country and across countries. Suicide comprises 10% of deaths among people of ages 25 to 34 years; 30% of deaths among university students; and is the second highest cause of adolescent death (Beers, Porter, & Jones, 2006). Men are more likely to die as the result of a suicide attempt, but women attempt suicide three times more frequently. Among some Native American tribes and Alaskan natives, the suicide rate is now several times the national average (Beers, Porter, & Jones, 2006; Medline Plus — Health Information, 2006).

Some conditions — such as behavioural abnormalities, social issues, physical disabilities, and mental disorders (especially depression) — have a somewhat higher association with suicidal behaviour than others. Although the majority of people with depression do not die by suicide, approximately 60% of people who commit suicide have been found to have a mood disorder (major depression, bipolar disorder, dysthymia). People with epilepsy have a five-fold increased risk of suicide compared to the general population, and those with temporal lobe epilepsy may have a twenty-five-fold increased risk. Depression is common in children and adolescents with epilepsy, but a connection with epilepsy and suicide is often overlooked. One study suggests that the cause of depression in such individuals is related to a number of factors, including seizure type, high seizure frequency, less than optimal pharmacological management, and lack of occupational and social activity (Mula, Bell, & Sander, 2010). Identification and treatment of depression need to be high priorities in people with epilepsy.

Recognizing the risk of suicide and respecting the seriousness of suicide attempts are major factors in its prevention. Physicians and other professionals have a responsibility to detect depression and thoughts or actions that might lead to suicidal behaviour, and to respond to it in a serious and constructive way. When a person threatens suicide, for example, he or she needs to be encouraged to communicate openly by having others listen to and understand the problem, remind him or her of the many people who care, and repeatedly use the person's name to acknowledge him or her as an individual. In addition, support needs to be offered and provided to alleviate immediate problems. In cases of suicide attempts, after receiving any necessary emergency medical aid (e.g., stomach pumping, bandaging), patients require psychiatric assessment and treatment either through a psychiatrist or a professional trained in suicide management. Follow-up is crucial, because 20% individuals who attempt suicide try again within 1 year, and 10% eventually complete it (Beers, Porter, & Jones, 2006).

Serious Conditions Associated With Abnormal Behaviours That Have Known Causes

In addition to those conditions mentioned above, a number of other serious conditions associated with abnormal behaviour have known biological causes. These include abnormal behaviours related to brain injury, neurological disorders, physical conditions causing pain, and reactions to certain drugs or their withdrawal.

Brain injury

Major causes of brain injury are physical impact (motor vehicle accidents, falls, bicycle accidents, sports injuries, assaults, bullet wounds), exposure to neurotoxic agents (e.g., lead poisoning, excessive alcohol use), disruption of cerebral blood supply (e.g., stroke), violent shaking of an infant's head, and hypoxia (lack of oxygen, e.g., from drowning or disruption of breathing at birth). Brain injury may result in mild to severe brain injury and death. It also can result in a broad range of abnormal behaviours, affecting neurocognitive and neurobehavioural functions. It is interesting to note that neonatal temporal lobe lesions in monkeys result in behavioural changes strikingly similar to those characteristic of autism (Bachevalier & Malkova, 2000). Typically, emotional problems resulting from brain injury take the form of depression, anxiety, emotional blunting, and irritability. A number of rare disorders can result from brain injury. Some examples include loss of ability to recognize faces (*prosopagnosia*) or believing that one's family and friends are imposters who just look like friends and family (*Capgras syndrome*). For more detail about brain injury, see Percy, Lewkis, & Brown, 2007, and the More Resources section.)

Neurological disorders

Serious neurological disorders can affect people with or without intellectual disability, and in some cases can cause cognitive impairment. Some disorders associated with neurobiological deterioration include Alzheimer's disease, Parkinson's disease, aphasia (not being able to use language properly), cerebrovascular disease (aneurisms and strokes), epilepsy, Creutzfeldt-Jakob disease, and Huntington disease. The most common neuromuscular disorder is multiple sclerosis, a progressive disease resulting from demyelination (loss of myelin sheaths of nerve fibres in the CNS). Neuro-oncological disorders include neurofibromatosis (Chapter 13) and brain tumours. The best known neuro-otological disorder is Meniere's disease, a disorder characterized by bouts of dizziness. (General sources: Beers, Porter, & Jones, 2005; Percy, Lewkis, & Brown, 2007.)

Pain disorders

These include migraines, sinus headaches, backaches, toothaches, sprains, strains and central pain syndrome resulting from stroke, brain and spinal cord injury, multiple sclerosis, reaction to medications, cancer and any condition that can cause damage to the nerves or brain.

Drug side effects and drug withdrawal

Some people experience serious side effects from drugs whereas others do not. Furthermore, interactions between different medications can have serious consequences. All doctors treating a patient need to be aware of all the medications that person is taking, including prescription drugs and over-the-counter medicines including vitamins, minerals, and herbal supplements.

People also need to discuss any alcohol or other drug use with their doctor. (See the National Institute of Mental Health (NIMH) website at *http://www.nimh.nih.gov/health/publications/mental-health-medications/complete-index.shtml* for a list of side effects of antipsychotic medications.) When a person stops using drugs or alcohol, there often is a rebound effect. Side effects from withdrawal of some drugs can produce physical, emotional, or mental symptoms. For example, sudden withdrawal from the barbiturate or certain benzodiazepines may result in delirium. (General sources: AddictionsandRecovery.com (n.d.) website at *www.addictionsandrecovery.org/withdrawal.htm.*)

Behavioural Phenotypes, Stereotypic, and Self-Injurious Behaviours

People with intellectual and developmental disabilities, like those without disabilities, have a wide range of behaviours. Most of their behaviours, both normal and abnormal, are similar to those of people without disabilities, although the range of what is accepted as normal behaviour for people with intellectual and developmental disabilities can be broader because some of their behaviours are understood to be a result of their disabilities.

In addition, abnormal behaviours that sometimes occur in people without disabilities occur more frequently in people with intellectual and developmental disabilities. Some abnormal behaviours that are assumed to be related to disabilities are not well understood, but others are. In addition, some abnormal behaviours appear to be unique to individuals, whereas others are common to many people because of the particular type of disability they have. These latter abnormal behaviours are part of a larger pattern of behaviours that are "typical" of the disability and that are referred to as *behavioural phenotypes*.

Table 2. Intellectual Disabilities with Behavioural Phenotypes*

Genetic syndromes

- Aicardi
- Angelman
- 22q11.2 deletion (including DiGeorge or velocar-diofacial)
- Cornelia de Lange
- Down
- Fragile X
- Lafora's disease
- Lesch-Nyhan
- Pallister Killian
- Noonan, Prader-Willi
- Smith-Lemli-Opitz
- Smith-Magenis
- Rett
- Sotos
- Tuberous sclerosis
- Turner
- Williams syndromes

Genetic syndromes alleviated by dietary intervention

- Aicardi
- Angelman

Multifactorial etiology

- Tourette syndrome
- Pervasive developmental disorder
- Autism

For additional information about particular intellectual disabilities, see Akbarzadeh, Akbarzadeh, & Akbarzadeh (2009); Dykens & Hodapp (2007); Chapter 13 and other chapters in this volume.

Behavioural phenotypes associated with particular developmental disabilities

Behavioural phenotypes (BPs) are patterns of behaviour that are characteristic of particular disorders. They are associated with distinct patterns of behaviour and personality, cognitive profiles, and patterns of learning difficulties. Defining BPs is expected to aid with development of effective treatment and educational approaches. BPs that are best understood are those evident for people with cer-

tain genetic disorders, although certain syndromes with an unidentified biological basis or known to have diverse causations also have characteristic behavioural phenotypes (Table 2). To note is that BPs are not necessarily unique to each syndrome. Moreover, not all individuals with a given syndrome necessarily show all of the patterns of the BP. Some behaviours within BPs are not considered to be particularly problematic or abnormal, but others are. For example, in Prader-Willi syndrome, the desire for enormous amounts of food, and the lengths that people with this disorder go to obtain and hoard food, is part of a BP that is considered abnormal because it is detrimental to the person's health and it often creates enormous problems within the family, school, and other social settings. Refer to Chapter 13 for information about the disorders listed in Table 2. (See also Akbarzadeh, Akbarzadeh, & Akvarzadeh, 2006; Dykens & Hodapp, 2007.)

Stereotypic or self-stimulatory behaviours

Some of the abnormal behaviours seen in people with disabilities are related to the cause of their disability, some are related to brain injury, and some are related to other mental or physical health problems. It is essential to determine whether disability, brain injury, mental health, or physical health (or a combination) is the underlying reason for abnormal behaviour to ensure that an appropriate intervention can be undertaken. Please refer to Chapter 36 for further discussion on the assessment.

People with intellectual and developmental disabilities can exhibit a wide array of abnormal behaviours, many of which can be classified as mental disorders described earlier in this chapter. Two forms of mental ill-health are singled out here because they are somewhat common, they can be quite serious, and they may or may not necessarily meet the full criteria of a mental disorder.

Stereotypic behaviour is a repetitive, invariant behaviour pattern with no obvious goal or function. It is sometimes referred to as *self-stimulatory*, or "stimming" behaviour. This can involve any of the senses or a combination of them. Stereotypic behaviour in humans can be categorized in these ways:

- Visual: staring at lights, blinking repetitively,

moving one's fingers in front of one's eyes, flapping one's hands
- Auditory: tapping ears, snapping fingers, making vocal sounds
- Tactile: rubbing the skin with one's hands or with another object, scratching
- Vestibular: rocking front to back, rocking side to side
- Taste: placing body parts or objects in one's mouth, licking objects
- Smell: smelling objects, sniffing people

Although such behaviours are seemingly purposeless, they may excite or arouse the nervous system and provide pleasure. Conversely, they may be calming. They interfere with attention and learning but can be a positive reinforcer if a person is allowed to do them after finishing a task. It is possible to reduce the frequency of stereotypic behaviours by providing alternative, more socially appropriate forms of stimulation such as chewing on a piece of rubber or silicon tubing, stimulation in a Snoezelen room (a room that excites the senses through provision of different lights, smells and touch sensations and helps to reduce anxiety and promote relaxation), or exercise. Drugs (e.g., risperidone) can be used to address such behaviours, but it is not known if these reduce the behaviours directly or indirectly by slowing down overall motor movement. As outlined in Chapters 16 and 24, intensive early behavioural intervention is reported to "normalize" some children with severe autism by reducing and/or eliminating stereotypical and other problem behaviours. (General sources: Garner, 2005; Percy, Brown, & Lewkis, 2007.)

Self-injurious behaviours

Self-injurious behaviours (SIBs) are the most devastating behaviours exhibited by people with or without intellectual and/or developmental disabilities. SIB often refers to any behaviour that causes tissue damage such as bruises, redness, and open wounds, regardless of any underlying disorder. In people with intellectual or developmental disability, the most common forms of SIBs include head banging, hand biting, and excessive self rubbing and scratching. SIB has an unusually high frequency in a number of disorders, including PDD, Tourette, Lesch-Nyhan, Cornelia de Lange, fragile X, and Smith-Magenis syndromes, schizophrenia, borderline personality disorder, and stereotypic movement disorder. It may occur as the result of abuse or incest. SIB does not include suicidal behaviour, but in people with schizophrenia, deliberate self-harm is a strong predictor of suicide. The causes and purposes of SIBs are not known, though physiological and social factors play a role as for stereotypic behaviours.

A variety of approaches are used in managing SIB, including psychotropic medication (e.g., antidepressants, anxiolytics, antipsychotics), mechanical restraint, cognitive-behavioural therapy, behavioural intervention, massage and/or sensory integration therapy, and group and family therapy. Deep brain stimulation and psychosurgery have been used in severe, refractory cases of Tourette syndrome. (General sources: Oliver & Richards, 2010; Percy, Brown & Lewkis, 2007; see also Chapters 13, 16, and 18.)

Future Directions

Research is exploding in the neurosciences. Researchers and clinicians in different fields are beginning to collaborate in order to provide new insight into the concepts of what it means to be human and what biological and molecular processes are involved in human behaviours. New advances in genetics (specifically in the fields of epigenetics and epigenomics — see Chapter 9) are beginning to reveal how environmental effects act on the genome and alter gene expression via biochemical mechanisms that are distinct from the DNA coding sequence. Our understanding of nervous system development and function, both normal and pathogenic, is expanding at an enormous rate.

New information about what causes abnormal behaviours, including excessive exposures to heavy metals, is raising the prospect of more effective treatments and interventions for them. Yet all of these advances are raising new social, ethical and legal questions not previously anticipated. (General sources: Mehler, 2010; Soghoian & Siebert, 2009; Chapters 9-12.)

Summary

In this chapter, we have attempted to approach the topic of abnormal behaviour from psychosocial and biomedical perspectives. We have introduced readers to the concepts of normal and abnormal behaviours, mental disorders, mental ill-health, and dual diagnosis, as well as to classification systems used in characterization of mental ill-health, suicidal behaviour and suicide. Various causes for abnormal behaviour are outlined. These include: stress and anxiety; attention problems; personality disorders; schizophrenia, depressive, eating, psychosocial, and sleeping disorders; pain disorders; substance abuse; medication side effects and withdrawal effects; brain injury; and various neurological disorders; and behavioural patterns associated with particular genetic syndromes and forms of intellectual and developmental disability. New research directions are elucidating the neurological processes that are involved in human behaviour, and also are raising new social, ethical and legal questions.

For Further Thought and Discussion

1. What types of behaviour might be considered abnormal by some people in society but might not really be abnormal?
2. Researchers are continuing to unravel the understanding of the biological mechanisms underlying abnormal behaviour. Do you think that such information may lead to new forms of stigmatization and to attempts to eliminate abnormal behaviours through genetic selection? Or might such information help to ameliorate different forms of mental ill-health and their consequences in society?

More Resources

Canadian Resources on Mental Health:

Canadian Mental Health Association
http://www.cmha.ca

Centre for Addiction and Mental Health (Toronto)
http://www.camh.net

The Human Face of Mental Health and Mental Illness in Canada (2006)
http://www.phac-aspc.gc.ca/publicat/human-humain06/pdf/human_face_e.pdf

Classification Systems of Mental Ill-Health:

American Psychiatric Association. DSM-5 development
http://www.dsm5.org/Pages/Default.aspx

DSM-IV Multiaxial System. PSYweb.com
http://psyweb.com/Mdisord/DSM_IV/jsp/dsm_iv.jsp

ICD 10 Online
http://apps.who.int/classifications/apps/icd/icd10online/

Brain Injury:

The Brain Injury Association of Canada
http://biac-aclc.ca/en/what-is-it/

Traumatic Brain Injury. Mayo Clinic
http://www.mayoclinic.com/health/traumatic-brain-injury/DS00552

General:

American Academy of Sleep Medicine. Information on sleep disorders and treatments
http://www.sleepeducation.com/

American Psychiatric Association. Mental health links *http://www.psych.org/SpecialGroups/MentalHealthResources.aspx*

American Psychological Association. Psychology topics
http://www.apa.org/topics/index.aspx

How Metals in Food Affect Your Child's Behaviour
www.eatingforlifebyellie.com/files/HowMetalsinFoodAffectYourChild.pdf

The Merck Manuals Online Medical Library
www.merckmanuals.com/professional/

National Institute of Mental Health (US). Mental health information
http://www.nimh.nih.gov/health/index.shtml

National Institute of Neurological Disorders and Stroke (US). Brain Basics — Know Your Brain
http://www.ninds.nih.gov/disorders/brain_basics/know_your_brain.htm

Perspectives on Abnormal Behaviour
http://www.ryerson.ca/~glassman/abnormal.html

The Royal College of Psychiatrists U.K. Mental Health Information for All. *http://www.rcpsych. ac.uk/mentalhealthinfoforall.aspx*

Society for Neuroscience. Brain Facts
http://www.sfn.org/index.aspx?pagename=brainfacts

Substance Abuse and Mental Health Services Administration (SAMHSA)
http://www.samhsa.gov/index.aspx

References

Abel, K. M., Drake, R., & Goldstein, J. M. (2010). Sex differences in schizophrenia. *International Review of Psychiatry, 22*(5), 417-428.

American Psychiatric Association. (2000). *Diagnostic and statistical manual of mental disorders* (4th ed., text rev.). Washington, DC: Author.

Akbarzadeh, M., Akbarzadeh, R., & Akbarzadeh, R. (2006). Behavioural phenotypes in genetic syndromes: A window on to the biology of behaviour. *Annals of General Psychiatry 2006, 5*(Suppl. 1), S264doi:10.1186/1744-859X-5-S1-S264.

Ashworth, M., Hirdes, J. P., & Martin, L. (2009). The social and recreational characteristics of adults with intellectual disability and pica living in institutions. *Research in Developmental Disabilities, 30*(3), 512-520.

Bassett, A. S., & Chow, E. W. (2008). Schizophrenia and 22q11.2 deletion syndrome. *Current Psychiatry Reports, 10*(2), 148-157.

Bachevalier, J., & Malkova, L. (2000). Neuropsychological indices of early medial temporal dysfunction in primates. In H. S. Levin & J. Grafman (Eds.), *Cerebral reorganization of function after brain damage.* New York: Oxford University Press.

Beers, M. H., Porter, R. S., & Jones, T. V. (Eds.). (2006). *The Merck manual of diagnosis and therapy* (18th ed.). Whitehouse Station, NJ: Merck Research Laboratories.

Bondy B. (2011). Genetics in psychiatry: Are the promises met? *World Journal of Biological Psychiatry, 12*(2), 81-88.

Canadian Network of Substance Abuse and Allied Professionals. (2010). Retrieved from http://www.rcptdc.ca/Eng/DevelopingTheWorkforce/SubstanceAbuseDisabilities/Pages/default.aspx

Cassidy, F. (2011). Risk factors of attempted suicide in bipolar disorder. *Suicide & Life-Threatening Behaviors, 41*(1), 6-11.

Dykens, E. M., & Hodapp, R. M. (2007). Three steps toward improving the measurement of behavior in behavioral phenotype research. *Child and Adolescent Psychiatric Clinics of North America, 16*(3), 617-630.

Fenton, W. S. (2000). Depression, suicide, and suicide prevention in schizophrenia. *Suicide & Life-Threatening Behavior, 30*(1), 34-49.

Fletcher, R., Loschen, E., Stavrakaki, C., & First, M. (Eds.). (2009a). *Diagnostic Manual-Intellectual Disability (DM-ID): A clinical guide for diagnosis of mental disorders in persons with intellectual disability.* Kingston, NY: NADD Press.

Fletcher, R. J., Loschen, E., Stavrakaki C., & First, M. (Eds.). (2009b). *Diagnostic Manual — Intellectual Disability (DM-ID): A textbook of diagnosis of mental disorders in persons with intellectual disability.* Kingston, NY: NADD Press.

Franke, J. (1999). Stress burnout and addiction. *Texas Medicine, 95*(3), 42-52.

Fung, W. L. A., Bhugra, D., & Jones, P. B. (2009). Ethnicity and mental health: The example of schizophrenia and related psychoses in migrant populations in the Western world. *Psychiatry, 8*(9), 335-341.

Fung, W. L. A., McEvilly, R., Fong, J., Chow, E. W. C., & Bassett, A. S. (2010). Elevated prevalence of generalized anxiety disorder in adults with 22q11.2 deletion syndrome. *American Journal of Psychiatry, 167*(8), 998.

Garner, J. P. (2005). Stereotypies and other abnormal repetitive behaviors: Potential impact on validity, reliability, and replicability of scientific outcomes. *ILAR Journal, 46*(2), 106-117. Retrieved December 9, 2010, from http://dels-old.nas.edu/ilar_n/ilarjournal/46_2/pdfs/v4602garner.pdf

Hassiotis, A., Barron, D. A., & Hall, I. (Eds.). (2009). *Intellectual disability psychiatry: A practical handbook.* Hoboken, NJ: Wiley.

Humphries, T. (2007). Attention deficit/hyperactivity disorder. In I. Brown & M. Percy (Eds.), *A comprehensive guide to intellectual and developmental disabilities* (pp. 295-307). Baltimore: Paul H. Brookes Publishing Co.

Insel, T. R. (2010). Rethinking schizophrenia. *Nature, 468*(7321), 187-193.

Jozsvai, E., Gajdos, L., Lean, M., & Hewitt, T. (2007). Prevalence of tobacco use and alcohol/drug problems among adults with developmental disabilities in Ontario. *Journal on Developmental Disabilities, 13*(3), 47-53.

Kirkbride, J. B., & Jones, P. B. (2011). The prevention of schizophrenia – What can we learn from eco-epidemiology? *Schizophrenia Bulletin, 37*(2), 262-271.

Kluger, J., & Song, S. (2002). Young and bipolar. *Time Magazine 160*(8), 38-46, 51.

Kordas, K. (2010). Iron, lead, and children's behavior and cognition. *Annual Review of Nutrition, 30,* 123-148.

Lin, Z., & Madras, B. K. (2006). Human genetics and pharmacology of neurotransmitter transporters. *Handbook of Experimental Pharmacology, 175,* 327-371.

McAdam, D. B., Sherman, J. A., Sheldon, J. B., & Napolitano, D. A. (2004). Behavioral interventions to reduce the pica of persons with developmental disabilities. *Behavior Modification, 28*(1), 45-72.

MedlinePlus — Health Information. (2011). Retrieved from *http://www.nlm.nih.gov/medlineplus/*

Mehler, M. F. (2010). Epigenetics and neuropsychiatric diseases: Introduction and meeting summary. *Annals of the New York Academy of Sciences, 1204* (Suppl), E1-7.

Mula, M., Bell, G. S., & Sander, J. W. (2010). Suicidality in epilepsy and possible effects of antiepileptic drugs. *Current Neurology & Neuroscience Reports, 10*(4), 27-32.

Oliver, C., & Richards, C. (2010). Self-injurious behaviour in people with intellectual disability. *Current Opinion in Psychiatry, 23*(5), 412-416. Retrieved from http://www.medscape.com/viewarticle/726769

Public Health Agency of Canada. (2002). Retrieved from *http://www.phac-aspc.gc.ca/publicat/miic-mmac/chap_4-eng.php*

Oquendo, M. A., Baca-García, E., Mann, J. J., & Giner, J. (2008). Issues for DSM-V: Suicidal behavior as a separate diagnosis on a separate axis. *American Journal of Psychiatry, 165,* 1383-1384, doi: 10.1176/appi.ajp.2008.08020281

Percy, M., Brown, I., & Lewkis, S. (2007). Abnormal behavior. In I. Brown & M. Percy (Eds.), *A comprehensive guide to intellectual & developmental disability* (pp. 309-361). Baltimore: Paul H. Brookes Publishing Co.

Roy, A., & Pompili, M. (2009). Management of schizophrenia with suicide risk. *Psychiatric Clinics of North America, 32*(4), 863-883.

Soghoian, S., & Siebert, R. H. (2009, November 5). (2009). Toxicity, heavy metals. EMedicine. Retrieved December 12, 2010, from *http://emedicine.medscape.com/article/814960-overview*

Stevens, L. J., Kuczek, T., Burgess, J. R., Hurt, E., & Arnold, L. E. (2010, Dec 2). Dietary sensitivities and ADHD symptoms: Thirty-five years of research. *Clinical Pediatrics*, Dec 2.

Verdoux, H., & Cougnard, A. (2006). Schizophrenia: Who is at risk? Who is a case? *International Clinical Psychopharmacology, 21*(Suppl. 2), S17-S19.

Wilens, T. E., & Spencer, T. J. (2010). Understanding attention-deficit/hyperactivity disorder from childhood to adulthood. *Postgraduate Medicine, 122*(5), 97-109.

Walton, J. R., Wang, M. X. (2009). APP expression, distribution and accumulation are altered by aluminum in a rodent model for Alzheimer's disease. *Journal of Inorganic Biochemistry, 103*(11), 1548-1554.

World Health Organization. (1992). International statistical classification of diseases and related health problems — tenth revision (ICD-10). Geneva: Author.

Young, A. H., & Newham, J. I. (2006). Lithium in maintenance therapy for bipolar disorder. *Journal of Psychopharmacology, 20*(2 Suppl.), 17-22.

Zimmerman, M., & Spitzer, R. L. (2009). 9. Classification in psychiatry: 9.1-Psychiatric classification. In B. J. Sadock, V. A. Sadock, & A. Ruiz (Eds.), *Kaplan & Sadock's comprehensive textbook of psychiatry* (Vol. I) (9th ed.) (pp. 1108-1138). Philadelphia: Lippincott Williams & Wilkins.

36

Developmental Disabilities and Mental Ill-Health

Jane Summers, Elspeth Bradley, and John Flannery

What you will learn:

- Understanding mental-ill health[1] in people with and without developmental disabilities
- Assessment and treatment of mental ill-health
- The mental health service system in Ontario

The view that people with developmental disabilities experience the same types of mental ill-health[1] that similarly affect the general population was not popularized in North America until fairly recently. For many years, the term "dual diagnosis" was applied almost exclusively to individuals with psychiatric disorders and concurrent addictions. This is no longer the case, as dual diagnosis is now more generally accepted as referring to people with developmental disabilities and mental ill-health (psychiatric, disorders, emotional disturbances, and/or behavioural problems). In this chapter, we will review key issues relating to the assessment and treatment of mental ill-health in people with developmental disabilities. Wherever possible, we will try to focus on the Ontario perspective by referring to provincial policies, relevant statistics, clinical practices, and

research. We will also try to identify factors that impact the provision of mental health services for this population and offer suggestions to overcome some of the difficulties that occur.

Understanding Mental Ill-Health and Developmental Disabilities

Types of mental ill-health

People with developmental disabilities experience similar kinds of mental ill-health that occur among the general population (Benson, 1985; Rutter et al., 1970). Some of the more common psychiatric conditions include mood and anxiety disorders, adjustment problems, personality disorders, and attention deficit hyperactivity disorder (Hassiotis, Barron, & Hall, 2009). These overlap considerably with behav-

---

[1] *Throughout this chapter, we use the term mental ill-health (cf. Cooper et al., 2007) in place of mental health problems to refer generally to any or all of behaviour problems, emotional disturbances, and psychiatric disorders.*

Developmental Disabilities and Mental Ill-Heath at a Glance

In this chapter, we use the term mental ill-health to refer broadly to psychiatric illness and disorders, emotional disturbances, and/or behavioural problems. Many readers will be familiar with the term dual diagnosis, which refers to the presence of two diagnoses. In Ontario, the term dual diagnosis is used to refer to people living with lifelong developmental disabilities and mental health needs. In many other parts of the world, however, dual diagnosis sometimes refers to people in the general population who have diagnosed psychiatric disorders and concurrent addiction disorders. To avoid this confusion, we have chosen to use the term mental ill-health. Mental ill-health applies to the general population and people with developmental disabilities alike, and ranges in severity and presentation from emotional and behavioural disturbances to diagnosable mental illness and disorders.

By referring to mental ill-health, we hope the reader will be aware of the complexity of mental and physical health-related conditions experienced by people with developmental disabilities and the need, therefore, for systematic approaches to their investigation and treatment.

Mental ill-health in people with developmental disabilities can be challenging to assess, diagnose, and treat. Reasons for this are discussed in detail in our chapter. We offer a systematic approach to assessment, treatment, and prevention. This systematic approach is based on the careful identification of causes and contributory factors to the mental ill-health. These factors include medical conditions, emotional issues, inadequate social supports, and inappropriate expectations for the client. We hope the reader will be able to apply this framework to better understand their own clients with developmental disabilities. We have provided further explanation and clinical examples to assist with this exploration.

When you are working with a client with developmental disability whose behaviour has changed, or one who is behaving in an unusual way, we suggest you use this framework to better understand what may be causing this behaviour. A diagnostic evaluation may be straight forward or may take many months to complete because of the complexities of the situation for the client and the range and availability of services and supports. Working within the context of an interdisciplinary team is often critical for a full understanding of these issues and for achieving successful outcomes.

ioural disturbances, which include verbal and physical aggression, self-injury, hyperactivity, attentional problems, and oppositional behaviour (e.g., Cooper, Smiley, Allan, et al., 2009; Cooper, Smiley, Jackson, et al., 2009; Jacobson, 1982; Jones et al., 2008; Lowe et al., 2007). Some conditions, such as autism and stereotypies, are seen more frequently in people with developmental disabilities than in the general population.

Basis of mental ill-health

Biological, psychosocial, and environmental factors play a major role in the occurrence of mental ill-health in people with developmental disabilities. Biological factors, which include genetic influences, brain injury, trauma, disease or infection, may directly underlie both the developmental disability and the mental ill-health (Holland, 1999; Rutter et al., 1970). Etiological circumstances giving rise to developmental disabilities may be associated with specific patterns of psychological, behavioural and mental ill-health (e.g., "behavioural phenotypes"; Shapiro & Accardo, 2009). In terms of environmental and psychosocial influences on mental ill-health, many people with developmental disabilities live in impoverished and isolated circumstances, lack meaningful employment, social opportunities and strong support systems, do not have control over many aspects of their lives, and feel removed from the mainstream of society (Emerson, 2007; Metzel, 2005). They may also have poor or inadequate social and coping skills and, when these conditions occur on top of the cognitive and communication deficits, feelings of frustration, sense of failure and an awareness of being "different" can be further heightened.

Prevalence of mental ill-health

There is mounting evidence that people with developmental disabilities are at greater risk of developing mental ill-health than their peers without such disabilities. Prevalence estimates vary widely, ranging from approximately 10% to 40% of adults with developmental disabilities (Cooper et al., 2007; Einfeld & Tonge, 1996; Rutter, Tizard, & Whitmore, 1970; for reviews see Cooper & Van der Speck, 2009; Whitaker & Read, 2006). According to one estimate, there are approximately 227,000 people in Ontario with developmental disabilities, of whom upwards of 85,000 are expected to have mental ill-health (Yu & Atkinson, 1993). These statistics are based on a 2.25% prevalence rate for developmental disabilities within the general population and an estimated 38% prevalence rate for mental ill-health in people with developmental disabilities.

Within the broader population of people with developmental disabilities, certain sub-groups may be especially prone to mental ill-health (Feinstein & Chahal, 2009; Moss & Howlin, 2009). An Ontario population-based study of adolescents and young adults with developmental disabilities (Bradley, Thompson, & Bryson, 2002; Bryson et al., 2008) found that individuals with autism, compared to those without co-existing autism, have a greater prevalence of new onset psychiatric illnesses such as mood and adjustment disorders (Bradley & Bolton, 2006), a greater prevalence of inattentive, hyperactive and impulsive behaviours (Bradley & Issacs, 2006), and are more than twice as likely to have one or more concurrent psychiatric disorders (Bradley & Bryson, 1998). In the same study, the frequency of psychiatric symptoms and behavioural disturbances was almost three times higher among those with severe intellectual disabilities and autism compared to those functioning at the same level but without a diagnosis of autism (Bradley, Summers, Wood, & Bryson, 2004). Co-existing autism may contribute different vulnerability to mental ill-health in young people (see also Brereton et al., 2006; Leyfer et al., 2006; Simonoff et al., 2008) compared to adults with developmental disabilities (Melville et al., 2008). If one considers that as many as 25,000 adults in Ontario may have

an autism spectrum disorder and developmental disabilities, there is a pressing need for specialized models of support and service that are linked to ongoing research on best practices (Autism Ontario, 2008).

Clinical challenges

A number of challenges exist in correctly diagnosing mental ill-health in individuals with developmental disabilities. *Diagnostic overshadowing* refers to the tendency of professionals to underestimate signs of psychiatric or emotional disturbance in this population (Reiss, Levitan, & Szysko, 1982). This phenomenon occurs when aberrant behaviours are viewed as an inherent part of the individual's developmental disability; hence, they are less likely to be seen as evidence of possible underlying mental ill-health. Another phenomenon that poses a challenge to diagnosing mental ill-health is known as *behavioural highlighting*, where severe or intense behaviour problems may make the detection of underlying health problems more difficult (Sovner & Hurley, 1986). Other diagnostic challenges are related to personal characteristics, such as severe communication and cognitive impairments that make it difficult for individuals to articulate the nature and source of their distress. In these situations, it is necessary to rely more heavily on information that is provided by caregivers than on self-reports (Barnhill, 2008). With increasing disability, it becomes more difficult to detect distinctive clinical patterns to assist with diagnosis as the behavioural presentation can be non-specific (e.g., when aggression or self-injury is the main referral problem) or even atypical in individuals with more severe impairments.

Co-morbidity, which is the co-existence of another medical or psychiatric condition, can further complicate the clinical picture. For instance, sensory impairments (e.g., vision and hearing problems), seizure disorders, and medical disorders (e.g., cardiovascular problems or abnormal thyroid functioning) can produce changes in behaviour that can be mistaken for symptoms of psychiatric disorders. Adults with severe developmental disabilities and co-morbid conditions may be particularly vulnerable to abuse and neglect. The tragic case of a young adult with autism and severe developmental dis-

Box 1: Clinical Scenario One

Background

Michelle, aged 29, was referred because of an escalation in severe self-injurious behaviours (SIB), which had been present from an early age. Michelle was mostly nonverbal and her functional skills were similar to those of an infant 18-24 months old. During her life, in response to severe escalations of the SIB, she had been seen by many specialists including medical, neurological, behavioural, and psychological. She was diagnosed as having autistic behaviours, and was being treated for an underactive thyroid. Various interventions were tried, including high doses of antipsychotic and other psychotropic medication and behavioural strategies, but these met with limited success. At the time of referral she had been in the same group home for a number of years, with a stable group of carers committed to ensuring optimum quality of life for their client. Carers were experienced in supporting persons with developmental disabilities and had an excellent working relationship with a consulting behaviour therapist; together they were able to provide Michelle with an environment that understood her developmental abilities, was emotionally nurturing, and had appropriate expectations of her, both in her day and residential settings. However, there continued to be concern about the excessive medication Michelle was taking (Michelle went on to develop a sudden abdominal obstruction requiring a piece of her bowel to be removed. This was likely related to the long term use of medication used to manage her SIB behaviours). Carers had managed to secure a psychiatric consultation and a medication change was recommended, but no psychiatric follow up was available. This medication change was carefully followed by the family doctor and carers, but when Michelle's behaviour started to escalate she was seen in the emergency room and was immediately reinstated on the original antipsychotic medication — but at higher doses! It was at this point she was referred for multidisciplinary assessment.

Comment

SIB (sometimes referred to as "challenging" behaviour) arises out of many circumstances, but can only begin to be adequately assessed in a continuous and stable setting where carers and involved health care staff share an understanding of: 1) the individual's developmental needs (e.g., psychological and adaptive functioning, communication, sensory issues), unique and atypical ways of communicating, and emotional responses (particularly when

---

ability from Ontario who died as a result of extreme neglect while in the care of family members,[2] heightens the need for adult protection legislation and increased public awareness of these issues.

Assessment

Overview of issues

As a group, people with developmental disabilities are over-medicated and under-treated (Deb et al., 2009; Matson & Neale, 2009; Reiss & Aman, 1998; Tsioris, 2010). Because of cognitive and language impairments, they are often limited in their capacity to reflect on their own internal mental and feeling states, and to communicate these subjective experiences to others. With increasing disability in these areas, they are more reliant on immediate caregivers to be sensitive to the pattern of their daily lives, and to understand the impact of daily events, such as changes in daily routines or inappropriate expectations, on their emotional responses and capacity to cope. If caregivers are unfamiliar with the usual responses of the individual, or are unaware of particular life events that may have occurred for that person, mental ill-health may be missed and remain untreated. For example, withdrawn behaviour and

---

[2] Shields, C. *Protecting vulnerable adults: Lessons from the past, recommendations for the future. November, 2008.* Available on Kerry's Place Autism Services website: www.kerrysplace.com/Latest%20News/Vulnerable%20Adults%20Dec.10%202008.pdf

in distress or medically ill); and 2) how the individual's environment and supports contribute to these behaviours. A multidisciplinary assessment approach should identify environmental and individual specific contributions to these behaviours and provide a comprehensive diagnostic formulation and treatment plan (Banks et al., 2007).

Michelle's care was continuous and stable as long as she remained within her day and residential settings, and as long as she had no medical problems or behavioural escalations requiring emergency medical or psychiatric intervention. The assessment of SIB may require trials of interventions, some of which may cause behavioural escalations. From the outset it is necessary, therefore, to map out the continuum of services that is required in order to allow an adequate assessment, and in particular to map out responses to crises that may arise so as to ensure continuity of assessment and treatment between inpatient and outpatient settings.

In Michelle's case, the following local services became partners in her care over the ensuing two years: Michelle's immediate care team (residential and day counsellors, supervisors and managers), consulting behaviour therapist, family physician, community psychiatrist and specialist assessment services, local pharmacist, emergency hospital services, inpatient psychiatric services, specialist medical services (e.g., neurology, surgical), community nursing, and the Office of the Official Guardian and Public Trustee (Michelle was unable to consent to her treatment and had no family).

Regular meetings occurred to review Michelle's progress and to ensure all partners in her care were informed as required. The anxiety was taken out of the crises. There was no longer the fear that Michelle's medication would be changed without adequate consultation with carers, and inpatient services no longer feared that Michelle would become a long term patient. As the crises abated for Michelle and for the systems of support, Michelle's behaviour stabilized, and a cyclic pattern to her behaviours emerged. She was treated with mood stabilizing medication and her antipsychotic medication was reduced. These changes resulted in significant improvement in her quality of life and reduction in SIB.

Key Point

The prescription of antipsychotic medication for challenging behaviours is no longer acceptable practice (Tyrer et al., 2008). Multidisciplinary assessment and treatment are required (Bradley et al., 2009; Deb et al., 2009).

loss of interest associated with depression may not be noticed or, if observed, may be incorrectly attributed to being a feature of the person's developmental disability (diagnostic overshadowing).

Those who engage in behaviours that are disruptive or cause damage to themselves or to others may be referred to mental health services or to emergency medical services. Health professionals (e.g., physicians, nurses) unfamiliar with the needs of people with developmental disabilities may also attribute this disturbed or unusual behaviour to the developmental disability and thus the behaviour may be managed with medication or other behavioural interventions, leaving the underlying problems undiagnosed and untreated. Emotional upsets, difficulties in coping with situations, frustrations with daily circumstances, physical illnesses and psy-

chiatric disorders most frequently present to emergency and mental health services as non-specific behavioural disturbance. The challenge for these service providers is, therefore, to understand what these disturbed or unusual behaviours "really mean" (or what these behaviours are "communicating"). Teasing out these issues apart requires coordinated teamwork involving the person with disabilities, his or her immediate caregivers, and access to specialists who have experience working both in the field of mental health and developmental disabilities and who are aware of the medical and mental health vulnerabilities of this population (Summers, Boyd, & Morgan, 2004).

In some jurisdictions, such as the United Kingdom, there are teams of professionals in each health locality (called Community Learning Disability Teams)

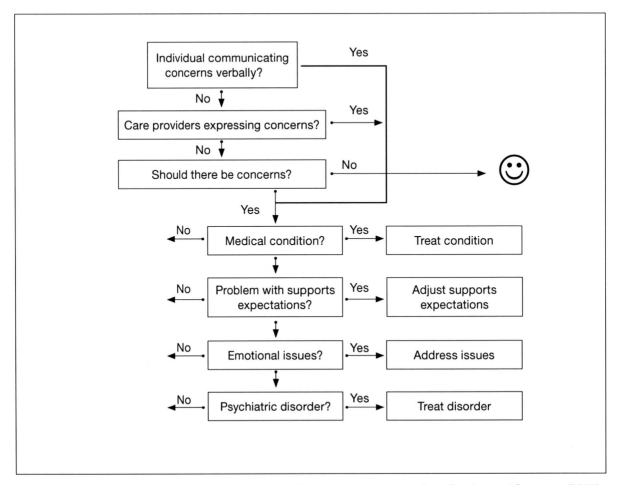

Figure 1. Mental health assessment: decision tree. *Redrawn by permission from Bradley and Summers (2003).*

who provide specialist support to people with developmental disabilities and mental ill-health and assist in coordinating access to the local generic health and mental health services. Formal training of mental health professionals is provided through university and college programs. However, in Ontario, as in much of Canada, the training of mental health professionals in developmental disabilities has been greatly neglected (see Costello et al., 2007; Lunsky & Bradley, 2001 regarding physician training). Services and systems have evolved somewhat differently; not infrequently, specialized support, if such is available, is developed around each individual only after recurrent failures of the generic services to provide appropriate care (see Box 1). In Ontario, there are few formal training programs available for

professionals in the area of mental health and developmental disabilities, and often access to generic medical, and particularly psychiatric, services is problematic as service providers may consider they do not have the expertise to deal with the individual with developmental disability. A more comprehensive discussion of mental health services in Ontario will follow in a later section.

Assessment of mental ill-health

When identifying whether behavioural disturbance is due to a psychiatric disorder, it is necessary to explore systematically all those areas that may give rise to behaviour disturbances. A brief outline of this process is provided in Figure 1 (Mental health assessment: decision tree) and Table 1 (Psychiatric assessment and treatment formulation).

In many instances, non-specific behavioural disturbance may be the final outcome of more than one related or unrelated causes, such as disruptive behaviour associated with a mood disorder but made worse by toothache. People with mild or moderate developmental disabilities will usually be able to assist in this exploration and will be able to share some of their inner discomforts, although time is usually required for them to feel comfortable with the interviewer, and for both to understand how the other communicates. Independent information from someone who knows the person well (an informant) should also be sought as the individual may not fully appreciate the larger context within which he/she feels distressed (e.g., the distress may be associated with an external event such as a bereavement).

For the individual with little or no language, the assessment rests primarily in understanding the meaning of the behavioural changes and in making inferences about internal feeling states from the characteristics and patterns of these changes in behaviour. Here, informants who know the individual well are key to a good assessment in terms of providing information on how the person usually communicates frustrations, emotions, physical pains, and so on. It is always helpful to meet with referred persons in settings where they normally live and spend their work and leisure time. Knowing and observing whether the behaviours of concern change in different settings provides clues as to what may be giving rise to these behaviours.

Circumstances giving rise to behavioural concerns

Physical health and medical issues: Individuals with mild developmental disabilities may be less able than their non-disabled peers to articulate or comment on their physical discomforts and pains, and often do not do so spontaneously. If a problem is suspected, it may be necessary to ask specific questions and to help the individual communicate his/her discomfort and pinpoint where the pain is located. Those individuals with more severe disabilities may be totally unable to communicate a pain or localize a

discomfort either verbally or even by gesture.

Chronic disorders (such as constipation), fluctuating pain (such as toothache), or side effects of medication may present to the caregiver and clinician as disruptive or irritable behaviour. As a group, people with developmental disabilities have a higher prevalence of other disabilities (such as visual and hearing impairments) and medical conditions (such as neurological impairments, including seizures and cerebral palsy). Those individuals with identifiable genetic or metabolic disorders, which may occur in up to 45% of those with severe developmental disabilities (for reviews see Curry et al., 1997; Raynham, Gibbons, Flint, & Higgs, 1996), may have associated physical and medical disorders and these can give rise to painful conditions (e.g., arthritis in adults with Down syndrome). Other problems, such as orthopaedic, gastrointestinal, nutritional, feeding, pulmonary, cardiac, endocrine, urological, gynaecological, dermatological, and dental problems may also give rise to pain and distress. Some syndromes (e.g., Autism, Fragile X, Williams, Prader-Willi) are associated with particular medical conditions and specific cognitive, linguistic, adaptive, and behavioural profiles ("behavioural phenotypes"; Dykens, Hodapp, & Finucane, 2000). Identifying the cause of the developmental disability, and these syndrome conditions, is an important part of the assessment, as this may direct attention to medical disorders and painful conditions that might otherwise remain hidden. In addition, Canadian consensus guidelines for primary health care are now available to assist the family doctor in caring for adult patients with intellectual disabilities (Sullivan et al., 2011).

Expectations and support needs: Developmental disabilities encompass significant impairments in cognitive and adaptive functioning. The latter involves deficits in communication and social skills, as well as skills in areas of self-care, home and community living, self-direction, health and safety, leisure and work, and functional academics. Each person with developmental disability is unique in his/her blend of adaptive abilities and skills, and he/she may demonstrate considerable strengths in some areas and considerable weaknesses in others. Some strengths may hide or mask weaknesses in

Table 1: Psychiatric Assessment and Treatment Formulation

Concerns*

- *What are the concerns, who is concerned, why the concern?*

History of concerns

- *What has been tried, for how long, what worked, what did not work, who was involved?*
- *When was client last at his/her best, how was a typical day spent then, how is the day spent now, what has changed?*

Background information — client**

- *Developmental level. Reports of psychological and adaptive functioning, communication assessments, school reports, developmental/pediatric assessments*
- *Communication skills. Verbal and non verbal, including how he/she communicates pain, bodily discomfort, emotional distress*
- *Social circumstances in past. Family and social supports, institutional care, losses, major life events, trauma, abuse, school, work, occupation, and leisure*
- *Recent changes/life events. Are these linked to onset of concerns?*
- *Medical. Hearing or visual impairments, cerebral palsy, seizures, biological cause of developmental disability, presence of a syndrome (e.g., Down or Fragile X), other medical disorders, medications past and present*
- *Other developmental conditions (e.g., autism spectrum disorders) and associated issues (e.g., sensory, affect regulation)*
- *Family history. Medical conditions, developmental disabilities, psychiatric disorders and responses to treatments*
- *Emotional and coping responses. Past response to stressors, life events*
- *Psychiatric history and pre-existing behaviours. Baseline behaviours (e.g., tics, self-injury, obsessions) before concerns*

Background information — supports

- *The understanding carers have of the developmental disability*
- *Social, emotional, physical (environmental), residential and day supports*
- *The structures and organization within which carers and staff work*
- *The appropriateness of services and expectations on clients*
- *Support for carers and staff*

---

other areas and give rise to unreasonable expectations by caregivers on the individual, which in turn can lead to emotional and psychiatric disturbance. For instance, good conversational and social skills may mask severe difficulties in understanding (as in Williams syndrome). Assessment of behavioural concerns, therefore, includes an assessment of the person's psychological profile, including adaptive functioning, and an assessment of the environment supporting that person, including the expectations of caregivers (and teachers if the individual is still attending school).

Emotional disturbances: People with developmental disabilities experience circumstances that might be expected to predispose them or give rise to emotional disturbances. Any associated disability, such

---

Background information — supports

- *The understanding carers have of the developmental disability*
- *Social, emotional, physical (environmental), residential and day supports*
- *The structures and organization within which carers and staff work*
- *The appropriateness of services and expectations on clients*
- *Support for carers and staff*

Examination

Client:

- *Physical (e.g., medical condition, is a syndrome present?)*
- *Interview/mental state*
- *Review of behavioural data*

Support System:

- *Are the physical and emotional environments optimally supportive?*
- *Are attitudes and expectations appropriate?*

Formulation

- *What is the problem?*
- *Where is the problem located?*
  - *Client. e.g., psychiatric or physical illness*
  - *Carers. e.g., inappropriate expectations, staffing structure*
  - *Support System. e.g., lack of appropriate service*
  - *Philosophy of care. e.g., insistence on chronological, rather than developmental, age-appropriate behaviours*
- *What further information or data is required?*
- *What further investigations and assessments are required?*
- *What intervention or treatment is needed — and for whom?*
  - *The client? carers? system?*

* Before gathering information, identify a reliable and knowledgeable informant

** Prior to, and since, outset of concerns

---

as language and communication disorder, sensory impairment, seizures, neurological impairment (including cerebral palsy), or pain and discomforts from physical disorders, has to be managed and accommodated.

Early experiences may have interfered with early bonding and personality development, adversely affecting the person's response to stress, coping strategies, and capacities to develop social supports and friendships. People with developmental disabilities are generally at risk of stigmatization, rejection and teasing by peers. They often develop poor self-esteem and self-image in a society that values achievement, independence and conformity. Opportunities for satisfactory work and leisure pursuits and for intimate relationships are often greatly

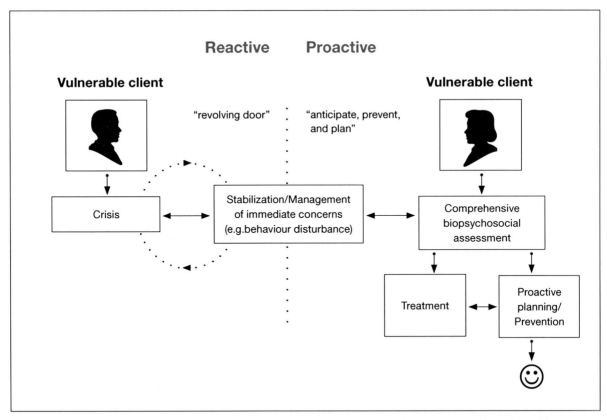

Figure 2. Reactive versus proactive responses to psychiatric/behavioral disturbances in vulnurable individuals.

limited. Most have experienced disadvantaged environments and some have lived in abusive situations. Not surprisingly, behavioural problems that are associated with emotional disturbances are often as severe as those associated with serious mental illness. Distinguishing between these two disorders, however, is often difficult as they frequently co-exist.

Psychiatric disorders: In jurisdictions where specialist psychiatric services for persons with developmental disabilities are still at an early stage (as is the case in Ontario), individuals with mental ill-health most frequently present in crisis to their family doctor or to local emergency services (Lunsky et al., 2007; Lunsky, Gracey, & Gelfand, 2008; Weiss et al., 2009). At these times, the immediate response may be to stabilize the situation with medication (Bradley & Lofchy, 2005; Sullivan et al., 2011). However, medication should be reviewed at the earliest opportunity and a more comprehensive assessment begun

so as to identify whether psychiatric illness is present or whether the problems are related to the other considerations outlined in the previous sections (i.e., physical health and medical issues, expectations and support needs, and emotional responses; Deb et al., 2009; Sullivan et al., 2011).

A decrease in behavioural disturbance in response to medications (such as antipsychotics) that are used at a time of crisis does not imply that a psychiatric disorder is present. Indeed, such medications are known to mask some conditions; most will contribute further to the developmental disability by impairing or slowing down the person's ability to focus and think clearly and many result in other side effects. In people who have difficulty already communicating bodily discomforts, these side effects may give rise to further behavioural disturbances. It is prudent, therefore, to distinguish clearly between managing the behavioural disturbances and treating the underlying

Box 2: Clinical Scenario Two

Background

Dave, age 22, was referred to the interdisciplinary mental health team by his community psychiatrist who felt "out of his depth" treating someone with developmental disability. Despite knowing Dave for many years and helping him through two periods of distress during adolescence, the underlying psychiatric diagnosis remained unclear and Dave was not responding to conventional treatment approaches.

Dave came from a family that valued academic achievement. He was identified as having mild developmental disability at an early age but this had largely been ignored. Dave set unrealistically high academic goals for himself and felt demoralized and worthless when he could not reach these goals. High school was a very difficult time for Dave since he did not fit in with the students who were preparing for university and he felt rejected by them. He succeeded in graduating from a modified high school program through hard work and an "understanding school principal." After finishing high school, Dave enrolled in college but eventually had to leave because it was too stressful. He started to hear voices, which he described as people calling him "retard." He was tearful and agitated and expressed feelings of not wanting to live. Dave had experienced a number of recent life events around the same time, including the breakup of a relationship and the realization that he was not able to cope with the demands of his college program. Physical examination and routine laboratory investigations were normal and Dave's psychiatrist started him on an antidepressant and recommended supportive psychotherapy.

Dave's mood improved but the voices remained. An antipsychotic was started, resulting in fewer experiences of voices most of the time. However, any attempt to reduce the antipsychotic medication resulted in a return of the voices, requiring the medication to be reinstated at higher doses. Even with the antipsychotic medication, Dave continued to hear voices at times of high anxiety (e.g., when his program was too stressful, when he was out in crowds, when he was seeking the approval of peers). The voices seemed to come from people he was unable to describe further in any detail and were always derogatory, calling him names like "retard" or "loser." Dave refused to talk about the voices when they were most bothersome and was reluctant to discuss them outside of these times. With his therapist, Dave started to share his intense and painful experiences of being teased and called names at school.

Comment

The underlying disorder(s) giving rise to Dave's behaviour and mental experiences is not clear from the information that is currently available. When Dave is well, his developmental disability and lack of abstract thinking limit his capacity to share, or to see the relevance of sharing, these experiences with his psychiatrist. Upon hearing the voices, however, he becomes hostile and paranoid and totally refuses to discuss them (perhaps because of cognitive confusion and fear).

A number of psychiatric disorders should be considered in Dave's case: psychotic disorder, including schizophrenia, major depressive disorder, anxiety disorder (including social phobia), and post traumatic stress disorder (flashbacks from experiences in school). Working within a biopsychosocial framework and taking into account the impact of Dave's developmental disability on his clinical presentation, a clinical diagnostic hypothesis can be generated rather than making a more definitive diagnosis based on inadequate information. An intervention or treatment plan can be formulated that includes a plan to identify and collect further information that would help to support (or refute) the working hypothesis. The intervention/treatment plan should include a process to review and revise the working diagnosis when new information becomes available, including Dave's responses to the intervention/treatment.

cause giving rise to these disturbances (see Figure 2; Bradley & Hollins, 2010; Sullivan et al., 2011).

Some syndromes are associated with a vulnerability to particular mental ill-health. For example, Down syndrome is associated with early onset dementia, autism with mood disorder, and Williams syndrome with anxiety disorders. Co-existing or concurrent conditions such as autism, attention deficit hyperactivity disorder (ADHD), stereotypies, anxiety, obsessive compulsive disorder (OCD), phobias and fears, and tics should be systematically identified where present. The clinical presentation of new onset disorders, such as mood and psychotic disorders, may be distorted by these pre-existing conditions, and, unless the latter are identified as background behaviours, misdiagnoses may be made. For example, an increase in "bizarre" self talk in someone with an autism spectrum disorder can easily be mistaken for schizophrenia, or an escalation of hyperactive or impulsive behaviours in someone with ADHD and limited verbal skills can be mistaken for mania. A good psychiatric assessment, therefore, requires a detailed description of "baseline" or usual behaviours for that client prior to the onset of the new disturbance.

In the assessment process, symptoms and changes in behaviour are examined to identify whether they meet standard diagnostic criteria, using classification systems such as DSM-IV (American Psychiatric Association, 1994) and ICD-10 (World Health Organization, 1992) for psychiatric disorders. Changes in behaviour can be used as markers (or "target behaviours") in monitoring the effectiveness of the treatment offered. The goal of the psychiatric assessment is to identify and diagnose any psychiatric disorder and to treat this optimally without further adding either to the developmental disability or to any medical condition. A further goal is to identify stressors and other circumstances that contribute to, or precipitate, mental ill-health so that further crises and relapses can be prevented. Not infrequently, because of the complexity in diagnosing psychiatric disorders in this population, there remains uncertainty as to the precise psychiatric diagnostic sub-type. When this occurs, the steps to follow are:

- Propose the clinical diagnosis that best fits the information currently available; in particular, the pattern of behaviours and symptoms currently and over time, the family history of mental ill-health, the life events, and other possible triggers.
- Collect data to confirm or refute this hypothesis.

- Review this data along with the results of the assessments in other areas (e.g., psychological, communication, behavioural, environmental, expectations).
- If the ongoing clinical data are not compatible with the working clinical diagnosis, review the diagnostic formulation.

By following this approach, it should be possible to minimize the potential for misdiagnosis and inappropriate treatment, particularly with psychotropic medication (see clinical scenario in Box 2).

Comprehensive psychiatric assessment of the individual with developmental disability is usually an ongoing and dynamic process that may take several months. It requires a coordinated approach across all the settings where the individual spends time, including out-patient and in-patient settings if hospital admission is required. Assessing and correctly diagnosing psychiatric disorders in people with developmental disabilities requires an understanding and experience of developmental disabilities and of psychiatric disorders. Assessment is best done within an interdisciplinary team context, working closely with caregivers who know the individual best (Summers et al., 2002). During the process of an assessment, specialist input may be required from many perspectives, including medicine (developmental pediatrics, genetics, psychiatry, neurology, family medicine, audiology, ophthalmology), nursing, psychology, speech and language pathology, behaviour therapy, and occupational and/or physiotherapy (see Bradley et al., 2009 for description of the multidisciplinary team).

An effective team will have developed a systematic approach to assessment and treatment based on the most up-to-date evidence, and will be using valid and reliable instruments and procedures. Team members, experienced in working with individuals with developmental disabilities, will be able to adapt their usual clinical approaches appropriately to the broad spectrum of functioning levels seen in this group. Such a team should be able to focus the assessment in appropriate areas, be able to coordinate the assessment findings in a meaningful manner, and also be able to provide a balanced formulation on which treatment recommendations should be based. Fragmented or incomplete assessments and those conducted by professionals who are unfamiliar with the emotional responses of people with developmental disabilities unfortunately contribute to misdiagnoses and inappropriate and sometimes harmful treatments.

The psychiatric assessment of the individual with developmental disability can be challenging, but there are now several helpful resources (e.g., Bradley & Hollins, 2010; Deb, Matthews, Holt, & Bouras, 2001; Silka & Hauser, 1997; Summers, Boyd, & Morgan, 2004). Standard manuals used in the mental ill-health field (i.e., DSM-IV-TR and the ICD-10) have been adapted for people with developmental disabilities and are more suitable for this population than the original manuals. The DSM-IV-TR adaptation is called DM-ID: Diagnostic Manual-Intellectual Disabilities (Fletcher, Loschen, Stavrakaki, & First, 2007); the ICD-10 adaptation is called DC/LD: Diagnostic Criteria for Psychiatric Disorders for use with Adults with Learning Disabilities/Mental Retardation (Royal College of Psychiatrists, 2001). These adapted manuals include helpful descriptions of symptoms and behaviours representing the range of psychiatric disorders that occur and the "atypical" presentations that may arise in people with developmental disabilities. Familiarity with both diagnostic systems and the rich descriptive clinical material contained in these manuals are recommended as invaluable resources to health professionals working with people with developmental disabilities and mental ill-health.

Treatment

A comprehensive assessment indicates the presence (or absence) of a psychiatric disorder and provides information not only on those circumstances that may be underlying the behavioural disturbances, but also on those circumstances that exacerbate or maintain these and other behaviours (even after the initial cause is no longer present). Treatment should emerge from a comprehensive assessment and address the needs that are identified by it.

Box 3: Treatment Principles

Decrease organic/biological contribution and prevent the occurrence of secondary disabilities and handicaps:

- *attention to sensory impairments (e.g., vision/ hearing)*
- *attention to physical impairments*
- *attention to sensory issues (e.g., sensitivity to sound/touch)*
- *treatment of seizures*
- *treatment of other medical disorders*
- *treatment of mental ill-health*

Decrease stress:

- *appropriate environments*
- *appropriate expectations*
- *appropriate supports to match level of functioning and adaptive skills*

Increase competence:

- *increase coping skills*
- *increase communication skills*
- *increase self-esteem*
- *increase social support systems*

Coordinated system approach:

- *continuity of care (e.g., inpatient to outpatient)*
- *identify spectrum of supports (e.g., physicians, nursing, behaviour support, case manager)*
- *proactive crisis management*

Assessment and formulation of treatment plans take time, however, so initially treatment may be more focussed on the immediate management of the behavioural disturbances until a clearer understanding of the cause of these behaviours is available (Bradley & Lofchy, 2005). Thus, during the assessment period, various "crisis" interventions (most often medication or behavioural) may be tried in response to the need to manage serious or dangerous behaviours. The responses of the individual to these interventions should also be monitored and documented carefully, as they may provide further insights into the underlying cause of the disturbance and may be relevant to future treatment recommendations (e.g., if the individual was hospitalized, how did he/she respond to this?). As a clearer understanding of the underlying etiology to the referring concerns becomes available, treatment becomes more focussed and individualized (see Boxes 3 and 4).

Following assessment and diagnostic formulation, which may identify a psychiatric disorder, medication is required only to the extent recommended for the optimal treatment of this disorder. Effective treatment will involve educating the individual with developmental disability and his/her caregivers about the disorder, about treatment options, and about strategies to minimize relapses and promote mental well-being. It is important to map out a proactive response to crisis or relapse, with a clear outline of the involvement of community, emergency, and inpatient services (Sullivan et al., 2006). This will help to stabilize the system supporting the individual and consolidate the treatment plan, will minimize anxiety and the escalation of distress in both the individual and his/her caregivers and, most importantly, will help ensure continuity of care and specialized treatment (an example of this approach is outlined in Box 1). With counselling or psychotherapy, people with developmental disabilities can be helped to develop alternative coping strategies, learn to modulate their emotional responses, and manage frustration and stress more effectively. However, caregivers have a key role in managing the amount of stress in the individual's environment (e.g., attending to noisy work environments when the person has a hearing impairment or ensuring appropriate expectations on the individual given his/her capacities) and in helping them to gain access to lifestyles that promote physical and emotional well-being (e.g., attention to physical health and medical disorders, friendships, and inclusion in work and recreational activities; see Box 4).

Research into the psychological and behavioural aspects of various syndromes has gained prominence in recent years (for a review of syndromes and behavioural phenotypes see Dykens, Hodapp, & Finucane, 2000; Moldavsky, Lev, & Lerman-Sagie, 2001; O'Brien & Yule, 1996). This new knowledge, coupled with autobiographical accounts by some more able individuals with these syndromes (for example, see Kingsley & Levitz, 1994 for Down syndrome; Lenhoff, Wang, Greenberg, & Bellugi, 1997 for Williams syndrome; and Grandin, 2008 for autism) offer opportunities to design environments and supports that are more sensitive to individual needs. Adolescents and young adults with autism and developmental disabilities, for example, are at greater risk for psychiatric disorders than peers with developmental disabilities alone (Bradley & Bolton, 2006; Brereton, Tonge, & Einfeld, 2006), and often present with severe behavioural disturbance. A broader understanding of the experience of individuals with autism and of the disabilities associated with autism allows a greater appreciation of, for example, how confusing and stressful their daily pattern of social life can be. These broader perspectives encourage the development of services that can optimally support individuals with autism and, in particular, minimize the stress they experience.

People with developmental disabilities and mental ill-health require regular follow-up and careful monitoring of their mediation. Shared care involving the psychiatrist, nurse, and family doctor with access to specialist services (such as psychology, behaviour therapy and counselling/psychotherapy) can work well. In some jurisdictions (e.g., the United Kingdom and some services in the United States), community psychiatric nurses are core members of the treatment team and play a crucial role in ensuring access to appropriate health care. In Ontario, however, the nursing role in supporting individuals with developmental disabilities and mental ill-health has not been fully appreciated or recognized (Summers et al., 2005), and few nurses are trained to practise in this area. In some localities, generic ("non-specialized") community nurses may become involved with specific clients for a limited time. Generally speaking, though, the relative roles of the nurse, psychiatrist, and family doctor at any time during treatment will be determined by the needs of the individual, the service context within which each of these professionals works, and the comfort level of each in working with people with developmental disabilities.

The Mental Health Service System in Ontario

Historical perspectives

In the past four decades a number of socio-political factors have helped shape the mental health and developmental services now available to people with developmental disabilities residing in Ontario (see Table 2). In 1971, a report commissioned by the government of Ontario, the "Williston Report" (Williston, 1971), recommended the downsizing of facilities for people with developmental disabilities and the establishment of community-based services to enable them to be supported in their local communities. In 1974, the *Developmental Services Act* came into effect in Ontario. This Act enabled responsibility for children and adults with developmental disabilities to be transferred from the Ministry of Health to the Ministry of Community and Social Services. This shift in government policy mirrored the increasingly popular view that a system that was based primarily on a medical model was not appropriate for the majority of people with developmental disabilities. Unfortunately, the decision to divest responsibility, instead of adopting a joint approach, may have set the stage for the gradual erosion and fragmentation of medical and mental health services for people with developmental disabilities, as the Ministry of Community and Social Services lacked the infrastructure and cross-sector linkages to provide or co-ordinate these types of services (Lunsky et al., 2007).

Another significant development occurred in 1987, when the government released a strategic plan for community living in a policy document entitled *Challenges and Opportunities: Community Living for People with Developmental Handicaps*. This document outlined a 25-year plan for the phasing out and eventual closure of provincial institutions for people with developmental disabilities. The infrastructure that had developed within the institutions to respond to the medical and mental health needs of people with developmental disabilities was starting to be dismantled, despite the lack of a co-ordinated plan to set up a comparable system of community-based care. Implicit in these policy changes was the notion

Box 4: Treatment Approaches

- *Counselling*
- *Psychotherapy (individual, family, group, cognitive, etc.)*
- *Behavioural support*
- *Communication assistance*
- *Sensory diet (for individuals with autism)*
- *Environmental alteration*
- *Psychopharmacology*
- *Education about developmental disabilities and mental health*
- *System interventions*
- *Caregiver and staff support*

that people with developmental disabilities would have their health care needs met by accessing generic services. However, many studies have now highlighted the specialist health care needs of this population which, if not met, will result in them not having access to the same standard of health care enjoyed by their non-disabled peers (Beange, 1996; Lennox, Diggens, & Ugoni, 1997; Lennox & Kerr, 1997).

In addition, over time, the realization took hold that people with developmental disabilities were even more vulnerable to mental ill-health than their non-disabled peers, yet had greater difficulty accessing appropriate services. Government strategies to address some of these issues relating to mental health services consisted of joint ministerial (Ministries of Health & Long Term Care and Community and Social Services) efforts to stimulate cross-sector activities and the development of policy guidelines (released in 1997 and revised in 2008) to encourage greater equity of access to generic mental health services (see Table 2).

In 2004, the Ministry of Community and Social Services made clear its intention to transform developmental services in Ontario, and in 2006 produced a document entitled *Opportunities and Action — Transforming Supports in Ontario for People Who Have a Developmental Disability*. This discussion document laid out the government's plan for transformation based on six key principles: citizen-

Table 2: The Ontario Perspective: Policies and Laws Affecting the Lives and Mental Well-Being of People with Developmental Disabilities

Year	Name of Discussion Paper, Policy Document or Bill	Ministry/Ministries Responsible	Important Key Elements
1971	*Present Arrangements for the Care and Supervision of Mentally Retarded Persons in Ontario ("Williston Report")*	*Health*	• *called for the development of comprehensive community-based services for people with developmental disability*
1974	*Developmental Services Act*	*MCSS[1]*	• *responsibility for people with developmental disability was transferred from Ministry of Health to Ministry of Community and Social Services*
1980	*Education Act, 1980 (Bill 82)*	*Education*	• *stipulated that school-age children with exceptionalities must receive appropriate special education services and programs*
1987	*Challenges and Opportunities*	*MCSS*	• *multi-year strategic plan for the phasing out and closure of provincial institutions for the developmentally disabled* • *called for comprehensive community-based service system to be established*
1988	*Building Community Support for People: A Plan for Mental Health in Ontario ("Graham Report")*	*Health*	• *people with a dual diagnosis were identified under special target groups as being susceptible to mental health problems and disadvantaged in terms of obtaining needed services*
1990	*Interministerial Initiative on Dual Diagnosis*	*Health and MCSS*	• *demonstration projects were funded to generate innovative ideas and improved cooperation among service providers to improve the health status and community integration of people with a dual diagnosis*

[1] *MCSS = Ministry of Community and Social Services*

Year	Name of Discussion Paper, Policy Document or Bill	Ministry Responsible	Important Elements
1993	*Putting People First (Mental Health Reform)*	*Health*	• *policy framework to reform mental health services in Ontario* • *recommendation to develop programs to provide comprehensive services for those with severe mental illness and unique needs* • *people with developmental disability are included as a "first priority population"*
1995	*Developmental Services Framework: Draft Paper*	*MCSS*	• *strategic plan for promoting integration of people with developmental disability into community supports and services*
1997	*Making Services Work for People*	*MCSS*	• *framework for reshaping services for people with developmental disability*
1997	*Policy Guideline for the Provision of Services for Persons with a Dual Diagnosis*	*MCSS and Health*	• *policy direction for the planning, delivery and coordination of cross-sector services for people with a dual diagnosis*
1997	*Reinvestment Strategy for Children and Youth; Reinvestment Strategy for Adults with a Developmental Disability*	*MCSS*	• *strategies to prevent or reduce the need for essential and long-term government supports, and increase the use of investment supports/services*
1998	*Individual Support Agreements for People with Developmental Disabilities*	*MCSS*	• *approach to enhancing accountability and individualized approaches to services and supports in the developmental services sector*

Table 2: The Ontario Perspective: Policies and Laws Affecting the Lives and Mental Well-Being of People with Developmental Disabilities (cont'd)

Year	Name of Discussion Paper, Policy Document or Bill	Ministry/Ministries Responsible	Important Key Elements
1999	*Making It Happen: Implementation Plan for Mental Health Reform and Operational Framework for the Delivery of Mental Health Services and Supports*	Health	• *framework for and implementation plan to improve the delivery of services and supports through the mental health reform process* • *individuals with a dual diagnosis (developmental disability with psychiatric disorder) are identified as one of the target populations who qualify for specialized services*
2005	*Accessibility for Ontarians with Disabilities Act*	MCSS	• *legislation that requires public and private businesses and organizations to develop, implement and enforce mandatory accessibility standards* • *under the act, "disability" may refer to an intellectual or developmental disability* • *act stipulates that persons with disabilities should be communicated with in a manner that takes into consideration their disability*
2005	*Community Networks of Specialized Care*	MCSS	• *creation of four networks across the province to coordinate specialized services for adults with developmental disabilities and mental illness or challenging behaviours* • *key roles of networks are to coordinate services, improve service delivery and increase capacity through education and training*
2006	*Opportunities and Action: Transforming Supports in Ontario for People Who Have a Developmental Disability*	MCSS	• *plan to transform developmental services in Ontario* • *underlying principles for developmental services include citizenship, equity and fairness, accessibility and portability, accountability and sustainability* • *calls for a network of independent planning teams and service "brokers," single points of access and a standardized application for services and supports*

Year	Name of Discussion Paper, Policy Document or Bill	Ministry/Ministries Responsible	Important Key Elements
2006	*Local Health System Integration Act*	*Health*	• *14 LHINs (Local Health Integration Networks) are established and given authority to manage local health systems* • *LHINs plan for and provide funding to divested psychiatric hospitals and community mental health and addiction centres*
2008	*Services and Supports to Promote the Social Inclusion of Persons with Developmental Disabilities Act (Bill 77)*	*MCSS*	• *legislation to replace the Developmental Services Act* • *plan to change the definition of developmental disability and designate independent "entities" to determine eligibility, assess need, allocate resources and prioritize applications for services and supports* • *bill would entrench individualized funding and wait lists in legislation*
2008	*Joint Policy Guideline for the Provision of Community Mental Health and Developmental Services for Adults with a Dual Diagnosis*	*Health and MCSS*	• *framework for the planning, coordination and delivery of community mental health and developmental services and supports for adults with a dual diagnosis* • *government expectation that LHINs and local developmental services planning forums (including networks of specialized care) will link to implement the guidelines*

ship; fairness and equity; accessibility and portability; safety and security; accountability; and sustainability. In 2008, the Ontario government created *the Services and Supports to Promote the Social Inclusion of Persons with Developmental Disabilities Act* (Bill 77), which replaces the *Developmental Services Act* that is more than 35 years old. Since announcing its intention to transform the developmental services system, several initiatives have been undertaken, including the closure of the last three remaining institutions in Ontario in 2009 and the creation of four Community Networks of Specialized Care in the province. In

July 2011, MCSS moved forward with establishing "Application Entities" to provide a centralized access point for developmental services in regions throughout Ontario (see Box 5 for other examples). Effective inter-ministerial planning for a full range of services, case management for coordination of services, and availability of knowledgeable staff for provision of services are key elements for optimizing community-based care for people with developmental disabilities (McCreary, 2008).

The need for access to well-funded, high-quality services and supports that are responsive to the

Box 5: Recent Initiatives in Ontario

Service Initiative: Mashkikiiwininiwag Maziinaatesijigan Wichiiiwewin (MMW) Program

The MMW program, first initiated as a pilot project in 2004, provides specialized clinical services through video-conference technology to people with developmental disabilities living in Northwestern Ontario. Acknowledging a significant lack of access to clinical services in the northern region of the province, Surrey Place Centre in Toronto collaborated with Sioux Lookout First Nations Health Authority and Community Living Dryden and Sioux Lookout to establish a clinical service that would enable people with developmental disabilities to access services closer to home and in their own communities. As a result of a partnership among Toronto agencies (Surrey Place Centre, The Centre for Addiction and Mental Health, Griffin Centre and George Brown College) and services in the north, people with developmental disabilities are able to access a range of services including psychology, psychiatry, behaviour therapy, nursing, counselling and other specialized services as needed. While these specialized services are primarily delivered through videoconference, clinical teams from Toronto make visits to northern communities from time to time throughout the year. The program targets adults with developmental disabilities who also have a mental health need and/or challenging behaviour. With hub sites in Sioux Lookout and Dryden, the program serves all of Northwestern Ontario including 32 First Nations communities and works closely with the North Network of Specialized Care to coordinate clinical services for this part of the province. The program also delivers a number of educational programs including a certificate program in dual diagnosis through George Brown College. For more information visit www.surreyplace.on.ca/Clinical-Programs/Developmental-Disabilities/Pages/Video-Conferencing.aspx

Service System Initiative: Community Networks of Specialized Care

As a key part of developmental services transformation in Ontario, the Ministry of Community and Social Services announced in May, 2005, the creation of four Community Networks of Specialized Care. The Networks were established to improve access to and enhance services for people with developmental disabilities who have mental health needs and/or challenging behaviours. Networks were created in Northern Ontario, Eastern Ontario, Central Ontario and Southern Ontario and lead agencies were identified in each of these four areas of the province to facilitate the development and coordination of Network activities. The Community Networks of Specialized Care represent a formal collaboration of specialized service providers to improve specialized service system coordination and access as well as build capacity within communities to deliver a range of specialized clinical services. Building effective cross sector collaborations, Network members represent providers from developmental services, mental health, health, justice, education and other sectors. For more information visit www.community-networks.ca

---

needs of individuals with developmental disabilities remains constant over time. But government policies and priorities change over time (see Table 2 for an historical overview of relevant laws and policies), and it is important to understand how these result in system changes that, in turn, impact the lives of people with developmental disabilities and their families (see Box 6 for one family's impressions of the service system).

Current services

When behavioural and mental health concerns arise, the family physician is usually the first point of contact and is the most common source for help ("primary level" health care). Depending on the nature and severity of the problem, the family physician has several options in terms of referring to more specialized services, such as an independent practice psychiatrist, community mental health program, general hospital outpatient or inpatient services ("secondary level" health care), or a specialized clinical program within the developmental service sector. Individuals in acute crisis may be referred to the nearest emergency department able to provide psychiatric service. Those with severe, intractable, and/or chronic disorders have, in the past, tended to receive service from the nearest Provincial Psychiatric Hospital ("tertiary level" health care).

In the 1980s, there were 10 Provincial Psychiatric Hospitals (PPHs) in Ontario. Many of these hospitals had wards or dual diagnosis programs (i.e., they had a service specifically for people with developmental disabilities and mental ill-health), offering long-term outpatient support and immediate access to inpatient beds at times of crisis. With the mental health restructuring of recent years (Ministry of Health & Long-Term Care, 1999a, 1999b), administrative authority for the PPHs was transferred to the public hospitals. Many of these former PPHs entered into agreements with existing public hospitals offering psychiatric services in their locality (previously the "secondary level" of health care), and have aligned their services to respond to local needs and priorities.

In terms of people with developmental disabilities and mental ill-health, each region/locality has to attend to the specialist needs of these individuals, either by offering services directly to them or, if such services are not directly available in that locality, by referring them elsewhere for service. Mental health restructuring provides new opportunities for people with developmental disabilities and mental ill-health to gain better and greater access to mental health programs in the locality in which they live; however, the history of mental health services for them has been one of exclusion. This situation is not likely to change unless mental health professionals receive specific training about people with developmental disabilities and a range of generic and specialist services are made available. In general, inpatient, outpatient, and community-based services are not linked closely; this can lead to fragmented, discontinuous care and can result in the individual with developmental disability and mental ill-health being held "captive" in a systems crisis that is often mistaken as a client crisis. A tenacious and committed effort to pursue coordinated and collaborative assessment, treatment, and discharge planning is fundamental to the provision of adequate mental health services for this population.

The most recent restructuring of the health care system in Ontario and the creation of Local Health Integration Networks (LHINs) across the province provide significant opportunity to address the challenges in responding to the health and mental health needs of people with developmental disabilities. With a mandate to plan for, fund, and manage health care services within their respective regions, many LHINs have identified mental health as a priority issue. While the LHINs are developing their mental health plans, therefore, it is crucial that the needs of people with developmental disabilities are acknowledged and addressed.

Barriers and bridges

Although people with developmental disabilities have, in principle, access to the full spectrum of services that are available to the citizens of Ontario, there are significant barriers that impede obtaining and benefitting from these services. For this population, it is relevant, therefore, to differentiate between access in principle and access in practice (sometimes referred to as equity of access). For many years, it has been consistently observed that people with developmental disabilities and mental ill-health tend to "fall through the cracks" for services. Factors that impact on the provision of services can be organized into three broad categories: a) infrastructure/systemic, b) clinical, and c) resources. These factors interact with each other in myriad and often complex ways (see Bradley & Cheetham (2010) for further discussion of the impact of these factors on care).

Infrastructure/systemic factors:

- Lack of a national health care policy for people with developmental disabilities to drive and support provincial and territorial initiatives and service provision.
- Absence of national, provincial and territorial a) clinical standards of care, and b) accreditation requirements in clinical education and training to ensure clinical standards are met.
- Exclusionary criteria for services, which result in many people with developmental disabilities being denied access to mainstream mental health services.

- Systems that are increasingly directed toward those "most in need"— that is, in crisis (and often least likely to become less dependent over time on expensive and highly specialized services). This perpetuates a crisis response mindset and overlooks the needs of the greater majority of people who could benefit from more timely and less expensive intervention approaches.
- Separation of authority and funding for health and developmental services without an accompanying infrastructure to mandate and oversee provision and coordination of services.

Comment: All efforts to bridge cross-Ministry mandates must be made if we are to improve services, and ultimately the health and mental health outcomes, for people with developmental disabilities and mental ill-health. The creation of the Local Health Integration Networks and Community Networks of Specialized Care represent some key opportunities to better integrate mental health and developmental services.

Clinical factors:
- Characteristics of people with developmental disabilities (e.g., the cognitive and communication impairments) that may contribute to their difficulties accessing services and receiving quality care.
- The fact that individuals with developmental disabilities do not always behave as "typical" patients, which can leave staff feeling bewildered or unskilled if their best treatments and intentions only result in further escalation of disruptive behaviours.
- Lack of systematic and robust professional and continuing education opportunities for medical and mental health professionals that result in reduced competence and confidence in providing care to people with developmental disabilities.

Comment: Model service-education programs may pave the way for linking clinical trainees and community service providers (McCreary, 2008). All efforts must be made to work collaboratively with academic institutions and regulatory colleges to ensure health care practitioners receive at least some level of training in the field of developmental disabilities.

Factors related to resources:
- Shortage of health care professionals impacts the entire population, but creates even more hardship for groups with more specialized needs such as people with developmental disabilities.
- Reimbursement schedules that do not permit physicians and other health care providers to be appropriately compensated for the amount of time many of these patients require (up to 4 times longer than for people without developmental disabilities).
- Lack of incentives to attract, recruit, and retain professionals to work in the field of developmental disabilities.
- Under-funding of services and economic disparities that place individuals with developmental disabilities at even greater disadvantage in trying to access appropriate services.

Developing an Ontario Vision of a Mental Health Service Sensitive to the Needs of People with Developmental Disabilities

Certain requirements stand out as being particularly pertinent in the planning and delivery of mental health services sensitive to the needs of people with developmental disabilities. Our vision includes a system that addresses the following specific needs:
- Recognition of the greater prevalence of health-related problems experienced by people with developmental disabilities so that: a) resources can be targeted to those most at risk, and b) problems can be anticipated and prevented.
- A sustained commitment to, and support for, developing a more integrated mental health system for people with developmental disabilities.
- The development of a spectrum of mental health and health-related services that are organized into a coordinated and cohesive

network of services including: primary level (e.g., family medicine), secondary level (e.g., crisis and emergency services, community psychiatric services, and access to general psychiatric inpatient services), and tertiary level (e.g., consultation, assessment and treatment of more complex problems and access to professionals with special expertise in developmental disabilities and mental ill-health). At each level, staff are needed who are experienced and comfortable working with people with developmental disabilities.

- The need for professionals and caregivers from relevant service sectors (health, social services, education and criminal justice) to enhance their knowledge of mental health issues and their knowledge of the range of the available community resources and supports.
- The need to integrate broad-based resources (including case management, respite, home-based services, employment options, social and leisure supports, education and housing) into the mental health service system so as to address people's needs from a holistic perspective.
- The need to promote clinical and service excellence and innovation by working in partnership with Academic Health Science Centres to develop training, education and research activities that focus on the needs of people with developmental disabilities.
- The need to develop a process to bring together service providers from relevant service systems to identify common issues and promote joint "ownership" through collaborative problem-solving efforts. In this regard, the Community Networks of Specialized Care may play an important role.

These issues must be addressed at the most meaningful administrative level, where the larger picture of needed services and supports can be appreciated, and where there is the capacity to implement change. For example, in Canada, a decision to develop mental health services within defined catchment areas would take place at the provincial level. However, issues relating to the education and training of professional staff may only be effectively addressed at a national level where, for example, professional colleges and National Examining Boards are better placed to ensure the development and maintenance of best clinical practices.

Meeting the challenges that are outlined above requires political will, ongoing commitment of resources, and involvement of clinicians, educators, service providers and service recipients. The dual diagnosis guidelines set out by Ontario's Ministry of Health and Ministry of Community and Social Services in 2008 (see Table 2) outline a framework for the joint provision of services, but do not specifically address the need for an integrated plan to create a mental health program attentive to the special needs of people with developmental disabilities. An undertaking of this magnitude is a formidable but not insurmountable task, as evidenced by the design and implementation of a province-wide initiative by the Ministry of Children and Youth Services (MCYS) to provide Intensive Behaviour Intervention (IBI) to children with autism spectrum disorders. In the case of the IBI program, the Ontario government set out objectives for the program, roles, responsibilities and qualifications for service providers, and expectations for the delivery of services. Some of the key elements of the IBI program that have relevance for a mental health program are that service providers are expected to provide high-quality intervention that is based on up-to-date scientific evidence, offer training and educational activities to enhance service capacity, establish collaborative relationships with a range of service providers and systematically collect clinical and statistical data that can assist with large-scale evaluations. The IBI program has helped to highlight the needs of individuals with ASD in general and has led to the creation of training and employment opportunities that have boosted capacity for diagnostic and intervention services within the field. Planning and implementing the IBI program illustrates how effective comprehensive services can be provided where there is a will to do so.

We envision a jointly-funded provincial network of interdisciplinary mental health teams supporting people with developmental disabilities and mental ill-health that are linked with hospitals, universi-

Box 6: Parents' Perspective: Impressions of the Service System for Those with a Dual Diagnosis[3]

We are offering these comments about the service system as the parents of two adult children with intellectual disabilities and mental health needs (dual diagnosis)[3]. While these comments reflect our personal experience, the concerns we raise are echoed by many parents we have come into contact with over the years.

One of our greatest concerns is how our children will fare after we have gone. There is a real feeling of relief when a family is able to get residential services and a full day program with an agency. Then we know that our children will have ongoing support. In recent years, however, it seems that the priority has been on providing residential and day services for those coming from institutions. Even now that the institutions are closed, there seems very little chance of obtaining residential care unless there is a severe crisis such as the death of a parent. Aging primary caregivers waiting for residential support (over 1500 are over 70 years old in Ontario) are finding it more difficult to support their children as they experience more physical limitations and as their children often start to experience early cognitive decline.

Recently, there have been planned changes to the system that are designed to improve accessibility and fairness. An emphasis on individualized funding is intended to allow families to design and staff day program activities and respite for their sons and daughters. Unfortunately, with the limited funding available it is difficult for a family on their own to develop effective individualized programs for their child who has a dual diagnosis. Moreover, families may not be able to take on the added responsibility of recruiting, training and supervising staff who understand both the intellectual disability and mental health issues to work with their son or daughter along with managing the financial arrangements. Families who are using individualized funding are concerned about what will happen when they are no longer able to manage the funds. Will the government take over? Many families are trying to set up their own mechanisms that will continue the support after they have passed away but it is not easy to maintain these arrangements over time.

Both agencies and families struggle to find and keep trained workers. While agencies may be able to provide on-the-job training, families are concerned about how to find individuals who have the appropriate qualifications and training to provide high-quality services or even to know how to judge the quality of services they provide. These issues take on greater importance when the person they are hired to work with has mental health needs. Regardless of whether services are provided by agency staff or workers that are hired through individualized funding, parents need to be educated about quality standards in order to become more "informed consumers."

Over the years, we have found it helpful to be able to consult with experts who are knowledgeable about both the developmental and mental health sectors, as opposed to our trying to learn everything from the ground up. However, finding the right doctor or psychiatrist who understands both intellectual disabilities and mental health issues has been a concern of ours and one that is shared by many families. We are aware of the initiative to develop primary health care guidelines for adults with intellectual disabilities and to train family physicians about these guidelines, and that is most welcome.

In summary, we have seen many changes to services and the broader system over the years but the situation of those caring for adults with a dual diagnosis at home seems unchanged. As the parents of adult children with intellectual disabilities and mental health needs, our wish is for them to lead full and productive lives which will continue after we can no longer care for them.

— Submitted by the parents of two adult children with intellectual disabilities and mental health needs.

---

[3] *Terms that are used by the parents, which we refer to as developmental disabilities and mental ill-health in the body of the text*

ties and developmental and mental health agencies as well as with each other. The mandate of these teams would be to provide clinical services, educate and train health, mental health and developmental providers and participate in research on topics and issues of importance to the field.

People with developmental disabilities and mental ill-health present service challenges that can only be embraced by a truly biopsychosocial approach. Their needs span the traditional administrative boundaries of health, social services, criminal justice, and education. Inter-ministerial initiatives and joint funding provide the solid bedrock on which integrated services develop.

Summary

In this chapter, we have presented key issues in the assessment and treatment of mental ill-health in people with developmental disabilities. In particular, we have learned that people with developmental disabilities experience similar kinds of mental ill-health as their peers without such disabilities, but are relatively more prone to mental ill-health. Emotional and psychiatric ill-health may present as behavioural problems. Left untreated, mental ill-health may become chronic and crippling, contributing further disability. Many emotional disturbances can be prevented, and both emotional and psychiatric disorders are significantly diminished with appropriate intervention and treatment.

We have also discussed how service systems impact on optimal assessment, treatment, and mental health support. With advances in genetics and the neurosciences, our understanding of people with developmental disabilities and mental ill-health is changing. By identifying and studying smaller groups of individuals with known genetic etiologies that give rise to their intellectual disabilities, a better appreciation for the complex interplay among biomedical and psychosocial factors has developed. The field is being enriched by the contributions of researchers, clinicians and students from different backgrounds and disciplines. It is imperative that effective research, academic (education and training), and clinical links are developed alongside the service systems responsible for the care and support of this vulnerable population (see Morris et al., 2007; Moss et al., 1997 for further exploration of these issues).

For Further Thought and Discussion

1. A friend has recently moved into your neighbourhood. She is worried about her teenage daughter Sophie who has started "to stay up late at night and has become oppositional and stubborn." Sophie has Down syndrome. What might be going on, what assistance is required, and how would you help your friend access appropriate services in your area?

2. Consider the origins of negative attitudes towards people with developmental disabilities. How do such attitudes affect access to good health care?

3. What is meant by a "proactive/preventive" and "crisis/reactive" health care service? Why is a proactive/preventive approach preferable to a crisis/reactive approach in the support of people with developmental disabilities?

More Resources

Websites:

Autism Ontario
1179 King Street West, Suite 004
Toronto, ON M6K 3C5
www.autismontario.com

Canadian Autism Intervention Research Network
The Offord Centre for Child Studies
Faculty of Health Sciences, McMaster University
107 Patterson Building, Chedoke Site
1200 Main Street West, Hamilton, ON L8N 3Z5
www.cairn-site.com
info@cairn-site.com

Canadian Association for Research and Education in Intellectual Disabilities (CARE-ID)
c/o Dual Diagnosis Program
Centre for Addiction and Mental Health
1001 Queen Street West, Unit 4, Room 115A
Toronto, ON M6J 1H4
careid@queensu.ca

Developmental Disabilities Division at the University of Western Ontario
850 Highbury Ave.. Room E126 London, Ontario N6A 4H1
www.ddd.uwo.ca
ddd@uwo.ca

NADD Ontario:
c/o CAMH
Dual Diagnosis Program
Unit 4 Room 112, 1001 Queen Street West
Toronto, ON M6J IH4
www.naddontario.org

NADD — An Association for Persons with Developmental Disabilities and Mental Health Needs
132 Fair St. Kingston, NY 12401
www.thenadd.org
info@thenadd.org

Ontario Association on Developmental Disabilities
2 Surrey Place
Toronto, ON M5S 2C2
www.oadd.org
oadd@oadd.org

Society for the Study of Behavioural Phenotypes
www.ssbp.co.uk

Understanding Intellectual Disability and Health — a UK-based website (St. George's, University of London) that provides information and learning resources for health care professionals and students
www.intellectualdisability.info

Statutes:

Developmental Services Act, 1974.

Education Amendment Act of 1980.

Accessibility for Ontarians with Disabilities Act, 2005.

Local Health System Integration Act, 2006.

Services and Supports to Promote the Social Inclusion of Persons with Developmental Disabilities Act, 2008.

Ontario Government Documents:

Ontario Ministry of Community and Social Services (1987). *Challenges and opportunities.* Toronto, ON: Queen's Printer.

Provincial Community Mental Health Committee (July, 1988). *Building community support for people: A plan for mental health in Ontario (The Graham Report).* Toronto, ON: Queen's Printer.

Ontario Ministries of Health and Community and Social Services (July, 1990). *Policy guideline for the provision of services for persons with a dual diagnosis* (developmental disability/mental health needs). Toronto, ON: Queen's Printer.

Ontario Ministry of Community and Social Services and Ministry of Health (1991). *Initiatives for persons with developmental disability and mental illness.* Toronto, ON: Queen's Printer.

Ontario Ministy of Health (1993). *Putting people first: Reform of the mental health services in Ontario.* Toronto, ON: Queen's Printer.

Ontario Ministry of Community and Social Services (March, 1995). *Developmental services: Draft paper.* Toronto, ON: Queen's Printer.

Ontario Ministry of Community and Social Services and Ministry of Health (1997). *Policy guideline for the provision of services for persons with a dual diagnosis.* Toronto, ON: Queen's Printer.

Ontario Ministry of Community and Social Services (April, 1997). *Making services work for people: A new framework for children and people with developmental disabilities.* Toronto, ON: Queen's Printer.

Ontario Ministry of Community and Social Services (October, 1997). *Reinvestment strategy for children and youth.* Toronto, ON: Queen's Printer.

Ontario Ministry of Community and Social Services (December, 1997). *Reinvestment strategy for adults with a developmental disability.* Toronto, ON: Queen's Printer.

Ontario Ministry of Health (1999a). *Making it happen: Operational framework for the delivery of mental health services and supports.* Toronto, ON: Queen's Printer.

Ontario Ministry of Health (1999b). *Making it happen: Implementation plan for the reformed mental health system.* Toronto, ON: Queen's Printer.

Ontario Ministry of Community and Social Services (May, 2006). *Opportunities and action: Transforming supports in Ontario for people who have a developmental disability.* Toronto, ON: Queen's Printer.

Ontario Ministry of Health and Long-Term Care and Ministry of Community and Social Services (December, 2008). *Joint policy guideline for the provision of community mental health and developmental services for adults with a dual diagnosis.* Toronto, ON: Queen's Printer.

General Reading:

Bouras, N., & Holt, G. (Eds.). (2007). *Psychiatric and behavioural disorders in intellectual disabilities* (2nd ed.). Cambridge: Cambridge University Press.

Brown, I., & Percy, M. (Eds.). (2007). *A comprehensive guide to intellectual & developmental disabilities.* Baltimore: Paul H. Brookes Publishing Co.

Griffiths, D. M., Stavrakaki, C., & Summers, J. (Eds.). (2002). *Dual diagnosis: An introduction to the mental health needs of persons with developmental disabilities.* Sudbury, ON: Habilitative Mental Health Resource Network.

Hassiotis, A., Barron, D. A., & Hall, I. P. (Eds.) (2009). *Intellectual disability psychiatry: A practical handbook.* Hoboken, NJ: Wiley.

References

American Psychiatric Association. (1994). *Diagnostic and statistical manual of mental disorders* (4th ed.). Washington, DC: Author.

Autism Ontario. (2008). *FORGOTTEN: Ontario adults with autism and adults with aspergers.* Retrieved from http://www.autismontario. com/client/aso/ao.nsf/adults/case+for+support? OpenDocument

Banks, R., Bush, A., Baker, P., Bradshaw, J., Carpenter, P., Deb, S., et al. (2007). *Challenging behaviour: A unified approach* (College Report No. CR 144). London: Royal College of Psychiatrists, British Psychological Society and Royal College of Speech and Language Therapists. Retrieved from http://www.

rcpsych.ac.uk/files/pdfversion/cr144.pdf

Barnhill, L. J. (2008). The diagnosis and treatment of individuals with mental illness and developmental disabilities: An overview. *Psychiatric Quarterly, 79,* 157-170.

Beange, H. P. (1996). Caring for a vulnerable population. *Medical Journal of Australia, 164,* 159-160.

Benson, B. A. (1985). Behavior disorders and mental retardation: Associations with age, sex and level of functioning in an outpatient clinic sample. *Applied Research in Mental Retardation, 6,* 79-85.

Bradley, E., & Bolton, P. (2006). Episodic psychiatric disorders in teenagers with learning disabilities with and without autism. *British Journal of Psychiatry, 189,* 361-366.

Bradley, E., & Bryson, S. (1998). *Psychiatric illness in mentally handicapped adolescents (and young adults) with autistic disability.* Report to the National Health Research and Development Program. Ottawa, ON: Health Canada.

Bradley, E., & Cheetham, T. (2010). The use of psychotropic medication for the management of problem behaviour in adults with intellectual disabilities living in Canada. *Journal of Mental Health and Intellectual Disabilities, 4*(3), 12-26.

Bradley, E., Goody, R., & McMillan, S. (2009). A to Z of disciplines that may contribute to the multi- and interdisciplinary work as applied to mood and anxiety disorders. In A. Hassiotis, D. A. Barron, & I. P. Hall (Eds.), *Intellectual disability psychiatry: A practical handbook* (pp. 257-263). Hoboken, NJ: Wiley.

Bradley, E., & Hollins, S. (2010). Assessment of patients with intellectual disabilities. In D. Goldbloom (Ed.), *Psychiatric clinical skills* (2nd ed.) (pp. 257-276). Toronto, ON: The Centre for Addiction and Mental Health.

Bradley, E. A., & Isaacs, B. J. (2006). Inattention, hyperactivity, and impulsivity in teenagers with intellectual disabilities, with and without autism. *Canadian Journal of Psychiatry, 51*(9), 598-606.

Bradley, E., & Lofchy, J. (2005). Assessment of psychiatric and/or behavioural disturbance in persons with learning disability in the A&E department. *Advances in Psychiatric Treatment, 11,* 45-57.

Bradley, E., & Summers, J. (2003). Developmental

disability and behavioural, emotional and psychiatric disturbances. In I. Brown & M. Percy (Eds.), *Developmental disabilities in Ontario* (2nd ed.) (pp. 751-774). Toronto, ON: Ontario Association on Developmental Disabilities.

Bradley, E. A., Summers, J. A., Wood, H. L., & Bryson, S. E. (2004). Comparing rates of psychiatric and behavior disorders in adolescents and young adults with severe intellectual disability with and without autism. *Journal of Autism and Developmental Disorders, 34*(2), 151-161.

Bradley, E. A., Thompson, A., & Bryson, S. (2002). Mental retardation in teenagers: Prevalence data from the Niagara Region, Ontario, Canada. *Canadian Journal of Psychiatry, 47*(7), 427-434.

Brereton, A. V., Tonge, B. J., & Einfeld, S. L. (2006). Psychopathology in children and adolescents with autism compared to young people with intellectual disability. *Journal of Autism and Developmental Disorders, 36,* 863-870.

Bryson, S. E., Bradley, E. A., Thompson, A., & Wainwright, A. (2008). Prevalence of autism among adolescents with intellectual disabilities. *Canadian Journal of Psychiatry, 53*(7), 449-459.

Caron, C., & Rutter, M. (1991). Comorbidity in child psychopathology: Concepts, issues and research strategies. *Journal of Child Psychology and Psychiatry, 32,* 1063-1080.

Cooper, S. A., Smiley E., Morrison J., Williamson A., & Allan, L. (2007). Mental ill- health in adults with intellectual disabilities: Prevalence and associated factors. *British Journal of Psychiatry, 190,* 27-33.

Cooper, S. A., Smiley, E., Allan, L. M., Jackson, A., Finlayson, J., Mantry, D., & Morrison, J. (2009). Adults with intellectual disabilities: Prevalence, incidence and remission of self-injurious behaviour, and related factors. *Journal of Intellectual Disability Research, 53*(3), 200-216.

Cooper, S. A., Smiley, E., Jackson, A., Finlayson, J., Allan, L., Mantry, D., & Morrison, J. (2009). Adults with intellectual disabilities: Prevalence, incidence and remission of aggressive behaviour and related factors. *Journal of Intellectual Disability Research, 53*(3), 217-232.

Cooper, S. A., & van der Speck, R. (2009). Epide-miology of mental ill health in adults with intellectual disabilities. *Current Opinion in Psychiatry, 22*(5), 431-436.

Costello, H., Holt, G., Cain, N., Bradley, E., Torr, J., Davis, R., Edwards, N., Lennox, N., & Weber, G. (2007). Professional training for those working with people with intellectual disabilities and mental health problems. In N. Bouras & G. Holt (Eds.), *Psychiatric and behavioural disorders in intellectual and developmental disabilities,* (2nd ed.) (pp. 400-411). Cambridge: Cambridge University Press.

Curry, C. J., Stevenson, R. E., Aughton, D., Byrne, J., Carey, J. C., & Cassidy, S. (1997). Evaluation of mental retardation: Recommendations of a consensus conference. *American Journal of Medical Genetics, 72,* 468-477.

Deb, S., Kwok, H., Bertelli, M., Salvador-Carulla, L., Bradley, E., Torr, J., & Barnhill, J. (2009). International guide to prescribing psychotropic medication for the management of problem behaviours in adults with intellectual disabilities. For the Guideline Development Group of the WPA Section on Psychiatry of Intellectual Disability. *World Psychiatry, 8,* 181-186.

Deb, S., Matthews, T., Holt, G., & Bouras, N. (Eds.) (2001). *Practice guidelines for assessment and diagnosis of mental health problems in adults with intellectual disability.* Brighton, United Kingdom: Pavilion Publishing.

Dykens, E. M., Hodapp, R. M., & Finucane, B. M. (2000). *Genetics and mental retardation syndromes: A new look at behavioral interventions.* Baltimore: Paul H. Brookes Publishing Co.

Einfeld, S. L., & Tonge, B. J. (1996). Population prevalence of psychopathology in children and adolescents with intellectual disability: II. Epidemiological findings. *Journal of Intellectual Disability Research, 40*(2), 99-109.

Emerson, E. (2007). Poverty and people with intellectual disabilities. *Mental Retardation and Developmental Disabilities Research Reviews, 13,* 107-113.

Feinstein, C., & Chahal, L. (2009). Psychiatric phenotypes associated with neurogenetic disorders. *Psychiatric Clinics of North America, 32*(1), 15-37.

Fletcher, R., Loschen, E., Stavrakaki, C., & First,

M. (Eds.). (2007). *Diagnostic Manual — Intellectual Disability (DM-ID): A textbook of diagnosis of mental disorders in persons with intellectual disability*. Kingston, NY: NADD Press.

Grandin, T. (2008). *The way I see it: A personal look at autism and Asperger's*. Arlington, TX: Future Horizons, Inc.

Hassiotis, A., Barron, D. A., & Hall, I. P. (Eds.). (2009). *Intellectual disability psychiatry: A practical handbook*. Hoboken, NJ: Wiley.

Holland, A. J. (1999). Psychiatry and mental retardation. *International Review of Psychiatry, 11*, 76-82.

Jacobson, J. W. (1982). Problem behavior and psychiatric impairment within a developmentally disabled population I: Behavior frequency. *Applied Research in Mental Retardation, 3*, 121-139.

Jones, S., Cooper, S. A., Smiley, E., Allan, L., Williamson, A., & Morrison, J. (2008). Prevalence of, and factors associated with, problem behaviors in adults with intellectual disabilities. *Journal of Nervous and Mental Disease, 196*, 678-686.

Kingsley, J., & Levitz, M. (1994). *Count us in: Growing up with Down syndrome*. New York: Harcourt Brace & Co.

Lenhoff, H. M., Wang, P. P., Greenberg, F., & Bellugi, V. (1997). Williams syndrome and the brain. *Scientific American, 277*, 68-73.

Lennox, N. G., Diggens, J. N., & Ugoni, A. M. (1997). The general practice care of people with intellectual disability: Barriers and solutions. *Journal of Intellectual Disability Research, 41*, 380-390.

Lennox, N. G., & Kerr, M. P. (1997). Primary care and people with an intellectual disability: The evidence base. *Journal of Intellectual Disability Research, 41*, 365-372.

Leyfer, O. T., Folstein, S. E., Bacalman, S., Davis, N. O., Dinh, E., Morgan, J., Tager-Flusberg, H., & Lainhart, J. E. (2006). Comorbid psychiatric disorders in children with autism: Interview development and rates of disorders. *Journal of Autism and Developmental Disorders, 36*, 849-861.

Lowe, K., Allen, D., Jones, E., Brophy, S., Moore, K., & Jones, W. (2007). Challenging behaviours: Prevalence and topography. *Journal of Intellectual Disability Research, 51*(8), 625-636.

Lunsky, Y., & Bradley, E. A. (2001). Developmental disability training in Canadian psychiatry residency programs. *Canadian Journal of Psychiatry, 46*, 63-67.

Lunsky, Y., Garcin, N., Morin, D., Cobigo, V., & Bradley, E. (2007). Mental health services for individuals with intellectual disabilities in Canada: Findings from a national survey. *Journal of Applied Research in Intellectual Disabilities, 20*(5), 439-447.

Lunsky, Y., Gracey, C., & Gelfand, S. (2008). Emergency psychiatric services for individuals with intellectual disabilities: Perspectives of hospital staff. *Intellectual and Developmental Disabilities, 46*, 446-455.

Matson, J. L., & Neal, D. (2009). Psychotropic medication use for challenging behaviors in persons with intellectual disabilities: An overview. *Research in Developmental Disabilities, 30*, 572-586.

McCreary, B. D. (2008). Deinstitutionalization in the care of persons with developmental disabilities: A psychiatrist's perspective. *Clinical Bulletin of the Developmental Disabilities Division, 19*(3-4), 1-10.

Melville, C. A., Cooper, S. A., Morrison, J., Smiley, E., Allan, L., Jackson, A., Finlayson, J., & Mantry, D. (2008). The prevalence and incidence of mental ill-health in adults with autism and intellectual disabilities. *Journal of Autism and Developmental Disorders, 38*, 1676-1688.

Metzel, D. S. (2005). Places of social poverty and service dependency of people with intellectual disabilities: A case study in Baltimore, Maryland. *Health & Place, 11*, 93-105.

Moldavsky, M., Lev, D., & Lerman-Sagie, T. (2001). Behavioral phenotypes of genetic syndromes: A reference guide for psychiatrists. *Journal of the American Academy of Child and Adolescent Psychiatry, 40*(7), 749-761.

Morris, S., Bishop, S., Gitta, M., Lunsky, Y., & Nugent, J. (2007). *Training, recruitment and retention in the field of developmental disabilities and dual diagnosis*. Task Group of the NADD Ontario Chapter.

Moss, S., Emerson, E., Bouras, N., & Holland, A. (1997). Mental disorders and problematic behaviours in people with intellectual disability: Future direction for research. *Journal of Intellectual Disability Research, 41*, 440-447.

Moss J., & Howlin P. (2009). Autism spectrum disorders in genetic syndromes: Implications for diagnosis, intervention and understanding the wider autism spectrum disorder population. *Journal of Intellectual Disability Research, 53*(10), 852-873.

O'Brien, G., & Yule, W. (Eds.). (1996). *Behavioural phenotypes. Clinics in Developmental Medicine (No. 138).* Cambridge, UK: McKeith Press.

Raynham, H., Gibbons, R., Flint, J., & Higgs, D. (1996). The genetic basis for mental retardation. *Quarterly Journal of Medicine, 89*, 169-175.

Reiss, S., & Aman, M. G. (1998). *Psychotropic medication and developmental disabilities: The international consensus handbook.* Columbus, OH: Ohio State University Nisonger Center.

Reiss, S., Levitan, G. W., & Szysko, J. (1982). Emotional disturbance and mental retardation: Diagnostic overshadowing. *American Journal of Mental Deficiency, 86*, 567-574.

Royal College of Psychiatrists. (2001). *DC/LD (Diagnostic criteria for psychiatric disorders for use with adults with learning disabilities/mental retardation.* London: Gaskell Press.

Rutter, M., Tizard, J., & Whitmore, K. (1970). *Education, health and behaviour.* London: Longman.

Shapiro, B. K., & Accardo, P. J. (2009). *Neurogenetic syndromes: Behavioral issues and their treatment.* Baltimore: Paul H. Brookes Publishing Co.

Silka, V. R., & Hauser, M. J. (1997). Psychiatric assessment of the person with mental retardation. *Psychiatric Annals, 27*, 162-169.

Simonoff, E., Pickles, A., Charman, T., Chandler, S., Loucas, T., & Baird G. (2008). Psychiatric disorders in children with autism spectrum disorders: Prevalence, comorbidity, and associated factors in a population-derived sample. *Journal of the American Academy of Child & Adolescent Psychiatry, 47*(8), 921-929.

Sovner, R., & Hurley, A. D. (1986). Managing aggressive behavior: A psychiatric approach. *Psychiatric Aspects of Mental Retardation Reviews, 5*, 16-21.

Sullivan, W., Berg, J., Bradley, E., Cheetham, T., Denton, R., Heng, J., Hennen, B., Joyce, D., Kelly, M., Korossy, M., Lunsky, Y. & McMillan, S. (2011). Primary care of adults with developmental disabilities: Canadian Consensus Guidelines. Canadian Family *Physician, 57*, 541-553.

Summers, J., Adamson, J., Bradley, E., Boyd, K., Collins, S., Levinson, A., & Morgan, J. (2005). The need for more community nursing for adults with intellectual disabilities and mental health problems. *Canadian Journal of Psychiatry, 5*(3), 222.

Summers, J., Boyd, K., & Morgan, J. (2004). Evaluating patients with intellectual disabilities and comorbid mental health problems. *Psychiatric Annals, 34*(3), 214-220.

Summers, J., Boyd, K., Reid, J., Adamson, J., Habjan, B., Gignac, V., & Meister, C. (2002). The interdisciplinary mental health team. In D. Griffiths, C. Stavrakaki, & J. Summers (Eds.), *An introduction to the mental health needs of persons with developmental disabilities* (pp. 325-357). Sudbury. ON: Habilitative Mental Health Resource Network.

Tyrer, P., Oliver-Africano, P. C., Ahmed, Z., Bouras, N., Cooray, S. et al. (2008). Risperidone, haloperidol, and placebo in the treatment of aggressive challenging behaviour in patients with intellectual disability: A randomised controlled trial. *Lancet, 371*, 57-63.

Tsiouris, J. A. (2010). Pharmacotherapy for aggressive behaviours in persons with intellectual disabilities: treatment or mistreatment? *Journal of Intellectual Disability Research, 54*, 1-16.

Weiss, J. A., Lunsky, Y., Gracey, C., Canrinus, M., & Morris S. (2009). Emergency psychiatric services for individuals with intellectual disabilities: Caregivers' perspectives. *Journal of Applied Research in Intellectual Disabilities, 22*(4), 354-62.

Whitaker, S., & Read, S. (2006). The prevalence of psychiatric disorders among people with intellectual disabilities: An analysis of the literature. *Journal of Applied Research in Intellectual Disabilities, 19*, 330-345.

Williston, W. B. (1971). *Present arrangement for the care and supervision of mentally retarded persons in Ontario.* Report to the Ontario Minister of Health. Toronto, ON: Ontario Department of Health.

World Health Organization. (1992). *The ICD-10 classification of mental and behavioural disorders. Clinical descriptions and diagnostic guidelines.* Geneva, Switzerland: Author.

Yu, D., & Atkinson, L. (1993). Developmental disability with and without psychiatric involvement: Prevalence estimates for Ontario. *Journal on Developmental Disabilities, 2*(1), 92-99.

37

Alzheimer's Disease: Implications in Down Syndrome and Other Developmental Disabilities

Vee Prasher, Maire Percy, Emoke Jozsvai, and Joseph Berg

What you will learn:

- Alzheimer's disease (AD) in the general population
- Normal aging and dementia
- Dementia of the Alzheimer's type (DAT) in people with Down syndrome (DS)
- Dementia and Alzheimer's disease in people with developmental disability other than DS
- Multidisciplinary approach to managing Alzheimer's disease, DAT and dementia

In 1907, Alois Alzheimer, a German neuropathologist, reported clinical and post-mortem neuropathological findings in a 56-year-old woman who had developed progressive severe loss of memory, disorientation, disturbance of language and paranoid ideas over the past 5 years of her life (Alzheimer, 1907). At autopsy, her brain tissue was treated with a newly developed silver stain and examined microscopically. It was found to be riddled with numerous diffuse deposits and intensely staining fibrils that now are called amyloid plaques and neurofibrillary tangles, respectively. This disease process, which was characterized by clinical dementia and unique changes in the brain, was apparently first named Alzheimer's disease by Kraepelin in 1910, a tribute that has become the general designation for the condition since then.

Alzheimer's disease can affect any adult as age advances. Understanding of this disorder in people with preceding developmental disability has lagged behind knowledge of the disease in the general population, with many clinical and biological issues still unresolved. In view of overall improvements in life expectancy, often dramatic in Down syndrome and other types of developmental disability, aging issues (including Alzheimer's disease) in people with developmental disabilities are bound to receive increasing attention, leading to prospects of better care for this often ignored section of society. This chapter provides an outline of Alzheimer's disease and considers its implications for people with Down syndrome and other types of developmental disability. It focusses on core issues and approaches, identified from previous chapters on this topic in earlier editions of *Developmental Disabilities in Ontario* and in Brown and Percy (2007), from reviews of the current literature, and from the many excellent websites listed in resources, drawing on the vast experiences of the authors in the field.

Alzheimer's Disease in the General Population

For the purpose of providing background, the chapter begins with an explanation of Alzheimer's disease in the general population. Topics discussed include abnormal brain features, prevalence, underlying causes and protective factors, changes associated with normal aging and with dementia, clinical manifestations, the need for diagnosis, and the diagnostic process.

Abnormal brain features

Neuropatholologically, Alzheimer's disease is a disease process characterized by the appearance of

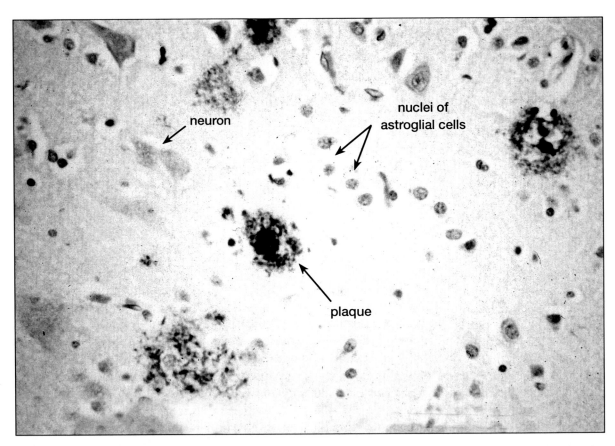

Figure 1a. Characteristic amyloid plaques of Alzheimer's disease. *The brain of all individuals with Alzheimer's disease is riddled with amyloid plaques. Brain tissue from the cortex of an individual with Alzheimer's disease was stained with antibody (Dako M872) that recognizes beta–amyloid, a breakdown product of amyloid precursor protein. The large, dense, roundish deposits in this section are amyloid plaques that have been stained with this antibody.*

numerous amyloid plaques and neurofibrillary tangles, principally in the outer part of the brain (cortex) but with some changes also in deeper regions (Wilcock & Esiri, 1982).

Amyloid plaques (also called senile or neuritic plaques) are areas of degeneration associated with a central core containing a protein often referred to as beta-amyloid, itself formed from another larger protein called amyloid precursor protein (APP), the gene for which is located on chromosome 21. In the healthy brain, beta-amyloid fragments either are not formed, or are broken down and eliminated. In Alzheimer's disease, the fragments accumulate to form hard insoluble plaques.

Neurofibrillary tangles are found within the nerve cells (neurons) and are paired helical filaments that disrupt cell function. They are insoluble twisted fibers that are formed inside of neurons. They primarily consist of a protein called tau, which forms part of a structure called a microtubule. The microtubules help transport nutrients and other important substances from one part of the neuron to another. In Alzheimer's disease, the tau is abnormal (it carries too many phosphate groups) and the microtubule structures collapse.

Plaques and tangles are not specific to Alzheimer's

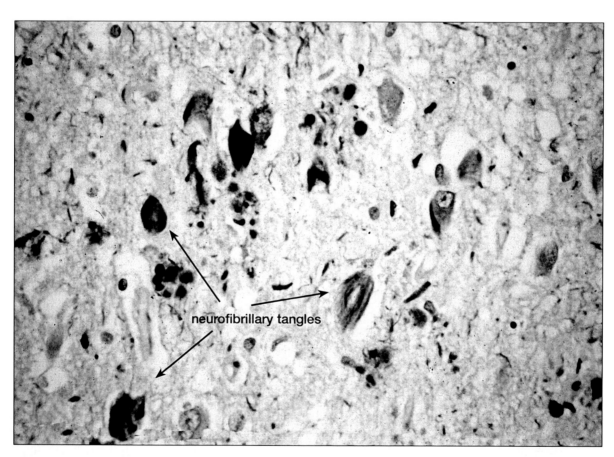

Figure 1b. Characteristic neurofibrillary tangles of Alzheimer's disease. *The brain of all individuals with Alzheimer's disease is also riddled with neurofibrillary tangles. Brain tissue from the cortex of an individual with Alzheimer's disease was stained with antibody (Sigma T5530) that recognizes tau protein in neurofibrillary tangles. The densely staining deposits that are present inside some of the neurons (triangular cells with a large, oval nucleus) are neurofibrillary tangles that have been stained with this antibody. We would like to thank Dr. Peter Barbar, Senior Lecturer in Pathology, University of Birmingham, U.K., for prints of the amyloid plaques and neurofibrillary tangles.*

Table 1: Quantitative Brain Changes in Alzheimer's Disease

Type of Change	Reduction
Brain weight	*7.5-18%*
Weight of cerebral cortex	*20-58%*
Thickness of cortex	*10-15%*
Hemispheral volume	*13-18%*
Number of nerve cells	*22-60%*

disease. They are found in other brain diseases such as Parkinson's disease (although in that disease the brain regions involved differ from those affected in Alzheimer's). They are also found in the brains of up to about 30% of intellectually normal elderly people. However, in adults who have been diagnosed with Alzheimer's disease on the basis of their clinical symptoms, the numbers of plaques and tangles in particular regions of the brain are markedly increased above the "normal limits" expected in persons of the same age without dementia. Thus, to reach a diagnosis of Alzheimer's disease after death on the basis of a brain autopsy, attention is necessary not just to the presence of plaques and tangles, but to how many there are and in which brain regions they are located (Khachaturian, 1985; Wilcock & Esiri, 1982). The two characteristic features of the Alzheimer's brain are shown in Figure 1a and Figure 1b. Along with plaques and tangles, which are microscopic abnormalities only seen with special staining techniques or with high-powered microscopes, other brain changes associated with Alzheimer's disease also occur as listed in Table 1.

Some 40 years after Alzheimer's initial account, an association between Alzheimer's disease and Down syndrome was established. It was recognized that the brains of virtually all people with Down syndrome over the age of about 40 years had features resembling those characteristic of Alzheimer's dis-

ease (Figure 2), although not all aging people with Down syndrome develop clinical manifestations of Alzheimer's disease. During the rest of the 20th century and beyond, there have been numerous reports concerning clinical, pathological and genetic links between Alzheimer's disease and Down syndrome, although investigations of Alzheimer's disease in relation to developmental disabilities other than Down syndrome have been much more limited.

The widespread changes in the brains of people with Alzheimer's disease not surprisingly result in disturbance of brain function. Chemicals called neurotransmitters (e.g., acetylcholine, noradrenalin and serotonin), that usually maintain communication between nerve cells and normal brain function, are progressively reduced as pathological changes increase. All of these brain changes result in the characteristic clinical picture of Alzheimer's disease (see section on clinical manifestations). See Chapter 11 for more information about the nervous systems.

Prevalence, underlying causes, and protective factors

The reported prevalence of Alzheimer's disease (i.e., the percentage of affected people in a population at a given time) in the general population varies in different studies and among different ethnic groups, but the striking age dependence of the disease is always evident. In North America, the prevalence of Alzheimer's disease doubles every 5 years beyond age 65. About one in 13 people over the age of 65, and about one in four over the age of 85, develop the disease. Some two-thirds of people diagnosed clinically are women (Diamond, 2008). About 40% of elderly people who had not been recognized to have dementia before they died have been found at autopsy to show neuropathological changes of Alzheimer's disease, indicating that the disease process likely begins many years prior to clinical symptoms becoming apparent. There is no single known cause of Alzheimer's disease, and no known cure. Furthermore, scientists are now asking if the deposition of beta-amyloid in the brain might play a protective role. However, it is generally accepted that Alzheimer's disease is the "end product" of a number of different pathways that all lead to the formation of plaques and tangles, and result in clinical dementia.

Some factors known to predispose to Alzheimer's disease are listed in Table 2. Advancing age of adults is the most obvious predisposing factor in all populations. In about 95% of people with Alzheimer's disease, the condition occurs sporadically (without any affected relative being apparent), for reasons that are not well understood (see below). Individuals with a first-degree relative (parent, sibling) with Alzheimer's disease have a greater chance of developing it. Studies of twins suggest that sporadic Alzheimer's disease likely results from the combination of genetic predisposition and potentially modifiable environmental triggers, although published concordance rates for Alzheimer's disease among both identical and fraternal twins differ substantially from one study to another (Gatz et al., 2006). Down

syndrome is a strong risk factor for Alzheimer's in the sense that clinical dementia resembling Alzheimer's occurs much earlier in persons with Down syndrome than in the general population. A gene that produces a protein called apolipoprotein E (ApoE) is involved in sporadic Alzheimer's disease. ApoE occurs in three major forms: E2, E3 and E4. Every person inherits one ApoE gene from each parent. The E4 form of the protein leads to earlier development of Alzheimer's disease in Caucasians. People with two copies of E4 tend to develop Alzheimer's disease several years earlier than those with one E4. However, not everyone with one or two E4s develops Alzheimer's disease. Type 2 diabetes and cardiovascular disease are considered to be predisposing factors for vascular dementia and may also predispose to Alzheimer's. Furthermore, brain glucose regula-

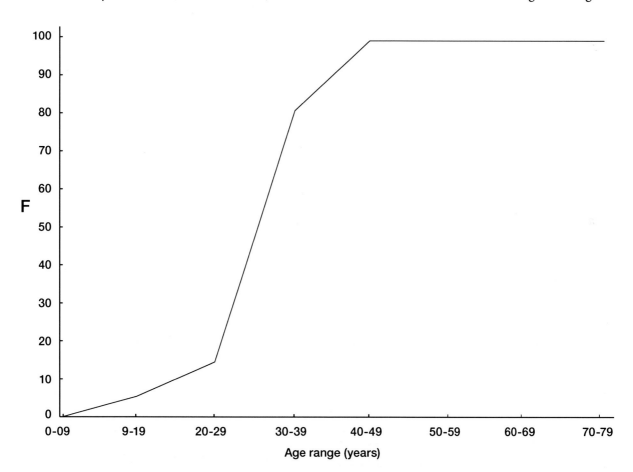

Figure 2. Cumulative frequency (F) of senile plaques and neurofibrillary tangles in people with Down syndrome.

Table 2: Factors That Predispose to Alzheimer's Disease*

Causes	Confirmed	Possible
Mutations in genes (APP, PS1, PS2)	*Advancing age*	*Inflammatory conditions*
	Family history of Alzheimer's	*Clinical depression*
	Apolipoprotein E4 gene	*Stress*
	Female gender	*Inadequate exercising of the brain*
	Down syndrome	*Herpes simplex virus 1 (HSV1) in the brain*
	Low levels of formal education	*Excessive metal ions (e.g., iron, copper, aluminum, zinc)*
	Mild cognitive impairment	*Vascular risk factors (e.g., cardiovascular disease and carotid artery atherosclerosis)*
		Type 2 diabetes
		Vitamin D deficiency

APP: amyloid precursor protein; PS1 and PS2: presenilin type 1 and type 2

* *Alzheimer Society of Canada (2010); CBS News (2010); Prasher et al. (2007)*

tion has been found to be abnormal in Alzheimer's and this disorder is considered by some to be Type 3 diabetes of the brain (de la Monte & Wands, 2008). In a small number of families, Alzheimer's disease can recur in an inherited form known as familial autosomal dominant that can be passed on from one generation to the next. This inherited form of Alzheimer's disease accounts for about 5–10% of all cases of the disease, and usually occurs below the age of 65 years, even as early as the 40's. Rare mutations in one of three genes — amyloid precursor protein (APP) and presenilins 1 and 2 (PS1 and PS2) — are considered to cause Alzheimer's disease in such families, because persons who carry one of these mutations almost always develop Alzheimer's in their lifetime (Alzheimer Society of Canada, 2010; Prasher, Percy, Jozsvai, Lovering, & Berg, 2007).

Because some identical twins develop Alzheimer's disease and others do not, and because the age of onset of the disease is not exactly the same in identical twins who both develop it, it is believed that adopting a good lifestyle may offer protection against Alzheimer's (Table 3). Factors associated with a good lifestyle include reducing risk factors for cardiovascular disease such as stress, obesity, high blood pressure and high cholesterol; increasing physical and mental activity; avoiding polluted air; eating a diet rich in green vegetables that contain folic acid and antioxidants such as spinach and broccoli; and drinking safe water (Prasher et al., 2007).

Some current research initiatives

Although scientists now have a good understanding about the biological processes that result in for-

Table 3: Some Factors That Might Protect Against Alzheimer's Disease*

Factors	Examples
Anti-oxidants	*Vitamin E, vitamin C, seligiline (deprenyl)*
Vitamins that regulate folate and homocysteine	*Folate, B6, B12*
Non-steroidal anti-inflammatory drugs	*Ibuprofen*
Conditions resulting in increased blood flow to the brain	*Physical exercise, intellectual stimulation, socializing*
Good diet	*Eating low fat foods (avoid beef), foods rich in antioxidants (certain fruits, nuts), omega-3 foods (such as oily fish). Best to check with a nutritionist.*

* Alzheimer Society of Canada (2010); Arab & Sabbagh (2010); Prasher et al. (2007).

mation of beta-amyloid from amyloid precursor protein and about biological abnormalities that correlate with this process, the physiological functions of beta-amyloid are not known, and there is controversy about whether the accumulation of beta-amyloid in the Alzheimer's brain is protective or harmful (Mondragón-Rodríguez et al., 2010). Because beta-amyloid binds iron, copper and zinc, hyperphosphorylated tau binds iron and aluminum, and metal ions catalyze the formation of free radicals in the presence of peroxide, the hypothesis that metal-loaded plaques and tangles might serve as free radical generators is under investigation. (Free radicals are very reactive molecules that can result in the oxidation (and destruction) of nucleic acids, proteins and fats, although they also have important physiological functions when present in small numbers.) An imbalance between the production of free radicals and the body's ability to easily neutralize these and repair the resulting damage results in a situation called *oxidative stress*. There is evidence that excessive oxidative stress occurs early in Alzheimer's disease and precedes the brain changes considered characteristic of the disease. Another research ini-

tiative to discover the function of beta-amyloid has demonstrated that this molecule possesses antimicrobial activity and may play a role in the body's *innate immune system*. (The innate immune system is comprised of cells and mechanisms that protect the host against infection by other organisms in a non-specific manner, but it does not confer long-lasting or protective immunity to the host.) This latter finding obviously has important implications for ongoing and future Alzheimer's disease treatment strategies (Soscia et al., 2010).

Although its involvement in Alzheimer's disease remains controversial, there continues to be interest in aluminum because some studies have found the brain levels of aluminum to be higher in people with Alzheimer disease than in healthy elderly persons. Furthermore, other studies have reported an association between elevated levels of aluminum in drinking water and an increased risk of Alzheimer's disease (McLachlan, Bergeron, Smith, Boomer, & Rifat, 1996). Evidence that dietary aluminum might trigger the Alzheimer's process has recently been described in an animal model (Walton & Wang, 2009). These findings do not provide justification for discarding aluminum cooking ware. However, it seems judicious to avoid cooking acidic food in aluminum pots (since the acid leaches aluminum from such pots into the food) and to avoid using deodorants, cosmetics and antacids that contain aluminum (Prasher et al., 2007).

The testing of new drugs for treatment of Alzheimer's is an active research area (see ClinicalTrials.gov, 2010). Unfortunately, aside from use of approved drugs that have minimal beneficial effects, no "magic bullet" has been found to cure or ward off Alzheimer's. The use of metal ion chelators continues to be of interest because these have the potential to reduce levels of oxidative stress, although challenges with their administration include how to target specific areas of the brain. Interest in the use of metal ion chelators was first generated by a report that the intramuscular administration of desferrioxamine, a chelator used for treatment of classic iron and aluminum overload, reduced the progression of Alzheimer's by approximately two-fold (Crapper-McLachlan et al., 1991). Other studies are examining the feasibility of vaccination or passive immunization to prevent brain accumulation of beta-amyloid. To date, however, such approaches have been disappointing. Some trials are being conducted in persons with mild cognitive impairment to see if physical exercise or mental exercise and health promotion might actually delay the onset of Alzheimer's. Some factors that might protect against Alzheimer's disease are listed in Table 3.

One research area that merits more intensive study stems from finding evidence of herpes simplex virus 1 (HSV1), the common cold sore virus, in the brains of persons with Alzheimer's, especially those who carry ApoE4 (Wozniak, Mee, & Itzhaki, 2009). Evidence that a virus is involved in Alzheimer's raises the possibility that antiviral agents might stop progression of the disease.

An exciting area of future research is the role that *single-nucleotide polymorphisms* (SNPs) play in the etiology of Alzheimer's disease in the general population (Potkin et al., 2009). (SNPs are DNA sequence variations that occur when a single nucleotide — an A, T, C or G — is altered. A variation must occur in at least 1% of the population to be considered an SNP.)

As indicated below, studies of dementia that occurs prematurely in people with Down syndrome are contributing unique insights to the etiology of Alzheimer's disease.

Normal aging and dementia

With normal aging into late life, mental and physical decline of varying extent is a general phenomenon among all people. Most persons, including many with developmental disability, maintain their cognitive abilities and adaptive behaviour skills fairly well throughout their adult lives. However, normal aging is associated with declines in some areas of cognitive functioning. Different cognitive abilities decline at different rates with advancing age. Abstract reasoning and verbal skills (expressive and receptive language ability) tend to remain relatively intact, whereas perceptual and motor skills decrease more substantially and earlier. As people age, they generally show some reduction in their capacity to learn and recall new information, their reaction time increases, and their motor movements become slower. There are many causes of age-related changes in cognitive functioning. The most prominent factors thought to affect cognitive functioning in old age include sensory deficits (particularly reduced hearing and vision), general health status and diminished motivation.

Beyond normal aging and extending into the realm of disease, dementia is a term used to designate the development, generally in adults, of serious cognitive and associated disorders with an often detectable pathological basis that affect the ability to cope on a day to day basis. More precisely in a diagnostic sense, Wherrett (1999) described the term as being applied "to persons in whom cognitive decline sufficient to impair personal, social, or occupational adaptation is the main presenting symptom, is persisting and progressive, and is associated with a chronic diffuse or multifocal brain disorder" (p. 91). There are many actual or potential causes of dementia (see Table 4) with various designations to indicate particular specific types with distinctive characteristics — for example, multi-infarct dementia, vascular dementia, and dementia pugilistica. Alzheimer's disease is the most common cause of

Table 4: Common Causes of Dementia Other Than Alzheimer's Disease

- *Vascular dementia*
- *Parkinson's disease*
- *Depression*
- *Pick disease*
- *Head trauma*
- *Hypothyroidism*
- *Alcohol abuse*
- *Drugs*
- *HIV infection*
- *Vitamin deficiencies (B12, folate, E and C)*
- *Bacterial, fungal and protozoan infections*
- *Normal pressure hydrocephalus*
- *Huntington disease*
- *Multiple sclerosis*
- *Heavy metal overload*
- *Brain tumour*

dementia in elderly persons. A disorder called mild cognitive impairment (MCI) is now recognized as a predisposing factor for Alzheimer's disease, though not everyone with MCI progresses to Alzheimer's.

Clinical manifestations of Alzheimer's disease

Symptoms of Alzheimer's disease range from early mild ones, which may go unnoticed and have little detrimental effect, to severe ones at the end stages of the disease process that can cause considerable stress to caregivers and lead to the individual requiring nursing care. The disorder can be artificially divided into three clinical stages (Table 5).

Onset of Alzheimer's disease is slow and gradual, with the precise age of onset often difficult to determine. The clinical symptoms of the disorder tend to develop gradually over a number of years. Those close to affected individuals frequently do not recognize that there is deterioration until it has become quite pronounced. As the disease progresses, it becomes increasingly apparent that there is progres-

sive and significant decline in memory and other mental functions sometimes associated with severe depression. There is a gradual loss of self-care skills and growing additional problems with day-to-day living. Onset of seizures may be the first indication for medical attention. The later stage of Alzheimer's disease is marked by cognitive and physical deterioration. Total dependency and inactivity with increased need for nursing care becomes evident. Pneumonia or urinary tract infection is often the immediate cause of death.

Alzheimer's disease manifestations vary among individuals. Some have a rapid, short illness, while others experience a longer, more gradual decline in health. Affected persons are unlikely to experience all symptoms and signs listed in Table 5, nor to decline precisely as outlined in the Table, which should be used only as a guide.

Diagnosis of Alzheimer's disease

For a confident diagnosis of Alzheimer's disease, the decline of memory and other cognitive functions should be present for at least one year and be irreversible. In Alzheimer's disease, deterioration of cognitive functioning is typically accompanied by personality, mood and behavioural changes. For the general population, there are reliable clinical diagnostic tests for Alzheimer's disease based on signs and symptoms, although diagnosis can be certain only on direct brain examination. In 1984, McKhann and his colleagues published criteria for the diagnosis of possible, probable and definite Alzheimer disease. Particularly in settings that specialize in Alzheimer disease and related disorders, these rigid diagnostic criteria enable an accurate clinical diagnosis to be made in 70% to 80% of patients. As of July, 2010, The National Institute on Aging and the U.S. Alzheimer's Association are leading an effort to update diagnostic criteria for Alzheimer's disease.

There are several important reasons for a diagnosis of Alzheimer's disease to be made.

This diagnosis enables:
- Families and caregivers to understand what is happening to the person concerned
- Families and caregivers to plan for the future

Table 5: Main Stages of Alzheimer's Disease

Stage I: Early (duration 1-3 years)

- *Memory loss (particularly short-term memory)*
- *Changes in personality*
- *Difficulties with language*
- *Disorientated in time*
- *Lost in familiar places*
- *Loss of motivation*
- *Signs of depression and aggression*
- *Loss of interest*

Stage II: Middle (duration 2-5 years)

- *Very forgetful*
- *Loss of self care skills*
- *Greater dependency on others*
- *Increased speech difficulties*
- *Wandering*
- *Seizures*
- *Reduced mobility*
- *Behavioural problems*
- *Hallucinations*

Stage III: Late (duration 4-8 years)

- *Marked intellectual deterioration*
- *Inability to recognize family, friends, carers*
- *Dependence on others for dressing, washing, feeding, toileting*
- *Immobility*
- *Bladder and bowel incontinence*
- *More severe seizures*
- *Limb rigidity and flexed postures*
- *Marked physical deterioration*

- Provision to be made, with support if necessary, for appropriate care
- Exclusion of other, often treatable, causes of intellectual decline
- Consideration of appropriate medication

A clinical diagnosis of Alzheimer's disease is principally based on initially identifying the presence of dementia and then excluding other possible treat-able causes of the dementia. Over time, the characteristic deterioration of Alzheimer's disease (see clinical manifestations in Table 5) often becomes evident. Diagnosis is generally made as shown in Figure 3. There are indications that the diagnosis of Alzheimer's disease may be aided by sensitive brain imaging techniques (e.g., computed or positron emission tomography and magnetic resonance imaging), or by measuring the amounts of particular substances in other bodily fluids and tissues such as peripheral blood and cerebrospinal fluid.

Dementia of the Alzheimer's Type in People with Down Syndrome

Prevalence

Interest in Alzheimer's disease in people with developmental disabilities has focussed primarily on the association between Down syndrome and dementia resembling Alzheimer's disease. As already mentioned, virtually all adults with Down syndrome over the age of 40 years have a considerable amount of beta-amyloid in their brains (Figure 2). Furthermore, people with Down syndrome are at risk of developing clinical dementia some 20 to 30 years earlier than is usually the case in the general population. In this chapter, we will refer to dementia that develops in older people with Down syndrome as dementia of the Alzheimer type (DAT). The high frequency of DAT in Down syndrome has become increasingly apparent as people with Down syndrome live longer, largely due to improved health care, nutrition, and housing conditions. In the 1920s, the life expectancy for Caucasians with Down syndrome was about 9 years, but by the 1980s it had reached about 35 years (Thase, 1982). In North America, the expected life span of a 1-year-old Caucasian child with Down syndrome and mild-to-moderate developmental disability is 55 years, and about a decade lower in those with profound cognitive impairment (Strauss & Eyman, 1996).

Although some studies have found no gender effect on life expectancy in Down syndrome (Day, Strauss, Shavelle, & Reynolds, 2005; Strauss & Eyman, 1996), one Australian study found that the life expectancy for females with Down syndrome was less than that for males (Glasson et al., 2003). Furthermore, the life expectancy of non-Caucasians with Down syndrome has often been considerably less than for Caucasians with the syndrome. This may in part be in related to possible factors such as access, use of, or quality of health care (Day et al., 2005; Yang, Rasmussen, & Friedman, 2002).

The frequency of DAT in Down syndrome increases from about 8% in those aged between 35 and 40 years, to approximately 75% in those over 60 years of age. In individuals with Down syndrome who have a mild-to-moderate level of disability, the average age of onset of dementia is approximately 55 years, but early signs of dementia may appear before the age of 50 in some (Prasher et al., 2007). Higher functioning individuals with Down syndrome tend to remain free of symptoms longer than low functioning individuals (Temple, Jozsvai, Konstantareos, & Hewitt, 2001). Caregivers must be alerted to this possibility and be knowledgeable about how to cope with it.

Factors predisposing to DAT

Although DAT research is not as extensive as for Alzheimer's disease in the general population, studies of Down syndrome are helping not only to clarify what causes DAT but also to clarify the controversy about what causes Alzheimer's. Because people with Down syndrome carry an extra chromosome 21, and the gene for amyloid precursor protein (APP) (which becomes degraded into beta-amyloid) is located on the long arm of that chromosome, over-production of APP is believed to be primarily responsible for DAT. However, a recent study by Jiang et al. (2010) has shown that a small derivative of APP and not the beta amyloid breakdown product of APP, is essential for induction of an abnormality found early in DAT and Alzheimer's called *endosome* dysfunction. (An endosome is a membrane bound compartment inside the cell that aids transport of large molecules from the plasma membrane of the cell to the lysosome (garbage disposal unit) or vice versa.) As in the general population, in Down syndrome the apolipoprotein E2 allele is associated with longevity and the preservation of cognitive functioning (Tyrrell et

Figure 3. Diagnosing Alzheimer's disease

Interview of family members/carers for evidence of mental deterioration and possible differential diagnosis

Formal assessment of mental condition including detailed psychological assessment of memory and other intellectual functions*

Comprehensive physical examination, including sensory testing, blood tests and urinalysis, to exclude treatable conditions

Electroencephalography, brain scan (computerized tomography, magnetic resonance imaging, single photon emission computerized tomography)*

Review of information and provisional diagnosis

Follow–up including further regular assessments to confirm diagnosis

* Dependent on availability of resources

al., 1998). However, in Down syndrome, the ApoE4 allele not only is associated with lower age of dementia in males, but it also has an independent and strong relation to early mortality even in non-demented persons with Down syndrome (Prasher et al., 2008). Furthermore, there is evidence that HSV1 infection may play a role in the development of DAT in Down syndrome as may be the case in the general population (Cheon, Bajo, Gulesserian, Cairns, & Lubec, 2001). Finally, among females with Down syndrome, a correlation has been noted between early age of menopause and frequency of dementia, and between the age of menopause and age of onset of dementia (Cosgrave, Tyrrell, McCarron, Gill, & Lawlor, 1999; Zigman & Lott, 2007). As in the general population, SNPs also may contribute to DAT. For example, a recent study suggests that subtle changes in the genetic make-up of individuals may explain why some individuals with Down syndrome get dementia and others do not, even when they have experienced the same environment (Patel et al., submitted).

Diagnosis of DAT in Down Syndrome

Problems distinguishing DAT from underlying cognitive disability

The clinical diagnosis of DAT remains problematic in people with Down syndrome and other types of developmental disability. Clinicians still have difficulty in distinguishing symptoms of dementia from cognitive deficits resulting from the preceding developmental disability. Because there is a wide variation in the degree of cognitive impairment among people Down syndrome, some tests that are used in dementia screening are too easy for some or too difficult for others. Also, there are a number of medical conditions that can mask as DAT (see below). Longitudinal neurological assessment is the best approach for diagnosing DAT in Down syndrome (also see below).

When onset of dementia is suspected in a person with Down syndrome, it is vital to determine as early as possible if there is a treatable cause. Such causes in people with Down syndrome that can be effectively treated include early vitamin B6, B12, or folate deficiency, early hypothyroidism, as well as severe depression and anxiety states.

Early signs of possible Alzheimer's disease in people with Down syndrome who have relatively higher levels of functional ability may include changes in personality (such as uncharacteristic irritability and mood swings), and reduced verbal communication. Initial symptoms often involve memory loss, problems in learning new things and changes in behaviour. As the disease progresses, activities of daily living are further impaired. For example, performance at work may gradually deteriorate, capacity to follow an instruction may decline, ability to use a telephone or to write may dissipate, and loss of language skills (especially word-finding abilities) may occur. At a more advanced stage, seizures frequently develop. The seizures, including myo-clonic ones (frequent small jerks of the body), often appear after two years of evidence of dementia, but usually occur somewhat later in higher functioning individuals with Down syndrome. Mobility typically becomes limited and there may be bowel and bladder incontinence. Hallucinations and delusions may also develop. In addition, weight loss is common in people with Down syndrome and DAT (Prasher et al., 2007).

For people with Down syndrome who have higher functioning abilities, early indicators of memory loss may be forgetting the location of commonly used objects such as a key, eye glasses, bus tickets, or a lunch bag. With lower functioning abilities and Down syndrome, the first indicators of possible DAT may be diminished social interaction, loss of interest in hobbies and previously enjoyed activities, or loss of self-care skills. As the disease progresses, memory deficits become more prominent and signs of spatial disorientation appear. The affected person may get lost in familiar surroundings and become unable to travel independently on previously familiar routes. Supervisors at a workshop may begin noticing poorer work performance than previously, with the need for increased supervision. Biological (diurnal) rhythms are sometimes disturbed with frequent confusion between day and night. Motor functions slow down and gait disturbances (problems with walking) may appear. The ability to perform the sequence of previously mastered complex tasks, such as toileting, dressing or setting the table, diminishes. Bladder or bowel incontinence may begin to develop. Individuals without a previous history of epilepsy may commence having seizures.

As the disease progresses further, affected individuals are unable to recall the names of, or even recognize, close relatives and friends. Ability to communicate awareness of recent life experiences diminishes. Symptoms differ in sequence and degree from one person to another, but some include: loss of purposeful activity, quiet resignation, delusional behaviour, visual and auditory hallucinations, and myoclonus (shocklike contraction of a muscle or group of muscles). At the late stages of their dementia, all verbal abilities and the ability to walk are typically lost, although not in a predictable sequence. Assistance with toileting and feeding is required. Death is frequently caused by infectious disease such as aspiration pneumonia, urinary tract infection, and infected bedsores; sometimes it simply results from a loss of basic life functions, such as the ability to swallow solid food and even liquids (Prasher et al., 2007).

Conditions that can mimic DAT

There are various physical conditions that can diminish cognitive function in older persons with Down syndrome, as is the case in the general population, and thus be mistaken for early evidence of Alzheimer disease. Hypothyroidism, which affects about 40% of people with Down syndrome, may precipitate decline by causing weight gain, apathy, mental slowing, and diminished levels of energy. Depression related to grief from loss of friends or relatives, or changes in residence and support workers, may lead to withdrawal or loss of daily living skills, and may be associated with the onset of incontinence, irritability, and insomnia.

Mental functions may deteriorate as a result of hearing loss and visual impairment. A large proportion of adults with Down syndrome (about half to three-quarters) experience hearing loss, and approximately half develop cataracts. Impaired hearing and vision leads to withdrawal, apathy and reduced interest in one's environment, mimicking early symptoms of DAT. Degenerative changes in the upper part of the cervical spine and joint problems in the hip and knee may cause pain and impair functioning in daily living. Vitamin B12 or folate deficiency and infectious diseases (e.g., pneumonia) may cause weightloss, tiredness and consequent decrease in activity levels. Excessive day-time sleepiness, chronic fatigue and irritability can also result from sleep apnea, a disorder characterized by frequent, brief respiratory pauses while asleep. Prescribed drugs (e.g., seizure medication, tranquillizers) can interfere with cognitive functioning. Cardiac disease and diabetes may produce functional decline in the general population and may have similar effects in people with Down syndrome. As well, celiac disease is associated with various neurological problems in people in the general population. It is important to identify all medical conditions that co-occur with deterioration of cognitive function in older people with Down syndrome since, with medical attention and treatment, cognitive functioning and skills of daily living often return to previous levels (Prasher et al., 2007).

Diagnosis of DAT

In the general population, dementia is diagnosed by comparing performance on cognitive tests to established standards (norms) for the person's age group. In Down syndrome, however, dementia is generally superimposed on already reduced cognitive functioning. Furthermore, there are significant individual differences in the abilities of non-demented people with Down syndrome. Some have strengths in the verbal domain but weaknesses in visual-spatial or motor abilities, and the opposite pattern occurs in other people. As noted above, there are other disorders that can mask as dementia. Hence people with Down syndrome suspected of developing DAT should undergo a multidisciplinary evaluation. Ideally, this should include a thorough physical examination that includes assessment of hearing and vision, screening for thyroid dysfunction and infectious diseases, blood work to identify vitamin B12 and folate deficiencies, psychiatric evaluation for depression or anxiety, and neuropsychological assessment to evaluate memory function, language functions, visual-spatial abilities, and adaptive behaviour skills. Interviews with various caregivers (e.g., relatives, supervisors at the workplace, or support workers in group homes) are an essential part of a neuropsychological assessment, as such persons are usually the first to notice signs of cognitive decline and to initiate referrals. Imaging or electroencephalography may also be considered to rule out disorders such as stroke or brain tumour (Prasher et al., 2007).

Until the early 1980s, there were a limited number of neurological tests available as aids for the diagnosis of dementia in people with developmental disabilities. Over the last 25 years, however, several new neurological measures have been developed (see Prasher, 2008). For example, for nonverbal individuals who cannot be assessed with formal test instruments, the Adaptive Behaviour Scale and/

Box 1: Case Report of K.D.

K.D. is a 59-year-old man with Down syndrome. He was referred for an assessment of cognitive functioning following a baseline evaluation. The referral was made by group home staff who had concerns about deterioration in his behaviour. He was reported to have episodes of confusion and his caregivers questioned his ability to distinguish fantasy from reality. K.D. was seen for one neuropsychological assessment in 1994, and another 6 months later in 1995. At that time, test results showed mild-to-moderate decline in verbal learning and memory for verbal material, as well as deterioration in fine motor control in his hands. Cognitive deterioration was coupled with the onset of seizures the following year,, at which time he was prescribed seizure medication by a neurologist. Staff from the group home where K.D. lived made referrals to screen for thyroid functions, as well as visual and hearing impairment. Blood tests were requested by his physician to test for possible vitamin B12 and folate deficiency. A psychiatric examination showed no overt signs of depression.

On examination, K.D. presented as a frail elderly man. He walked slowly with assistance. He was unable to follow test instructions. Consequently, formal testing could not be implemented. Instead, information was gathered from caregivers regarding K.D.'s current difficulties. Interviews with staff at K.D.'s residence revealed significant deterioration in his cognitive functioning and skills of adaptive behaviour over the past two years. According to reports from residential support workers, K.D. frequently misplaced objects, forgot the names of people he knew, and partly lost track of familiar routines. Over the past two years, his speech had slowed and had become difficult to understand. K.D. got lost several times while alone in the community and, more recently, he had experienced difficulty finding his own bedroom. He was no longer able to dress or bathe himself and required assistance feeding. He was regularly incontinent of feces and urine if he was not prompted to use the toilet. There were incidents suggesting that he experienced hallucinations and paranoid ideas. At times, K.D. complained of imaginary people wanting to beat him up, putting him into a closet, or attacking him. Sometimes he got angry for no apparent reason, banging his head into, or kicking, the walls.

Residential support staff expressed concerns about the deterioration of K.D.'s functioning and arranged to have him transferred to a long-term care facility. In the meantime, supervision of K.D. at the group home was intensified and he was given assistance with bathing, feeding and walking. The safety of his current environment was assessed by an occupational therapist and modifications were made to prevent injury. K.D. was issued a Medic-Alert identification bracelet and was registered at the Alzheimer's Society.

or the Dementia Scale for Down Syndrome developed by Gedye may be administered to caregivers to elicit information about changes in functioning. In a large, international multisite trial of vitamin E in older persons with Down syndrome, a brief praxis test was used as the primary outcome measure to monitor cognitive functions expressed as performances of simple, short, sequences of voluntary movements every 6 months over a 35 month period. This simple praxis test can be administered by almost any trained individual, including the primary care provider. It is available on request from Dr. A. J. Dalton (personal communication) or from either of the first two authors of the chapter.

Because DAT occurs so early in people with Down syndrome, it is recommended that all adults be evaluated at least once in early adulthood (by age 25 years) to establish a record of baseline cognitive functioning. When DAT is suspected, such earlier baseline data are useful for comparison with current test data to ascertain the nature and magnitude of changes in various areas of functioning. Such testing may be available in hospital clinics that specialize in Alzheimer's disease and related disorders, as well as in some settings serving adults with Down syndrome and other developmental disabilities.

The case report of K.D. (Box 1) illustrates clinical manifestations and progression of DAT often observed in persons with Down syndrome. Readers are also referred to the paper by Devenny et al. (2005) that follows the course of decline of a woman with Down syndrome and DAT over an 11-year period until her death at age 57. As stated by the authors:

> *This case illustrates features of premature aging that are typically associated with Down syndrome, and the progressive changes in memory and cognition that are usually associated with DAT. Although the subject's cardiovascular condition and thyroid disorder were treated, they may have contributed to the decline of her memory. This case shows the difficulty in diagnosing dementia in an individual with mental retardation who suffered comorbid episodes of depression and psychosis. (p. 1)*

Histopathological findings revealed upon brain autopsy are included in this report. The Devenny et al. study shows the invaluable contribution that detailed studies of only one individual can make to the field, and the key role that caregivers can make by collaborating with researchers and by facilitating the donation of brain tissue from their family members to "brain banks."

Dementia and Alzheimer's Disease in People with Developmental Disability other than Down Syndrome

People with developmental disabilities other than Down syndrome also are living into middle age and beyond, and the development of psychiatric symptomatology and dementia in this adult population also is receiving increasing attention. In some respects, elucidation of these issues is more complex than is the case with Down syndrome since, because unlike Down syndrome, developmental disabilities constitute a wide-ranging "mixed bag" of entities with diverse etiology and symptomatology. However, while bearing the above considerations in mind, some notable findings (although not always consistent) with significant implications have been documented, aspects of which are referred to below.

There have been discrepancies in the limited studies of the frequency with which dementia occurs in elderly adults with developmental disabilities other than Down syndrome. Evenhuis (1997) noted that the age-related frequency (and natural history) of dementia in this group was comparable to that in the general population. Zigman and Lott (2007) reported the rate of dementia in adults with developmental disability over age 64 years to be equivalent or lower than would be expected compared to general population rates. Strydom, Livingston, King, & Hassiotis (2007) determined the prevalence of criteria-defined dementia in a group with developmental disability without Down syndrome (age 65 years or more) and concluded that this was 2–3 times more common than in the general population. In a recent review, Cooper and van der Speck (2009) reported that the prevalence of dementia in persons with developmental disability is four times that of people over age 64 in the general population. Discrepant findings in these regards are not surprising in view of such factors as relatively small sample sizes from different sources, with variable etiologies (most unknown), intellectual levels, age distributions and dementia diagnostic criteria — all this in circumstances where preceding cognitive, behavioural and chronic physical health problems (e.g., sensory and motor impairments) can seriously hamper accurate diagnosis of dementia.

In the studies referred to above, there is some mention of a diagnosis of Alzheimer's disease in a number of persons in the groups investigated, but the information available is not sufficiently extensive for firm generalizations. As outlined in Prasher et al. (2007), there have been reports (albeit scanty in number) of postmortem brain examinations focussed on Alzheimer's disease neuropathology in groups of non-Down syndrome adults with developmental disabilities. In these studies, the range was in keeping with that that in a number of comparably-aged population groups of intellectually normal non-demented persons. However, from the retrospective clinical data available in each of the studies referred to, it was uncertain to what extent the neuropathology noted was associated with dementia.

It can be anticipated that further exploration and clarification of these issues will lead to improved therapeutic, quality of life, and even preventive prospects for those actually or potentially affected. These considerations become increasingly important as people live longer.

Virtually no published information exists about risk factors that predispose or protect to dementia in people with developmental disabilities who do not have Down syndrome. Approaches for the diagnosis of dementia in this group are the same as for those who have Down syndrome (see above). As for people with Down syndrome, multidisciplinary, longitudinal assessment is strongly recommended for all older people with developmental disability to ensure that service provision in their later years is adequate.

Management of Dementia in People With or Without Developmental Disability

Multidisciplinary approach for management

There is no cure for Alzheimer's disease. However, appropriate management of the disease in people with or without developmental disability improves the quality of life of those affected and their caregivers. Such management involves a multi-disciplinary approach combining medication, psychological therapies, environmental changes and support for caregivers. Treatment may involve trying to minimize the disease process, dealing with specific symptoms, and assisting caregivers to cope in the best way possible. Clinical trials in the general population of proposed medication for Alzheimer's disease are common. Until recently, such trials usually excluded people with developmental disability. However, these people are now more often the focus of attention in these regards.

Medication

Treatment of Alzheimer disease per se: There is no drug that can cure or stop Alzheimer's disease. At present, most approved drugs are intended to increase availability of neurotransmitters (especially acetylcholine) and have effects that are minor and only temporary. In Canada, there are four drugs being used for intervention in Alzheimer's disease: AriceptTM (donepezil), ExelonTM (rivastigmine),

ReminylTM (galantamine hydrobromide), and memantine (EbixaR). The first three prevent the breakdown of acetylcholine, and have been approved by Health Canada for use in persons with mild to moderate Alzheimer's. The fourth blocks effects of excessive glutamic acid and has been conditionally approved for the treatment of symptoms of moderate to advanced Alzheimer's. These drugs also are being used to treat Alzheimer's disease in persons with Down syndrome and other developmental disabilities. Potential new drugs continue to be tested. For a list of clinical trials that are underway, refer to *ClinicalTrials.gov*, a service provided by the U.S. National Institutes of Health.

Treatment of specific symptoms: Medications to alleviate specific distressing symptoms that can occur in Alzheimer's disease should be used cautiously, with regular review and usually only on a temporary basis. Such medications include:

- Hypnotics for night sedation
- Low dose neuroleptics for aggression, restlessness, and paranoid behaviour
- Antidepressants for low mood
- Anticonvulsants for seizures
- Antibiotics for infections

Psychological therapies

Reality orientation and reminiscence therapy: These forms of therapy aim to prevent, halt, or reverse intellectual impairment and to maximize remaining abilities. Reality orientation tries to keep the affected person oriented in time and place as much as possible by having caregivers provide appropriate clues (e.g., "It's noon — time for the bathroom; it's one o'clock — time for your lunch"). The environment may be modified by the use of signs and colours (e.g., blue doors for toilets). Reminiscence therapy uses prompts (e.g., objects, photographs) to help people with Alzheimer's disease relive past memories and thereby enable them to remain stimulated and to adjust to recent changes.

Behavioural therapy: This can enhance maintenance of pre-existing skills such as dressing, washing, feeding and communication. The therapy can also reduce difficult behaviours including restlessness, agitation and aggression. Suitable behaviours are targeted and encouraged with positive consequences. Conversely, undesirable behaviours are discouraged by avoiding the situations that lead to these and excluding confrontation about them. It is important to establish and maintain routines, avoid confrontation, keep tasks simple, speak clearly in short sentences, and try to maintain existing abilities. Support that emphasizes action (behaviour) often works better than that based on verbal exchange (conversation and reasoning) for people with Alzheimer disease, especially after the understanding of words deteriorates.

Environmental changes

The home must be made safe to prevent serious accidents. Safety assessments are valuable in providing guidelines for accidents in the kitchen, bathroom, stairs, and other places. Some simple, low-cost physical arrangements can be made that enhance safety and independence in family and group homes or supervised apartments with resident aging people who have developmental disabilities. These arrangements include even external walkways and steps, easily grasped and sturdy railings, adequate lighting, accessible closets and cabinets, and minimal clutter. Wandering can be reduced by use of enclosed areas, door alarms, and safety gates. Also beneficial outside the home are "wandering registries" and Medic Alert identification bracelets that can be obtained at a nominal cost. Incontinence is a major cause of burnout in caregivers, so that advice should be readily available regarding incontinence management and the use of a waterproof mattress, commode, bedpan or bed bottle. Group homes are often supportive about allowing residents with dementia or Alzheimer's disease to remain living there as long as possible. However, nursing home placement may be required if a high level of nursing care becomes necessary and the individual becomes completely dependent. Major causes of death include aspiration pneumonia, urinary tract infections, and bedsores. High quality nursing care is critical to avoiding these complications.

Other approaches

Meaningful activity that promotes health, and that uses and strengthens remaining daily living skills and abilities prevents these qualities from deteriorating and provides a sense of accomplishment, improves mood, and increases overall physical fitness. Exercise can be beneficial by serving as a means for other social, memory, and language stimulation activities. Local "day" programs specifically for people with Alzheimer's disease provide opportunities for such activities and reduce continuous pressure on caregivers. The involvement of volunteers in the life of persons with all forms of dementia cannot be underestimated.

Support of caregivers

Support of caregivers of individuals with dementia or Alzheimer's disease, particularly long-standing caregivers who are family members, is essential. Such support includes emotional backing, information, advice, practical aids, and help with future planning. The many aspects of care, which vary as the disease progresses, require maintenance of the affected person's dignity, retaining a sense of humour and understanding, and making sure that the home is safe. This includes encouraging those with the disease to themselves attend to such needs as dressing, washing and eating. For example, if clothes are laid out in order in which they are usually put on, and are easy to put on, distress can be minimized.

Caregivers and family members need guidance over time in coping with new negative emotions that can result from their experience with someone who has dementia or Alzheimer's disease. These emotions can involve feelings of loss, guilt, frustration, unrealistic hope, bitterness, sadness, and depression. It is important for others to recognize the challenges that caregivers and family members are going through, particularly as the behaviour of persons with dementia or Alzheimer disease distressingly changes from previously familiar patterns.

Typically, support for primary caregivers is essential, in some cases including financial support. Generally, there is a need for caregivers and family members to learn more about the nature of Alzheimer's disease, its manifestations, and necessary practical changes to facilitate effective coping.

Table 6. Needs of People with Dementia, and of their Caregivers

Service

- *Differential diagnosis of dementia (to distinguish reversible and treatable forms from Alzheimer disease)*
- *Counselling*
- *Advocacy*
- *Case management and coordination*
- *Adult day care programs*
- *Home care*
- *Home chores*
- *Home safety assessment by occupational therapists*
- *Delivered meals*
- *Respite care for temporary relief of caregivers*
- *Nursing assistance*
- *Nursing homes*
- *Wandering person's registries*
- *Support groups*

Education

- *Brochures, guides, manuals, videos*
- *Internet information*
- *Conferences, workshops, forums and symposia*
- *Courses and study programs*
- *Help lines*
- *Legal and financial assistance*

Research

- *Proposed therapeutic interventions*
- *Longitudinal studies of the development of dementia*
- *Donation of brain tissue for research*

Caregiving help is almost always required, including practical in-house support from home-care workers and emotional backing from relatives, friends and various professionals. An important beneficial source of guidance is presence of a local Alzheimer's Support Group. Joining such a group makes it possible to meet others who are facing similar issues with Alzheimer disease and enables sharing of information, feelings, and practical suggestions for coping and for helping a person with the disease to enjoy life as fully as possible.

Services and resources needed by people with dementia and their caregivers

Early detection of Alzheimer's disease facilitates prompt attention by family and other caregivers to learn about the nature of the condition, to establish a support network, and to plan for the possibility of future alternative living arrangements. Service and other resources that are needed for people with Alzheimer's disease, whether with or without preceding developmental disability, are listed in Table 6. The availability of such attention varies substantially even among communities in the same country.

Some social services systems have implemented person-centered long-term planning to provide individualized services. This involves comprehensive examination of such issues as residential, financial and legal ones requiring individual resolution. Planning for guardianship and residential changes benefit from an interdisciplinary approach, with the affected person's needs and desires being taken into account. High-standard nursing is an aspect of dementia care that is essential for a reasonable quality of life, since people with dementia have complex medical and other needs. Supporting such people in small group-home settings or in their family residences as long as possible tends to respectfully enhance their dignity even in difficult times. Also, an effective support system is needed to assist those concerned with the emotionally draining process of dealing with terminal illness and death.

Accessing support services and community resources

Even in the early stages of dementia, increased supervision of the affected person in his or her home is necessary with consideration of various compensatory cognitive and environmental strategies to lessen the impact of the disease. Residential support staff are usually very cooperative in applying such strategies, but nursing home placement may be necessary if care requirements become too onerous.

Information about available services, community resources, and intervention strategies can be elicited from multiple sources, including Alzheimer's societies and family support groups, social service agencies that provide dementia screening, Alzheimer's disease and related disorder clinics, religious organizations, the Internet, and home care and safety agencies. Please also refer to Chapters 14 and 49.

Summary

Alzheimer's disease is the commonest form of dementia. This disease is characterized by the presence of large quantities of amyloid plaques and neurofibrillary tangles in particular areas of the brain. The first clinical evidence of Alzheimer's disease tends to be memory loss, but other areas of intellectual functioning are progressively affected, leading to loss of self-care, social skills, and marked deterioration of physical health. The prevalence of Alzheimer's disease increases with increasing age in the general population and in people with developmental disability. When older people begin to show signs of developing dementia, it is important that a differential diagnosis be undertaken promptly, since there are various reversible causes of dementia.

Dementia of the Alzheimer's type (DAT) is more common (though not inevitable) in middle-aged and older adults with Down syndrome than in similarly aged adults in the general population or in those with developmental disability not due to Down syndrome. The association of DAT with Down syndrome is thought to be principally due to the trisomy 21 in Down syndrome, resulting in three copies of the amyloid precursor protein gene instead of the normal two. People with Down syndrome are at risk of developing DAT at a much earlier age than is the case in the general population. Because they are now living longer, more will be affected by this disorder than heretofore. The diagnosis of DAT in people with Down syndrome and other developmental disabilities is more difficult than in the general population because dementia must be distinguished from the previously existing cognitive impairment. Diagnosis may require a multidisciplinary longitudinal assessment. A baseline assessment at about 25 years of age is an advantageous reference in identifying later changes in function. Suspicious manifestations should be thoroughly evaluated because there are many treatable medical conditions that can mask as Alzheimer's disease.

Dementia has not been as extensively studied in people with developmental disability other than that in Down syndrome, although it appears to be at least as prevalent as in the general population. New drugs are now available to slow down the Alzheimer's disease process, but they are not curative. Despite absence of a cure for Alzheimer's disease, diagnosing and managing it effectively improves the quality of life of those who are affected and of their caregivers. Family and caregiver support is an essential part of care management. People with dementia and their caregivers play a key role in better understanding dementia by collaborating with researchers and donating brain tissue to brain banks.

For Further Thought and Discussion

1. To what degree do people with developmental disability lose cognitive and behavioural skills as they get older?
2. If you are a caregiver of a person aged about 40 years who has Down syndrome, what do you need to know about Alzheimer's disease and dementia?
3. If you notice evidence of seeming dementia in a person under your care, what steps should you take to gather more information and pursue the matter further?
4. Discuss what it might mean to: 1) professionals and 2) family members to have an understanding of the possible causes and characteristics of Alzheimer's disease.
5. Should recent drug therapies advocated for the general population be used for people with developmental disabilities? Why or why not?
6. How can caregivers improve their roles in attending to relatives with Alzheimer's disease, including changes in daily routines, in communication and in attitude?
7. What services are available in your area to help support people with Alzheimer's disease and their families?
8. Do you think that it is important for people

with Alzheimer's disease to take part in research studies and for their brains to be donated to brain research banks? If not, why not? If so, how can these activities be facilitated?

9. How much is Alzheimer's disease due to one's genetic makeup or due to the environment we live in?

More Resources

Alzheimer's disease:

Alzheimer Society of Canada
http://www.alzheimer.ca

Alzheimer Society Ontario
http://alzheimerontario.org/

Percy, M. E., Pogue, A. I., Kruck, T., & Lukiw, W. (in press). Towards the prevention of potential aluminum toxic effects an effective treatment for Alzheimer's Disease. *Journal of Inorganic Biochemistry.*

Down syndrome:

Alzheimer Disease in Individuals with Down Syndrome.
http://emedicine.medscape.com/article/1136117 –overview

Down's Syndrome Scotland
http://www.dsscotland.org.uk/

Recommended Down syndrome Sites on the Internet; compiled by Len Leshin, MD, FAAP
http://www.ds-health.com/ds_sites.htm

Intellectual Disabilities:

Alzheimer Disease and People with Mental Retardation
http://www.thearc.org/NetCommunity/Document. Doc?&id=95

Dementia & Intellectual Disabilities
http://www.alz.co.uk/adi/pdf/ intellectualdisabilities.pdf

Dementia in Older Adults with Intellectual Disabilities
http://www.rrtcadd.org/TA/Dementia_Care/ Resources/assets/State%20of%20Science%20on%20 Dementia.pdf

Intellectual Disabilities, Aging & Dementia
http://www.albany.edu/aging/IDD/r-id.htm

Janicki, M. P. (2011). Quality outcomes in group home dementia care for adults with intellectual disabilities. *Journal of Intellectual Disability Research, 55*(8), 763-766.

Learning About Intellectual Disabilities and Health (St. George's University of London, U.K.)
http://www.intellectualdisability.info

Resources on Alzheimer's Disease and Dementias (University of Illinois at Chicago)
http://www.rrtcadd.org/TA/Dementia_Care/ Resources/Info.html.

Clinical Trials:

ClinicalTrials.gov

References

Alzheimer, A. (1907). Über eine eigenartige Erkrankung der Hirnrinde. *Allgemeine Zeitschrift für Psychiatrie und Psychisch-Gerichtliche Medizin, Berlin, 64,* 146–148.

Alzheimer Society of Canada. (2010). Retrieved from http://www.alzheimer.ca

Arab, L., & Sabbagh, M. N. (2010). Are certain lifestyle habits associated with lower Alzheimer's disease risk? *Journal of Alzheimers Disease, 20*(3), 785–794.

CBS News. (July 12, 2010). *Vitamin D, exercise: Big factors in keeping Alzheimer's at bay.* Retrieved from http://www.cbsnews.com/8301-504763_162-20010239-10391704.html

Cheon, M. S., Bajo, M., Gulesserian, T., Cairns, N., & Lubec, G. (2001). Evidence for the relation of herpes simplex virus type 1 to Down syndrome and Alzheimer's disease. *Electrophoresis, 22,* 445–448.

Cooper, S. A, & van der Speck, R. (2009). Epidemiology of mental ill health in adults with intellectual disabilities. *Current Opinion in Psychiatry, 22*(5), 431–436.

Cosgrave, M. P., Tyrrell, J., McCarron, M., Gill, M., & Lawlor, B. A. (1999). Age at onset of dementia and age of menopause in women with Down's syndrome. *Journal of Intellectual Disabilities Research,*

43(Pt 6), 461–465.

Crapper-McLachlan, D. R., Dalton, A. J., Kruck, T. P. A., Bell, M. Y., Smith, W., Kalow, W., et al. (1991). Intramuscular desferrioxamine in patients with Alzheimer's disease. *Lancet, 337*, 1304–1308.

Day, S. M., Strauss, D. J., Shavelle, R. M., & Reynolds, R. J. (2005). Mortality and causes of death in persons with Down syndrome in California. *Developmental Medicine and Child Neurology, 47*(3), 171–176.

de la Monte, S. M., & Wands, J. R. (2008). Alzheimer's disease is type 3 diabetes-evidence reviewed. *Journal of Diabetes Science and Technology, 2*(6), 1101–1113.

Devenny, D. A., Wegiel, J., Schupf, N., Jenkins, E., Zigman, W., Krinsky-McHale, S. J., et al. (8 April, 2005). Dementia of the Alzheimer's type and accelerated aging in Down syndrome. *Science of Aging Knowledge Environment: SAGE KE [electric resource], 14*, dn1.

Diamond, J. (2008). *Rising tide: The impact of dementia on Canada.* Retrieved from the Alzheimer Society of Canada website at http://www.alzheimer.ca/docs/RisingTide/Rising%20Tide_Full%20Report_Eng_FINAL_Secured%20version.pdf

Evenhuis, H. M. (1997). The natural history of dementia in ageing people with intellectual disability. *Journal of Intellectual Disability Research, 41*, 92–96.

Gatz, M., Reynolds, C. A., Fratiglioni, L., Johansson, B., Mortimer, J. A., Berg, S., et al. (2006). Role of genes and environments for explaining Alzheimer disease. *Archives of General Psychiatry, 63*(2), 168–174.

Glasson, E. J., Sullivan, S. G., Hussain, R., Petterson, B. A., Montgomery, P. D., & Bittles, A. H. (2003). Comparative survival advantage of males with Down syndrome. *American Journal of Human Biology, 15*, 192–195.

Jiang, Y., Mullaney, K. A., Peterhoff, C. M., Che, S., Schmidt, S. D., Boyer-Boiteau, A., et al. (2010). Alzheimer's-related endosome dysfunction in Down syndrome is Abeta-independent but requires APP and is reversed by BACE-1 inhibition. *Proceedings of the National Academy of Sciences U.S.A., 107*(4), 1630–1635.

Khachaturian, Z. S. (1985). Diagnosis of Alzheimer's disease. *Archives of Neurology, 42*, 1097–1104.

McKhann, G., Drachman, D., Folstein, M., Katzman, R., Price, D., & Stadlan, E. M. (1984). Clinical diagnosis of Alzheimer's disease: Report of the NINCDS-ADRDA Work Group under the auspices of Department of Health and Human Services Task Force on Alzheimer's disease. *Neurology, 34*, 939–944.

McLachlan, D. R., Bergeron, C., Smith, J. E., Boomer, D., & Rifat, S. L. (1996). Risk for neuropathologically confirmed Alzheimer's disease and residual aluminum in municipal drinking water employing weighted residential histories. *Neurology, 46*, 401–440.

Mondragón-Rodríguez, S., Basurto-Islas, G., Lee, H. G., Perry, G., Zhu, X., Castellani, R. J., et al. (2010). Causes versus effects: the increasing complexities of Alzheimer's disease pathogenesis. *Expert Review of Neurotherapeutics, 10*(5), 683–691.

Patel, A., Rees, S. D., Kelly, M. A., Bain, S. C., Barnett, A. H., Thalitaya, D., et al. (2011). Association of variants within APOE, SORL1, RUNX1, BACE1 and ALDH18A1 with dementia in Alzheimer's disease in subjects with Down syndrome. *Neuroscience letters, 487*(2), 144-148.

Potkin, S. G., Guffanti, G., Lakatos, A., Turner, J. A., Kruggel, F., Fallon, J. H., et al. (2009). Alzheimer's Disease Neuroimaging Initiative. Hippocampal atrophy as a quantitative trait in a genome-wide association study identifying novel susceptibility genes for Alzheimer's disease. *PLoS One, 4*(8), e6501.

Prasher, V., Percy, M., Jozsvai, E., Lovering, J. S., & Berg, J. (2007). Implications of Alzheimer's disease for people with Down syndrome and other intellectual disabilities. In I. Brown & M. Percy, *A comprehensive guide to intellectual and developmental disabilities* (pp. 681–702). Baltimore: Paul H. Brookes Publishing.

Prasher, V. P. (Ed.). (2008). *Neuropsychological assessments of dementia in Down syndrome and intellectual disabilities.* New York: Springer.

Prasher, V. P., Sajith, S. G., Rees, S. D., Patel, A., Tewari, S., Schupf, N., et al. (2008). Significant effect of APOE epsilon 4 genotype on the risk of dementia in Alzheimer's disease and mortality in persons with Down syndrome. *International Journal of Geriatric Psychiatry, 23*(11), 1134–1140.

Soscia, S. J., Kirby, J. E., Washicosky, K. J., Tucker, S. M., Ingelsson, M., Hyman, B., et al. (2010). The Alzheimer's disease-associated amyloid beta-protein is an antimicrobial peptide. *PLoS On, 5*(3), e9505.

Strauss, D., & Eyman, R. K. (1996). Mortality of people with mental retardation in California with and without Down syndrome, 1986–1991. *American Journal on Mental Retardation, 100*(6), 643–653.

Strydom, A., Livingston, G., King, M., & Hassiotis, A. (2007). Prevalence of dementia in intellectual disability using different diagnostic criteria. *British Journal of Psychiatry, 191*, 150–157.

Temple, V., Jozsvai, E., Konstantareos, M. M., & Hewitt, T. A. (2001). Alzheimer dementia in Down syndrome: The relevance of cognitive ability. *Journal of Intellectual Disability Research, 45*, 47–55.

Thase, M. E. (1982). Longevity and mortality in Down's syndrome. *Journal of Mental Deficiency Research, 16*, 177–192.

Tyrrell, J., Cosgrave, M., Hawi, Z., McPherson, J., O'Brien, C., McCalvert, J., et al. (1998). A protective effect of apolipoprotein E e2 allele on dementia in Down's syndrome. *Biological Psychiatry, 43*, 397–400.

Walton, J. R., & Wang, M. X. (2009). APP expression, distribution and accumulation are altered by aluminum in a rodent model for Alzheimer's disease. *Journal of Inorganic Biochemistry, 103*(11), 1548–1554.

Wherrett, J. R. (1999). Neurological aspects. In M. P. Janicki & A. J. Dalton (Eds.), *Dementia, aging and intellectual disabilities: A handbook* (pp. 90–102). Philadelphia: Taylor & Francis.

Wilcock, G. K., & Esiri, M. M. (1982). Plaques, tangles and dementia: A quantitative study. *Journal of the Neurological Sciences, 56*, 343–356.

Wozniak, M. A., Mee, A. P., & Itzhaki, R. F. (2009). Herpes simplex virus type 1 DNA is located within Alzheimer's disease amyloid plaques. *Journal of*

Pathology, 217(1), 131–138.

Yang, Q., Rasmussen, S. A., & Friedman, J. M. (2002). Mortality associated with Down's syndrome in the USA from 1983 to 1997: A population-based study. *Lancet, 359*, 1019–1025.

Zigman, W. B., & Lott. I. T. (2007). Alzheimer's disease in Down syndrome: Neurobiology and risk. *Mental Retardation and Developmental Disabilities Research Reviews, 13*(3), 237–246.

Part V

Developmental Disabilities Through the Lifespan

38

Prenatal and Early Life

Karolina Machalek, Maire Percy, Melissa Carter, and Ivan Brown

What you will learn:

- Issues in prenatal development
- Issues in early life
- Issues for parents

Three things are crucial to a young child's development: health of the parents prior to conception, the perinatal environment (what occurs around birth), and the first 3 years of a child's life. The purposes of this chapter are to provide an introduction to issues relevant to prenatal and early life, and to highlight issues important for parents and families. The information in this chapter is for educational purposes only, and readers should consult professionals for guidance with health issues.

Issues in Prenatal Development

Preconceptual and prenatal health

The fetus is very vulnerable to interference in development. The nutrition of parents prior to conception and the nutrition of the mother during pregnancy are thought to be key factors for normal development. On average, a pregnant woman needs about 300 calories per day more than she did before she was pregnant to support the growth of her fetus

and to maintain her own health (March of Dimes, 2010). An enormous variety of factors can result in developmental disabilities or low birth weight (a factor often related to developmental disabilities). Many of these factors are discussed in Chapters 9, 10, and 12, and include the following:

- Genetic and environmental factors
- Blood type incompatibility
- Metabolic and/or endocrine disorders in the mother, including hypothyroidism and diabetes
- Prematurity for any reason, including multiple gestation, HIV infection and other infections such as malaria
- Maternal alcohol or other substance abuse
- Lead or mercury poisoning
- Smoking and indoor air pollution
- Pediatric traumatic brain injury

As many as 30% of all pregnancies involve fetuses with abnormalities, but most of these are lost as the result of natural miscarriage. Problems with a mother's immune system may interfere with natural

Table 1: Vitamins and Minerals Important for a Healthy Pregnancy

Vitamin or Mineral	Importance	Natural Sources
Folic acid *RDA: 0.4 mg for adults* *0.6 mg for pregnant women* *0.4-1 mg for women of childbearing age with risk factor for neural tube defect*	*Synthesis of the nucleic acids adenine and thymine; use of the essential amino acid methionine; preventing elevated levels of the amino acid homocysteine; lowering risk of birth defects such as neural tube defects (spina bifida and anencephaly)*	*Fortified cereals, whole wheat breads, dark green vegetables, navy beans, kidney beans, lentils, liver, milk, cheese, beef, chicken, pork, tuna, mushrooms, oranges, barley, brown rice*
Iodine *RDA: 80-90 mcg for children* *150 mcg for adults*	*Production of thyroxine, which helps regulate blood cell production, body temperature, growth production, metabolic rate and nerve and muscle function; prevention of goitre; prevention of iodine deficiency, which causes miscarriages and stillbirths, and retards fetal growth and brain development*	*Bread, iodized salt, lobster, marine fish, milk, oysters (cooked), shrimp, milk, seaweed*
Iron *RDA: 18-30 mg for women* *15-25 mg for men*	*Production of hemoglobin and function of red blood cells; function of the immune system; prevention of anemia; prevention of iron deficiency during pregnancy which contributes to maternal and perinatal mortality*	*Iron fortified cereals, green leafy vegetables, beef, soybeans, eggs, fish, liver, whole grains, nuts, avocados, beets, peaches, lentils, raisins, sesame seeds, baked potatoes, clams, pumpkin seeds*
Vitamin A *RDA: 500 mcg for children* *1000 mcg for adults* *100,000 mcg is toxic*	*Proper function of the immune system; prevention of vitamin A deficiency, which causes blindness in children and night blindness in pregnant mother*	*Fish liver oils, liver, egg yolks, butter, cream, carrots, pumpkins, yams, cantaloupe, mangos, spinach, tuna, turnip, beet greens*

Key: RDA – Recommended Daily Allowance; mg – milligrams; mcg – micrograms
Sources: Chapter 12; Joint SOGC-Motherisk Clinical Practice Guideline No. 201, 2007; Machalek, Percy, & Brown, 2007; the Merck Manuals Online Medical Library, 2010; Prenatal Nutrition, 2010.

miscarriage and promote the carrying of a fetus with a serious abnormality to term. Standard early and continuous measures can be taken to prevent some abnormalities. In North America, early care before pregnancy includes eating a well-balanced diet and ensuring adequate intake of iron and folic acid.

It should be pointed out, however, that different ethnic groups have different requirements and tolerances for essential nutrients and different protective or adverse responses to foods and dietary substances. For example, people who live in malarial regions actually are protected against malarial infection by having low levels of body iron (Moalem, Weinberg, & Percy, 2004). Nevertheless, during pregnancy, proper and sufficient nutrition should be maintained, adequate intake of iron and folate being particularly important (Moore & Davies, 2005). (For more information, see the section on nutrition in Chapters 10 and 12, and Ramakrishnan, 2004.) Additional preventative measures include avoiding alcohol, cigarettes and illicit drugs, avoiding X-rays, hot tubs and saunas (which predispose a fetus to neural tube defects), and limiting caffeine intake and low-impact exercise (Chapter 12; Larsson & Lindqvist, 2005; Prenatal Care, 2010). See also Melzer, Schutz, Boulvain, & Kayser (2010) for additional information about the benefits of exercise.

Issues for professionals

Professionals involved in supporting parents through a pregnancy should promote healthy nutrition and a healthy lifestyle, and encourage women to avoid alcohol and other abusive substances, especially those that may have teratogenic effects (Chapters 9, 10, 12, and 19). They should also arrange for regular visits to health professionals to monitor fetal and maternal health and to provide information about maternal serum screening and other forms of testing. If there is a known genetic problem in the family, or if the parents have another child with some type of disability, professionals should discuss with the parents the added risk of having a child with a disability. A genetic counsellor can inform parents about the risk of the disability occurring again, options for diagnostic testing and, if the disorder is likely to affect other relatives in the blood line, about appropriate ways to inform other family members and friends.

Prenatal care

The rationale for providing prenatal care is to screen pregnant women in order to detect early signs of, or risk factors for, abnormal conditions or diseases and to follow this detection with effective and timely intervention.

Suggested general care

The recommended prenatal care program in developing countries is often the same as the programs used in developed countries. However, in developing countries there is wide variation in the proportion of women who receive prenatal care. The World Health Organization (WHO) randomized trial of prenatal care and the WHO systematic review indicated that a model of care that provided fewer prenatal visits could be introduced into clinical practice without causing adverse consequences to the woman or the fetus (Lumbiganon, Winiyakul, Chongsomchai, & Chaisiri, 2005). Follow-up care during pregnancy typically involves the following:

- Determining the mother's blood group
- Testing for anemia and anti-Rh antibodies (see below)
- Checking the growth of the uterus
- Listening to the fetal heart beat
- Checking the urine for protein (testing kidney function)
- Checking the urine for sugar (testing for diabetes)
- Monitoring blood pressure
- Checking for other concerns such as blurred vision, leg cramps, abdominal cramps, and unusual headaches
- Optimizing oral health
- Offering and facilitating genetic screening if warranted (see below)

Testing for infections such as hepatitis B virus, rubella (measles), syphilis, and HIV is standard care. HIV is a very serious issue; since it was first identified, over 60 million people worldwide have become affected, and over 20 million have already died. In 2008, an estimated 31.1 to 35.8 million people were affected with HIV, 14.2 to 17.2 million of these being women and 1.2 to 2.9 million being children under the age of 15 years (World HIV & AIDS Statistics, n.d.). Since HIV affects females as well as males, an HIV infection in the mother is sometimes spread to her baby. In 2008, there were an estimated 240,000 to 610,0000 new cases of HIV in children under the age of 15 years. HIV has been referred to as the epidemic of the 21st century, and more outreach and education is needed to prevent the spread of the virus. As explained in Chapter 20, HIV can be transmitted from a mother to her fetus or baby while it is still in the uterus, during the delivery process, and through breast-feeding. There is strong evidence that use of antiviral medications during pregnancy can reduce transmission of HIV from mother to fetus. Thus, testing pregnant women for HIV can be an extremely important aspect of prenatal health. One survey in the United States indicated that routine HIV testing is a reasonable option for identifying HIV infections in the primary care setting, as this is non-discriminatory, allows for increased awareness of actual risk for infection, and provides an opportunity for earlier detection of HIV (Simmons, Rogers, Frierson, Beckwith, & Flanigan, 2005). If a father is HIV positive and a mother HIV negative, there is still risk of fetal infection if the mother becomes HIV positive. In some European countries, in vitro fertilization with washed sperm is being used to lower such risk (Chapter 10).

Screening for Down syndrome, trisomy 18, and neural tube defects by ultrasound and maternal serum screening is a routine part of prenatal care in many countries (see below and Chapter 10). Midwifery care is an integrated part of some prenatal health care systems. This can provide enormous emotional support for a pregnant woman and a natural approach to birthing. Finally, it has been recommended that a nutritionist should be appointed to mother and child clinics, as professional caregivers sometimes are lacking in nutritional knowledge (Endevelt, Blau, Neville, Shvartzman, & Shvarts, 2003). For more information, see the websites: Midwifery in Ontario, 2003; Prenatal Care, 2010; and Prenatal Nutrition, 2010.

Types of prenatal measures and tests

As noted in the pervious section, numerous types of screening are recommended. This section provides further details on various measures and tests that may take place prior to conception and birth.

Genetic counselling: Genetic counselling is a growing need, especially to families with an inherited disorder. Genetic counsellors are professionals specifically trained to help individuals and families face the implications of the diagnosis and make decisions on the basis of both medical and non-medical options. The service offered by genetic counsellors provides parents and other family members with accurate, full, and unbiased information. It should offer non-directive support in the decision-making process and should seek to help families understand the implications of an inherited disorder. Although family physicians typically have some knowledge about inherited genetic disorders, they may not be prepared to offer counselling to their patients. Because of this, it is often useful to involve genetic counsellors after a need is identified by the family physician and prior to any prenatal diagnostic tests or interventions. For perspectives on genetic counselling, see Ensenauer, Michels, & Reinke, 2005; Genetic Resources Ontario, 2009.

Ultrasound to monitor fetal development: Fetal development is now routinely monitored by ultrasound (Chapter 10). This procedure is considered to be safe, non-invasive, accurate, and cost-effective. Ultrasound is used to help in the assessment of early pregnancy, to check fetal viability in the case of threatened miscarriage, to determine gestational age (the time since conception) and assess fetus size, to check the localization of the placenta, to determine the number of fetuses, and to check for fetal malformation as well as other conditions. Many different structural abnormalities in the fetus, including neural tube defects, and congenital cardiac abnormalities, can be recognized before 20 weeks of pregnancy (Hourrier, Salomon, Dreux, & Muller, 2010). Ultrasound is also used to assist in other diagnostic procedures including amniocentesis, chorionic villus sampling, and percutaneous umbilical cord sampling (see below).

Prenatal testing for Down syndrome and trisomy 18: In many countries, any pregnant woman may choose to have a blood test in the second trimester to screen for Down syndrome, trisomy 18 and open neural tube defects in the fetus. This testing is known in Ontario as Maternal Serum Screening or MSS. In one Canadian study, the detection rate of MSS for Down syndrome was found to be 70.6% with a false positive rate of 7.2%; that for neural tube defects was 72.7% with a false positive rate of 2.0%, and for trisomy 18 was 50.0% with a false positive rate of 0.2% (Summers, Farrell, Huang, Meier, & Wyatt, 2005). Some health centres combine specialized first trimester ultrasound with MSS. In Ontario, this is called Integrated Prenatal Screening, or IPS. This enhanced screening method was developed to increase the sensitivity and specificity of prenatal testing for Down syndrome and trisomy 18 by measuring maternal serum markers twice during pregnancy, and adding an ultrasound measurement of fetal nuchal translucency (a fluid-filled space behind the neck). IPS has a higher detection rate for Down syndrome than MSS alone, detecting up to 90% of fetuses with Down syndrome. The false positive rate of IPS is 2-4% (See also Wald, 2010).

Women with negative results on prenatal screening tests usually have no further follow-up testing. Women with positive results may arrange to have a detailed (Level 2) ultrasound and a more invasive diagnostic test such as amniocentesis, chorionic villus sampling, or percutaneous umbilical cord sampling (see below) to rule out or confirm the results of the serum tests. These procedures are considered to be invasive, as they pose some risks to the health of the fetus.

Amniocentesis is usually done in the second trimester and involves removing a small sample of amniotic fluid from the mother's womb and analyzing the chromosomes in cells of that fluid. To obtain amniotic fluid, a needle is inserted through the woman's abdomen into the uterus and amniotic sac. Even though it is a relatively common procedure, amniocentesis before 14 weeks of gestation has been associated with an increased risk of postural deformities, and amniocentesis at 14 and 15 weeks with an increased risk of respiratory disturbances (Cederholm, Haglund, & Axelsson, 2005). There is also about a 1% risk of miscarriage following amniocentesis. Chorionic villus sampling (CVS) may be performed in the first trimester of pregnancy (8-10 weeks after conception). Chorionic villi are actively dividing cells of fetal origin that contain a full complement of chromosomes; the villi are found within the trophoblastic layer. CVS procedures can be transabdominal (through the abdomen) or transcervical (through the cervix), although the transabdominal

procedure is more commonly used. Because invasive sampling procedures are associated with some risk of miscarriage and causing deformities — though the rates are low — there currently is much interest in developing better non-invasive methods for obtaining intact fetal cells from the pregnant woman's blood. This would allow accurate prenatal diagnosis for aneuploidy (having an incomplete set of chromosomes because of a missing or damaged chromosome) and single gene disorders while avoiding the risks associated with invasive testing. It might also increase the use of prenatal diagnosis by women at risk (Simpson, 2010; Zimmermann et al., 2008); see also Chapter 10 for diagrams of amniocentesis and CVS. See Cunniff & Hudgins, 2010, and Ferguson-Smith, 2008, for additional information about prenatal genetic screening.

Before diagnostic testing, however, women should consider what they would do if the diagnostic results were positive. It is important for a woman to receive emotional support from her spouse, partner, family and/or friends before and after receiving the diagnosis, since many women have not seriously considered the possibility of having a child with a disability. Women should also consider talking about the diagnosis with their relatives and friends, and having them present at the time of learning the diagnosis for emotional support. Women can also seek advice and help from genetic counsellors, usually available in the hospital setting to answer any questions the women may have about the diagnosis. Follow-up testing is also important to confirm the diagnosis and to rule out a false positive test result.

Prenatal testing for other inherited disorders: If parents know that they are at higher risk of having a baby with an inherited genetic condition other than Down syndrome, neural tube defects or trisomy 18, diagnostic prenatal testing can be arranged to test for such a condition in the fetus. This is also done on amniotic fluid or CVS cells. Percutaneous umbilical blood sampling (PUBS), or cordocentesis, is sometimes performed at 18-27 weeks of pregnancy. The risk of miscarriage associated with PUBS is higher than for amniocentesis or CVS, at about 2%. The PUBS technique is similar to amniocentesis, except that a blood sample is obtained from the fetal circulation via the placental cord. DNA or RNA analysis can then be used to identify inherited genetic conditions in the fetal cells, and to test for the presence or absence or the amount of a particular protein. PUBS is also used to check the Rh status of the fetus if a mother is known to make anti-Rh antibodies (see below), or to assess fetal renal (kidney) function. In some places (e.g., Ontario), if there is no known potential risk to the mother or the fetus, and therefore no medically justified reason for a non-routine genetic test, requests for invasive testing are not usually accepted, although individual practice may vary. However, women whose requests for tests are not accepted have the option of being tested for a fee in the United States or elsewhere.

Testing and prevention of Rhesus disease: One of the simplest, least invasive, and most important tests that parents can have done is a blood test for Rhesus or Rh factor, a substance present in red cells of some people. Individuals who make Rh factor are Rh-positive; those who do not are Rh-negative. If an Rh-negative woman with an Rh-positive partner has an Rh-positive baby, then her fetus is at risk of developing Rhesus disease. If this occurs, it is essential that parents obtain proper medical follow-up to ensure that their baby does not develop Rhesus disease. If medical intervention is not sought for Rhesus disease, untreated babies may develop severe brain or nerve damage (including cerebral palsy, hydrops fetalis, and kernicterus), and require life-long support.

Fetal red cells can enter a mother's circulation under a number of circumstances: during a spontaneous miscarriage or even during a threatened one, an ectopic pregnancy, chorionic villus sampling or amniocentesis performed for genetic reasons (see below), or as the result of a motor vehicle collision or other accident (Harrod, Hanson, VandeVusse, & Heywood, 2003). If a mother is Rh-negative and the fetal cells are Rh-positive, the mother may begin to make antibodies to the fetal Rh-positive cells. If these cross from the mother's circulation to her unborn child during pregnancy, destruction of the fetal red cells (a process called hemolysis) may occur, and result in a low blood count in the fetus (anemia) or even fetal death. Because this fetal dis-

order results from destruction of red cells secondary to anti-Rh-antibodies produced by the mother, it is called hemolytic disease of the newborn secondary to Rhesus disease, or simply Rhesus disease. In the United States, the prevalence of this disorder is about 1 per 1,000 live born infants. If the fetal anemia is severe, the fetus may require blood transfusions while still in the uterus via the umbilical cord. Once a mother begins to produce anti-Rh antibodies, the severity of Rhesus disease in her fetus increases with each successive pregnancy. Medication called Rhesus immune globulin (or RhoGAM) is available to prevent Rhesus disease. RhoGAM should be given to all Rh-negative women at 28 weeks of pregnancy and after the delivery of an Rh-positive baby. Similar medications are not yet available to prevent fetal hemolytic disease resulting from maternal antibodies produced against factors on fetal red cells that are rarer than Rh factor. (Reviewed by Salem & Singer, 2010.)

Accuracy of prenatal testing

Accuracy of prenatal testing depends on a number of factors, including the sensitivity and specificity of the test and its false negative and false positive rates. The term *sensitivity* refers to the ability of the test to detect true positives (i.e., individuals who really have the disorder). The term *specificity* refers to the ability of the test to detect true negatives (i.e., individuals who really do not have the disorder). A *false positive test result* refers to a positive test result in an individual who does not have the disorder. A *false negative test result* refers to a negative test result in an individual who does have the disorder. When considering prenatal testing, prospective parents should work with a genetic counsellor to make sure that they understand the information that the test is likely to yield, as well as the options that are available to them after the testing has been done, particularly if the test results are positive.

Ethical issues associated with genetic testing

As of the early 21st century, guidelines for genetic testing focus on a thorough examination of the psychological, social, and medical implications of a test result for the individual being tested (Robertson &

Table 2: Potential Disadvantages and Potential Advantages of Genetic Testing in Children

Potential Disadvantages

- *Negative parental attitudes towards the child*
- *Low self-esteem on the part of the child*
- *Psychological maladjustment, including depression and suicide*
- *Parental guilt*
- *Social discrimination, including future employment and insurance discrimination*

Potential Advantages

- *Decreased parental and child anxiety*
- *Decreased uncertainty about the future*
- *Minimizes the possibility of psychological maladjustment in life resulting from late discovery of status*
- *More realistic life choices*
- *Option of treatment and therapy*
- *More openness about genetic conditions within the family and in society in general*

Savulescu, 2001). In research ethics, the autonomy of the individual is of utmost importance. However, genetic information is by its very nature information about families. Detecting a genetic mutation in a person will, in effect, yield information about the risk-status of family members who may or may not wish to be informed. Genetic testing done on a research basis sometimes can have unpredicted adverse effects; furthermore, useful guidelines on how to handle genetic information in research are simply not available (Quaid, Jessup, & Meslin, 2005).

Discovering that there is a genetic disorder in a family may result in a range of reactions and emotions from partners and relatives including love, affection, obligation, gratitude, jealousy, advice, support, criticism, fear of disapproval, argument, and security or insecurity (Cranley Glass et al., 1996). It is impossible to control and to determine how families will deal with genetic issues. The individuals being tested and the professionals who are guiding them must always think ahead, and consider the effects that genetic knowledge might have for other members of the family and for more distant relatives. Especially in families where this is a potential problem, genetic counselling and other forms of support should be arranged before genetic testing is initiated. Genetic testing and genetic counselling can be done prenatally or postnatally at any age. It is more complex in children than in adults, since children do not have the freedom to choose whether to be tested or not, whereas adults can choose for themselves. When deciding to test a child for a genetic disorder, it is important to examine the advantages and the disadvantages (Policy Statement Archives, 1995; Robertson & Savulescu, 2001). Some of these are outlined in Table 2.

Family planning

After prenatal testing or planning for subsequent children, some parents might consider alternative methods for family planning such as assisted reproductive technology or adoption, in conjunction with the prevention of birth through sterilization and/or contraception (see Greydanus, Rimza, & Matytsina (2005) and Johnson (2005) for additional information about contraception). Others might choose to prevent/terminate a fetus found to have a condition that they are not prepared to deal with; abortion may be carried out as early as 3 weeks in the first trimester of pregnancy, or as late as in the third trimester.

It should be noted, however, that having an induced abortion involves some difficulties. It may lead to problems with future pregnancies, and previous induced abortion is associated with an increased risk of premature delivery (Moreau et al., 2005). As discussed in Chapter 12, the more premature or underweight the newborn, the greater the risks of illness (infection, respiratory distress or other problems), cognitive disabilities such as cerebral palsy and learning problems, hearing and vision problems, and death (Haas et al., 2005; Machalek et al., 2007). In addition, induced abortion may have negative physical and psychological effects on women who choose to terminate their pregnancies. Some publications have observed an association between induced abortion and subsequent serious mental health problems such as depression, anxiety, suicidal behaviours, and substance abuse (Fergusson, Horwood, & Ridder, 2006). Other studies have reported an association between induced abortion and breast cancer (e.g., Hajian-Tilaki & Kaveh-Ahangar, 2010), though this association is not generally recognized. More immediately, the termination of pregnancy due to a genetic defect may cause grief, guilt, and depression (Ring-Cassidy & Gentles, 2003). The links between induced abortion and complications such as pelvic inflammatory disease, ectopic pregnancies, endometriosis, and other infections, as well as cancers of the reproductive tract, have not been firmly established, but some studies point to these associations (Ring-Cassidy & Gentles, 2003). Induced abortion may also have a negative effect on the siblings of the unborn child and on other family members (Coleman, Reardon, & Cougle, 2002; Ring-Cassidy & Gentles, 2003). It is therefore important that pregnant women and their partners be informed about the possible impact of abortion on them and their families; they should also be provided with information on the care of children with disabilities to enable them to make a truly informed decision based on all the available information.

There are also a number of natural family planning methods available, one of the most effective being the Billings Ovulation Method. The Billings Ovulation Method is a scientifically validated method of natural fertility control, which allows a woman to assess her level of fertility based on observations of her cervical mucus secretions (Billings & Westmore, 1998). This method can be used to achieve or to avoid pregnancy. (See also relevant websites in More Resources.)

Assisted reproductive technologies

Assisted reproductive technology includes procedures known as in vitro fertilization (IVF), intracytoplasmic sperm injection (ICSI), gamete intrafallopian transfer (GIFT) and zygote intrafallopian transfer (ZIFT), the newest technology. IVF involves fertilizing ova (eggs) with sperm in the laboratory and implanting embryos into the uterus. ICSI involves fertilizing an ovum with a single sperm by injection with a fine needle. GIFT involves the implantation of sperm and ova into the fallopian tube where fertilization occurs *in vivo*. ZIFT involves the implantation of ova fertilized *in vitro* into the fallopian tube. The risks of assisted reproductive technology include failure, ectopic pregnancy (the fertilized ovum developing outside the uterus, such as in the fallopian tube), multiple pregnancy, drug side effects and associated complications resulting from anaesthesia and surgery.

The adoption and implantation of *frozen* embryos is yet another variation of an assisted reproductive technology used by some couples to have a healthy baby. With multiple pregnancies (for whatever reason) comes the risk of premature birth, which might lead to developmental disability in the baby. The costs for assisted reproductive technology are high, and are beyond the means of some people. Having a surrogate mother bring a baby to term is another approach used by couples not able to conceive. In Canada, health falls under provincial jurisdiction, and most Canadian provinces do not financially support assisted reproduction treatments. Since 1994, Ontario has paid for three IVF cycles only if women have both fallopian tubes blocked. As of August 5, 2010, Quebec pays for infertile couples to get three treatment cycles, and for single women and lesbian couples to get free sperm donations (Hilborn, 2010). (See also relevant websites in More Resources.)

When using assisted reproductive technology to conceive, genetic disorders may be screened for by the biopsy of follicles that are collected after egg retrieval is initiated (i.e., polar body analysis), and/or by the analysis of single cells that are harvested from embryos at the 8-cell stage prior to implantation (Cooper & Jungheim, 2010; Lashwood, 2005).

Pregnancy avoidance and adoption

Pregnancy can be avoided by choice, by male or female sterilization, and by the use of contraceptives. Sterilization should be carefully considered before undertaking, as it is not always reversible or 100% effective in preventing pregnancy. The procedure involves blocking the passageway of sperm or the egg by clips, rings, cutting or cauterizing. Various contraceptive methods are also currently available. The combined oral contraceptive pill and progesterone only pill is extremely effective, at approximately the 99% mark. Other methods include emergency contraceptive drugs. Hormonal implants, or injections such as Norplant and Depo-Provera are ranked at greater than 99% effective. Barrier methods such as female and male condoms, cervical caps and diaphragms also are commonly available methods of contraception. The copper-releasing intrauterine device and progestin-releasing intrauterine device also are options. The Billings Ovulation Method is an effective and non-invasive form of pregnancy avoidance and natural family planning. This method teaches a woman to interpret her natural signs of fertility throughout the duration of her cycle. When followed, the method is close to 100% effective at preventing pregnancy (Machalek et al., 2007).

Adoption is often considered by couples not able to conceive and by single individuals. Parents considering putting up a child for adoption may benefit from invaluable information available at Adoption Centres and by communicating with other surrendering parents. Parents considering adoption should also contact Adoption Centres for information on the types of adoption and the adoption process. Like natural-born children, adopted children may or may not present with medical and developmental concerns. If growth stunting, abnormal behaviour, and delays in motor, speech and language development are identified, intervention protocols that will help adopted children assimilate into their new families should be developed as soon as possible (Mason & Narad, 2005). Adoption from other countries has become an option for many families. (See Licenced International Adoption Agencies (n.d.) for information about international adoption in Ontario.)

Personal values regarding testing and related decisions

For many people, having a therapeutic abortion in order to prevent disability, resorting to assisted reproductive technology in order to have a healthy baby, or even taking measures to prevent pregnancy are options that are not morally or ethically acceptable. In addition, some people may not want to partake in prenatal testing since the results will not change the course of the pregnancy in any case. Furthermore, attitudes of different cultural groups to prenatal testing are different (Singer, Antonucci, & Van Hoewyk, 2004). Thus, decisions about whether or not to perform prenatal testing, and decisions based on their results, should be made on an individual basis, in accordance with personal value systems and beliefs.

Issues in Early Life

Issues in early life arise from the birth process, development over the first months after being born, recognizing developmental delay (sometimes in the form of a formal diagnosis), and beginning to receive specialized support. These and related issues are discussed in this section.

Disabilities arising from birth

Babies who are born too early, or babies who do not get enough oxygen during the birthing process, are at risk of developing brain damage. Complaints of infection in mothers and babies, especially after a home birth, should always be considered seriously. Developments in medical knowledge and technology now save the lives of many premature babies who would have died in earlier years. However, these lives are at an increased risk of brain damage or even severe disability (Anderson & Doyle, 2003). As it is not possible to predict which babies will have problems of this nature, medical advances in neonatal care are posing challenging ethical dilemmas for which solutions are not obvious.

Case Study 1: Samantha

When Samantha was a month and a half old, her parents started noticing problems with her eyes, and that she did not react to her surroundings. They visited their family doctor many times and he insisted that she was fine. Samantha's parents knew that there was something seriously wrong with her and that the doctor was not telling them everything. When Samantha was six months old, her parents decided to take her to their nearest hospital. The pediatrician who examined Samantha asked her parents whether they wanted to know what was wrong with her. This was the first time anyone had asked them if they wanted to know and if they could handle it. The parents did want to know what Samantha's problems were, because they thought that once they knew what was wrong, they could get help for her. That was their main concern.

When the pediatrician told Samantha's parents that she had cerebral palsy and was developmentally delayed, she was surprised at how well they accepted the diagnosis. For the parents, it was a relief to have someone finally say what they had feared for so long. They now felt that they could move forward and do the best for their daughter.

Neonatal care and testing

All infants and toddlers deserve the best possible support to ensure the best quality of life. As discussed in Chapter 10, positive social interactions play a strong role in the proper development of a baby's brain. Medical support includes all aspects of health care, including medications and pharmacological interventions, surgical interventions, dental intervention, and intervention for any vision or hearing problems that might exist. Other forms of support include physiotherapy, speech and language therapy, interventions designated as assistive, infant stimulation programs, early childhood intervention programs, and other types of programs.

Some developmental disabilities such as Down syndrome, fragile X syndrome, cerebral palsy and autism have particular needs of which professionals should be aware (see other chapters in this volume about these disorders). In most developed countries, newborns are screened for at least congenital hypothyroidism, phenylketonuria, and galactosemia. This screening is done on small blood samples, usually taken from a baby's heel. In Ontario, as of 2010, screening is done for at least 28 metabolic, endocrine, and blood disorders. These disorders include the 3 congenital problems mentioned above and cystic fibrosis. Individually, these disorders are rare, but will, as a group, affect approximately 150 out of 140,000 newborns. (See the Ontario Newborn

Screening Program, 2003, for additional information.) Treatments for such conditions do exist and are immediately implemented for babies with these conditions. If a baby is born with a cardiac or gastrointestinal problem, surgical intervention is carried out (if warranted).

It also is important to have a baby's hearing and vision checked as early as possible and to provide remediation if there is a problem. Blocked hearing due to middle ear infection is a common condition that can lead to language difficulty in young children. In many countries, consideration is now being given to the implementation of routine newborn screening programs for hearing. In Canada, this is done routinely (see More Resources for information about hearing tests). There are many different causes of vision impairment in newborns. Corrective measures should be taken as soon as possible to ensure that children do not become blind as the result of potentially correctable causes, such as cataracts and retinopathy of prematurity (Rudanko & Laatikainen, 2004).

It is estimated that another 15% to 18% of children (in the U.S.) have some degree of intellectual/developmental or behavioural disability that would benefit from intervention. An additional 7% to 10% experience school failure and drop out before completion of high school. Overall, one in four children has serious psychosocial problems. To ensure that such children are identified early and that their dif-

Case Study 2: Matt

The family doctor finally told Dianne that her son Matt had Down syndrome. The doctor explained that he had suspected this at birth, but wanted Matt's parents to learn to love him and know him as a person before they were told. The doctor believed that this bonding process would ensure that they made the right decisions with respect to raising their child. Dianne was surprised that the doctor knew about her son's disability all along and did not say anything to her, but she also appreciated the concern the doctor had for her child and their whole family.

ficulties are addressed, it has been recommended that pediatricians use screening tools at each health supervision visit (Glascoe, 2000). It is not always possible to perform effective screening for developmental disability. In some countries, doctors are reluctant to carry out such testing because they consider that they are not adequately reimbursed. For those doctors willing to perform the screening, young patients are not always compliant and their families are not always interested.

Recognizing and diagnosing disability in the preschool years

Chapters 10, 12 and 13 discuss a number of different ways that developmental disability can first be recognized. Observant parents, other family members, friends, family doctors, or other professionals may recognize particular developmental characteristics, or realize that a child is not meeting his or her developmental milestones. These principal milestones include sitting at 6 months, crawling at 9 months followed by creeping, walking at about a year, and putting words together in meaningful ways beginning at about age 2 (later for boys) (see also Chapter 10 and Resources).

Identifying developmental disability in a young child can be a challenge for doctors and psychologists, especially if the child is non-verbal, has behaviour problems, or has a disability that is borderline. Determining the primary cause of the disability is a process that sometimes takes a number of years, and for many children the cause is never known. Certain disorders are screened for or are recognizable at birth, but a great many go unnoticed for months or even years due to their mildness and the lack of observed, delayed milestones necessary for diagnosis. Sometimes the diagnosis is not made until the child starts school and has trouble keeping up with other children (see Chapter 41 for information on comprehensive pre-school systems for children with intellectual/developmental delays).

Although learning about their child's disability within minutes or days after birth may be a shock to parents, experiencing anxiety for months or years after a child is born because of suspicion that there might be a problem can be disabling for families. For most parents, it is better to know early, even if it is a shock, so that action to help the child and the family can be taken. Parents' and other people's concerns about a child's development should always be taken seriously. Most family physicians are responsive and helpful, and readily refer the family to a specialist, such as a pediatrician, who has more knowledge of childhood disabilities. At times, though, parents or advocates may need to pursue more formal diagnostic procedures aggressively with their doctors, as some physicians are overly reliant on "clinical judgement," which has been shown in some research studies to detect fewer than 30% of children with developmental disability. It is not uncommon for parents of a child subsequently found to have a developmental disability to have been told by their doctor that "the child is just being herself," or that their parenting skills may not be the best. In many countries, the diagnosis of developmental disability or a specific

Case Study 3: Tommy

Tommy's pediatrician told his parents that he was developing typically. When Tommy's mother insisted that there was a problem, the doctor told her not to worry about Tommy not talking and that he would begin talking when he was ready. When Tommy was 3 years old, his parents took him to see a child psychologist at their local mental health clinic. The psychologist recognized that Tommy showed classic symptoms of autism.

type of developmental disability must be done by a physician or a psychologist, but the process can be initiated by anyone. (See Chapters 1, 13 and others for further information about how to obtain a diagnosis of developmental disability).

As hinted in Case Study 1, doctors sometimes underestimate how well parents can take the diagnosis. Some withhold the information for fear of being the "bearer of bad news." It is likely that parents are more accepting of a physician deliberately holding back diagnostic information if there is a specific benefit for the child. As in the case presented in Case Study 2, a family physician may think it best for parents to bond with their child before the child's disability is revealed to them. Studies have determined that not all mothers experience feelings of love for their baby in the first hours or even days after birth. One U.S. study found that even though 41% of mothers feel love for their baby even before the baby is born, 35% of mothers feel love for the child only after more than a week's time of nurturing and being with the child (MacFarlane et al., 1978).

Advice for parents on getting the diagnosis

Parents spend much more time with their child than any professional does, and are often the first to become aware of a problem. If parents suspect that their child may have a disability, it is important to do the following:

- Check a list of warning signs and symptoms provided by the relevant disability organization (see also Chapter 13 of this book).
- Visit a local library or search the Internet for additional reading material or information on

the disability (not all Internet sites are credible and some may not have fully accurate information on the disability; parents are recommended to visit Internet sites associated with recognized organizations for people with disabilities; see the Resources section for examples).

- Ask for a second opinion. Some professionals are more knowledgeable on the topic of disabilities than others.
- Keep track of the child's progress and possible manifestations of disability, such as missed milestones, that suggest he or she may be delayed.

Getting a referral to a specialist

Once parents are made aware of a problem, they may be referred by a family doctor, pediatrician, or clinic to a specialist or a diagnostic group. Parents may also self-refer (see Case Study 3).

When parents are not sure what the child's problem is or whether a problem even exists, the search for a specialist can be complicated. It can be helpful to conduct the search through a community healthcare or social service organization. In searching for knowledgeable professionals, parents should remember that a multifaceted team can offer more information and can evaluate the child more comprehensively than a single specialist. This team may consist of such professionals as a pediatrician, a children's education specialist, a physical therapist, an occupational therapist, a speech language pathologist, an orthopedic surgeon, a psychologist, a psychiatrist, an ophthalmologist, and an audiologist, among others. Teams of specialists are often found at larger hospitals, especially those classified as university teaching hospitals.

Understanding the diagnosis

Obtaining the diagnosis from a professional or diagnostic group is one step forward for the child. Understanding the meaning of the diagnosis and its immediate and long-term implications are just as important for parents. It is important for professionals to simplify the diagnosis into terms that the parents are able to fully comprehend. It is also important for parents to learn as much as possible about their child's disability so that, in time, they will become familiar with special terms and the many other aspects of the disability.

There has been a dramatic increase and improvement in the quality of information available on the Internet. However, not all web sites portray credible and accurate information. The following questions should be considered when trying to judge the quality of the Internet information:

- Who is presenting the information?
- With whom are they affiliated?
- What is their background?
- When was the information last updated?
- Is this web site linked with or sponsored by companies?
- Is there disclosure of sponsorship, advertising policies, and conflicts of interest?
- Where is the information coming from?

Other valuable sources of information come from articles included in PubMed, PsycInfo, and other databases. In order to have free access to full articles in the PubMed and PsycInfo databases, a library card from an organization that subscribes to these facilities is usually required. Another good option is to visit sites associated with recognized organizations for people with disabilities.

Parent-professional communication

The importance of communication between parents and professionals cannot be overemphasized. Often, because parents are so highly motivated to become educated and to take constructive action, their knowledge about the disorder and available resources may exceed that of the professionals with whom they are interacting. Professionals should be receptive to learning from parents and be respectful of their knowledge, their attitudes, and their concerns. Occasionally, barriers to communication can lead to difficulties in relationships between professionals and families/caregivers. Strategies for dealing with such difficulties are discussed in detail in Chapter 25.

Issues for Parents

As noted in the preceding section, parents of young children with disabilities face recognizing and understanding the nature of their child's delay, and almost always must establish links and communications with specialized professionals. This section presents other issues that are specific to these parents.

Challenges and rewards of having a child with developmental disability

Parenting a child with a developmental disability can be very challenging indeed. But it also brings rewards, and provides opportunities for parents and siblings to learn and experience many new things. In one study (Renwick, Brown, & Raphael, 1998), in which 35 sets of parents were interviewed in depth, parents explained that their lives were enriched by having a child with a disability in a wide variety of ways. On the other hand, they readily identified a long list of challenges that they faced as parents. It is essential for new parents of a child with a disability to understand that:

- Their lives will be enriched in some ways.
- They will face many challenges that they would not face with a non-disabled child.
- They are not alone — there are many other parents who share their experiences.
- Medical and other professionals do not necessarily have expertise on disability.
- It is probably best to look for support and practical help from a variety of sources.

Grief and accepting disability

When parents first learn about their child's disability and have not been prepared for this possibility, it is not uncommon for them to feel shocked and numb. Parents may feel overwhelmed by feelings of denial, rejection, guilt, suffering, withdrawal, and other emotions. Nearly all parents and other family members of children with disabilities go through periods of grief, even though individuals experience and show their grief in different ways and to different degrees. Mothers may become furious at spouses who seem to be taking the situation calmly, but the fathers may still feel upset. It is less common for men to grieve openly — their grief may emerge as unusual quietness (Dickman & Gordon, 1985).

Discovering that their child has a disability may cause parents to cry, shout, scream, or curse. These may well be the best ways to handle the situation — to get the feelings out into the open in order to get on with living. Many couples go through a stage of asking, "Why did it happen to us?" All feelings and thoughts are valid and are neither "good" nor "bad." However, it is important not to become overwhelmed by these feelings or a combination of conflicting emotions. As one parent put it, "Feelings are not 'bad' or 'good.' It is what you do about these feelings that is 'bad' or 'good.'" Parents must find the strength to move forward from their grief.

Supportive family and friends may be helpful when parents of a disabled child are overwhelmed by feelings of grief. They have the power to persuade their loved ones to "get on with it." Other parents who have a child with a disability and have had similar experiences can offer a special kind of understanding and solace that neither family, friends or professionals can. Joining such a support group and networking in other ways with parents of children with disabilities provides relief for many parents. (See Resources section of this chapter for contact information of such organizations.)

Sometimes, parents are so deeply caught up in despair that they require comfort and help beyond the level that close friends and family can provide. People who cannot cope may benefit enormously from professional counselling. These parents should ask their family doctors to refer them to a counsellor or refer themselves by contacting a local clinic.

Programs to assist in child care

Both parents-to-be and new parents are encouraged to take advantage of prenatal education classes, well-baby clinics, and visits from public health nurses. A new birth can be very demanding, and families, especially mothers, often need additional help at this time. In many places, there are groups for new mothers that provide them with opportunities for socializing, having adult conversation, and babysitting. Some new mothers have become inspired to form such groups themselves, if they are not available in the community. Mothers of babies and young children, with or without disabilities, take part in such groups.

The first 3 years are considered the most important for a child's development; therefore, the implementation of home-based programs for a child with special needs should be considered as early as possible. Home-based programs can help families access community resources, help parents identify and achieve personal goals, provide up to date information on children's growth and development, help to access developmental screening, and provide assistance with transportation to appointments. If a family is particularly strained, some respite services exist that provide caregivers with time to themselves. Family support programs can provide support and information to parents and to assist in personal and family crises.

Family support programs can also provide referrals, information about disabilities and genetic counselling, short-term care management, and crisis and stress relief. The programs' general health, safety and technical advice ranges from feeding, playing, toilet training, hygiene, and taking medication to finding schools, advocacy groups, and facilitating friendships. The support programs are also a source of information about entitlements, guardianship and legal issues, as well as various types of counselling. Parent matching groups connect families that have similar children. Such parent groups frequently provide a lot of information and support. Parents can also seek advice from guides for parents with a child who has a disability. One such guide is *One Miracle at a Time: A Guide for Parents of Disabled Children* (Dickman & Gordon, 1985).

Parenting a child with a disability

Effective parenting of a child with a disability includes learning as much as possible about the disability and keeping detailed records about the child. Detailed record keeping is essential for monitoring the child's progress. It is also important to provide such information to doctors, psychologists and other professionals involved in the care of the child. Parents may have a binder or notebook of contacts and telephone numbers. The following are some kinds of information that can be included:

- *Emergency telephone numbers*: First aid, ambulance, fire, police, important suppliers and providers for the child, depending on the disability.
- *The child's and parent's ID numbers*: These include social security numbers, health care numbers, and private insurance numbers.
- *The child's medical history*: If the child was born with the disability, this includes prenatal information about the child and parents, genetic background and other relevant data. Details about birth and shortly after birth are also relevant. Copies of hospital and medical records should be included where possible.
- *The child's medication record*: It is easy to forget the names of drugs or medications, why, when and for what purpose they were prescribed and whether they accomplished that purpose. Negative side effects should also be noted.
- *Informal notes on conferences, consultations, and conversations (face-to-face or on the phone)*: Parents can take note of questions asked and answers given at consultations with professionals, their recommendations and follow-up. When attending conferences, the purpose, participants, conclusions and suggestions should be noted. It may be a good idea to tape the conference, where permissible. Notes should also be taken on conversations with agency and school officials. Their names and telephone numbers should be recorded for follow-up purposes.
- *Correspondence*: This should include any letters to and from government and voluntary agencies, suppliers, school officials and others who have been contacted about the child's needs and problems.
- *The child's educational history*: This includes preschool programs and schools attended, infant stimulation and early intervention programs (with dates), names of teachers, therapists and resource personnel who work with the child; copies of report cards, test results, comments, assessments, individual education programs (IEPs) or other educational plans, and so forth.
- *The parent's observations of the child's behaviour*: Parents are often experts on their child. Parental observations are helpful and welcomed by physicians, therapists, teachers and other professionals. These observations are worth keeping; they identify problems and act as evidence that the child is making progress. Keeping a record can be therapeutic on its own for parents and other caregivers.

Managing care for a child with a disability

The arrival of a child with a disability can create stresses in a family and can be very challenging. However, the following things are known based on evidence from parents' experiences, as reported by Dickman and Gordon (1985):

- A family with a disabled child does not have to be disabled in any way.
- A family with a disabled child does not have to disintegrate under stress.
- It is not the child's disability specifically that creates family difficulties; rather, these difficulties are caused by the way that family members react to the disability and to one another.

Finding ways to deal with the added stresses, to minimize them and to overcome them by sharing them can draw a marriage and a family closer.

When a child with a disability becomes part of the family, tension may begin to mount, and it is not uncommon for some parents to find fault with and to blame one another. Yet, other parents say that the experience of bringing up a child with a disability has brought them closer together, making their marriage stronger. Essential to the well being of the marriage *and* the child is communication between the parents. Couples must find a way to talk together about their child. This often means bringing other people, such as the child's siblings, into the discussion. Each family needs to work out an effective communication pattern. For some families, this may mean sitting around the kitchen table once a week. For others, communicating might occur more sporadically. Whatever the case, feelings should be shared, as this will foster an inclusive environment where all family members feel validated. When parents cannot cope with managing a child with a disability, they should seek professional counselling and help.

Siblings are an important part of the support network for the disabled child. The child's brothers and sisters should be informed as much as possible about the nature of the disability, according to each sibling's age and ability to understand and deal with the information. One way to improve sibling adjustment to, and understanding of, the disability is to join a sibling group or a sibling-parent group. This understanding will make it easier to reconcile the extra time parents must spend on the care of the child with a disability. Although siblings may understand this at an intellectual level, on an emotional level they may still feel jealous, neglected or shortchanged. In families that have one child with a disability, it is often not possible for parents to spend equal amounts of time with their other children. This can be frustrating for parents who want the best for all of their children. One way to manage this is to set aside "special time" for every child in the family (Dickman & Gordon, 1985). The length of time is not as important as the fact that special attention and nurturing is given to the siblings. One study noted that children appreciated when parents tried to be equitable about dividing their time, even when parents were often unsuccessful, and that children also appreciated open communication and time spent together (Pit-Ten Cate & Loots, 2000).

Respite care for the child with the disability can provide parents with the time and opportunity to spend time with their other children. Many parents also find it helpful to provide special rewards, such as praise or privileges, to both sons and daughters for helping to care for and look out for their sibling with a disability. Even though some children may find it normal that they help with the care of their brother or sister with a disability, parents should take care to ensure that children do not bear an "undue burden of care," which is often the case with older siblings

(especially girls) of children with disabilities (Pit-Ten Cate & Loos, 2000).

Siblings can make an extremely important contribution to the development of the child with disabilities, to the degree to which he or she is accepted by peers, and to the stability of family life. This contribution needs to be recognized.

Dealing with family and friends

New parents will probably need guidance and practical assistance to deal positively with family and friends. Two particular studies with parents of children with developmental disabilities point to this need (Brown, Anand, Fung, Isaacs, & Baum, 2003; Renwick et al., 1998). In these studies, most parents considered care and responsibility for their children with disabilities to be an "in family" concern and, as a consequence, they relied little on others. Their reasons for doing so were as follows:

- People other than family members do not understand a child with a disability.
- People other than family members do not know how to handle or talk to a child with a disability.
- Parents feel embarrassed about the behaviour of their child.
- Parents do not want to burden other people with their child's disability.

However, these parents did not identify acceptance by other people as being a particular problem for them. It appeared from their responses that relatives, friends, and people in the general public are often much more accepting of disability than many parents at first believe. Still, there are many ways that new parents can help relatives, friends and others understand and accept disability in their child. First, they need to discuss the disability openly, explain its nature and what can be expected in the future. Second, they can provide opportunities for others to interact with, and care for, their child with disabilities — as they would for a child who does not have disabilities. Third, they can include the child with disabilities in their social activities to the extent that is comfortable — again, as they would a child without disabilities. Finally, they may need to make extra efforts to instruct others on what they should say, what they should do and how they should react. It is important to realize that most other people do not have experience with children who have disabilities and simply may not know what they should do. Typically, they welcome some helpful pointers from the parents.

As noted, siblings of children with developmental disabilities share the experience of disability in their families and often form a special bond with a sister or brother who has a developmental disability (Lamb & Sutton-Smith, 1982; McPhail, 1996). However, types of sibling relationships can vary enormously, depending on a great many factors. Factors that appear to help include setting a positive family atmosphere and interacting with others in positive ways (Greenberg et al., 1999; McPhail, 1996). Yet parents should be aware that siblings of a child with developmental disabilities often feel an ongoing sense of loss and sometimes experience ridicule from other children (McPhail, 1996). For both parents and siblings, it is important to take initiative in dealing with relatives, friends and others in positive ways. Because parents and siblings usually do not have experience with this and may be dealing with considerable adjustment themselves, they very often need some help and guidance. Knowledgeable counsellors, or health, early childhood, or social services professionals can be very helpful in this regard. There are also numerous parent and family support groups (known to local social service organizations; see also More Resources) that provide invaluable help to new parents of infants with developmental disabilities. Many families find it very helpful to connect to these groups as soon as possible.

Summary

Preconceptional and prenatal health are pivotal for the healthy development of babies. Families can sometimes choose whether to have children with certain types of disabilities or genetic disorders. Such choices may involve the use of genetic counselling, the decision not to continue a pregnancy for which prenatal testing indicates disability in the fetus, and avoidance of pregnancy if parents know

there is a risk for having a child with a disability. However, such approaches for prevention are not acceptable to everyone.

The first 3 years of a child's life are considered to be the most influential in their development. General early life issues include good nutrition, good medical care, good parenting methods and procedures that ensure the best development and quality of life for the child. Early life issues in families of a child with a suspected disability include getting a diagnosis, understanding the diagnosis, communicating a diagnosis to families and friends, coping with grief, establishing a good rapport with health care and other professionals involved in the child's care (sometimes educating the professionals), and getting all forms of supports needed for the child with the disability and for family members.

For Further Thought and Discussion

1. Marta has just found out that her 4-year-old son has Fragile X syndrome and that she is a carrier of the fragile X mutation. Marta's parents decided to be tested for the fragile X mutation as well. Marta found out that she inherited a Fragile X mutation from her mother. Marta and her parents know that Marta's sister, Joy, wants very much to have a baby, and that Joy may or may not have inherited a fragile X mutation from her mother. They do not know if they should tell Joy, as Joy once mentioned that she would never consider genetic counselling for an inherited disorder in the family. How would you handle the situation if you were Marta or her parents?

2. Rose is a single mother of a 5 year old girl with severe cerebral palsy. She has a job that enables her to manage financially. Until recently, she had a wonderful live-in caregiver for her daughter. Unfortunately, the caregiver became very ill and Rose had to arrange for nursing care from an agency. Each week, a different nurse comes to the house, and Rose has to spend an enormous amount of time training each new person about her daughter's needs. Rose's employer has become concerned about the amount of time

Rose takes off from work. Also, professional nursing assistance is far more expensive than live-in care, and Rose knows that this cannot continue indefinitely. What course of action would you recommend?

3. Riva and Invid have a son with autism who requires a great deal of their time. Their other son is engaging in challenging behaviour because he feels neglected. What can Riva and Invid do to help both their children and improve their family life?

More Resources

Assisted reproduction:

Assisted Reproduction. The Reproductive Sciences Center, La Jolla, CA.
http://www.fertile.com/

Assisted Reproductive Technology in Canada
http://www.cadth.ca/index.php/en/hta/ reports-publications/health-technology-update/ issue-10-september-2008/assisted-reproductive

Billings ovulation method:

Billings Ovulation Method Effectiveness Studies
http://www.naomi.ie/effect.htm

World Organisation Ovulation Method Billings (WOOMB
www.woomb.org

Ontario Ministry of Children and Youth Services:

Can Your Baby Hear?
http://www.children.gov.on.ca/htdocs/English/topics/ earlychildhood/hearing/brochure_hear.aspx

Infant Hearing Program Locations
http://www.children.gov.on.ca/htdocs/English/topics/ earlychildhood/hearing/where.aspx

Prenatal Testing:

Prenatal Testing
http://www.nlm.nih.gov/medlineplus/prenataltesting. html.

Prenatal screening tests for the detection of Down syndrome, trisomy 18 and open neural tube defects. Reference guide for health care providers.
http://www.beststart.org/events/detail/ bsannualconf08/presentations/B2_1_ho.pdf

Other Resources:

Levine, M. D., Carey, W. B., & Crocker, A. C. (1992). *Developmental-behavioural pediatrics*, (2nd ed.) Philadelphia: W.B. Saunders Company.

References

Anderson, P., & Doyle, L. W. (2003). Victorian Infant Collaborative Study Group. Neurobehavioral outcomes of school-age children born extremely low birth weight or very preterm in the 1990s. *The Journal of the American Medical Association, 289,* 3264-3272.

Assisted human reproduction: Regulating and treating conception problems (Feb. 5, 2009). *CBC News*. Retrieved from http://www.cbc.ca/health/ story/2009/02/05/f-reprotech.html

Billings, E., & Westmore, A. (1998). *The Billings method: Controlling fertility without drugs or devices.* Toronto, ON: Life Cycle Books.

Brown, I., Anand, S., Fung, W. L. A., Isaacs, B., & Baum, N. (2003). Family quality of life: Canadian results from an international study. *Journal of Developmental and Physical Disabilities, 15,* 207-230.

Cederholm, M., Haglund, B., & Axelsson, O. (2005). Infant morbidity following amniocentesis and chorionic villus sampling for prenatal karyotyping. *BJOG: An International Journal of Obstetrics and Gynaecology, 112,* 394-402.

Coleman, P. K., Reardon, D. C., & Cougle, J. (2002). The quality of the caregiving environment and child developmental outcomes associated with maternal history of abortion using the NLYS data. *Journal of Child Psychology and Psychiatry, 43,* 743-757.

Cooper, A. R., & Jungheim, E. S. (2010). Preimplantation genetic testing: Indications and controversies. *Clinics in Laboratory Medicine, 30*(3), 519-531.

Cranley Glass, K., Weijer, C., Palmour, R. M., Shapiro, S. H., Lemmens, T. M., & Lebacqz, K. (1996). Structuring the review of human genetics protocols: Gene localization and identification studies. *IRB: A Review of Human Subjects Research, 18*(4), 1-9.

Cunniff, C., & Hudgins, L. (2010). Prenatal genetic screening and diagnosis for pediatricians. *Current Opinion in Pediatrics,* Sep 8.

Dickman, I. R., & Gordon, S. (1985). *One miracle at a time: A guide for parents of disabled children.* New York: Simon and Schuster.

Endevelt, R., Blau, A., Neville, A., Shvartzman, P., & Shvarts, S. (2003). [Mothers know best] *Harefuah, 142,* 728-733, 808.

Ensenauer, R. E., Michels, V. V, & Reinke, S. S. (2005). Genetic testing: Practical, ethical, and counseling considerations. *Mayo Clinic Proceedings, 80,* 63-73.

Ferguson-Smith, M. A. (2008). Cytogenetics and the evolution of medical genetics. *Genetics in Medicine, 10*(8), 553-559.

Fergusson, D. M., Horwood, L. J., & Ridder, E. M. (2006). Abortion in young women and subsequent mental health. *Journal of Child Psychology and Psychiatry, 47,* 267-273.

Genetic Resources Ontario. (2009). Retrieved from http://www.geneticresourcesontario.ca/

Glascoe, F. P. (2000). Early detection of developmental and behavioral problems. *Pediatrics in Review, 21*(8), 272-280.

Greenberg, J. S., Seltzer, M. M., Orsmond, G. I., & Krauss, M. W. (1999). Siblings of adults with mental illness or mental retardation: Current involvement and the expectation of future care giving. *Psychiatry Services, 50,* 1214-1219.

Greydanus, D. E., Rimsza, M. E., & Matytsina, L. (2005). Contraception for college students. *Pediatric Clinics of North America, 52,* 135-161.

Hajian-Tilaki, K. O., & Kaveh-Ahangar, T. (2010). Reproductive factors associated with breast cancer risk in northern Iran. *Medical Oncology,* Apr 3. [Epub ahead of print].

Harrod, K. S., Hanson, L., VandeVusse, L., & Heywood, P. (2003). Rh negative status and isoimmunization update: A case-based approach to care. *Journal of Perinatal & Neonatal Nursing, 17,* 106-178.

Haas, J. S., Fuentes-Afflick, E., Stewart, A. L., Jack-son, R. A., Dean, M. L., Brawarsky, P., & Escobar, G. J. (2005). Pepregnancy health status and the risk of preterm delivery. *Archives of Pediatric & Adolescent Medicine, 159,* 58-63.

Hilborn, R. (Sept. 16, 2010). Provincial help for the infertile in Canada—free IVF in Québec; tax help in Manitoba; Ontario balks. *Fertility Helper.* Retrieved from http://www.familyhelper.net/iy/news/100917quebecivf.html

Hourrier, S., Salomon, L. J., Dreux, S., & Muller, F. (2010). Screening for adverse pregnancy outcome at early gestational age. *Clinica Chimica Acta, 411*(21-22), 1547-1552.

Huang, T., Hoffman, B., Meschino, W., Kingdom, J., & Okun, N. (2010). Prediction of adverse pregnancy outcomes by combinations of first and second trimester biochemistry markers used in the routine prenatal screening of Down syndrome. *Prenatal Diagnosis, 30*(5), 471-417.

Joint SOGC-Motherisk Clinical Practice Guideline No. 201. (2007). Retrieved from http://www.sogc.org/media/pdf/advisories/JOGC-dec-07-FOLIC.pdf

Johnson, B. A. (2005). Insertion and removal of intrauterine devices. *American Family Physician, 71,* 95-102.

Lamb, M. E., & Sutton-Smith, B. (1982). *Sibling relationships.* Hillsdale, NJ: Lawrence Erlbaum.

Larsson, L., & Lindqvist, P. G. (2005). Low-impact exercise during pregnancy − a study of safety. *Acta Obstetricia et Gynecologica Scandinavica, 84,* 34-38.

Lashwood, A. (2005). Preimplantation genetic diagnosis to prevent disorders in children. *British Journal of Nursing, 14*(2), 64-70.

Licenced International Adoption Agencies, Ministry of Children and Youth Services. (n.d.). Retrieved from http://www.children.gov.on.ca/htdocs/English/topics/adoption/internationaladoption.aspx

Lumbiganon, P., Winiyakul, N., Chongsomchai, C., & Chaisiri K. (2004). From research to practice: The example of antenatal care in Thailand. *Bulletin of the World Health Organization, 82,* 746-749.

Machalek, K., Percy, M., & Brown, I. (2007). Prenatal and early life. In I. Brown & M. Percy (Eds.),

A *comprehensive guide to intellectual and developmental disabilities* (pp. 433-450). Baltimore: Paul H. Brookes Publishing Co.

March of Dimes. (2010). *Working together for stronger, healthier babies.* Retrieved from http://www.marchofdimes.com/pregnancy/pregnancy.html

Mason, P., & Narad, C. (2005). International adoption: A health and developmental perspective. *Seminars on Speech and language, 26,* 1-9.

McPhail, E. (1996). A parent's perspective: Quality of life in families with a member with disabilities. In R. Renwick, I. Brown, & M. Nagler (Eds.), *Quality of life in health promotion and rehabilitation* (pp. 279-289). Thousand Oaks, CA: Sage Publications.

Melzer, K., Schutz, Y., Boulvain, M., & Kayser, B. (2010). Physical activity and pregnancy: Cardiovascular adaptations, recommendations and pregnancy outcomes. *Sports Medicine, 40*(6), 493-507.

The Merck Manuals Online Medical Library. Home Edition. (2010). Retrieved from http://www.merck.com/mmhe/index.html

Midwifery Links, Canadian Association of Midwives. (n.d.). Retrieved from http://www.naho.ca/inuit/midwifery/MidwiferyLinks.php

Midwifery in Ontario, Ministry of Health and Long Term Care. (2003). Retrieved from http://www.health.gov.on.ca/english/public/program/midwife/midwife_mn.html

Moalem, S., Weinberg, E. D., & Percy, M. E. (2004). Hemochromatosis and the enigma of misplaced iron: Implications for infectious disease and survival. *Biometals, 17,* 135-139.

Moore, V. M., & Davies, M. J. (2005). Diet during pregnancy, neonatal outcomes and later health. *Reproduction, Fertility, and Development, 17,* 341-348.

Moreau, C., Kaminski, M., Yves Ancel, P., Bouyer, J., Escande, B., Thiriez, G., Boulot, P., Fresson, J., Arnaud, C., Subtil, D., Marpeau, L., Roze, J-C., Maillard, F., Larroque, B., & EPIPAGE Group. (2005). Previous induced abortions and the risk of very preterm delivery: Results of the EPIPAGE study. BJOG: *An International Journal of Obstetrics and Gynaecology, 112,* 430-437.

Ontario Newborn Screening Program, Ministry of Health and Long-Term Care. (2003). Retrieved from http://www.health.gov.on.ca/english/providers/program/child/screening/screen_sum.html

Pit-Ten Cate, I. M., & Loots, G. M. (2000). Experiences of siblings of children with physical disabilities: An empirical investigation. *Disability and Rehabilitation, 22,* 309-408.

Policy Statement Archives. (1995). Points to consider: Ethical, legal, and psychosocial implications of genetic testing in children and adolescents. *American Journal of Human Genetics, 57,* 1233-1241. Retrieved from http://www.ashg.org/pages/statement_ajhg57.shtml

Prenatal Care. (2010). Retrieved from http://www.nlm.nih.gov/medlineplus/prenatalcare.html

Prenatal Nutrition, Health Canada. (2010). Retrieved from http://www.hc-sc.gc.ca/fn-an/nutrition/prenatal/index-eng.php

Quaid, K. A., Jessup, N. M., & Meslin, E. M. (2004). Disclosure of genetic information obtained through research. *Genetic Testing, 8,* 347-355.

Ramakrishnan, U. (2004). Nutrition and low birth weight: From research to practice. *The American Journal of Clinical Nutrition, 79,* 17-21.

Renwick, R., Brown, I., & Raphael, D. (1997). *The family quality of life project: Final report. Report to the Ontario Ministry of Community and Social Services, Developmental Services Branch.* Toronto, ON: Centre for Health Promotion, University of Toronto.

Ring-Cassidy, E., & Gentles, I. (2003). *Women's health after abortion: The medical and psychological evidence* (2nd ed.). Toronto, ON: The deVeber Institute for Bioethics and Social Research.

Robertson, S., & Savulescu, J. (2001). Is there a case in favour of predictive genetic testing in young children? *Bioethics, 15,* 26-49.

Rudanko, S. L., & Laatikainen, L. (2004). Visual impairment in children born at full term from 1972 through 1989 in Finland. *Opthalmology, 111,* 2307-2312.

Salem, L., & Singer, K. R. (2010). Rh Incompatibility. *E-Medicine.* Retrieved from http://emedicine.medscape.com/article/797150-overview

Simmons, E. M., Rogers, M. L., Frierson, G. M., Beckwith, C. G., & Flanigan, T. P. (2005). Racial/ethnic attitudes towards HIV testing in the primary care setting. *Journal of the National Medical Association, 97*, 46-52.

Simpson, J. L. (2010). Preimplantation genetic diagnosis at 20 years. *Prenatal Diagnosis, 30*(7), 682-695.

Singer, E., Antonucci, T., & Van Hoewyk, J. (2004). Racial and ethnic variations in knowledge and attitudes about genetic testing. *Genetic Testing, 8,* 31-43.

Summers, A. M., Farrell, S. A., Huang, T., Meier, C., & Wyatt, P. R. (2003). Maternal serum screening in Ontario using the triple marker test. *Journal of Medical Screening, 10,* 107-111.

Wagle, S., & Deshpande, P. G. (2010). Hemolytic disease of newborn. *Emedicine.* Retrieved from http://www.emedicine.com/ped/topic959.htm

Wald, N. J. (2010). Prenatal screening for open neural tube defects and Down syndrome: Three decades of progress. *Prenatal Diagnosis, 30*(7), 619-621.

World HIV & AIDS Statistics. (n.d.). Retrieved from http://www.avert.org/worldstats.htm

Zimmermann, B. G., Grill, S., Holzgreve, W., Zhong, X. Y., Jackson, L. G., & Hahn, S. (2008). Digital PCR: A powerful new tool for noninvasive prenatal diagnosis? *Prenatal Diagnosis, 28*(12), 1087-1093.

Early Intervention for Young Children

Elaine B. Frankel and Kathryn Underwood

What you will learn:

- Children grow and develop at different rates as they explore their environments and interact with family and significant caregivers

- Biological disposition, cultural expectation and environmental experience all impact on and affect the young child's healthy development

- Some children are at risk for developmental delays because biological or environmental conditions impact development

- Central to the child's development is the care and education each receives from conception to age six, when the foundation for the child's social, emotional, intellectual and physical growth is set

- It is critical to intervene and provide services at an early stage of growth to children at risk for developmental delay and their families

- Inclusive, family-centred and collaborative team practices are the preferred way to support the child and family in the community

Sunny Hills Public School provides a full-day early learning program to its community as part of the Ontario early learning initiative. Situated within the school is Creative Kids, a childcare centre, and Creative Families, a family resource program. Jessica, Carlos, Nidi, and Matthew arrive at their childcare centre giggling at each other's hair styles — done up for "wacky hair day" at the centre. They are followed by their parents, who bring them to the centre each morning. They are each three years old and live in the same neighbourhood. Jessica has a congenital hearing impairment. Her mothers have been teaching her sign language since she was an infant.

Carlos has fragile medical conditions that have impacted his development. Nidi and her family recently emigrated from India. They are struggling with language barriers and a sense of isolation since extended family members still live in India. Matthew has Fragile X syndrome and has recently been diagnosed with autism. His family's first language is Korean.

Eileen, the childcare centre's director, arranges transdisciplinary team meetings for each family throughout the year to review the child's progress. The team includes the family, the centre director, the classroom early childhood educators, the centre's resource con-

sultant, and other professionals appropriate to each child and family's challenges. For Jessica, a speech-language therapist and audiologist are included. Nidi's meeting includes an interpreter who speaks Hindi and a settlement specialist from the family resource program. Included in Matthew's meeting are his occupational therapist, intensive behavioural therapist, and an interpreter who speaks Korean. Since Matthew will be turning 4 this year and will soon enter the all day kindergarten program at Sunny Hills Public School, the junior kindergarten receiving teacher also attends a transition meeting. Together they identify the child and family's strengths, abilities, challenges and goals. Through this collaborative effort, the team produces an inclusion plan that provides environmental adaptations and teaching strategies to best support each child in his or her development, learning, and success.

All young children require environments and experiences that optimize their growth, learning and development. For infants and young children at risk for developmental delays, it becomes essential that early intervention services that promote healthy child development are available to them and their families. These services identify young children in the community who are at risk for developmental delays and support their development. Early identification and intervention services are critical to minimizing and even eliminating the effects of conditions associated with children at risk for delays in development (Carpenter, 2005, p. 95). Some children may be developmentally at risk because of biological factors such as low birth-weight; others are born with established conditions, including chromosomal disorders; and still others must cope with poverty, violence, poor nutrition, and other environmental conditions. Wolery and Bailey (2002) described the expected outcomes of early intervention as those that have an impact on the child and family including:

1. To promote children's engagement, independence, and mastery
2. To promote children's development in key domains
3. To build children's social competence
4. To promote children's generalized use of skills

5. To prepare children for normalized life experiences in the community and in the school
6. To prevent the emergence of future problems or disabilities
7. To achieve positive family perceptions of the early intervention experience
8. To achieve positive family perceptions of the impact of the early intervention on the child and family

Neuroscientific investigations continue to support the importance of providing appropriate early experiences and environments for optimal brain development (Shonkoff & Phillips, 2000). In the early years of a child's development, the brain's rapid growth and ability to self-correct offers a window of opportunity to reverse or minimize the effects of risk conditions such as brain injury, chromosomal anomalies or environmental stress (McCain & Mustard, 1999). Positive effects are enhanced when children are identified and referred to appropriate intervention services early in their development. Over time, most children at-risk for delays, who have received adapted early learning experiences and individualized interventions, present with less severe developmental problems and improved quality of life outcomes (Brown, Odom, & Conroy, 2001; Odom et al., 2004).

The underlying principle of early intervention that it is better to intervene at an early age for children at-risk for developmental delays than not to intervene assumes high quality early learning and care for all children. Mackenzie-Keating and Kysela (1997) have called early intervention the "least dangerous assumption." This chapter describes the legislative, theoretical, and empirical understandings of the positive and perceived benefits of early intervention for children and families.

Legislative Context

Early intervention in Ontario today assumes a rights-based approach to children's care, development, and education. The United Nations *Convention on the Rights of the Child* (1989), to which Canada is signatory, stipulates that all children with physical or mental disabilities "should enjoy a full and decent life, in conditions which ensure dignity, promote self-reliance, and facilitate the child's active participation in the community" (A. 23, s.1). The United Nations *Convention on the Rights of Persons with Disabilities* (2006) further states that children with disabilities have a right to early intervention (A. 25 s.b) and to education "on an equal basis with others in the communities in which they live" (A. 24 s.2b.). This convention has been ratified by the Government of Canada (United Nations, 2010).

Both the Canadian Charter of Rights and Freedoms (1982) and the Ontario Human Rights Code (1990) legislate the rights of all individuals to equal treatment and protection under the law without discrimination in respect to services and facilities. This right includes access to and equal participation in education for children with disabilities. In cases where supports are not provided, but are required for a child's full participation in education, the child's stated right is considered to be infringed upon. This right may include providing support to families for fostering their child's development and education (Dunst & Dempsey, 2007).

The Ontario Day Nurseries Act (1990) and its regulations support inclusion for children with developmental disabilities. However, the decision to include a child with developmental disabilities in an early childhood setting requires administrators and staff to change and modify policies and instructional practices (Frankel & McKay, 1997; Sandall, McLean, & Smith, 2000) and to increase access to inclusive education (Pivak, McComas, & LaFlamme, 2002). This change is a process that involves all participants over time (Frankel & McKay, 1997; Fullan, 2007).

Early Intervention in Ontario

In Ontario today, early intervention services are acknowledged as foundational to the provincial strategy in support of young children, their healthy development and their school success. High quality early intervention services in the child's community are guided by the principles of: a) inclusion, b) family-centred care, and c) collaborative team approaches. Each of these is described more fully below.

Early intervention and inclusion

Early childhood inclusion values the right of every child to belong as an active full participant in the family, community and society in which he or she lives (Division for Early Childhood [DEC]/National Association of the Education of Young Children [NAEYC], 2009). Inclusion promotes policies and practices that provide opportunities for children with and without disabilities to participate together in programs with the recognition that each child will receive individualized attention based on his or her abilities. Inclusive early intervention services for infants and young children with developmental delays is based on the philosophy that all children belong together and can learn together in all aspects of community life. This includes such things as going to the park, neighbourhood early childhood programs, or going to the local library with peers.

At the core of successful inclusive early intervention are high quality services that provide access, full participation and appropriate supports to enhance each child's learning and development (DEC/NAEYC, 2009). Within inclusive early childhood settings, children may have very different learning needs, learning styles and rates of learning, yet each child's growth is appreciated and encouraged.

Converging evidence suggests that the positive developmental outcomes associated with early intervention can be achieved in inclusive early childhood settings where children with developmental delays play and learn alongside their typically developing peers (for a review of the research see Odom et al., 2004). In inclusive settings, children with developmental delays begin to imitate the more sophisticated play, language and social interactions of their peer models (Guralnick, 1992; Odom & Brown, 1993). Children with severe disabilities in inclusive settings are reported to perform better on standardized indicators of development (Hundert, Mahoney, Mundy, & Vernon, 1998), and on measures of language and social skills development than those in segregated settings (Rafferty, Piscitelli, & Boettcher, 2003). Greater gains in social-emotional functioning were made in inclusive settings than in self-contained settings by chil-

Box 1: Why Inclusion?

- *It's the law! Laws and human rights codes support inclusion.*

- *It's the right thing to do! Morally, segregation on the grounds of disabling conditions unfairly excludes one group from the culturally normative setting, and is thus never appropriate.*

- *It works! Research supports the benefits of inclusion for children and families with and without disabilities.*

- *Society benefits! An inclusive environment encourages acceptance of diversity, tolerance, understanding and cooperation in all children.*

Sources: Bailey, McWilliam, & Wesley (1998); Irwin, Lero, & Brophy (2004).

dren with moderate social-emotional needs, while for children at a lower level of social-emotional growth gains were equal in inclusive and specialized programs (Holahan & Costenbader, 2000). These empirical findings give support to inclusion, not only as a moral and ethical imperative, but as a strategy to achieve positive developmental and educational outcomes for children.

In an inclusive early childhood setting, all children benefit. They become more sensitive, tolerant, and accepting of persons with disabilities (Diamond & Carpenter, 2000; Hestenes & Carroll, 2000). They learn to appreciate and embrace diversity.

An assessment of the early childhood inclusive environment can provide guidance for embedding interventions for a child with a developmental delay in the classroom (Hollingsworth, Boone, & Crais, 2009) and can promote professional development of staff (Buysse & Hollingsworth, 2009). Ecobehavioural assessments of classroom environments and behavioural interactions between a child with disabilities and adults and peers show that positive social interactions of children with disabilities are established in inclusive settings (Tsao, Odom, Buysse, Skinner, West, & Vitztum-Komanecki, 2008). In Canada the SpeciaLink Childcare Inclusion Practices Profile and Principles Scale (Lero, 2010) has been validated

to enable childcare programs to rate themselves as they move to full inclusion. The *Checklist for Quality Inclusive Education* (Early Childhood Resource Teacher Network of Ontario [ECRTNO], 1997), developed in Ontario, enables practitioners to review the environment and inclusive practices of childcare programs and provides staff with strategies for making classrooms more inclusive.

This is not to suggest, however, that a quality early childhood program that offers developmentally appropriate programming for its children is enough to assure continued gains for children with developmental delays. In other words, mere proximity to typically developing peers does not guarantee developmental advances for the child with a disability. Research now informs us that in order to promote successful developmental growth, individualized interventions must be provided that allow children with developmental delays to learn and apply functional behaviours and communication skills (Blackman, 2003; Guralnick, 1990).

Beyond educational and ethical rationales for early intervention services, there is a strong economic rationale for providing quality care and education to every child in Canada. Research shows that in Canada every $1 invested in childcare returns $1.45 to the economy (Prentice & McCracken, 2004). These benefits include increased opportunities for parents to work or pursue higher education, increased family income, decreased poverty and social assistance, and better short- and long-term outcomes for children through early identification of learning disabilities (Child Care Advocacy Association of Canada, 2008; Cleveland & Krashinsky, 1998; Prentice & McCracken, 2004). Money spent in early intervention and education will be paid back by adults who become productive contributing members of society.

Early intervention and family involvement

Families reflect diverse cultures, diverse languages, diverse economic backgrounds and diverse family forms. Today, our definition of family refers not only to the traditional family where the main care providers are two parents, but also to those with a single parent, same sex parents, step-parents, grandparents or other caregivers and child relationships. In addition, many families are coping with increased stress, whether it is due to negotiating supports for a child with a known developmental disability such as autism, or to conditions of marital breakdown, poverty, substance abuse, violence, unemployment or cultural adjustment. A study completed with Canadian Postal Workers highlighted the increased stress of families in finding appropriate and affordable child care for their children with disabilities when they are at work (Irwin & Lero, 2004).

To serve the needs of families, parent involvement and family support have become central components of early intervention programs and services (Carpenter, 2005; Dunlap & Fox, 2007; Dunst & Trivette, 2009; Singer, Biegel, & Ethridge, 2009; Wang & Brown, 2009). Evidence suggests that family participation in early intervention services promotes positive parent attitudes and expectations for their child and changes family processes. These family changes are found to have positive long-term effects on child development outcomes (Conyers, Reynolds, & Ou, 2003).

Parent involvement and family support relate to both the type and nature of interventions that impact on child, parent and family functioning. Professionals assist families in a variety of functions such as providing parent education programs, providing information about disabilities, and supporting families in acquiring resources for themselves and their child. While providing these services, it is essential that practitioners consider the nature of the help-giving relationship with families. Family-centered approaches that promote mutual trust, open communication and shared decision-making between professionals and families have been advocated as building parent competence, confidence and capabilities (Bailey, 2001).

Inclusive practices assure that a broad range of early intervention services are available that are sensitive to and respectful of diverse cultural, religious and social values and priorities. Some children with developmental delays and their families will experience barriers to participation in inclusive programs in the community. Barriers can include fragile health, age, few available child care spaces, cultural

preferences, transportation, and parent discomfort with sending their child out into the world. A relationship of trust and acceptance between the early interventionist and the family will slowly enable the family to move into the community with confidence. Therefore, a variety of informal and formal services, including speech and language programs, programs that provide intensive behavioural interventions for children with autism spectrum disorders, and family resource drop-in programs for parents, must be available in each community to match with the individualized needs of the child and the preferences of the family (See Box 2: Carlos in the Community).

Early intervention in communities

Children and families requiring support and assistance are everywhere in our communities. They attend infant development programs, child care centres, family resource centres, library events and community health clinics. The first step to successful early intervention requires universal screening programs that identify children at risk for compromised healthy child development. Liaising with community-based medical, health and educational professionals can assist early interventionists in identifying and referring children at risk for developmental delays and their families (Strain, Wolery, & Izeman, 1998).

In Ontario, Best Start is a networking strategy to integrate child development, quality childcare, and family services in the early years (Ministry of Children and Youth Services [MCYS], 2009). In addition, Healthy Babies, Healthy Children (HBHC) promotes the optimal development of all children. All newborns and their families in the province are screened for factors associated with child developmental outcomes using the Healthy Babies, Healthy Children Parkyn Postpartum Screening Tool (Ministry of Health and Long Term Care [MHLTC], 2009) and a post-partum telephone interview conducted by public health nurses. Every child in Ontario is screened through an enhanced 18-month well-baby visit often using the Nipissing District Developmental Screen (NDDS) and the Rourke Baby Record (Expert Panel on the 18-month Well Baby Visit, 2005). For families

Box 2: Carlos in the Community

When Carlos was born, his doctor detected a heart murmur. After consultation with a paediatric cardiologist, Carlos was diagnosed with Atrial Septal Defect (ASD), a congenital heart defect. Carlos's ASD was determined to be of moderate severity but puts him at risk for chronic fatigue, poor physical development, and frequent lung infections.

Carlos's family emigrated from Peru. They now live in a small home in an urban community in Ontario. They speak Spanish at home, although they are learning to speak English. Carlos' mother is now five months pregnant and healthy. During Carlos' infancy, a public health nurse made regular home visits to provide Carlos and his family with health care and support for his illnesses and physical development. In the first year of his life, Carlos had four lung infections, one of which was pneumonia that required hospitalization. When Carlos turned two, he had not yet learned to walk. He also showed difficulty with endurance during physical activities, such as crawling and pulling himself up to standing. The public health nurse referred the family to a family resource program (FRP) in the community, where they met with an early childhood resource consultant who noted other global developmental delays. The consultant visited with Carlos and his family regularly at their home and the FRP. The resource consultant referred Carlos and his family to an occupational therapist and recommended childcare for Carlos. But his parents were hesitant to allow him to attend at age 2.

When Carlos was almost three, he began receiving support from an occupational therapist, which enhanced his physical development. As Carlos became stronger his parents began to feel more comfortable with allowing him to attend childcare. After a 3-month wait, Carlos' mother and father were able to receive subsidized childcare three days a week for him. The separation was difficult on the family at first but the support of the resource consultant and early childhood educators at the childcare centre alleviated some of that stress and, over time, Carlos' progress has been evident to everyone. His occupational therapist visits once a week and leads the program's circle time, engaging all the children in movement with music, fingerplays, and children's yoga. Because Carlos has respiratory illnesses, he and his family make frequent trips to his doctor and Carlos often requires hospitalized care. In the past year, he has spent more than 70 nights in the hospital receiving treatment for lung infections. His last hospital stay required that Carlos miss over a month of childcare. This added to his parent's stress. During that time, the subsidy his parents were receiving was withdrawn and they were required to re-apply before Carlos could return to childcare. During the wait for subsidy, Carlos' resource consultant, occupational therapist, and friends from school made regular visits to his home. Carlos continues to grow and make new discoveries everyday.

where risk factors are flagged, an in-depth assessment of families is then conducted in the home to identify the level of risk and to assess their needs. Using a blended model of service delivery, public health nurses and lay home visitors are available to support those children and families assessed as high risk. By home visiting families, linking families to appropriate services and providing service coordination with an interdisciplinary team of professionals, Healthy Babies, Healthy Children supports the healthy growth and development of children with developmental challenges.

Information provided in popular media, including newspapers, television and the Internet, that emphasizes the importance of the early years in the child's healthy development are alerting parents and professionals to potential concerns in a child's development. Local community screening and assessment clinics are now available for parents to take their children from infancy to 5 years of age. Programs, such as the Prevention Early Identification Program (PEP-Start) in Peel Region, Ontario, are collaborative ventures among infant development, speech and language, and developmental and behavioural specialists for screening and identifying children with special needs. Parents are provided with the opportunity to consult with these professionals about their child's development and to identify developmental issues at an early age when interventions can be most successful.

The effects of merely identifying children and families are limited if resources are not available in the community to support their special needs. Early intervention services can range in intensity and degree depending on the child and family's strengths and priorities.

Early intervention services in Ontario are provided in a variety of forms such as supports in child care, preschool, kindergartens and primary classrooms and special education supports or specialized intervention programs (Underwood & Killoran, 2009). Early intervention services are also available through community, health and family resource programs with a variety of titles to describe professionals who provide these services, including resource teachers/consultants, developmental consultants, and early interventionists. Early interventionists may support children and families through weekly home visits. These intense interactions are intended to be transitional responses to family needs. They offer a bridge between the family and their community. In all situations, community programs must be flexible to allow for creative planning and programming solutions for each child and family.

Several early intervention initiatives have recently been funded by the province of Ontario to support inclusion for children with disabilities in their own communities. These include the Blind-Low Vision Early Intervention Program for children from birth to Grade One, the Infant Hearing Program (IHP), and the Preschool Speech and Language (PSL) initiative (MCYS, 2009). The purpose of IHP and PSL is to provide early identification of hearing or speech and language difficulties and to enhance the system of speech and language services for preschool children (MCYS, 2009). These services are provided in a variety of ways that are unique to the needs of the children being serviced and the community in which they live.

The Ontario government provides some funding for early behavioural interventions for children with autism (MCYS, 2007). This program augments services already in place by providing intensive behavioural interventions and assistance in accessing a range of other supports for these children and their families. Applied Behaviour Analysis (ABA) tech-

niques are also now being used in Ontario schools (Ministry of Education, 2007)

Currently in Ontario, agencies in each community are working together in a spirit of collaboration. This allows families to access a variety of programs through one central intake and coordination of services committee. The service integration plan provided is unique to each community.

Providing Inclusive Programs

Providing inclusive early intervention services challenges us as professionals to think about how we work with young children. It requires us to look at our beliefs and stereotypes and challenges us to view children with developmental disabilities as valued members of society. Despite legal and moral obligations inclusive programs are still elusive for many children with disabilities and their families. In a study on inclusive practices within Toronto preschools, Killoran, Tymon, and Frempong (2007) found that over 59% of supervisors of childcare centres surveyed would refuse a child based on disability. In centres that were inclusive, 95% of children with disabilities were able to participate with some accommodations made by staff. Ultimately, the decision to include a child with developmental disabilities is determined by staff values, attitudes and beliefs about inclusion, staff perceptions of whether they have the skills to best meet the needs of the child, and by the availability of additional resources such as resource teachers and resource consultants to support their efforts (Frankel, 2006; Killoran et al., 2007; Pivak et al., 2002). These attitudes and beliefs have been found to be further affected by the experiences centre staff and directors have had with inclusion (Irwin, Lero, & Brophy, 2000). Positive experiences with children with disabilities in their programs were found to enhance the staff's commitment and self-confidence in accepting children with greater challenges.

Inclusive practices may vary from program to program depending on staff dynamics, needs of children in the program, and numbers of children with special needs being included. Characteristics that serve as quality indicators of best practices in inclusive environments include:

1. *A Philosophy of Inclusion.* Inclusion begins with a vision. One of the primary characteristics of a successful inclusive program is a well articulated philosophy of inclusion (DEC/NAEYC, 2009). It requires that all staff, from the directors and supervisors, to the front line early childhood educators, to the cook, share in a philosophy of inclusion. This vision is based on the unconditional acceptance of all children and the belief that it is each child's right to attend the same early childhood program as their siblings and other neighbourhood children.

2. *A Policy of Inclusion.* Boards of directors and supervisors need to be able to clearly articulate the philosophy of inclusion to staff and families. By having a written policy, position, or mission statement affirming inclusion, administrators demonstrate a commitment to ensuring children have access to both equity and quality in all aspects of their early childhood experience. Staff and families should participate in the process of developing inclusive policies in the early childhood setting (Frankel & McKay, 1997).

3. *Inclusion as a Planned Process.* Although an inclusive philosophy and clear policies are the cornerstones of inclusion, there needs to be a planned process to ensure that the vision is carried out effectively. Administrators, families, early childhood educators, resource teachers, and resource consultants have key roles as agents of change and must work together to plan, problem-solve and decide on how to include a child with developmental disabilities in all aspects of the program (Frankel, 2006; Sandall, Schwartz, & Joseph, 2001).

4. *Families as Partners.* Inclusive early childhood programs should be based on the premise that the child's family is central to the child's life. Family-centred practices take into account the lifestyles, culture, values and priorities of the child's primary caregivers. To ensure family involvement, accommodations may need to occur in methods of communication, the time and frequency of team meetings, and the location of meetings.

5. *Enrollment.* Wait lists and admission practices should ensure equitable access. The number of children with developmental disabilities in an inclusive early childhood setting should reflect the prevalence of disability in each community. This allows all children in the community to come together in early childhood settings.

6. *Intentional Relationships.* The promotion of relationships, social competence and close friendships between children with developmental disabilities and their typical peers needs to be intentionally encouraged and developed by early childhood educators and caregivers. These intentional interactions provide opportunities for children to learn how to relate to each other as playmates and friends. They also help develop friendships that continue outside the early childhood program.

7. *Staff Development.* In an inclusive early childhood program, all members of staff take responsibility for all children and are involved in all children's learning on a daily basis. It is critical that staff feel comfortable and competent working with all children. Staff development, therefore, is an essential component of the success of an inclusive program (Leatherman, 2007; Leatherman & Niemeyer, 2005). Research has documented the need for staff training to address issues of fear and anxiety, values, skill development, program adaptation, team process, and effective communications (Chang, Early, & Winton, 2005). An ecological approach, where all staff and administrative personnel partake in all training, has been identified as the most effective training procedure (Miller & Stayton, 2000). Training supports for staff may include attending workshops, having access to recent research, books, ongoing in-service training and consultative assistance.

8. *Interagency Collaboration and Communication.* Children with developmental disabilities and their families are often involved with service agencies and organizations other than early intervention (e.g., special services at home, respite care). By cooperating, collaborating and communicating with other service delivery pro-

grams, staff in the early childhood program can help to increase the quality of life for the child and family (Salisbury, Crawford, Marlowe, & Husband, 2003).

9. *Transdisciplinary Team Approach.* A transdisciplinary team approach has been recognized as the ideal model for inclusive early childhood settings (Linder, 1993; Odom & McEvoy, 1990). A transdisciplinary team is characterized by interprofessional 'role release' and 'role acceptance' (Carpenter, 2005). Families, early childhood educators, resource teachers, and specialized consultants (e.g., speech and language pathologist, occupational therapist, physiotherapist) share roles, cross traditional discipline-specific boundaries, and collaborate in order to assess a child's learning, plan program goals and objectives for the child's success, determine environmental accommodations and teaching strategies, and evaluate the effectiveness of the program. The transdisciplinary team ensures that the whole child is supported, resulting in more meaningful assessments, programming, and evaluation (Linder, 1993).

10. *Individual Program Planning.* In Ontario, an Individual Program Plan (IPP) based on observations and assessments must be developed within the first month of the child's enrollment into an early childhood setting, and updated every six months. The IPP developed by the transdisciplinary team focuses on developmental goals for children that include their strengths, interests and an implementation plan that outlines teaching and learning strategies (See Box 3: Individual Program Plan for Jessica). Because children with developmental disabilities are included in a variety of early childhood programs, including group child care centres, nursery schools, drop-in centres, family resource centres and private home child care, the way that individualized goals and instructional approaches are implemented may be different from program to program. Some early childhood settings develop an Individualized Family Service Plan (IFSP) or Individualized Family Inclusion Plan (IFIP) to include family priori-

ties and goals. It is important to ensure that the goals and approaches in individual program planning take into account not only the abilities and needs of the child, but also the environment in which the program will be implemented and the interactive skills of the caregiver who will implement them (Sandall et al., 2001). When an IPP is in place, it should be used to inform the Individual Education Plan (IEP) that will be developed later in elementary schools (Ministry of Education, 2000).

11. *Program Adaptations.* Staff are responsible for implementing a child's individualized goals within the daily program, but they are also responsible for developing activities that are interesting and promote the involvement of all children (Sandall et al., 2001). Discussion of possible adaptations that allow the child with developmental disabilities to participate should occur during the program planning process. Considering the learning objectives of each scheduled activity, Hopkins (1994) suggested that adaptations may occur in:

- Order, sequence of routines or activities. For example, providing indoor active play right after sleep time, rather than going outside, to accommodate longer sleeping needs of some children.
- Location of activities. For example, moving the water table to an open area to allow for easier access to a child who uses a wheelchair.
- Adult-child groupings. For example, having several small, short group activities to accommodate younger or less focused children and encourage socialization.
- Developmental variability. For example, providing single inset puzzles as well as jigsaw puzzles to meet the range of developmental skills of children within the group.
- Number of toys. For example, are there too many toys, leading children to be overwhelmed, or is the variety of toys too limited, resulting in boredom?
- Physical location of toys and activities. For example, putting toys and activities on lower

Box 3: Individual Program Plan for Jessica

Child: Jessica

Chronological Age: 3 years, 2 months

Team Members Present:
H. Reid (Parent); T. Jack (Parent); E. Sloan (Supervisor); C. Kwiatkowski (Resource Consultant); L. Davis (ECE); J. Perry (Speech Language Therapist), T. Lang (Audiologist)

Areas of Development	Child's Strengths	Child's Interests	Short-Term Objectives	Long-Term Goal(s) (Fundamental Skills and Concepts)
Language & Communication: Expressive Speech	Expressive signing well developed	Story books Puppets Creative/Expressive Art	Jessica will: Read pictures to peers and teachers Describe own art/pictures Choose books from library to read at home and school	Jessica will: Use verbal language with sign language to make requests Use verbal language for sequencing events
Social/Emotional: Self Esteem	Engages in parallel play with peers Attends to and engages in large group activities	Sociodramatic play Large group games Sensory exploration (sand, playdough)	Jessica will: Initiate play with peers Label emotions Join small group activities with teacher support	Jessica will: Engage in associative play with peers Participate independently in play activities
Implementation Plan (services to be provided):	1. Independent picture drawing	2. Library Walks (once per week)	3. Dramatic Play Area	4. Visual, Verbal, and Behavioural Teaching Strategies
	ECE and Speech Language Therapist will encourage and record children's verbal description of creative art work ECE will verbalize signed descriptions	ECE will pair children with a different partner each week Children will choose books to borrow Children will describe pictures in books	ECE will invite and record children's ideas for dramatic play area themes during circle Dramatic area will change each week to reflect children's ideas Resource Consultant will lead small-group art experiences that emphasize self knowledge (i.e. body tracing)	ECE will encourage emotional expression daily using verbal prompts ECE will encourage Jessica's entry into small group sensory play using verbal prompts and physical proximity for support ECE will use positive verbal and behavioural reinforcement when Jessica is engaged in play with peers

shelves to ensure they are accessible to all children.

- Types of materials or equipment used. For example, providing adapted eating utensils, or seat supports to ensure a child's participation in all activities.
- Cues or visual aids. For example, using such things as labels and symbols to aid in instruction and provide reminders for following directions.
- Teacher interactions and communication strategies. For example, using verbal or physical prompts, instructions that reflect various learning styles.
- Peer interactions and communication strategies. For example, teaching children to use alternative communication strategies, like sign language and picture exchange systems with each other.

12. *Evaluation.* Evaluation is critical to the continued improvement and expansion of inclusive early childhood programs (Guralnick, 2004). In addition to measuring growth in children in all developmental domains, staff should be encouraged to evaluate all aspects of their programs, including professional development and family satisfaction. By using the quality indicators of an inclusive early childhood program, staff, families, resource teachers, resource consultants and inclusion facilitators can work together to create high quality programs for all children.

Creating Partnerships with Families

Families of children with developmental delays experience stress related to the quality of supports available to them (Bailey, Golden, Roberts, & Ford, 2007; Boyd, 2002; Tehee, Honan, & Hevey, 2009). For this reason, early intervention programs that effectively meet the special needs of individual children must also recognize and serve the needs of the whole family. Intervention programs that recognize the importance of the child's family, the social context in which the family operates, and the family's enduring relationship with its child are known

as family-centred programs. There is a growing body of evidence indicating that interventions that are family-centred are more likely to have broad-based positive influences on a number of aspects of child, parent and family functioning (Turnbull & Turnbull, 2001).

Guidelines for family-centred practice should be based on the core principle that supports to the child need to be embedded in an understanding of the family members and the living situation of the family as a whole. However, such guidelines should also stipulate that children with disabilities should be part of decisions that affect them, and be informed in a manner appropriate to their ages and development. The United Nations *Convention on the Rights of the Child* (1989) states that the "views of the child should be given due weight" in decisions that affect them (A. 12, s.1), or a representative should be heard on the child's behalf. This means that we should be including families as children's representatives and, where appropriate, keeping children informed. The child should therefore be central to family-centred practice.

Research supports that family-centred programs are guided by the following beliefs (Dempsey & Keen, 2008; Dunst & Dempsey, 2009; Dunst, Trivette, & Hamby, 2007; Hogan, Linden, & Najarian, 2002):

- Strengthening and supporting the family in conjunction with the child will have a positive impact on all members of the family.
- Families and children should be empowered to become competent and capable rather than dependent on professional help-giving systems. This is accomplished by creating opportunities for families to acquire knowledge and skills to navigate the ongoing challenges that life presents.
- A proactive approach to families and children involves the acceptance of individual differences and the recognition of individual strengths, and encourages the acquisition of skills that will allow families and children increased control and decision making power.
- Needs and aspirations identified by the family and children, and not by the professionals, should become the target for intervention. It

Box 4: Individualized Family Inclusion Plan for Nidi

Child: Nidi
Chronological age: 3 years, 3 months
Collaborative Team:

Parents: M. and H. Wahid
Supervisor: E. Sloan
Resource Consultant: R. Graham

Early Childhood Educator: J. Thompson
Language Interpreter: R. Kandola
Settlement Specialist: L. Rogers

The Family's Narrative

Nidi and her parents emigrated from India one year ago. The family's language of origin and language spoken at home is Hindi. The parents have limited ability in English and still struggle with verbal language and comprehension. Both parents work shifts, alternating days and nights. They live in a bachelor apartment and Nidi must play quietly when one of her parents sleeps during the day. The parents have high expectations for Nidi's future and are motivated to foster all areas of her development. The family was part of a close knit community in India but their current social network includes only a few acquaintances. The extended family members assisted with Nidi's care when the family lived in India. But since their arrival in Canada, Nidi's parents have only been able to rely on their neighbour to care for Nidi when both parents must work at night. Nidi's mother has expressed feelings of isolation and increased depression. In her free time, which is limited, she and Nidi enjoy watching television, reading books, and preparing meals together. They look forward to a better future for Nidi.

Nidi's current level of functioning

- *Proficient receptive language in both Hindi and English*
- *Limited expressive language in both Hindi and English*
- *Enjoys some physical activity such as dancing and playing on the climbing apparatus in the playground*
- *Displays self-help skills when dressing, toileting, and eating*
- *Occasionally interacts with other children through associative play*
- *Has difficulty with daily transitions and separation from her mother*

Statement of Concerns

Teachers report that Nidi never speaks in the childcare centre. She primarily plays in the dramatic play centre alongside her peers. Nidi's parents are concerned about Nidi's language development. They feel unable to provide her with support in English due to their limited ability to speak English. They also worry that Nidi will lose her ability to communicate in Hindi, especially with the absence of their extended family. Nidi's mother is concerned that Nidi has difficulty separating from her when she brings Nidi to the child care centre. Her parents would like her to play, interact and learn with other children.

Statement of Priorities

Nidi's parents and teachers want to extend Nidi's English expressive language skills. Her parents also want to maintain her ability to communicate in Hindi. Nidi's parents want to learn ways in which they can help foster Nidi's development, including her social development. Nidi's parents and teachers want Nidi to verbally make requests and express her thoughts and emotions to teachers and children when at the child care centre. Her teachers want to extend her interests in activity centres beyond sociodramatic play to promote her physical and social skills.

Child and Family Goals

- *Mother and father will increase English language proficiency*
- *Family will extend social network*
- *Nidi will extend her play interests and themes*
- *Nidi will initiate and maintain play with peers*
- *Nidi will transition comfortably between home and school and between daily activities*
- *Childcare providers will learn some basic words in Hindi*

Early Intervention Supports

- *Resource consultant and early childhood educators will collaboratively develop an IPP for Nidi based on the parents' and childcare providers' observations of Nidi's strengths and challenges, with a focus on social engagement in activities with peers and expressive language*
- *The settlement specialist will collaborate with the family resource centre director to provide weekend ELL classes at the resource centre that Nidi's parents can attend*
- *Mother will attend the family literacy program at the family resource centre in support of Nidi's language development*
- *Childcare providers will introduce Nidi's parents to other parents of children in the childcare centre at a planned family activity*
- *Childcare providers and supervisor will attend a workshop to learn basic Hindi words and phrases*
- *Childcare supervisor will have written information for parents translated into Hindi, including information on ways the parents can facilitate Nidi's development*

should be the role of the family to determine what is in the best interests of the family.

- All families and children have strengths, and these strengths should be recognized and built upon. Focusing on correcting deficits will prevent the development of a meaningful and productive relationship between families and professionals.
- Families often have informal social networks that can provide resources and support that families need. It should be the aim of intervention programs to strengthen and build social networks for families and children, not to replace them with professional services.
- The relationship between parents, children and professionals should be considered a partnership in which the individual partners all have capabilities that become enhanced through the sharing of knowledge, skills and resources.

Early interventionists are including families as integral members of the transdisciplinary team. Family-driven assessments allow the family to take the lead in articulating the strengths and needs of the child (Boone & Crais, 1999). Not only are families involved in assessing needs, but also they collaborate with the professionals to establish goals and develop intervention plans as part of an Individualized Family Inclusion Plan (IFIP). The IFIP is based on the expressed strengths and requirements of the family with a young child who is at risk for developmental delays (See Box 4: IFIP for Nidi).

There remains, however, tremendous diversity in the ways in which family-centred programs are designed and delivered in Ontario. Dunst, Johanson, Trivette, and Hamby (1991) proposed a framework for differentiating between four classes of family-oriented program paradigms. They include:

- Professionally-centred models view profession-

Box 5: Collaborative Team Transition Meeting Notes

Child: Matthew

Chronological Age: 3 years, 7 months

Collaborative Team:

F. Hong (Parent); M. Hong (Parent); E. Sloan (Supervisor); C. Kwiatkowski (Resource Consultant); L. Davis (ECE); L. Wan (Developmental Pediatrician); F. Frankfurt (Occupational Therapist); and G. Park (Kindergarten Teacher)

The collaborative team met to begin the process of transitioning Matthew into the junior kindergarten class next September. Mr. Hong expressed that he wanted Matthew to be a part of the class like the other children he had seen when visiting the school. He hoped that Matthew would have friends and participate in all areas of the program. He and Ms. Hong expressed concern that Matthew's physical and cognitive development may interfere with his ability to play and learn like the other children. Ms. Hong shared that Matthew enjoys looking at storybooks and listening to music. Everyone on the team agreed that it would benefit Matthew to learn to speak both English and Korean. Dr. Wan supported Mr. Hong's interest in Matthew's social skills development. Fabian, the occupational therapist, wanted to continue sensory integration experiences. Leah, the ECE teacher, provided examples of how the teachers in the childcare promote Matthew's social interactions with peers and engagement with sensory activities that reflect his interests. Fabian made some recommendations for environmental adaptations in the kindergarten room. Carol, the resource consultant, offered to observe Matthew's first few visits to the junior kindergarten room and to provide suggestions for activities that could be embedded in the curriculum and involve all children. Gloria, the kindergarten teacher, expressed concern that Matthew's wandering through the room would be a distraction to the other children. She was invited to observe Matthew's routines in the childcare centre prior to the start of school in September. The team scheduled a time for the next team meeting.

---

als as experts who determine family needs from their own, rather than the family's perspective.

- Family-allied models see families as agents of professionals, whose role it is to implement interventions that the professional has deemed necessary.

- Family-focused models have professionals provide a selection of services for families to choose from. Services are determined to be necessary or desirable for the family by the professional.

- Family-centred models view professionals as serving families by helping them to meet their own needs in ways that support and strengthen family functioning (see also Dunst, 2002; Dunst & Trivette, 2009).

These four models vary according to the established power relationship between the family and professionals. In the professionally-centred models, professionals lead the intervention process, making decisions based on their own views of the needs of the child and family. In family-centred practices, the relationship between the family and professionals is seen as a partnership that emphasizes the family's power to make decisions and determine what is best for the family. Within a family-centred intervention model, the role of the professional has shifted from "expert" to that of facilitator for a change process. The professionals support, encourage and help to create opportunities for families to achieve successes. The professional role is a positive one, helping families to recognize and develop their strengths and to use them most effectively in their lives. The professional assists the family in acquiring the services and skills needed to realize their goals.

Family-centred early intervention is a dynamic ongoing process of:

1. Listening to the unique narratives of each family (Ali, Corson, & Frankel, 2009).

2. Defining, articulating and prioritizing fam-

ily and children's strengths, concerns and aspirations.

3. Supporting the choices made by the families and children.

4. Identifying supports, information and resources (formal and informal) for meeting family and children's needs and aspirations.

5. Creating opportunities for the development of skills and capabilities that will ensure that families and children will be able to adapt to, and cope with, future challenges.

Some barriers may exist to optimal parental involvement in the intervention process. These barriers include the presence of overwhelming family stresses, the level of confidence and ability of parents to coordinate their own services, and the parents' degree of interest and energy to participate in the process. Professional barriers to family-centred intervention include administrative policies, regulations or procedures that limit family involvement, the lack of available resources and the family's resistance to changing established patterns of service delivery (Bailey, Buysse, Edmondson, & Smith, 1992; Dodd, Saggers, & Wildy, 2009). In spite of these barriers, family-centred practices in early intervention achieve a high level of family involvement and family satisfaction.

Forming Collaborative Teams

In Ontario, resource teachers and resource consultants have been instrumental in supporting the delivery of early intervention services to young children with developmental disabilities and delays in community-based early childhood settings (Frankel, 1994, 2006). These early interventionists are now striving to use a collaborative team model to facilitate inclusion. As noted earlier, the team consists of the early interventionist, family members, early childhood educators and all specialized personnel involved with the child and family. All members work together to take a transdisciplinary approach to the assessment, problem-solving, program planning and decision-making functions of the team. Research suggests that when early interventionists collaborate with families and other professionals to facilitate inclusion, all members develop a common understanding of the issues, take ownership of the problems and share responsibility for the solutions (Frankel & McKay, 1997).

By using a collaborative team approach, specialized consultants teach, learn and work with early childhood educators and families within the context of the early childhood setting. Resource consultants in collaborative teams are most effective in promoting change in teacher practices when they start with the skills and abilities that teachers already demonstrate and then modify them according to the individual needs of the child (Frankel, 2006). Pull-out practices for assessments and therapy are discouraged. Rather, the goal of the specialized consultant is to provide strategies that maximize the child's participation in the regular program by incorporating adaptations into activities and routines presented to all children by early childhood educators (Winton, 1996). For example, the speech-language pathologist teaches sign language to a group of children during circle time or the physiotherapist participates in indoor and outdoor games that stretch and strengthen the large muscles of the child with a developmental disability while all children participate. Instructional strategies and specialized techniques that are modeled by consultants can then be integrated into the daily activities and routines planned by the early childhood educators.

Successful teams must demonstrate specific characteristics to be collaborative. Six of the most important are:

1. *Equality.* Hierarchical power relationships are dismissed in favour of equal partnerships. A collaborative team approach requires that all members of the team are equal partners in the process of providing services to children with developmental disabilities and their families. The perspectives, priorities and goals of the family are as equally valued and considered as those of the professionals on the team. Each member of the team has an opportunity to share his or her observations of the child and to suggest critical goals for development.

2. *Communication.* Effective interpersonal com-

munication skills assist all team members in listening and responding to the opinions and perspectives of others on the team. This requires participants to maintain an open mind, to show empathy to others, and to put aside the priorities of their own discipline to incorporate the views of others when appropriate.

3. *Trust and mutual respect.* An environment of trust is most beneficial to the work of a collaborative team. When individuals feel supported and respected, they can, in turn, support and respect the views of others. Creative solutions can flow more freely in an atmosphere of trust and cooperation. Each participant feels freer to express ideas without fear of criticism (Keen, 2007).

4. *Accepting conflict.* Conflict has been seen as an inevitable part of the change process (Frankel & McKay, 1997). It is common for administrators, early childhood educators, families, and specialists to cling to previously held conceptions of practice when including children with developmental disabilities in their classrooms and programs. It should be remembered that conflict does lead to growth and change. Differences of opinion should be viewed as opportunities to consider all perspectives, to be flexible and to implement new intervention strategies.

5. *Group decision-making.* The IPP and IFIP that results from the collaborative team's efforts are based on observations and assessments and guide the intervention. Group members exchange knowledge, share expertise and make program recommendations. Decisions derived from group problem-solving and decision-making are superior to those that can be developed by any one individual alone. Ultimately, though, it is the family — as the consumer — that holds the power to make final decisions related to the IPP and IFIP.

6. *Regeneration.* A collaborative team continually evaluates its efforts. Members leave the team as their expertise is no longer required and new members may be added as the needs of the child and family change. The collaborative team is dynamic, with participants working together to plan strategies for including children with developmental disabilities in early childhood programs.

Summary

This chapter describes early intervention services in Ontario for young children at risk for developmental delays. Best practice in early intervention reflects the principles of inclusion, family-centred practice, and collaborative team approaches. Families, early childhood educators and specialized consultants form the transdisciplinary team. The team has responsibility to assess the abilities and requirements of the child and the family, to seek creative solutions for achieving goals, and to make mutual decisions about service. Based on the family's priorities, goals and personal preferences, the Individualized Program Plan and Individualized Family Inclusion Plan are formulated. These plans direct services for the family and the individualized education plan for the child. With the implementation of adapted instructional activities and family services in inclusive early intervention programs, all children like Jessica, Nidi, Carlos and Matthew will have an opportunity to reach their optimal developmental potential.

For Further Thought and Discussion

1. What is the importance of early intervention for children at risk for developmental delays?
2. How would you define inclusion for young children with developmental delays?
3. What benefits are derived from including families in the collaborative team?
4. Attend a transdisciplinary team meeting. What characteristics does the team demonstrate? How would you determine if it is a collaborative team?

Acknowledgements

The authors acknowledge contributions from other versions of this chapter authored by Dr. Elaine B. Frankel and Dr. Susan Gold (2007), and Dr. Elaine B. Frankel, Susan Howson and Ingrid Fish (2003). The authors thank Colleen Thornton for her research assistance.

More Resources

Ministry of Children and Youth Services (MCYS)
http://www.children.gov.on.ca/htdocs/English/index.aspx

MCYS Local Preschool Speech and Language programs contact information:
http://www.children.gov.on.ca/htdocs/English/topics/earlychildhood/speechlanguage/locations.aspx

Ministry of Health and Long-term Care
http://www.health.gov.on.ca/en/

Early Childhood Resource Teacher Network of Ontario
http://www.ecrtno.ca/

Infant Mental Health Promotion Project Department of Psychiatry
http://www.sickkids.ca/imp/

SpeciaLink: The National Centre for Child Care Inclusion
http://www.specialinkcanada.org

References

Ali, M., Corson, P., & Frankel, E. (2009). *Listening to families: Reframing services.* Toronto, ON: Chestnut Press.

Bailey, D. B. (2001). Evaluating parent involvement and family support in early intervention and preschool programs: Three levels of accountability. *Journal of Early Intervention, 24,* 1-14.

Bailey, D. B., Buysse, V. M., Edmondson, R., & Smith, T. M. (1992). Creating family-centred services in early intervention: Perceptions of professionals in four states. *Exceptional Children, 58,* 298-309.

Bailey, D. B., Golden, R. N., Roberts, J., & Ford, A. (2007). Maternal depression and developmental disability: Research critique. *Mental Retardation and Developmental Disabilities Research Reviews, 13,* 321-329.

Bailey, D. M., McWilliam, R. A., Buysse, V., & Wesley, P. W. (1998). Inclusion in the context of competing values in early childhood education. *Early Childhood Research Quarterly, 13,* 27-47.

Blackman, J. A., (2003). Early intervention: An overview. In S. L. Odom, M. J. Hanson, J. A. Blackman, & S. Kaul (Eds.), *Early intervention practices around the world* (pp. 1-23). Baltimore: Paul H. Brooks Publishing.

Boone, H. A., & Crais, E. (1999). Strategies for achieving family-driven assessment and intervention planning. *Young Exceptional Children, 3*(1), 2-11.

Boyd, B. A. (2002). Examining the relationship between stress and lack of social support in mothers of children with autism. *Focus on Autism and Other Developmental Disabilities, 17,* 208-215.

Brown, W., Odom, S., & Conroy, M. A. (2001). An intervention hierarchy for promoting young children's peer interactions in natural environments. *Topics in Early Childhood Special Education, 21,* 162-175.

Buysse, V., & Hollingsworth, H. L. (2009). Program quality and early childhood inclusion. *Topics in Early Childhood Special Education, 29,* 119-128.

Canadian Charter of Rights and Freedoms. (1982). Retrieved from *http://www.efc.ca/pages/law/charter/charter.sect.html*

Carpenter, B. (2005). Early childhood intervention: Possibilities and prospects for professionals, families, and children. *British Journal of Special Education, 32,* 176-183.

Chang, F., Early, D. M., & Winton, P. J. (2005). Early childhood teacher preparation in special education at 2- and 4-year institutions of higher education. *Journal of Early Intervention, 27,* 110-124.

Child Care Advocacy Association of Canada. (2008). *Child care services: Economic stimulus with long term benefits for Canada. Pre-2009 Federal budget consultation brief.* Ottawa, ON: Author.

Cleveland, G., & Krashinsky, M. (1998). *The benefits and costs of good child care: The economic rationale for public investments in young children.* Toronto, ON: Childcare Resource and Research Unit.

Conyers, L. M., Reynolds, A. J., & Ou, S. (2003). The effect of early childhood intervention and subsequent special education services: Findings from the Chicago child-parent centres. *Educational Evaluation and Policy Analysis, 25,* 75-95.

Dempsey, I., & Keen, D. (2008). A review of processes and outcomes in family-centered services for children with a disability. *Topics in Early Childhood Special Education, 28,* 42-52.

Diamond, K. E., & Carpenter, E. S. (2000). Participation in inclusive preschool programs and sensitivity to the needs of others. *Journal of Early Intervention, 23,* 81-91.

Division for Early Childhood/National Association of the Education of Young Children. (2009). *Early childhood inclusion: A summary.* Chapel Hill, NC: The University of North Carolina. FPG Child Development Institute.

Dodd, J., Saggers, S., & Wildy, H. (2009). Constructing the ideal family for family-centred practice: Challenges for delivery. *Disability & Society, 24,* 173-186.

Dunlap, G., & Fox, L. (2007). Parent-professional partnerships: A valuable context for addressing challenging behaviours. *International Journal of Disability, Development, and Education, 54*(3), 273-285.

Dunst, C. J. (2002). Family-centered practices: Birth through high school. *The Journal of Special Education, 36,* 139-147.

Dunst, C. J., & Dempsey, I. (2007). Family-professional partnerships and parenting competence, confidence, and enjoyment. *International Journal of Disability, Development, and Education, 54,* 305-318.

Dunst, C. J., & Trivette, C. M. (2009). Capacity-building family-systems intervention practices. *Journal of Family Social Work, 12,* 119-143.

Dunst, C. J., Johanson, C., Trivette, C. M., & Hamby, D. (1991). Family-oriented early intervention policies and practices: Family-centred or not? *Exceptional Children, 58,* 115-126.

Dunst, C. J., Trivette, C. M., & Hamby, D. W. (2007). Meta-analysis of family-centred helpgiving practices research. *Mental Retardation and Developmental Disabilities Research Reviews, 13,* 370-378.

Early Childhood Resource Teacher Network of Ontario. (1997). *Checklist for quality inclusive education: A self-assessment tool and manual for early childhood settings.* Haliburton, ON: Author.

Expert Panel on the 18 Month Well Baby Visit. (2005). *Getting it right at 18 months ...Making it right for a lifetime: Report of the Expert Panel on the 18 Month Well Baby Visit.* Retrieved from *http://www.ocfp.on.ca/local/files/CME/Research/Final-Rpt-18MonthPrjct-ENG.pdf*

Frankel, E. B. (1994). Resource teachers in integrated children's centres: Implications for staff development. *International Journal of Early Childhood, 26*(2), 13-20.

Frankel, E. B. (2006). The knowledge, skills, and personal qualities of early childhood resource consultants as agents of change. *Exceptionality Education Canada, 16*(2), 35-58.

Frankel, E. B., & McKay, D. (1997). Embarking on integration of preschool programs: Creating positive change. *Early Child Development and Care, 138,* 57-70.

Fullan, M. (2007). *The new meaning of educational change* (4th ed.). New York: Teacher's College Press.

Guralnick, M. J. (1990). Major accomplishments and future directions in early childhood mainstreaming. *Topics in Early Childhood Special Education, 10*(2), 1-17.

Guralnick, M. J. (1992). A hierarchical model for understanding children's peer-related social competence. In S. L. Odom, S. R. McConnell, & M. A. McEvoy (Eds.), *Social competence of young children with disabilities: Issues and strategies for intervention* (pp. 37-64). Baltimore: Paul H. Brookes Publishing.

Guralnick, M. J. (2004). Effectiveness of early intervention for vulnerable children: A developmental perspective. In M. A. Feldman (Ed.), *Early Intervention: The essential readings* (pp. 9-50). Oxford, United Kingdom: Blackwell Publishing.

Hestenes, L., & Carroll, D. (2000). The play interactions of young children with and without disabilities: Individual and environmental influences. *Early Childhood Research Quarterly, 15*(2), 229-246.

Hogan, B. E., Linden, W., & Najarian, B. (2002). Social support interventions: Do they work? *Clinical Psychology Review, 22,* 381-440.

Holahan, A., & Costenbader, V. (2000). A comparison of developmental gains for preschool children with disabilities in inclusive and self-contained classrooms. *Topics in Early Childhood Special Edu-*

cation, *20*, 224-235.

Hollingsworth, H. L., Boone, H. A., & Crais, E. R. (2009). Individualized inclusion plans at work in early childhood classrooms. *Young Exceptional Children, 13*(1), 19-35.

Hopkins, B. (1994). *Inclusion and early intervention: A resource manual for early childhood settings in Ontario*. Hamilton, ON: St. Matthew's House.

Hundert, J., Mahoney, B., Mundy, F., & Vernon, M. L. (1998). A descriptive analysis of developmental and social gains of children with severe disabilities in segregated and inclusive preschools in southern Ontario. *Early Childhood Research Quarterly, 13*(1), 49-65.

Irwin, S. H., Lero, D. S., & Brophy, K. (2000). *A matter of urgency: Including children with special needs in child care in Canada*. Wreck Cove, NS: Breton Books.

Irwin, S. H., & Lero, D. S. (2004). *In our way: Child care barriers to full workforce participation experienced by parents of children with special needs — and potential remedies*. Retrieved from *http://www.specialinkcanada.org/books/iow_summary.html*

Irwin, S. H., Lero, D. S., & Brophy, K. (2004). *Inclusion: The next generation of child care in Canada*. Wreck Cove, NS: Breton Books.

Keen, D. (2007). Parents, families and partnerships: Issues and considerations. *International Journal of Disability, Development and Education, 54*, 339-349.

Killoran, I., Tymon. D., & Frempong, G. (2007). Disabilities and inclusive practices within Toronto preschools. *International Journal of Inclusive Education, 11*(1), 81-95.

Leatherman, J. M., & Niemeyer, J. A. (2005). Teachers' attitudes toward inclusion: Factors influencing classroom practice. *Journal of Early Childhood Teacher Education, 26*, 23-36.

Leatherman, J. M. (2007). "I just see all children": Teachers' perceptions about inclusion. *The Qualitative Report, 12*, 594-611.

Lero, D. S. (2010). *Assessing inclusion quality in early learning and child care in Canada with the SpeciaLink Child Care Inclusion Practices Profile and Principles Scale*. Winnipeg, MB: SpeciaLink.

Linder, T. W. (1993). *Transdisciplinary play-based assessment: A functional approach to working with young children* (rev. ed.). Baltimore: Paul H. Brookes Publishing.

Mackenzie-Keating, S. E., & Kysela, G. M. (1997). Efficacy of early intervention: Fact or fantasy? *Exceptionality Education Canada, 7*(1&2), 21-28.

McCain, M. N., & Mustard, J. F. (1999). *Revising the real brain drain: Early years study — Final report*. Toronto, ON: Publications Ontario.

Miller, P. S. & Stayton, V. D. (2000). DEC Recommended practices in personnel preparation. In S. Sandall, M. E. McLean, & B. J. Smith (Eds.), *DEC Recommended practices in early intervention early childhood special education* (pp. 77-81). Longmont, CO: Sopris West.

Ministry of Children and Youth Services. (2007). Newsletter for parents of children and youth with autism, January 2007, Issue 2. Toronto, ON: Author.

Ministry of Children and Youth Services. (2009). *Ontario's Best Start plan*. Retrieved from *http://www.children.gov.on.ca/htdocs/English/news/backgrounders/01292007.aspx*

Ministry of Education. (2000). *Individual education plans: Standards for development, program planning and implementation*. Toronto, ON: Queen's Printer for Ontario. Retrieved from *http://www.edu.gov.on.ca/eng/general/elemsec/speced/iep/iep.pdf*

Ministry of Education. (2007). *Policy/Program Memorandum No. 140*. Toronto, ON: Queen's Printer for Ontario. Retrieved from *http://www.edu.gov.on.ca/extra/eng/ppm/140.html*

Ministry of Health and Long Term Care. (2009). *Postpartum implementation guidelines for the healthy babies, healthy children program*. Retrieved from *http://www.health.gov.on.ca/english/providers/pub/child/hbabies/postpartum.html*

Odom, S. L., & Brown, W. H. (1993). Social interaction skills interventions for young children with disabilities in integrated settings. In C. A. Peck, S. L. Odom, & D. D. Bricker (Eds.), *Integrating young children with disabilities into community programs: Ecological perspectives on research and implementation* (pp. 39-64). Baltimore: Paul H. Brooks

Publishing.

Odom, S. L., & McEvoy, M. A. (1990). Mainstreaming at the preschool level: Potential barriers and tasks for the field. *Topics in Early Childhood Special Education, 10,* 48-61.

Odom, S. L., Vitztum, J., Wolery, R., Lieber, J., Sandall, S., Hanson, M. et al. (2004). Preschool inclusion in the United States: A review of research from an ecological systems perspective. *Journal of Research in Special Education Needs, 4*(1), 17-49.

Ontario Day Nurseries Act. R.S.O. 1990, Chapter D2. Retrieved from *http://www.e-laws.gov.on.ca/html/statutes/english/elaws_statutes_90d02_e.htm*

Ontario Human Rights Code. R.S.O. 1990, Chapter H.19. Retrieved from *http://www.e-laws.gov.on.ca/html/statutes/english/elaws_statutes_90h19_e.htm*

Pivak, J., McComas, J., & LaFlamme, M. (2002). Barriers and facilitators to inclusive education. Exceptional Children, 69(1), 97-107.

Prentice, S., & McCracken, M. (2004). *Time for action: An economic and social analysis of childcare in Winnipeg.* Winnipeg, MB: Child Care Coalition of Manitoba.

Rafferty, Y., Piscitelli, V., & Boettcher, C. (2003). The impact of inclusion on language development and social competence among preschoolers with disabilities. *Exceptional Children, 69,* 467-479.

Salisbury, C. L., Crawford, W., Marlowe, D., & Husband, P. (2003). Integrating education and human service plans: The interagency planning and support project. *Journal of Early Intervention, 26*(1), 59-75.

Sandall, S., McLean, M. E., & Smith, B. J. (Eds.). (2000). DEC recommended practices in early intervention early childhood special education. Longmont, CO: Sopris West.

Sandall, S., Schwartz, I., & Joseph, G. (2001). A building blocks model for effective instruction in inclusive early childhood settings. *Young Exceptional Children, 4*(3), 3-9.

Shonkoff, J. P., & Phillips, D. (2000). *From neurons to neighborhoods: The science of early childhood development.* Washington, DC: National Academy Press.

Singer, G. H. S., Biegel, D. E., & Ethridge, B. L. (2009). Toward a cross disability view of family support for caregiving families. *Journal of Family Social Work, 12,* 97–118.

Strain, P. S., Wolery, M., & Izeman, S. (1998). Considerations for administrators in the design of service options for young children with autism and their families. *Young Exceptional Children, 1*(2), 8-16.

Tehee, E., Honan, R., & Hevey, D. (2009). Factors contributing to stress in parents of individuals with autistic spectrum disorders. *Journal of Applied Research in Intellectual Disabilities, 22,* 34-42.

Tsao, L., Odom, S. L., Buysse, V., Skinner, M., West, T., & Vitztum-Komanecki, J. (2008). Social participation of children with disabilities in inclusive preschool programs: Program typology and ecological features. *Exceptionality, 16*(3), 125-140.

Turnbull, A. P., & Turnbull, H. R. (2001). *Families, professionals, and exceptionality: Collaborating for empowerment* (4th ed.). Upper Saddler River, NJ: Prentice Hall.

Underwood, K., & Killoran, I. (2009). Early intervention practice and research in Ontario, Canada: Listening to the field. *Journal of Early Childhood Teacher Education, 30,* 298-305.

United Nations. (1989). *Convention on the Rights of the Child.* A. 12, s.1. Retrieved from *http://www2.ohchr.org/english/law/crc.htm*

United Nations. (2006). *Convention on the Rights of Persons with Disabilities.* Retrieved from *http://www.un.org/disabilities/convention/conventionfull.shtml*

United Nations. (2010). *Convention and Optional Protocol Signatures and Ratifications.* Retrieved from *http://www.un.org/disabilities/countries.asp?navid=17&pid=166)*

Wang, M., & Brown, R. I. (2009). Family quality of life: A framework for policy and social service provisions to support families of children with disabilities. *Journal of Family Social Work, 12,* 144-167.

Winton, P. J. (1996). Family-professional partnerships and integrated services. In R. A. McWilliam (Ed.), *Rethinking pull-out services in early intervention: A professional resource* (pp. 49-69). Baltimore: Paul H. Brookes Publishing.

Wolery, M., & Bailey, D. B. (2002). Early childhood special education research. *Journal of Early Intervention, 25,* 88-99.

40

Developmental Disabilities and Child Maltreatment

Ann Fudge Schormans

What you will learn:

- The historical and current contexts
- The association between maltreatment and developmental disability
- Some of the indicators, characteristics, and impacts of maltreatment for children with developmental disability
- The responsibility of professionals involved with people with developmental disabilities

The right to live free from fear and from want is a basic human right with a long legislative history. It was set out by the United Nations (UN) in the 1948 *International Declaration of Human Rights* and later expanded to extend protections to people with disabilities in 1971 (*Declaration on the Rights of Mentally Retarded Persons*), 1975 (*Declaration on the Rights of Disabled Persons*), 1982 (*World Program of Actions Concerning Disabled Persons*), and 1994 (*Standard Rules on Equalization of Opportunities for Persons with Disabilities*). More recently, the UN *Convention on the Rights of Persons with Disabilities* and its *Optional Protocol* were adopted by the UN

General Assembly on December 13, 2006. Canada was one of the first countries to sign the Convention, doing so on March 30, 2007. There is also the UN's *Convention on the Rights of the Child* (1989). Ratified by both developed and developing countries, this document guarantees every child the right of freedom from maltreatment. As articulated in Article 23 of the Convention, children with intellectual and physical disabilities share these rights and signatory states are responsible to ensure their special needs are met. Nationally, the *Canadian Charter of Rights and Freedoms* also promises equal protection of the law for individuals with disabilities (see Chapters 5 and 6 for Canadian legislation and entitlements). These declarations have prompted many developed and developing nations — including Canada — to begin to design policies, legislation, and practice to ensure these rights. Yet, despite these fundamental protections, child maltreatment remains a major problem for children worldwide and an even more severe problem for children with disabilities (Fudge Schormans & Sobsey, 2007).

What is Meant by the Term Child Maltreatment

The term *child maltreatment* (or *child abuse*), just like the term *disability*, is a socially constructed concept. Consequently, how the term is understood varies across class, culture, geography, gender, and generations. Even the definition of *child* varies according to laws and customs that set out the ages at which individuals are considered adults. It is not possible for this chapter to adequately address this multiplicity of meaning, particularly as it pertains to similarities and contrasts among different countries. The tremendous social, economic, and political variability prohibits a universal understanding. The definitions that apply in Ontario are contained in various sections of Canada's Criminal Code and within the 1999 Child and Family Services Amendment Act (CFSA), which is the provincial child protection legislation governing mandated child welfare/child protective services (Covell & Howe, 2001). Section 72 (1) of the CFSA defines a "child in need of protection" as one requiring protection from physical, sexual, and emotional abuse; neglect; and harm (see Box 1). Child welfare services are involved in the majority of reported cases of child maltreatment; therefore, it is from the CFSA statutory framework that this chapter will proceed.

Historical and Contemporary Contexts

References to the abuse of children, both with and without developmental disabilities, can be found in some of our earliest historical recordings of children's lives (Fudge Schormans & Sobsey, 2007).

The existence of an organized concern with, and response to, the maltreatment of children is, however, a relatively recent phenomenon. In Ontario, it was established in 1887 with the founding of the Toronto Humane Society whose intended purpose was the prevention of cruelty to both animals and children. This led to the passing of both the provincial Children's Protection Act (1888), making child abuse, for the first time, an indictable offence, and to the organization of Ontario's first Children's Aid Society (CAS) in 1891 (Macintyre, 1993).

In many ways, the development of a systemic response to child abuse parallels the path of service provision to children with developmental disabilities; the phenomena of child abuse and developmental disability seem to be inextricably linked. Two unfortunate ways that services for children with developmental disabilities and services for maltreated children were similar were that 1) both produced institutional care, and 2) institutional care often produced more abuse (Fudge Schormans & Sobsey, 2007).

Prior to the late 1800s, children in Ontario were granted few protections from abuse. The "laissez-faire" ideology of government, combined with the liberal idea of the sanctity of the family, minimized the provision of social supports to children and deterred state intervention in situations involving disability and/or the abuse of children by their parents. Children, with and without developmental disabilities, were considered the responsibility — and property — of parents. Foundling homes operated by churches, charitable organizations, or private philanthropists provided an alternative to the infanticide of unwanted children and a temporary refuge for very young children orphaned or abandoned to the streets or churchyards (Macintyre, 1993). The generally deplorable conditions resulted in reported child mortality rates as high as 50-80% (Steinhauer, 1991). Almshouses, workhouses, or apprenticeship arrangements were the only options available for older children who had been deserted or orphaned, or who had run away from abusive family situations. Without rights or recourse, at the mercy of their benefactors, and typically housed with adults exhibiting a host of social, emotional, and psychological problems, the risk of maltreatment in these environments was great (Macintyre, 1993; Sobsey, 1994). It was not until the latter half of the nineteenth century that the need of all children for protection from abuse, nurturance, and the conditions necessary for healthy growth and development, began to be recognized and the state's responsibility in this task acknowledged.

Several factors can be identified as having contributed to this development. Before industrialization and urbanization, the "family" in Western society typically functioned as a productive unit. With each member (often including members with a disability) contributing to the livelihood of the family, children (with and without disabilities) were not necessarily distinguished from other members of the family. The advent of industrialization found children of families from lower socio-economic classes working alongside adults in factories. Treated as "little adults," they were exploited (overworked and underpaid) as child labourers and regularly subjected to poor child-rearing practices, lack of protection and, frequently, severe punishment (Macintyre, 1993).

For children with developmental disabilities, a production-based economy created a situation of disadvantage. A growing awareness of the impact of these conditions on the well-being of children combined with the emergence of a strong middle class and the evolution of what we now understand to be the traditional patriarchal family model to foster both the notion of childhood as a separate stage of human development and a patriarchal model of helping that has proven tenacious (Macintyre, 1993). In addition, with rising cultural standards of health and welfare, standards of behaviour towards children accepted as normal in previous centuries came to be regarded as intolerable (Chadwick, 1999). For children with developmental disabilities, a growing belief that they could be educated, along with recognition of their vulnerability, led to the rise of an institutional care system intended to provide them with the specialized care and training they would require to take their place in society. The growth of institutions was, however, powerfully fuelled by another important trend: a strong eugenics movement that used institutions as an avenue by which to segregate (for life)

those considered to be of "inferior stock" with little pretense of training to enable children to return to the community (Sobsey, 1994).

The child-saving movement in Ontario

Out of this new middle class emerged a social reform movement intent upon rescuing children from the deplorable conditions created, in part, by industrialization and urbanization. Private philanthropic and volunteer efforts played important roles in this child-saving movement. Other influences included the animal-saving movement, the women's suffragette movement, the abolitionist movement, and the labour movement (that recognized the threat posed by child labourers to the economic value of adult labourers). These reformers advocated for moving beyond the traditional charitable model of provision for children towards a social welfare model with government legislation for the protection of neglected and maltreated children (Sobsey, 1994; Waldfogel, 1998). Patriarchal conceptions of family shaped a *parens patriae* model of child protection legislation, *parens patriae* being a Latin term meaning "protector" and "father of the country" (Macintyre, 1993, p. 20). Through legislated child welfare agencies, the state acted as a substitute benevolent parent. Within this framework, the state had the right, in the best interests of the child, to suspend the authority of the family through its legislative and court systems, to make determinations of "good" or "bad" parenting, to define acceptable living conditions for children, to establish services on behalf of children, and to remove from their homes children believed in need of protection (Macintyre, 1993). For children with developmental disabilities, the "best interests" rationale similarly permitted removal from their homes and placement in institutions.

The child-saving movement, however, operated from a particular moral standpoint. Rescuing children from abusive and neglectful families was not just about protecting children from victimization: it was also perceived as the best method to protect society from moral degeneration and social unrest. Adopting an individual pathology approach, the blame was placed on immoral parents — the optimal

Box 1: Child and Family Services Amendment Act (Child Welfare Reform) (1999) s.37 (2)

A child is deemed in need of protection when:

a)   The child has suffered physical harm, inflicted by the person having charge of the child, or caused by, or resulting from that person's:

   i.   failure to adequately care for, provide for, supervise or protect the child, or

   ii.   pattern of neglect in caring for, providing for, supervising or protecting the child;

b)   There is a risk that the child is likely to suffer physical harm inflicted by the person having charge of the child or caused by or resulting from that person's:

   i.   failure to adequately care for, provide for, supervise or protect the child, or

   ii.   pattern of neglect in caring for, providing for, supervising or protecting the child;

c)   The child has been sexually molested or sexually exploited, including child pornography, by the person having charge of the child or by another person where the person having charge of the child knows or should know of the possibility of sexual molestation or sexual exploitation and fails to protect the child;

d)   There is a risk that the child is likely to be sexually molested or sexually exploited as described in paragraph 3;

e)   The child requires medical treatment to cure, prevent or alleviate physical harm or suffering, and the child's parent or the person having charge of the child does not provide, or refuses or is unavailable or unable to consent the treatment;

f)   The child has suffered emotional harm, demonstrated by serious:

   i.   anxiety,

   ii.   depression,

   iii.   withdrawal,

   iv.   self-destructive or aggressive behaviour, or

   v.   delayed development,and there are reasonable grounds to believe that the emotional harm suffered by the child results from the actions, failure to act or pattern of neglect on the part of the child's parent or the person having charge of the child;

Source: Government of Ontario, Canada (Last Ammendment: 2010a).

solution was to remove "good children" from these "moral imbeciles" (Carlson, 2001, p. 126) before they grew up to be immoral adults themselves. In this way, legislators ignored the social and economic factors involved in child abuse. This same concern with protecting society from moral decay was at the root of moving children with developmental disabilities to segregated institutions (Carlson, 2001).

The child welfare system and the institutional system operated in parallel for the next 60-70 years. Although child protection legislation did not specifically exclude maltreated children with developmental disabilities, the typical response of child welfare services was to transfer the child and responsibil-

ity for the "problem" to the institutions (Simmons, 1982). Institutions thus retained control over the investigation and management of abuses occurring in those settings.

The current context of child protection and developmental disabilities

The 1950s and 1960s were witness to a renewed interest in both child maltreatment and developmental disability, prompted again by feminist and civil rights movements. The identification of battered child syndrome (1962) was a key factor leading to a medical model approach to child protection focussed on physical abuse and rescuing children from physi-

f.1) *The child has suffered emotional harm of the kind described in subclause (f) i, ii, iii, iv or v and the child's parent or the person having charge of the child does not provide, or refuses or is unavailable or unable to consent to, services or treatment to remedy or alleviate the harm;*

g) *There is a risk that the child is likely to suffer emotional harm of the kind described in subclause (f) i, ii, iii, iv or v resulting from the actions, failure to act or pattern of neglect on the part of the child's parent or the person having charge of the child;*

g.1) *There is a risk that the child is likely to suffer emotional harm of the kind described in Subclause (f) i, ii, iii, iv or v of paragraph 6 and that the child's parent or the person having charge of the child does not provide, or refuses or is unavailable or unable to consent to, services or treatment to prevent the harm;*

h) *The child suffers from a mental, emotional or developmental condition that, if not remedied, could seriously impair the child's development and the child's parent or the person having charge of the child does not provide, or refuses or is unavailable or unable to consent to, treatment to remedy or alleviate the condition;*

i) *The child has been abandoned, the child's parent has died or is unavailable to exercise his or her custodial rights over the child and has not made adequate provision for the child's care and custody, or the child is in a residential placement and the parent refuses or is unable or unwilling to resume the child's care and custody;*

j) *The child is less than 12 years old and has killed or seriously injured another person or caused serious damage to another person's property, services or treatment are necessary to prevent a recurrence and the child's parent or the person having charge of the child does not provide, or refuses or is unavailable or unable to consent to, those services or treatment;*

k) *The child is less than 12 years old and has on more than one occasion injured another person or caused loss or damage to another person's property, with the encouragement of the person having charge of the child or because of that person's failure or inability to supervise the child adequately.*

l) *The child's parent is unable to care for the child and the child is brought before the court with the parent's consent and, where the child is twelve years of age or older, with the child's consent, to be dealt with under this Part. R.S.O. 1990, c. C.11, s. 37 (2); 1999, c. 2, s. 9.*

cally abusive parents (Waldfogel, 1998). The primary impetus for change with respect to developmental disability came from a growing movement of parents alarmed by the appalling conditions and abuses prevalent in institutions. Rescuing their children from institutional settings and returning them to their home communities became a strong advocacy focus, and de-institutionalization policies and practices gradually took hold (Radford & Park, 2003).

Throughout the 1970s and 1980s, as more children with developmental disabilities remained in the community with their families, they were increasingly likely to become involved with child welfare services. This was initially restricted to reasons of child maltreatment, but around this time many state and provincial governments also began to develop family support services intended to assist families with the care of their child with a disability. The development of these programs was driven both by a philosophical commitment to preserve families and by simple economics, which suggested that relatively modest investments in families could save the high costs of institutionalization (Fudge Schormans & Sobsey, 2007). In Ontario, the 1984 Child and Family Services Act, under Section 30(1), made provision for parents to enter into a voluntary Special Needs Agreement (SNA) with child welfare agencies if they were unable to provide for their child's special needs. As the economic recession of the 1980s progressed and developmental disability services became more difficult to access, more and more parents entered into an SNA as a means of accessing residential and specialized services for their children — services they could not otherwise access. Although this provision remains in the 1999 CFSA, the economic costs incurred by the high number of children with developmental disabilities in child welfare care under SNAs, combined with the belief that the needs of families of children with disabilities are best met in the community, led governmental child welfare authorities to call for a return to a focus on child protection, making this option very difficult for families of children with developmental disabilities to access. The most recent review of the CFSA reinforces that unless a protection issue exists, parents of children with disabilities cannot access the residential care system through the child welfare system (Government of Ontario, 2010b).

Paralleling de-institutionalization and normalization philosophies in developmental disabilities, child protection services also shifted towards a family preservation model. Respect for parental rights and the integrity of the family were prioritized over children's rights, thus making it more difficult to bring any child into protective care. This response was a reaction to criticisms of earlier policies that permitted greater state intrusion into family life. It was fuelled also by concerns over the abuse of children in state care and the negative impacts of state care and removal from the family home on a child's well-being. At this time, there was also a growing interest in preventing and prosecuting child sexual abuse, which resulted in amendments to criminal justice legislation modifying investigative and court procedures that made it easier for children to testify (Covell & Howe, 2001).

The recognition in the late 1990s that family preservation policies were no more effective in protecting children from maltreatment than were earlier models coincided with two other developments to return child protection services to a social welfare model. First, acceptance grew for the idea of children's rights, such as the right to protection from abuse and neglect and the right to a stable and healthy childhood; this was facilitated by, and reflected in, the 1989 United Nations' *Convention on the Rights of the Child*. Second, reports of child deaths caused by abuse inflamed concerns that children's needs and rights were not being adequately addressed. In Ontario, the legislation was amended (*Child and Family Services Amendment Act,* 1999) — its stated purpose was to promote the best interests of the child by rescuing them from neglectful or abusive parents. In lowering the threshold for risk of harm, this legislation encouraged earlier intervention in cases of child maltreatment. The emphasis had also shifted again, focusing on neglect and emotional abuse (Covell & Howe, 2001).

A return to the social welfare model, however, was not without competing interests. Both historical and contemporary child protection legislation and practice are rooted in liberal ideologies and a *parens patriae* approach that struggles with the competing demands of reducing child welfare costs, preserving and yet not intruding upon families, and protecting children. As a result, current legislation remains, for the most part, reactive as opposed to proactive — it is not charged with preventing child maltreatment, only with responding to it once it has occurred (Covell & Howe, 2001; Macintyre, 1993). In response, Ontario child welfare practice has most recently adopted a differential response paradigm (Ontario Child Welfare Transformation, 2005). Such an approach allows children's aid societies to differentiate its response to reports of child maltreatment (Alaggia, Jenney, Mazzuca, & Redmond, 2007). In situations of substantiated maltreatment, and for families deemed to be at high risk, typical child protection interventions are used. Families reported for child maltreatment who are deemed to be at low to moderate risk and who fall below the intervention line for child protection services, are instead offered supportive and preventative services that they might not otherwise have been eligible to receive (Conley, 2007). Research into the effectiveness of differential response paradigms is only just emerging; much more is critically needed to determine whether this paradigm better meets the needs of children and families — with and without developmental disabilities — at risk of child maltreatment.

Developmental Disability and Child Maltreatment

Just as there is no singular understanding of what constitutes "child maltreatment," there is no universal definition of disability. Across the vast array of world cultures can be found a similarly vast number of understandings of, and responses to, children and adults labelled "developmentally disabled." A review of the international literature, however, reveals a strong connection between developmental disability and maltreatment. As this literature does not always distinguish between children and adults, the following discussion makes reference to both (Fudge Schormans & Sobsey, 2007).

INCIDENCE OF CHILD MALTREATMENT

It is increasingly recognized that the risk of abuse for individuals with developmental disabilities is greater than that for individuals without developmental disabilities. As early as 1967, Elmer and Gregg reported that 50% of the abused children they examined had developmental disabilities. More recently, Randall, Parilla, and Sobsey (2000) suggested the risk may be as much as ten times greater. Manders & Stoneman (2009) identify a long list of research studies that document this increased risk. Although there is no epidemiological consensus in the literature, children with developmental disabilities are typically found to be at a much greater risk for abuse than are their peers without disabilities.

Examining data from the Canadian Incidence Study of Reported Child Abuse and Neglect (CIS-2003), Canada's second national study examining the incidence of reported child maltreatment and the characteristics of children and families coming into contact with child welfare services (Trocmé et al., 2005), it was found that children with developmental disabilities were over-represented in the child welfare system (Fudge Schormans & Fallon, 2009). Of the CIS-2003 core sample of 11,562 child maltreatment investigations (excluding Quebec), 8.9%, involved children identified as having developmental delay. Child maltreatment is substantiated more often in cases involving children with developmental delay (54.0%) than in cases involving children with no developmental delay (46.5%). Neglect remains the most frequently substantiated form of maltreatment for all children reported to child protection services. Physical abuse is the second most common form, emotional maltreatment occupies third place, and sexual abuse is the least frequently occurring category of substantiated maltreatment. Children with developmental delay experience more neglect than do children without developmental delay: in particular, higher rates of medical and educational neglect. They are also more likely to experience maltreatment over longer periods of time. Only 22.2% of investigations for this group involved single incidents, as contrasted with 33.1% for children with no developmental delay. Caregivers of children with developmental delay are more likely to use spanking as a form of discipline (27.6%) than are caregivers of children without developmental delay (21.4%). In addition, children with developmental delay are more likely to experience physical harm — harm requiring medical treatment — as a result of maltreatment than children with no developmental delay (17.0% & 9.1%, respectively). They are also more likely to demonstrate signs of emotional harm as a result of the maltreatment incident(s). Thirty-seven percent of children with developmental delay (18.5% of children without delay) were reported to exhibit such signs of harm — harm which, once again, is more likely to require therapeutic treatment (Fudge Schormans & Fallon, 2009).

The findings from the CIS-2003 resemble those from Sullivan and Knutson's (2000) study of a large cohort of more than 50,000 children attending school in Omaha, Nebraska in the United States. Like the CIS-2003, Sullivan and Knutson's cohort design allowed the same definitions of disability to be applied to children. Unlike the CIS-2003, this study was not limited to child welfare records and cases of intrafamilial abuse and was thus able to incorporate data from a wider range of databases. Sullivan and Knutson (2000) found that children identified by their schools as requiring special education services were 3.4 times as likely to be maltreated as children not needing these services. This meant that almost one-quarter (22%) of children with a history of maltreatment were identified as

Table 1: Common Indicators of Child Maltreatment*

A. Physical Abuse:

Child Physical Signs	Child Behavioural Signs	Parent Behavioural Signs
• Abrasions	• Atypical attachment	• Lack of empathy for child
• Bites	• Disclosure	• Unrealistic expectations of child
• Bruises	• Fearfulness	• Holding child overly responsible for his or her behaviour and blaming child for negative outcomes
• Burns and scalds	• Learning disabilities	
• Lacerations	• Noncompliance	
• Ligature marks	• Regression	• Interpreting child's behaviour negatively and judging misbehaviour too harshly
• Welts	• Sleep disturbances	
• Dislocations	• Withdrawal	• Coercive or threatening to child
• Broken bones	• Acting-out behaviour	• Difficulty managing stress
• Dental injuries		• Overly tense, depressed, angry, confused, or impulsive
• Ear Injuries		
• Eye Injuries		• Involved in domestic violence
• Coma		

B. Sexual Abuse:

Child Physical Signs	Child Behavioural Signs	Parent Behavioural Signs
• Bruises or genital abnormalities	• Atypical attachment	• Antisocial behaviour
• Genital discomfort	• Avoidance of specific adults or settings	• Lack of effective social skills
• Pregnancy	• Development of new fears	• Social anxiety
• Sexually transmitted disease	• Depression	• Sociopathology
• Signs of physical abuse	• Dissociation	• Lack of empathy for child
• Torn or missing clothing	• Eating disorder	• Cognitive distortions that encourage exploitative relationships
	• Learning difficulties,	• Impulsivity; lack of Inhibitions
	• Deterioration in school performance	• Seductive or sexually explicit behaviour with child in presence of others
	• Low self-esteem	
	• Noncompliance	• Overly protective of child
	• Behavioural regression	• Extremely authoritative
	• Resists physical examination	• Criminality, previous conviction for sexual assault
	• Self-injurious behaviour	
	• Sexualized behaviour	• Isolating child and family
	• Sleep disturbance	• Seeking isolated contact with children
	• Substance abuse	
	• Withdrawal or acting-out behaviour	
	• Excessive fantasy behaviour	

C. Neglect:

Child Physical Signs	Child Behavioural Signs	Parent Behavioural Signs
• Failure to thrive (i.e., growth falls below satisfactory levels) • Illness • Malnourishment • Poor hygiene	• Apathy • Avoidance or resistance to attachment • Coercive • Displays more frustration than typical for age • Insecure attachment • Isolated at playtime • Less effective coping • Less positive and more low self-esteem • Negative affect • Passive behaviour • Poor problem-solving ability • Reduced prosocial behaviour • Self-centered behaviour • Withdrawal	• Expecting child to fill adult emotional needs • Withdrawn, depressed, psychologically unavailable • Failure to recognize and attend to child's need for attention • Failure to address child's emotional or behaviour disorders • Exposing child to parent's mental illness or substance abuse or to domestic violence • Failure to provide adequate physical care • Failure to provide adequate clothing, shelter, or nourishment • Failure to provide adequate medical care or treatment • Age-innappropriate expectations of child (e.g., very young child expected to feed him- or herself) • Lack of appropriate supervision • Repeated separations or moves

D. Emotional Abuse/Psychological Maltreatment:

Child Physical Signs	Child Behavioural Signs	Parent Behavioural Signs
• Poor growth	• Anxiety and fear • Age-inappropriate responsibility (too much or too little expected of child) • Decline in cognitive ability • Lessened problem-solving capacity • Lower educational attainment • Poor peer relationships (withdrawn) • Poor school attendance • Self-abuse	• Degrading, hostile, or rejecting • Exploitative and/or corrupting • Not emotionally responsive to child; detached and uninvolved • Denial of services promoting child development and well-being • Isolates child • Neglectful • Comments that shame, insult, or ridicule child • Terrorizing and/or threatening behaviour • Lack of understanding of child's needs and how to meet them • Lack of empathy for child

* The reader is cautioned to remember that there are no absolute indicators of child maltreatment; maltreatment is the result of a complex interaction of multiple factors and many different responses are possible. Although current research and practice offers some support for the indicators listed, the indicators will not necessarily apply in each and every case.

Sources: Garbarino, Brookhouser, Authier, et al. (1987); Macdonald (2001); and Sobsey (1994).

Box 2: Responsibility to Report a Child in Need of Protection as Mandated by the Child and Family Services Amendment Act (Child Welfare Reform),s. 72 (1-8).

The welfare of children is the responsibility of all members of society. Despite the provisions of any other Act, if a person, including a person who performs professional or official duties with respect to children has reasonable grounds to suspect that a child is, or may be, in need of protection, they are legally mandated to report these suspicions to a children's aid society.

Professionals affected include (but are not limited to) the following:

- *health care professionals, including physicians, nurses, dentists, pharmacists and psychologists*
- *teachers, early childhood educators, and school principals*
- *social workers and family counsellors*
- *operators or employees of day nurseries*
- *youth and recreation workers (not volunteers)*
- *priests, rabbis and other members of the clergy*
- *mediators and arbitrators*
- *peace officers and coroners*
- *solicitors*
- *service providers and employees of service providers*
- *any other person who performs professional or official duties with respect to a child.*

It is an offence not to report the suspicion that a child is in need of protection, and a penalty exists for professionals who fail to do so. A person who has a duty to report must make the report themselves and cannot rely on any other person to report on her or his behalf.

Except as required or permitted in the course of a judicial proceeding, in the context of the provision of child welfare services, otherwise by law, or with the written consent of an informant, no person shall disclose the identity of the information to the family of the child reported to be in need of protection, or to the person who is believed to have caused the child to be in need of protection. No person shall dismiss, suspend, demote, discipline, harass, interfere with or otherwise disadvantage an informant under this section.

The duty to report is an ongoing one, and any further grounds to suspect abuse would necessitate further reporting.

The duty to report overrides any other provincial statute including those that prohibit disclosure of confidential information (solicitor client privilege is exempt).

Unless there is proof that a person who has reported has acted maliciously or without reasonable grounds, the legislation provides protection from liability.

Source: Government of Ontario (Last Ammendment: 2010a).

needing special education, and almost one-third (31%) of children in special education had a confirmed history of child maltreatment. Children with intellectual disabilities were 3.7 times more likely to have a confirmed history of neglect, 3.8 times more likely to have a confirmed history of physical abuse, 3.8 times more likely to have a confirmed history of emotional abuse, and 4.0 times more likely to have a history of sexual abuse than children with no identified disability. Among all maltreated children, 24.1% had intellectual disabilities.

Despite a lack of consensus around the actual incidence rates, research findings typically demonstrate this greater risk for people with developmental. Determining the exact scope of this problem is complicated by three factors:

- reporting issues
- variability in research methodology
- lack of clarity in understanding the association

Issues in reporting

Given its multiple causes and manifestations, developmental disability is believed to be under-diagnosed in the general population and is often neither identified nor noted in the records of child protective services (Sullivan & Knutson, 2000). In Ontario children's aid societies, documenting the presence of a developmental disability is not part of standard record keeping. As a result, there is no means of obtaining accurate statistics of the number of children with developmental disabilities involved with the societies at any given time.

Child maltreatment is also believed to be under-reported, often because people are not familiar with the indicators of maltreatment (see Table 1). In Canada, where reporting suspected child abuse it mandatory (see Box 2), people may not be aware of their legislated responsibility to report suspected maltreatment, or how and to whom to report their suspicions. Variable and changing reporting laws within and between jurisdictions may also create confusion and affect rates of reporting (Hibbard, Desch, Committee on Child Abuse and Neglect, and Council on Children with Disabilities, 2007). Even when maltreatment is recognized, there may be reluctance to report. It is estimated that 50-75% of all cases of suspected child maltreatment are not reported (Fallon, Trocmé, Fluke, MacLaurin, Tonmyr, & Yuan, 2010). People may believe that reporting will have negative repercussions for them-selves, the child, and/or the family; that it will cause more harm; or, that nothing will be done. Children who have been abused may not report if they have been manipulated or threatened by the abuser; if they believe the abuse to have been their fault; if they fear being punished for reporting; and/or if they feel ashamed (Department of Justice, 2001). Even assuming that the proportion of reported to unre-ported cases of abuse is approximately equal, any figure we arrive at is likely a gross underestimation of the problem (Fudge Schormans & Sobsey, 2007).

Among children with developmental disabilities, abuse is both significantly under diagnosed and underreported. Children and adults with develop-mental disabilities are less likely to disclose abuse themselves, for several reasons that are typical for people with and without disabilities: fear of repri-sal from abuser, feelings of guilt or shame, fear of consequences to self and family (i.e., child sepa-rated from family, father jailed, becoming homeless, and losing support network), and fear of not being believed. Many people with developmental disabili-ties (and those with other disabilities as well) may not have the vocabulary or communication skills needed to make a disclosure (Garbarino et al., 1987; Strickler, 2001). As a result, reports most often come from a third party. However, considerable variation exists regarding the competence of caregivers, staff, and professionals to detect abuse (Beail & Warden, 1995). When communication difficulties impede a child's ability to verbally disclose abuse, the child may instead demonstrate emotional or behavioural signs of having been maltreated (Ammerman et al., 1989). As these signs are less conclusive than a ver-bal disclosure, they are often overlooked, misdiag-nosed as a symptom of a mental health problem, or improperly labelled as a function of the disability. By attributing the cause of the aberrant behaviour or emotional response to the disability, the true cause — child abuse — is overlooked (see Box 3).

Other factors are believed to play a role in the underreporting of abuse of people with develop-mental disabilities, such as changes in societal atti-tudes and understandings of both "disability" and "maltreatment." In addition, child welfare workers typically receive insufficient training to identify developmental disabilities at the time child abuse is being investigated (Hibbard et al., 2007). The abuse of children with disabilities may be less likely to be reported and investigated if the characteristics of the disability (uncontrolled movements of children with cerebral palsy, poor gross motor skills, etc.) are seen as a reasonable explanation for the injuries (Manders & Stoneman, 2009). Cooke and Standen (2002) reported that social workers in Britain believe there is often a conscious and unconscious tendency for people not to see (and thus not to report) the mal-

Box 3: Case study - Nina

Nina was born with a congenital syndrome that resulted in both physical and developmental disabilities. This syndrome was progressive in nature. It was anticipated at her birth that Nina would require increasing levels of care and that she would likely die before reaching adulthood. Nina's parents had no family support here to assist with her care. Nina's father was unwilling to accept respite or in home support services. Feeling unable to cope with her daughter's care needs and impending death, Nina's mother abandoned her to her father's care when she was 9 years old. Her father began to sexually abuse her once she reached puberty. This continued for more than a year. A neighbour, who had known Nina for several years, suspected that Nina was being abused after observing changes in Nina's behaviour with her father. Unable to speak, Nina would close her eyes and turn her head away whenever her father spoke to her or approached her. Previously a friendly child, her apparent sadness also prompted the neighbour's suspicions. When questioned by police and child protective services, Nina's father admitted to abusing his daughter but asserted his belief that he had acted within his rights as Nina's father.

Source: Fudge Schormans (2003).

treatment of children with disabilities. Because of the variation in reporting and substantiation rates for children with and without disabilities, relative rates of confirmed abuse may be misleading (Fudge Schormans & Sobsey, 2007).

Methodological variability

Variability in research methodology complicates the ability to get an accurate understanding of the rate of maltreatment in children with developmental disabilities (see Govinshenoy & Spencer, 2006). Research samples tend to be selective, targeting individuals who share a particular diagnosis (e.g., Down syndrome), thus failing to represent the broad range of diagnoses and abilities captured under the label "developmental disability." Many studies focus on only one type of abuse. In addition, incidence studies rarely control for age in comparing children with and without disabilities (Dufour & Chamberland, 2003; Hibbard et al., 2007). When data is collected from child protective service records, the lower socioeconomic classes and ethnic minorities may be overrepresented in the results (Gorman-Smith & Matson, 1992).

Although children with developmental disabilities reside in a wide variety of settings (i.e., family homes, foster and adoptive homes, group homes, and institutions), samples tend to be drawn from very specific (typically clinical) settings (Perlman & Erikson, 1992). Estimates drawn from the records of

child protective services typically include only cases of intrafamilial abuse, thereby excluding situations of extrafamilial abuse investigated by the police (Fudge Schormans & Fallon, 2009; Hibbard et al., 2007). For example, drawing on data taken from child protective services records alone, Sullivan and Knutson (2000) determined the incidence of maltreatment among children with developmental disabilities to be 1.7 times greater than for children without developmental disabilities. Examining data derived by merging a number of sources (i.e., school, police, and child protective services records), children with developmental disabilities were found to be 3.4 times more likely to experience abuse.

Also of concern is the Eurocentric bias to research. Although approximately 80% of people with disabilities live in developing countries, most available research originates from developed countries, specifically Western Europe and North America (Priestley, 2001). Differential definitions and understanding of the terms *developmental disability* and *abuse* further confound knowledge of incidence and prevalence worldwide (Govindshenoy & Spencer, 2006; Hibbard et al., 2007).

Lack of clarity in understanding the association

Another concern is that studies relating developmental disability to maltreatment do not typically clarify the nature of the association. They do not indicate whether children who already have disabilities are at increased risk, whether maltreatment results in the overrepresentation of cases of children with disabilities, or whether some other factors increase the risk for both disabilities and maltreatment. These three factors suggest that any estimates to date are most likely an underreporting of the true extent of the problem (Fudge Schormans & Sobsey, 2007). While it is clear that children with developmental disabilities are overrepresented in maltreatment, a lack of recent research into this association is of concern. There is a critical need for research that examines and makes clear this relationship for practice and policy to be effective (Govindshenoy & Spencer, 2006; Hibbard et al., 2007; Horner-Johnson & Drum, 2006; Mersky, Berger, Reynolds, & Gromoske, 2009; Stith et al., 2009).

Child maltreatment, like all forms of violence, cannot be understood to result from any single determinant. The most accepted theoretical framework in much contemporary research is the integrative ecological model (Macdonald, 2001). From this perspective, child abuse and neglect are the result of the dynamic interplay of genetic, biological, psychological, environmental, and sociological factors that combine to create the conditions necessary for maltreatment to occur. Some of these factors act to increase the risk of maltreatment, whereas others protect the child from harm. Some factors are distal and have long-lasting or cumulative effects (e.g., attachment disruptions). Current, or recent, factors are defined as proximal factors (e.g., loss of housing). An understanding of maltreatment is best accomplished through an assessment of the interplay among the relevant factors over both space (i.e., the individuals involved and the environment) and time (past and present), and across four levels of analysis: the level of the individual (child and caregiver), family, community, and society (Macdonald, 2001).

DEVELOPMENTAL DISABILITY AS BOTH RISK FOR, AND CONSEQUENCE OF, MALTREATMENT

There is a well-established association between maltreatment and developmental disability. Child maltreatment is implicated in a substantial number of developmental disabilities and, as has been demonstrated, children with developmental disabilities are at an increased risk of experiencing maltreatment (Fudge Schormans & Fallon, 2009; Vig & Kaminer, 2002). Sobsey (1994) suggested that 3-6% of all maltreated children will have some degree of permanent developmental disability as a result of the abuse and that child maltreatment is a factor in 10-25% of all developmental disabilities. This is, however, not a simple cause and effect relationship. Neither is it universal nor inevitable. Yet it can, for some people, create a cycle of maltreatment and disability: childhood maltreatment leading to permanent developmental disability that precipitates life-long risk and vulnerability to further maltreatment. These two concepts are discussed in detail next.

Child maltreatment increases the risk of developmental disability

There are three primary mechanisms by which developmental disability becomes an outcome of child maltreatment: 1) physical trauma, 2) neglect, and 3) the emotional and psychological effects of maltreatment. As more is learned about how emotional and psychological effects produce physiological, and even anatomical, effects in developing children, the line between these primary categories begins to blur (Fudge Schormans & Sobsey, 2007).

Physical trauma: Physical trauma leading to neurological damage may result in developmental disability. Permanent brain damage may be a sequelae of physical abuse and may be implicated in developmental disability, cerebral palsy, epilepsy, neuromotor disabilities, speech and language deficits, and growth deficits. Shaken-baby syndrome and physical assault of a child are two well-known examples. Women face an increased risk of physical assault during pregnancy. Sobsey (1994) identified that this may be a result of a number of factors: marital stress, sexual frustration, a response to changes in the woman's affect and/or behaviour during pregnancy, a conscious or unconscious desire to hurt the fetus, or the woman's decreased capacity to defend herself during pregnancy. Both the assaults and the stress associated with spousal violence can result in traumatogenic developmental disabilities or low birth weights (which are also associated with developmental disability) (Teixeira, Fisk, & Glover, 1999). Maternal prenatal substance abuse (e.g., alcohol, street drugs, inhalants) also interferes with typical fetal development and may lead to serious, lifelong developmental problems (e.g., fetal alcohol spectrum disorder). The role of violence in pregnancy is relevant both because: 1) it is associated with maternal substance abuse, poor nutrition, and poor prenatal care, and 2) because prenatal family violence is a risk factor for postnatal child maltreatment. Although there is debate over whether assault to a developing fetus is definable as child maltreatment, the numbers of children born affected after assault warrants inclusion of this category in this discussion (see Covell & Howe, 2001).

Neglect: Neglect affects a child's development in several ways. Poor maternal nutrition and prenatal care negatively affects fetal development. Inadequate nutrition, especially in the first two years of life when the brain and central nervous system are growing rapidly, may stunt the child's development. Poverty is an important consideration here — many maltreated children live in poverty and living in poverty is associated with an increased vulnerability to conditions associated with disability (Vig & Kaminer, 2002). Inadequate supervision of children is implicated in child fatalities, serious injury, and exposure to toxic or poisonous substances. As well, developmental disability may be a consequence of neglect of the child's needs for attention, stimulation, and learning opportunities (Fudge Schormans & Sobsey, 2007).

Emotional and psychological effects: Emotional and psychological effects of maltreatment frequently include delayed or arrested cognitive development. When a child's energies are directed toward surviving and/or trying to cope with extreme stress, learning and adaptive deficits may follow (see Box 4). Research also suggests that emotional and psychological trauma can result in temporary and permanent changes to the child's developing brain (e.g., atypical brain wave patterns, higher than expected rates of seizure disorder), which affects cognition and learning and possibly increases the risk for future psychiatric disorders (Bremner &

Vermetten, 2001; De Bellis & Thomas, 2003; Penza, Heim, & Nemeroff, 2003).

Developmental disability increases the risk of maltreatment

How do we understand this increased risk and vulnerability to maltreatment? Children with disabilities are not substantially different from children without disabilities, and therefore share those risk factors common to all children (see Table 2). Reflecting a social model understanding of disability, people with developmental disabilities are, however, believed to be more vulnerable as a result of a number of factors specific to them as a group. Most of these factors do not apply to everyone with developmental disabilities, nor are they necessarily the result of immutable characteristics of people with disabilities. Instead, they reflect the typical life experiences of many people with disabilities in a society that does not adequately understand, value, or protect them. The relationship between disability and maltreatment is not a causal one — disability, in and of itself, does not cause maltreatment. To assume a causal relationship serves only to engage in blaming the victim and to obscure the social, material, political, and economic variables that contribute to both maltreatment and disability.

A number of tenacious myths have sprung up around the abuse of people with developmental disabilities and have serious consequences:

- Children and adults with developmental disabilities are never abused.
- The abuse of people with developmental disabilities is not a serious issue because they will neither understand what happened to them nor be affected as severely as would people who do not have developmental disabilities.
- The abuse of people with developmental disabilities is acceptable because it is a natural response to the burden of having to care for someone with a disability.
- People with developmental disabilities are not sexually desirable — no one would want to sexually abuse them.
- People with developmental disabilities are unable to provide a credible account of what

Box 4: Case study - Kathryn

Kathryn was born following an uneventful and typical pregnancy. Her mother had a history of psychiatric problems but, with support from the community mental health services, had maintained both employment and housing for several years. Kathryn's early developmental scores were in the average range, and early hospital records reported Kathryn to be developing along normative parameters until approximately 3 years of age.

At this time, her mother became involved with a new partner, whom she later married. Over the next 4 years, the family situation steadily deteriorated. Kathryn's mother discontinued her involvement with the community mental health services and, as her behaviour became more erratic, she lost her job. The family was frequently homeless or living in shelters. Kathryn was both witness to domestic violence between her mother and stepfather and the victim of repeated incidents of physical and emotional abuse. Kathryn stopped speaking. Following an incident of physical abuse by her mother, which was witnessed by a shelter staff person, Kathryn was brought into the care of child protective services. At Kathryn's admission to care, it appeared that she had developmental disabilities.

Kathryn soon started to speak again and disclosed to her foster mother long-standing sexual abuse by her stepfather. Even after several years of intensive support and intervention, as a teenager Kathryn remained several grade levels behind her peers and functioned at a level typical of a much younger child. Her psychologist believed the effects of the abuse on her development to be permanent.

Source: Fudge Schormans (2003).

happened; therefore, there is no point in dealing with their disclosure.

Acceptance of these myths serves as a rationale for denying the existence of maltreatment in this population; minimizing the seriousness of the problem; failing to report suspected or disclosed abuse; failing to pursue conviction of the alleged perpetrator; and/or failing to provide appropriate support and interventions to the person who has been abused. Some of the most frequently cited risk factors specific to this population are presented next (Gorman Smith & Matson, 1992; Hibbard et al., 2007; Kvam, 2000; Manders & Stoneman, 2009; Mazzucchelli, 2001; Perlman & Erikson, 1992; Randall et al., 2000; Strickler, 2001; Tharinger, Burrows Horton, & Millea, 1990; Vig & Kaminer, 2002). Note, however, that this is not an exhaustive list.

1. *In a society that devalues disability, the presence of a developmental disability in their child may, for some families, be more than they can manage.* Parents may mourn the loss of the "normal" child they had expected. The anger that often accompanies mourning may be directed

at the child. Family members' perceptions of the child as being different can impede their ability to form an attachment or provide appropriate care for their child — a situation that may be made more difficult if extended family members and friends appear to reject the child. It may also precipitate sufficient emotional stress to create a family crisis, thus increasing the child's risk of and vulnerability to abuse. This can be exacerbated for families without access to adequate social and professional supports. It is important to understand, however, that not all families respond this way to the birth of a child with a developmental disability — to assume all families interpret the birth of a child with a disability as a tragedy is erroneous and can also result in negative consequences for the child and family.

2. *Dependence upon others increases vulnerability to maltreatment.* Children and adults with developmental disabilities may be more dependent upon carers for their basic needs and for the provision of intimate personal care. In many cases, this may be a lifelong dependence. In addition,

Table 2: Common Risk Factors for Maltreatment of Children With and Without Disabilities

Risk factors at the level of the child

- Childhood
- Gender (there are gender differences associated with types of maltreatment; for example, girls are more likely to experience sexual abuse and boys are more likely to experience physical abuse)
- Prematurity/birth anomalies
- Exposure to toxins in utero
- Chronic or serious illness
- Disability (developmental, physical, or learning disability)
- Temperament (e,g., fussy, feeding problems, does not readily engage)
- Behaviour (e.g., activity level, noncompliance)
- Childhood trauma
- Antisocial peer group

Risk factors at the level of the parent / caregiver

- Parental/caregiver psychopathology
- Parental/caregiver substance abuse
- Parent/caregiver negative affect
- Parental/caregiver history of abuse
- Low parental/caregiver self-esteem and self-efficacy
- Poor child management skills
- Unrealistic expectations of child
- Poor impulse control
- Poor conflict resolution skills
- Parental/caregiver illness or disability
- Parental/caregiver lack of empathy
- Death of parent or sibling

Risk factors at the level of family environment

- Conflict between parents
- Separation and/or divorce (especially high-conflict divorce)
- Parental/caregiver negative affect
- Domestic violence
- Family disorganization
- Harsh or aversive parenting/caregiving style
- High levels of family stress
- Family size

Risk factors at the level of community environment

- Poverty
- Homelessness or housing instability
- Unemployment
- Poor access to medical care and social services
- Lack of child care
- Community violence
- Exposure to discrimination
- Exposure to environmental toxins
- Poor schools
- Social isolation
- Single parenthood with lack of support

Societal and cultural risk factors

- Societal attitudes and response to violence
- Perceptions regarding the sanctity and integrity of the family unit, rights of parents, status of children, and use of physical punishment
- Societal attitudes toward the provisions of social supports and educational resources
- Societal attitudes and response to minority groups (including disability) and discrimination
- Societal mechanisms for identifying and responding to abuse

Sources: Garbarino et al. (1987); Macdonald (2001); and Sobsey (1994).

they may have multiple caregivers across a wide variety of situations (e.g., home, school, respite home, therapy centre, day program), exponentially increasing the risk of maltreatment.

3. *Compliance training is a common experience for many people with developmental disabilities.* Compliance is often overemphasized at the expense of assertiveness or independence. An unintended consequence is an increased vulnerability, as it places the person in a situation of unusual trust while enhancing the possibility of coercion.

4. *The overuse and/or misuse of specialized interventions or treatments, such as aversive behavioural techniques, restraints, and pharmacological interventions, creates risk.* Aversive behavioural techniques and restraints — especially if administered improperly, by insufficiently trained persons, or in an aggressive or overly punitive manner — can create a situation of risk. The overuse or misuse of pharmacological interventions can similarly result in the risk of harm.

5. *Social powerlessness* stems from power inequities in the settings designed to protect people with developmental disabilities (e.g., school, foster care, respite care, group homes, institutions). In these settings, children and adults with developmental disabilities generally have little real control and limited influence on decision-making.

6. *Limited communication skills can play a role.* Such limited skills may affect the ability to report abuse, to have one's disclosure understood or viewed as credible, to say "no," and/or to call for help. This may lead to some perpetrators identifying persons with developmental disabilities as an "easy mark."

7. *Additional physical or mobility impairments* may also pose a risk. They may impede the ability to defend oneself, to ward off an attack, or to run away.

8. *The need or desire to "fit in" and to feel accepted can also work to create risk.* Low self-esteem, emotional and social insecurities, and an eagerness to please can make one more vulnerable to coercion.

9. *Insufficient education and training regarding sex-uality, personal rights, self-protection, and abuse can create risk.* People with developmental disabilities frequently have not been equipped to recognize dangerous situations, protect themselves, or report what has happened to them. Some parents and service providers are reluctant to provide this information. They may believe that persons with developmental disabilities are not sexual, that sexual behaviour is not appropriate for people with developmental disabilities, or that providing this information will lead to inappropriate behaviour. Most often, this kind of instruction and training is provided only after maltreatment has occurred.

10. *A lack of personal privacy also increases vulnerability.* This is most notably a concern for people with developmental disabilities living in large, congregate settings. As the number of residents and staff increases, so does risk.

11. *Social devaluation is a particularly powerful risk factor.* It decreases both internal inhibitions and social restraints against the abuse of people with developmental disabilities. Also, when societal devaluation is internalized by the person being devalued it can facilitate an ongoing sense of powerlessness to resist or report abuse.

12. *Segregation and out-of-home care arrangements are more likely for people with developmental disabilities, especially for those with more severe impairments.* Segregated school, therapeutic, and leisure settings, and/or residential placement in foster care, group homes, or institutional settings inflate the risk of maltreatment. This is due to an increased exposure to potential offenders, fewer available protections, and more limited access to individuals who will act on disclosures. It should be noted, however, that most reported child maltreatment occurs in the family home (Fudge Schormans & Brown, 2002; Fudge Schormans & Fallon, 2009).

From an ecological perspective, we cannot look only at personal characteristics of children and adults with developmental disabilities in our attempts to understand why they are maltreated more often than their non-disabled peers. Numerous factors are involved, not the least of which are related to the devaluation and latent assumptions and prejudices about people with developmental disabilities in contemporary culture. See Table 3 for Sobsey's (1994) application of an integrated ecological model of abuse of persons with developmental disabilities.

CHARACTERISTICS OF MALTREATMENT AND DEVELOPMENTAL DISABILITY

Children with developmental disabilities are subject to the same types of maltreatment experiences as children without developmental disabilities, yet significant differences also exist. A few of the more significant similarities and differences will be presented next.

Most common type of maltreatment

For children with and without developmental disabilities, neglect is the type of maltreatment that is reported to occur most often — more often than physical abuse, sexual abuse, or emotional maltreatment. In addition, both groups of children are reported to frequently experience multiple forms of maltreatment either simultaneously or at different times or ages. What is also evident, however, is that children with developmental disabilities appear to experience both neglect and multiple categories of maltreatment at significantly higher rates (Fudge Schormans & Fallon, 2009; Sullivan & Knutson, 2000; Trocmé et al., 2005; Verdugo, Bermejo & Fuertes, 1995). One hypothesis put forth to explain the high incidence of neglect is that the increased care demands of this group of children places them at greater risk (Ammerman et al., 1989; Vig & Kaminer, 2002), especially if the supports and services they and their families require are not readily available or accessible. Families of children with developmental disabilities with substantiated maltreatment experience higher rates of reliance on social assistance, more precarious and unsafe housing, higher rates of additional caregiver stressors and fewer social supports (Fudge Schormans & Fallon, 2009). There was no agreement in the literature reviewed as to which type of maltreatment was reported most often after neglect. To maintain relevance to the situation in Ontario, findings from

the CIS indicate physical abuse to be the second most frequently substantiated form of maltreatment, followed by emotional maltreatment and then sexual abuse. Findings also demonstrate comparable or higher rates of all categories of maltreatment for children with developmental disabilities (Fudge Schormans & Fallon, 2009; Lightfoot, Hill, & LaLiberte, 2011).

Severity

There is strong literature support for the belief that the maltreatment of people with developmental disabilities is more severe than for people without developmental disabilities. This is evident in the areas of physical abuse and emotional maltreatment as people with developmental disabilities appear to sustain more physical injuries and experience more emotional harm as a result of maltreatment (Ammerman et al., 1989; Fudge Schormans & Fallon, 2009; Tharinger et al., 1990). More severe abuse occurs as well in sexual abuse: having a developmental disability increases the likelihood of experiencing contact sexual abuse (e.g., inappropriate touching; oral, anal, or vaginal penetration; attempted penetration) as opposed to noncontact sexual abuse (e.g., indecent exposure, invitation to touch). This means that in addition to being subjected to more severe sexual abuse, people with developmental disabilities are also put at a greater risk of exposure to HIV/AIDS and other sexually transmitted diseases (Ammerman et al., 1989; Beail & Warden, 1995; Sobsey, 1994; Tharinger et al., 1990).

Chronic versus acute nature

Abuse and neglect for people with developmental disabilities tends also to be chronic. They are much more likely than people without disabilities to experience multiple episodes of maltreatment spanning a longer time period. While this may be partially explained by higher rates of neglect (Fudge Schormans & Fallon, 2009), Sullivan & Knutson (2000) found that 71% of their sample of children identified as having a developmental disability reported repeated abuse, as opposed to 60.1% of their sample without an identified developmental disability. When we look at sexual abuse specifically, this may be even more pronounced for younger children and for children with more significant disabilities (Sobsey, 1994).

Degree of developmental disability

The degree of disability is an important parameter for consideration. A common assumption is that people with more severe developmental disabilities are at greater risk of abuse and neglect, primarily as a result of several of the risk factors that were previously identified: increased dependence, the potential for more caregivers, less well-developed communication skills, additional motor impairments, and more involvement with out-of-home care and segregated services. A review of the literature, however, indicates that people with mild or moderate levels of developmental disability appear to be at greater risk. One explanation is that children with more severe disabilities elicit more sympathy than anger, which serves somehow to protect them. A second explanation is that they are less able to engage in behaviours that may trigger an abusive incident (i.e., aggressive or self-stimulating behaviour) (Ammerman et al., 1989). Strickler (2001) suggested they are less capable of interacting with others or reacting to a potential abuser in a way that precipitates abuse. Benedict et al. (1990) argued that because caregivers expect less from them, caregiver frustration (leading to abuse) is a less common response. It must be remembered, however, that maltreatment is far less likely to be verbally disclosed by people with more severe developmental disabilities (largely a result of more limited communication abilities). Also, if abuse is disclosed behaviourally or emotionally, there is less chance it will be correctly identified by others, especially by people unfamiliar with indicators of maltreatment and/or the individual's nonverbal communication methods (Balogh et al., 2001; Kvam, 2000). Sobsey (1994) found that people with mild to moderate or severe to profound developmental disabilities are almost equally represented in reported cases of sexual abuse. More recently, Herman's study of maltreatment in preschool-aged children in the United States indicated that the risk of physical and sexual abuse increases in proportion to the severity and multiplicity of disability (2007). This suggests the need to investigate this area further.

Age

Two patterns start to emerge when age is examined. First, the maltreatment of children with developmental disabilities tends to begin at a younger age than for children without developmental disabilities. More preschool aged children with developmental disabilities are reported for all types of maltreatment than are their counterparts without developmental disabilities (Benedict et al., 1990; Sullivan & Knutson, 2000). In an investigation of a sample of children with multiple disabilities in psychiatric hospitals, Ammerman et al. (1989) found that before the age of 2 years, 46% of the children in this sample had been physically abused, 49% had been sexually abused, and 68% had experienced neglect. For both children with and without developmental disabilities, younger children are typically at greater risk for physical abuse and neglect, whereas the risk of sexual abuse increases in adolescence (Ammerman et al., 1989; Beail & Warden, 1995; Trocmé et al., 2005).

Second, an inverse relationship between age and maltreatment exists for children without developmental disabilities: as age increases, the rate of maltreatment decreases. As children grow, they typically develop better communication skills and self-protection skills and are physically better able to ward off an attack. With maturity frequently comes an improved capacity to escape or avoid abusive situations (Randall et al., 2000). This is not always the case for children with developmental disabilities (especially for children with more severe disability) who may develop such skills later or not at all. For this group, age is not necessarily a protective factor and vulnerability to maltreatment generally extends across the life span (Randall, et al., 2001; Verdugo et al., 1995).

Gender

The effect of gender is not equal for children with and without developmental disabilities. Among children without developmental disabilities, Sullivan and Knutson (2000) noted that girls are abused more often

Table 3: Individual, Environmental, and Cultural Aspects of Maltreatment of People with Developmental Disabilities

Potential victim

- *Impaired physical defences*
- *Impaired communicative functioning*
- *Lacks critical information*
- *Learned helplessness*
- *Learned compliance*
- *Covers up allegations*
- *Undeveloped sense of personal space*
- *Dependency*

Potential offender

- *Devaluing attitudes*
- *Need for control*
- *Authoritarian*
- *Low self-esteem*
- *Displaced aggression*
- *Exposure to abusive models*
- *Little attachment to victim*
- *Impulsive behaviour*

Environment

- *Dehumanizes potential victims*
- *Emphasizes control*
- *Attracts abusers*
- *Isolated from society*
- *Provides awarded models of aggression*
- *Covers up allegations*
- *Many caregivers*
- *Transient caregivers*
- *Eliminates nonabusers (discourages them from staying and/or reporting maltreatment)*
- *Clusters risks*
- *Discourages attachment*

Culture

- *Disinhibits aggressions*
- *Devalues victims*
- *Objectifies victims*
- *Teaches compliance*
- *Emphasizes vulnerabilities*
- *Denies problems*
- *Discourages attachment*
- *Discourages solutions*

From Sobsey, D. (1994). Violence and abuse in the lives of people with disabilities: The end of silent acceptance? (p. 163). Baltimore: Paul H. Brookes Publishing Co.; adapted by permission.

(56%) than boys (42%), whereas Trocmé et al. (2005) found an almost equal distribution (49.1% girls and 50.9% boys). It is interesting to note that boys with developmental disabilities are overrepresented in all categories of substantiated maltreatment: 63.8% of children with developmental disabilities reported for child maltreatment are boys and 36.2% are girls (Fudge Schormans & Fallon, 2009).

Does disability status actually increase the risk of abuse for boys? Children with developmental disability are more likely to have paid caregivers and, for boys, these are more likely to be male. The characteristics "paid caregiver" and "male" are sometimes correlated with perpetrator status which potentially

contributes to an elevated risk of maltreatment for boys with developmental disabilities (Randall et al., 2000). Sullivan and Knutson (2000) offered another explanation, noting that more boys than girls are identified as having developmental disabilities. The greater prevalence of maltreated boys may simply reflect the increased prevalence of boys in the developmental disability population. The differences may be further accounted for by reporting issues. Maltreated boys with developmental disabilities are more likely to act out, to demonstrate behavioural concerns that bring them into contact with professionals, thus potentially increasing the probability of being reported for maltreatment. As a group, their female counterparts tend more towards withdrawal and other emotional and behavioural expressions that do not create the same type of problems for their caregivers as the behaviours exhibited by boys. A consequence is that girls are thus less likely to be diagnosed as being abused (Beail & Warden, 1995).

To complicate matters, it is speculated that both developmental disability and maltreatment are underreported more often for girls than for boys (Randall et al., 2000). Furthermore, although boys seem to be more reluctant to disclose abuse — especially sexual abuse — than do girls, girls are less likely to be believed. This not only affects understanding of the rates of maltreatment but also, more seriously, it results in the threat of continued maltreatment for girls (Beail & Warden, 1995; Randall et al., 2000). In addition, as contrasted with their peers without a disability, disclosures by both girls and boys with developmental disabilities are significantly less likely to be believed (Kvam, 2000). These factors skew understanding of the intersection between gender, disability, and maltreatment and point to the need for further investigation.

Alleged perpetrator

For all children, irrespective of disability, the alleged perpetrator of maltreatment is usually someone the child knows. "Stranger" abuse is actually a rare event, accounting for less than 1% (Trocmé et al., 2005) to 6.6% (Sobsey, 1994) of child maltreatment. Across the world, the alleged perpetrator of child maltreatment is most often a family member. In Canada, the CIS-2003 reported that only 3% of child maltreatment was committed by a nonfamily member such as a teacher, professional, baby sitter, parental girlfriend/boyfriend, peer, or stranger (Trocmé et al., 2003). This figure is perhaps an underestimation, as many instances of non-familial abuse may have been investigated by the police rather than child protective services. For children without a developmental disability, and for many children with developmental disability, immediate family members are believed to be responsible for the majority of neglect, physical, and emotional abuse. Extended family or nonfamily members are implicated more often in sexual abuse cases. Mothers and fathers are equally represented as perpetrators of physical abuse, with more mothers reported for neglect and emotional abuse, and more fathers for sexual abuse. It must be remembered, however, that in Western culture the responsibility for child care often still rests primarily with mothers. In addition, more single-parent families (a risk factor for child maltreatment) are headed by more mothers than by fathers (Sobsey, 1994; Sullivan & Knutson, 2000; Trocmé et al., 2005).

Debate exists in the literature as to whether people with developmental disabilities are at greater risk of familial or nonfamilial maltreatment. While some studies report high levels of familial abuse (Ammerman et al., 1989; Beail & Warden , 1995; Tharinger et al., 1990), contradictory findings suggest that maltreatment at the hands of service providers is a greater threat. Sobsey (1994) reported that for those included in his sample, 56% of sexual abuse was perpetrated by service providers, compared with 28% by caregivers. The issue is muddied by the variety, multiplicity, and complexity of living arrangements for this group. Although deinstitutionalization policies have resulted in more people with developmental disabilities living in their family homes, the reality is that a significant number still reside in out-of-home placements. These placements may be permanent (i.e., group homes or institutional settings) or temporary (i.e., respite care). Multiple moves are not uncommon (especially in the foster care system, where children sometimes bounce from one placement to the next). One outcome of such discontinuity of care and involvement with the developmental disability service system is an increased vulnerability to maltreatment by nonfamily members. This is not restricted to alternative caregivers or staff persons alone. A consequence of residential and day program settings, in which several people with developmental disabilities are congregated together, is a higher risk of maltreatment by a peer who also has a developmental disability (Balogh et al., 2001).

Potential for abuse in institutions

The Government of Ontario closed its last three institutions in the spring of 2009, and there had not been any children housed in any of Ontario's institutions since the early 1990s. There are still institutions operating in some other Canadian provinces, however (see Chapter 2 for more information), and certainly in other countries around the world. Thus, although the discussion here does not describe the situation for Ontario children, it is still highly relevant for children elsewhere.

Specific to children and adults with developmental disabilities is the notion that institutionally sanctioned services and procedures may be abusive or neglectful. In some instances administrative structures, philosophies, and institutional cultures can permit, condone, or even encourage three forms of institutional maltreatment that are then enacted by employees. Institutional child abuse involves the use of physical punishment, aversive behaviour management techniques, excessive isolation, physical or mechanical restraints, or the abuse or misuse of psychotropic drugs. Institutional child neglect refers to failure to provide needed services, stimulation and educational opportunities and negligent attitudes toward the use of punishment, restraints, and medication. Wrongful abrogation of personal rights includes such actions as improper segregation and restrictions on personal choice, decision-making, communications, or socialization preferences (Garbarino et al., 1987).

IMPACT OF MALTREATMENT ON CHILDREN AND ADULTS WITH DEVELOPMENTAL DISABILITIES

The impact of maltreatment on children with developmental disabilities appears to be similar to but more severe than the impact on children without disabilities. Mansell, Sobsey, and Moskall (1998), for example, compared clinical findings from two samples of age- and gender-matched Canadian children served by the same treatment agency: children with developmental disabilities who had been sexually abused and children without disabilities who had been sexually abused. Clinical characteristics were similar, but the children with disabilities exhibited a higher number of clinically significant problems (e.g., increased vulnerability to sexual abuse, withdrawal into fantasy and self-abuse). This finding is supported by Fudge Schormans and Fallon (2009) in their analysis of the CIS-2 (2003) data: maltreated

children with developmental delay were reported to demonstrate more signs of emotional harm (e.g., nightmares, bed wetting, social withdrawal) — harm requiring therapeutic treatment — than their non-disabled counterparts.

Kvam (2000) cautioned us that, for each individual, the impact is affected by: the seriousness of the abuse, the age of onset, single or multiple episodes of maltreatment, characteristics of the individual, family response to disclosure, family situation, and the individual's relationship to the abuser (remember, the first five have already been identified as significant factors in the maltreatment of persons with developmental disabilities). People with developmental disabilities typically experience the same outcomes as do people without developmental disabilities (see Table 4). Heeding Kvam's caution, this list is not applicable to everyone who experiences maltreatment, nor is it exhaustive, nor is it likely that any one person will experience all of these outcomes.

In addition to being at risk for experiencing the same impacts of maltreatment as their non-disabled peers, there are additional impacts of maltreatment unique to persons with developmental disabilities. These include the following (Fudge Schormans & Sobsey, 2007; Gorman-Smith & Matson, 1992; Perlman & Erikson, 1992; Sobsey, 1994; Strickler, 2001; Tharinger et al., 1990; Vig & Kaminer, 2002):

1. The experience of maltreatment exacerbates the feelings of social isolation and of "being different" that are common to this group.

2. People with developmental disabilities are already stigmatized in our society; further stigmatization may accrue as a result of maltreatment.

3. There is a tendency for individuals to believe they were abused because they have a developmental disability.

4. Notably higher rates of psychiatric disorder have been correlated with maltreatment for children and adults with developmental disabilities.

5. Because of frequent misdiagnosis of the emotional, social, and behavioural symptomatology of maltreatment, people with developmental disabilities are more likely to be mistreated and prescribed intrusive behaviour management, inappropriate psychotropic medication,

hospitalization, and/or unnecessary placement changes. There may be the mistaken belief that behavioural and/or emotional indicators of abuse are, instead, just part of the individual's "syndrome". Self-injurious behaviour, for example, is a common clinical finding among abused children with and without developmental disabilities. Using punishment procedures to reduce or eliminate this behaviour — without understanding why the behaviour is occurring — will likely result in further trauma and harm.

6. There is a mistaken belief that maltreated persons with developmental disabilities are unable to benefit from therapeutic interventions. This is one reason why these services are rarely made available to them. Even if they are available, generic services are frequently unable to accommodate the unique needs of this group. Specialized therapeutic services are limited in number and are consequently more difficult to access. This increases the risk that the impacts of maltreatment will be more severe, longer lasting, and may precipitate emotional, behavioural, or psychological crises.

INVESTIGATING MALTREATMENT OF CHILDREN AND ADULTS WITH DEVELOPMENTAL DISABILITIES

Despite investigations of alleged maltreatment, the abuse of people with developmental disabilities is punished less often than might be expected. Much of the research reports that alleged perpetrators are rarely criminally charged, tried, and/or convicted and, as a result, the abuser often continues to live with (or to provide care for) the person with the developmental disability (Balogh et al., 2001; Beail & Warden, 1995; Trocmé et al., 2001). Interestingly, the findings of the CIS-2003 suggest no significant difference in rates of police investigations, consideration of criminal charges, or the laying of criminal charges between children with and without developmental disabilities (Fudge Schormans & Fallon, 2009). The CIS-2003 data does not, however, provide for an explanation for this shift.

Canada, like other developed countries, offers two legal means of providing protection from abuse.

Canada's Criminal Code legislates protections for children and adults from physical and sexual abuse and/or deprivation of necessities of life. Falling under the domain of the criminal judicial system, this legislation is, however, dependant upon the "burden of proof," of proving the guilt of the alleged perpetrator beyond a reasonable doubt. One consequence of this is that many cases of suspected child abuse are not pursued successfully through criminal law; obtaining sufficient evidence to establish guilt beyond a reasonable doubt is often more difficult when dealing with child maltreatment.

Protection is also afforded through provincial and territorial child protection legislation governing child protection agencies. Applying exclusively to children, this legislation is premised on the less demanding civil law standard of proof of the preponderance of the evidence in the family court system. Whereas criminal proceedings are intended to determine guilt and to punish criminal behaviour, child welfare proceedings are intended to determine whether a child is in need of protection and to do what is best for the child (Fudge Schormans & Sobsey, 2007).

Child protective services are primarily responsible for investigating reports of child maltreatment when the alleged perpetrator is someone acting in a caregiving capacity (e.g., family member, babysitter, teacher, child care provider, foster parent, group home staff member). Joint investigations typically occur between child protective services and the police if the allegation involves sexual abuse, serious physical harm, criminal activity, and/or a child who has been left unattended or abandoned. The police are less likely to participate in situations involving neglect or emotional abuse unless domestic violence has been identified as a factor in the emotional abuse. The police maintain responsibility for investigating alleged child maltreatment if the alleged perpetrator is a stranger or non-family member. It is not uncommon, however, for the police to include child protective services in such investigations to take advantage of their expertise in interviewing children and linking maltreated children and their families to community supports and services. Adult protective services have been

Table 4: Common Effects of Maltreatment for People With and Without Developmental Disabilities

Social

- *Difficulty forming or maintaining relationships*
- *Social isolation*
- *Social stigmatization*
- *Less sensitive to social/emotional contexts*
- *Impaired ability to discriminate between safe situations and potentially abusive situations*
- *Increased risk of victimization*

Personality

- *Negative self-concept*
- *Low self-esteem*
- *More egocentric*
- *Inability to trust*
- *Increased dependency*
- *Overly sensitive to approval/threats*
- *More introspective*
- *Secretive*
- *More cautious*
- *More serious*

Behavioural

- *Behaviour disturbances*
- *Eating disorders*
- *Sleep disturbances*
- *Sexually inappropriate behaviour*
- *Impaired adaptive functioning*
- *Overly friendly with strangers*
- *Antisocial behaviour*
- *Aggressive behaviour*
- *Undercontrolled behaviour*
- *Running away*
- *Health-risk behaviours (e.g., substance abuse)*
- *Inability to regulate behaviour*

Cognitive

- *Impaired cognitive functioning*
- *Poor school performance*
- *Neurological consequences to brain development & function*

Psychological/emotional

- *Emotional withdrawal*
- *Emotional distress*
- *Depression*
- *Anxiety*
- *Feelings of helplessness*
- *Suicidal ideation and attempts*
- *Impaired ability to discriminate what and who is "safe"*
- *Diminished coping skills*
- *Hypervigilance*
- *Fears/phobias*
- *Guilt*
- *Anger*
- *Shame*
- *Problems with sexuality, sexual behaviour, and sexual relationships*
- *Unusual thought processes*
- *Psychopathology*
- *Posttraumatic stress disorder*
- *Overly sensitive to approval/threats*
- *Dissociative disorder*
- *Attention deficit symptomatology*

Sources: Garbarino, Brookhouser, Authier, et al. (1987); Macdonald (2001); Sobsey (1994); Vig & Kaminer (2002).

Box 5: Case study - Child protection investigation

A social worker received a call from a teacher. The teacher said that a 6-year-old boy and his 5-year-old sister had been sexually abused by their father. Both children had developmental disabilities. The girl was nonverbal, and her disability was more severe. The teacher conveyed the following: the mother forced father to leave the home after witnessing father in the act of abusing the children; the abuse was ongoing; the boy was anxious, frightened and was threatened by father not to tell; mother also had a developmental disability; and the school had ongoing concerns about the children's nutrition, clothing, and hygiene.

The worker completed a standardized tool for assessing risk and discussed the situation with her supervisor. They decided that eligibility criteria for service have been met. According to local government guidelines, the children had to be seen within 12 hours. This would be a joint investigation with police and would take place at the school. To account for the children's disabilities, to minimize trauma, and to maximize information obtained, the social worker tried to arrange for assistance from an expert in developmental disabilities. The social worker wanted the person to accompany her, and a police officer, to the school. No such support person was available that day, so the social worker arranged for the children's classroom aides to be present during the interview. Although the social worker and the police officer knew this had potential to contaminate evidence, they believed it would best facilitate information gathering.

In case the children were later unable to testify in court, the interview was videotaped. During the interview, the boy was anxious, distractible, and unable to give dates, but his aide kept him focussed. Consistent details of sexual, physical, and emotional abuse of both children emerged from the boy's report. Despite the presence of her aide, the sister was unable to provide any information.

The mother was called and requested to accompany the children and the worker to the hospital's sexual assault unit l, where she was interviewed and the children were examined. The boy complied with being examined. Although no physical evidence could be obtained, the physician noted that his behaviour during the exam was consistent with abuse. The physician was unable to complete an exam of the girl, as she was distraught, even with her mother's support. Because the prosecuting attorney would need to prove guilt beyond a reasonable doubt, it became apparent that the lack of physical evidence may compromise prosecution of father. The mother was interviewed and confirmed her son's account of the abuse. However, mother reported that the father had returned home, and she felt unable to protect the children at that time. Because the children were clearly not safe, she agreed with the worker's plan to place the children in foster care until parenting supports could be arranged.

The police found the father at the family home. After questioning him, they decided to charge him despite his denial of wrongdoing and the lack of physical evidence. The boy's disclosure and behavioural indicators warranted this decision. Even if no conviction was obtained, it was hoped this would be a deterrent in the future. The boy was referred to a victim witness program to be prepared for criminal court. His sister would not testify, as her communication was determined to be neither consistent nor reliable. Her brother was deemed competent as a witness because he knew right from wrong and the importance of telling the truth. He testified but, in part because of his cognitive, memory and language difficulties, he was easily confused by the defense attorney and his credibility was damaged. Although behavioural evidence existed, the lack of physical evidence and the boy's difficulties in testifying due to his developmental disabilities meant that the father was found not guilty. The mother refused to testify. Later, it was learned that she has also been the victim of violence at the father's hands. During supervised access visits with the children at the social services agency offices, however, the mother recanted her disclosure and stated her decision to remain with father. The children became wards of the state.

Source: Fudge Schormans (2003).

developed in many provinces, including Ontario. While these are an attempt to provide a system of protections for adults with developmental disabilities who are vulnerable to maltreatment, they vary substantially from one province to another (Fudge Schormans & Sobsey, 2007).

The current issues and debates associated with the investigation of maltreatment, for people with and without developmental disabilities, are complex. For people with developmental disabilities, Boxes 5 and 6 present cases that reveal some of the myriad factors that complicate this process and have repercussions for the child, family, and alleged perpetrator. (The reader is directed to Cederberg & Lamb, 2006; Erikson, Isaacs, & Perlman, 2003; Griffiths & Marini, 2000; and Sobsey, 1994).

There is research that indicates a differential response to the maltreatment of children with developmental disabilities by child welfare workers — even when the abuse is severe. The beliefs, attitudes and biases of child welfare workers can influence decision-making (Manders & Stoneman, 2009). Children with disabilities are more likely to be seen by child welfare workers as having characteristics that contributed to — or "provoked" — the abuse and are thus believed to be at least partially responsible for their own abuse (Manders & Stoneman, 2009). While caregiver stress may play a role in triggering outbursts of abuse, empirical evidence refutes a dependency-stress model that suggests that the caregiving needs or challenging behaviours of children with disabilities causes maltreatment (Sobsey, 2002). Despite this, many child welfare workers still rely on an understanding of children with disabilities as causing undue parental stress and burden (Manders & Stoneman, 2009). As a result, workers may be more likely to feel some empathy towards abusive parents of children with disabilities (especially if the child had emotional or behavioural disabilities) — because of the perceived stress and burden these children place upon their caregivers. The negative view of the child that follows from this thinking may mean that the abuse of children with disabilities is thus somehow easier to understand and may serve to partially excuse maltreatment. Abuse is thus less likely to be substantiated and more likely to continue (Manders & Stoneman, 2009; Sobsey, 1994). In addition, if workers are somehow blaming the child with a disability for her/his abuse, the solution would seem to be to "fix" the child, to make the child a "better child," one who is less likely to provoke or drive the parents to abuse. Services are then more likely to be child-focused: fewer parent-focused services (e.g., anger management) are rec-

ommended for families of children with disabilities (Manders & Stoneman, 2009).

What has become apparent is that children with developmental disabilities with substantiated maltreatment are more likely to be removed from the care of their families, to have multiple and longer stays in foster and other out-of-home care arrangements, and are less likely to be returned to parental care than their non-disabled counterparts (Fudge Schormans & Brown, 2002; Fudge Schormans, Coniega, & Renwick, 2006; Fudge Schormans & Fallon, 2009; Lightfoot et al., 2011; Manders & Stoneman, 2009; Rosenberg & Robinson, 2004). While we do not have a clear understanding of the reasons for this higher rate of out-of-home care (Lightfoot, 2011), this trend is troubling. The implications of this trend — on children with disabilities, their families, and the foster families responsible for their care — are unknown. This is of even greater concern when we consider that many foster parents indicate they receive insufficient training and inadequate supports to provide safe and nurturing care to children with developmental disabilities (Brown & Roger, 2009; Fudge Schormans et al., 2006; Lightfoot et al., 2011).

Summary

Historically, societal attitudes about developmental disability in Ontario are reflected in our legislated and practised responses to the maltreatment of people with developmental disabilities. In addition, we still do not have a clear understanding of the scope of the problem. There is a critical lack of research on how to identify and respond to people with developmental disabilities who have been, or are at risk for, being maltreated. Regrettably, children and adults with developmental disabilities are frequently not taught to recognize abuse and maltreatment or important self-protection skills (Doughty & Kane, 2010). This is compounded by insufficient training for child welfare workers, foster parents, caregivers, involved professionals, and the police and criminal justice system on recognizing developmental disabilities and abuse and on supporting children with developmental disabilities who have been

Box 6: Case study - Police investigation

A 31-year-old woman with developmental disabilities was a frequent customer at a neighbourhood variety store down the street from her home. Although nonverbal, she had some alternative communication abilities, and the shop keeper came to know her well. During the day, the woman attended an adult day program funded by the local government.

Over time, the shop keeper began to notice disturbing changes in the woman's behaviour. She appeared overly interested in men in the store but also frightened of them. She openly masturbated in their presence and began to exhibit self-injurious behaviours (e.g., head slapping). Concerned that she had been abused, the shop keeper attempted to engage the woman in conversation and suggested that if she had been abused she should call the police and not let anyone hurt her. The woman was clearly distressed by this conversation. The shop-keeper decided to call the police, who advised her that if the woman could not or would not make a disclosure herself, then the shop keeper could register a third-party complaint. This was done, and several days later the police met with the shop keeper. The shop keeper could provide little information about the woman's family. The police were reluctant to go the woman's home, fearing this might place her at greater risk. Deciding to meet with the woman at the store, the police were unsuccessful in their attempts to speak with her, but they were convinced by observing her behaviour that something had happened to her. As a result, the police decided to speak with the woman's family.

The woman lived alone with her mother. Appearing devastated by the suspicions of abuse, the mother agreed to facilitate a police interview with her daughter. The mother, able to communicate with her daughter using a system of "yes"/"no" responses to questions, elicited from her daughter that she had been sexually touched by staff at the day program. The daughter was then informed of her rights and her options but it was not clear how much she understood. She refused to go to the hospital for an examination, and she did not agree to press charges. Because of her age, the woman was deemed responsible to make her own decisions. The police were unable to proceed without her consent. They reviewed with the mother the option of having her daughter legally declared incompetent so that they could go forward with the investigation. The mother refused, as she saw the risks this posed to her daughter's future ability to make decisions for herself. The police referred the woman and her mother to a local sexual assault centre in an effort to assist them to receive information and support.

Source: Fudge Schormans (2003).

maltreated. This is particularly important because people with developmental disabilities are typically involved with numerous different professionals over the course of their lives to an extent that is greater than their non-disabled counterparts. Existing literature stresses that training should emphasize attitudes as well as knowledge and skills (Hibbard et al., 2007; Manders & Stoneman, 2009; Rosenberg & Robinson, 2004; Sobsey, 1994; Vig & Kaminer, 2002). Differential treatment for this group from social service, child protection, and criminal justice systems is not uncommon, and can serve to perpetuate, condone, or even authorize further maltreatment. Our present structures are inadequate to effectively address this problem: what is required is acknowledgment that they are both part of the problem and

of the solution. A stronger collaboration among all the parties involved with this issue is required: child protection services, developmental disability services, police officers, lawyers, judges, school staff, child care providers, health care professionals, therapeutic service professionals, service planners and administrators, governmental administrators and policy makers, and advocates. Researchers are also implicated — Kendall-Tackett, Lyon, Taliaferro and Little (2005) entreat all researchers studying child maltreatment to add disability status to their studies. People with developmental disabilities and their families are a key element to the development of a more responsive system of protections, possessing invaluable insights into the factors contributing to maltreatment, and what is required for prevention, protection, and healthy recoveries.

Maltreatment is a reality in the daily lives of many people with developmental disabilities. People with developmental disabilities face a much higher risk of, and vulnerability to, maltreatment. Their experiences of maltreatment are both similar to and unique from that experienced by people without disabilities. Yet, maltreatment of these individuals all too often is unreported and/or undetected or reports are not believed and, therefore, it is untreated. Three things are required to work towards change. First, recognition, acknowledgement, and a clearer understanding of the magnitude and seriousness of this issue are necessary. Second, legislation, policies, and practices are needed that are preventative rather than reactive. Third, society needs to value people with developmental disabilities, demand active condemnation of the violence perpetrated against them, and challenge the devaluation that lies at the root of such maltreatment.

For Further Thought and Discussion

1. What might be the consequences of conceptualizing maltreatment of children with disabilities in the following ways: an individual pathology issue, a social welfare issue, a public health issue, a public safety issue, or a human rights issue?

2. One thing that people with developmental disabilities share with other oppressed groups is a concern over the language used to describe them. For example, the current practice for many people labelled as having mental health concerns is to use the term psychiatric "survivor" rather than "victim." Explain the pros and cons of the use of each of these terms in relation to children and adults with developmental disabilities who experience maltreatment.

3. Discuss the issue of prenatal practices resulting in developmental disabilities (e.g., alcohol or drug use by pregnant women). Should this be defined as child abuse? Do these practices constitute a criminal offence? What role, if any, should child protection services play in cases where an expectant mother is known to be put-

ting her unborn child at risk for developmental disability?

4. The child protection system lacks expertise in the area of developmental disability. The developmental disability service system lacks expertise in the area of child maltreatment. Which service system do you feel is most appropriate to deal with the issue of the maltreatment of children with developmental disabilities, and why? What alternatives might be possible?

5. Should people with developmental disabilities be treated as a "special case" within child welfare legislation and/or criminal law in light of their particular vulnerabilities and the systemic issues that have been identified?

More Resources

Journals:

Child Abuse & Neglect: The International Journal

Children and Youth Services Review

Reports:

Public Health Agency of Canada. Canadian Incidence Study of Reported Child Abuse and Neglect – 2008: Major Findings. Ottawa, 2010. Available from: *www.phac-aspc.gc.ca/cm-vee/pub lic-eng.php*

Sexuality and Developmental Disability: A Guide for Parents. CPRI. 2009 *http://cpri.ca/uploads/section000033/2010 1209120903_668p_Sexuality%20and%20 Developmental%20Disability.pdf*

Electronic Resources:

Canadian Child Welfare Research Portal
www.cwrp.ca

Canadian Health Network
www.canadian-health-network.ca/faq-faq/sexuality_ reproductive_healthsexualite_reproduction/8e.html

Ontario Sexuality and Developmental Disability Network
c/o Sex Information and Education Council of Canada (SIECCAN)
www.sieccan.org

The British Columbia Coalition of People with Disabilities
http://www.bccpd.bc.ca

The JP Das Developmental Disabilities Centre
Dick Sobsey, Director
dick.sobsey@ualberta.ca
www.ualberta.ca/~jpdasddc/INDEX.html

The National Information Center for Children and Youth with Disabilities (USA)
http://www.nichcy.org

Key Services and Supports

Arch Disability Law Centre
www.archdisabilitylaw.ca/

Canadian Coalition for the Rights of Children
www.rightsofchildren.ca/

Justice for Children and Youth
www.jfcy.org/

Ontario Association of Children's Aid Societies
www.oacas.org

Surrey Place Centre
www.surreyplace.on.ca

References

Alaggia, R., Jenney, A., Mazzuca, J., & Redmond, M. (2007). In whose best interest? A Canadian case study on the impact of child welfare policies in cases of domestic violence. *Brief Treatment and Crisis Intervention, 7*(4), 275-290.

Ammerman, R.T., Van Hasselt, V.B., Hersen, M., et al. (1989). Abuse and neglect in psychiatrically hospitalized multihandicapped children. *Child Abuse & Neglect, 13*, 335–343.

Balogh, R., Bretherton, K., Whibley, S., et al. (2001). Sexual abuse in children and adolescents with intellectual disability. *Journal of Intellectual Disability Research, 45*, 194–201.

Beail, N., & Warden, S. (1995). Sexual abuse of adults with learning disabilities. *Journal of Intellectual Disability Research, 39*, 382–387.

Benedict, M. I., White, R. B., Wulff, L. M., et al. (1990). Reported maltreatment in children with multiple disabilities. *Child Abuse & Neglect, 14*, 207–217.

Bremner, J. D., & Vermetten, E. (2001). Stress and development: Behavioural and biological consequences. *Development and Psychopathology, 13*, 473–489.

Brown, J., & Rodger, S. (2009). Children with disabilities: Problems faced by foster parents. *Children and Youth Services Review, 31*, 40-46.

Carlson, L. (2001). Cognitive ableism and disability studies: Feminist reflections on the history of mental retardation. *Hypatia, 16*, 124–146.

Cederberg, A., & Lamb, M. E. (2006). How does the legal system respond when children with learning difficulties are victimized? *Child Abuse & Neglect, 30*(5), 537-547.

Chadwick, D.L. (1999). The message. *Child Abuse & Neglect, 23*, 957–961.

Child Welfare Transformation. (2005). *A strategic plan for a flexible, sustainable and outcome oriented service delivery model.* Ministry of Children and Youth Services, Ontario, Canada. Available from http://www.cdrcp.com/pdf/CWTransformation-FINAL-rev'd%20July%2011-ek.pdf

Conley, A. (2007). Differential response: A critical examination of a secondary prevention model. *Children and Youth Services Review, 29*, 1454-1468.

Cooke, P., & Standen, P. J. (2002). Abuse and disabled children: Hidden needs. . .? *Child Abuse Review, 11*, 1–18.

Covell, K., & Howe, R. B. (2001). *The challenge of children's rights for Canada.* Waterloo, ON: Wilfred Laurier University Press.

De Bellis, M. D., & Thomas, L. A. (2003). Biologic findings of post-traumatic stress disorder and child maltreatment. *Current Psychiatry Reports, 5*(2), 108–117.

Department of Justice. (2001). *Family Justice Initiative.* Retrieved from http://www.justice.gc.ca/eng/piwww.justice.gc.ca/eng/pi/fv-vf/facts-info/child-enf.html

Doughty, A. H., & Kane, L. M. (2010). Teaching abuse-protection skills to people with intellectual disabilities: A review of the literature. *Research in Developmental Disabilities, 31*(2), 331-337.

Dufour, S., & Chamberland, C. (2003). *The effectiveness of child welfare interventions: A systematic review.* Retrieved from http://www.cecw-cepb.ca/

PubsAll.shtml

Elmer, E., & Gregg, G. S. (1967). Developmental characteristics of abused children. *Pediatrics 40*(4), 596–602.

Fallon, B., Trocmé, N., Fluke, J., MacLaurin, B., Tonmyr, L., & Yuan, Y. (2010). Methodological challenges in measuring child maltreatment. *Child Abuse & Neglect, 34*(1), 70-79.

Fudge Schormans, A., & Brown, I. (2002). An investigation into the characteristics of the maltreatment of children with developmental delays and the alleged perpetrators of this maltreatment. *Journal on Developmental Disabilities, 9*(1), 1–19.

Fudge Schormans, A., Coniega, M., & Renwick, R. (2006). Placement stability: Enhancing quality of life for children with developmental disabilities. *Families in Society, 87*(4), 521–528.

Fudge Schormans, A., & Fallon, B. (2009, August). *Children with developmental disability and substantiation of child maltreatment.* Paper presented at American Psychological Association 117th Annual Convention, Toronto, ON.

Fudge Schormans, A., & Sobsey, D. (2007). Maltreatment and developmental disability. In I. Brown & M. Percy (Eds.), *A comprehensive guide to intellectual and developmental disabilities* (pp. 467-487). Baltimore: Paul H. Brookes Publishing Co.

Garbarino, J., Brookhouser, P. E., Authier, K., et al. (1987). *Special children, special risk: The maltreatment of children with disabilities.* New York: Aldine De Gruyter.

Gorman-Smith, D., & Matson, J. L. (1992). Sexual abuse and persons with mental retardation. In W. O'Donohue & J. H. Geer (Eds.), *The sexual abuse of children: Theory and research volume I* (pp. 285–306). Mahwah, NJ: Lawrence Erlbaum Associates.

Government of Ontario. (Last Amendment: 2010a). *Child and Family Services Act.* Retrieved from http://www.e-laws.gov.on.ca/html/statutes/english/elaws_statutes_90c11_e.htm

Government of Ontario. (2010b). *Report on the 2010 Review of the Child and Family Services Act.* Retieved from http://www.children.gov.on.ca/htdocs/English/documents/about/2010%20CFSA%20Discussion%20document.pdf

Govindshenoy, M., & Spencer, N. (2006). Abuse of the disabled child: A systematic review of population-based studies. Child: Care, health and development, *33*(5), 552-558.

Griffiths, D., & Marini, Z. (2000). Interacting with the legal system regarding a sexual offence: Social and cognitive considerations for persons with developmental disabilities. *Journal on Developmental Disabilities, 7,* 76–121.

Hibbard, R. A., Desch, L. W., & the Committee on Child Abuse and Neglect and Council on Children with Disabilities. (2007). Maltreatment of children with disabilities. *Pediatrics, 119*(5), 1018-1025.

Horner-Johnston, W., & Drum, C. E. (2006). Prevalence of maltreatment of people with intellectual disabilities: A review of recently published research. *Mental Retardation and Developmental Disabilities Research Reviews, 12,*I 57-69.

Kendall-Tackett, K., Lyon, T., Taliaferro, G., & Little, L. (2005). Why child maltreatment researchers should include disability status in their maltreatment studies. *Child Abuse & Neglect, 29,* 147-151.

Kvam, M. H. (2000). Is sexual abuse of children with disabilities disclosed? A retrospective analysis of child disability and the likelihood of sexual abuse among those attending Norwegian hospitals. *Child Abuse & Neglect, 24,* 1073–1084.

Lightfoot, E., Hill, K. & LaLiberte, T. (2011). Prevalence of children with disabilities in the child welfare system and out of home placement: An examination of administrative records, *Children and Youth Services Review.* doi: 10.1016/j.childyouth.2011.02.019

Macdonald, G. (2001). *Effective interventions for child abuse and neglect: An evidence-based approach to planning and evaluating interventions.* Hoboken, NJ: John Wiley & Sons.

Macintyre, E. (1993). The historical context of child welfare in Canada. In B. Wharf (Ed.), *Rethinking child welfare in Canada* (pp. 13–36). Toronto, ON: McClelland & Stewart.

Manders, J. E., & Stoneman, Z. (2009). Children with disabilities in the child protective services system: An analog study of investigation and case management. *Child Abuse & Neglect, 33*(4), 229-237.

Mansell, S., Sobsey, D., & Moskal, R. (1998). Clinical findings among sexually abused children with and without developmental disabilities. *Mental Retardation, 36*(1), 12–22.

Mazzucchelli, T. G. (2001). Feel Safe: A pilot study of a protective behaviours programme for people with intellectual disability. *Journal of Intellectual and Developmental Disability, 26*, 115–126.

Mersky, J. P., Berger, L. M., Reynolds, A. J., & Gromoske, A. N. (2009). Risk factors for child and adolescent maltreatment: A longitudinal investigation of a cohort of inner-city youth. *Child Maltreatment, 14*(1), 73-88.

Penza, K. M., Heim, C., & Nemeroff, C. B. (2003). Neurobiological effects of childhood abuse: Implications for the pathophysiology of depression and anxiety. *Archives of Women's Mental Health, 6*(1), 15–22.

Perlman, N., & Erikson, C. (1992). Issues related to sexual abuse of persons with developmental disabilities: An overview. *Journal on Developmental Disabilities, 1*, 19–23.

Priestly, M. (2001). Introduction: The global context of disability. In M. Priestley (Ed.), *Disability and the life course: Global perspectives* (pp. 3–14). Cambridge, United Kingdom: Cambridge University Press.

Radford, J. P., & Park, D. C. (2003). Historical overview of developmental disabilities in Ontario. In I. Brown & M. Percy (Eds.), *Developmental disabilities in Ontario* (2nd ed.) (pp. 3–18). Toronto, ON: Ontario Association on Developmental Disabilities.

Randall, W., Parilla, R., & Sobsey, D. (2000). Gender, disability status and risk for sexual abuse in children. *Journal on Developmental Disabilities, 7*, 1–15.

Rosenberg, S. A., & Robinson, C. (2004). Out-of-home placement for young children with developmental and medical conditions. *Children and Youth Services Review, 26*, 711-723.

Simmons, H. G. (1982). *From asylum to welfare.* Toronto, ON: National Institute on Mental Retardation.

Sobsey, D. (1994). *Violence and abuse in the lives of people with disabilities: The end of silent acceptance?* Baltimore: Paul H. Brookes Publishing Co.

Steinhauer, P. D. (1991). *The least detrimental alternative: A systematic guide to case planning and decision making for children in care.* Toronto, ON: University of Toronto Press.

Stith. S. M., Liu, T., Davies, L. C., Boykin, E. L., Alder, M. D., Harris, J. M., et al. (2009). Risk factors in child maltreatment: A meta-analytic review of the literature. *Aggression and Violent Behaviour, 14*(1), 13-29.

Strickler, H. (2001). Interaction between family violence and mental retardation. *Mental Retardation, 39*, 461–471.

Sullivan, P., & Knutson, J. F. (2000). Maltreatment and disabilities: A population-based epidemiological study. *Child Abuse & Neglect, 24*, 1257–1273.

Teixeira, J. M., Fisk, N. M., & Glover, V. (1999). Association between maternal anxiety in pregnancy and increased uterine artery resistance index: Cohort based study. *British Medical Journal, 318*, 153–157.

Tharinger, D., Burrows Horton, C., & Millea, S. (1990). Sexual abuse and exploitation of children and adults with mental retardation and other handicaps. *Child Abuse & Neglect, 14*, 301–312.

Trocmé, N., Fallon, B., MacLaurin, B., et al. (2005). *Canadian Incidence Study of Reported Child Abuse and Neglect (CIS-2003): Major Findings.* Ottawa, ON: Minister of Public Works and Government Services Canada.

Verdugo, M. A., Bermejo, B., & Fuertes, J. (1995). The maltreatment of intellectually handicapped children and adolescents. *Child Abuse & Neglect, 19*, 201–215.

Vig, S., & Kaminer, R. (2002). Maltreatment and developmental disabilities in children. *Journal of Developmental and Physical Disabilities, 14*(4), 371-386.

Waldfogel, J. (1998). *The future of child protection.* Cambridge, MA: Harvard University Press.

41

Developmental Disabilities and Ontario's Schools

Eileen C. Winter and Ester Cole

What you will learn:

- The historical development of special education in Ontario
- Ontario legislation and policy for students with developmental disabilities
- The identification of exceptional students
- Placement and programming for students with developmental disabilities
- Funding of special education in Ontario
- Collaboration between special education teachers and other professionals

Early Development of Special Education in Ontario

The province of Ontario began to develop a public responsibility for providing for children with special needs in the latter years of the 1800s. There had been considerable debate about the education of children with disabilities during the 1800s, especially in Europe, and these discussions paved the way for many of the changes in special education that occurred during the 20th century in Canada. In 1831, Ronald McDonald opened a school for the deaf in Quebec. This venture is widely regarded as Canada's first real effort in special education. A similar school opened in Ontario in 1858. The Ontario Institution for the Education and Instruction of the

Deaf and Dumb (1870) in Belleville, and the Ontario Institute for the Education and Instruction of the Blind (1872) in Brantford are other early examples of institutions that made provisions for students with special needs.

The establishment of these, and other institutions that followed, suggests that society was beginning to recognize its responsibility for people with disabilities in the province, although the language used to describe the students and the education they received might not bear scrutiny today. Even in the 1800s, some problems began to be associated with institutionalization. Winzer (1990) suggested that many of the children who came to reside in the institutions were, in fact, abandoned or rejected by their families. She noted also that, in institutional life, there was little attention paid to the individual needs of the children. In most cases, the children only received "care" and little in the way of education. At this period in our history, persons who would now be described as having developmental disabilities were generally considered "ineducable," and were often abandoned by their parents to live in institutions with little stimulation and where growth potential went unrecognized and unfulfilled. Although the institutions might be considered extremely problematic by today's standards, their establishment does indicate a growing degree of social responsibility and an awareness of people with disabilities (Weber & Bennett, 1999). The quality of the education might be questionable, but "the mere existence of residential schools was an especially striking development for the time, in light of the fact that education for the so-called 'normal' population was still far from universal" (Weber & Bennett, 1999, p. 7).

In 1876, the first Canadian institution specifically for people with developmental disabilities (at the time referred to as feeble-minded and later as mentally retarded) opened in Orillia, Ontario. Some years later, in 1888, this facility was reorganized to include a kindergarten program, physical education, music, and some academic programming (Smith, Luckasson, & Crealock, 1995). By the end of the 1800s, the emphasis in the institutions began to change. Reformers suggested that education and training would equip the residents with the skills to become more self-sufficient, enabling them to contribute to the ongoing maintenance of the institutions themselves. As a consequence, an emphasis on vocational training began to emerge. The passing of the Special Classes Act in 1910 made it legal to have segregated classes in Ontario schools. This focus on educating persons with disabilities in segregated settings continued until after World War I, when the return of many war veterans, disabled in the war, began to challenge the commonly-held assumption that people with disabilities should be segregated and trained to perform only menial tasks (Winzer, Rogow, & David, 1987). As the assumptions about people with disabilities began to be debated and subsequently to change, the number of special classes

grew, and in 1916 the first courses for teachers of special classes began in Toronto.

Factors influencing early special education

Two of the most pervasive and dominant notions that influenced progress towards the education of persons with developmental disabilities, until approximately the 1950s, were intelligence testing and the eugenics movement.

Intelligence testing: Intelligence testing was developed in France and later in the United States and elsewhere because of a perceived need to identify those children who were considered unable to benefit from publicly funded education due to lower intelligence. As the tests developed over time, so did the practice of using their results (IQ scores) to classify and segregate developmentally disabled children from their peers and to remove them from regular classes in schools. The IQ scores came to be regarded as finite and immutable predictors of future potential. The immutability issue was reinforced by opinions such as that of Doll (1941), who described mental deficiency as "essentially incurable through treatment, and unremediable through training except as treatment and training instill habits, which superficially or temporarily compensate for the limitations of the person so affected" (p. 217). Doll's views were widely accepted for many years and the resulting limits that were put on the education of children with developmental disabilities have been significant.

In discussing the impact of IQ scores on the lives and the education of many children over the years, Weber and Bennett (1999) stated "although doubts about the real value — and the abuse — of testing instruments were raised as early as the 1930s, the general public's faith in them had taken a long time to fade" (p. 9). Considerable rethinking and challenging of the early notions of intelligence have been published over the years (Gardner, 1993; Luther, Cole, & Gamlin, 1996; Prifitera, Saklofske, & Weiss, 2005; Sternberg, 1985). To date, intelligence tests such as the Wechsler Intelligence Scale for Children (WISC IV) continue to be used today to help identify certain areas of exceptionality in the Ontario school system (Wechsler, 2003).

Eugenics: The second major influence on the development of special education during the 1900s was the decline in the widely-held beliefs of the eugenics movement that advocated for the protection of society from the "feeble-minded." Eugenics itself emerged from Social Darwinism, a philosophy that held that societies, like individual species, could be improved if populations and living conditions were shaped in ways that were thought to be beneficial. Eugenics focused on the drawbacks of allowing growth in the uneducated and "feeble-minded" segments of the population, and on the benefits of promoting the educated and more able population. The eugenics movement led to the practice of encouraging procreation among desirable individuals, such as the wealthy and the educated, and of segregating and forbidding procreation among those considered to be undesirable. Eugenics, as both philosophy and practice, was popular in some parts of Europe, Canada, Australia, and elsewhere, and especially in some parts of the United States, during the early part of the 1900s.

After World War II, support for the eugenics movement and the notion that certain individuals would contaminate the population through procreation and, therefore, should be kept away from the rest of society gradually decreased. It should be noted, however, that well into the 1960s, large institutions were still being built in relatively isolated areas of Ontario. This isolation resulted in people with disabilities being placed well away from the mainstream of society, often for life.

An Era of Change

Toward training and education

As eugenic beliefs weakened, society at large began to move towards the idea of "normalization" with the growing belief that there was value in educating and training children with disabilities. By the 1920s, special education classes could be found throughout the education system, and teachers were being trained to teach these classes. A further impetus for change came in 1922 when the Council for Exceptional Children (CEC) was founded; this was a professional organization for teachers, administrators, parents, and other advocates for the rights of students with disabilities. Today, the CEC remains one of the major driving forces in innovation and advancement in special education.

Throughout the 1940s, parents of children with developmental disabilities became more organized and more vocal, and began to take action regarding the education of their children. It was at this time that parents and educators joined forces to form organizations such as the Canadian Association for the Mentally Retarded, now known as the Canadian Association for Community Living. Groups of parents and advocates lobbied persistently for the education of children with developmental disabilities. Many parent groups started schools of their own and, eventually, through fund-raising initiatives and the support of various foundations, special schools came into existence. Parents took on the roles of teachers and, although extremely committed, lacked the formal training given to teachers in mainstream schools.

In spite of such changes, a great many children classified as "mentally deficient" or "mentally retarded" remained in institutions throughout the 1900s. Arguments against institutionalization and for normalization, however, slowly began to take hold and gained considerable support in the early 1970s through the work of Wolf Wolfensberger and the National Institute on Mental Retardation (now the G. Allen Roeher Institute). This movement was strongly supported by parents who were committed to bringing about changes in an educational system that continued to exclude their children on the grounds of their limited cognitive capacity.

Role of the Ministry of Education

Eventually, by the late 1950s, the Ontario Ministry of Education took over the administration and funding of the schools and these new "Ministry" schools began to operate under the Retarded Children's Education Authorities. In 1969, further progress was made when local school boards assumed responsibility for the education of children with developmental disabilities. The Ministry of Education now governed the special schools and their teachers through Ontario's Education Act. The regulations pertaining to special schools required that all of the teachers of students with developmental disabilities in the schools be specially trained. The required course, "Teaching the Trainable Mentally Retarded," was run by The Ministry of Education in summer sessions. The course qualified teachers to teach in schools or classes for children identified as Trainable Mentally Retarded (TMR) but not in mainstream classes, essentially segregating not only the children, but the teachers as well.

Important as these legislative changes were, some inherent problems became evident. The legislation was regarded as "permissive," in that it allowed school boards to provide education for the children but did not mandate that they do so. The result was that, under Section 34 of the Education Act, some children could still be excluded from school for such things as being deemed "unable to profit from instruction" or for exhibiting behaviours considered to be "inappropriate." Keeton-Wilson (1983) described this section of the Act as "the infamous 'exclusions clause' since the child who was considered to be unable to profit from the available instruction could be excluded from school" (p. 8).

It should be noted, however, that the Ministry of Education was taking steps to encourage inclusion of children with special needs in regular schools. In 1979, the Ministry published a Curriculum Ideas for Teachers document entitled *Children with Mild Intellectual Handicaps* (Ontario Ministry of Education, 1997). The document was intended to "assist teachers in developing and implementing programs for pupils in regular classrooms or in special settings in the Primary and Junior divisions who are functioning below their age group" (p. 2). The document offered program suggestions across a range of subject areas. The ideas were intended to help the child who, "because of slow mental development, is unable to profit sufficiently from programs in regular classrooms" (p. 3). It was anticipated that these students would be able to "function independently in society" (p. 3).

This document was followed in 1981 by a similar document entitled *Children with Moderate and Severe Intellectual Handicaps* that addressed the needs of children with more severe disabilities

(Ontario Ministry of Education, 1981). Both these publications, available in French and English, were designed to assist teachers in developing programs for learners with special needs.

Although progress was being made regarding the students who were in school, parents continued to voice their concerns about exclusions and to press for a school system that welcomed all children, regardless of their special needs. They argued for a "zero-reject" policy in education, insisting that all students had the right to have equal access to education and equal opportunity for success. This activism by parents and other advocacy groups had a powerful impact on educational policy over the years. In Ontario's schools today, parents play a significant role, and nowhere is this more evident than in the field of special education.

A New Era

The 1970s heralded a time of immense change in educational policy. The trend for provincial education ministries to mandate appropriate educational programs and services for all children, regardless of any disabling condition, became prevalent. Two provinces, Saskatchewan (1971) and Nova Scotia (1973), led the way in passing legislation mandating educational programs and services for students with special needs. In the United States, a landmark piece of legislation in 1975 had a significant impact on the rest of Canada. *The Education for All Handicapped Children Act* that came to be known by its working title of PL (Public Law) 94-142, mandated appropriate education for every handicapped student in the U.S. This law provided advocates in Canada with the impetus needed to pursue similar legislation for all provinces.

In Ontario, a similar private members bill in 1977 did not make it through the legislature, but all of these events did, eventually, lead to significant amendments to the Education Act. In December 1980, the *Education Amendment Act* (often referred to as Bill 82) was passed in the legislature (Ontario Ministry of Education, 1980). The stipulations of this Act are generally regarded as the most stringent and mandatory of any provincial education legislation in Canada. Embedded in the changes are five major principles. As described by Keeton-Wilson (1983), they are:

- *Universal access.* The right of all exceptional pupils to have access to appropriate education programs.
- *Education at public expense.* Education is provided without additional fees charged to the pupil and family.
- *Appeal process.* The right of exceptional pupils to have their interests represented, including the right of parents to appeal the identification and placement, or to request a review on behalf of their child.
- *Appropriate program.* The right of exceptional pupils to a program that includes a plan containing specific objectives and an outline of the services that meet the needs of the exceptional pupil.
- *Ongoing identification and continuous assessment and review.* The provision for identification, and continuous assessment and evaluation of each pupil's progress, including an annual review of the suitability of the placement.

Changes to education of students with developmental disabilities

The 1980 *Education Amendment Act* had a number of specific aspects that are worthy of particular note, especially for children with developmental disabilities:

- School boards now had a legal responsibility for providing special education and services for all exceptional students.
- No child could be excluded on the grounds of a disabling condition.
- Parents now had the right to appeal a child's program and/or placement.
- The Ministry of Education now funded all programs for "trainable retarded" (TR) pupils, and for school-aged children in government-approved care and treatment facilities.
- Specific and explicit directions regarding the education of students who were identified under the descriptor of "trainable retarded"

were included.
- Each school board was required to have an Advisory Committee whose focus was on schools for the Trainable Retarded pupils (TRAC).

Including children, who were labelled at the time as "trainable retarded," was a monumental step forward for both parents and advocates who had lobbied long and hard for the inclusion of their children in the school system. The admissibility requirements that had existed previously were now removed and students identified as TR could at last have open access to the programs established for them (Sections 20(3); 32(5,6); 39(3)). According to Keeton-Wilson (1983), the *Education Amended Act* did the following for children with more than mild disabilities:

[It] provides some striking new provisions for such students. The five principles of law are specified separately for this group of pupils. The principle of universality of access is established by defining trainable retarded children as exceptional pupils thereby admitting them to the same provisions as other exceptional pupils. (p. 9)

The amendments confirmed that TR students had the right to attend TR schools or have classes set up for them. They also had the right to instruction in either English or French (Sec. 72). Further, the costs associated with the education of the students were addressed. School boards had the option of setting up TR schools or of purchasing this service from another board. The cost of purchase rested with the sending board, and the responsibility for the program rested with the receiving one. Any lodging or transport costs involved in this process also rested with the sending board.

Two other important aspects of the new regulations should be noted. First, Catholic School Boards, previously not permitted to provide TR programs, could now do so. This allowed children identified as TR to attend separate schools if appropriate. Second, TR students could attend school until the end of the school year following their 21st birthday, the fees for this extension being paid by the board that served

Table 1: The Identification and Placement of Exceptional Pupils: Ontario Regulation 181/98

The goal of the regulation is to improve the IPRC process, and to make the process more user friendly for parents and older students. The information below highlights changes in the regulation. Please refer to the complete version on the Ministry of Education's website.

Communication: *Part I, Section 4*

Information must be provided through Braille, large print or audio-cassette formats upon request.

Parent/Pupil Participation: *Part I, subsection 5(1)*

Entitlement of parents and 16 year old pupils to participate in all discussions.

Representative: *Part I, subsection 5(3)*

Entitlement to have a representative present to speak on behalf of, or otherwise support, the parent or pupil (if over 16 years old).

Parent Guide: *Part III, Section 13*

1. *Expanded Parent Guide will provide additional information concerning:*
2. *IPRC's duty to list pupil's strengths and needs;*
3. *IPRC's duty to include exceptionality and definition in statement of decision;*
4. *names and addresses of provincial and demonstration schools;*
5. *list of local parent organizations eligible to be on SEAC.*

Parent Guide must be available in alternate formats.

Appeal Board: *Part VI, subsection 27(1)*

An appeal board will be comprised of:

1. *one member selected by parent;*
2. *one member selected by school board;*
3. *chair selected jointly by the two.*

Where no agreement on chair, appropriate manager of ministry district office to select chair.

IPRC Statement of Decision: *Part IV, subsection 18(2) and 18(3)*

IPRC statement of decision to include:

1. *description of students strengths and needs;*
2. *pupils exceptionality identification and definition;*
3. *the placement decision;*
4. *reasons for placement in a special class;*
5. *IPRC may make recommendations re: programs and services.*

Integration: *Part IV, Section 17*

IPRC shall decide to place an exceptional pupil in a regular class when such a placement meets the pupil's needs, and is in accordance with parental preferences. Other placement still to be available as per the Ministry's 1994 policy statement on integration.

Placement and Services: *Part IV, Subsection 16(1) and (2)*

The IPRC may discuss and make recommendations for special education programs and services that may meet the pupil's needs.

  a. *Timelines*

More specific timelines are included for carrying out the responsibilities related to the identification and placement of exceptional pupils.

Individual Education Plan (IEP): *Part I, Section 6*

Principal shall take into consideration any recommendations of the IPRC in the development of the IEP. An IEP must include:

1. *learning expectation for the pupil;*
2. *an outline of special education programs and services;*
3. *how the pupil's progress will be evaluated;*
4. *a transition plan for every pupil over 14 years old (except for students identified as Gifted).*

the area within which the student resided (Sections 47(1); 73(1)).

The "Regulation" issued by the Ministry of Education, and related to the amendments, set out these legal responsibilities. They also provided information on the identification of exceptional students, and their placement in educational settings where their needs could best be met. Ontario Regulation 554/81 (O. Reg 554, subsequently revised as O. Reg 305, and most recently as O. Reg 181/98; see Table 1 for details) provided the legal basis for the procedures involved in the identification, placement, and review of exceptional pupils. Each school board was required to set up an Identification, Placement, and Review Committee (IPRC), the responsibilities of which were set out in the regulation. One of these responsibilities was to identify students under one of the categories described in the Education Act 1980 (Ch. 129, subsection 8. 2).

The impact of the 1980 amendment in Ontario was enormous. The changes required that school boards provide, or purchase from another board, special education programs and services for all exceptional students. To facilitate this, school boards in the province were given a five-year implementation period. This was not a difficult task for boards with programs and services already in place, but boards that lacked them faced a much more challenging task. Despite these challenges, the overwhelming bureaucracy, and considerable paperwork involved in the new procedures, special education became an integral part of the day-to-day functioning of Ontario's school boards (Weber & Bennett, 1999).

Two categories of students

Although the changes to the *Education Act* applied to all exceptional students, some aspects were more significant for children with developmental disabilities. The new legislation required school boards to identify exceptional students according to specific categories laid out by the ministry. Of importance here was the category entitled Intellectual. Two subcategories under intellectual were outlined in the original legislation, and, as a consequence, were the widely used labels within Ontario school systems during the 1980s and 1990s:

Educable Retardation: Definition: A learning disorder characterized by:

a. an ability to profit educationally within the regular class with the aid of considerable curriculum modification and supportive services
b. an inability to profit educationally within a regular class because of slow intellectual development
c. a potential for academic learning, independent social adjustment, and economic self-support

Trainable Retardation: Definition: A severe learning disorder characterized by:

a. an inability to profit from a special education program for the educable retarded because of slow intellectual development
b. an ability to profit from a special education program that is designed to accommodate slow intellectual development
c. a limited potential for academic learning, independent social adjustment, and economic self-support

It was not until 1993 that the Ministry of Education repealed the term "trainable retarded" from the *Education Act* and later, in 1998, renamed the two sub-categories above as Mild Intellectual Disability and Developmental Disability respectively. The descriptions remained the same in the Ministry's 2001 *Special Education Handbook* (Ontario Ministry of Education, 2001a).

The debate around using categories

The issue of categorizing or "labelling" in special education has been a difficult and often controversial one, as it has been in the broader field of developmental disabilities. A large literature describes the advantages and disadvantages of both applying and using labels (see Coulby, 1997; Kliewer & Bilkin, 1996; Winzer, 1999), and this has resulted in a generally-held convention today maintaining that categories and labels are useful only when the result is to improve understanding, life conditions, or services (see Chapter 1 for more information).

This literature has also clarified our understanding of categories and labels to a considerable degree.

There do not appear to be any descriptors for this population that are entirely free from negative connotations and inappropriate usage. On one hand, labels can be stigmatizing and misleading; on the other hand, labels often facilitate professional communications and educational responses to the unique needs of the students. As the educational provision for students with developmental disabilities has grown, the labels have become more educational in their focus. Smith (1998) pointed out that the classifications "were used to describe both the anticipated level of educational achievement of these students and the corresponding placements to which they were assigned" (p. 74).

Vocal opponents of labelling have argued for a "non-categorical" approach to special needs that has "a focus on behaviours and learning patterns rather than on diagnostic categories" (Winzer, 1999, pp. 11-12). Others favour a cross-categorical approach that "pays more attention to students' learning needs than to their labels" (Friend, Bursuck, & Hutchinson, 1998, p. 23). The "anti-labelling" stance has, however, also come under attack. Soder (1989) criticized anti-labelling as inherently dangerous, focusing more on integration and on a search for less expensive alternatives. This, in turn, has been criticized as misrepresenting the anti-labelling movement (Booth, 1991).

Oliver (1992) suggested that the anti-labelling discussion has little to do with any genuine commitment to disabled people. He argued that terminology such as "people with disabilities" is a "linguistic attempt to deny the reality of disability" (p. 21). Instead, disability needs to be viewed as a social construct, and as a result of discrimination and ignorance within social, political and organizational systems, and society at large. It is society's response to some of its own members that creates the phenomenon we think of as disability (Oliver, 1996).

Social and professional views of people with lesser abilities and intelligence will, no doubt, continue to evolve. Weber and Bennett (1999) suggested that "there are indications that, as the new century begins, the matter of labels and categories and definitions has declined significantly as an issue for debate" (p. 25). They claimed that, in the future, the

issue of labels and descriptors will not "stir passions as it once did" (p. 25).

At the present time in Ontario, the Ministry of Education still requires school boards to identify exceptional students according to specific categories to determine their eligibility for services. School boards are also required to report the numbers of students in each category to the Ministry on an annual basis. Part of the rationale for this reporting procedure is linked to the funds made available for special needs students.

Limitations of Ontario's legislation

The 1980s legislation represented a tremendous step forward for special education in Ontario. At the same time, there were some important omissions in comparison to the earlier U.S. legislation. These omissions were considered by some to be a pragmatic response to what might otherwise be difficult legal requirements, but others considered them limitations to full and inclusive special education in Ontario.

First, in Ontario, parents could appeal whether or not the child was identified as exceptional, and/or whether or not the placement was suitable, but they could not appeal the program. Thus, as long as school boards were providing programs, or purchasing them from another board, they were fulfilling their responsibilities. Even if the program was not considered by the parents to be the most suitable, there was no legal recourse.

Second, the issue of placement, required in the U.S. legislation to be in the "least restrictive environment" or as close as possible to the regular classroom setting, was not included in Ontario. Although influenced by the trend toward inclusion of children with special needs in regular classes, individual Boards of Education could still place children in special education classes that were often organized according to the student's "category" or "label" (e.g., Behaviour; Learning Disability).

Third, the stringent requirements of the Individual Education Plan (IEP) that appeared in the U.S. legislation were not mandated in Ontario in 1980. Ontario's only stipulation was that there had to be a plan containing specific objectives and an outline of services. Although many school boards did adopt some type of IEP for their identified students, the form and substance of the plans were specific to individual Boards of Education. In Ontario, IEPs were not mandated until 1998, and even then, they did not stipulate some of the details required in the US PL 94-142. Recent changes in U.S. special education legislation in 2004 (Individuals with Disabilities Education Improvement Act, 2004) resulted in a reconceptualization of the process that schools could use to identify eligibility for special education under the category of specific learning disabilities, including response to intervention (PL108-446; Shinn, 2007).

School teams

The composition of Multidisciplinary Teams is closely tied to school policies and organizational goals. The roles of members and the functions of Teams vary. In the U.S., for example, legislation required that Multidisciplinary Teams provide for the assessment and programming of special education students. In Ontario, Teams are not mandated by special education legislation, and thus there is considerable flexibility to adopt a wide variety of roles.

In schools facing a rapid transformation of communities, Teams have focused on consultation and coordination of education and early intervention programs (Cole & Brown, 2003). The consultative problem-solving that Teams develop may be described as including six phases:

a. *Clarification of presenting problem.* A clear definition of the presenting problem is crucial for planning appropriate interventions. In order to avoid ambiguity, Team members must discuss and state the issues in concrete, explicit terms.

b. *Analysis of identified problem(s).* Presenting students' problems should be assessed by eliciting information from multiple sources, including background information, review of school records, and observational data. During Team meeting(s), teachers and Team members can clarify the needs of individuals or groups of students. Questions asked during discussion often lead to a better understanding of needs in the context of the current learning environment.

c. *Brainstorming alternative solutions.* Once the problem analysis has been completed, the Team should consider, together with invited members, as many solutions as possible. All alternatives should be discussed without making value judgements. By being open minded, all participants will feel that their ideas are listened to and respected.

d. *Developing plans for intervention.* During this phase, Team members choose among alternative strategies. Short and long term action plans for class, school and/or community-based supports are selected by consensus.

e. *Assigning responsibilities and time lines.* Once recommendations have been obtained by consensus, Team members have to assume responsibility for different aspects of the agreed upon solutions. In addition, time lines for program implementation have to be stated clearly. The questions *Why? Who? What? When? Where?* must be answered before the conclusion of the consultation meeting.

f. *Monitoring interventions and follow-up.* Follow-up meeting dates have to be established in advance in order to evaluate the effectiveness of interventions. This phase provides the Team with opportunities to review programs and receive feedback about services. By evaluating the effectiveness of programs, the Team can make additional recommendations or adjustments on an as-needed basis.

Identifying Exceptional Students in Ontario

Recent requirement changes

Since 1980, the Education Act has required that school boards provide, or purchase from another board, special education programs and services for all identified exceptional students. In the intervening years, a few changes have been made to the original legislation. The most significant of these changes came in 1998 with the new Ontario Regulation 181, entitled *Identification and Placement of Exceptional*

Pupils (O. Reg. 181/98), that replaced the old Regulation 305. This regulation updated the legal requirements and the process for identifying a student as exceptional. It also revised the process for determining an appropriate placement for the exceptional student in Ontario (see Table 1).

The aims of the revised regulation were to strengthen parental involvement and participation in the identification process, to tighten up the procedures, to ensure that each identified student had an Individual Education Plan (IEP), and to provide transition plans where appropriate. The new elements of this regulation that came into force on September 1, 1998, specified:

- An IEP must be prepared for each exceptional student in Ontario. The IEP must take into consideration the assessments and recommendations from the IPRC, parents, and support staff. The intent of the IEP is to ensure that identified students receive effective and appropriate programs, to provide a measure of accountability, and to assist in the ongoing assessment of each student's progress.
- Every student age 14 and over has to have a transition plan included in the IEP. Only students identified as gifted are exempt from this requirement.
- The original recommendation that school boards produce a Parents' Guide has been very clearly reinforced in the new regulation. School boards are now required to produce a "parent friendly" guide interpreting Reg. 181/98, and to ensure that parents receive a copy of this guide prior to any involvement with a formal identification process.
- The role of parents is strengthened in that they are now entitled to participate in all discussions related to the identification and placement of their child, and to be present when IPRC decisions are made.
- The IPRC must now make a decision regarding the student's placement. If this placement is to be in a special class, the committee must provide a rationale for this decision. The Ontario Ministry of Education remains committed to "regular class" as the placement of first choice

where the placement meets the student's needs and is in accordance with parental preferences.

To assist school boards with these updated requirements, the Ministry of Education in Ontario developed an *Individual Education Plan (IEP) Resource Guide* (2004). One of the Resource Guide's objectives was to promote a consistent process for developing IEPs and "to help teachers and others working with exceptional pupils to develop, implement and monitor high-quality IEPs" (p. 4). Sample IEPs were developed using the provincial electronic IEP template, with 47 samples posted in English and French. These can be accessed at *http://www.ontariodirectors.ca*. The *Resource Guide*, along with a sample Parents' Guide for use in school boards, is available on the Ministry website (www. edu. gov. on. ca)

Identifying students with developmental disabilities

It is important to understand that students with developmental disabilities comprise a relatively small percentage of the student population identified as exceptional in Ontario's schools. Identifying students with developmental disabilities may be especially important for two reasons:

- Those who are officially identified must have the appropriate placement, program, and an IEP.
- Teachers need as much information as possible to make informed educational decisions.

Information used to determine exceptionality: Intelligence tests have, for many decades, played a significant role in helping to identify students with developmental disabilities. Their role, and the role of other standardized tests, has declined substantially in recent years, partly due to strong criticism regarding the validity of the tests for this population (McDonnell, Hardman, McDonnell, & Kiefer-O'Donnell, 1995). More emphasis is now placed on a functional assessment of the student, especially where the disability is more severe. That assessment typically focusses on the skills necessary for students to function as fully as possible in contexts such as home, school, and community.

Functional assessments: A functional assessment

is based on specific observable behaviours in the student's repertoire. According to Winzer (1999), there are two major components of a functional assessment. These are "to identify skills that will increase a child's ability to interact with people and objects in the daily environment," and "whether the skill will have to be performed by someone else if the child has not been taught to do it" (p. 60). In providing a further description of a functional assessment, Gaylord-Ross and Browder (1991, p. 45) suggested that it:

- Focusses on practical independent living skills that enable the person to survive and succeed in the real world
- Has a strong ecological emphasis that looks at the individual functioning in his or her surrounding environment
- Examines the process of learning and performance
- Suggests intervention techniques that may be successful
- Specifies ongoing monitoring procedures that can evaluate treatment progress

The assessment process usually involves a full medical workup, a range of tests and scales, and an adaptive behaviour inventory. Psychologists and other qualified personnel use such things as clinical interviews, cognitive measures, behavioural observation scales, and social-emotional measures.

In spite of a wide range of both formal and informal assessment tools, an accurate assessment of the potential of a student with developmental disabilities remains challenging. In the educational context, students with moderate to severe disabilities often enter school with existing diagnoses and program plans. These data can be used for identification and placement purposes under the regulation once the student is attending school. Many cases of mild disability, however, may not be evident until the student enters school. Information from kindergarten screening may suggest a need for further investigation. In these instances, a full educational assessment is required for identification, program and placement purposes (IPRC).

It is also possible for some students with developmental disabilities not to be officially identified through an IPRC and not, therefore, to be formally recognized in the school system. This may be due to a number of factors, but three of the most important are:

- Parental reluctance to have the student "categorized and labelled"
- No special placement is required
- There is no need for special funding

In such cases, children can still be recognized within the school system as having special learning needs and receive individual programming, and may also have an IEP developed as needed.

Educational Placement

At the time of the 1980 amendments, most school boards in Ontario placed exceptional students in self-contained classes according to educational needs. Students in these classes were segregated from the regular students on the grounds that their needs would be better served in a small class environment. Most students with developmental disabilities were placed in these classes, and had little opportunity to mix with their peers. Over time, with considerable pressure from parents and advocacy groups, full time placement in a regular class has become the norm in Ontario. This practice, however, does not have the support of all parents. Some parents prefer the smaller segregated class option, often feeling alienated and pressured by advocates who strongly and vociferously support full inclusion for all students.

The Council of Administrators of Special Education (CASE) in Canada supports the philosophy of inclusion, but in a 1997 statement indicated that a "continuum of service delivery options must always be available" (p. 3). This point of view is consistent with the approach in Ontario where the regular class is considered the placement of first choice for all exceptional students, with decisions being made on an individual basis. The Ministry of Education itself has not used the term "inclusion" in any of its legislation, preferring to use "integration" in discussions about placement, and encouraging school boards to maintain a full range of educational placements. This "middle of the road" position appears to be an attempt to satisfy all interested parties.

Arguments about the most appropriate placement have, at times, been the source of considerable stress for both school boards and parents. In a number of instances, the matter of placement has had to be settled by a court decision. The issue of placement in a special class being in violation of the Canadian Charter of Rights and Freedoms was the subject of a high court decision in 1996 (see Table 2 for details).

In making decisions about the educational placement of a student with developmental disabilities, a number of factors must be taken into consideration (Winzer, 1999). Developmental disabilities must be viewed on a continuum, where students with mild disabilities are likely to benefit most from placement in a regular class among their age peers with support from an educational assistant or resource teacher. In cases of more severe disability, many students will need more extensive modifications to the regular grade level curricula. Others may be following a totally alternative curriculum specifically designed to meet their individual needs.

Whatever the placement decision, all accommodations and/or modifications must be stated in the students' IEPs. In planning appropriate programs, teachers should ensure that activities are age-appropriate, interactive, and functional. Expectations should be appropriately challenging, with opportunities for students to develop skills that build towards becoming independent and productive members of the community.

Programming

In October 2001, the Ministry of Education released its updated version of the 1984 *Special Education Handbook* (Ontario Ministry of Education, 2001a). This document includes a section on curriculum policy that applies to all Ontario students, including those identified as exceptional. The educational needs of students with developmental disabilities, however, are not specifically addressed.

Currently, there are no Ministry of Education publications dealing specifically with students with developmental disabilities. Although out of print, the 1990 publication *Planning for Independence:*

A Support Document for Teachers of Students with Intellectual Disabilities remains an excellent resource for teachers (Ontario Ministry of Education, 1990). This document emphasizes that "each student is a unique individual who has the potential to learn and develop with the help of a carefully planned and judiciously executed program" (p. 5). Care is taken to avoid labelling and to keep the focus on the students as "a highly heterogeneous group with a wide range of learning strengths, needs, and abilities" (p. 5). The document also emphasizes that the intellectual challenges faced by the students result in challenges in academic and social skills, and often create considerable difficulties with communication. Further, this document presents a useful model for program planning. It outlines a process for assessing student needs, developing programs, implementing the programs, and evaluating their effectiveness. It also suggests that, in the best interests of students, "programs should prepare them for effective participation in the community, because everyone has the right to a full and rewarding life" (p. 5). Such a life includes opportunities to:

- Live as independently as possible, in a home rather than an institution
- Be productive through independent or supported employment, volunteer work, and participation in home life
- Use all community facilities and services
- Interact with others and make friends
- Enroll in continuing education programs, including literacy programs, and a wide range of interest courses
- Enjoy leisure activities

A program with an emphasis on real life skills, or a "functional curriculum," appears to be the most appropriate for students with moderate to severe developmental disabilities (Ford, Davern, & Schnorr, 1990; York, Vandercook, & Stave, 1990). In class, teachers must be aware of the rate of learning, which in many cases is extremely slow. Students may have difficulty working with abstract ideas and transferring their learning, and may require much repetition and practice to maintain their learning. Both reading and math may also present problems

Table 2: Eaton vs Brant County Board of Education

In 1997, the Supreme Court of Canada sent down a decision on the integration of an Ontario student that is likely to have far-reaching implications throughout Canada. Emily Eaton, a student with quite extensive special needs, spent three years in a regular class placement in her local school. At the end of this time, the IPRC recommended a special class placement in another school. Emily's parents disagreed with this decision and appealed right through to the Supreme Court on the grounds that the placement was in violation of the Canadian Charter of Rights.

The Supreme Court decided in favour of the School Board for the following reasons:

1. *There is no Charter presumption in favour of integration*
2. *The parents' view of their child's best interests does not determine the question*
3. *Emily was not discriminated against*
4. *The Board of Education used appropriate criteria in its decision*
5. *A segregated placement may be required where an integrated setting cannot reasonably be adapted*
6. *The placement decision was in the best interests of the child*

for many such students.

Students with more severe disabilities may require more intensive support in order to learn basic skills such as personal care, throwing a ball, or using eating utensils. Often these students need ongoing support from a range of personnel such as physiotherapists, occupational therapists, speech and language pathologists, social workers, and psychologists. Limitations in both receptive and expressive language skills may significantly impair the communication necessary for the demands of everyday life. These individuals are likely to require personal care and supervision in the course of their everyday lives. In school situations, students with severe disabilities are often placed in classrooms equipped to meet their ongoing needs and with a high level of adult support through teachers, educational assistants, and other caregivers. Teachers can find additional programming suggestions in the Learning Accommodations section of the Ministry of Education's *Special Education Guide* (Curriculum Unit Planner CD; Ontario Ministry of Education, 2001b).

Reporting Procedures

The issue of reporting the achievement of students with exceptionalities and the use of the Provincial Report Card can often be challenging for teachers. This can become more complex for students with developmental disabilities where their learning expectations differ considerably from the provincial curricula.

Ongoing assessment and evaluation of students is essential in monitoring student learning. One resource for this is the set of guidelines on reporting achievement outlined in *Special Education: A Guide for Educators* (Ontario Ministry of Education, 2001c). As stated in this guideline, "the student's achievement of the goals and expectations identified in the IEP must be reflected in his or her report card" (p. C24).

The Education Quality and Accountability Office (EQAO) also expects all students to participate in the provincial assessments carried out in Grades 3, 6, and 9, and in the Grade 10 Literacy Test. During the assessments, exceptional students are entitled to the accommodations that are outlined in their IEPs. Information on deferrals and exemptions can be found in the EQAO's policy on provincial assessments (http://www. eqao.com) and in the Ministry's Policy Program Memo No. 27. Exemptions are considered on an individual basis and currently, according to Hutchinson (2002), comprise less than 2% of the school population across Canada. She suggests

Box 1: One Mother's Comment

My daughter, G. has Down syndrome. Although she is only two years old, I have spent some time trying to imagine her school experiences in the future. What comes to mind is the teacher and the teacher's attitude. A teacher can have all the skills in the world, but if she does not use these in a caring, kind, supportive, safe, warm and comfortable way, then G. will not thrive. She may survive, but she will not thrive. In this teacher's classroom, all students are special, all students have abilities, all students have strengths.

"that only those students who have severe disabilities or who might be harmed by participating in the assessments were exempted" (p. 232).

Funding Special Education in Ontario

Funding of education is complex and often bewildering. In recent years, the cost of funding public education has been a major political issue in Ontario. Questions about how funds are allocated, how effectively they are used, and how accountable school boards are in their use of public funds have been topics of ongoing discussion.

Historically in Ontario, school funding was a municipal responsibility. On January 1, 1998, however, the Ontario government ended this responsibility and assumed full control of educational funding in the province. Since that date, all funding allotted to school boards is provided through specific grants delineated by the government of Ontario.

Ontario has moved to a "layered" or "staged" model of funding in Special Education that allocates funding based on student needs. The intent is to allocate higher levels of funds for students with higher needs. In commenting on this funding model, Weber and Bennett (1999) claimed that since "no jurisdiction in North America has yet found an entirely satisfactory way of making staged funding work, [this] likely means that Ontario will not either" (p. 23).

Special Education Funding: School boards receive a Foundation Grant for every student enrolled. This base grant covers the basic cost of classroom education, including personnel and materials. Boards also receive funding through a Special Education Grant, which is in what the Ministry calls a "protected envelope," meaning that the funds must be used solely for special education programs and services. The Special Education Grant has two distinct components:

1. The Special Education per Pupil Amount (SEPPA), which is based on the total number of students in a school board, not just the identified students. This is a general grant intended to fund programs and services for the majority of exceptional students in a school board.
2. The Intensive Support Amount (ISA), which is generated on the basis of stated and identified student need, not enrolment.

There are four levels of ISA funds available to school boards and these are only given if specifically requested. The Ministry has prerequisite eligibility criteria for each level, and school boards must demonstrate that all criteria are met in order for a student to be considered eligible for the funds. Students do not have to be identified as exceptional, but must have an IEP. A fifth level of funds, called a Special Incidence Portion (SIP), is also available and is intended to support students with extremely high health and safety needs. Full details on Special Education funding can be found in the *Resource Manual for the Special Education Grant Intensive Support Amount (ISA): Guidelines for School Boards* (Ontario Ministry of Education, 2001d), which is available on the Ministry's website.

To be eligible for an ISA grant, it must be demonstrated that the student has significant additional needs as itemized in the IEP, and that these needs meet the stringent criteria set out by the Ministry of Education. The amount of additional funding received by a school board reflects the number of eligible students for whom claims have been submitted to, and accepted by, the Ministry of Education. All applications to the Ministry are subject to close scrutiny to ensure that funding is directed to the students with the highest needs. All claims are also subject to Ministry audit.

The changes in the funding model and the paperwork involved in ensuring that ISA claims meet the ministry requirements have placed considerable additional demands on teachers' and administrators' time in schools and boards. Applications for ISA grants on behalf of students with developmental disabilities can be made regardless of the educational placement. Providing students are placed on an IEP, and are receiving special education services, an ISA claim can be made. It is extremely important, however, that school board personnel keep up to date with the Ministry's requirements for ISA funds.

Teacher Qualifications

According to the regulations in Ontario (Reg. 298), teachers holding Special Education positions must have additional qualifications. To be recommended by the Ontario College of Teachers, candidates must complete at least Part 1 of the additional qualifications courses in Special Education. Parts 2 and 3 of these additional qualifications are often preferred for specific positions in school boards. Although these courses are currently under review by the Ontario College of Teachers and may be subject to change, at the present time, each part consists of a core component, plus an elective chosen by the candidate. Electives focus on a range of specific exceptionalities, such as learning disabilities or developmental disabilities.

In selecting teachers for segregated classes or special schools for students with developmental disabilities, principals usually prefer individuals who have completed an elective course dealing specifically with this area of exceptionality. It should be noted that where students with developmental disabilities are included in the regular class, there is no stipulation that the teacher have any additional qualifications.

Collaboration with Other Professionals

Teachers working with students who have developmental disabilities frequently have to be involved with professionals from a number of other disciplines. This team often includes physiotherapists, occupational therapists, nurses, classroom assistants, special services coordinators, interpreters, and other personal care assistants. In providing services to students with severe developmental disabilities, this team-based approach may be necessary. It is essential that team members collaborate in an atmosphere of mutual trust and respect in order to maximize the potential of every student. Ogletree, Bull, Drew and Lunnen (2001) stated that "professionals need each other's disciplinary expertise to understand all aspects of children" (p. 138). They provided some options and guidelines for successful team-based service delivery.

The key people in the collaboration picture, however, are the parents. They have the right, as indicated above, to be involved in all aspects of their child's education and can be a wonderful source of information for educators. In the school context, parents are the classroom teacher's strongest allies. Parents may also involve an advocate to serve as their advisor and spokesperson, especially in formal meetings such as the IPRC. According to Friend, Bursuck & Hutchinson (1998), involvement of an advocate may occur for a number of reasons, such as parents feeling that they are not knowledgeable enough about the policies and procedures that govern special education,…are not sure school personnel are acting in the best interests of their children,…[or] may be uncomfortable interacting with school personnel because of language or cultural differences (p. 46).

It is imperative that educators be sensitive to parental needs and concerns about their child, even in situations where the communication is difficult. Davern (1996) conducted a series of interviews with parents of children with disabilities, and identified formal meetings such as IPRCs as being very difficult for parents. She said, "They used such phrases as 'very intimidating' to describe them, adding that they felt at times like token participants in the discussions about their children" (p. 181). Parents found the informal meetings and contacts more comfortable and beneficial for them.

Results of studies like this should send important messages to educators of children with developmental disabilities. Parents spend considerable amounts of time just keeping their lives organized and meeting the needs of other family members, while responding to the additional needs of the child with a developmental disability. These parents' rich experience can be a valuable source of information for school personnel, and it must be welcomed, valued, and respected.

Summary

The education of students with developmental disabilities in Ontario has come a long way since classes and schools were established in the early 1900s. Today, all Ontario school boards are required to provide education for all school-age children with disabilities, and the trend is increasingly to see such students included with their peers in regular classes. Although programming can be challenging, the teacher plays a crucial role in the success of each student. Inclusion can be successful for many students if the necessary supports are in place. Each person who is in contact with the student has a key role to play, regardless of the student's educational placement. Teachers, parents, and other professionals must work together to ensure that students reach their full potential.

For Further Thought and Discussion

1. Is full inclusion always the best option for students with developmental disabilities?
2. Does legislation guarantee the most appropriate program?
3. What is the role of parents in the education of students with developmental disabilities?
4. Given the importance of a "team approach" to meeting the needs of students, how do we ensure that team members collaborate in the best interests of the child?

More Resources

Printed Material:

Batshaw, M. L., Pellegrino, L., & Roizen, N. J. (2007). *Children with disabilities* (6th ed.). Baltimore: Paul H. Brookes Publishing.

Friend, M. (2008). *Special education: Contemporary perspectives for school professionals* (2nd ed.). Columbus, OH: Charles E. Merrill Publishing Company.

Salvia, J., Ysseldyke, J. E., & Bolt, S. (2010). *Assessment in special and inclusive education* (11th ed.). Florence, KY: Wadsworth Publishing.

Electronic Material:

Council for Exceptional Children
www.cec.sped.org

Learning Disabilities Association of Ontario
www.ldao.ca

Ontario Ministry of Education
www.edu.gov.on.ca

Ontario Ministry of Education: Special Education
www.edu.gov.on.ca/eng/general/elemsec/speced/speced.html

Special Education Resources on the Internet
www.seriweb.com

University of Toronto: Ontario Institute for Studies in Education (OISE) Library. Special Collections
http://oise.library.utoronto.ca/special-collections

References

Booth, A. (1991). Integration, disability and commitment: A response to Marten Soder. *European Journal of Special Needs*, 6, 1-16.

Cole, E., & Brown, R. (2003). Multidisciplinary school teams: A five-year follow-up study. In E. Cole, & J. Siegel (Eds.), *Effective consultation in school psychology* (2nd ed.) (pp. 24-44). Toronto, ON: Hogrefe & Huber.

Council of Administrators of Special Education (CASE) Inc. (1997, fall). Position paper on delivery of services to students with disabilities. *Keeping in Touch, 3.*

Coulby, D. (1997). Modernist knowledge and prejudice: Special educational needs. In J. Dwyfor Davies, & P. Garner (Eds.), *At the crossroads: Special educational needs and teacher education* (pp. 19-28). London: David Fulton Publishers Ltd.

Davern, L. (1996). Listening to parents of children with disabilities. *Educational Leadership*, 53(4), 61-63.

Doll, R. (1941). The essentials of an inclusive concept of mental deficiency. *American Journal of Mental Deficiency, 46*, 214-219.

Ford, A., Davern, L., & Schnorr, R. (1990). Inclusive education: "Making sense" of the curriculum. In S. Stainback, & W. Stainback (Eds.), *Curriculum considerations in inclusive classrooms: Facilitating learning for all students.* Baltimore: Paul H. Brookes.

Friend, M., Bursuck, W., & Hutchinson, N. (1998). *Including exceptional students: A practical guide for classroom teachers* (Canadian edition). Scarborough, ON: Allyn & Bacon Canada.

Gardner, H. (1993). Creating minds. New York: Basic Books.

Gaylord-Ross, R., & Browder, D. (1991). Functional assessment: Dynamic and domain properties. In L. H. Meyer, C. A. Peck, & L. Brown (Eds.), *Critical issues in the lives of people with severe disabilities* (pp. 45-66). Baltimore: Paul H. Brookes.

Hutchinson, N. (2002). *Inclusion of exceptional learners on Canadian schools: A practical handbook.* Toronto, ON: Pearson Education Canada.

Individuals with Disabilities Education Improvement Act. (2004). Pub. L. No. 108, 446.

Keeton-Wilson, A. (1983). *A consumers guide to Bill 82: Special education in Ontario.* Toronto, ON: OISE Press.

Kliewer, C., & Bilkin, D. (1996). Labeling: Who wants to be called retarded? In W. Stainback, & S. Stainback (Eds.), *Controversial issues confronting special education: Divergent perspectives* (2nd ed.) (pp. 83-95). Boston: Allyn & Bacon.

Luther, M., Cole, E., & Gamlin, P. (Eds.). (1996). *Dynamic assessment for instruction: From theory to application.* Toronto, ON: Captus University Publications.

McDonnell, J. J., Hardman, M. L., McDonnell, A. P., & Kiefer-O'Donnell, R. (1995). *An introduction to persons with severe disabilities: Educational and social issues.* Needham Heights, MA: Allyn & Bacon.

Ogletree, B. T., Bull, J., Drew, R., & Lunnen, K. Y. (2001). Team-based service delivery for students with disabilities: Practice options and guidelines for success. *Intervention in School and Clinic, 36*, 138-145.

Oliver, M. (1992). Intellectual masturbation: A rejoinder to Soder and Booth. European *Journal of Special Needs, 7*, 20-28.

Oliver, M. (1996). Defining impairment and disability: Issues at stake. In C. Barnes, & G. Mercer (Eds.), *Exploring the divide: Illness and disability* (pp. 39-54). Leeds, UK: Disability Press.

Ontario Ministry of Education. (1979). *Children with mild intellectual handicaps.* Toronto, ON: Queen's Printer.

Ontario Ministry of Education. (1980). *Education Amendment Act.* Toronto, ON: Queen's Printer.

Ontario Ministry of Education. (1981). *Children with moderate and severe intellectual handicaps.* Toronto, ON: Queen's Printer.

Ontario Ministry of Education. (1990). *Planning for independence: A support document for teachers of students with intellectual disabilities.* Toronto, ON: Queen's Printer.

Ontario Ministry of Education. (2004). *Individual Education Plan (IEP): Resource guide.* Toronto, ON: Queen's Printer.

Ontario Ministry of Education. (2001a). *Special education handbook.* Toronto, ON: Queen's Printer.

Ontario Ministry of Education. (2001b). *Curriculum unit planner — CD: Special education guide.* Toronto, ON: Queen's Printer.

Ontario Ministry of Education. (2001c). *Special education: A guide for educators.* Toronto, ON: Queen's Printer.

Ontario Ministry of Education (2001d). *Resource manual for the special education grant Intensive Support Amount (ISA): Guidelines for school boards.* Toronto, ON: Queen's Printer.

Ontario Ministry of Education and Training. (1998). *Regulation 181: Identification and placement of exceptional pupils.* Toronto, ON: Queen's Printer.

Prifitera, A., Saklofske, D., & Weiss, L. (Eds.). (2005). *WISC-IV: Clinical use and interpretation.* New York: Elsevier Academic Press.

Shinn, M., (2007). Identifying students at risk, monitoring performance, and determining eligibility within response to intervention: Research on educational need and benefit from academic intervention. *School Psychology Review, 36*, 601-617.

Smith, D. D. (1998). *Introduction to special educa-

tion (3rd ed.). Boston: Allyn & Bacon.

Smith, D. D., Luckasson, R., & Crealock, C. (1995). *Introduction to special education in Canada: Teaching in an age of challenge.* Scarborough, ON: Allyn & Bacon Canada.

Soder, M. (1989). Disability as a social construct: The labeling approach revisited. *European Journal of Special Needs Education, 4,* 117-119.

Sternberg, R. J. (1985). *Beyond IQ: A triarchic theory of human intelligence.* New York: Cambridge University Press.

Weber, K., & Bennett, S. (1999). *Special education in Ontario schools* (4th ed.). Thornhill, ON: Highland Press.

Wechsler, D. (2003). *Wechsler Intelligence Scale for Children* (4th ed.). San Antonio, TX: The Psychological Corporation.

Winzer, M. (1990). *Children with exceptionalities: A Canadian perspective* (2nd ed.). Toronto, ON: Prentice Hall.

Winzer, M. (1999). *Children with exceptionalities in Canadian classrooms* (5th ed.). Scarborough, ON: Prentice Hall Allyn & Bacon Canada.

Winzer, M., Rogow, S., & David, C. (1987). *Exceptional children in Canada.* Toronto, ON: Prentice Hall.

York, J., Vandercook, T., & Stave, K. (1990). Recreation and leisure activities: Determining the favourite for middle school students. *Teaching Exceptional Children, 22*(4), 10-13.

42

The Transition from School to Adult Life

Ivan Brown and Lynn Martin

What you will learn:

- Key transition support questions
- Theoretical foundations for transition support
- Preparing for transition to adult life
- Special transition support to individuals with severe disabilities and their families

All people experience many changes over the span of their lifetimes. Many of these changes are small, but there are certain times in most people's lives when major changes must be made. When making major changes, people with developmental disabilities may require more, or more specialized, assistance from support personnel, family members, and others.

For this reason, in the field of developmental disabilities there is a focus on identifying times of life when there is major change for many people with disabilities. Through developing and sharing conceptual frameworks, research findings, and service knowledge, the field is exploring ways to ensure that needed support is available to the individual as he or she experiences major life changes, and that both the individuals' short-term and long-term wants and needs are addressed in a quality way. The term transition is used in the field to describe times of major

change, but also to refer to the expanding body of literature in this area.

There are a number of key transitions that affect the lives of many people with developmental disabilities. Transitions arise from health and biology (e.g., growing up, losing parents, entering a later-life care facility), social norms (e.g., moving out of parents' home, getting married), societal organization (e.g., entering or leaving school, entering or retiring from employment), and from current demographic trends (e.g., moving away from family, getting separated or divorced) (Brown, 2004). Thus, transitions differ in nature from one region to another, due to social, cultural, and economic differences. For example, in some places, community-based residential opportunities are few, and so individuals with developmental disabilities may continue to live with their parents well into adulthood. Transitions also differ in nature and importance from one individual to another. For example, one person may retire after working for 30 years and experience the transition in a positive way, whereas another person may find this transition to be problematic.

One transition that affects almost every person with developmental disabilities (as well as young people without disabilities) is the transition from school to adult life. As a consequence, this is the transition that has attracted the most attention and the most research to date in the disabilities field. There are a number of major changes in the lives of most people as they move from school to adult life, particularly those that affect people's places of residence and employment and their social interactions (Blacher, 2001). Wehman (2001) has identified seven common changes for youth with disabilities in the transition from school to adult life: employment, living arrangements, getting around the community, financial independence, making friends, sexuality and self-esteem, and having fun. Table 1 lists the major lifestyle changes that are common and that underlie such transitions.

Key Transition Support Questions

As noted previously, the transition from school to adult life is a period when a number of changes can be expected and during which young people with developmental disabilities may require specialized support. What, then, are the key questions or issues that need to be addressed when preparing for and providing this specialized support?

- *Theoretical foundations for support*: From what theoretical foundations is work in the transitions area drawn?
- *Support to individuals and families:* How do individuals and families prepare for the transition to adult life?
- *Special support to individuals with severe disabilities and their families:* What options are currently available for young people with profound and complex learning disabilities after the age of 16?

The following three sections do not address these questions fully; rather, they outline much of the progress that has been made to date.

Theoretical Foundations for Transition Support

The transition from school to adult life draws on theory from a number of sources. In a review of the literature, Eisenman (2003) pointed out that the transition literature does not have a strong theoretical foundation. Instead, theory from a number of perspectives informs transition from school to adult roles, including:

Critical studies
- Critical disability theory suggests that young adults with developmental disabilities have been subject to historic discrimination and oppression because our societies have not provided the means to equal access to adult life.

Vocational psychology
- Person-environment fit theories suggest that positive work outcomes result from a good match between worker skills and abilities and the requirements of the job and work environment.
- Career development theories refer to people's awareness of, planning for, and response to work opportunities.

Learning and cognitive psychology
- Learning and socio-cognitive theories propose that such things as individuals' cognitive skills, motivation, perceptions, goals, attitudes, and expected rewards are key to successful adjustment.

Quality of life
- Quality of life theory proposes that addressing core quality of life concepts — such as allowing independence; including what is important to the individual; satisfying personal needs and wishes; and providing opportunities, choice, and social connectedness — is key to positive life adjustment outcomes.

Sociology
- Status attainment theories look to social status and cognitive abilities as being most relevant to availability of opportunities and attainment of life and career goals.
- Structuralist theories examine the relationship between major social institutions (e.g.,

Table 1: Issues Related to the Transition from School to Adult Life

From	To
Going to school	*Going to a job or training or having no occupational activity*
Seeing oneself as a student	*Seeing oneself as an adult*
Living with parents or other family	*Living in one's own home or in a shared accommodation*
Identifying as a member of parental family	*Identifying as an independent adult or as a member of one's own family*
Socializing with family and schoolmates	*Socializing with work colleagues and community-based friends*
Engaging mostly in child and youth leisure	*Engaging mostly in adult, community-based leisure and recreation*
Relying on parents, siblings, and others	*Being responsible for more decisions about oneself*

Source: Brown (2004).

schools, labour markets, health and social services, social policy) and an individual's characteristics.

- Gender- and race-based theories focus on differences and inequities.
- Workplace culture theories emphasize the social patterns and behavioural norms that occur within workplaces.

These examples illustrate the eclectic nature of the theory that informs the area of transitions to adult life. On the other hand, drawing from a variety of theoretical sources may add to the richness of this relatively new field of study, which involves virtually all aspects of a person's life. Some aspects of life are more important to individuals than others in times of change so, for specific individuals, one perspective may be more useful than others.

APPROACHES TO TRANSITION ARISING FROM THEORY

Reflecting the eclectic nature of its theoretical foundations, the practical work associated with successful transition from school to adult life appears to be multifaceted and, consequently, to reflect more than one theoretical approach. Eisenman (2003) summarized the approach most commonly used for work in the area of transition from school to adult life as being not strictly theory based but, rather, as focused on solving problems that arise in the various environments (e.g., schools, businesses, community services) and with the various people involved (i.e., family members, teachers, employers, social service workers) throughout the transition process.

There are many ways to look at the transition from school to adult life, though each pursues the same ultimate goal — successful adjustment to adult life. For example:

1. *Developmental life span*: Emphasizes opportunity-seeking skills, involving support groups, and making choices that are suited to the individual's competencies and that will benefit him or her in the long term (e.g., Morningstar, 1997, and Rojewski, Maddy-Bernstein, Meers, Jones, & West, 1996, as cited in Eisenman, 2003, p. 97).

2. *Quality of life*: Emphasizes addressing basic needs, then enhancing the quality of a person's life experiences to promote enjoyment of life

and reduce life problems (Kirby, 1997; Kraemer, McIntyre, & Blacher, 2003; see also Brown & Brown, 2003).

3. *Family*: Emphasizes the involvement of the family in transition planning and activities and the effects of transition on both individual family members and the family as a whole (Blacher, 2001; Wehman, 2001).

4. *Social and psychological adjustment*: Emphasizes the stressful nature of the social and psychological changes that face young people as they move from school to adult life (Hepper & Garralda, 2001).

5. *Supports needed*: Emphasizes policy, service, workforce, and family supports needed for successful transition to adult life.

CONCEPTUALIZATIONS OF TRANSITION EMERGING FROM THEORY

A number of conceptual frameworks for transition have been developed since the mid-1960s that are useful for transition planning and putting transition plans into practice. Readers are invited to explore the cited sources for more details.

A brief history of conceptual frameworks

In the last fifty years, numerous models of transitions have been presented, and each includes different components and outcomes of transitions to adult life. A brief review of early models is presented here, but the reader is encouraged to consult Whetstone & Browning (2002) for more details. In the 1960s, ideas related to vocational preparation for youth with disabilities surfaced. At that time, *work-study models* with curriculum based on academic, social, and work skills were developed in an attempt to provide students with the knowledge and skill set needed for a successful work life. In the 1970s, *career education models* emerged, from which seven major goals were advanced that remain among the fundamental principles of the transition movement today: 1) career awareness, exploration, and decision-making; 2) employability and adaptability skills; 3) private sector and public school partnerships; 4) interfacing education and work; 5) career

emphasis in the classroom; 6) work as a meaningful part of life; and 7) reducing prejudice and stereotypes to protect the individual's freedom to choose his or her career. In the mid 1980s, the *bridges model* (also called the Office of Special Education and Rehabilitative Services (OSERS) model) emphasized the service linkages (i.e., "bridges") that were needed to successfully transition youth from school to work (see Will, 1984, 1985). Shortly thereafter, a *community adjustment model* was introduced that proposed other components of adult life that should be included as outcomes in the transition to adult life — namely, residential environments and social and interpersonal networks (Halpern, 1985). While each of these models offers practical methods for promoting the importance of both academic and life skills, Halpern's (1985) community adjustment model is the one upon which much of today's transition-related legislation, policies, and practices are based (Whetstone & Browning, 2002).

Conceptualizations using a family perspective

In the time of transitioning from school to adult life, youth with disabilities face a number of complex choices that are often limited in scope. In most cases, family members play an important role in the transition process (Kohler & Field, 2003) because they are in a unique position to inform on the quality of both the process and outcomes of transition (Davies & Beamish, 2009). Blacher (2001) offered a useful conceptual model that "considers transition from a family perspective, with family well-being as the primary outcome of interest" (p. 173).

In Blacher's conceptual model, three interacting types of factors influence transition success: 1) individual factors (e.g., cognitive level, adaptive behaviour, psychiatric status); 2) environment and culture (e.g., social supports, socioeconomic status, service supports, religious connectedness, cohesion/families, acculturation); and 3) involvement/detachment (e.g., behavioural, cognitive, emotional). Transition success (i.e., residential placement, work/vocational opportunities, socialization, and quality of life), in turn, is seen as a major influence on family well-being during the transition period. Family well-being is described as both positive and negative indicators of adjustment (individual, dyadic or two-person interactions, and family) considered all together (Blacher, 2001).

In their study, Davies and Beamish (2009) sought to understand the transition experience and outcomes from the parental perspective. They found that, although parents were satisfied with transition planning, they were dissatisfied with its outcomes, in particular with the "difficulties experienced by families when desired outcomes related to employment, community living, and social networking were not realised" (p. 255). For example, difficulties included economic hardship (as some parents had to quit working in order to stay at home with their children during the day) and transportation issues. In spite of efforts related to improving the transition planning process, it appears much work remains to be done as the post-school situation of youth with disabilities and their families has remained relatively unchanged (Davies & Beamish, 2009).

From conceptualization to action

Just as transition models have expanded to include outcomes other than employment, the way in which the transition process is operationalized has also changed. There is no single "true" definition of the transition to adult life, and there is no one single way to best support individuals with disabilities who are facing this transition. However, the following key elements of successful transition programs have been identified and still are relevant today: individualized transition planning; integration with mainstream settings; paid work experiences; active family involvement; coordination of data and services; job-seeking and placement; and follow-up or follow-along (Rojewski, 1992).

The Taxonomy for Transition Programming (Kohler, 1996) more explicitly sets out concepts, sub-concepts, and action objectives that are useful for carrying out transition plans and evaluating transition systems. The taxonomy comprises five key concepts:

1. *Student-focused planning*: the student actively participates in planning activities
2. *Student development*: e.g., life skills, employment skills, assessment, support services
3. *Interagency collaboration*: collaborative frameworks and models of service delivery
4. *Program structure*: philosophy, policies, strategic planning, program evaluation, resources
5. *Family involvement*: the family actively participates in planning activities

A recent review of evidence-based practices in the transition to adult life identified 32 practices that aligned with Kohler's (1996) taxonomy (Test, Fowler, et al., 2009). For the most part, the practices had only a moderate level of evidence to support their use. The authors concluded that their findings "provide practitioners with a set of evidence-based practices for improving transition services and researchers with an agenda for conducting future research" (p.115).

The same year, an Ontario-based research team published best practice guidelines and an evidence-based model for the transition to adult life, called "The Best Journey to Adult Life" model (see Stewart et al., 2009). A hot air balloon is used to depict the journey to adulthood. The guidelines for this journey have been organized into six main themes: 1) collaboration; 2) capacity-building; 3) navigation; 4) information; 5) education; and 6) research. Further, three key phases of the transition process were identified: preparation, journey, and landing. For each of the six themes identified, guidelines are offered for each of the three phases of the transition process. This model builds on the belief that various "landings" exist in the journey to adulthood, and that a number of people are needed to support the youth throughout the process. It is also based on the core values reflected in Kohler's (1996) work (e.g., must be person-centred), but also expands it to include other values related to cultural sensitivity, equity, flexibility, life-course perspective, supportive environments, and promotion of wellness.

Outcomes

Ultimately, the transition process aims to support an individual as he or she moves from one point to another. Thus, transition planning is outcome-based, and requires evaluation to ensure that the desired outcomes are achieved.

Hughes, Eisenman, Hwang, Kim, Scott, and Killian (1997) have developed an outcomes measures synthesis that provides a helpful way of thinking about the methods used to evaluate success for youth transitioning from school to adult life. Eleven categories were constructed based on their literature review findings: Employment (44), Social interaction (39), Community adjustment, competence, and independent living (35), Psychological well-being and personal satisfaction (31), Personal development and fulfillment (25), Recreation and leisure (23), Social acceptance, social status, and ecological-fit (19), Self-determination, autonomy, and personal choice (17), Physical and material well-being (17), Individual and social demographic indicators (13), and Civic responsibility and activity (6).

In a more recent review, sixteen evidence-based in-school factors were identified that correlated to post-secondary education, employment, and independent living: career awareness; community experiences; diploma status; inclusion in general education; interagency collaboration; occupational courses; paid employment and work experiences; parental involvement; program of study; self-determination or self-advocacy; self-care skills; social skills; student support; transition program; vocational education; and work study (Test, Mazzotti, et al., 2009). The results highlight the fact that a number of transition program characteristics are significantly linked to post-school success among youth with disabilities. However, work that is able to establish more than a correlation between these in-school variables and post-school outcomes are needed. Cobb and Alwell (2009) have found that well-designed scientifically-based research studies of the transition to adult life are generally lacking.

Preparing for Transition to Adult Life

The point at which young people graduate from school has come to be seen as the true beginning of adult life. It is a significant milestone that is marked in a number of social ways, such as graduation ceremonies, physical moves, and the beginning of work. It is a rite of passage and, as Ferguson, Ferguson, and Jones (1988) pointed out a number of years ago, it can

be a stressful time because of the changes it entails.

Yet, it is also a time of heightened expectations and hope for the future (Thorin, Yovanoff, & Irvin, 1996). It is a time to begin new activities, make new friends, live in new places, and learn new skills. Both stress and heightened expectations can create interesting challenges for those who work with individuals and families to support successful transitions. Many of these are related to the overall dilemma inherent in letting go of young adults with developmental disabilities and encouraging them to take greater charge of managing their own lives and their own futures in ways that are helpful and safe.

THE DILEMMA INHERENT IN LETTING GO

The transition from school to adult life is a period when most parents (of children without disabilities) naturally relinquish most of the control they had over the lives of their sons and daughters. This transition also marks a time when most young people (without disabilities) assume control and independence. They begin setting up their independent lives in the areas of their own accommodation, employment, and finances; making the final decisions about almost everything that affects their lives; and sometimes starting families of their own.

For families that include a transition-age youth who has a developmental disability, however, the shift is usually not nearly as straightforward. The problem these families face is that, at the very time when it would be natural for their sons and daughters to be assuming independence and for families (especially parents) to be letting go, the demands on families (especially parents) increase. A number of reasons for this — reasons that vary from family to family, and from country to country — have emerged in the literature and have remained remarkably consistent over the past 20 years (Bramston & Cummins, 1998; Brown & Renwick, 1998; Capie, Contardi, and Doehring, 2006; Lichtenstein & Nisbet, 1992; Richardson, 1989; Ryan, 1997; Smull & Bellamy, 1991; Thorin et al., 1996; Todd, Young, Shearn, & Jones, 2004; Zetlin & Turner, 2002):

- Some youth with disabilities do not want to leave school because they have become accustomed to a way of life they enjoy.

- Youth with disabilities do not have the life skills to assume control and independence.
- Parents and other family members do not know how to help the person with disabilities plan for or adjust to adult living.
- Parents and other family members feel worn out from many years of providing care and support, and lack hope and energy to address the future.
- Parents' friends (with children who do not have disabilities) are beginning lives free from child-rearing responsibilities.
- Established routines, such as preparing for school, travelling to and from school, and taking part in the daily school schedules, are no longer available and this can be experienced as loss; in addition, there can be a feeling of void if lost routines are not replaced by other routines.
- There are few local options available for youth with disabilities.
- Formal supports (services) are under-funded, with insufficient staff and program alternatives.
- Moving to independent or shared living has a great many challenges that parents recognize, but youth with developmental disabilities may perceive this as a positive event that lowers stress.
- People with disabilities face unemployment, underemployment, long-term dependency, inappropriate living conditions, inadequate financial resources, restricted opportunities for education and training, limited opportunities for leisure activities, and (in some countries) inadequate health care — all in larger measure than their peers without disabilities.

As a consequence, parents of children with disabilities are faced with a number of dilemmas. On the one hand, they want their children to become more independent and begin leading their own lives. On the other hand, they want to ensure that their children have both opportunities and supports for their lives ahead. Thorin et al. (1996) identified six such dilemmas, and found them to be important to the 103 families they studied for reasons and to degrees that differ among families:

Dilemma 1: Wanting to create opportunities for independence for the young adult, and wanting to assure that health and safety needs are met.

Dilemma 2: Wanting a life separate from the young adult, and wanting to do whatever is necessary to assure a good life for him or her.

Dilemma 3: Wanting to provide stability and predictability in the family life, and wanting to meet the changing needs of the young adult and family.

Dilemma 4: Wanting to create a separate social life for the young adult, and wanting to have less involvement in his or her life.

Dilemma 5: Wanting to avoid burnout, and wanting to do everything possible for the young adult.

Dilemma 6: Wanting to maximize the young adult's growth and potential, and wanting to accept the young adult as he or she is. (pp. 118–119)

Two other factors, in particular, complicate what parents want for their sons and daughters with disabilities who are facing young adulthood. First, raising a child with a disability can be stressful, but there are also many positive emotional and practical advantages (Blacher & Hatton, 2001; Brown & Renwick, 1998). For example, many parents enjoy ongoing caregiving and, as a result, a person with disabilities sometimes becomes a valued and central figure in a family. Some people with disabilities are helpful in carrying out household chores, and some families rely on disability pensions to support their household income; many parents are reluctant to give these up. Second, by the time youth reach transition age, most parents have invested a tremendous amount of time and energy in understanding the youth's personal skills, abilities, and personal characteristics, as well as in trying to develop strategies that make the youth's life as successful as possible (Todd et al., 2004; Zetlin & Turner, 2002). Quite understandably, many parents see themselves as the experts on their son's or daughter's life. Even though they may wish to have a break from caregiving, they are rather wary of handing the main responsibility for support to paid support workers who are less experienced (Brown & Renwick, 1998). There are several legitimate reasons for this. The most important are: some transition age youth choose to turn to those who are closest to them (usually parents or other family members) for additional emotional support in times of change; adult services are not always available; and, if services are available, front line paid support workers do not always know the youth well, are often relatively inexperienced, and typically have limited time to spend with the youth.

Thus, the challenge of "letting go" is not as easy as most family members might wish it to be. The fault, if there is one, lies not in one place, but in many. The framework set out by Ferguson et al., (1988) — which identified bureaucracy, family life, and adult status as areas in which transition problems emerge — unfortunately still seems fully relevant today. Problems still emerge from these sources. Equally applicable and equally unfortunate is Wells' (1991) observation that anxieties prevail in families during times of transition because they realize the young person's dependency will not conclude but, rather, will continue into adulthood. Box 1 presents a parent's perspective on how these factors often influence the behaviour of youth with developmental disabilities.

LEGAL INDEPENDENCE

One factor that complicates the issues of letting go and accepting responsibility in the transition years is that they occur at about the age when people with disabilities who do not demonstrate incompetence become legally independent of their parents or guardians. What this means is that, in Canada, adults who are not deemed incompetent are not legally subject to the direction of others at all (e.g., see Millar, 2003). Such legal independence means not only that young people with developmental disabilities are entitled to make their own decisions, but also that they are responsible for both making decisions and being accountable for the outcomes of those decisions.

On one hand, legal independence is an assertion of equal rights for people with disabilities and encourages them to function among others adults in their societies in responsible ways. On the other hand, it sometimes creates stress for family members who feel unsure that their youth with disabilities can make sound decisions and who fear that their youth may be held legally accountable for adverse consequences of unsound decisions.

IMPORTANCE OF PLANNING

A dominant theme of the transitions literature is the importance of planning. Numerous planning principles and methods are available from a number of sources that are available on the Internet and in professional and academic journals. As Capie et al. (2006) cautioned, however, prepared plans may not be helpful for addressing the specific needs of some youth; thus, all should be tailored to the specific needs and circumstances of the individual. Generally accepted principles in transition planning include the following:

- *Self-determination*: Above all, transition planning must reflect the perspective of the youth with a disability and include his or her wishes, dreams, goals for the future, perceptions of themselves as adults, and preferred ways of doing things.
- *Multi-sector participation*: Transition planning should include representatives — who are in a position to effect change — of the person's family, friends, other support group(s), school, adult services, and so forth.
- *Person–planning fit*: Transition planning should be carried out in a way that the person with the disability can understand. For those who express themselves verbally, this may require modifying or adjusting both the process and the content of the plan. For those who do not express themselves verbally, this may require direct experience, such as visiting places and introducing new people and carefully noting nonverbal expressions of likes and dislikes.

Generally accepted methods for helping youth with disabilities and those who support them plan successfully include these approaches:

- Provide the needed human and environmental support to a person with a disability throughout the planning process to allow full participation.

- Prepare the person for his or her roles in future planning.
- Provide the person with opportunities from which to choose.
- Have accurate information about the opportunities that are available.
- Ensure the person has the skills and feels free to express his or her choices independently.
- Expose the person to a variety of experiences to enable him or her to make life-enhancing choices.
- Allow adequate time for planning and for revisiting plans.
- Allow the person to make poor choices and to act on opportunities to learn from those experiences.

Additional information about planning, from the family's point of view, is presented in Box 2.

Things that families can do

The most important thing that families can do is to ensure that a transition plan is in place and that those who have assumed responsibility for putting it into action are doing so. The various responsibilities associated with transition may be taken by school or community agency staff, by a family member, or by another person such as a paid consultant. Most transitions work better, however, if parents participate in the process and have an active voice in how it is carried out (Cooney, 2002; Wehman, 2001). This view has been supported by Blacher (2001) and by Mizutani, Hiruma, and Yanagimoto (2003), who recommended that parents keep involved in the transition planning through the school years and when the youth becomes involved in services from community agencies. Box 3 illustrates the importance of parents advocating on behalf of their sons and daughters to ensure their needs are being addressed.

One aspect of entering adult life that is often viewed as a family concern, and thus that families can have a strong part in supporting, is addressing sexuality in transition youth, including both procreation and the role of sexuality in social relationships (Hayes Hammer, Holloway, DePrato, & Weiss, 2000;

Box 1: A Parent's Perspective: Transition and Behaviour

Young people react to transition in various ways. They may not realize a change is about to occur, and when it does they may exhibit stress-related changes in their behaviour. Conversely, many such youth are glad to leave school. They see their peers leaving, and they see what other young people are doing on television and in other media. They wish to do the same. They are ready to move into the adult phase of their lives. Yet, they may not have the skills to do this independently and become frustrated in their attempts when they set out to live like other young adults who do not have disabilities. Also, their parents may perceive that they do not have these skills, and either curtail their activities or try to provide supports that the youths do not wish to have. Such situations can cause additional problems and can bring on negative behaviour.
– Lawrence Spiro, parent.

Source: Brown (2007).

Zetlin & Turner, 2002). Although these topics may well have been covered in the school curriculum, families can help by providing additional sex education, offering practical help and advice, and above all being open to ongoing discussions about emerging issues related to sexuality. Some aspects of sexuality continue to be considered from a moral perspective (i.e., specific sexual acts are considered to be right or wrong) within some families and some cultures, and families can be helpful in explaining socially acceptable methods of satisfying adult sexual needs, dealing with the possibility of pregnancy, being a partner in a sexual relationship, and addressing concerns that arise from engaging in sexual activity.

Things that policy makers can do

Making the transition from school to adult living is a relatively new focus for policy in the field of developmental disabilities. The Ontario government has introduced and refined a number of policy initiatives that are designed to facilitate such a transition (see Chapter 23 for additional details):

- Schools are required to include a transition plan for post-secondary school activities in the

Box 2: A Parent's Perspective: Planning and Being Prepared

Family preparedness is an important aspect in the youth's transition from school to adult life. Some parents are very prepared and have set up sources of income, arranged daily activities, and ensured that ongoing social contacts are in place. Other parents have given little thought to what will happen in the future, and are caught off guard when their children finish school. Such youth may move into an unplanned and unstructured life to which they are unaccustomed.

Regardless of the degree of preparedness of the family, the transition from school to community can be very stressful. Most families find that "just letting things happen" is not a good way to manage and that more systemic planning is preferable. To begin, families must think about the options that face their son or daughter. If work placement is not an option, families must consider what else is available. Planning can be done informally, through simple family discussion or in a more formal way. Creating a life plan for a young person with an intellectual disability is one more formal way of planning for the future. This can be done in many ways but, in general, it is a collection of ideas, preferably generated by a circle of supporters with input from the youth. Its first phase does not need to be practical — all that is required are dreams and aspirations. The plan will change as a young person develops, but at least it starts a process that should be beneficial to the youth and to his or her family. For many young people with developmental disabilities, having such a structured plan is very empowering and stress relieving. — Lawrence Spiro, parent.

Source: Brown (2007).

Individual Education Plan (IEP) of all students 14 years of age or over who are exceptional because of developmental disability (Ontario Ministry of Education, 2010a, 2010b).

- The "Passport" program was developed for persons who are no longer eligible to receive school-based supports and who would benefit from support to facilitate community participation (Ontario Ministry of Community and Social Services, 2009). The program provides funding to individuals who are not otherwise eligible for Ontario Disability Support Program (ODSP) for activities that promote personal growth, use of community programs, development of occupational skills, and achievement of personal goals. Typical categories of support under this initiative include those related to communication and social abilities, personal supports, behaviour, personal health and medical care, and supervision (Ontario Ministry of Community and Social Services, 2010). The Passport funding may be used by individuals to purchase their own supports and services, to obtain services from community-based agencies, or to acquire supports through a combination of the two. Persons must complete an application that covers a three-year period, and must re-apply to receive additional funding.

When introducing these policy initiatives, Ontario has learned from research and scholarly discussion in other jurisdictions. Legislation enhancing supported employment has existed in the United States (see Wehman, 2001, for a description of U.S. legislation) and many other countries since the mid-1980s (Kirby, 1997). As Eisenman (2003) noted in her review, there have been some helpful policy discussions about how to integrate transition into special education curricula, especially in relation to how this might more positively affect employment and other measures of successful living for youth after they leave school. Some helpful ideas for what policy makers should be focusing on include the following:

- Address the issue of fair wages for people with disabilities by setting clear rules and guidelines (Kirby, 1997).
- Develop helpful databases for the purposes of evaluating the effectiveness of transitions activities such as making transition plans; putting plans into effect; gaining employment or other

Box 3: A Parent's Perspective: The Importance of Advocacy

Most parents have a positive attitude about the skills of their young sons or daughters. Parents who advocate strongly for their children and youth are more likely to get needed support, to be well informed about the resources available, and to have realistic aspirations for their children. Proactive parents show up at school meetings and interact with community agencies as needed. Often, they interact with one another and belong to parent or other disability-related groups. Such involvement is time consuming and it can take a toll on personal resources. Yet, some parents find their advocacy work to be a source of strength and satisfaction in their lives.

Some parents simply do not advocate at all. They do not interact with the service system and, in fact, may feel threatened by it. This may occur because they have not come to terms with their child's disability, or because of any number of other social and cultural reasons. While the children of such parents are in the school system, school staff can provide some support, but once they leave, the families are usually on their own. It is essential for schools and community services to be aware of such families so that they can be supported in ways that will be most beneficial to their young adult children during the important transition years. – Lawrence Spiro, parent.

Source: Brown (2007).

meaningful daily activity; acquiring independent accommodation; becoming interconnected with community services, people, and activities; and providing for financial independence (Kirby, 1997).

- Enhance the mandates of government-funded agencies to fully address transition issues (Kirby, 1997).
- Promote greater independence in early adult life by taking measures to ensure personal safety, financial security, and access to public transportation (Ramcharan, 2003).
- Promote within industry the value of employing workers with disabilities and responsibility for doing so, providing incentives if necessary.
- Put into place programs that clearly link transition planning in the schools to assistance to youth after they leave school (Mizutani & Yanagimoto, 2003).
- Set out policy for training of non-disabled managers and workers in industry (Kirby, 1997).

Things that schools can do

In Ontario, schools develop transition plans for all students who are exceptional because of developmental disability at age 14. These plans are developed with input from the youth with disabilities, parents or guardians, teachers, principals or other school personnel, and representatives of community agencies or organizations. According to the Ontario Ministry of Education (2010a), the plan must feature the student's own goals and wishes and include:

- Specific goals for the student's transition to postsecondary activities. The goals must be realistic and must reflect the strengths, needs and interests of the student.
- The actions required, now and in the future, to achieve the stated goals. The actions identified must build on the student's identified strengths, needs, and interests.
- The person or agency (the student, parents, educators, providers of specialized support and services, community agencies) responsible for or involved in completing or providing assistance in the completion of each of the identified actions.
- Timelines for the implementation of each of the identified actions.

The Ontario requirement for developing transition plans is consistent with similar requirements in some other provinces and countries, but not all. For example, in a 2004 review, Bouck noted that despite progressive legislation in the United States — including the *Education for All Handicapped Children Act* of 1975 (PL 94-142) and the *Individuals with*

Disabilities Education Act (IDEA) of 1990 (PL 101-476), its 1997 amendments (PL 105-17), and its 2004 reauthorization (PL 108446) — there are no specific requirements for transition to be part of the curriculum and it is not always included. If transition planning is in place and carried out effectively, there is some evidence that it results in improved outcomes for youth after they graduate from school (e.g., Frank & Sitlington, 2000; Nietupski et al., 2004). However, even where transition is included in the curriculum, the quality varies considerably (Bassett & Smith, 1996; Ramcharan, 2003). As a first step, then, schools can ensure that quality transition planning and development of skills to support successful transition are part of their curricula.

Transition research has begun to explore skills that are essential to successful transition, such as problem solving (Crites & Dunn, 2004), learning how to express points of view and to ensure that those points of view are heard (Cameron & Murphy, 2002), and adapting to specific objectives set out in transition curricula and other materials (e.g., Martin, Mithaug, Husch, Oliphint, & Frazier, 2002). It will be necessary to engage in evaluation research to develop knowledge about which skills are most effective for successful transition.

In the meantime, there are a number of helpful strategies and resources available for teachers and other school personnel for ensuring that their transition plans are successful (Hughes & Carter, 2000; Wehman, 2001, 2002; Wehman & Walsh, 1999):

- Advocate with policy makers for ongoing training and adult learning.
- Keep transition planning student-centered (Miner & Bates, 1997).
- Involve parents and professionals from community agencies in planning for postgraduation activities (Mizutani et al., 2003).
- Involve youth in their own planning to a greater degree (Attanasio, 2003; Braithwaite, 2003; Martin et al., 2002; Mizutani et al., 2003; Ramcharan, 2003; Wehman, 2001; Zhang & Stecker, 2001).
- Provide meaningful work experience for students (Kirby, 1997).
- Provide more accessible information to stu-

dents to assist with choices (Ramcharan, 2003).
- Refer students to community disability programs that are most likely to meet their needs (Attanasio, 2003).
- Take into full consideration the possibility of attending college (Getzel & Wehman, 2005). Transfer to community social service agencies information about numbers of students with special needs and descriptions of those needs well before the students leave school (Wehman, 2001; Wells, 1991).
- Undertake continuous improvement of transition planning (Kirby, 1997).

Things that service providers can do

One of the major problems in transition from school to adult living is that community service organizations very often do not plan for or make themselves available to students who will be graduating from school. This trend has been changing gradually in Ontario and elsewhere. Although it is not required in Ontario, some schools and community service organizations have now developed joint programs to address transition in a systematic way. For example, the Bloorview MacMillan Children's Centre operates the Skills for Transition Program for youth with various disabilities aged 15 to 21 years, which is funded by the Ontario Ministry of Health and Long-term Care (Community Living Research Project, 2006). This program "focuses on the development of life skills required for managing daily tasks at home, at school, and in the community", develops "strategies for practical, hands on learning that specific to the unique needs of the individual", and collaborates "with youth, families, educators, and health care providers with regard to identified issues and goals" (p. 62). "Door 2 Adulthood" is an online resource in Ontario that provides information for youth with all types of disabilities on various transition-related topics (see *www.ablelink.org/public/door2adulthood. htm;* Community Living Research Project, 2006). The site also provides opportunities for youth in transition to communicate with their peers.

Similar scattered programs, some of which are funded by governments, have arisen in various parts of the world (e.g., see Wehman, 2001). In all of these programs, including those in Ontario, change has been slow, primarily because education and adult social services are administered and funded by separate government ministries. In addition, the relatively low level of funding of community services for adults can result in people waiting for services that are sometimes many years long. Where this is the case, it is somewhat understandable that organizations focused on adult services do not reach out to graduating students.

For those community service organizations that are in a position to take some action, important aspects of their role that have been suggested in the disability literature are:

- Take action to coordinate the services that youth with disabilities get while they are in school and the services they will need when they leave school, especially health and social services (Ramcharan, 2003; Wells, 1991).
- Provide comprehensive case management (Wehman & Walsh, 1999).
- Increase the number of options that are available to youth to engage in meaningful life activity (Braithwaite, 2003).
- Put in place personnel who have training, skill, and experience in helping young adults move from school to adult life (Wells, 1991).
- Ensure that service workers do not give up on youth and stop helping them (Ferguson et al., 1988).
- Train youth in self-development and self-advocacy skills to promote themselves in workplace and other community settings (Martin et al., 2002).
- Invest time and energy in developing relationships with current and potential employers (Luecking, Fabian, & Tilson, 2004).
- Seriously consider self-employment as one option (Griffin & Hammis, 2003).
- Train youth in ways and times to disclose their disabilities to others for helpful purposes (Hagedorn, Bond, & Hatt, 2001).

Things that employers can do

In spite of sustained efforts to involve people with developmental disabilities in paid, community-based employment, Kirby (1997) noted that large numbers of youth with disabilities continue to be unemployed. This may still be the case in the more developed countries of the world today, although reliable statistics are not always available. Information that is available suggests that more than 50% of youth leaving school (Wehman & Walsh, 1999) and 60% of adults (Wehman & Kregel, 1998) with disabilities are unemployed. In Ontario, a large study (Brown, Raphael, & Renwick, 1997) found that, although 71% of people with developmental disabilities known to the service system had daily occupational activities, only 17% of such activities were paid jobs or supported community employment. Moreover, this study estimated that only approximately 26% of adults with developmental disabilities were actually involved with the service system, and it is unlikely that the employment rate among those not involved would be even as high. More recently, employment rates of less than 30% have been reported for persons with developmental disabilities in Canada (Prince, 2010; Statistics Canada, 2008). The question of who needs to assume strong leadership in attempting to redress these long-standing problems (e.g., governments, business, disability organizations, parents and individuals with disabilities) has not yet been resolved. In the absence of such leadership, a great many employers simply take no active role in attempting to include young people with disabilities in their workforces.

For those employers who do take an active role, there are a number of guides readily available to assist them to better accommodate people with disabilities in their workplaces (e.g., Australian Government, 1998; Conference Board of Canada, 2001; DAWN Ontario, 2003; Epilepsy Ontario, 2006; Government of Canada, 2004; U.S. Social Security Administration, n.d.). The Conference Board of Canada guide provides practical advice to employers under three main headings: recruitment, workplace accommodations, and training and education in the workplace. In addition, almost all community agencies have staff who have specialized training in placing youth with disabilities in appropriate workplaces, providing on-the-job support, and assisting employers with training and accommodation. Such guides and personnel provide a great deal of practical help for employers.

Employers, too, must be willing to play their part if youth are to be successfully included. They need to be open to providing a variety of job possibilities within their workplace for which youth might be trained, moving beyond thinking only of the types of work that are repetitive and not mentally challenging (Braithwaite, 2003; Ramcharan, 2003). They also need to be open to providing training for staff without disabilities to be effective in their support for the employees who have disabilities.

Special Transition Support to Individuals with Severe Disabilities and Their Families

Successful transition to adult life is most challenging for people with severe developmental disabilities, yet is so essential to positive life outcomes (Clark & Davis, 2000; Johnson, McGrew, Bloomberg, Bruininks, & Lin, 1997). It might be assumed that lower levels of cognitive or other skills might be problematic to putting transition plans into effect, but Cooney (2002) noted that students were remarkably articulate about post-school plans. Rather, Cooney claimed, problems appeared to stem primarily from lack of available opportunities. This view is supported by a large study of 3,084 students 14 years of age and older with severe intellectual disability in England and Wales, where students were found to have few opportunities to participate in the community life of adults (Florian, Dee, Byers, & Maudslay, 2000).

Central to the special support needed by individuals with severe disabilities is the inescapable realization that dependency will continue into adulthood. Wells pointed this out in 1991, but it is just as relevant today. This realization may contribute to families, schools, and community service organizations considering fewer options for people with severe disabilities. For example, youth, especially men, with challenging behaviour problems are likely in the early transition years to enter residential care (Alborz, 2003). Regarding occupational activity, Kraemer and Blacher (2001) noted that more than

half of youth with severe disabilities in their U.S.-based study worked in segregated environments. Similarly, Brown et al. (1997) found that in a random sample of people with (mostly severe) intellectual disabilities who lived in group homes in Canada, 83% attended a major day program, but only 9% were in supported employment or other community work. Another important finding of this survey was that 60% of those who lived in group homes and had a major daily activity had no input into the decision to be placed in the program, and another 17% had limited input.

Family involvement may be especially important in broadening opportunities for youth with severe disabilities. One study illustrated that employment seeking that is initiated by schools or community agencies may be most likely to result in sheltered work, whereas employment seeking that is initiated by family members may be linked closer to inclusive options such as continuing education or self-employment (Devlieger & Trach, 1999). Yet, what parents would like to happen does not always match their ability to recognize diverse opportunities (Cooney, 2002) or what they consider to be realistic (Kraemer & Blacher, 2001). Thus, parents' dreams and initiatives appear to be helpful in expanding ideas and opportunities but may not always be able to be realized to the extent that they might wish.

In Ontario, there is some special help available for young adults with severe disabilities. The Special Services at Home (SSAH) program helps families to pay for special services needed for their family member (child or adult) to live at home in the community (MCSS, 2008). SSAH funds may be used to hire an individual to provide respite to the family, or to teach or enhance skills (e.g., communication, self-care) that will promote independence. Note that funding is not available if the individual is already receiving residential support. Similarly, the Assistance for Children with Severe Disabilities (ACSD) program helps families pay for the ongoing costs of providing for a child with a severe disability who is under the age of 18 years and living at home (Ministry of Child and Youth Services, 2010). Funding is based on family income, the severity of the child's disability, the type and extent of difficulties experienced by the child, and the associated costs. Parents may receive up to $440 per month to help defray costs associated with travel for appointments, assistive devices (e.g., wheelchair, hearing aid, and eyeglasses), prescription medication, and family respite support.

Overall, individuals with severe disabilities typically need to have some specialized support to help them successfully negotiate transition to adult life. For most people with severe disabilities continued success needs to include ongoing personal and professional support. The specific methods for providing such supports are numerous and need to be person specific. However, some general actions that have been described or suggested in the literature and that are helpful to almost all people are to:

- Begin with, and integrate throughout the transition process, a full assessment for all youth with severe disabilities (Sax & Thoma, 2002).
- Carry out a thorough assessment of behaviours during transition times to understand the true nature of what people with severe disabilities are responding to and inferring (Clark & Davis, 2000; also see Kern & Vorndran, 2000, for an interesting example).
- Facilitate social interaction in community settings in an ongoing way to help community integration (Souza & Kennedy, 2003).
- Involve families, individuals with disabilities, schools, community agencies, and other support people in the ongoing planning and implementation of transition activities.
- Provide a wide variety of community-based experience (Black & Langone, 1997).
- Provide employment support in the form of employment specialists and trained co-workers (Wehman, Gibson, Brooke, & Unger, 1998).

Summary

All young people, whether or not they have disabilities, experience considerable change when they leave school and begin their adult lives. A smooth transition from school to adult life is one of the major keys to the successful inclusion of young adults into community life. The theoretical foundation for transitioning to adult living borrows from several differ-

ent sources, but helpful theoretical and conceptual frameworks are available. In Ontario, there have been changes in recent years that are designed to facilitate transition to post-school life, but there are still many things families, policymakers, schools, service organizations, and employers can do to make the process better. People with severe disabilities require additional support to move into their adult lives, and some help is available in Ontario for this purpose. It is important to recognize that no one person, no one family, and no one service organization can provide the full range of services needed by an individual or his or her family. If the best ways to bring about smooth transitions for youth to adult life are to be found, governments, services, communities, and families will have to find a way to share and blend their responsibility for doing so.

For Further Thought and Discussion

1. What could be done to better connect the "two solitudes" — the school system for students and the community supports for adults?
2. Consider the case of one youth with disabilities. What factors are most helpful to him or her adjusting to adult life in the community? How many of these factors pertain to most youth with intellectual or developmental disabilities? How many are unique to the person you have selected to describe?
3. Think of a family you know or have heard about that has a teenager with an intellectual or developmental disability. Now imagine that the parents are not satisfied that a transition plan is being developed in the school. What courses of action might the parents take? Discuss the advantages and disadvantages of each course of action.
4. Many employers are interested in helping people with disabilities, even if they are not required to do so. What can interested employers do to promote opportunities within their workplaces?
5. Not all families connect with community services when their children leave the school system. These families are sometimes described as "falling between the cracks" because their chil-

dren need services but are not obtaining them. What can policy makers do to ensure that families do not fall between the cracks? What can community service organizations do? What can schools do?

References

Alborz, A. (2003). Transitions: Placing a son or daughter with intellectual disability and challenging behaviour in alternative residential provision. *Journal of Applied Research in Intellectual Disabilities, 16*, 75–88.

Attanasio, M. E. (2003). The relationship between locus of control, residential setting, and employment status within a sample of adults with mental retardation. *Dissertation Abstracts International: Section B: The Sciences & Engineering, 64*(6-B), 2904.

Australian Government. (1998). *Practitioner's handbook for public sector employers and employees: Workplace diversity.* Canberra, Australia: Commonwealth of Australia, Legislative Services.

Bassett, D. S., & Smith, T. E. C. (1996). Transition in an era of reform. *Journal of Learning Disabilities, 29*, 161–166.

Blacher, J. (2001). Transition to adulthood: Mental retardation, families, and culture. *American Journal on Mental Retardation, 106*, 173–188.

Blacher, J., & Hatton, C. (2001). Current perspectives on family research in mental retardation. *Current Opinion in Psychiatry, 14*, 477–482.

Black, R. S., & Langone, J. (1997). Social awareness and transition to employment for adolescents with mental retardation. *Remedial and Special Education, 18*, 214–222.

Bouck, E. C. (2004). State of curriculum for secondary students with mild mental retardation. *Education & Training in Developmental Disabilities, 39*, 169–176.

Braithwaite, M. (2003). Transition and changes in the lives of people with intellectual disabilities. *International Journal of Disability, Development & Education, 50*, 225–226.

Bramston, P., & Cummins, R. A. (1998). Stress and the move into community accommodation. *Journal of Intellectual & Developmental Disability, 23*, 295–308.

Brown, I. (2007). The transition from school to adult life. In I. Brown, & M. Percy (Eds.), *A comprehensive guide to intellectual & developmental disabilities* (pp. 511–525). Baltimore: Paul H. Brookes.

Brown, I., & Brown, R. I. (2003). *Quality of life and disability: An approach for community practitioners.* London: Jessica Kingsley Publishers.

Brown, I., Raphael, D., & Renwick, R. (1997). *Quality of life: dream or reality? Life for people with developmental disabilities in Ontario.* Toronto: Centre for Health Promotion.

Brown, I., & Renwick, R. (1998). *Family quality of life: A report to the Ministry of Community and Social Services, Government of Ontario.* Toronto: University of Toronto, Faculty of Social Work.

Brown, R. I. (2004). Life for adults with Down syndrome: New opportunities, new challenges. In R. I. Brown (Ed.), *Life for adults with Down syndrome: New opportunities, new challenges (series).* Southsea, UK: The Down Syndrome Educational Trust.

Cameron, L., & Murphy, J. (2002). Enabling young people with a learning disability to make choices at a time of transition. *British Journal of Learning Disabilities, 30*, 105–112.

Capie, A., Contardi, A., & Doehring, D. (2006). Transition to employment. In R. I. Brown (Ed.), *Life for adults with Down syndrome: New opportunities, new challenges (series).* Southsea, UK: The Down Syndrome Educational Trust.

Clark, H. B., & Davis, M. (Eds.). (2000). *Transition to adulthood: A resource for assisting young people with emotional or behavioral difficulties.* Baltimore: Paul H. Brookes Publishing Co.

Cobb, R. B., & Alwell, M. (2009). Transition planning/coordinating interventions for youth with disabilities: A systematic review. *Career Development for Exceptional Individuals, 32*, 70-81.

Community Living Research Project. (2006). *Young adults with developmental disabilities: Transition from high school to adult life: Literature and initial program review.* Retrieved from http://www.communitylivingbc.ca/news_and_events/documents/YoungAdultsTransitionDocument_feb07.pdf

Conference Board of Canada. (2001). *Tapping the*

talents of people with disabilities: A guide for employers. Retrieved from http://www.conference-board.ca/documents.asp?rnext=85

Cooney, B. F. (2002). Exploring perspectives on transition of youth with disabilities: Voices of young adults, parents, and professionals. *Mental Retardation, 40,* 425–435.

Crites, S. A., & Dunn, C. (2004). Teaching social problem solving to individuals with mental retardation. *Education & Training in Developmental Disabilities, 39,* 301–309.

Davies, M. D., & Beamish, W. (2009). Transitions from school for young adults with intellectual disability: Parental perspectives on "life as an adjustment." *Journal of Intellectual and Developmental Disabilities, 34,* 248–257.

DAWN Ontario. (2003). *Barrier-free employers: Practical guide for employment accommodation for people with disabilities.* Retrieved from http://dawn.thot.net/employment_accommodation.html

Devlieger, P. L., & Trach, J. S. (1999). Mediation as a transition process: The impact on postschool employment outcomes. *Exceptional Children, 65,* 507–523.

Education for All Handicapped Children Act of 1975, PL 94142,20 U.S.C. §§ 1400 et seq.

Eisenman, L. T. (2003). Theories in practice: School-to-work transitions for youth with mild disabilities. *Exceptionality, 11,* 89–102.

Epilepsy Ontario. (2006). *Employers guide to employing people with epilepsy.* Retrieved from http://epilepsyontario.org/client/EO/EOWeb.nsf/web/Employers'+Guide

Ferguson, P. M., Ferguson, D. L., & Jones, D. (1988). Generations of hope: Parental perspectives on the transitions of their children with severe retardation from school to adult life. *Journal of The Association for Persons with Severe Handicaps, 13,* 177–187.

Florian, L., Dee, L., Byers, R., & Maudslay, L. (2000). What happens after the age of 14? Mapping transitions for pupils with profound and complex learning difficulties. *British Journal of Special Education, 27*(3), 124–128.

Frank, A. R., & Sitlington, P. L. (2000). Young adults with mental disabilities — does transition lanning make a difference? *Education & Training in Men-*

tal Retardation & Developmental Disabilities, 35, 119–134.

Getzel, E. E., & Wehman, P. (Eds.). (2005). *Going to college: Expanding opportunities for people with disabilities.* Baltimore: Paul H. Brookes Publishing Co.

Government of Canada. (2004). *Working together: An employer's resource for workplace accommodation.* Retrieved from http://www.hrsdc.gc.ca/en/on/epb/disabilities/pdf/workplace_accommodation.pdf

Griffin, C., & Hammis, D. (2003). *Making self-employment work for people with disabilities.* Baltimore: Paul H. Brookes Publishing Co.

Hagedorn, L., Bond, J., & Hatt, P. (2001). *Learning disabilities: Best practice and innovations.* Retrieved from http://www.on.literacy.ca/pubs/best/learndis/insidcov.htm

Halpern, A. S. (1985). Transition: A look at the foundations. *Exceptional Children, 51,* 479–486.

Hayes Hammer, J., Holloway, J., DePrato, D. K., & Weiss, K. J. (2000). Transitioning individuals with mental retardation and developmental disability: The other sister. *Journal of the American Academy of Psychiatry & the Law, 28,* 202–205.

Hepper, F., & Garralda, M. E. (2001). Psychiatric adjustment to leaving school in adolescents with intellectual disability: A pilot study. *Journal of Intellectual Disability Research, 45,* 521–525.

Hughes, C., & Carter, E. W. (2000). *The transition handbook: Strategies high school teachers use that work!* Baltimore: Paul H. Brookes Publishing Co.

Hughes, C., Eisenman, L. T., Hwang, B., Kim, J., Scott, S. V., & Killian, D. J. (1997). Transition from secondary special education to adult life: A review and analysis of empirical measures. *Education and Training in Mental Retardation & Developmental Disabilities, 32,* 85–104.

Individuals with Disabilities Education Act Amendments of 1997, PL 105-17, 20 U.S.C. §§ 1400 et seq.

Individuals with Disabilities Education Act (IDEA) of 1990, PL 101-476, 20 U.S.C. §§ 1400 et seq.

Individuals with Disabilities Education Improvement Act of 2004, PL 108-446, 20 U.S.C. §§ 1400 et seq.

Johnson, D. R., McGrew, K. S., Bloomberg, L., Bruininks, R. H., & Lin, H. (1997). Results of a national follow-up study of young adults with severe disabilities. *Journal of Vocational Rehabilitation, 8,* 119–133.

Kern, L., & Vorndran, C. M. (2000). Functional assessment and intervention for transition difficulties. *Journal of The Association for Persons with Severe Handicaps, 25,* 212–216.

Kirby, N. (1997). Employment and mental retardation. In N. W. Bray (Ed.), *International review of research in mental retardation: Vol. 20* (pp. 191–249). San Diego: Academic Press.

Kohler, P. D. (1996). *Taxonomy for transition.* Champaign, IL: University of Illinois. Also available at homepages.wmich.edu/~kohlerp/pdf/Taxonomy.pdf)

Kohler, P. D., & Field, S. (2003). Transition-focused education: Foundation for the future. *The Journal of Special Education, 37,* 174–183.

Kraemer, B. R., & Blacher, J. (2001). Transition for young adults with severe mental retardation: School, preparation, parent expectations, and family involvement. *Mental Retardation, 39,* 423–435.

Kraemer, B. R., McIntyre, L. L., & Blacher, J. (2003). Quality of life for young adults with mental retardation during transition. *Mental Retardation, 41,* 250–262.

Lichtenstein, S., & Nisbet, J. (1992). *New Hampshire Transition Initiative: From school to adult life. Young adults in transition: A national and state overview.* Durham, NH: University of New Hampshire, Institute on Disability.

Luecking, R. G., Fabian, E. S., & Tilson, G. P. (2004). *Working relationships: Creating career opportunities for job seekers with disabilities through employer partnerships.* Baltimore: Paul H. Brookes Publishing Co.

Martin, J. E., Mithaug, D. E., Husch, J. V., Oliphint, J. H., & Frazier, E. S. (2002). *Self-directed employment: A handbook for transition teachers and employment specialists.* Baltimore: Paul H. Brookes Publishing Co.

Millar, D. S. (2003). Age of majority, transfer of rights and guardianship: Considerations for families and educators. *Education & Training in Developmental Disabilities, 38,* 378–397.

Miner, C. A., & Bates, P. E. (1997). The effect of person centered planning activities on the IEP/transition planning process. *Education & Training in Mental Retardation & Developmental Disabilities, 32,* 105–112.

Mizutani, Y., Hiruma, T., & Yanagimoto, Y. (2003). A nationwide investigation of individualized plans in Japanese special high schools: Implications for the collaborative practices of individualized transition support plans. *Japanese Journal of Special Education, 39,* 41–58.

Mizutani, Y., & Yanagimoto, Y. (2003). Transition support system in Japanese Special High Schools for students with intellectual disabilities: A comparison with the ITP process in the United States. *Japanese Journal of Special Education, 40,* 713–722.

Nietupski, J., McQuillen, T., Duncan Berg, D., Weyant, J., Daugherty, V., Bildstein, S., O,Connor, A., Warth, J., & Hamre-Nietupski, S. (2004). Iowa's High School High Tech Goes to College Program: Preparing students with mild disabilities for careers in technology. *Journal of Developmental and Physical Disabilities, 16,* 179–192.

Ontario Ministry of Children and Youth Services. (2010). *Assistance for children with severe disabilities.* Retrieved from http://www.children.gov.on.ca/htdocs/English/topics/specialneeds/disabilities/index.aspx

Ontario Ministry of Community and Social Services. (2008). *Services and supports for people with a developmental disability: Special Services at Home.* Retrieved from http://www.mcss.gov.on.ca/en/mcss/programs/developmental/servicesAndSupport/specialServicesAtHome.aspx

Ontario Ministry of Community and Social Services. (2009). *Services and supports for people with a developmental disability: Passport.* Retrieved from http://www.mcss.gov.on.ca/en/mcss/programs/developmental/servicesAndSupport/passport.aspx

Ontario Ministry of Community and Social Services. (2010). *Appendix C: Typical characteristics and categories of support for individuals accessing community participation supports.* Retrieved from http://www.mcss.gov.on.ca/en/mcss/publications/developmentalServices/passportGuidlines/appendixC.aspx

Ontario Ministry of Eduction. (2010a). *Transition planning*. Retrieved from http://www.edu.gov.on.ca/eng/general/elemsec/speced/transiti.html

Ontario Ministry of Eduction. (2010b). *Transition planning: A resource guide, 2002*. Retrieved from http://www.edu.gov.on.ca/eng/general/elemsec/speced/transiti/transition.html

Prince, M. J., (2010). People with disabilities, labour markets, public policies, and Canadian federalism. Disabilities Health Research Network Speaker Series, February 3, 2010, Vancouver, BC.

Ramcharan, P. (2003). Bridging the divide at transition: What happens for young people with learning difficulties and their families. *Journal of Learning Disabilities, 7*, 283–284.

Richardson, A. (1989). Letting go: A mother's view. *Disability, Handicap & Society, 4*, 81–92.

Rojewski, J. W. (1992). Key components of model transition services for students with learning disabilities. *Learning Disability Quarterly, 15*, 135-150.

Ryan, T. (1997). *Making our way: Transition from school to adulthood in the lives of people who have learning difficulties*. London: Values into Action.

Sax, C. L., & Thoma, C. A. (2002). *Transition assessment: Wise practices for quality lives*. Baltimore. Paul H. Brookes Publishing Co.

Smull, M. W., & Bellamy, G. T. (1991). Community services for adults with disabilities: Policy challenges in the emerging support paradigm. In L. H. Meyer, C. A. Peck, & L. Brown (Eds.), *Critical issues in the lives of people with severe disabilities* (pp. 527–536). Baltimore: Paul H. Brookes Publishing Co.

Souza, G., & Kennedy, C. H. (2003). Facilitating social interactions in the community for a transition-age student with severe disabilities. *Journal of Positive Behavior Interventions, 5*, 179–182.

Statistics Canada. (2008). Participation and Activity Limitation Survey: Employment. The Daily, July 24, 2008. Retrieved from http://www.statcan.gc.ca/daily-quotidien/080724/dq080724a-eng.htm

Stewart, D., Freeman, M., Law, M., Healy, H., Burke-Gaffney, J., Forhan, M., Young, N., & Guenther, S. (2009). "*The Best Journey to Adult Life*" *for youth with disabilities: An evidence-based model and best practice guidelines for the transi-tion to adulthood for youth with disabilities*. CanChild Centre for Childhood Disability Research. Retrieved from http://transitions.canchild.ca/en/OurResearch/resources/BestPractices.pdf

Test, D. W., Fowler, C. H., Richter, S. M., White, J., Mazzotti, V., Walker, A. R., Kohler, P., & Kortering, L. (2009). Evidence-based practices in secondary transition. *Career Development for Exceptional Individuals, 32*, 115–128.

Test, D. W., Mazzotti, V. L., Mustian, A. L., Fowler, C. H., Kortering, L., & Kohler, P. (2009). Evidence-based secondary transition predictors for improving postschool outcomes for students with disabilities. *Career Development for Exceptional Individuals, 32*, 160–181.

Thorin, E., Yovanoff, P., & Irvin, L. (1996). Dilemmas faced by families during their young adults' transitions to adulthood: A brief report. *Mental Retardation, 34*, 117–120.

Todd, S., Young, P., Shearn, J., & Jones, S. (2004). Family quality of life in Wales. In A. Turnbull, I. Brown, & H. R. Turnbull (Eds.), *Families and people with mental retardation and quality of life: International perspectives* (pp. 101–147). Washington, DC: American Association on Mental Retardation.

U.S. Social Security Administration. (n.d.). *Americans with Disabilities Act: A guide for people with disabilities seeking employment* [Publication Number ADA-0001 ICN 951750]. Retrieved from http://www.eeoc.gov/facts/adaguide.html

Wehman, P. (2001). *Life beyond the classroom: Transition strategies for young people with disabilities* (3rd ed.). Baltimore: Paul H. Brookes Publishing Co.

Wehman, P. (2002). *Individual transition plans: The teacher's curriculum guide for helping youth with special needs*. Austin, TX: PRO-ED.

Wehman, P., Gibson, K., Brooke, V., & Unger, D. (1998). Transition from school to competitive employment: Illustrations of competence for two young women with severe mental retardation. *Focus on Autism & Other Developmental Disabilities, 13*, 130–143.

Wehman, P., & Kregel, J. (Eds.). (1998). *More than a job: Securing satisfying careers for people with disabilities*. Baltimore: Paul H. Brookes Publishing Co.

Wehman, P., & Walsh, P. N. (1999). Transition from school to adulthood. In P. Retish, & S. Reiter (Eds.), *Adults with disabilities: International perspectives in the community* (pp. 3–31). Mahwah, NJ: Lawrence Erlbaum Associates.

Wells, I. (1991). Severe learning difficulties in Northern Ireland: Leaving school. *British Journal of Special Education, 18*(2), 63–66.

Whetstone, M., & Browning, P. (2002). Transition: A frame of reference. *Alabama Federation Council for Exceptional Children (AFCEC) Online Journal, 1*(Special Issue). Retrieved from http://www.afcec.org/pubs/journal/vol1/02F_definition1.pdf

Will, M. (1984). *OSERS programming for the transition of youth with disabilities: Bridges from school to working life.* Washington, DC: Office of Special Education and Rehabilitative Services, U.S. Office of Education.

Will, M. (1985). Transition: Linking disabled youth to a productive future. *OSERS News in Print.* Washington, DC: U.S. Department of Education, Office of Special Education and Rehabilitative Services, *1*(1), 1.

Zetlin, A. G., & Turner, J. L. (2002). Transition from adolescence to adulthood: Perspectives of mentally retarded individuals and their families. In J. Blacher & B. L. Baker (Eds.), *The best of AAMR: Families and mental retardation. A collection of notable AAMR journal articles across the 20th century* (pp. 193–201). Washington, DC: American Association on Mental Retardation.

Zhang, D., & Stecker, P. M. (2001). Student involvement in transition planning: Are we there yet? *Education & Training in Mental Retardation & Developmental Disabilities, 36,* 293–303.

43

Work and Employment for People with Developmental Disabilities in Ontario

Judith Sandys

What you will learn:

- The historical development of work-related supports and services for people with developmental disabilities in Ontario
- The current situation for people with developmental disabilities
- Devaluation and the importance of valued social roles
- Operation and funding of work-related supports and services
- Work options for people with developmental disabilities
- Non-work alternatives

Note: *Words related to employment and disability, as well as acronyms used throughout this chapter, are explained in the Special Terms section following the Summary.*

Work is an important and central focus in the lives of most adults. When most of us talk about going to work, we are talking about engaging in an activity for which we expect to receive pay. Certainly, there are activities that involve a great deal of effort (perhaps even more than our paid work) that we are not paid for — caring for children, cooking, taking care of our garden, or cleaning the garage, to name a few. In fact, other people may be paid to do the very same things that we do without pay (and vice versa). Almost any activity may be "paid work" for some people and unpaid for others. Therefore it is

the element of pay, rather than the nature of the activity itself, that defines something as belonging in the "work-as-employment" category.

Of course, some people may not work, either because they are unable to find work or because there are other priorities in their lives at a particular moment. They may, for example, be involved in caring for children or other relatives, or may choose to focus on volunteer community service or particular creative pursuits. It is certainly possible to have a fulfilling life without engaging in paid work. Most of the time in today's society, however, people expect and are expected to work for much of their adult lives.

Needless to say, we work to earn money to buy the things we need and want; paid employment represents the major way that resources are distributed

Box 1

Good work:

- *is interesting and challenging*
- *makes us feel that we are contributing*
- *fills our days with meaningful activities*
- *pays a fair wage*
- *is consistent with our interests and skills*
- *is valued by society*
- *connects us to our community*
- *enables us to interact with others*
- *provides opportunities to develop relationships*
- *enhances our existing skills and lets us develop new ones*
- *promotes enhanced levels of responsibility*

in our society. The need for money is not the only (or always the most important) reason why we work or why we choose to do a specific kind of work. In addition to the money it generates, work serves a number of other functions. The work we do influences how we think about ourselves and how others think about us. When we meet someone new, "What do you do?" is usually one of the first questions that we pose. The work we do, or hope to do, influences how we spend our days (or nights), who we interact with, what we learn, and many other things.

Not all jobs have these positive outcomes. Many people, with and without disabilities, may find themselves trapped in jobs that pay poorly and/or that provide little satisfaction. People may find their working conditions dull and unchallenging, harsh and exploitive, or isolating. There are times when having no job at all may be preferable to having a terrible job. However, most people find working, even in less than ideal conditions, preferable to not working at all. Further, even if they cannot always achieve it, most people seek work that provides satisfactions beyond the pay they receive.

If work plays such an important role in our own lives, it is logical to assume that it plays an equally important role in the lives of most adults with devel-

opmental disabilities. Why would one presume that people with developmental disabilities do not need interesting and challenging work, opportunities to develop relationships, a chance to make a difference, the respect of the broader society and, ideally, the resources that work generates? Not surprisingly, programs for people with developmental disabilities have often included some focus on work, and are often referred to as vocational services. We refer to them here as work-related supports and services.

The Historical Developments of Work-Related Supports and Services for People with Developmental Disabilities in Ontario

In the mid 1800s, large institutions for people with developmental disabilities were built in Ontario (see Little, 1993; Sandys, 2008; Simmons, 1982). There were many reasons why people were admitted to institutions. Sometimes it was because there was no one in the community who could or would provide them with the care they needed. Other times it was because their behaviour was considered delinquent, dangerous, or immoral. Whatever the reason, a stated purpose of early institutions was to educate and train people with developmental disabilities so that they could be returned to the community as productive members. It was commonly believed that this training could help some people learn the skills needed to function in the community.

The earliest work programs for those with developmental disabilities started within these institutions. Sometimes the "inmates" performed various maintenance tasks or took care of residents with more severe disabilities, probably to reduce the cost of running the institution. However, work was also believed to be of therapeutic value; it was hoped that these work activities would prepare some people for subsequent employment in the community. It was the desire to provide more training in a wider range of work tasks that led to the development of workshops within institutions.

Work oriented programs for people with developmental disabilities outside of institutions did not appear in Ontario until the 1950s. At that time, parents were forming themselves into organizations to promote the development of community based services for their sons and daughters. One of the earliest kinds of programs started by "local associations" was sheltered workshops, where people with developmental disabilities could engage in various kinds of work activities in a protected environment. Beginning in the 1950s, advocacy by parent groups and some professionals increased pressure to close or phase down institutions. Developing sheltered workshops in the community was seen as a necessary part of this deinstitutionalization thrust.

Sheltered workshops were usually developed with two goals in mind. One of these was to train people so that they could acquire the skills needed to work in the community. The other was to provide long term work activities in a protected environment for the people who, it was thought, could not be prepared for community employment. Many sheltered workshops tried to do both of these things at the same time. However, some organizations emphasized one goal over another, or had separate programs for each of them. For example, an organization might have a separate place where people would come for a period of time so that they could receive training. At the end of that time, if they were considered employable, people would be helped to find a job. Otherwise, they would go to a sheltered workshop on a long term basis. In fact, only a small proportion of the people admitted to sheltered workshops moved on to competitive employment. Over the next decades, and until recently, workshops continued to increase in number and size.

By the 1970s, people were becoming quite critical of workshops, which were not successful at training people for competitive employment. The work that people did in workshops most often consisted of simple, dull, and repetitive tasks for which they earned very little money. There were efforts during this period to improve workshops. Two people, both Americans, who had a significant impact were Michael Gold (1980) and Tom Bellamy (see for example, Bellamy, Peterson, & Close, 1975). Both demonstrated that when work activities were broken down into small, manageable steps with systematic teaching strategies, people with major developmental disabilities could learn very complex assembly tasks. Still another American, John DuRand, suggested that introducing a small number of non-disabled "model workers" into the workshop would improve the behaviour of the disabled workers and the overall productivity of the workshop. He called these settings *affirmative industries* (DuRand & DuRand, 1978). In other instances, workshops began to disperse by developing enclaves, work stations, or mobile work crews, in which a number of disabled workers and a supervisor worked in the community or a regular industry. Many more organizations began job placement programs to find employment for the people whom the workshops had trained.

All these developments had a significant impact in Ontario, where efforts were made to incorporate many of these new elements into existing sheltered workshops. The different components were perceived as a part of a continuum through which individuals could progress on their route to competitive employment (DuRand & Neufeldt, 1980; Murphy & Rogan, 1995). Nevertheless, criticisms of sheltered workshops continued as there was no evidence that workshops were doing significantly better in terms of preparing people for employment. Perhaps even more important were changing philosophies. An ever-increasing emphasis on community participation and inclusion (see, for example, Taylor, Biklen, & Knoll, 1987), and a heightened appreciation of the need to promote valued social roles for people with developmental disabilities (Osburn, 1998; Wolfensberger, 1980, 1992) led people to question traditional service models. As a result, many came to consider all segregated settings, including sheltered workshops, unacceptable (see for example, McCallum, 1989; Murphy & Rogan, 1995).

If the theme of the 1970s and early 1980s was to try to make workshops better, the central theme of the mid-1980s and the 1990s was on developing work/employment-related alternatives to sheltered workshops. A major development, beginning in Ontario in the early 1980s and continuing today, has been the development of supported employment. Along with this have been efforts to enable people with developmental disabilities to become self-employed, either individually, or as part of a group.

The Current Situation for People with Developmental Disabilities

Most people with developmental disabilities are not working in paid employment. In Canada, the rate of employment for people with developmental disabilities is said to be 25.5% as compared to 75.5% for people without disabilities, with little change occurring in recent years (Canadian Association for Community Living, 2009; Crawford, 2008). Of course, since these statistics are based on the number of people working or "available to work" (excluding those who are perceived as unable to work), the actual proportion of people with developmental disabilities is much higher. Those who are employed are most often people with mild developmental disabilities, and even for this group, employment is most often in part time, low paying jobs. For people with significant developmental disabilities, lack of paid work is the norm.

Nonetheless, some people with significant developmental disabilities are being supported to work in the community through supported employment programs or with individual support. Some may engage in work activities that do not pay a regular wage or that do not pay anything at all. Such work may happen in the context of segregated settings like sheltered workshops or worker co-ops. Other people may engage in volunteer work or other activity in a regular workplace without pay. A seemingly increasing number of people are not working at all, either on a paid or unpaid basis. Sometimes this is a temporary situation as, for example, when someone is involved in an educational program. But in other situations, people are involved on a long term basis in various kinds of day programs that have a largely recreational focus. The extent to which this is a positive development is highly questionable.

By March 31, 2009, the government of Ontario had closed the last of the government operated facilities for people with developmental disabilities. As a result, more and more people with developmental disabilities are living in the community.

Nevertheless, many experience life conditions that most of us would consider unacceptable for ourselves. People with developmental disabilities are often poor, have little control over their lives, are isolated, have few opportunities for growth and development or meaningful activity, and continue to encounter discrimination and exclusion on a regular basis.

Devaluation and the Importance of Valued Social Roles

The most significant reason that people with developmental disabilities are so often denied the opportunity to work is that, as a group, such individuals are devalued within our society. Devaluation is to attach negative value to a person or thing (see for example, Wolfensberger, 2000). Because our society values characteristics such as intelligence, productivity, independence, beauty, wealth, and others, those who are perceived to lack these characteristics often experience poor treatment. Societal stereotypes develop that reflect and reinforce this devaluation. Thus, people with developmental disabilities are often perceived as childlike, as objects of pity or ridicule, as a burden or a menace, and are treated accordingly.

The devaluation of people with developmental disabilities sets of a negative spiral that entrenches and increases the devaluation, and decreases the likelihood of them becoming working adults. For example, devaluation results in other people having low expectations of people with developmental disabilities, which results in poor schooling and fewer opportunities to learn about potential jobs or to acquire the skills and behaviours required for these. All of this serves to reinforce the existing stereotypes.

Wolfensberger (1998) contended that one strategy for addressing devaluation is to enable devalued people to have valued social roles. Each of us has many roles and for most of us, many of these roles are positive — these include some roles that we do not choose, such as being a loved child or sibling. However, many are roles that we move into, perhaps with the encouragement and support of others. These roles may include being a spouse or a parent, an athlete or musician, a homeowner, a student, a friend, and — very often — a worker. Of course, being a worker is not the only valued role, but it is a central one for most adults. Our society expects adults to work and does not treat kindly those who do not.

To enable a person with a developmental disability to have the valued role of worker, we need to be providing the supports that will enable that person to acquire the work and social skills associated with being a worker. At the same time, we need to provide support that will enable the person to be perceived positively, perhaps providing coaching around dress, grooming and workplace behaviour. Just as devaluation sets off a negative spiral, a valued social role creates a positive one. A person who is working is likely to be perceived as more competent. Others are likely to have higher expectations and, consequently, to create opportunities to acquire more skills.

People with developmental disabilities do have cognitive impairments and some may not be able to work, at least not in a paying job. However, much of the societal rejection and exclusion that people with developmental disabilities experience relates far more to societal devaluation than to the impairment itself. Supporting a person with a developmental disability to have the valued social role of being a worker can have a profound impact on that person's life.

Operation and Funding of Work-Related Supports and Services

How work-related supports and services operate

In Ontario, work-related supports and services for people with developmental disabilities are operated by many different kinds of organizations, including a variety of community agencies. Every Association for Community Living (ACL) in Ontario offers work-related supports and services. Other community agencies that provide such programs include some that 1) offer a range of services to people with developmental disabilities; 2) offer only work-related supports and services to people with developmental disabilities; and 3) offer such programs to people with a wide range of disabilities (i.e., not only to people with developmental disabilities).

In addition, some individuals with developmental disabilities may access work-related supports on an individual basis, outside the context of organized services and programs, using an individualized funding model. In this model, the funding is attached to the person rather than to a specific program. The person, ideally with the involvement of family and/or other supportive friends and relatives, decides on the nature and type of support that is required and "purchases" it from whoever is considered most appropriate. Individualized funding approaches have been used to provide a wide range of supports to people with developmental disabilities (Lord, 1998; Lord & Hutchison, 2008), including work-related support, but most typically supported or self-employment.

Although some organizations may operate only one kind of work-related program, it is more typical for organizations to offer a range of services, either as a series of separate programs, or within a broader structure. Thus, there are many ACLs that operate a sheltered workshop, a supported employment program, some non-work alternative day programs, and perhaps a co-op in development. People may attend more than one program, each on a part-time basis.

How work-related supports and services are funded

In Canada, labour issues are a national responsibility and federal funds do provide some support for employment programs for people with developmental disabilities through federal-provincial agreements, including Labour Market Agreements and Labour Market Development Agreements (Crawford, 2004, 2006). Such agreements may provide direct funding to employment programs that assist people with disabilities to find and keep jobs. In other instances, federal funds are allocated to the provinces, which then use them towards the costs of employment programs for people with disabilities.

One federally funded department, Human Resources and Skills Development Canada (HRSDC), provides funding for employment supports for people with disabilities through the

Opportunities Fund. Working in partnership with organizations and employers, the Opportunities Fund supports a range of activities to encourage employers to hire people with disabilities, to enable people with disabilities to enhance their skills, to provide supports needed for workforce participation, and to support people with disabilities who wish to start their own businesses. The Opportunities Fund is provided to programs directed at people with disabilities who are unemployed and not eligible for Employment Insurance Benefits. HRSDC also funds Targeted Wage Subsidies through which an employer who hires a person with a disability can receive a substantial subsidy for up to a year and a half (although more typically 26 to 30 weeks).

Within Ontario, the Ontario Disability Support Program (ODSP) provides income support and funds employment supports directed at enabling people with disabilities to become and remain employed. This latter part of the program is referred to as Ontario Disability Support Program-Employment Supports (ODSP-ES). ODSP-ES provides individualized funding so that individuals with disabilities can access the employment-related supports and services that they require. In order to receive these funds, individuals must first have an approved plan that outlines the needed services. People may use their allocated funds to "buy" the approved services they need from whomever they wish, including private providers, the local ACL, or other agencies. ODSP-ES funding is intended to support a range of activities, including planning and preparing for a job; training; technical aids; interpreter, reader, note taker or intervener; job coaching and searching; and assistance with transportation during the job training phase. ODSP-ES is designed for people who are presumed to be able to be gainfully employed if provided with these kinds of support. It is designed to be a relatively short term program that will enable people to be employed, independent of paid support. When first implemented, funding was limited to 6 months, but more recently has been extended to 12 months. In some instances funding has continued longer.

The Ontario Ministry of Community and Social Services (MCSS) funds a range of programs for people with intellectual disabilities, including work-related supports and services. In recent years, there has been a significant decline in the number of sheltered workshops; those that remained at the time this book was printed were funded under the *Services and Supports to Promote Social Inclusion of Persons with Developmental Disabilities Act, 2008*, generally referred to as the Social Inclusion Act. Some supported employment programs may still be funded in whole or in part through the DSA. MCSS also provides funding, through the PASSPORTs program, to assist young adults with developmental disabilities to transition from school to the community. While the funding does not have an explicit employment preparation or support focus, it may be used to that end.

In addition to funding provided through the provincial and federal governments, organizations for people with disabilities have always sought out funding from a variety of private sources, including the United Way, foundations, donations, and fundraising events. Some funds may be used to support short term pilot projects, others to support ongoing activities.

Each of these funding sources has its own eligibility criteria and application process, creating a complex and confusing situation for agencies and individuals. A great many organizations are funded through a combination of these various sources as they seek to find the funds necessary to meet the needs of the people they are supporting.

Work Options for People with Developmental Disabilities

Segregated work programs

Until recently, the most common type of work-related program for people with developmental disabilities in Ontario was the sheltered workshop. Even today there are many people remaining in these types of settings, although the programs may be called by another name — affirmative business, social purpose enterprise, or worker co-op for example.

Whatever they are called, these are all settings in

which people with developmental (and sometimes other) disabilities are brought together to engage in work and related activities. The underlying, often unstated, assumption in such segregated settings is that many people with developmental disabilities are unable to work in the community, at least until they have been "trained," and perhaps never. (As we will see later, others have challenged this assumption.) The primary focus of sheltered workshops is (or should be) work, although many engage in various kinds of training. This training often, but not always, has some relationship to work, such as providing people with skills that will enhance their work capacity. Some kinds of training include: work skills (e.g., how to operate a particular kind of machinery); academic skills (e.g., literacy & numeracy); community skills (e.g., how to use public transit), and social/behavioural skills (e.g., communication).

In general, the majority of the work in sheltered workshops is done on site, though some may also involve people working in settings outside the workshop (e.g., mobile work crews). The most typical kind of work undertaken has been packaging and assembly, but can also include such things as: collating, stuffing envelopes, labelling, mailing, woodworking, printing, janitorial work, clerical work, crafts, ceramics, sewing, and recycling. Most often, workshops get contracts from regular businesses to do certain jobs. Because workshops are not considered "real" places of work, participants do not have the legal status of "employee" and are not covered by minimum wage legislation. Some people feel that some businesses take advantage of sheltered workshops by paying rates that are unrealistically low. The workshops may accept this work since even low paying work is better than none. It is worth noting, however, that there are some sheltered settings where people do engage in work that is challenging and may be paid more than one typically receives in such a setting. For example, there is an "affirmative industry" in which people manufacture a variety of wood products, including lawn furniture, which is sold through a large and popular store in the community.

As noted earlier, some workshops have seen their role as providing long term sheltered employment to

Box 2: Robert

Robert has been attending the sheltered workshop for many years. He has many friends there and enjoys the work. The major work activity at this workshop is packaging. The shop has a number of different kinds of heat sealing machines — blister packaging, shrink and vacuum packaging. Robert gets great satisfaction out of working on these machines and is known to be a safe and reliable worker. The staff of the workshop are encouraging Robert to get a job through the supported employment program, but Robert doesn't really want to. He has friends who are working and most of them only work a few hours a week and the work they do does not always sound very interesting. Some of them have lost their jobs a number of times and some of them say that other people are not very nice to them. Robert has heard that they are going to close this workshop and he is worried about what will happen to him.

some, if not all, people who attend. However, some provide a training environment in which people may also engage primarily in work activities, but the expectation is that after a certain period of time, they will leave to work elsewhere. Almost invariably, the goal is that they will be able to get a job. If this is not feasible, then they will be referred to another program, often another kind of training program, or a long term sheltered workshop. The potential advantage of a training focussed program is that it may enable the program to make decisions based on the training needs of the person rather than the production needs of the program, thereby providing more individualized, specialized training in particular skills. For some people with disabilities, an environment that is defined as a training environment may be more acceptable, since it carries with it the hope of something better at the end. For the most part, though, this "readiness" model does not seem very effective for people with developmental disabilities. There are many people with developmental (and other) disabilities who move from one segregated training environment to another, never achieving that elusive "real" job.

Some segregated work programs may use community placements for assessment and training pur-

Box 3: Michael

Michael's first job was working part time at a garden centre. He then found a job working 10 to 15 hours a week with Mr. Grocer, a job he has now held for seven years. A member of his support group recently connected him to a stockbroker friend, and Michael finally got to have his own small business. The stockbroker produces a newsletter, which a courier delivers to Michael. He then prepares it for mailing. The first time he did this job, he found an important error in the newsletter mailing list, which was corrected before the mailing went out.

Source: Excerpted from Kappel, In Lord (1998, p. xiv).

poses. People may be placed in community settings for short (or not so short) periods of time to help determine their interests and abilities, or to learn particular skills. Although this has merit, it also has limitations. Employers often do not have the same expectations when people are placed for only a short period of time, and so the assessment may not provide an accurate reflection of how the individual will perform in a real job. Further, moving from one work setting to another is likely to be stressful for many people with disabilities; most people, disabled or not, find adjusting to a new work setting somewhat stressful.

Finally, in some workshops, people are involved in purely recreational activities during part of the regular workshop day (e.g., going swimming once a week). The appropriateness of this is questionable. Other criticisms of sheltered workshops include:

1. The work in sheltered workshops is most often simple, repetitive work (although there are some exceptions to this).
2. People in workshops almost always receive very little pay.
3. People in workshops have little choice — either about the people with whom they work or about the kind of work they do.
4. In an environment where everyone is disabled, people are likely to have low expectations.
5. In an environment where there are low expectations, people are less likely to learn.
6. All of us learn from the people around us; seg-

regated environments provide fewer opportunities for learning.
7. People in sheltered workshops learn the skills they need to be a sheltered workshop worker, not the skills they need to work in the community.
8. Workshops do not do a good job of enabling people to get jobs.
9. When people with developmental disabilities are kept in sheltered workshops, we give the message that they belong there, rather than in regular work places in the community.
10. As a result of all the above, sheltered workshops create and sustain low expectations and reinforce devalued status. They make it more likely that people with developmental disabilities will be treated poorly within our society.

While these are very real issues, it is important to remember that at this time a good many people with developmental disabilities in Ontario are still attending segregated work programs of one kind or another. For many, workshops provide a place to go each day where they can interact with other people and engage in various kinds of work activities. For most, the workshop is the only place they have ever worked and it is important to them. They define it as their work and like the opportunity to socialize with their friends. For many families, sheltered workshops represent a safe and secure place where their family member is cared for and kept busy. For all these reasons, it is important that efforts to develop alternatives to workshops are well planned and sensitive to the needs of individuals and families.

Despite their inherent limitations, there are "good" (or at least better) workshops and "bad" ones. The better ones ensure that people with developmental disabilities are treated with dignity and respect. They try to find work that is interesting, challenging, and that pays as much as possible. They continue to look for ways to improve the work environment. They also strive to enable people to move out of workshop settings, and are often involved in developing new and better ways of supporting people to work in the community.

As has been noted, workshops have very much fallen out of favour, and many ACLs and other organizations have closed their sheltered workshops or converted them into other kinds of programs. For those who have long advocated for the closure of sheltered workshops, this would seem to be good news. However, some of the alternatives that have been developed do not always appear to be very different or to be an improvement.

Self-employment

Another service model that is currently receiving a considerable degree of attention is self-employment (Canadian Association for Community Living, 1996; Lemon & Lemon, 2003). Self-employment refers to a situation where a person is not employed by someone, but works for her/himself. This might mean that the person is an independent contractor doing specific tasks for someone else in return for pay, or that the person actually has her/his own business and regularly sells a product or service. Another type of self-employment that has emerged in Ontario is the worker co-op, where a group of people jointly own and manage their own business (see, for example, Lemon & Lemon, 2003). Some of the kinds of self-employment situations in which people with developmental disabilities have engaged include: refurbishing nuts and bolts; catering; baking; document processing; packaging and assembly; cleaning and maintenance; recycling, salvage; pet grooming and dog walking; restaurant; and mailing service.

Self-employment has been on the rise in our society for some time. This growth reflects changes in the labour market, a response to downsizing, contracting out, layoffs, and other factors (HRDC, 2000). Thus, it is not surprising that it would be considered as a possible model for people with developmental disabilities. At the same time, we have a context in which the very real shortcomings of sheltered workshops have been identified, and the frustrations that many service providers have encountered in their efforts to implement supported employment programs. If sheltered workshops are outdated and supported employment is just too challenging, what other options are there? Self-employment seems an appealing concept for some people.

Self-employment may also provide greater stability and avoid the ups and downs of the labour market and the insensitivities encountered in some workplaces. Those who promote this model note that, within our society, having one's own business is a valued social role that commands some respect; therefore it is likely to have a positive impact on an individual's status and self-esteem. They suggest that self-employment maximizes choice and self-determination and enables people to earn more money. Adding to this attractiveness is the fact that self-employment may be perceived to be a relatively low cost option.

It is possible that this view of self-employment is somewhat romanticized. The study by HRDC (2000) presented a more realistic view of self-employment drawing on the actual accounts of people who have chosen self-employment. Though this study did not focus on people with disabilities, the findings are most certainly relevant. The study suggests that self-employment is more likely to have positive outcomes for managers, professionals, and white collar workers, and less chance of success with people with fewer skills (and less access to capital). Lack of benefits, isolation, lack of training opportunities, and negative attitudes of others were some of the disadvantages cited. The study does not suggest that self-employment outcomes are always negative, but it does identify some of the challenges inherent in making it successful, such as personality factors, expectations, job requirements (niche markets, advanced technologies), skills, and access to needed business training.

There are relatively little data available on the outcomes of self-employment for people with developmental disabilities. There is some evidence that the level of satisfaction of those involved is very high, and that people take pride in being self-employed (Neufeldt, Sandys, Fuchs, & Logan, 2000; Sandys, 1999a; Smith, Wilson, Webber, & Graffam, 2004). Dale (2002) noted that the people in a study reported were somewhat more stable in their employment situation, compared to general employment. These same studies suggest that people in self-employment tend to work fewer hours and earn less than those in supported employment programs.

There are some risks associated with self-employment. When a person has a business, the amount of money earned depends on the success of the business. The person may earn a great deal, a modest amount, very little, or nothing at all. The person may end up with less money than he/she began with. Nothing prevents an entrepreneur from operating at a loss. To date, it seems that people with developmental disabilities who are self-employed tend to generate very limited amounts of money, often only marginally more than they earned in the workshop and certainly less, on average, than those who are working in the community through supported employment programs. Also, since they are generating income through self-employment, they are not covered by minimum wage legislation. In one particularly egregious example, co-op workers received no pay for many months while the co-op manager, hired to provide support, and the person who was hired to get contracts for the co-op did receive their regular salary.

A number of co-ops have been developed by ACLs; often, the contracts held by the sheltered workshop have been turned over to a small group of workshop participants. Not surprisingly, some of these workshops-turned-co-ops have shown an increase in per person earnings, likely because the members of the co-op were selected from among the best workers, with the others being directed to the non-vocational options.

In these situations, the work people do through self-employment is most likely to be similar to what they did in the sheltered workshop. Almost invariably, people work alone and risk being very isolated, or work with other people with disabilities in small (or not so small) segregated settings. In many instances, people with developmental disabilities who are self-employed (whether on their own or as part of a co-op) work a very limited number of hours. A pilot study of developing co-ops in Ontario (Sandys, 1999b) found that these tended to be very closely tied to the sheltered workshop, so that in reality people had little choice over such things as the nature of the work to be done, the pricing of contracts, how the work was to be done, or the people with whom they worked. While there may be an illusion created that co-op members are "in charge," in fact, the range of decisions to be made may be very small as compared to a typical business.

Starting a business — even a small one — is a challenge for anyone. Although some new businesses prosper, many do not. Few business enterprises can escape the impact of hard economic times. Nonetheless, being self-employed is something that many people do find appealing, and one would not want to deny this opportunity to people with developmental disabilities. The extent to which this is a realistic option for many people with developmental disabilities remains, at this writing, an open question.

Supported employment

There are certainly some people with developmental disabilities who are able to get and keep a job with relatively little extra support. However, such individuals tend to move quickly away from the service system. By and large the focus of attention of most organizations is on those who need at least some support on an ongoing basis.

In the early 1980s, a new program model arrived on the scene in Ontario that drew on experiences in the US, and most notably the work of Paul Wehman. Supported employment provided a new way of thinking about and responding to the issue of employment for people with developmental disabilities. The Ontario MCSS (1990) defined supported employment as "paid employment in an integrated, competitive work setting where on-going, individualized training and support is provided to a person with a disability" (p. 5).

As we have noted, workshops have tried to train people and, when they are considered "ready," to find jobs for them. Supported employment programs work in reverse. They help a person find a job and then they provide the training and support that is necessary to ensure success. Instead of a train-then-place approach, they use a place-then-train-and-support approach. The underlying assumption of supported employment programs is that people with developmental disabilities can work successfully if they are provided with the appropriate amount and type of support. Supported employment was and is more than simply a new strategy for preparing people for the world of work. It reflects a fundamental change in philosophy. It says that the

Box 4: Sarah

Sarah was assisted to get a job through the supported employment program attached to the sheltered workshop she was attending. She works in a medical laboratory four mornings a week and is paid slightly more than minimum wage. She performs a number of simple tasks preparing supplies required by the technicians including, for example, putting coloured caps on tubes, cutting gauze to specified lengths, and cutting tips off paper cones. Sarah exhibits a number of disruptive behaviours including "faking seizures" and her employer has had to work closely with the staff of the supported employment program to develop strategies for dealing with these. Sarah's supervisor says that Sarah has improved greatly and that she has found working with her very rewarding. The supervisor thinks that having Sarah work there has been good for everyone. The work that Sarah does contributes to overall efficiency by freeing up the laboratory technologists for more complex tasks. However, beyond this, the supervisor comments: "People look out for each other now. We're more of a team."

Adapted from Sandys (1993).

opportunity to work in the community should be widely available to people with developmental disabilities and that the best place to learn to work in the community is in the community.

Supported employment programs have enabled people with developmental disabilities to work in a wide variety of settings, including offices, factories, hospitals, restaurants, car dealerships, laboratories, schools, colleges and universities. The jobs are as varied as the settings and include, for example: clerical work; food preparation, food serving; maintenance, janitorial; manufacturing, packaging, and assembly; laundry; mail room, internal mail delivery; shipping and receiving; document assembly; assistant in medical laboratory; and car detailing.

There are no reliable data available about the number of people with developmental disabilities in Ontario, but in recent years there seems to have been a levelling off of interest in the supported employment model. While we will explore some of the reasons why this may be in a later section, it is important to emphasize that this is not the case elsewhere. Jenaro,

Mank, Bottomley, Doose, and Tuckerman (2002) discussed supported employment in the international context and noted that it exists in places as diverse as Peru, Zambia, Spain, Germany, England, and Australia. Wehman, Revell, and Kregel (1998) titled their article "Supported Employment: A Decade of Rapid Growth and Impact." The existence of American Association for Persons in Supported Employment (AAPSE) with chapters in most states and the Canadian Association for Supported Employment (CASE) with a number of provincial organizations, and the rich literature on supported employment, primarily from the United States, all speak to a continuing lively interest in supported employment. The rich and vibrant literature on supported employment (see for example, Beyer, Brown, Akandi, & Rapley, 2010; Cramm, Finkenflugel, Kuijsten, & van Exel, 2009; Grant, 2008; Kober & Eggleton, 2005; Migliore, Mank, Grossi, & Rogan, 2007; Wehman, 2006) speaks to the continuing interest in and commitment to supported employment in North America and beyond (see for example, Shearn, Beyer, & Felce, 2000; Stevens & Martin, 1999; Saloviita, 2000).

The supported employment process

Much has been written about the supported employment process. The following brief overview draws on numerous sources including: Callahan & Bradley, 1997; Hagner & DiLeo, 1993; Little, 1993; McLoughlin, Garner, & Callahan, 1987; Sandys, 2002; Wehman & Moon, 1988; Wehman, Sale, & Parent, 1992.

A number of issues must be addressed for an individual with a developmental disability to succeed in the workplace. In order to find a suitable position, the support worker must have a very thorough understanding of the interests, characteristics, and talents of the individual for whom a job is being sought. What kinds of environments will the person be most comfortable in? How does the individual learn? What kinds of supports are likely to be required? What adaptations? Generally this means spending a considerable amount of time with the individual and, often, with those who know him or her best.

As well as information about the individual, the

Box 5: Harry

Harry has been working at a pizza restaurant for three years. He works every day from 9:00 a.m. to 2:30 p.m., although he occasionally works extra hours. His responsibilities include the morning maintenance tasks: sweeping and mopping the front lobby, cleaning the bathrooms, vacuuming the carpets, and oiling the aluminum frames. As well, he sets up the dish room for lunch, washes and dries dishes through the lunch period, and does any other cleaning that is required before he leaves.

Harry was placed in this job through a supported employment program (SEP). When he first began, the restaurant paid a sum of money (less than the equivalent of minimum wage) to the program which, in turn, paid Harry. However, about a year ago the decision was made to pay Harry directly and he began getting minimum wage. He has had two raises since then. When Harry started working, the SEP support worker would come around frequently. This has diminished over time to the point where the worker telephones about once per month or less to check how things are going.

Source: Sandys (1993).

support worker needs to know about the kinds of jobs that might be available. Since we know that many jobs may never be advertised, it is helpful to look at any personal contacts the individual may have through family or friends as a strategy for identifying potential jobs. A high degree of creativity is required in the job finding process. Often, support workers work with employers to "carve" out a job suitable for a particular individual. While this may involve some redistribution of work tasks within a particular setting, it can result in a job that is tailor-made to fit the supported employee's needs at the same time as it meets the employer's needs very effectively (e.g., Sarah's job in Box 4).

Once a suitable job has been located, the supported employment staff will be available to provide a range of supports to the supported employee and to the work site. In the early days of supported employment, it was assumed that the support worker would provide on-site training and support to the individual, intensively at first, and phasing out their involvement as the person learned the required skills and adapted to the workplace. In more recent years, it has been recognized that success depends, in large measure, on the support that is provided to the individual by the workplace. As much as possible, the goal is for the supported employee to be a regular employee, with supervision, training and support provided by the employer and co-workers. The term natural support (Nisbet, 1992; West, Kregel, Hernandez, & Hock, 1997) is often used to

refer to this kind of support — support that is generated "naturally" by the work place, as distinguished from the external support provided and paid for by the service agency.

The emphasis on natural support has sometimes been interpreted to mean that support workers did not need to provide much in the way of services. We now know that the support worker has a key role to play in providing support to the workplace so that it can effectively meet the needs of the supported employee. Employers may need assistance in designing modifications or job adaptations. Supervisors and co-workers may be quite willing to provide direction, mentoring, and other supports to the employee, but may not always know how to go about doing this. Especially at the outset, but often on an ongoing basis, the support worker can play a critically important role as facilitator, supporter, problem-solver, and coach.

Success in the workplace does not only depend on the individual's ability to acquire specific work skills, but also in learning non-work routines. For example, they may require assistance regarding appropriate grooming and dress, development of appropriate behaviours and social skills, buying lunch at the cafeteria, using the time clock, or travelling to work by public transit.

The support worker must continue to monitor the situation to ensure that the individual is paid equitably for the work done, and to deal with any concerns that arise. As well, the support worker, in collaboration with the employer, must continue to engage in a process of "job-building" to ensure that the supported employee's job continues to grow as the individual acquires competencies. In the ideal situation, the supported employee will have opportunities over time to participate in a wider range of tasks, with ever-increasing levels of responsibility and complexity, longer hours of work, and higher rates of pay.

Most people change jobs periodically, usually because they choose to, but sometimes as a result of performance problems or layoffs. The support worker must be available should the supported employee lose the job or decide that a change would be desirable.

How duccessful are supported employment programs?

A number of studies indicate that successful supported employment programs have made a significant difference in the lives of many people with developmental disabilities (Dale, 2002; Moseley, 1988; Pedlar, Lord, & Van Loon, 1989; Wehman & Kregel, 1994). Through supported employment programs, people with developmental disabilities are working in a large variety of settings, doing many different kinds of work. Overall, these people are earning more than they earned in the sheltered workshop, sometimes at rates of pay that are well above the legal minimum wage. These studies have indicated that, in general, people in successful supported employment programs are proud of working in the community (and prefer it to working in a sheltered workshop), enjoy the work they do, and get along well with their co-workers. When Migliore, Mank, Grossi, and Rogan (2007) asked parents, staff and people with disabilities about their preferences, all expressed a preference for work outside the workshop setting.

Kober and Eggleton (2005), comparing the effects of different forms of employment, reported that people with developmental disabilities who were working in a non-sheltered setting were "integrating more with their community," and expressed "greater feeling of social belonging" and "an increased feelings of empowerment/independence" (p. 759). In a similar vein, Cramm, Finkenflugel, Kuijsten, and

van Exel (2009) noted the positive impact of supported employment. They reported that for some respondents the benefits seemed related primarily to the structure that work provided, while for others these related to the opportunity for participation and belonging. However, regardless of the nature of the benefit, the consensus was that supported employment "had a positive effect on the well-being of people with intellectual disabilities" and that respondents "valued supported employment more than their prior work experience" (p. 519).

Employers who have hired people with developmental disabilities usually say that they are good workers: they work hard, learn new skills, are well liked, and are an asset to the workplace. Some employers have observed that when co-workers become involved in supporting a person with a developmental disability, this sometimes carries over to other relationships at work; people may become more supportive of one another — not only supportive of the person with the disability. Finally, many employers take great pride and derive great personal satisfaction from having had such a positive impact on the life of a person with a developmental disability (Sandys, 1999a).

Regardless of many potentially positive outcomes of supported employment, the picture is not entirely rosy. Opportunities to find supported employment jobs are at the mercy of a not always welcoming labour market. Employers may not be willing to hire people with developmental disabilities or, if they do, may give them only dull, poor paying, part time jobs. Social inclusion is likely not to be as high as for co-workers (Fillary & Perneice, 2006). Supported employees may be seen by employers and co-workers as child-like and in need of being taken care of, rather than as a colleague (Sandys, 1999a).

It is clear that supported employment programs have not had the results that many people expected (Mank, 1994). When supported employment programs first began, there was a feeling that this new approach would help to find community employment for many people with developmental disabilities and that, as a result, many sheltered workshops would close. Sadly, this has not happened. It is hard to know exactly why. Certainly, fluctuating economic conditions has been one factor. During times of economic slowdown, many supported employees lose their jobs, and finding new jobs for people with developmental disabilities is much more difficult.

Another factor has been that we have not always found people "good" jobs. Some so-called supported employment jobs do not provide a real wage (or perhaps anything at all). Some involve people in work activities far worse than what they had done in the sheltered workshop. Some people work in very isolated situations with no opportunities to interact with anyone, disabled or not. Or they work on only a very part-time basis, perhaps a few hours a week, leaving many empty hours with nothing to do. Even when people do have good jobs and are making a real contribution to the work, employers and co-workers may treat them as though they are children. Sometimes, supported employment programs have not provided enough — or perhaps the right kind of — support. Also, well-intentioned employers may not know how to deal with the challenges that the disabled individual presents. They may become discouraged when positive changes in behaviour or productivity are not forthcoming.

Undoubtedly, uncertain funding for supported employment has impeded its development in Ontario. While funding through ODSP-ES is certainly positive, it may have increased the tendency to draw a line between those considered to have the potential to become employed and those who do not. In order to receive funding through ODSP-ES, an individual must develop, and have approved, an employment plan, a process that can be quite long and complicated. When first implemented, job support was only available through ODSP-ES for a maximum of six months; however, it can now be extended to a year. (Some organizations appear to have been able to negotiate for a second year for some individuals, but it is not clear how frequently this occurs.)

A study reported by Dale (2002) noted that in areas serving primarily people with developmental disabilities (as compared to those serving people with a range of disabilities) there were "lower levels of individuals achieving independence on the job and much higher levels of support needs" (p. 27). This study also noted that people are more likely to maintain

their jobs when supports are not limited. The time limitations on the length of time a person may be provided with support through ODSP is a significant disincentive to involving people with developmental disabilities, since many are likely to require support on a continuing, rather than a time limited basis.

All these factors together have, for at least some people, taken the "shine" off supported employment. Some organizations and staff who have worked very hard finding jobs for people with developmental disabilities have become discouraged and have begun to question whether supported employment really "works." We have been unprepared for how difficult it can be to enable people, some with significant degrees of impairment, and many who have spent years and years in segregated workshops, to work in the community. Perhaps we have tended to give up too easily when things have not worked out as we had hoped. We need to remember that even the most positive program model will not work well if we do not implement it well. We know that supported employment has the potential to work very well for many people. The challenge is to make it work well for many more.

Payment for work

Some people with developmental disabilities may work at a significantly slower pace, making it unlikely that they will be hired if the employer must pay the full wage. As a solution, some disability organizations have entered into a contract with the employer so that the employer pays the organization a specified amount for the work done, and then the organization pays the worker. (Workshops have been doing this for some time for work stations and mobile work crews.) Since the individual is not an employee of the organization, that organization need not pay minimum wage. Another "strategy" that has been used is for an employer to hire a person for a portion of the day at minimum wage standards, and then allow the person to remain at the work place for additional hours for "training" purposes. For example, the person may be at the work site for seven hours but only receive pay for four. People with developmental disabilities may also do "volunteer" work, or simply work in a regular place and not be paid.

Without a doubt, these approaches are problematic. At their worst, they may create a situation where a person is not being paid fairly for the work she or he is doing. At another level, they may inadvertently give a message that it is acceptable not to pay a person with a developmental disability. All this notwithstanding, it is interesting to note that, by and large, no one gets upset at the thought of someone working for little or no pay in a workshop or co-op. It is only when the person is working in the community that this becomes an issue. If we accept that some people with developmental disabilities may not be paid, despite ours and their best efforts, would we rather this happen in a segregated environment or in a community setting?

For some people, there may be substantial benefits to working in the community, even without pay. Wolfensberger and Thomas (2009) provided a very thoughtful discussion of many of these, including the opportunity to learn new skills, to develop work habits, or to increase one's stamina. Being seen by others to be working is likely to increase one's status in the eyes of others. Working in the community, even if not paid, creates opportunities to meet new people and to form new relationships. In some situations the combination of how one is perceived, the skills one acquires and the relationships that one develops may, in time, lead to a paying job. But even if it does not, it is hard to think that the person would be better off in a segregated program that is not work focussed and/or that provides little challenge.

Should everybody work?

Ours is a society that values freedom and autonomy. While almost all of us are constrained by factors over which we may have little control, we do make many decisions on a regular basis. We may not get into exactly the college or university program we want to, but we are likely to have a number of choices available to us. We may not get exactly the job we want, but usually we have some control over the kind of work we do. We may have limited resources, but no one tells us where we have to live or with whom we have to live. No one in our society is forced to work — although for most of us there are very powerful incentives to do so.

As we seek to promote positive life experiences for people with developmental disabilities, there has been an increasing emphasis on ensuring that individuals are, to the maximum extent possible, involved in making the decisions that affect their lives, including decisions about whether to work. Given the important role that work plays in our own lives and the impact that working has on all of us, it is important to examine the context in which some people with developmental disabilities choose not to work. Does this constitute an informed and meaningful choice? What are the potential consequences of such a choice?

Why, we may ask, would an individual make a choice that is not in their own best interests? Perhaps such a choice reflects the fact that the work available to developmentally disabled people often does not meet the criterion of "good" work? Enabling people to work at good jobs in the community often requires an enormous amount of energy and skill on the part of the manager. Perhaps we have low expectations about whether or not a person with a developmental disability is able to work. Perhaps we are encouraging people to "choose" those options that are easier for us to provide.

Ramsey (2007), who has developed an approach to planning he calls "Roles based planning," noted that when people with developmental disabilities were simply asked what they wanted to do, they often chose recreational activities. But when they were encouraged to choose among a variety of work activities that would confer a valued role, they were much more likely to choose to work. To a large extent the choices that are available to people, and the choices they make, are shaped by the expectations that others have of them. Of course, we want to demonstrate our respect for people with developmental disabilities by honouring their wishes. But perhaps by not encouraging them to develop a work identity and work ethic, we are limiting their options for a more satisfying and self-determining life in the future.

Full-time or part-time work?

It has become increasingly common for people with developmental disabilities who are working, to be working only on a part-time basis. Sometimes they are working only a few hours a week, or working in several different places, each for a limited amount of time. Sometimes people's time is divided between work (paid or unpaid) and participation in various non-work activities. There are a number of reasons for this. In some instances, a person may need a high level of paid support and there are insufficient funds available to provide it. Other times the employer may not have enough work to provide more than a few hours of employment. Yet another reason is that there is concern about the person losing their disability benefits. These are real and sometimes unavoidable reasons. However, there are other, more questionable, reasons that one hears frequently. One is that the person is not able to work longer hours because of a lack of stamina. Or, we are told, the person "chooses" to work part time.

While there may indeed be situations where it is not possible for a person to work full time, our experience has been that it is, for the most part, a matter of expectations. Most of us work full time and most people with developmental disabilities can do so also. Further, working full time provides many more opportunities for learning new skills, making a contribution, developing relationships, and being seen as a work colleague. There is much informal communication in any workplace that plays an important role in how people get along in that place. When someone is only there for a few hours, they are not likely to have access to this informal network and this further disadvantages them.

Non-Work Alternatives

A section on activities that do not focus on work and employment perhaps appears misplaced in a chapter such as this. However, given that such programs are being developed at an ever more rapid rate than employment programs, a brief discussion is required.

In recent years, there has been a growing trend to developing a range of non-work activities for people with developmental disabilities as an alternative to work. As service providers have felt thwarted in their efforts to promote community employment and self-employment opportunities for people, and as

they have felt the effects of funding cutbacks, many organizations have sought to develop other options that would provide people with an opportunity to participate in activities that, although not necessarily work related, would be meaningful to the individual. In some situations, people are perceived to be too disabled to engage in work in a meaningful way, and so other activities are developed for them. In other situations, people with developmental disabilities indicate that they do not want to work, and service providers feel that this "choice" must be respected. Still another practice is to involve "older" adults with developmental disabilities in leisure activities more typical of retirement, even though they may still be in their 40s and 50s. The programs may be seen as filling a gap when people are working on a very part time basis, or perhaps during periods of unemployment.

Typically, people can access such programs for as much or as little of the day as they wish, and they involve a range of activities (e.g., literacy training, cooking classes, computer classes, art, music, recreational activities, and community outings). Funding for these programs is often quite low and may be provided through developmental services or, in part, through individualized funding that individuals are able to access.

On the positive side, these programs provide an opportunity to socialize and perhaps to learn new skills. They provide some structure to a person's life so that there is something to do each day. They ensure that family members are not responsible for providing support all day, every day. They prevent people from having to hang around all day with nothing to do. Undoubtedly, these are important benefits. However, although some of the individual activities may be quite age appropriate, overall these programs often seem more like day camps than places typical, valued adults are likely to attend. For people who may be able to work, or who are perhaps between jobs, it is hard to see how this kind of program will enhance their chances of finding employment.

As segregated settings, these programs contain all the disadvantages that we noted at the outset in our discussion of sheltered workshops. Whenever we operate segregated programs, we are giving society the message that people with developmental disabilities need to be kept separate and cannot be an integral part of the community. There is an irony in giving out this message — another part of the same organization may be trying to communicate exactly the opposite message through its supported employment program. Perhaps the greatest risk with these programs is that they distract us from focussing on work and employment for people with developmental disabilities. Instead of continuing to seek more effective ways of implementing supported employment programs, to assist more people with meaningful self-employment, trying to develop co-ops that are truly self-managed (and perhaps integrated), and advocating for legislation that will provide ongoing employment support for people who need it, we content ourselves with a renamed and somewhat dressed up segregated day activity program for people with developmental disabilities — and we call it progress.

Summary

In this chapter, we examined the nature and importance of work and discussed the historical development of work-related supports and services in Ontario. We looked at three service models (i.e., sheltered workshops, self-employment, and supported employment), the rationale behind each service model, as well as the associated positive outcomes and challenges experienced by some people. We also discussed the development of non work-related day programs and some of the issues that they present.

All this served to emphasize that there is no one model that is perfect or that can meet the needs of all people with developmental disabilities. Nonetheless, each of us, in whatever setting we find ourselves, can contribute to promoting positive work experiences for the people we support. Undoubtedly, much remains to be done in terms of developing strategies that will enable people with developmental disabilities to have opportunities to participate in work that is integrated, meaningful, challenging and profitable.

For Further Thought and Discussion

1. Compare work situations you have experienced yourself with the work situations of some people with developmental disabilities with whom you are familiar. How are they similar or different?
2. Should sheltered workshops be eliminated? Why or why not?
3. Why do you think the implementation of supported employment programs has proven to be so difficult? Do you think mandatory employment equity would result in more people with developmental disabilities being hired? What are the potential advantages and disadvantages?
4. Is it okay for a person to work in the community and get less than minimum wage? No pay at all?
5. What are your feelings about self-employment? Co-ops? What are the advantages and disadvantages of these approaches as compared to: a) sheltered workshops, and b) supported employment? How might these approaches be made more effective?
6. What should we do when an individual say he or she doesn't want to work?
7. To what extent do existing policies and legislation promote or impede the employment of people with developmental disabilities?
8. Which do you think is a better option: unpaid work, or a non-vocational alternative? Why?
9. With regard to employment, do you think that things are getting better or worse for people with developmental disabilities? What evidence is there for your position?

Special Terms

Many terms are used (not always consistently) to refer to different kinds of work and employment programs. Some of the most typical terms, along with their most common usage, are described below.

Co-operatives: (sometimes inaccurately referred to as worker co-ops). A number of people jointly own the "business" in which they all work. They make decisions jointly and share in the profits or losses of the business. (At least, this is the theory.)

Competitive employment: The individual works

in a regular setting in the community and is paid a regular salary at or above the legal minimum wage.

Enclave: A small group of people with disabilities working as a group within a larger work environment in the community. An example of this is a group of people with developmental disabilities who, with a supervisor, work in a factory where all the other people are not disabled. Most often the individuals involved are paid through the sheltered workshop or vocational program rather than directly by the employer (may also be called a work station).

Individualized funding: Funding is provided to the individual rather than to the program. The individual, often with the support of family and/or relatives and friends, determines her/his goals and uses these funds to purchase needed supports. (Such funds may be used to address a variety of support needs including, but not limited to, employment support.)

Job training program: A program designed to prepare people for competitive employment. It may be conducted within a sheltered workshop, as a standalone segregated program, or within a community environment.

Mobile work crew: A small group of people with disabilities who, generally with a supervisor, work in the community. Unlike a work station or enclave, there may not be other non-disabled workers in the same environment, when the work is being done. Typical examples are crews that clean buildings or bus shelters when there are no other workers around. Most often the individuals involved are paid through the sheltered workshop or vocational program rather than directly by the organization for whom the work is performed.

Non-work alternatives: This is a "catch all" term for a variety of day activity programs for people who are perceived as not wanting, or not being able, to engage in work activities. These activities/day programs may take place in integrated or segregated environments.

Self-employment: The individual does not work for an employer but works as an independent contractor or has her/his own business.

Sheltered workshop: A segregated work program for people with disabilities. May provide job training and/or long term sheltered employment.

Supported employment: The individual works in a regular setting in the community and is paid by the employer. The vocational program provides a support worker or job coach who is available to provide training and support to the individual. The support worker/job coach may also work with the employer and co-workers so that they can provide the supported employee with the required supports. In theory, supported employees are paid at least minimum wage.

Supported self-employment: Same as self-employment, with support provided by a support worker/job coach.

Unpaid work: In some environments, people with developmental disabilities may work without pay, doing the kind of work for which other people in that environment are paid. Where this is a short term situation, it would come under the definition of work experience. At other times it may be referred to (inaccurately) as "volunteer work," although it does not resemble work that is typically done on a volunteer basis.

Work experience: An individual with a disability works in the community in order to gain some knowledge about community work and/or in order that her/his work skills can be assessed. Often part of a job training program. Typically the person is not paid for the work done.

Work station: See *enclave*.

Acronyms used in this chapter

ACL: Association for Community Living

CAP: Canada Assistance Plan

DSA: Developmental Services Act

EAPD: Employability Assistance for Persons with Disabilities

HRSDC: Human Resources and Skills Development Canada

MCSS: (Ontario) Ministry of Community and Social Services

ODSP-ES: Ontario Disability Support Program -Employment Supports

More Resources

Journals:

- Canadian Journal of Rehabilitation
- Disability & Society
- Education and Training in Mental Retardation
- Journal of Rehabilitation
- Journal on Developmental Disabilities
- Journal of Vocational Rehabilitation
- Journal of Applied Research in Intellectual Disabilities
- Journal of Intellectual Disability Research
- Social Role Valorization Journal

Websites:

A web search using the key words: supported employment, self-employment, sheltered workshops, and vocational rehabilitation will yield many sites. Some sites that you may find helpful include the following:

- Canadian Association on Supported Employment
- Canadian Centre for Disability Studies
- Human Resources and Skills Development Canada
- Ontario Ministry of Community and Social Services
- Research and Training Centre (RRTC):
- Virginia Commonwealth University
- The Centre on Human Policy, Syracuse University
- The Office of Disability Issues, Government of Saskatchewan
- *worksupport.com*

Books:

Canadian Association for Community Living. (1996). *A guide to self employment: A creative career choice for persons with an intellectual disability.* North York, ON: Author.

CGA Management Consultants. (1997). *The will to work: An employment related service needs assessment for persons with disabilities in Metropolitan Toronto.* Toronto, ON: Human Resources Development Canada.

Wehman, P., Inge, K. J., Revell, W. G., & Brooke, V. A. (2007). *Real work for real pay: Inclusive employment for people with disabilities.* Baltimore: Paul H. Brooks Publishing Co.

References

Bellamy, T., Peterson, L., & Close, D. (1975). Habilitation of the severely and profoundly handicapped: Illustrations of competence. *Education and Training of the Mentally Retarded, 10,* 174-187.

Beyer, S., Brown, T., Akandi, R., & Rapley, M. (2010). A comparison of quality of life outcomes for people with intellectual disabilities in supported employment, day services and employment enterprises. *Journal of Applied Research in Intellectual Disabilities, 23*(3), 290-295.

Callahan, M. J., & Bradley, G. (1997). *Keys to the workplace: Skills and supports for people with disabilities.* Baltimore: Paul H. Brooks.

Canadian Association for Community Living. (1996). *Everybody's business: Self employment issues and opportunities for people with a disability.* North York, ON: Author.

Canadian Association for Community Living. (2009). *National Report Card 2009: Inclusion of Canadians with intellectual disabilities.* Retrieved from http://www.cacl.ca/english/reportcard.asp

Cramm, J. M., Finkenflügel, H., Kuijsten, R., & van Exel, N. J. A. (2009). How employment support and social integration programmes are viewed by the intellectually disabled. *Journal of Intellectual Disability Research, 53*(6), 512-520.

Crawford, C. (2004). *Improving the odds: Employment disability and public policy programs in Canada.* Toronto, ON: The Roeher Institute.

Crawford, C. (2006). *Tapping into Labour Market Development Agreements to improve the employment prospects of people with intellectual disabilities.* Toronto, ON: The Roeher Institute.

Crawford, C. (2008). *Employment, education and intellectual disability: A statistical snapshot.* Unpublished paper, Roeher Institute, Toronto, ON.

Dale, J. (2002). *Community involvement council — Employment outcomes project.* Tillsonburg,

ON: Community Involvement Council and The Employment Outcomes Steering Committee.

DuRand, J., & DuRand, L. (1978). *The affirmative industry*. St. Paul, MN: Minnesota Diversified Industries.

DuRand, J., & Neufeldt, A. (1980). Comprehensive vocational services. In R. Flynn, & K. Nitsch (Eds.), *Normalization, integration and community services* (pp. 283-298). Baltimore: University Park Press.

Filary, R., & Pernice, R. (2006).Social inclusion in workplaces where people with intellectual disabilities are employed: Implications for supported employment professionals. *International Journal of Rehabilitation Research, 29*(1), 31-36.

Gold, M. (1980). *Try another way: Training manual*. Champagne, IL: Research Press.

Grant, J. (2008). Paid work – A valued social role that is empowering more people with an intellectual disability and providing employers with dedicated employees! *Journal of Intellectual and Developmental Disability Research, 33*(1), 95-97.

Hagner, D., & DiLeo, D. (1993). *Working together: Workplace culture, supported employment and people with disabilities*. Cambridge: Brookline Books.

Human Resources Development Canada. (2000). *Own-account self-employment in Canada: Lessons learned, final report*. Retrieved from http://www11.hrdc-drhc.gc.ca/pls/edd/ OASECTR1.html

Jenaro, C., Mank, D., Bottomley, J., Doose, S., & Tuckerman, P. (2002) Supported employment in the international context: An analysis of processes and outcomes. *Journal of Vocational Rehabilitation, 17*, 5-21.

Kober, R., & Eggleton, I. R. C. (2005). The effect of different types of employment on quality of life. *Journal of Intellectual Disability Research, 49*(10), 756-760.

Lemon, C., & Lemon, J. (2003). Community-based cooperative ventures for adults with intellectual disabilities. *The Canadian Geographer, 47*(4), 414-428.

Little, T. (1993). *Streetwise guide to supported employment*. Toronto, ON: Central Marketing Consulting Services.

Lord, J. (1998). *The Nabors experience: Lessons in building community*. Toronto, ON: Green Dragon Press.

Lord, J., & Hutchison, P. (2008). Individualized funding in Ontario: Report of a provincial study. *Journal on Developmental Disabilities, 14*(2), 44-53.

Mank, D. (1994). The underachievement of supported employment: A call for reinvestment. *Journal of Disability Policy Studies, 5*(2), 1-24.

McCallum, D. (1989). Discrimination of the invisible minority. Paper presented at the 4th Canadian Congress of Rehabilitation, Toronto, ON.

McLoughlin, C., Garner, J., & Callahan, M. (1987). *Getting employed, staying employed*. Baltimore: Paul H. Brookes.

Migliore, A., Mank, D., Grossi, T., & Rogan, P. (2007). Integrated employment or sheltered workshops: Preferences of adults with intellectual disabilities, their families and staff. *Journal of Vocational Rehabilitation, 26*, 5-19.

Moseley, C. R. (1988). Job satisfaction research: Implications for supported employment. *Journal of the Association for Persons with Severe Disabilities, 13*(3), 211-219.

Murphy, S., & Rogan, P. (1995). *Closing the shop: Conversion from sheltered to integrated work*. Baltimore, MD: Paul H. Brookes.

Neufeldt, A., Sandys, J., Fuchs, D., & Logan, M. (2000). Supported and self-directed support initiatives in Canada: An overview of issues. *International Journal of Practical Approaches to Disability, 23*(3), 24-36.

Nisbet, J. (Ed.). (1992). *Natural supports in school, at work, and in the community for people with severe disabilities*. Baltimore: Paul H. Brookes.

Ontario Ministry of Community and Social Services. (1990). *Supported employment provisional guidelines*. Toronto, ON: Author.

Osburn, J. (1998). An overview of social role valorization theory. *The Social Role Valorization Journal, 3*(1), 7-12.

Pedlar, A., Lord, J., & Van Loon, M. (1989). *The process of supported employment and quality of life*. Kitchener, ON: Centre for Research and Education in Human Services.

Ramsey, S. (2007). Roles Based Planning: A thoughtful approach to social inclusion and empowerment. *The Social Role Valorization Journal, 2*(1), 4-12.

Saloviita, T. (2000). Supported employment as a paradigm shift and a cause of legitimation crisis. *Disability & Society, 15*(1), 87-98.

Sandys, J. (1993). "It does my heart good": The perceptions of employers who have hired people with intellectual disabilities through supported employment programs. Unpublished doctoral dissertation, University of Toronto, Toronto, ON.

Sandys, J. (1999a). "It does my heart good": How employers perceive supported employees. In R. J. Flynn, & R. Lemay (Eds.), *A quarter-century of normalization and social role valorization*. Ottawa, ON: University of Ottawa Press.

Sandys, J. (1999b). Worker co-ops for people with intellectual disabilities. Paper presented at the 1999 Annual Conference of the Society for Disability Studies. Toronto, ON: Ryerson University.

Sandys, J. (2002). *Evaluating your supported employment program*. Winnipeg, MB: Network South Enterprises, Inc. (NSEI).

Sandys, J. (2008). *A turning point in history*. Paper presented at the Annual Conference of Community Living Ontario. Toronto, ON: Ryerson University.

Shearn, J., Beyer, S., & Felce, D. (2000). The cost-effectiveness of supported employment for people with severe intellectual disabilities and high support needs: A pilot study. *Journal of Applied Research in Intellectual Disabilities, 13*(1), 29-37.

Simmons, H. (1982). *From asylum to welfare.* Downsview, ON: National Institute on Mental Retardation.

Smith, K., Wilson, C., Webber, L., & Graffam, J. (2004). Employment and intellectual disability: Achieving successful employment outcomes. *International Review of Research in Mental Retardation, 29*, 261-289.

Stevens. P., & Martin, N. (Eds.). (1999). Supporting individuals with intellectual disability and challenging behaviour in integrated work settings: An overview and a model for service provision. *Journal of Intellectual Disability Research, 43*(1), 19-29.

Taylor, S., Biklen, D., & Knoll, J. (Eds.). (1987). *Community integration for people with severe disabilities.* New York: Teachers College Press.

Wehman, P. (2006). Integrated employment: If not now, when? If not us, who? *Research and Practice for Persons with Severe Disabilities, 33*(2), 122-126.

Wehman, P., & Kregel, J. (1994). *At the crossroads: Supported employment ten years later.* Richmond, VG: Commonwealth University.

Wehman, P., & Moon, M. (Eds.). (1988). *Vocational rehabilitation and supported employment.* Baltimore: Paul H. Brookes.

Wehman, P., Revell, G., & Kregel, J. (1998). Supported employment: A decade of rapid growth and impact. *American Rehabilitation, 24*(1), 31-43.

Wehman, P., Sale, M., & Parent, W. (1992). *Supported employment for persons with severe disabilities: From research to practice.* Andover, MA: Andover Medical Publishers.

West, M. D., Kregel, J., Hernandez, A., & Hock, T. (1997). Everybody's doing it: A national study of the use of natural supports in supported employment. *Focus on Autism and Other Developmental Disabilities, 12*(3), 175-181.

Wolfensberger, W. (1980). The definition of normalization: Update, problems, disagreements, and misunderstandings. In R. Flynn, & K. Nitsch (Eds.), *Normalization, integration and community services* (pp. 71-115). Baltimore: University Park Press.

Wolfensberger, W. (1992). *A brief introduction to social role valorization as a high order concept for structuring human services* (rev. ed.). Syracuse, NY: Training Institute for Human Service Planning, Leadership and Change Agentry, Syracuse University.

Wolfensberger, W. (1998). *A brief introduction to social role valorization: A high-order concept for addressing the plight of societally devalued people, and for structuring human services* (3rd ed.). Syracuse, NY: Training Institute for Human Services Planning, Leadership & Change Agentry (Syracuse University).

Wolfensberger, W. (2000). A brief overview of social role valorization. *Mental Retardation, 38*(2), 105-123.

Wolfensberger, W., & Thomas, S. (2009). Some thoughts on the role valorizing merits of valued paid and unpaid activities. *The Social Role Valorization Journal, 4*(2), 12-18.

44

Lifestyles of Adults with Developmental Disabilities in Ontario

M. Katherine Buell, Jonathan Weiss, and Ivan Brown

What you will learn:

- How the lifestyles of adults with developmental disabilities have changed
- The varied lifestyles of people with developmental disabilities
- The importance of family, self-determination, and inclusion as lifestyle issues
- Current support for independent lifestyles, and challenges that are still ahead

Lifestyle is a word we have come to use to refer to the way people carry out their lives — the places where they are, the people with whom they interact, and all the many things they do in the course of simply living their lives. Lifestyles are different for every human being because every human being is unique, each with his or her own characteristics and behaviours. Still, it is possible to group people together and look at the ways they carry out their lives generally. By doing this, it is possible to describe the lifestyles of groups of people. In this chapter, the lifestyles of groups of adults with developmental disabilities are described (see Chapters 1 and 2 for historical and contemporary use of terms).

Historical Influences

The lifestyles of adults with developmental disabilities today can be more clearly understood by examining the sociohistorical and cultural per-spectives on disability (Harbour & Maulik, 2010). Some of the important influences on modern lifestyles of adults with developmental disabilities began in the 18th century in Western Europe and North America. During that century, there developed a growing interest in both education for this group, and in humanitarianism. Interest in education for people who were often formerly considered not to be educable blossomed, incorporating ideas from the rich philosophical groundwork that evolved in Europe (e.g., Condillac's sensationalism, which claimed that learning results from information gained from using our five senses, and from our internal thinking and imagining; Stanford Encyclopedia of Philosophy, 2010). In particular, Itard's 1801 demonstration of learning by Victor, the "enfant-sauvage" or "wild boy of Aveyron," brought on a revolution in thinking about the treatment of people who were different. People saw first-hand that Victor could learn a large number of new skills,

A Family Reunion

Sheila Appleby-Williams couldn't ignore the butterflies in her stomach as she made her way from Toronto to Napanee on the 401 on a rainy Thursday morning. Only a few hours ago she had been at her home in California pondering one of the most important decisions in her life. Now with her mind firmly set, she was about to reunite with a brother she hadn't seen for 50 years.

The early 1950s were a tough time for families with children who had developmental disabilities. The stigmas that surrounded these families forced some parents to make tough decisions and Sheila's family was no different. Her older brother Arthur was diagnosed with autism and was placed in an institution, away from his family, at the recommendation of his family doctor.

"My father was angry and bitter about Arthur's condition and most of his feelings were directed at my mother as if it was her fault," says Appleby-Williams. "My mother wasn't allowed to mention Arthur's name or have any photos of him in the house. She was forced to hide any items that she sent to him and never really recovered from the guilt, shame and pain of giving away her only son. I therefore never spoke about my brother or knew where he was."

After a 10 year battle with Alzheimer's, Sheila's mother passed away. After her passing Sheila found a photo of her brother at four years old as well as his birth certificate. She still had no contact name or address. Recently, when her father passed away, Sheila received a clue that she believed may lead her to her long lost sibling.

"My parents divorced when I was a teenager and I hadn't seen my father for years. He had apparently taken on the paperwork concerning Arthur once my mother became ill. While reading my father's will, I learned that he had left some money for Arthur to provide him with any items he needed for his comfort. At that time I finally decided it was time to find my brother."

After some exhaustive searches on the internet, Sheila was led to the Rideau Regional Centre in Smiths Falls. A contact at Rideau Regional, after some research herself, was then able to point Sheila to Ongwanada. Arthur had been transferred to Prince Edward Heights in Picton in 1970 and was later moved to Napanee.

"After speaking with a few people who worked for Ongwanada, I was put in contact with the Social Worker . She called me back and informed me that they were currently also searching for Arthur's next of kin. She asked me if I would take on that role and be interested in coming to visit my brother in person.

Reprinted by permission from: Ongwanada The Horizon, Summer (2009).

when taught in a logical sequence, and that these new skills helped him to behave in ways that were close to the ways others around him behaved. From Itard, Eduoard Seguin developed systematic methods to educate the "feebleminded" at Salpetrière Hospital in Paris (Harbour & Maulik, 2010). Many others began to believe that it might be possible for all people to learn new skills if appropriate teaching methods could be discovered and followed.

Related to the growing interest in education in the 18th century was a corresponding growth in humanitarianism. Humanitarianism is a philosophical perspective that views the differences among people in a kindly, sympathetic manner and that treats people with differences in humane ways. The growth of humanitarianism during this period represented a change from previous philosophy that attributed differences to various causes — even, at times, to possession by the devil that warranted punishment.

The role of institutions

As a result of this humanitarian influence, educational programs (sometimes formalized as schools) and whole lifestyle programs (sometimes formalized as communities or hospitals) were set up in France, Switzerland, the United States, and elsewhere to provide good diet, exercise, medical care, and skill development. The idea was that appropriate training could increase a person's competency so that they would be able, eventually, to live in their communities.

These programs were, for the most part, implemented by well-meaning people who attempted to

"It was a difficult decision to make. When I last saw my brother as a child, he was completely non-communicative and would rock back and forth for long periods of time. Would he remember me? Would this reunion bring peace and closure to a difficult part of my life? Was I prepared to meet him after searching for him for so long?"

Sheila confided in several friends who suggested that a visit might prove to be too painful and bring little closure. But, despite those sentiments she decided that she would travel back to Ontario with little expectations. Ongwanada staff sent her pictures of her brother, so that she would be prepared for her brother's appearance which had changed significantly since she last saw him. But she still wasn't fully prepared for what she saw when she arrived at his community residence.

"I didn't expect to see a tall slender man lounging in a blue recliner. He looked at me and I saw so much life in his eyes, this wasn't the vacant stare that I saw so many years ago. I was overwhelmed and burst into tears, he wasn't my long lost brother any longer, he was a person!"

Over the next five hours Sheila was able to learn all about her brother. "He loves new clothes, receiving cards, lounging in his pajamas in his favourite chair. These are all family traditions! I was able to see his bedroom and understand him better. It is difficult to express the comfort that I felt, the relief at seeing how content he is and how well he has been taken care of."

"When I went to see my brother, I was hoping to connect with others in a similar situation and have learned that I was not alone. A number of people of my generation are just now discovering the whereabouts or even existence of a sibling "locked away" for so many years. I can't begin to express the healing and release of the shame and pain that I carried with me for so many years. It seems that we have come very far in acknowledging Autism and creating acceptance. However, I have discovered that it is still mainly the mothers who are left to fight for their child's rights and refuse to give up hope. This was my mother's struggle — over 50 years ago."

"I have since learned how important of a role Ongwanada has played in the effort to move residents out of institutions and into community homes. I want to share my sincere thanks and appreciation for the environment and care that my brother has and still is receiving. This has been an amazing and healing experience for me. I began my search wanting answers to many questions, but now I have brother that I can finally acknowledge and keep in contact with."

develop what they considered to be the best possible environments and training. Some programs were set up in modern, elaborate buildings with extensive grounds that were designed to bring tranquility to those who were there to benefit from them. Even at the beginning of the 20th century, many institutions for people with disabilities were "model" self-supporting communities, providing work, training, social support, and many other advantages. Because this was a lifestyle that was thought by many to be appropriate for people with developmental disabilities, there was considerable general support for making it one that appeared to be pleasant and fulfilling (see Brown & Brown, 2003; Simmons, 1982).

In spite of the apparently good intentions of those who founded and built such educational and broader lifestyle programs, over time these places of residence became larger and more people with various disabilities and differences were sent to live in them for longer periods of time. These places, based on humanitarian beliefs that people with disabilities could be taught to lead better lives, gradually became the overcrowded and underfunded institutions of the 20th century. The first institution for people with developmental disabilities in Ontario formally opened in Orillia in 1876. By the mid 1970s, Ontario had 19 government-operated institutions providing care to children and adults with developmental disabilities. In the late 1980s, Ontario institutions shifted to providing care only to adults, and in March 2009 all institutions for persons with developmental disability in Ontario closed (see Chapter 2 for more details).

Decline of standards in institutions

Why did this change in standards take place? A number of interrelated factors contributed to the change, but among the most important were periods of economic hardship that resulted in reduced support, the growing number of poor working and non-working people who emerged out of industrialization, and shifting social values. Social values were influenced, in particular, by the growth of science and the triumph of rational thought and scientific theories over faith, superstition, and adherence to doctrine. The growing interest in, and acceptance of, Darwin's theories illustrated the rise of science over belief. Darwin's ideas of survival of the fittest and natural selection produced a more biological view of human functioning (Stanford Encyclopedia of Philosophy, 2010).

One of the phenomena that arose from this line of thinking was "eugenic alarm" (Meyers & Blacher, 1987), a set of beliefs that developmental disabilities (described at the time as feeblemindedness) and criminality were closely related, and that both were inherited. The rise of eugenics was strongly influenced by Darwin's cousin, Sir Francis Galton, whose publication *Hereditary Genius* in 1869 was widely read and discussed (Beirne-Smith, Pattong, & Kim, 2006). In eugenic thinking, feebleminded people were thought to be inferior and potentially dangerous, and needed to be protected from society within institutions for the good of themselves and others. Further, it was thought important for the general well-being of society to protect itself against such people having children since, through propagation, they would only add to the "problem" of feeblemindedness that threatened the vitality of society. By taking measures such as these, society could be improved in ways that were similar to, but faster than, the naturally-occurring evolutionary process (i.e., survival of the fittest).

The growing urbanization of society that resulted from industrialization also contributed to changing attitudes toward people with differences. Urbanization concentrated larger numbers of people into smaller geographic locations, and people with differences became highly visible. At the same time, living in towns and cities was more complex and required a higher level of daily living skills than living in rural areas. In addition, greater mobility, the absence of extended family networks, and the dense concentration of people all detracted from informal or "natural" supports for persons who lived in towns and cities. Combined, these factors fostered a growing need in urban areas for more formal programs for people with disabilities and other needs.

These influences all put pressure on programs not only to educate but also to house people. The increased numbers of people being admitted to programs resulted in too many demands on the resources available and hence in increasing numbers of failures. The slowdown in returning people to the community, and the rise in the numbers being admitted, resulted in the schools and other programs becoming overcrowded institutions.

The decision that institutional living should be the standard defining lifestyle characteristic for the people who lived in them was not reversed until the mid 1970s when the normalization philosophy was introduced (in Ontario by Benjt Nirje and shortly afterward to an international audience by Wolf Wolfensberger in 1972). This philosophy was interpreted, somewhat erroneously over the years following its introduction, to mean that people with developmental disabilities should live in ways that made them blend into the larger culture and live as closely as possible to the ways "normal" people live.

Becoming part of the community again

The widespread adoption of the normalization philosophy into service policies and procedures had a profound influence on the lifestyles of persons with developmental disabilities both inside and outside institutions. Ontario, like other jurisdictions in the more developed countries of the world, initiated a series of reforms and advances in services for people with developmental disabilities that markedly changed lifestyles. In the early 1970s in Ontario, there began to be a rethinking of what services should be made available to people with developmental disabilities. The idea was gradually accepted that there was a need to reduce and eventually close the institutions, and to provide considerably more

George's Story

My brother George had spent the majority of his 61 years at the Rideau Regional Centre and when it was proposed that he was to be moved to a group home in Gananoque my wife and I had major reservations. Would George get the care and attention he required? What professionals would be available (medical doctor, nurse, dietician, therapist, counsellor, etc.)? How would he respond to a residential setting? After all, Rideau Regional had been his home for so long.

A year and a half has passed since the move and we can honestly say that our concerns were not warranted. In a matter of weeks the house has become his home. We visit regularly, something we did not do at Rideau Regional Centre, and are welcomed each and every time by residents and staff. The staff keeps us informed by phone and mail of upcoming activities that we may want to get involved with such as outings, Christmas dinner, planning meetings, and so on. It is inspiring to see the care and dedication put forth by the home supervisor and his team who have created an atmosphere that can simply be described as family. On our last visit my wife took her sewing machine to shorten some pants for her brother-in-law. At one end of the kitchen table George and I did puzzles while at the other end the sewing machine whirred — a very homey experience.

The visits have moved beyond us visiting the home to George making his first visit to our home. In late January George's primary residential counsellor brought George the 60 km and after a visit the three amigos (Shawn, George and I) went out to dinner for, as Shawn stated "a boys night out." Thank you Shawn for creating a very memorable evening for two brothers.

Finally, Sandra and I would like to congratulate the Ongwanada staff on creating a home for five very special residents.

Sincerely,

Colin Campbell

Reprinted by permission from Ongwanada The Source, March 2010.

resources to support community-based services. The overall intent of this shift in thinking was that institutional living as a lifestyle should be phased out, and community living as a lifestyle should be encouraged and supported.

This shift in thinking received support from the government of Ontario in 1973 through the publication of its policy report *Community Living for the Mentally Retarded in Ontario: A New Policy Focus* (Ministry of Health, 1973). This report emphasized the need for community, rather than institutional, services for both children and adults with developmental disabilities (deSilva & Faflak, 1976). One result of the 1973 report was the enactment of the *Developmental Services Act* (Ministry of Community and Social Services, 1974). This Act transferred the responsibility for services to people with developmental disabilities from the Ministry of Health, which regulated health-related policies and services, to the Ministry of Community and Social Services

(MCSS), which regulated social service policies and services. Among other things, this shift in ministerial responsibility represented a move away from developmental disability being viewed as an illness and a deficit, and toward it being viewed as a set of unique characteristics of a portion of the province's overall population. This shift in perspective resulted in developmental disability being seen as a much broader social issue than had been the case previously. The legislation itself added to this change in perception by requiring that recreational, medical, dental, spiritual, and other services be provided within the community. On the whole, the transfer of Developmental Services to MCSS supported the perception that the Ontario government was actively seeking to initiate a change in lifestyle for people with developmental disabilities away from institutional living and toward community living.

Although it took longer than anticipated for this trend to develop in Ontario (Stainton, 1995), a long-term policy on deinstitutionalization (moving people from institutional living to community living) was outlined in the document *Challenges and Opportunities: Community Living For People With Developmental Handicaps* (Ministry of Community and Social Services, 1987). Acting on the recommendations of this report, MCSS set out a general plan to reduce institutions gradually over 25 years, and to establish a comprehensive community service system. The priorities of the 25-year plan underwent some changes as a result of subsequent policy developments (MCSS, 1997a; MCSS, 1997b; MCSS 1998a; MCSS, 1998b). In 2004, MCSS formally announced its intention to close the three remaining residential institutions for adults with developmental disabilities, which occurred in March 2009 with the closure of Huronia Regional Centre (Orillia), Rideau Regional Centre (Smith Falls), and Southwestern Regional Centre (Blenheim)). These closures ended 133 years of institutional lifestyles for people with developmental disabilities in Ontario.

Try this exercise: Think of some technological advance available 5 years ago, 10 years ago, 20 years ago. Is that technology relevant or obsolete today? What about today's latest technology?

Lifestyles: Nine Areas of Life

One of the interesting questions associated with increasing support for community living lifestyles is whether or not this lifestyle is actually better for people with developmental disabilities. Are they happier? Are they more fulfilled? Is this a better way of life? MCSS made a commitment in 1990 to address this question by funding the Quality of Life Project, an Ontario-wide initiative to look at the quality of life, over several years, of adults with developmental disabilities who were associated in various ways with the Ontario service system. The Quality of Life Project, completed in December 1998, supported the view that, although quality of life for people with developmental disabilities in Ontario is not especially good when contrasted with people in the general population, those pursuing lifestyles that involve more independent living in communi-

ties and the use of stronger community living skills have higher quality of life scores than those who do not (Brown, Raphael, & Renwick, 1997; Brown, Renwick, & Raphael, 1999).

The Quality of Life Project also provided, for the first time, a wealth of information about the lifestyles of adults with developmental disabilities in Ontario who receive services, and is still the most comprehensive source of information available. Because the sample of 504 people for this project was drawn randomly from all the service organizations, including institutions, across Ontario, its results could be reliably generalized to the population of adults with developmental disabilities in Ontario who received some type of service from the Ontario service system. It should be noted, however, that those who receive MCSS-funded services do not represent all people who might be assessed as having developmental disabilities in Ontario. It was estimated by Brown et al. (1997) that about 23% of adults with developmental disabilities were associated with MCSS-funded services in 1995. The Quality of Life Project inquired about nine aspects of lifestyle, presented below (for full details, see Brown et al., 1997).

1. Where do people live?

In 1995, approximately 10% of adults with developmental disabilities receiving MCSS services lived in large care facilities, 19% lived in community-based small care residences, 46% lived with families, and 25% lived independently. Since the completion of both the Project and follow-up related to the Project, the number of people living in long term care facilities continued to decline (see Chapter 2). This trend continued until the 2009 closure of the last of the MCSS-funded institutions. Almost all people who lived independently in communities chose their own homes and the location of their homes, although often they had help choosing. About three-quarters of those who lived in small residences had little or no choice about where they lived. Almost half of the adults who lived with families did not perceive that they had yet experienced an opportunity to choose their living arrangement. Of the remainder, surprisingly few considered that they were living with families because of personal choice.

2. What are people's homes like?

Taken from the Quality of Life Project, a list of twenty characteristics of homes is shown in Table 1 for people with developmental disabilities in Ontario who lived in small care community homes, on their own, and with their families. This is not an exhaustive list, but it includes many of the important things that are typical of most people's homes. It is interesting to compare the characteristics of people with developmental disabilities who lived in these four types of residences with the characteristics of your own home. Note, for example, that the only group where everyone can play the radio at any time — something we probably all take for granted — is those people who live independently.

Try this exercise: Think of your own home. Answer yes or no to each characteristic on the list in Table 1. Put a star beside the items that you consider important to have.

3. What are people able to do?

People's ability to do things is an important factor in what their lifestyles are like. Forty percent of people with developmental disabilities in Ontario were described as also having some type of physical disability. People were also asked how many life activities they could do on their own. Twenty-six percent of people could do most activities on their own, 35% could do many activities on their own, 22% could do only some life activities on their own, and 17% were able to do few life activities independently. This suggests that about three-quarters of the adults with developmental disabilities need to have assistance from others, at least some of the time, to do the things people do in expressing their lifestyles.

4. Going to community places and events

Most people with developmental disabilities who lived in Ontario communities did things in their communities — including entertainment and recreation — at least once a week, and many of them did so almost every day. By contrast, about two-thirds of those who lived in institutions did things in their communities less than once a week. Cost was some-what more of a barrier to doing things in one's community for people who lived independently than it was for people who lived in more structured environments. Getting around was a problem for one-third or fewer of people with disabilities, somewhat more so for people who lived in community homes than for people who lived independently or with their families.

Ten things were identified as helping people with developmental disabilities to go places and do things in their communities. These were:

- Wanting to go — showing initiative
- Encouragement from staff
- Encouragement from friends, family, and volunteers
- Having places and activities to go to
- Knowing the community and being known in the community
- Accepting people in the community
- Having skills to get around the community
- Having skills to interact with people in the community
- Having transportation readily available
- Living in a small community that is easy to navigate

5. Occupational activities

In our culture, occupational activity — what we "do" during the day — plays a large role in how we live our lives and how we see ourselves fitting in with those around us. For people with developmental disabilities in Ontario, the Quality of Life Project indicated that about 70% had a major occupational activity of some type. That is, they attended work, school, or a program regularly at least half days. This varied slightly by where people lived: 83% of people who lived with families, 83% of people who lived in community homes, and 67% of people who lived independently had a major occupational activity of some type.

For something that is as central to lifestyle as occupational activity, personal choice is an important factor to consider. Only about 25% of people with developmental disabilities in Ontario chose their occupational activity (some on their own, others with assistance from others). By contrast, 60% had

Table 1: Percentage of People Who Answered Yes to 20 Characteristics of Their Homes

Characteristic of home	Where people live		
	Small care	*Independent*	*With family*
Has own bedroom	78	96	94
Has private space	87	97	85
Has own furniture	91	95	85
Has own door key	24	96	49
Has own money to spend	59	94	35
Can come and go any time	25	93	36
Can eat at any time	67	98	78
Can watch television any time	88	99	91
Can play radio any time	89	100	92
Can engage in consensual sex	56	91	6
Can invite guests to home	78	95	71
Has own television	39	94	61
Has own stereo	60	87	68
Has own VCR	20	67	37
Has enhanced TV connection	33	85	44
Has own telephone line	17	85	18
Has pets	13	32	39
Has plants	19	42	22
Has hobbies in home	86	83	79
Receives mail in own name	96	98	84

The reader is encouraged to see additional information on characteristics of homes in Anderson (1993).

no part of the decision about what they do during the day. The remainder had some limited choice.

6. Financial support

The amount of money people have, and the ways they choose to use their money impacts, to a considerable degree, on their lifestyles. About 93% of adults with developmental disabilities in Ontario who received services from service organizations were supported financially by government pensions. The remainder earned their own incomes, or were supported in other ways (usually by family). Control over finances varied by where the study participants lived. Other people controlled the finances for 87% of those in community homes. This can be partly explained, perhaps, by the low levels of daily living skills of people who lived there. It was perhaps somewhat surprising that other people controlled the finances of 84% of those who lived with families. Even for those who lived independently, only 30% controlled their own finances, while 31% had help and 39% had their finances controlled by someone else.

7. Services people get

The number and types of services that people receive play a major role in defining the way people lead their lives. This is especially so for the one-third of adults with developmental disabilities in Ontario for whom services affect most areas of their lives, and even for the one-third for whom services affect some or many areas of their lives. Ten general categories of services provide an indication of the range of services that are most commonly used by adults with developmental disabilities (see Table 2).

8. Health

Health is a central lifestyle issue, especially since health is increasingly seen in recent years as a resource for daily living (World Health Organization, 1996). Thirteen percent of the respondents (or their proxies) in the Quality of Life Project were noted to have a serious illness (more than a cold or flu, something that was physical in nature, and that required special medical attention) in the six months prior to the survey, and nearly all of these required hospitalization. Data from large-scale studies that compare the health of adults with developmental disabilities to adults without disabilities in similar countries reveals a disturbing pattern: adults with developmental disabilities are significantly more likely to have poor physical and mental health than their peers. These issues include poorer cardiovascular fitness levels (suggesting a more sedentary lifestyle), lower vaccination levels, higher rates of mental health disorders, poorer dental health, and fewer health screenings (Walsh, Kerr, & van Schrojenstein Lantman-de Valk, 2003).

9. Friends, family, and other people

The people around us — those with whom we interact — make up an important part of our lifestyles. For people with developmental disabilities in Ontario, almost all in the Quality of Life Project identified staff or other professional people as the ones who provided both practical and emotional support. About half or fewer of the people who lived outside institutions received support from friends and family, although most of those who lived with their families received support from their parents. About one-third of those who lived independently received support from a spouse or special person, and about one-quarter of these same people received support from other people they knew in the community. All other types of support from other people were low.

Try this exercise: Think about your lifestyle, and about how many people help or support you across the 9 aspects described.

Key Concepts for Healthy Lifestyles

The "snapshot" provided in the previous section referred to people with developmental disabilities in general. Some reference was made, however, to overarching concepts that are critical for the successful promotion of healthy lifestyles of adults with developmental disabilities. Three of the most important of these are explored in more detail below.

HAVING SUPPORTIVE FAMILY ENVIRONMENTS

The place where people live is a critical factor in determining lifestyles of people with developmental

Table 2: Percentage of Adults Who Use Ten Categories of Services

Service categories	%
Occupational programs provided/work support	61
Residences provided/support in independent living	52
Recreation provided or supported	51
Life skills supports	50
Physical health	46
Financial management or support with money	39
Mental health	35
Transportation provided or supported	31
Spiritual aspects of living	18
Other types of service	10

disabilities. In the past few decades, children with developmental disabilities have become increasingly likely to live in their family homes with their parents well into adulthood. Data regarding adults with developmental disabilities in the United States indicate a similar trend — of adults with developmental disabilities receiving U.S. Medicaid waivers, there has been a decreasing trend regarding the number of adults living in institutions, and an increasing trend of adults living with family members, rising from approximately 6% in 1992 to 39% in 2006 (Lakin, Prouty, & Coucouvanis, 2007). There are likely four reasons why this trend is occurring in Ontario:

1. Except for maltreatment or extreme behaviour, children do not live in residential care.
2. Local school boards have been required since the 1980 legislation *An Amendment to the Education Act* to provide education for all exceptional students. This allows almost all children with disabilities to attend school in their local communities and thus to live in their family homes.
3. There has been growth in MCSS programs that offer financial support to parents who have children living at home, and programs that address transition from family and school life to adult community life (see Chapter 23 for details).
4. An explicit policy shift, beginning in 1997 with *Making Services Work for People* (Ministry of Community and Social Services, 1997a) and continuing with other MCSS documents, has made clear that the responsibility for children and adults with developmental disabilities is now shared among families, communities, and governments. This has resulted in an open expectation that families, if they are able, will act as the main caregivers of their own children with disabilities. In practice, this means that more children and adults are continuing to live in their family homes, usually with their parents.

BEING SELF-DETERMINED AND PERSON-DIRECTED

One important philosophical shift that impacts the lifestyles of individuals with developmental disabilities is acceptance of the concept of self-determination. Self-determination refers to an individual's ability to have control over one's life and destiny, as well as a group's right for self-governance (Wehmeyer & Bolding, 2008). Self-determination occurs when a person's skills, knowledge, and motivation for independence are supported by the environment in which one lives, as well as by the broader society (Abery & Stancliffe, 1996). Self-determination is the opposite of learned helplessness, which occurs when people believe they do not have control or agency over their lives. People with developmental disabilities are at tremendous risk for learned helplessness when: they are provided with few opportunities to make active choices; they are presented with messages that they cannot be involved in the decision-making process or will fail in the process; and their choice not to be involved in the process is encouraged by others (Wehmeyer & Bolding, 2008). In contrast, self-determination means being self-directed and goal-oriented. It involves personal choice, which includes the ability to make decisions and having available options to make decisions

Roberto: Life in a Community Home

Roberto is a 48 year old man who lives with three other men in a newly constructed single dwelling home in a small rural Ontario town. Each man has his own bedroom in this rambling bungalow. There are always two paid staff members in the home to assist the men with most aspects of their day-to-day lives. Roberto can speak well, but at times it is necessary to encourage him to express his feelings and wishes.

Roberto needs the assistance of staff to manage his meals and routines, his finances, and any medical problems that arise. One staff is designated as his case manager and advocates for his needs and wants. Roberto has a number of interests and it is important to him to be active. He especially enjoys golf and attending hockey games. He also reads the newspaper in order to follow his favourite team. Staff assist him in maintaining his interests in bowling and swimming, and often the staff and all four men are involved in activities together on the weekend.

The home has a van, which allows the staff to provide the transportation Roberto requires for his interests as well as to and from his daily education program. This program, which involves a class of his peers with a teacher and a teacher's aide, is very important to him. He is studying numeracy and literacy skills, and is making good progress. His program is also focused on building community skills, and the class is often out in the community learning appropriate social or financial skills, or just becoming familiar with resources of their community.

Roberto receives ODSP, which is managed by his case manager with input from his family. His family is supportive of him, and visit him — or he visits them — on a regular basis.

about (Brown & Brown, 2009). As Wehmeyer (1996) suggested, people with developmental disabilities can be self-determined when they are able to act autonomously, can control their own behaviours, feel empowered in the process, and are aware that they have the right to make the choices. Obviously, being self-determined has a tremendous impact on one's lifestyle.

There are a number of factors that are important to consider when addressing personal choice and self-determination. A person with developmental disability is entitled to the same rights and freedoms as any other person in Ontario. These rights apply to any decisions the person makes and should include any opportunities available to any person in Ontario (see Chapter 5). However, because of the limitations posed by developmental disabilities, and the cautious paternalism (often called protection) that is sometimes exercised by those people who support them, these rights and opportunities are often overlooked. One way of ensuring personal choice is to embrace the idea that people with developmental disabilities should be afforded the "dignity of risk," that is, allowed to make their own choices and

pursue opportunities that interest them, even if it appears to others that such choices and opportunities involve some risk. Another closely-linked way is to allow for the learning value associated with making "bad" choices. Adopting such strategies is often difficult for people providing support, but, if used wisely, they can be valuable tools for supporting personal choice over choice by others, and for fostering learning of new life skills. In fact, most judicious parents and teachers use this very strategy to help typically developing individuals learn life lessons.

Promoting self-determination requires promoting a system that encourages people with developmental disabilities to make their own choices about their lifestyles, a movement that is often called "person-centred planning" or "person-directed planning." According to MCSS and the Individualized Funding Coalition for Ontario (Dingwall, Kemp, & Fowke, 2006), person-directed planning is an ongoing process that starts with understanding what a person with developmental disability wants for his or her own life, often taking into account the thoughts of families, friends, and members of the social network. In person-directed planning, the person with

Sarah: Life with the Family

Sarah is a 40 year old woman with Down syndrome who has lived in her family home all her life. Her family now consists of just her and her 75 year old father. Sarah's mother died a couple of years ago, and there are no other siblings available to help with the support needs. Their single dwelling home is in a middle class neighbourhood in a small Ontario town. Sarah and her father are in the process of making future plans for her accommodation but, for now, the only time they are apart is when Sarah goes to her day program. Sarah's father helps her with meals, self maintenance, manages all the money needs, and health needs. He also usually drives her to her day program, although she sometimes takes the access bus. However, Sarah has a habit of hoarding access bus tickets and does not have a physical disability, so she often is disallowed from this transportation.

Sarah attends a recreational day program every day, where she participates in a rotating schedule of activities with other adults with developmental disabilities. Because she does not have much verbal communication, she makes her needs and opinions known through gestures and actions. Some of her actions can be quite intense and often require the support of staff to figure out what the need or opinion is. Sarah makes social contact with others at her day program, and is involved in some evening and weekend activities provided by a local service agency.

As both Sarah and her father age, they worry about long term placement, social and emotional contacts, and continuity of services. One agency involved with the family is trying to assist the family with these concerns.

developmental disability directs the pace, rhythm, and content of the decision-making process, with the support from others when needed. Everyone involved views the person with developmental disability as being the decision maker of his or her own life, and is committed to build and maintain relationships with that person. Services that will provide the person with the opportunity to fully contribute and participate in society are explored, and safeguards are put in place to deal with challenges. Importantly, this process is intended to lead to action — concrete steps are to be taken to help the person with developmental disability achieve their goals. A number of guidebooks now exist to help create person-directed plans (go to *http://www. individualizedfunding.ca* to learn more).

One critical step in person-directed planning, and helping individuals with developmental disabilities live self-determined lives, involves understanding an individuals support needs. Once desired life experiences and goals are developed, a support needs assessment should be undertaken to develop an individualized support plan that a) prioritizes preferences and identifies the supports needed to achieve these preferences, b) identifies the support sources that are needed as well as those that are cur-

rently in place, and c) monitors the progress of realizing the person's goals and challenges to engaging the services (Thompson, 2008).

A number of tools have been developed in recent years to help practitioners assess support needs. One of the best known is the Supports Intensity Scale (SIS; Thompson et al., 2004), now being used in numerous jurisdictions; in Ontario it is being used as part of a battery of needs assessment tools. The SIS asks about the supports that are needed and the intensity of the supports needed, in order that people may achieve their goals in their home, community, lifelong learning, employment, health and safety, and social domains. Understanding support needs is fast becoming a critical aspect of promoting self-determined lifestyles for adults with developmental disabilities. For example, more than 15 states and provinces in North America have officially adopted the SIS to understand and analyze the service needs of their citizens with developmental disability (Schalock, Thompson, & Tassé, 2008).

INCLUSION

One of the major issues with respect to the lifestyles of adults with developmental disabilities today is fostering inclusion. People with developmental

Andrea: A Family Beyond the Institution

Andrea is a 78 year old woman who has lived with a family in rural Ontario for 5 years. Prior to this, Andrea lived in a large congregate care facility in Eastern Ontario. Andrea has a history of mental illness which requires psychiatric intervention on an intermittent basis. Because of this, when plans for closing her large congregate care facility were being made, it was originally planned that Andrea would move into a small care home in the community.

However, Andrea moved into the home of a couple in their 50s who are paid a per diem fee for supporting Andrea. She is very proud of her independence, but has been accepted into the family's routines and activities — becoming part of their family. The couple helps her with her medical needs, and monitors her day to day decisions and activities. Andrea has no next of kin of her own, and appreciates the love and support of her new family. It is the couple's intention to have Andrea with them as long as they can and they are currently planning for this.

Andrea also receives case management through the community agency that recruited the family. A case worker is in frequent contact, and is responsible for coordinating the supports for Andrea.

Andrea's institutional history has left its mark. Andrea smokes, even though she has been advised not to for medical reasons. Unsuspected things can trigger swearing and physical outbursts, but these are occurring less frequently as she adjusts to her new home.

It is important to Andrea to keep in touch with the people she once lived with in the institution. Though she is of retirement age, Andrea attends a seniors program with her old friends. The program is located in a beautifully restored old home close to a small town. This program involves crafts, use of the pool, trips, and various other activities. All these activities are supported by a number of staff. Andrea views this centre as her job, attends 3 days a week, and is given a stipend by her case manager there on a weekly basis.

disabilities need to be "included" in, rather than "excluded" from, the general or prevailing culture.

The first step to inclusion involves supporting individuals in ways that help them live in their communities among other people, and ensures that people are "in the community," but does not necessarily mean they are "of the community." Being "of the community," a major goal of inclusion, means living in, enjoying, being accepted and valued by others, as well as contributing to one's community. Two important aspects of inclusion are discussed here: integration, and social support.

Inclusion in the community – being integrated

The goal of integration is for people with developmental disabilities to belong within the larger culture and to form part of it. A useful way of looking at integration is to take an acculturation perspective (Berry, 1984; Buell, 1998; Buell & Minnes, 1994). An acculturation perspective focuses on identifying the unique needs of individuals, and on blending support

for these needs with involvement with non-disabled people in community settings. Table 3 illustrates the role of two questions relating to support and community involvement in contributing to descriptions of integration (the goal), segregation, assimilation, and marginalization (Buell & Minnes, 1994).

The acculturation perspective also recognizes that people with developmental disabilities form a small and diverse cultural group within the broader culture. The larger culture often makes some accommodations (e.g., wheelchair ramps, or the use or pictures rather than words on signs), but the needs of this smaller culture group, for the most part, define what has to be supported so that they will be able to live within the larger group. One such method of measuring inclusion is through the use of the Assimilation, Integration, Marginalization, Segregation (AIMS) Interview and Checklist (Buell, 2003). Using the AIMS, Minnes, Buell, Feldman, McColl, & McCreary (2002) found that adults with developmental disabilities in Ontario often expe-

Clifford: Being Independent

Clifford is a 40 year old man who lives in a semi-detached house with one other 30 year old man in a working class neighbourhood in an Ontario town. He and his roommate share the household tasks, and Clifford maintains responsibility for his room and the designated areas of the house. Cost for his home is subsidized by an organization funded by the Ministry of Community and Social Services. He has lived in his home since 8 years ago, when he moved out of a commercial boarding home where he fended for himself.

Clifford has a volunteer position with the housekeeping staff at an organization, where his duties include assisting with the general upkeep of the offices. He works with a colleague at times, but generally goes about his job independently. He views this position as his job and receives a small amount of money at the end of each week. Others would view Clifford's job as a volunteer position, but he is adamant that it is his "job." It certainly is what he "does" during the week, and thus it plays a central role in how he thinks of himself.

Clifford is supported primarily by one case manager who helps him with shopping and the general chores around the house. He has regular contact with this "worker" a couple of hours a week, but has 24-hour access to help if he needs it. It was with the help of his case manager that Clifford was able to find both his home and his job. Clifford also has the support of a dietician who helps to manage his diabetes through diet and insulin, which he gives himself.

Clifford has several close friends in the community, rides the city bus to get about, and pays for and uses his phone for contact with his friends. He enjoys fishing, gardening, music, going to garage sales, and using his CB (citizens' band) radio. Clifford makes regular visits to his family in Peterborough, generally making the arrangements himself. Clifford is fiercely independent and usually makes his own decisions about his life. At times, however, it is considered necessary by his support workers to assist him with some of his choices, especially around his diet, but they are careful to help him to make the choice that is in his best interest.

rience more "integration" with regard to medical services, dental services, social activities, housing, and community involvement, but more "marginalized" experiences with regard to education, volunteer activities, and employment. The integration as acculturation perspective is complemented by the identification of needed supports provided by instruments like the SIS, which define unique needs in context.

Inclusion with other people — having social support

A second important aspect of inclusion is social support. Social support means the practical and the emotional ties people have with others — ties that make life both easier to live and more enjoyable (Brown et al., 1997). Social support emerges from having people involved in your daily life, having people to share personal interests and experiences, and having people who are connected to all the various things you do in the course of carrying out your daily life. Social support means feeling accepted, respected, being able to give and receive trust, feeling there is someone who is respectful of your dignity, having someone to turn to when practical and emotional needs arise, and having people with whom to share close bonds.

Because many people with developmental disabilities have limited social skills, social support is especially important for them and contributes a great deal to their lifestyles. Unfortunately, a great deal of the social support for people who receive services comes from professional staff. For example, almost all people surveyed by Brown et al. (1997), regardless of type of living situation, identified professional staff as sources of practical and emotional support. There were other sources of social support as well — especially from parents of adults with developmental disabilities who lived at home — but the survey results suggested that it is not nearly as strong nor as broadly-based as might be hoped. A major ongoing challenge for improving the lifestyles of adults

Table 3: Conditions for Integration and Related Terms Through an Acculturation Perspective

		Is it considered valuable for persons with disabilities to maintain relationships with other groups and with the culture at large?	
		Yes	**No**
Is it considered valuable to recognize and support the unique characteristics of persons with disabilities?	**Yes**	**Integration** *the person is supported and involved in an individual way within the community*	**Assimilation** *the person is involved in an individual way within the community*
	No	**Segregation** *the person is supported and involved in an individual way*	**Marginalization** *the person is uninvolved within the community*

with developmental disabilities is to expand social support networks beyond professional staff into the larger culture. The overwhelming reliance of adults with developmental disabilities who receive services on professional staff for social support underscores the need for having knowledgeable, trained, and skilled people as the professional staff. Through various professional activities, staff members are instrumental in supporting the lifestyles of people with developmental disabilities, and as members of the larger culture, staff act as ambassadors and educators for expanding social support. Practitioners' very jobs involve providing social support, and thus a challenge they face is how to provide support but not to be the only source of support.

What About the Future?

A number of factors will influence the lifestyles of adults with developmental disabilities in Ontario in the future. Ten factors that are considered to be important are:

1. How happy people with developmental disabilities are, and what we do to increase their happiness.

2. The material resources people with developmental disabilities have available to them so that they may lead full and dignified lives.

3. The degree to which people with developmental disabilities exercise self-determination.

4. The degree to which inclusion of people with disabilities continues to be a value and a priority within the general culture of Ontario.

5. The degree to which the Ontario government provides resources for supporting healthy and fulfilling lifestyles of persons with developmental disabilities.

6. Engaging the general public in assisting people with developmental disabilities to improve their lifestyles.

7. The degree to which families will be called upon to support their sons and daughters.

8. The education, training, and experience of people who work in the field of developmental disabilities.

9. The role of professionals who work in the field of developmental disabilities.

10. The way in which the support and care provided to people with developmental disabilities

is monitored and evaluated. Currently, support is evaluated by many community agencies, but there is little formal evaluation of support workers who are employed by families or through other arrangements. Yet, this support work can have a very large influence on the lifestyles of people with developmental disabilities.

Try this exercise: Which aspects of these 10 factors can you influence?

A number of factors need to be in place for community living to improve the quality of lifestyles for people with developmental disabilities in the future. Four of the most important are highlighted here. First, people with developmental disabilities themselves, and the field of developmental disabilities as a whole, need to be valued. Second, because this value and the required supportive actions that are associated with them are unlikely to occur without direct government intervention, governments need to continue to accept responsibility for putting forward legislation and policies that strongly support inclusionary practices. Third, resources that promote being involved in the community in a worthwhile way, and thus promote independent lifestyles, need to be available to people with developmental disabilities and sometimes to their families. Fourth, there need to be well trained professionals who are knowledgeable in the field of developmental disabilities who can advocate for the needs of individuals and who can both keep the system accountable, and advocate for helpful systemic changes.

Summary

Over the years, the lifestyles of people with developmental disabilities have been influenced by prevailing philosophies and cultural ideas. As cultures have changed over time, so also have lifestyles for people with developmental disabilities. In developed countries, the past century has seen tremendous change in our approach to developmental disabilities: the eugenics movement, increased urbanization resulting in the decline of informal supports, over-expansion and under-funding within the institutional system, and a community living movement based on the principles of inclusions and recognition of individual dignity. The current emphasis is on community-based or generic services that support people with developmental disabilities, and often their families, in a lifestyle that promotes being involved in their communities in a worthwhile way.

For Further Thought and Discussion

1. Think about how the prevailing philosophies have over time influenced the lifestyles of people with developmental disabilities. Identify the current philosophies prevalent in today's society. How are these ideas influencing the lifestyles of people with developmental disabilities?
2. Refer to Table 3 on the acculturation perspective of integration. Discuss the differences among integration, segregation, assimilation, and marginalization. How do you think the larger cultural group would answer the questions posed, and how would they view these four terms?
3. What aspects of lifestyle do you think are the most important?
4. Think of one person with developmental disabilities. How would you help improve that person's lifestyle?
5. Think about examples that show that you are self-determined. How can you foster this in someone else?

More Resources

Ontario Government Resources:

Ministry of Community and Social Services
http://www.mcss.gov.on.ca

MCSS Developmental Services
http://www.mcss.gov.on.ca/en/mcss/programs/developmental/index.aspx

Ministry of Education
http://www.edu.gov.ca/eng

Publications
http://www.gov.on.ca/CSS/page/brochure/pub.html

Historical Resources:

Bibliography of the history of idiocy
http://www.dundee.ac.uk/~mksimpso/histories.html

History of developmental disability
http://www.familyvillage.wisc.edu/lib_cdmr.htm

Disability Resources:

yourAble.com
http://www.disabilitynet.co.uk/
yourAble.com is a worldwide disability information and news service, offering a wide range of services for everyone with an interest in disability issues.

Disability resources
http://www.nchrtm.okstate.edu
Includes pointers to many interesting sites.

National Association of Developmental Disabilities Councils
http://www.naddc.org
The NADDC promotes national policy that provides individuals with developmental disabilities the opportunity to make choices regarding the quality of their lives and be included in the community.

Lifestyle Resources:

Provincial Association of Associate Families and Specialized Foster Care
Contact: Geoff Gifford, Chair, Ongwanada, 191 Portsmouth Ave., Kingston, ON, K7M 8A6.

Canada's Community Inclusion Initiative
http://www.communityinclusion.ca/

Community Inclusion
http://www.connectability.ca

Individualized Funding Coalition of Ontario
http://www.individualizedfunding.ca

Community Living Ontario
http://www.communitylivingontario.ca/

Pomona: Health Indicators for People with Intellectual Disabilities
http://www.pomonaproject.org/

Quality of Life:

Brown, I., & Renwick, R. (1997). Understanding what we mean by quality of life [Editorial]. *Journal*

on Developmental Disabilities, 5(2), i-vii.

Brown, I., Raphael, D., & Renwick, R. (1997). *Quality of life — dream or reality? The lives of people with developmental disabilities in Ontario.* Toronto, ON: Centre for Health Promotion, University of Toronto.

McLaughlin, J. F., & Bjornson, K. F. (1998). Quality of life and developmental disabilities [Editorial]. *Developmental Medicine and Child Neurology,* 40(7), 435.

Ontario Quality of Life Project
http://www.utoronto.ca/qol

References

Abery, B., & Stancliffe R. (1996). The ecology of self-determination. In D. J. Sands & M. L. Wehmeyer (Eds.), *Self-determination across the life span: Independence and choice for people with disabilities* (pp. 111–146). Baltimore: Paul H. Brookes Publishing Co.

Anderson, D. J. (1993). Social inclusion of adults with mental retardation. In E. Sutton, A. R. Factor, B. A. Hawkins, et al. (Eds.), *Older adults with developmental disabilities: Optimizing choice and change* (pp. 79-93). Baltimore: Paul H. Brookes Publishing Co.

Beirne-Smith, M., Patton, J. R., & Kim, S. H. (2006). *Mental retardation: An introduction to intellectual disabilities* (7th ed.). Upper Saddle River, NJ: Pearson Merrill Prentice Hall.

Berry, J. W. (1984). Cultural relations in a plural society: Alternatives to segregation and their sociopsychological implications. In N. Miller & M. B. Brewer (Eds.), *Groups in contact: The psychology of desegregation* (pp. 11-27). San Francisco: Academic Press, Inc.

Brown, I., & Brown, R. I. (2003). *Quality of life and disability: An approach for community practitioners.* London: Jessica Kingsley Publishing.

Brown, I., & Brown, R. I. (2009). Choice as an aspect of quality of life for people with intellectual disabilities. *Journal of Policy and Practice in Intellectual Disabilities,* 6(1), 11-18.

Brown, I., Raphael, D., & Renwick, R. (1997). *Quality of life — dream or reality? The lives of people with developmental disabilities in Ontario.* Toronto, ON: Centre for Health Promotion, University of Toronto.

Brown, I., Renwick, R., & Raphael, D. (1999). *The Quality of Life Project: Results from the follow up studies.* Report to the Ontario Ministry of Community and Social Services by the Centre for Health Promotion, University of Toronto.

Buell, M. K. (1998, April). Integration: The service of bringing a group into the community. Keynote speech at the annual meeting of the Research Special Interest Group, Ontario Association on Developmental Disabilities, Niagara Falls, Ontario.

Buell, M. K. (2003). Integration as acculturation: Developmental disability, deinstitutionalization and service delivery implications. *International Review of Research in Mental Retardation, 26,* 221-260.

Buell, M. K., & Minnes, P. (1994). An acculturation perspective on deinstitutionalization, normalization and service delivery. *Journal on Developmental Disabilities, 3*(2), 94-107.

deSilva, R. M., & Faflak, P. (1976). From institution to community. Mental Retardation, *14,* 25-28.

Dingwall, C., Kemp, K., & Fowke, B. (2006). *Creating a good life in community: A guide on person-directed planning.* Retrieved from http://www.individualizedfunding.ca/Guide%20on%20Person-directed%20Planning.pdf

Harbour, C., & Maulik, P. (2010). History of intellectual disability. In J. H. Stone & M. Blouin, (Eds.), *International encyclopedia of rehabilitation.* Retrieved from http://cirrie.buffalo.edu/encyclopedia/article.php?id=143&language=en

Lakin, K. C., Prouty, R., & Coucouvanis, K. (2007). HCBS recipients are increasingly likely to live with parents or other relatives. *Intellectual and Developmental Disabilities, 45*(5), 359-361.

Meyers, C. E., & Blacher, J. (1987). Historical determinants of residential care. In S. Landesman & P. Vietze (Eds.), *Living environments and mental retardation* (pp. 3-16). Washington, DC: American Association on Mental Retardation.

Ministry of Community and Social Services. (1974). *Developmental Services Act.* Toronto, ON: Author.

Ministry of Community and Social Services. (1987). *Challenges and opportunities: Community living for people with developmental handicaps.* Toronto, ON: Author.

Ministry of Community and Social Services. (1997a). *Making services work for people: A new framework for children and for people with developmental disabilities.* Toronto, ON: Author.

Ministry of Community and Social Services. (1997b). *Reinvestment strategy for adults with a developmental disability.* Toronto, ON: Author.

Ministry of Community and Social Services. (1998a). *Ministry of Community and Social Services 1998-1998 Business Plan.* Toronto, ON: Author.

Ministry of Community and Social Services. (1998b). *Individual Support Agreements for people with developmental disability.* Toronto, ON: Author.

Ministry of Education. (1984). *The Education Act.* Toronto, ON: Author.

Ministry of Health. (1973). *Community living for the mentally retarded in Ontario: A new policy focus.* Toronto, ON: Author. Also available at http://www.mcss.gov.on.ca/documents/en/mcss/dshistory/legislation/Welch%20Report.pdf

Minnes, P., Buell, K., Feldman, M. A., McColl, M. A., & McCreary, B. (2002). Community integration as acculturation: Preliminary validation of the AIMS interview. *Journal of Applied Research in Intellectual Disabilities, 15*(4), 377-387.

Simmons, H. G. (1982). *From asylum to welfare.* Toronto, ON: Roeher Institute.

Schalock, J. R., Thompson, J. R., & Tassé, M. J. (2008). *International implementation of the Supports Intensity Scale.* Washington, DC: American Association on Intellectual and Developmental Disabilities.

Stainton, T. (1995). Bureaucracy and ideology: A case study of the development of community living policy in Ontario in the 1970s. *Journal on Developmental Disabilities, 4*(1), 75-97.

Stanford Encyclopedia of Philosophy. (2010). *Darwinism.* Retrieved from http://plato.stanford.edu/entries/darwinism/

Stanford Encyclopedia of Philosophy. (2010). *Étienne Bonnot de Condillac.* Retrieved from http://plato.stanford.edu/entries/condillac/

Thompson, J. R. (2008). Using the four-component assessment and planning process in ISP development and monitoring. In R. L. Schalock, J. R. Thompson, & M. J. Tassé (Eds.), *Relating Supports Intensity Scale information to individual service-plans*. Washington, DC: American Association on Intellectual and Developmental Disabilities.

Thompson, J. R., Bryant, B. R., Campbell, E. M., Craig, E. M., Hughes, C., Rotholz, D., et al., (2004). *The Supports Intensity Scale (SIS): Users manual*. Washington, DC: American Association on Mental Retardation.

Walsh, P. N., Kerr, M., & van Schrojenstein Lantman-de Valk, H. M. J. (2003). Health indicators for people with intellectual disabilities: A European perspective. *European Journal of Public Health, 13*(3 supplement), 47-50.

Wehmeyer, M. L. (1996). Self-determination as an educational outcome: Why is it important to children, youth and adults with disabilities? In D. J. Sands & M. L. Wehmeyer (Eds.), *Self-determination across the life span: Independence and choice for people with disabilities* (pp. 15-34). Baltimore: Paul H. Brookes Publishing Co.

Wehmeyer, M. L., & Bolding, N. (2008). Enhanced self-determination of adults with intellectual disability as an outcome of moving to community-based work or living evironments. *Journal of Intellectual Disability Research, 45*(5), 371-383.

Wolfensberger, W. (1972). *Normalization*. Toronto, ON: National Institute on Mental Retardation (now the Roeher Institute).

World Health Organization. (1996). *Ottawa charter for health promotion*. Geneva, Switzerland: Author.

45

Family Life and Developmental Disability

Patricia Minnes and Julie Burbidge

What you will learn:

- The changing roles of parents and professionals
- The parent as advocate, therapist/mediator, educator, and caregiver
- Aging parents and changing roles
- The roles of other family members
- Evolving roles for parents in the 21st century

With the closure of the last institution for individuals with developmental disabilities in 2009, all individuals with disabilities are now accommodated in the community. As a result, increasing numbers of persons with disabilities are being integrated into community activities, into the educational mainstream, and into supported employment. Although such changes in philosophical orientation have had many beneficial effects for persons with disabilities over the past 50 years, they also have had major implications for families.

The Changing Roles of Parents and Professionals

For the first half of the 20th century, services for persons with developmental disabilities were guided primarily by the *medical model* and people with developmental disabilities were viewed as patients with diseases or organically based disorders. Physicians and disability professionals were viewed as experts, and parents often had relatively little involvement in the treatment and care of their children with disabilities. However, in the late 1960s and 1970s, with the introduction of behavioural techniques based on operant conditioning, there was a gradual shift from the medical model to a more *developmental model*, which focussed on education and training for people with developmental disabilities. Greater parental involvement was encouraged and parents and caregivers were trained to carry out programs with their children. This approach, known as the *mediator model*, was widely adopted.

Such changes, although beneficial for people with

developmental disabilities in a variety of ways, added to the responsibilities and burden of care for families. Compared to the 1970s, when the move to community-based services began, the last two decades have been times of considerable financial restraint that limit the expansion of supports for families caring for an individual with a disability in the community. Although the mediator model continues today, reduced funding has sometimes meant that there is a greater reliance upon pharmaceutical interventions to manage difficult behaviours.

In addition, with many new developments in genetic, physical health, and pharmaceutical knowledge, *biological models* may be gaining increasing acceptance. In many instances, interventions based on these models can be helpful in conjunction with behavioural strategies, especially with individuals whose behaviours are particularly challenging in the community. Well-controlled research is needed, however, to determine the relative effectiveness of behavioural and pharmaceutical interventions and the impact of such treatments upon the quality of life of persons with developmental disabilities and their families (see also Chapter 34).

Since the 1970s, parents have become increasingly active, advocating for the rights of their children and lobbying governments to improve services and supports. At first, many parents who were disillusioned with professionals took matters into their own hands but, in recent years, parents and professionals alike have begun to work toward developing more collaborative relationships and partnerships. The Ontario government has responded over the years to the needs of individuals with developmental disabilities and their families through legislation and a series of policy documents. In 1974, the Ontario government committed to a major change in services for people with developmental disabilities, shifting the focus from institution-based care to community-based services. This shift was partly in response to the apparent failure of the institutional system, and partly because many parents indicated the wish to care for their children with developmental disabilities at home but required assistance.

In 1987, the Ontario Ministry of Community and Social Services released a document entitled *Challenges and Opportunities: Community Living for People with Developmental Handicaps*, which outlined new service goals resulting from consultations with consumer and interest groups and agencies offering programs to individuals with disabilities and their families. In addition to its major long-term goal to establish a comprehensive community service system that would provide support to individuals with developmental disabilities in their home communities, the report described initiatives designed to strengthen supports for families caring for children with developmental disabilities at home and to develop new supported independent living arrangements for adults. Services such as special day care programs, respite care services, and Handicapped Children's Benefits under the Special Services at Home Program were introduced. Such changes were clearly designed to provide additional support for persons with developmental disabilities and their families. What was not clear — and is still not clear today — was how parents learn about such programs and how much additional burden parents experience if they need to connect with new agency personnel, learn about the application process, and complete an application for support. In some parts of Ontario, language is a major barrier, especially for immigrant families who do not speak English well or are unfamiliar with our service systems. Evaluation of these processes, their impact on parents, and factors contributing to successful outcomes are topics that have received very little attention in the literature to date.

In 1997, a new initiative titled *Making Services Work for People* outlined the Ontario government's plans to update the social service system and strategies not only to alter the services offered to families but also to improve the delivery of such services. The Ministry of Community and Social Services (then called Ministry of Community, Family and Children's Services) set out nine goals for reshaping social services in Ontario, including a commitment to ensure the maintenance of essential supports, greater integration of services, earlier and better provision of services for families and individuals with disabilities, and more consistent provision of core services across the province.

As described in the *Making Services Work for People* document, these changes included four shifts in direction: 1) a shift from services that respond only to entrenched problems to services that anticipate problems, respond earlier and reduce the need for future services; 2) a shift from services organized by agencies to services organized to respond to the needs of individuals and families in general; 3) a shift in emphasis from viewing increased funding as the major impetus for change to the view that service delivery can be improved using existing resources; and 4) a shift from government responsibility to shared responsibility. The impact of these changes for family members and the success of these initiatives have yet to be fully evaluated.

In 2008, the *Services and Supports to Promote the Social Inclusion of Persons with Developmental Disabilities Act* was passed in the Ontario legislature. As of 2011, the Ministry of Community and Social Services was developing policy directives and regulations required before the Act can become law (*www. ontario.ca/community*). This legislation replaces the *Developmental Services Act* (1974). Changes to the new Act include new criteria regarding eligibility for government funding, more flexibility regarding the types of support and who can provide them, and providing more choices for services and supports (e.g., person-directed planning; direct funding to permit individuals to manage their supports and make their own decisions rather than working through community agencies). To date, it is not clear what impact such changes will have on parents and community agencies. The process of implementation of such legislation often takes several years and critical issues related to evaluation of outcomes may be overlooked until several years after the programs have been in place.

The Multiple Roles of Parents

The role of parents as advocates

In order to face the challenges involved in raising a child with a developmental disability, parents often take on the role of "advocate." Munro (1991) defined effective advocacy as "a non-violent empowerment and support process, through which families with disabled relatives can constructively express dissatisfaction and contribute creative solutions to problems existing in human service systems" (p. 1). In order to become advocates, parents need to expand their function as parent and caregiver to include the jobs of information seeker, problem solver, committee member, public educator, political activist and, most importantly, spokesperson for the needs of a child who may be unable to communicate his or her own needs to those in power. In order to advocate effectively, parents need to be aware of their social, economic, and political environments and become aware of changing service philosophies, legislation, and budgetary issues.

A parent of an individual with a developmental disability may advocate in a variety of different situations and in many different ways. Parents can be advocates individually or as part of a group. They can write letters, make phone calls, and enlist the help of the media in furthering their cause. They may focus on their own child or the needs of all children with developmental disabilities. Their actions may occur at the community, national, or international level. A parent may view advocacy as a necessary evil, as something that just needs to be done, or as a full-time career. For parents to be successful advocates within a service delivery system — health, education, or social services — there needs to be a sense of partnership between the professional and caregiver, and they must learn to cooperate as equals. Unfortunately, the parent-professional partnership is an ideal notion that may be complicated by reality. While some parents have been able to immerse themselves in the role of collaborator, some professionals may be unprepared to deal with the "parent-as-expert." A sense of resentment may build in situations where parents are unable to discriminate between "what is legally their right and what privileges go beyond the scope of their power" (Nelson, Howard, & McLaughlin, 1993, p. 64). Open communication, mutual respect and trust, shared decision making, and parental empowerment, as well as recognition of the knowledge and skills of both parents and professionals, have been found to be important components of successful parent-professional partnerships (Davies & Hall; 2005; Minnes &

Box 1

Mary Ann is the mother of two children. Eric is 10 and has an intellectual disability due to unknown cause and epilepsy. Eric's younger brother Robbie has joined Cub Scouts and Mary Ann would like Eric to be able to attend as well. During a discussion with the Cub Scout pack leader, it became clear to Mary Ann that inclusion of Eric would be problematic. He would need someone to assist him in activities and the leader had safety concerns due to the severity of Eric's seizures. He also was concerned that he and others would need training to deal with the seizures. The leader reluctantly said that they would not be able to take Eric into the Cub Scout troop until these issues were addressed. Since Mary Ann is a single mother with limited finances, she was not able to hire someone to go to Cubs with Eric and she did not want to limit Robbie's activities by giving him extra responsibilities for his brother. Mary Ann also did not want to wait until she could find suitable supports. As a result, Mary Ann and a friend decided to set up their own Cub Scout group at home so that Eric could participate. Robbie and some of his friends have joined this new cub scout group and other children have expressed an interest. This initiative has provided new opportunities for Eric to interact with typically developing children.

Steiner, 2009).

A qualitative study by Nachshen and Jamieson (2000) explored the outcome of the role of advocacy, in relation to parents' sense of well-being. It was found that six factors contributed significantly to the perception of advocacy as a positive or negative experience. The first factor, *the role of advocacy*, referred to the parents' own sense that their advocacy role was a strategy to achieve change and not just an extra struggle. *The outcome of advocacy* related to the parents' belief that their actions would exert a positive effect on their environment. A third important factor was *the role of professionals*, which focused on professionals' negative or supportive response to the parents' efforts. Whether the parents were advocating for things to come or past injustices was the basis of the fourth factor, *the focus of advocacy*. The fifth factor, *the effect on personal life* emphasized the need for advocacy actions to create interpersonal links, rather than to destroy them. As well, parents spoke of the need to balance the need for advocacy with other personal needs, such as time, money, and relaxation. Personal *emotional issues* was the final factor, accentuating the relevance of parents' own emotional response. Advocacy could inspire feelings of confidence and empowerment, or depression, guilt, and anxiety.

In recent years, parents of children with autism have become particularly strong advocates, pressuring governments for funding to support early intensive behavioural intervention for their chil-

dren. Parents have argued that failure to fund such programs is an infringement of their children's equality rights under the *Canada Health Act*. Such efforts, however, have had mixed results. For example, in 2002 the British Columbia Court of Appeal ruled that: "It is discriminatory under the Canadian Charter of Rights and the United Nations Convention on the Rights of the Child to not provide universal access to intensive behavioural intervention (IBI) for children with autism." The judgement concluded that "IBI is the most effective known therapy for children with autism and that it is a medically necessary intervention without which prognosis is poor" (Couper, 2004, p. 559). However, in a British Columbia government appeal, the Supreme Court of Canada refused to order the provincial government to fund IBI treatment (The Globe and Mail, November 20, 2004). Similarly, in Ontario a class action suit filed in 2004 by parents seeking assurances that their children with autism would have access to IBI in school was unsuccessful and in 2008, the Supreme Court rejected their application to appeal the decision (*http://www.autismontario.com/client/aso/ao.nsf*). Nevertheless, Boards of Education in Ontario and advocacy groups such as Autism Ontario subsequently began to work together on this issue. For example, Public Policy Memo 140 has been developed to provide guidance and support to school boards in the use of applied behaviour analysis (ABA) with students with autism spectrum disorders.

Box 2

Joanna and her husband Rick have twin boys. Both have been diagnosed with autism and they are on a waiting list for publically funded IBI. As an Occupational Therapist, Joanna is very eager for her boys to have IBI as soon as possible. She has done training courses and has been trying to work on skills with the boys but both she and her husband need to work. They also have an older daughter who needs their time and attention. Joanna has a friend who works at a local community college where there is a training program for behaviour therapists. Joanna and her friend developed a creative idea whereby a practicum placement would be set up in Joanna's home and students would work under supervision with her boys. This is just an interim measure while Joanna waits for funding and she is concerned that there will be gaps when the students are writing exams or on holidays. However, this is one example of an innovative approach and a win-win situation for the children, the parents and for the students who will gain valuable training and experience.

The role of parents as mediators/therapists

The mediator model is based on family involvement, enlisting family members as therapists to implement treatment programs. This model allows more families to be served by a small number of trained professionals. The professional meets with the family several times at the beginning of the intervention to do an assessment, formulate a treatment plan and train the family in carrying out the intervention. Following this, the family carries out the intervention in the home. The professional then collects and analyzes the data from the family and provides ongoing feedback. The ability of the family to carry out the intervention on a day-to-day basis allows the trained professional to work with many families at the same time.

An important advantage of this model is that it involves families in the process of change. The family's expertise and knowledge of their family member with a disability are an integral part of the assessment and critical to the implementation of the intervention. This collaboration between professionals and family members should result in the family feeling a sense of ownership of the process. However, many parents who are in need of services delivered in this fashion do not have the time, energy, or personal resources to be able to carry out the role of mediator. Often, these families are at the end of their own resources when they contact agencies for support. The expectation that the family can take on the extra burden of carrying out the intervention may not be realistic in many cases, and may be setting up

the intervention and the family to fail. Some families are not good candidates to be mediators because of their own physical, cognitive, or emotional challenges. In the mediator model, a family member takes on the role of home therapist. To take on this role, the family member must be highly motivated, follow through consistently, and carry out the dual roles of caregiver and therapist. These blurred boundaries between professional and personal roles can make it difficult for the family member to serve as a good mediator and can put stress on the family system. When services are only offered in terms of the mediator model, many families are placed in a no-win situation where either they cannot engage the services and carry on as is when they need more support or they become engaged in a process that they are unable to carry out successfully. Such situations put added pressure on a family system that is already heavily burdened.

Despite the absence of research evidence supporting the importance of family involvement, the mediator model has been used extensively in a wide variety of interventions. One of the best known is the involvement of parents of children with autism spectrum disorders in the implementation of intensive behavioural interventions (IBI; Solish & Perry, 2008). Recent research focussing on factors contributing to parent involvement has highlighted parental self-efficacy or confidence in their ability as a significant predictor of parental involvement. Parental knowledge and belief in IBI were found to be correlated with involvement; however, they did not emerge as predictors of involvement. Although

Box 3

Bruce, who is 32 and has Down syndrome, was diagnosed last year with depression. For a time, doctors thought that Bruce was showing signs of early dementia (e.g., confusion, withdrawal, irritability, loss of skills). His mother, Barbara, researched the topic and found that diagnostic overshadowing (i.e., attributing symptoms to intellectual disability) can often lead to misdiagnosis. Once Bruce was referred to a dual diagnosis team, his problems were recognized as being related to depression but also to hypothyroidism, which is common in people with Down syndrome. Bruce was given medication to address these issues. Barbara and her son have since become involved in the Clinical Learning Centre at the local university. They regularly participate in education sessions for medical students about developmental disabilities, and Bruce has become a standardized patient helping medical students to improve their interviewing and communication skills.

the mediator model continues to be viewed as a useful and important model of service delivery in the field of developmental disabilities, further research is needed to evaluate its effectiveness.

The role of parents as educators

Ignorance is often cited by parents of a child with special needs as being one of the major challenges they face. In addition to parents becoming increasingly involved in programs designed to facilitate their child's development, many parents find themselves taking on the role of educator with professionals as well as with the public at large. Many parents feel that they have no choice but to try to meet their child's needs, first by informing themselves and then by passing on the information to others. Parents and professionals alike have highlighted the need for more education about developmental disabilities (Minnes, Lauckner, & Recoskie, 2007; Minnes & Steiner, 2009; Phillips, Morrison, & Davis, 2004). Parents also have suggested that they are better equipped to deal with professionals if they are well informed. One parent wrote, *"I have had good success with my doctors. I tell my doctors things they didn't know about Down syndrome"* (Nachshen, 1996). Educating others about their child's disability also helps many parents to deal with those around them. A parent explained: *"Most of the time when I name the syndrome, people have never heard of it and want to know more about this syndrome because it's so uncommon. I have had great experiences with explaining her condition. People have really accepted her."* Other suggestions from parents include the development of readily available and understandable information for the general public, grandparents and friends. Research is needed to explore the role of the media in providing such information. For example, television programs such as *Life Goes On*, have been shown to have potential in educating the public and changing attitudes about developmental disabilities (Hall & Minnes, 1999). Although many parents appreciate their role as educator, it is important to note that this may also be an added burden for parents. Many parents cope with the challenges they face in dealing with the public by trusting their own judgement. One parent wrote, *"We just do what we have to for our son, and if other people can't understand that, then we don't waste our time on them."* Another parent offered this advice: *"Ignore those who disapprove."*

The role of parents as caregivers

Despite the pressures on parents of individuals with developmental disabilities to be therapists and advocates, the main role of these parents, as with most parents, is that of caregiver. When a child with a developmental disability is born into a family, much of the family's energy is spent caring for their child with special needs. Families face a variety of challenges across the lifespan. Some of these are related to developmental transitions that take place in all families, including the child's progression through early developmental stages such as learning to walk and talk and later transitions such as starting school, puberty, developing friendships, and making plans for the future. Other challenges are related to events that are not experienced by parents of nondisabled children, including disability-related issues such as diagnosis, having to deal with problem behaviours, and making plans for future accommodation and guardianship.

The stress experienced by parents of children with disabilities has been well documented in the research literature (e.g., Schneider, Wedgewood, Llewellyn, & McConnell, 2006). Some studies support a "wear-and-tear" hypothesis suggesting that family stress increases over time. Ongoing concerns may accumulate and contribute to chronic stress across the child's lifespan (Webster, Majnemer, Platt, & Shevell, 2008). In contrast to the view that stress in parents of children with developmental disabilities is chronic, many parents indicate intermittent periods of emotional distress corresponding to significant transition periods and stages in their child's development (Minnes & Woodford, 2004; Wikler, 1986). For example, parents are often concerned about their children meeting developmental milestones (e.g., walking, talking, puberty, leaving school). Moreover, differences between children with and without developmental disabilities are often highlighted during these periods and present unique challenges for families with children with disabilities.

Caregiver stress has been found to vary according to a number of factors, such as the age of the child (Baker, Blacher, Crnic, & Edelbrock, 2002), the type and degree of disability, and behavioural challenges (Hastings & Johnson, 2001; Nachshen, Garcin, & Minnes, 2005). Differences in parental stress may not only be the result of differences in the child's temperament, social responsiveness, and behaviour, but also the availability of support services. Although greater caregiving stress frequently is found with greater dependency and management needs and more severe degrees of disability, some researchers have found that parents of children with milder disabilities report more caregiving stress. The behaviour and appearance of children with milder disabilities may be closer to what is perceived as normal or typical and, as a result, parents may develop unrealistic expectations for their child, whereas parents of children with more severe disabilities may be less able to deny or overlook problems (Minnes, 1988b).

In a study conducted in Ontario (Nachshen, 1996),

parents of children with developmental disabilities, including fragile X syndrome, Down syndrome or developmental disability due to other causes, indicated that the diagnosis of their child as having a developmental disability was a major issue for their family. Qualitative studies (Minnes, Laukner, & Recoskie, 2007; Minnes & Steiner, 2009) also have highlighted challenges associated with the diagnostic process, particularly for parents of children with fragile X syndrome and autism. Parents often sense that something is not right about their child's development but these concerns may not be taken seriously by professionals. Parents of children with fragile X syndrome found physicians' lack of interest in learning about the condition and a series of misdiagnoses to be major challenges. Parents of children with autism spoke of the difficulty of obtaining a timely diagnosis in order to access services. In such cases, a number of parents resorted to paying privately rather than waiting for public diagnostic services (Minnes et al., 2008; Minnes & Steiner, 2009).

Other issues of parental concern include: explaining to others about their child's disability; dealing with professionals in general; creating and/or finding opportunities for their child to make friends and participate in activities; meeting their own personal needs; choosing the best level of integration for their child; dealing with teachers and the education system; and dealing with their feelings about the cause of their child's disability (Nachshen, 1996).

Positive outcomes

A theme within the literature on parenting and families has been the considerable stress experienced by parents of children with developmental disabilities compared to parents of children without disabilities. There has been some concern, however, that too much emphasis on this tends to pathologize parents (Glidden, 1993) and, as a consequence, the focus of research has shifted in the past decade. Research has shown that many such families often cope well, and may not be distinguishable from families that do not have a child with disabilities (Perry, Harris, & Minnes, 2004). Indeed, many parents report positive impacts of having a child with a disability (Hastings & Taunt, 2002), including opportunities for personal growth, improved relations with others, and changes in philosophical or spiritual values (Scorgie & Sobsey, 2000), satisfaction with providing care (Rapanaro, Bartu, & Lee, 2008), and empowerment (Nachshen & Minnes, 2005). Reported positive impacts have also been shown to vary across cultural groups (Blacher & Baker, 2007).

Factors That Help Parents in Their Role as Caregiver

The stress associated with caring for a child with a developmental disability can be buffered by a number of individual and family resources. Four of the most important are highlighted below.

Family resources

Family adjustment and adaptation to change or stress have been associated with a number of resources that contribute to resiliency (McCubbin & McCubbin, 1996). In addition to personal resources and coping strategies used by individuals within a family, family system resources such as cohesiveness, communication, organization, control, and flexibility can often assist families under stress. Family cohesion or unity refers to the amount of bonding, trust, respect, and support in a family (McCubbin & McCubbin, 1996). Families that are cohesive tend to be encouraging, use listening skills, negotiate to avoid conflict, and foster a sense of belonging (Spina, Ziviani, & Nixon, 2005). Open communication patterns, use of organizational skills, and flexibility have also been found to contribute to family adaptation (McCubbin & McCubbin, 1996). The degree to which a family can find a balance between cohesiveness and independence, and between organization, control, and flexibility contributes to adaptation (Minnes, 1988a).

Financial resources are a critical factor for all families, but families of children with developmental disabilities are more likely to have lower socioeconomic status (Emerson, Hatton, Llewellyn, Blacher, & Graham, 2006; Lopes, 2008). Being of lower socioeconomic status and having additional expenses associated with the costs of raising a child with a disability can impose increased stress on the family (Lopes, 2008). Poverty can also be associated with poor parental health, a decreased sense of well-being, and poorer parenting practices, all of which can have adverse effects on children (Emerson, 2004).

Social support

Informal social support networks also can have a positive impact on family quality of life (Flynt, Wood, & Scott, 1992; Minnes et al., 1989; Trivette & Dunst, 1992). In addition, informal support has been found to be strongly related to confidence in parenting and optimism (Bailey, Nelson, Hebbeler, & Spiker, 2007). On the other hand, there is evidence to suggest that some, but not all, families of children with disabilities become socially isolated. Informal support from extended family, friends, and neighbours can be helpful, although parents frequently indicate that people beyond their immediate family do not understand their situations (Renwick & Brown, 1998).

An Ontario study (Nachshen, 1996) highlighted the support needs of parents. One mother spoke of her need for informal support stating, *"I felt ignored by my family and friends while in the hospital. Only one friend came to visit, and only because I didn't tell her the circumstances. People in general didn't know how to react, and [were] likely uncomfortable so they stayed away. I desperately needed people around me to support me and maybe say congratulations."* Parents also reported that ignorance and insensitivity in the general public are frequent challenges. When describing her experiences with people in the neighbourhood, one parent said, *"People who barely know us make comments on our situation and our child's condition or behaviour. I don't like being put on the spot, even if people 'mean well' with their remarks."*

Despite the challenges, parents still indicate that family life can be enjoyable and that other people in their lives can be supportive. This was one theme in a compilation of thoughtful reflections by professionals who were also parents of children with developmental disabilities in the United States (Turnbull & Turnbull, 1985), and was highlighted in a Toronto-based qualitative study of family quality of life (Renwick & Brown, 1998). One parent in the

Nachshen study (1996) stated that her spouse was optimistic about their son's capabilities and was very understanding about their child's needs: "*There are times when we need a break, (but) our family and friends are there.*"

Professional support

Although formal services are often assumed to provide support, and thus reduce family stress, this is not always the case. Families who use more services may have higher levels of stress and thus higher needs for services, or they may have lower levels of stress due to service-related assistance. Services can also potentially increase stress if the nature of service delivery is not effective (Blacher, Neece, & Paczkowski, 2005) or is not sufficiently family-centred (Trute, Hiebert-Murphy, & Wright, 2007). Furthermore, due to the changing availability of services at different ages (i.e., services for children and adults are often funded by different government Ministries), parents often need to seek out new services at transition points, which can add to already elevated stress levels.

Although it is generally assumed that more formal support from professionals and service agencies is beneficial for families of children with developmental disabilities, interactions with professionals have often been reported to contribute to parental distress rather than reducing it (Baxter, 1987). Many parents feel that professionals can be an important resource, but parents also describe problems when dealing with professionals (Nachshen, 1996). One parent noted at the time she was told of her son's diagnosis, "*It was very disappointing because two strange doctors brought my son to me and described what his condition was. It was not my own doctor.*" Another parent discovered her child's condition when she read the newborn's chart, which had accidentally been left open. Often, however, parents feel that the diagnosis of their child was made easier because of professionals who were thoughtful and caring, and had a positive attitude.

Physicians have often been criticized for being uninformed about developmental disabilities. "*They make important decisions for our children, but they are not as informed as they should be.*" Interestingly,

many parents feel that some professionals also lack information on their child's disability (Minnes & Steiner, 2009). One parent wrote, "*I find many times I'm more of an expert on Down syndrome, and particularly my son, than the so-called professionals.*" Efforts to educate professionals are not always met with success, as one parent pointed out: "*...all the literature I have given [my doctor] has been tucked away. He as much as told me he doesn't have time to read it*" (Nachshen, 1996). Older parents also have expressed concerns in this regard: "*[The doctors] won't do what you want them to do. It is difficult for medical people to accept ideas that come from parents.*" Another parent suggested that "*there needs to be increased understanding, education, and flexibility within the medical profession.*" In response to some of the concerns expressed by parents and others, Canadian guidelines for primary health care of individuals with developmental disabilities (Sullivan, Heng, Cameron, Lunsky, Cheetham, et al., 2006) have recently been developed in an effort to help family physicians better meet the needs of patients with developmental disabilities and their families.

In addition to feeling that others are ignorant of their child's condition, many parents feel that they do not have enough information themselves to deal adequately with the challenges that they face. One parent wrote, "*Not having enough information about fragile X makes it difficult to explain.*" In making decisions concerning integration in school, one respondent felt that it was "*difficult to get information [about the] successes and problems of full integration.*" This lack of information has also been highlighted by those dealing with their child's sexuality: "*We would like to know what others do about this. We are totally ignorant about how to handle this and it worries us very, very much!*"

Parents have indicated that teachers can be an important source of support. "*Her first kindergarten teacher was great and talked to me about her all the time — for example, her accomplishments, friends, hardships, etc. It made us feel good about her and her life around her.*" However, teachers frequently are also criticized for creating difficulties for the family. "*A teacher centred us out by speaking loudly about our son amongst other parents and children.*"

She should have been discreet and spoken privately to me" (Nachshen, 1996). All families are different and have different needs. However, one common complaint is that schools and community organizations are not flexible enough to meet those needs. Most parents seek full integration in the school system. Although some achieve success in that respect (often after years of struggling), many remain unsatisfied, feeling that the schools are reluctant to integrate and modify programs. One parent who felt more strongly about this issue, stated that *"forced integration [is a] farce — [there's] no such thing."* Another parent whose children were fully integrated was not satisfied for a different reason: *"I don't think integration into normal classrooms helps with our kids' social lives. Yes, they are well liked as a rule, but not invited to things by normal kids. They need opportunities to be with their peers — they seem to make the best friends with people like themselves."* Many parents feel that schools are not equipped to deal with their children appropriately, complaining of untrained teachers and a lack of one-on-one teaching for their child (Nachshen, 1996).

Support groups

Growing numbers of parents are participating in support groups in person or online. Research with parents of children with developmental disabilities has reported that parents involved in a support group report significant positive changes in their perceptions of their child compared to parents in a wait-list control group (Singer et al., 1999). Mandell & Salzer (2007) found that 66% of parents of children with autism spectrum disorders had participated in support groups. Potential benefits of such groups include providing emotional support, coping strategies, role models, a sense of belonging, and a sense of mastery or control (Solomon, Pistrang, & Barker, 2001). Online groups can be relatively cost-effective, include families in rural and remote areas, and reduce the need for travel and child care (Clifford & Minnes, 2010). Parents report that online support groups can be helpful for seeking information, connecting with other parents, and promoting advocacy, although parents also report frustration with confusing, unreliable, or overwhelmingly negative informa-

tion (Carter, 2009).

Opportunities to talk with other parents of children with similar challenges can be very helpful for parents. In the Nachshen (1996) study, the diagnosis of their child as having a developmental disability was made easier for one parent when *"a professional parent having experience with her own child with Down syndrome visited us and asked if we would like any information. We readily accepted and I started reading information before I left the hospital."* The same parent suggested that a list of parents who are interested in offering support to new parents of disabled children at the hospital for anyone who would like support would help to make the experience of the diagnosis easier for others in a similar situation. A support group would be extremely helpful to one parent who said, *"Most people do not want to hear about any difficulties or problems you're having."* Parents also have suggested that support groups for their nondisabled children would be helpful.

Coping with Caregiving Across the Lifespan

Some of the most commonly cited coping strategies for managing stress are problem-focused, emotion-focused, and appraisal or perception-focused coping (Folkman, Lazarus, Dunkel-Schetter, DeLongis, & Gruen, 1986). Parents who use problem-focused coping (i.e., attempting to alter the problem or situation), as opposed to emotion-focused coping strategies (i.e., attempting to reduce the emotional distress caused by the situation), have been found to report less stress and greater well-being (Glidden, Kiphart, Willoughby, & Bush, 1993; Shapiro, Blacher, & Lopez, 1998). Furthermore, parents with a greater internal locus of control, who rely on themselves rather than others, have been found to report less depression than those who report high external locus of control.

Cognitive appraisals (i.e., perception-focused coping) have also been found to contribute to parental adaptation (Hastings & Brown, 2002; Plant & Sanders, 2007). For example, older parents' perceptions of aging and stress have been found to mediate the relationship between parent health and depression (Minnes, Woodford, & Passey, 2007).

Table 1: Issues of Concern to Older Parents

Issue	Percent Rating Issue as Stressful	Mean Stress Score of Parents who Rated this Issue as Stressful (0-4)
Long-term planning for accommodation	83%	3.11
Planning for emotional and social support	68%	2.63
Creating opportunities	56%	2.53
Meeting your own personal needs	55%	2.16
Decision about accommodation in the home or in the community	54%	2.91
Time apart from offspring	51%	2.41
Planning for wills, trusts and guardianships	50%	2.68
Dealing with health professionals	50%	2.03
Transportation	48%	2.79
Financial issues	48%	2.55
Employment for child	46%	2.46
Diagnosis of disability	44%	2.43
Feelings about the cause of disability	39%	2.42
Explaining to others about the disability	39%	1.98
Level of integration	38%	2.5
Assistance with day to day care	38%	2.23
Meeting the needs of spouse	36%	2.14
Meeting the needs of other children	34%	2.3
Dealing with people day to day	33%	2
Maintaining satisfying friendships for self	31%	2.04
Dealing with child's sexuality	30%	2.33
Dealing with legal professionals	23%	2.59

Adapted with permission from Minnes & Woodford (2004); Minnes, Woodford, & Passey (2007).

Table 2: Service and Support Use and Needs of Older Parents for their Children

Services and Support for Offspring	Service Use	Service Need	t	p
Social/Recreational Activities	48%	76%	4.34	0.0001*
Case Management	63%	69%	2.06	0.044
Respite Care	44%	63%	4.28	0.0001*
Supported Employment	29%	63%	4.9	0.0001*
Day Program	32%	58%	5.31	0.0001*
Residential Placement	15%	53%	6.89	0.0001*
Special Medical	36%	37%	1.43	0.159
In-home Support	22%	36%	3.03	0.004*
Speech Language Therapy	9%	36%	4.49	0.0001*
Counselling	11%	28%	3.62	0.0001*
Social Work	16%	25%	2.32	0.024
Assistive Devices	22%	22%	-	-
Behaviour Management	6%	22%	3.74	.0001*
Physical Therapy	11%	14%	1.76	0.083
Occupational Therapy	5%	13%	2.06	0.044
Psychology	7%	13%	1.35	0.182

*p<.01   *Adapted with permission from Minnes & Woodford (2004); Minnes, Woodford, & Passey (2007).*

Other cognitive appraisals associated with positive adaptation in mothers include: 1) a sense of meaning in their experiences as parents of a child with special needs, 2) a sense of mastery and control, 3) an optimistic outlook and trust in others who care (Affleck & Tennen, 1993), 4) focussing on the positive or reframing (Hastings, Allen, McDermott, & Still, 2002), 5) persistence, and 6) information seeking (Nachshen, 1996). Although spirituality or religiosity have received limited attention in the literature, there is some evidence indicating that they also can be a resource. Parents may gain social support from other members of the spiritual or religious community and spiritual or religious beliefs may contribute to a sense of meaning or empowerment (Speraw, 2006).

The Changing Roles of Aging Parents

Improvements in lifestyles, environments, and health care have led to increased numbers of people with developmental disabilities living into their 50s, 60s and beyond. For many of these people, parents and other family members continue to provide care at home. The burden of care is very often greater at this stage, however, because of aging parents' declining health, strength, and patience, and because of age-related changes in the health, ability, and behaviour of older individuals with developmental disabilities.

The well-being of older parents of adults with developmental disabilities has been studied in relation to stresses associated with both caregiving responsibilities and their own aging (Minnes & Woodford, 2004; Minnes, Woodford, & Passey, 2007; see Table 1). Long-term planning for accommodation for individuals with developmental disabilities is a primary concern of older parents. For example, Minnes & Woodford (2000) found that 83% of parents rated this issue as stressful. One parent explained: *"Our family was on a waiting list for five years and only moved from 87th to 85th place. As older parents, that's just not acceptable or realistic"* (Minnes & Woodford, 2000, p. 39). Accommodation is not the only concern, however. Even parents who have found accommodation for their child express concern about ensuring that the child's ongoing emotional and social support needs will be met: *"It is very difficult to plan for an adult. I am trying to think of what is best for [my son]. Caregivers must consider the unique needs of the individual"* (Minnes & Woodford, 2000, p. 50). Another parent commented: *"Will they have the time to do little things for our son that we do now?...Is there enough time to look after the little...nice things in life...take him for a walk, or to a movie or to town?"* (Minnes & Woodford, 2000, p. 39). Transportation is also a major concern for older parents: *"I have to do it all myself if my son is going to do anything. I spend $400/*

month on taxis. The only other option is that my son sits at home and does nothing" (Minnes & Woodford, 2000, p. 52).

Although the older parents in this study rated their life satisfaction as high, they also indicated that they had many unmet service and support needs, particularly in terms of productive activities for their adult children, parent relief services, and residential placements (see Table 2).

Older parents expressed concerns about finding accommodation. They reported dissatisfaction with the range of accommodation options, concerns for their child's feelings about moving away from the family home, and concerns about the adequacy of care. In addition to their concerns, however, parents also made the following recommendations about how to improve their lives (Minnes & Woodford, 2000, p. 68):

1. Assist older parents to plan for alternative accommodation, while providing ongoing emotional and social support for their sons and daughters with developmental disabilities; in addition, assist with wills, trusts, and guardianship with:
   i. more readily available and detailed information about options,
   ii. parent support groups and educational packages to facilitate information exchange,
   iii. more training for lawyers, doctors and health professionals about developmental disabilities, and
   iv. a change in legislation to allow parents to leave their homes to their child without it affecting their disability pensions.
2. Ease concerns of older parents regarding the nature of alternative accommodation through:
   i. development of permanent homes for less than four individuals, and
   ii. improvements to community residences, including more family-like environments (less structure), a better standard of living, and greater continuity of staff and care.
3. Ease the burden of care experienced by parents of adults with developmental disabilities and ease the transition from home to community by providing:

i. more day programs for senior citizens with developmental disabilities, and

ii. more readily available respite care.

4. Ease problems associated with transportation by providing:

i. funding for specialized transportation for persons with developmental disabilities and/or an allowance to help pay for taxis or to hire someone to accompany their offspring on public transport.

The Roles of Other Family Members

Although the presence of a child with a disability in the family can be particularly challenging for parents, the impact is often felt by other members of the family as well. Parents often face challenges in meeting the needs of the other children in the family (Minnes & Nachshen, 1997). Some families feel that their nondisabled children are forced to grow up too fast. As one parent stated, *"Having a handicapped little brother, at times, has created stress for my daughter and son. He doesn't learn as quickly as a non-handicapped child. Often, he makes messes and gets into mischief. Sometimes the older two are frustrated because we depend on them so much to help us with their little brother. I sometimes feel guilty for robbing them of their childhood."* Other parents feel that their nondisabled children receive less attention than they deserve.

Studies of in-home interactions, activities of older and younger children with developmental disabilities and their nondisabled siblings indicate that the role of siblings is often important (Stoneman, Brody, Davis, Crapps, & Malone, 1991). Relationships between disabled and nondisabled siblings are frequently different in that the responsibility for caregiving and the role of teacher are assumed by siblings, especially sisters. These differences have been found to increase with age and with greater language and adaptive skill deficits in the younger sibling. Similar patterns of role relationships have been found between younger siblings of older children with developmental disabilities where younger siblings commonly assumed roles normally held by the oldest children in the family. In contrast to older sib-

lings of nondisabled children, who tended to assume the dominant role, the younger siblings of disabled children were found to be more involved in teaching and behaviour management. However, contrary to expectation, older siblings with developmental disabilities were also found to adopt teacher and helper roles more frequently than nondisabled older siblings. This behaviour may have been learned through modelling of the younger sibling's helping behaviour (Brody, Stoneman, Davis, & Crapps, 1991).

In adulthood, many nondisabled siblings maintain high levels of contact with their brother or sister with a disability (Seltzer, Greenberg, Orsmond, & Lounds, 2005). On average, siblings make up about one-quarter of the social network of disabled adults (Krauss, Seltzer, & Goodman, 1992). Gender plays a role in sibling involvement, with sisters typically providing more emotional and instrumental support to their disabled siblings than brothers (Orsmond & Seltzer, 2000). Additionally, sisters are more likely to expect future caregiving roles and to expect to co-reside with their disabled sibling when parents are no longer able to provide support (Greenberg, Seltzer, Orsmond, & Krauss, 1999). In a meta-analysis of sibling research, Heller and Keileing Arnold (2010) concluded that, despite mixed results, the psychosocial outcomes for siblings are generally positive.

Many parents of disabled adult children have not completed future planning for their sons and daughters, including making decisions about guardianship, caregiving, and residential needs (Heller & Kramer, 2009). Additionally, parents are often hesitant to involve their nondisabled children in planning for the future of their disabled son or daughter (Heller & Caldwell, 2006). Siblings are most likely to be involved in residential planning and identifying a future caregiver, and they are less often involved in more formal matters, such as establishing powers of attorney and creating letters of intent (Heller & Kramer, 2009).

Despite the expectations of co-residence held by many siblings, longitudinal research shows that most adults with disabilities do not co-reside with their siblings after transitioning out of their parents' homes (Freedman, Krauss, & Seltzer, 1997). However, many siblings still do play an active role

Box 4

Sandra is a 51-year-old woman who lives with her husband and her two teenage sons. She works part-time as a nurse and her husband owns a small business. Sandra's younger brother Gerald has Down syndrome, and he lives with their mother. Their father passed away 3 years ago. Sandra and Gerald's mother is 82 years old, and she is experiencing increased difficulty with living independently and acting as Gerald's caregiver. Sandra recently spoke to her mother about moving to an assisted living facility and finding a home in the community for Gerald; her mother is reluctant to have Gerald live with someone other than a family member. Sandra and Gerald have a good relationship, and they see each other weekly. Sandra is concerned about Gerald's future and she wants to be involved in his life; however, she does not believe that she has the time or resources to become Gerald's full time caregiver. It is possible for Gerald to move into the assisted living facility with their mother; however, Sandra believes that living in a facility designed for seniors would limit Gerald's ability to spend time with friends his own age. Sandra and her mother worked with Gerald's case manager to develop a solution. Through a community agency, they found an associate family for Gerald to live with full time. This will allow Gerald to live in a safe, family environment within the community where he can continue to work at his part-time job and spend time with his friends while still having regular visits with his mother.

in the lives of disabled individuals after the transition out of parental care. Most commonly, siblings are involved in making important life decisions, managing finances, and advocating for services for their disabled sister or brother. In addition, adult siblings may be involved in monitoring service provisions, managing medical care, coordinating social contacts, fulfilling legal roles (e.g., legal guardian), providing primary care, and providing support to others who provide primary care (Bigby, 1997).

While struggling to meet the needs of their non-disabled children, many parents also feel that they have been unable to fully meet the needs of their spouse or partner (Renwick & Brown, 1998). A lack of free time to spend alone together is often given as the main reason for this difficulty. A lack of time may also make it difficult for parents to meet their own needs.

Grandparents are often overlooked as people who sometimes play an important role in families of children with developmental disabilities. In some instances, grandparents can help to relieve some of the burden of parenting borne by their children by acting as extra caregivers for their grandchildren with or without a disability. In other families, however, where parents are unable to care for their children, grandparents become the primary caregivers. As a result, grandparents also may need information and support. Curricula have been developed

specifically to help grandparents. Such programs provide up-to-date information on a variety of topics related to developmental disability and help to prevent additional family stress caused by grandparents who may give their children inaccurate or outdated advice about what they should do to help their grandchild (Meyer & Vadasy, 1986).

Meeting the Needs of Families in the 21st Century

The primary role of families continues to be care for their family member with a disability. However, with the shift from institutional to community-based care, caregiving responsibilities have extended across the lifespan. Unfortunately, service provision tends to focus primarily on the needs of the identified person and the needs of family members may be overlooked. Although disability services and supports frequently focus on the needs of parents of young children with disabilities, experience and recent research are now helping us to understand that the needs of families are ongoing and that a variety of services is required for all members of families at different stages of the development of the child with a disability.

Although community-based accommodation and services for persons with developmental disabilities have been the preferred approach for at least

Box 5

Marion and her daughter Sue live in a rural area. Sue has an intellectual disability but has many independent living skills and was a great help when her father was terminally ill. Marion and her husband have run a business in the small town where they live for many years and Marion decided to continue after her husband's death. Sue would like to enroll in a continuing education program at a community college in the city, but there is no public transport available and her mother is not able to take the time for the 90 minute drive. Sue also would like to participate in other activities such as Special Olympics, not offered in her area. Marion contacted the Association for Community Living in the city and they were able to find accommodation for Sue during the week with an associate family. Sue has become more independent since her move to the city. She has learned to use public transport, she enjoys helping her associate family with their young children and has made new friends through her college program and Special Olympics activities.

the past 40 years, and parents now routinely keep their children at home, there is an ongoing need for out-of-home placements. The decision to house a child outside the family home is often an extremely difficult one for parents. Research regarding such decisions indicates that placement decisions depend upon a complex combination of factors, including the availability and use of formal support services as well as parental thoughts and feelings (Bromley & Blacher, 1989). Higher placement rates have been related to the child's level of dependency and maladaptive behaviour, day-to-day stressful events, disruption in family relations, and family mental health problems (Black, Molaison, & Smull, 1990). Parents' feelings of attachment to the child and guilt, as well as the availability of formal support services, helped to delay placement (Bromley & Blacher, 1991). Respite care is often considered to be a factor preventing out-of-home placement, although research by Perry and Black (1997) suggested that use of respite care may indeed reflect a transitional stage between the child living at home and the child being placed in the community.

Respite care and out-of-home placement are critical supports for many older parents. Still, older parents are frequently more reluctant than younger parents to use such services. They often continue to care for their child with a disability for as long as possible due to the interdependence with the child, the sense of purpose derived from caregiving, and concern over the lack of acceptable services (Heller & Factor, 1991). In one study, 40% of younger caregivers were found to use residential services, compared to only

8% of older caregivers (Rinck & Calkins, 1995).

In Ontario, finding appropriate community placements for adult children with developmental disabilities can be extremely difficult for older parents. Research has shown that older parents find long term planning to be very stressful (Minnes & Woodford, 2004; Smith, Majesky, & McClenny, 1996) and long waiting lists add to the problem. As a result, residential placement of adults with developmental disabilities who have lived at home often does not occur until after the death of the parent (Heller, 1995).

Clearly there is a need for a range of respite care and accommodation services to address the needs of families across the lifespan. Furthermore, introducing parents early to the importance of future planning and discussion of options across the lifespan could be very helpful to parents and individuals with developmental disabilities.

Evolving family and professional roles: directions for the future

Turnbull & Turnbull (1986) documented how much the roles of parents have changed since the 1950s. Parents originally were seen as clients, and in many cases as "the problem." In more recent years, parents have taken on the role of educators and advocates, and often the most important sources of care and support. Professionals are also sometimes seen as advocates, but at other times they are viewed as adversarial or obstructionist, not helpful, and not understanding. Accounts in the literature have indicated strong parental dissatisfaction with professionals and services, and point to the need for professional services to carefully evaluate what they are doing (Baxter, 1989; Brown, 2010).

The development of parent/professional partnerships is an important goal for clinicians, parents, and researchers alike. Recent efforts to adopt more family-centred approaches to service delivery and efforts to evaluate the positive outcomes for families (Trute et al., 2008) are important developments that merit greater attention in research and practice. The quality of life of individuals with developmental disabilities and their families rests in the balance.

Summary

In the past 40 years, the roles of parents and families and the roles of professionals in relation to families have changed within a changing socio-political context. With the move to community-based care, the need for more parent-professional partnerships has become clear. As with coping and adjustment to other unexpected, non-normative events with long-term consequences for families, the adjustment of parents of children with developmental disabilities depends upon a number of factors, including the characteristics of the child, the resources available within and beyond the immediate family, individual perceptions and coping strategies, and the ability to develop and change over time. Research with families indicates that parents do not always feel heard or respected by professionals and caregivers. Moreover, research has provided some important insights into the experiences of family members and the factors that contribute to coping and adjustment. In light of this, the following are a few guidelines to consider when helping families:

1. Recognize transition periods and acknowledge that such times can be stressful for families.
2. Consider and anticipate new and changing roles that may occur at such times.
3. Listen carefully to parents and respect their priorities, which may not be the same as yours.
4. Take an individualized approach that incorporates the specific wishes of the family.
   Remember to consider the needs of all family members.
5. Be flexible and be prepared to learn.

For Further Thought and Discussion

1. What are your assumptions about the impact of having a person with a disability in the family?
2. How can we as professionals, paid caregivers, or volunteers be more supportive of families?
3. When working with families of children with developmental disabilities:
   a. Are we asking too much of families or too little, given their levels of stress and resources?
   b. Are we giving too much or too little?
   c. Are our suggestions consistent with the family's priorities?
   d. Are our priorities consistent with the family's stage in the life cycle?

More Resources

G. Allen Roeher Institute
http://indie.ca/roeher
The Roeher Institute is a source of research information focussing on factors promoting the equality, participation, and self-determination of people with intellectual and other disabilities with a view to reducing societal barriers that limit the well-being of people with disabilities.

Ontario Association for Community Living
www.communitylivingontario.ca/
The Ontario Association for Community Living mandate includes advocacy and promotion of full inclusion for people who have an intellectual disability in all aspects of community life.

Family Village
http://www.familyvillage.wisc.edu/
Family Village provides web-based information and resources, and communication opportunities for persons with intellectual and other disabilities, for their families, and for service providers.

The Beach Center on Disability
http://www.beachcenter.org/
http://www.lsi.ukans.edu/beach/beachhp.htm
The Beach Center on Disability located on the University of Kansas campus. Their website provides extensive resources for parents, including guides on a wide range of topics such as: parent to parent support, transition into school, care coordination. It

also provides relevant journal articles, research, and policy information.

Children's Disabilities Information

http://www.childrensdisabilities.info

This website provides articles and resources with a view to empowering parents of children with disabilities and special needs.

Association for Birth Defect Children, Inc. (ABDC)

http://www.birthdefects.org

Birth Defect Research for Children, Inc. (BDRC) provides parents with information about birth defects and support services for their children. BDRC has a parent-matching program that helps families of children with birth defects to communicate with similar families. BDRC also sponsors the National Birth Defect Registry, which supports research investigating links between birth defects and exposure to environmental toxins.

Miriam Foundation

http://www.miriamfoundation.ca

The Miram Foundation provides funding in support of rehabilitation, and vocational services and residential accommodation for individuals with intellectual disabilities or Autism Spectrum Disorders. In addition to promoting increased socialization and community integration, the Miriam Foundation, through the Abe Gold Learning & Research Centre, supports research and educational initiatives and publishes and publishes Exceptional Family, a magazine for parents and caregivers of children with disabilities.

Exceptional Parent Magazine &
The Family Education Network

http://www.families.com/sr.asp?ch_no=20

This organization focuses on all disabilities.

The Autism Treatment Network – Toronto

http://www.autismspeaks.org/science/programs/atn/

The ATN is a network of treatment and research centres dedicated to improving medical care for children and adolescents with autism.

The Canadian Down Syndrome Society

http://www.cdss.ca

The Canadian Down Syndrome Society provides information and education about Down syndrome to parents, individuals with Down syndrome and families across the lifespan.

Autism Ontario (formerly Autism Society Ontario)

autismontario.com

Autism Ontario provides information and education, supports research, and advocates for programs and services for individuals with autism spectrum disorders and their families and caregivers.

Links to Learning

Linkstolearning.ca

This website was developed by parents to provide resources for parents and families.

Autism Spectrum Disorders Canadian-American Research Consortium

www.autismresearch.ca

ASD-CARC is a multi-disciplinary team of researchers and clinicians working with families in Canada and internationally.

Autism Connects

www.asdcarc.com

Autism Connects provides opportunities for participation in research, updates on resources and events.

Sibling Support Project

http://www.siblingsupport.org/

This website focuses on increasing awareness of the needs and contributions of siblings of individuals with disabilities. It also provides information on developing workshops, listserves, and websites for young and adult siblings.

Association for Children with a Disability

http://www.acd.org.au/siblings/index.htm

This website provides web resources for parents and siblings in Australia.

Chromosome Deletion Outreach (CDO)

http://members.aol.com:80/cdousa/cdo.htm

This organization focuses on chromosome deletions, inversions, and additions.

References

Affleck, G., & Tennen, H. (1993). Cognitive adaptation to adversity: Insights from parents of medically fragile infants. In A. P. Turnbull, J. M. Patterson, S. K. Behr, D. L. Murphy, J. G. Marquis, & M. J. Blue-Banning (Eds.), *Cognitive coping, families and disability* (pp. 135-150). Baltimore: Paul H. Brookes.

Bailey, Jr., D. B., Nelson, L., Hebbeler, K., & Spiker, D. (2007). Modeling the impact of formal and informal supports for young children with disabilities and their families. *Pediatrics, 120,* e992-e1001.

Baker, B., & Blacher, J., Crnic, K., & Edelbrock, C. (2002). Behavior problems and parenting stress in families of three year old children with and without developmental delays. *American Journal on Mental Retardation, 107,* 433-444.

Baxter, C. (1987). Professional services as support: Perceptions of parents. *Australia and New Zealand Journal of Developmental Disabilities, 13,* 243-253.

Baxter, C. (1989). Parent-perceived attitudes of professionals: Implications for service providers. *Disability, Handicap & Society, 4,* 259-269.

Bigby, C. (1997). Parental substitutes? The role of siblings in the lives of older people with intellectual disability. *Journal of Gerontological Social Work, 29,* 3-21.

Blacher, J., & Baker, B. (2007). Positive impact of intellectual disability on families. *American Journal on Mental Retardation, 112,* 330-348.

Blacher, J., Neece, C. L., & Paczkowski, E. (2005). Families and intellectual disability. *Current Opinion in Psychiatry, 18* (5), 507-513.

Black, M. M., Molaison, V. A., & Smull, M. W. (1990). Families caring for a young adult with mental retardation: Service needs and urgency of community living requests. *American Journal on Mental Retardation, 95,* 32-39.

Brody, G. H., Stoneman, Z., Davis, C. H., & Crapps. J. M. (1991). Observations of the role relations and behavior between older children with mental retardation and their younger siblings. *American Journal on Mental Retardation, 95,* 527-536.

Bromley, B., & Blacher, J. (1991). Parental reasons for out-of-home placement of children with severe handicaps. *Mental Retardation, 29,* 275-280.

Brown, I. (2010). Family quality of life: A comparison of trends in eight countries. In. V. P. Prasher (Ed.), *Comtempory issues in intellectual disabilities* (pp. 255-264). New York: Nova Publishers.

Carter, I. (2009). Positive and negative experiences of parents involved in online self-help groups for Autism. *Journal on Developmental Disabilities, 15,* 44-52.

Clifford, T., & Minnes, P. (2010). *Developing an online support group for parents of children with Autism Spectrum Disorders: Lessons learned.* Poster presented at the Ontario Association on Developmental Disabilities Research Special Interest Group conference. Toronto, March 31, 2010.

Couper, J. (2004). Who should pay for intensive behavioural intervention in autism? A parent's view. *Journal of Paediatric Child Health, 40,* 559–561.

Davies, S., & Hall, D. (2005). Contact a family: Professionals and parents in partnership. *Archives of Diseases in Children, 90,* 1053–1057.

Emerson, E. (2004). Poverty and children with intellectual disabilities in the world's richer countries. *Journal of Intellectual & Developmental Disability, 29,* 319-338.

Emerson, E., Hatton, C., Llewellyn, G., Blacher, J., & Graham, H. (2006). Socio-economic position, household composition, health status and indicators of well-being of mothers of children with and without intellectual disabilities. *Journal of Intellectual Disability Research, 50,* 862-873.

Flynt, S. W., Wood, T. A., & Scott, R. L. (1992). Social support of mothers of children with mental retardation. *American Journal of Mental Retardation, 4,* 233-236.

Folkman, S., Lazarus, R. S., Dunkel-Schetter, C., DeLongis, A., & Gruen, R. (1986). The dynamics of a stressful encounter: Cognitive appraisal, coping, and encounter outcomes. *Journal of Personality and Social Psychology, 50,* 992-1003.

Freedman, R., Krauss, M., & Seltzer, M. (1997). Aging parents' residential plans for adults with mental retardation. *Mental Retardation, 35,* 114-135.

Glidden, L. M. (1993). What we do not know about families with children who have developmental disabilities: Questionnaire on Resources and Stress as a case study. *American Journal on Mental Retardation, 97,* 481-495.

Glidden, L. M., Kiphart, M. J., Willoughby, J. C., & Bush, B. A. (1993). Family functioning when rearing children with developmental disabilities. In A. P. Turnbull, J. M. Patterson, S. K. Behr, D. L. Murphy, J. G. Marquis, & M. J. Blue-Banning (Eds.), *Cognitive coping, families and disability* (pp. 183-194). Baltimore: Paul H. Brookes.

Greenberg, J. S., Seltzer, M. M., Orsmond, C. I., & Krauss, M. W. (1999). Siblings of adults with mental illness or mental retardation: Current involvement and expectation of future caregiving. *Psychiatric Services, 5*, 1214-1219.

Hall, H., & Minnes, P. (1999). Attitudes toward persons with Down syndrome: The impact of television. *Journal of Developmental and Physical Disabilities, 11*, 61-76.

Hastings, R. P., Allen, R., McDermott, K., & Still, D. (2002). Factors related to positive perceptions in mothers of children with intellectual disabilities. *Journal of Applied Research in Intellectual Disabilities, 15*, 269-275.

Hastings, R. P., & Brown T. (2002). Behavior problems of children with autism, parental self-efficacy, and mental health. *American Journal on Mental Retardation, 107*, 222-232.

Hastings, R., & Johnson, E. (2001). Stress in UK families conducting intensive home-based behavioural interventions for their young child with autism. *Journal of Autism and Developmental Disorders, 31*(3), 327-336.

Hastings, R. P., & Taunt, H. M. (2002). Positive perceptions in families of children with developmental disabilities. *American Journal on Mental Retardation, 107*, 116-127.

Hastings, R. P., & Taunt H. M. (2002). Positive perceptions in families of children with developmental disabilities. *American Journal on Mental Retardation, 107*, 116-127.

Heller, T. (1995). Aging caregivers of persons with disabilities: Changes in burden and placement desire. In K. A. Roberto (Ed.), *The elderly caregiver: Caring for adults with developmental disabilities* (pp. 21-38). Thousand Oaks, CA: Sage Publications.

Heller, T., & Caldwell, J. (2006). Supporting aging caregivers and adults with developmental disabilities in future planning. *Mental Retardation, 44*(3), 189-202.

Heller, T., & Factor, A. (1991). Permanency planning for adults with mental retardation living with family caregivers. *American Journal on Mental Retardation, 96*, 163-176.

Heller, T., & Keiling Arnold, C. (2010). Siblings of adults with developmental disabilities: Psychosocial outcomes, relationships and future planning. *Journal of Policy and Practice in Intellectual Disabilities, 7*, 16-25.

Heller, T., & Kramer, J. (2009). Involvement of adult siblings of people with developmental disabilities in future planning. *Intellectual and Developmental Disabilities, 47*, 208-219.

Krauss, M. W., Seltzer, M. M., & Goodman, S. J. (1992). Social support networks of adults with retardation who live at home. *American Journal on Mental Retardation, 96*, 432-441.

Lopes, V. (2008). *Factors contributing to the successful transition of preschoolers with and without developmental delay into school.* Unpublished master's thesis, Queen's University, Kingston, ON.

Mandell, D. S., & Salzer, M .S. (2007). Who joins support groups among parents of children with autism? *Autism, 11*, 111-122.

McCubbin, M. A., & McCubbin, H. I . (1996). Resiliency in families: A conceptual model of family adjustment in response to stress and crises. In H. I. McCubbin, A. I. Thompson, & M. A. McCubbin (Eds.), *Family assessment: Resiliency, coping and adaptation — Inventories for research and practice* (pp. 1–64). Madison, WI: University of Wisconsin.

Meyer, D., & Vadasy, P. (1986). *Grandparents workshops: How to organize workshops for grandparents of children with handicaps.* Seattle, WA: University of Washington Press.

Minnes, P. (1988a). Family resources and stress associated with a mentally retarded child. *American Journal on Mental Retardation, 93*, 184-192.

Minnes, P. (1988b). Family stress associated with a developmentally handicapped child. In N. Ellis & N. Bray (Eds.), *International review of research in mental retardation, vol. 15* (pp. 195-226). New York: Academic Press.

Minnes, P., Lauckner, H., & Recoskie, K. (2007). Healthcare concerns of parents of individuals with fragile X syndrome: Preliminary results from qualitative analyses. *Journal on Developmental Disabilities, 13*, 119-132.

Minnes, P., McShane, J., Forkes, S., Green, S., Clement, B., & Card, L. (1989). Coping resources of parents of developmentally handicapped children living in rural communities. *Australia and New Zealand Journal of Developmental Disabilities, 15,* 109-118.

Minnes, P. M., & Nachshen, J. S. (1997). The Family Stress and Support Questionnaire: Focussing on the needs of parents. *Journal on Developmental Disabilities, 5,* 67-77.

Minnes, P., & Steiner, K. (2009). Parent views on enhancing the quality of healthcare for their children with Fragile X syndrome, Autism or Down syndrome. *Child Care, Health & Development, 35*(2), 250–256.

Minnes, P., & Woodford, L. (2000). *Well-being of older caregivers of adults with developmental disabilities.* Unpublished report to the Ontario Ministry of Community and Social Services, Developmental Services Branch.

Minnes, P., & Woodford, L. (2004). Well-being in aging parents caring for an adult with a developmental disability. *Journal on Developmental Disabilities, 11,* 47-66.

Minnes, P., Woodford, L., & Passey, J. (2007). Mediators of well-being in aging family caregivers of adults with intellectual disabilities. *Journal of Applied Research in Intellectual Disability, 20,* 539-552.

Munro, J. D. (1991). Training families in the "step approach model" for effective advocacy. *Canada's Mental Health, 39,* 1-6.

Nachshen, J. S. (1996). *Parental stress in families of children with developmental disabilities: A pilot study using the Family Stress and Support Questionnaire.* Unpublished B.A. Honours thesis. Department of Psychology, Queen's University at Kingston, Canada.

Nachshen, J. S., Garcin, N., & Minnes, P. (2005). Problem behaviour in children with intellectual disabilities: Parenting stress, empowerment, and school services. *Mental Health Aspects of Developmental Disabilities, 8,* 105-114.

Nachshen, J. S., & Jamieson, J. (2000). Advocacy, stress and quality of life in parents of children with developmental disabilities. *Developmental Disabilities Bulletin, 28,* 39-55.

Nachshen, J. S., & Minnes P. (2005). Empowerment in parents of school-aged children with and with-out developmental disabilities. *Journal of Intellectual Disability Research, 49,* 889-904.

Nelson, D., Howard, V. F., & McLaughlin, T. F. (1993). Empowering parents to become advocates for their own children with disabilities. *B.C. Journal of Special Education, 17,* 62-72.

Orsmond, G. I., & Seltzer, M. (2000). Brothers and sisters with mental retardation: Gendered nature of the sibling relationship. *American Journal on Mental Retardation, 105,* 486-508.

Perry, A., & Black, A. (1997). A prospective study of out-of-home placement tendency in families of children with autism. *Journal on Developmental Disabilities, 5,* 1-23.

Perry, A., Harris, K., & Minnes, P. (2004). Family environments and family harmony: An exploration across severity, age, and type of developmental disability. *Journal on Developmental Disability, 11,* 15-24.

Phillips, A., Morrison, J., & Davis, R. W. (2004). General practitioners' educational needs in intellectual disability health. *Journal of Intellectual Disability Research, 48,* 142-149.

Plant, K. M., & Sanders, M. R. (2007). Predictors of care-giver stress in families of preschool-aged children with developmental disabilities. *Journal of Intellectual Disability Research, 51*(2), 109-124.

Rapanaro, C., Bartu, A., & Lee, A. H. (2008). Perceived benefits and negative impact of challenges encountered in caring for young adults with intellectual disabilities in the transition to adulthood. *Journal of Applied Research in Intellectual Disabilities, 21,* 34-47.

Renwick, R., & Brown, I. (1998). *The family quality of life project.* Report to Developmental Services Branch, Ontario Ministry of Community and Social Services, Toronto, Ontario.

Rinck, C., & Calkins, C. (1995). Family satisfaction with case management and service provision: Rural and urban perspectives for older families of persons with developmental disabilities. In K. A. Roberto (Ed.), *The elderly caregiver: Caring for adults with developmental disabilities* (pp. 125-145). Thousand Oaks, CA: Sage Publications.

Schneider, J., Wedgwood, N., Llewellyn, G., & McConnell D. (2006). Families challenged by and accommodating to the adolescent years. *Journal of Intellectual Disability Research, 50*, 926-936.

Scorgie, K., & Sobsey, D. (2000). Transformational outcomes associated with parenting children who have cisabilities. *Mental Retardation, 38*, 195-206.

Seltzer, M. M., Greenberg, J. S., Orsmond, G. I., & Lounds, J. (2005). Life course studies of siblings of individuals with developmental disabilities. *Mental Retardation, 43*, 354-359.

Shapiro, J., Blacher, J., & Lopez, S. R. (1998). Maternal reactions to children with mental retardation. In J. A. Burack, R. M. Hodapp, & E. Zigler (Eds.), *Handbook of mental retardation and development* (pp. 606-636). Cambridge, MA: Cambridge University Press.

Singer, G. H. S., Marquis, J., Powers, L. K., Blanchard, L., Divenere, N., Santelli, B., Ainbinder, J., & Sharp, M. (1999). A multi-site evaluation of parent to parents programs for parents of children with disabilities. *Journal of Early Intervention, 22*, 217-229.

Smith, G. C., Majeski, R. A., & McClenny, B. (1996). Psychoeducational support groups for aging parents: Development and preliminary outcomes. *Mental Retardation, 34*, 172-181.

Solish, A., & Perry, A. (2008). Parents' involvement in their children's behavioural intervention programs: Parent and therapist perspectives, *Research in Autism Spectrum Disorders 2*, 728-738.

Solomon, M., Pistrang, N., & Barker, C. (2001). The benefits of mutual support groups for parents of children with disabilities. *American Journal of Community Psychology, 29*, 113-132.

Sperow, S. (2006), Spiritual experiences of parents and caregivers who have children with disabilities or special needs. *Issues in Mental Health Nursing, 27*, 213–230.

Spina, S., Ziviani, J., & Nixon, J. (2005). Children, brain injury and the resiliency model of family adaptation. *Brain Impairment, 6*, 33–44.

Stoneman, Z., Brody, G. H., Davis, C. H., Crapps, J. M., & Malone, D. M. (1991). Ascribed role relations between children with mental retardation and their younger siblings. *American Journal on Mental Retardation, 95*, 537-550.

Sullivan, W. F., Heng, J., Cameron, D., Lunsky, Y.,

Cheetham, T., Hennen, B., Bradley, E. A., Berg, J. M., Korossy, M., Forster-Gibson, C., Gitta, M., Stavrakaki, C., McCreary, B., & Swift, I. (2006). Consensus guidelines for primary health care of adults with developmental disabilities. *Canadian Family Physician, 52*, 1410-1418.

Trivette, C. M., & Dunst, C. J. (1992). Characteristics and influences of role division and social support among mothers of preschool children with disabilities. *Topics in Early Childhood Special Education, 12*, 367-385.

Trute, B., Hiebert-Murphy, D., & Wright, A. (2008). Family-centred service coordination in childhood health and disability services: The search for meaningful service outcome measures. *Child: Care, Health and Development, 34*(3), 367-372.

Turnbull, H. R., & Turnbull, A. P. (1985). *Parent speak out: Then and now.* Columbus, OH: C. E. Merrill.

Turnbull, H. R., & Turnbull, A. P. (1986). *Families, professionals and exceptionality: A special partnership.* Columbus, OH: Merrill Publishing.

Webster, R. I., Majnemer, A., Platt, R. W., & Shevell, M. I. (2008). Child health and parental stress in school-age children with a preschool diagnosis of developmental delay. *Journal of Child Neurology, 23*(1), 32-38.

Wikler, L. M. (1986). Periodic stresses in families of children with mental retardation. *American Journal of Mental Deficiency, 90*, 703-706.

46

Sexuality and Developmental Disability: From Myth to Emerging Practices

Dorothy Griffiths

What you will learn:

- Seven common myths about sexuality and disability
- Facts that dispel the seven myths
- How sexual policy is changing
- The value and nature of sexuality education
- The history and practice of birth control and issues of parenting
- Issues related to sexual diversity
- The range and nature of sexual victimization
- Treatment and counselling for sexual problems

Sexuality is often overlooked in relation to people who have developmental disabilities. This chapter explores the subject in terms of myths and facts, matters related to changing sexual policy, socio-sexual education, birth control, sexual diversity, sexual victimization and treatment and counselling.

Myths and Facts

The topic of sexuality of people with developmental disabilities conjures up many myths. It is surprising that myths that were commonly believed at the beginning of the last century still exist in the 21st century. Seven of the most common are listed in Table 1. After reading them, it may appear that some of the myths contradict others. However, all of them have the same effect: they give the impression that the sexuality of people who have a developmental disability is outside of the "normal" range. Such myths allow society to continue to deny this aspect of life to people with developmental disabilities.

Dispelling the Myths

The myth that people with developmental disabilities are eternal children is based on a misunderstanding that mental age is a predictor of all aspects

Table 1: Seven Common Myths About the Sexuality of People Who Have Developmental Disabilities

Myths	Dispelling the myths
1. *People with developmental disabilities are eternal children and are asexual.*	*Most people who have developmental disabilities develop secondary sexual characteristics at about the same rate as non-disabled people. Individuals may vary in their rate of development, however, especially individuals with certain genetic or endocrine dysfunctions.* *Generally, individuals with developmental disabilities will have sexual feelings and responses to the same kinds of things as do non-disabled persons.*
2. *People with developmental disabilities need to live in environments that restrict and inhibit their sexuality to protect themselves and others.*	*People who have developmental disabilities require environments that provide the types of learning about one's sexuality that are generally taught in our culture.* *Like others in the general population, people with developmental disabilities benefit from an environment that models and teaches personal, moral, social and legal responsibility regarding sexuality.*
3. *People with developmental disabilities should not be provided with sex education, as it will only encourage inappropriate behaviour.*	*Socio-sexual education helps individuals to understand their changing bodies and feelings and provides the knowledge and guidance necessary to learn responsibility about one's sexuality.* *There appears to be a correlation between socio-sexual education and a reduced frequency of abuse (Hard, 1986 as cited in Roeher institute, 1988).* *Socio-sexual education provides, for people who may be demonstrating inappropriate sexual behaviour, knowledge and skills to replace their current inappropriate sexual behaviour.*
4. *People with developmental disabilities should be sterilized because they will give birth to children who are also disabled.*	*Eighty-five percent of adult disability is caused after the age of 13, and more than ninety percent of infant disability is due to social, not genetic, causes (Rioux, 1996). Thus, most people with developmental disabilities are not disabled because of a known genetic abnormality. There is no physical reason for people with developmental disabilities to give birth to children with disabilities, unless there is a genetic cause for the disability. It should also be noted that the disabling condition for some people with developmental disabilities, especially those with genetic causes, is such that they can never procreate (Griffiths, Richards, Fedoroff & Watson, 2002).*
5. *People with developmental disabilities are more likely to develop diverse, unusual, or deviant sexual behaviour.*	*The sexual development of people with developmental disabilities can be affected by many factors: lack of sexual education, deprivation of peer group interactions, family restrictions on activities, lack of social exposure, and even lack of motor co-ordination.* *People with developmental disabilities do not develop any more sexually inappropriate behaviour than the general population if they have normal opportunities to learn about their sexuality.*

Myths	Dispelling the myths
6. *People with developmental disabilities are over-sexed, promiscuous, sexually indis-criminate, and dangerous; children should not be left unattended with them.*	*While it appears that persons with developmental disabilities may be somewhat over-represented in the population of people who are convicted of sexual offences, these data may reflect that they are more likely to get caught, confess, and waive their rights, rather than indicating an increased rate of offence.*
	When people with developmental disablties act inappropriately in a sexual way (e.g., public masturbation), it is often less serious than offences committed by non-disabled people. Some clinicians have suggested that sexual deviance may be less common in this popu-lation than among people who are non-disabled (Day, 1994).
	People with developmental disabilities are more likely to be the victims of sexual offences, rather than the victimizers.
7. *People with dvelopmental disabilities cannot benefit from sexual counselling or treatment.*	*There is a growing body of literature that has demonstrated that people who have developmental disabilities can benefit from treat-ment or intervention directed at: (i) sexual abuse counselling or (ii) teaching appropriate socio-sexual behaviour to replace sexually inappropriate behaviour.*

of the person's life, rather than just being a number on an intelligence test. According to Johnson (1973) "there does not seem to be a high correlation between sex IQ and general IQ" (p. 60). Just because a person's mental age is equivalent to that of a child, it does not mean that he or she is child-like in all respects. An adult with a mental age of seven does not act like a seven-year-old. This person is physically mature, emotionally different, and has additional years of learning experiences that significantly change how they will react to life events. A mental age of seven simply means that the number of questions answered correctly on an intelligence test was equivalent to the number answered correctly by a typical seven-year-old.

People with developmental disabilities typically show an interest in closeness, affection, and contact with others, as do nondisabled people. However, from the moment of birth, others often treat people with developmental disabilities as asexual. They are often denied, through isolation from the general public and especially from people of the opposite sex, the usual cultural experiences through which to learn about, and understand, their sexuality.

Early in the twentieth century, institutions for people with developmental disabilities grew in size. The fear of procreation was one of the reasons for segregating and institutionalizing these individuals. This way of thinking began to change over time, however, and when Wolfensberger (1972) wrote his classic book *Normalization,* he emphasized the importance of providing the most culturally normative life experiences possible for people with developmental disabilities. This included those experiences relating to socio-sexual needs.

In the remainder of this chapter, some of the key issues revolving around sexuality and the field of developmental disabilities will be explored: sexuality policy, socio-sexual education, birth control, sexual diversity, victimization, counselling and treatment. For expanded discussions of these and other topics the reader is referred to *Ethical Dilemmas: Sexuality and Persons with Developmental Disabilities,* edited by Griffiths et al. (2002).

Changing Sexuality Policy

People with developmental disabilities have the right to be treated in the same way as anyone else, and this includes the realm of sexuality. In both Canada and the United States, this right is implied in various laws. The Canadian Charter of Rights (1982) guarantees protections against discrimination based on disability. The American Bill of Rights and the Rehabilitation Act of 1973 protect rights for privacy, choice of marital status, and freedom to procreate and raise a family. Globally, the United Nations Declaration of Rights for Retarded Persons (1971) proclaimed that people with developmental disabilities have the right to cohabitate and marry. However, when it comes to sexuality, these rights have been routinely denied to people with developmental disabilities.

In March of 2010, Canada ratified the United Nations Convention on the Rights of Persons with Disabilities (United Nations, 2006). This Convention clearly states that persons who have a disability must not be denied their rights with regard to their sexuality and parenting. It goes further to state that nations must provide support to individuals to assure them opportunities to assert these rights, including education, counselling, and abuse prevention. This Convention moves Canada beyond the rhetoric of recognition of the rights of persons with disabilities to bearing responsibility for creating a positive climate that respects and supports people's opportunities to understand and express their sexuality to the same degree that other citizens do.

In the past few years, there has been a growing awareness of the need for community agencies and other organizations to develop socio-sexual policies to ensure that the rights of people with developmental disabilities are respected. Policies are vital in ensuring that a consistent and responsible atmosphere in which to learn about culturally appropriate socio-sexual interactions exists. Unless there are clear guidelines for staff in a school or community agency to provide direction on socio-sexual issues, each staff member might come up with his or her individual approach. This would lead to great inconsistencies in what is being taught. Certain behaviours might at times be accepted and at other times punished, depending on which staff member is present. This type of inconsistent treatment creates an environment in which it is very difficult for people to learn to take responsibility for their own behaviour.

To create a positive atmosphere in which to teach appropriate and responsible socio-sexual behaviour, it is recommended that a school or community agency commit in policy:

- A statement that recognizes the sexuality of people with developmental disabilities and recognizes related rights
- An educational program to ensure that staff respond to socio-sexual issues, whether appropriate or inappropriate, in a consistent manner across staff and over time
- Opportunities for people with developmental disabilities to learn appropriate socio-sexual education and behaviour
- Access for people with developmental disabilities to medical and counselling intervention, as needed, for sexual issues, including abuse counselling and treatment for inappropriate sexual behaviour
- A clear policy and set of procedures to prevent abuse, and procedures to follow should there be a suspicion of abuse

In more recent years, parents have become more verbal and less conservative about sexuality. They have recognized the importance of sex education for their children because of the growing awareness that without it, their children could be at greater risk of abuse (Johnson & Davies, 1989). Staff attitudes have also become generally more accepting toward sexual behaviour between consenting adults in private settings (Adams, Tallon, & Alcorn, 1982), but there are still inconsistent attitudes regarding abortion, sterilization and homosexuality (Johnson & Davies, 1989). The rigid disapproval that existed in earlier years is now giving way to indecision (Griffiths & Lunsky, 2000). Policy is the only means by which agencies can ensure that the sexuality of persons with developmental disabilities will be responsibly, consistently and proactively addressed.

Socio-Sexual Education

Early sex education programs focussed on behavioural control of inappropriate sexual activities, particularly inappropriate masturbation (Mitchell, Doctor, & Butler, 1978) and neglected issues such as "dating, relationships, gender security, [and] exploitation" (Rowe & Savage, 1987, p. 11). By the late 1970s, most facilities reported teaching sex education to some degree, but sexual activity, with the exception of masturbation, continued to be met with disapproval and prohibition (Coleman & Murphy, 1980). Mitchell, Doctor, and Butler (1978) conducted research on attitudes of institutional staff and found that educators generally omitted explicit discussion of sexual behaviour from sex education reading materials in keeping with the conservative attitudes held by parents and staff.

Pioneer sexuality educators, such as Kempton (1975) and Gordon (1971), began to move away from this moralistic approach to sex education. Sex education became more focussed on the socio-sexual learning needs of persons with developmental disabilities. In addition to education about anatomy, birth control, sexual intercourse, hygiene and venereal disease, educators now incorporate an increased emphasis on relationships, social behaviour, self esteem, decision making, sexual lifestyles, and abuse into their curricula (see Kempton, 1993).

Griffiths and Lunsky (2000) identified an increased emphasis on socio-sexual education in recent decades and a shift in the priorities of education. The reasons for this are fourfold: awareness of abuse, attention to inappropriate sexual expression, HIV/AIDS, and interest in preventative health.

First, Dick Sobsey and his colleagues from the University of Alberta produced a profound and thoughtful stream of research demonstrating that: persons with developmental disabilities are far more vulnerable to abuse than nondisabled persons; abuse is most likely perpetrated by persons known to the victim; and the perpetrator, often a caregiver, gains access and opportunity to abuse through the disability system (Sobsey & Doe, 1991). Hard (as cited in Roeher Institute, 1988) presented correlational data that showed that among persons who had been provided with sex education, abuse rates were considerably lower than for those who had not. Sex education, therefore, became identified as a key factor in the reduction of abuse.

Second, it is being recognized that a lack of sexuality education not only leaves persons with developmental disabilities vulnerable to abuse, but also leads to developing socially inappropriate expressions of their own sexuality (Griffiths, Quinsey, & Hingsburger, 1989). Treating inappropriate expressions of sexuality that developed in this way can sometime require clinically complex interventions (Griffiths, 2002), although Hingsburger, Griffiths, and Quinsey (1991) presented case examples of persons with developmental disabilities for whom the treatment for certain inappropriate sexual behaviours was sex education alone.

Third, the discovery of HIV/AIDS changed society's perspective on sex education. Persons with developmental disabilities are typically presented with little information about what HIV/AIDS is, or about how to minimize their risk of contracting it (McGillvray, 1999). Agencies are beginning to recognize the critical importance of evaluating and documenting the effectiveness of their educational programs and the need for accountability regarding the quality of sexuality education.

Fourth, preventive health care has become an emerging concern. Recent initiatives focus on preventative health methods, including sexual health, that go beyond simple hygiene (e.g., Lunsky, Armstrong, & Straiko, 1999).

Learning about sexuality does not take place in six one-hour sessions, nor is it restricted to a single period in a person's life. It is a life-long process. This means that people with developmental disabilities, just like non-disabled people, will learn about sexuality throughout their lives. People need access to accurate information when it is age-appropriate and contextually relevant for them to know it. Parents and staff can capitalize on these moments to teach about different parts of sexuality. Examples of natural "teachable moments" for sexuality education are when children begin to ask questions about their bodies, when they want to know where babies come from, or when they experience body changes during puberty.

In addition to these "teachable moments," people who have developmental disabilities benefit from formal socio-sexual education programs. There are some excellent programs that are available commercially today. One of the most widely used is the Life Horizons I and II program by Winifred Kempton (1988). This program is very comprehensive and includes hundreds of slides to aid instruction. Winifred Kempton, one of the most important founding educators in this field, suggests that a good socio-sexual education program should include male and female anatomy, human reproduction, birth control, and sexual health (including safer sex practices). However, she also recommends that training should include the moral, social, and legal aspects of sexuality; male and female socio-sexual behaviour; dating, parenting, and marriage; prevention of and coping with abuse; building self-esteem; and establishing relationships. A fundamental part of socio-sexual education is teaching that there are responsibilities that come with sexual expression.

Although most professionals today agree that sex education should be provided for people with developmental disabilities, there are several major challenges with the way in which socio-sexual education is provided. It is generally:

1. Provided sporadically, or only in response to a problem
2. Based upon educational programs that have very little, if any, empirical evidence of effectiveness
3. Incomplete and fails to address the full range of topics to allow for a comprehensive understanding of sexuality
4. Not evaluated for effectiveness, generalization or transfer of skill to the person's life

Consequently, although there is significant consensus about the value of socio-sexual education, the practice of it often does not follow.

Birth Control

Beginning from the early part of last century, sexuality in persons with developmental disabilities was dominated by a concern about procreation (see Scheerenberger, 1983). During World War II, about 300,000 people with developmental disabilities in Nazi-occupied countries underwent forced sterilization because of a fear of procreation. Primarily for the same reason, similar forced sterilization occurred throughout other parts of the world, including North America, until the 1970s. Sterilization of people with developmental disabilities was based on beliefs that arose from the eugenics movement — popular both in North America and in Europe — that "feeble-mindedness" was largely inherited. Intelligence tests were being used to determine if individuals should be institutionalized or sterilized to prevent procreation. Since institutionalization was expensive, people with developmental disabilities were often sterilized so that they could then be put to work in the community.

Eugenics beliefs have long been discredited. It has been known for some time that many of the causes of disabling conditions are not linked to genetic factors. Non-genetic causes, such as child maltreatment, infections, accident, injury, and fetal alcohol syndrome and related conditions, account for a considerable percentage of disabling conditions. Even if a person with developmental disabilities is disabled because of a genetic condition, it is not always passed on (e.g., recessive genes need to be paired with similar recessive genes). If a dominant gene created the disability, then the chance of passing the disability to a child is still only fifty percent (see Chapter 12, for more detail about primary causes of developmental disability).

The right to procreate and parent has stirred heated debate in the field of developmental disabilities. In Canada during the 1970s, the classic case of Eve (Rioux & Yarmol, 1987) provided very clear consent guidelines for nontherapeutic sterilization. Today, in Canada and in many states in the United States, parents do not have the right to consent to nontherapeutic sterilization for their child, whether an adult or a child. For a person who is developmentally disabled to give consent to nontherapeutic sterilization, the nature and consequences of consenting to the procedure must be established.

The right to procreate and raise children does not end with the topic of sterilization. Concern is often expressed as to whether people with developmental disabilities can be adequate parents. It is common for a parent who is developmentally disabled to be subject to considerable scrutiny regarding his or her ability to raise the child free from neglect or harm. Chapter 48 describes a specialized program that has been developed to support parents with disabilities in learning parenting skills. Currently, it is commonly held that the rights of the child must supersede the rights of parents, even if the latter have developmental disabilities. This is consistent with current views on the rights of children in our culture. The decision to have a child carries with it great responsibility. Counselling and support is very often vital to help people with disabilities make the right decision for themselves and their future child.

Sexual Diversity

It is currently thought that the population of people with developmental disabilities exhibits the same range of sexual expression that occurs in the nondisabled population, including heterosexual, homosexual, and bisexual relationships, dating, petting, masturbation, premarital coitus, and marriage.

Some individuals with developmental disabilities are limited in their sexual expression by physical challenges, interest, or opportunity. However, many people with developmental disabilities are limited by the environments in which they live and by the attitudes of caregivers and of society overall. A great number of people with developmental disabilities live in sex-segregated environments where it is almost impossible to develop a heterosexual relationship. In some environments, there are severe restrictions on sexual behaviour of people with developmental disabilities, and the rights of association or privacy that would be afforded to nondisabled people are denied. In addition, people with developmental disabilities have been punished or even abused for their sexuality. There have been instances of people with developmental disabilities being beaten, drugged, or emotionally berated for engaging in sexual behaviour. Inappropriate sexual behaviour can develop as a result, as a means of adapting to an aberrant environment.

As with non-disabled persons, individuals with developmental disabilities may choose to express or not to express their sexuality in various ways, depending on their learning experiences, family values, or religious background. However, some people with developmental disabilities have experienced very different learning histories with regard to their sexuality. They are often sheltered from sexual knowledge and typical experiences that would assist them in developing a healthy understanding of their sexuality. Inappropriate sexual behaviour can sometimes develop as a result of a lack of sexual knowledge and understanding. People with developmental disabilities do not inherently have more unusual or inappropriate sexual behaviour than nondisabled people, but it is common for them to encounter very different learning experiences about their sexuality. For this reason, they have sometimes learned unusual or inappropriate sexual behaviours through atypical life and learning experiences, such as abuse and institutional living.

Sexual Victimization

Research has provided convincing evidence that the sexual abuse of people who are developmentally disabled is widespread in North American society (Sobsey, 1993). It has been suggested that people with developmental disabilities are one and a half times more likely to be sexually abused than nondisabled people (Doucette, 1986). Sobsey (1993) reported that abuse occurs across all levels of disability, with the victims both female (83%) and male (17%). The majority of offenders against people with developmental disabilities were males who were known to the person. In 43.7% of the cases, the offender's relationship with the person with a developmental disability was related to the victim's disability. The offenders were often people who held a trusted, care-giving role in the life of the victim. The offences frequently occurred in the natural environments of the person with developmental disabilities. Often, the abuse experiences were repeated.

The increased vulnerability for abuse of people with developmental disabilities is not related directly to the nature of the person's disability. Rather, abuse is more likely to occur because of the way society treats and views people with developmental disabilities and their sexuality, and because of the systems in which people with developmental disabilities live. In these systems, people with developmental disabilities have little or no power, choice, or control over many aspects of their lives. Sexual abuse is not just a sexual act, it is an expression of power.

Theorists believe that there is a need for a multi-dimensional approach to the reduction of abuse of persons with developmental disabilities (Sobsey, 1994). This approach would include changing systems in terms of policy, screening staff, individual empowerment, addressing attitudes that dehumanize people with disabilities, and providing education for staff and individuals who are developmentally disabled about healthy boundaries.

Treatment and Counselling

Until the 1980s, it was widely assumed that people with developmental disabilities would not benefit from counselling or treatment for sexual issues. Traditional insight-oriented therapy was considered inappropriate for people with developmental disabilities. In recent decades, these therapies have developed in keeping with the cognitive abilities of people with developmental disabilities.

The two primary areas of counselling and treatment of sexually-related issues are victim (survivor) counselling and treatment of inappropriate sexual behaviour.

Victim (Survivor) Counselling: Although persons with developmental disabilities have been sexually abused at higher rates than nondisabled persons, their access to appropriate supports and counselling services has been largely ignored until recent years. There is now, however, an emerging body of literature to help clinicians who work with sexual abuse survivors who have adapted their counselling procedures to support persons who are developmentally disabled. One contribution to the field includes a book entitled *Counselling People with Developmental Disabilities who have been Sexually Abused*, and a training video, *Alone in a Crowd*, created by two of the leaders in this field (Mansell & Sobsey, 2001).

Treatment of Sexually Inappropriate Behaviour: Edgerton (1973) suggested that persons with developmental disabilities do not demonstrate any more sexually inappropriate behaviour than non-disabled persons if they are provided with a normative learning experience. However, the sexual learning experience of many persons with developmental disabilities has often been anything but normative. Population statistics have shown that individuals with developmental disabilities are over-represented in the population of convicted sexual offenders (e.g., Shapiro, 1986). The reader should be cautious about the interpretation of these rates. Persons with developmental disabilities may be over-represented because they are more likely to get caught, confess and be unable to mount a suitable defence (Santamour & West, 1978). Moreover, the nature of their offences are more likely to be inappropriate behaviours such as public masturbation, exhibitionism and voyeurism (rather than serious sexual violations) than is the case for nondisabled persons (Gilby, Wolf, & Goldberg, 1989).

Paraphilia is rare among persons with developmental disabilities (Day, 1994), but can occur in males and females of all intellectual levels (Fedoroff, 2000). Paraphilia means "recurrent, intense sexually arousing fantasies, sexual urges, or behaviours generally involving 1) nonhuman objects, 2) the suffering or humiliation of oneself or one's partner, or 3) children or other non-consenting persons that occur over a period of at least 6 months" (APA, 1994, pp. 522-523). When paraphilia does occur in people with developmental disaiblties, it is often misdiagnosed. The *Diagnostic and Statistic Manual of Mental Disorders - Fourth Edition* (DSM-IV-TR) states that persons with developmental disabilities may present a "decrease in judgment, social skills, or impulse control that, in rare cases, leads to unusual sexual behavior" distinguishable from paraphilia (APA, 2000, p. 525). In 2007, the National Association for the Dually Diagnosed developed a companion manual to the DSM-IV-TR in which it is recommended that diagnosis of paraphilia in persons with developmental disabilities should not be made until the individual has been evaluated for "counterfeit deviance" (Fletcher, Leoschen, Stavrakaki, & First, 2007). The term "counterfeit deviance" was used in an article by Hingsburger, Griffiths, and Quinsey (1991) to illustrate that the sexual misbehaviour of persons with developmental disabilities is often the product of experiential, environmental, or medical factors, rather than paraphilia. This distinction often requires a comprehensive biopsychosocial assessment.

In the past two decades, an increasingly rich body of clinical literature on intervention has emerged (see Griffiths, 2002). More recently, the treatment focus has shifted toward promotion of the development of adaptive sexual behaviours. Griffiths, Richards, Watson, and Fedoroff (2002) suggested that treatment strategies for inappropriate sexual behaviour include teaching and reinforcing alternative replacement, altering the conditions sustaining the behaviour, and the judicious use of medication or hormonal therapy, if appropriate.

Based on a growing body of clinical experience, specialized treatment providers have reported that sexuality problems of persons with developmental disabilities, particularly the mildly and moderately disabled, have been surprisingly responsive to treatment (Lackey & Knopp, 1989). The clinical literature provides convincing evidence of effective sexual treatment and counselling strategies that have been developed for persons with developmental disabilities, although there is a lack of empirical research in this area. Specialized treatment for persons who are dually diagnosed (mental health needs and developmentally challenged) is not available in all areas and often requires coordination with generic mental health and correctional resources that may be reluctant or ill-informed to adapt resources for this population (see Griffiths, Stavrakaki, & Summers, 2002).

Summary

It is important to dispel the seven myths described at the beginning of this chapter. Even today, these myths continue to influence how some people in society treat people with developmental disabilities with respect to their sexuality. People with developmental disabilities have been sexually abused throughout history. Available research and clinical evidence con-

tradicts the myths, demonstrating that people with developmental disabilities are sexual people and, like nondisabled people, need knowledge and a normal learning environment to understand and learn to act responsibly on their natural feelings.

For Further Thought and Discussion

Discuss the following in groups:

1. What would you do if you came across two residents alone in the family room of a five-person group home engaged in petting?
   a. What would the major issues be in this situation?
   b. Would their level of cognitive functioning change your response?
   c. What if both individuals were consenting?
   d. What if one was not consenting?
   e. Would your response differ if the couple was a man and a woman or a couple of the same sex?
   f. Where is an appropriate place to engage in petting behaviour in a group home?
   g. What teaching programs might be recommended?

2. Why do you believe that persons with developmental disabilities are at greater risk for sexual abuse? What systemic changes could occur to minimize this risk?

Respond to the following individually:

1. Did you believe any of the myths before reading this paper? Do you still believe some? Why? What do you think most people in Ontario believe?

2. Do you think people with developmental disabilities have the same sexual rights as nondisabled people? Why do you think these rights are so often denied?

3. Why do you think the sexuality of people with developmental disabilities makes so many people uncomfortable?

4. Why do you think people with developmental disabilities are more likely to be sexually abused? What could be done to reduce this?

More Resources

Dual diagnosis

Griffiths, D. M., Stavrakaki, C., & Summers, J. (Eds.) (2002). *Dual diagnosis: An introduction to the mental health needs of persons with developmental disabilities*. Sudbury, ON: Habilitative Mental Health Resource Network.

Ethical dilemmas

Griffiths, D. M., Richards, D., Fedoroff, P., & Watson, S. L. (2002). *Ethical dilemmas: Sexuality and developmental disabilities*. Kingston, NY: NADD.

Parenting reading

Hingsburger, D. (1993). *I openers. Parents ask questions about sexuality and children with developmental disabilities*. Vancouver, BC: Family Supports Institute Press.

Parents with developmental disabilities

Feldman, M. (2002). Parents with intellectual disabilities: Impediments and supports. In D. M. Griffiths, D. Richards, P. Fedoroff, & S. L. Watson (Eds.), *Ethical dilemmas: Sexuality and developmental disabilities* (pp.255-293). Kingston, NY: NADD.

Policies on sexuality

Owen, F., Griffiths, D., & Arbus-Nevestuk, K. (2002). Sexual policies in agencies supporting persons who have developmental disabilities: Ethical and organizational issues. In D. M. Griffiths, D. Richards, P. Fedoroff, & S. L. Watson (Eds.), *Ethical dilemmas: Sexuality and developmental disabilities* (pp. 53-77). Kingston, NY: NADD.

Griffiths, D., Owen, F., & Arbus-Nevestuk, K. (2002). Sexual policies in agencies supporting persons who have developmental disabilities: Practice and implementation issues. In D. M. Griffiths, D. Richards, P. Fedoroff, & S. L. Watson (Eds.), *Ethical dilemmas: Sexuality and developmental disabilities* (pp. 78-132). Kingston, NY: NADD.

Kastner, T., DeLotto, P., Scagnelli, B., & Testa, W. R. (1990). Proposed guidelines for agencies serving persons with developmental disabilities and HIV infection. *Mental Retardation, 28*, 139-145.

Relationship training

Champagne, M. P., & Walker-Hirsch, L. (1993). *Circles: Intimacy and relationships*. Santa Barbara, CA: James Stanfield Publishing.

Sexual abuse

Mansell, S. & Sobsey, D. (2001). *Counselling people with developmental disabilities who have been sexually abused*. Kingston, NY: NADD.

Mansell, S., & Sobsey, D. (2001). *Alone in a crowd* [Training video]. Kingston, NY:NADD.

Sobsey, D. (1994). *Violence and abuse in the lives of people with disabilities*. Baltimore: Paul H. Brookes.

The Roeher Institute (1988). *Vulnerable*. Toronto, ON: Author.

Sexuality and people with developmental disabilities

Fegan, L., Rauch, A., & McCarthy, W. (1993). *Sexuality and people with intellectual disability* (2nd ed.). Baltimore: Paul H. Brookes.

Griffiths, D., Richards, D., Watson, S., & Fedoroff, P. (2002). Sexuality and mental health issues. In D. M. Griffihs, C. Stavrakaki, & J. Summers (Eds.), *Dual diagnosis- An introduction to the mental health needs of persons with developmental disabilities* (pp. 419-482). Sudbury, ON: Habilitative Mental Health Resource Network.

Rowe, W., & Savage, S. (1987). *Sexuality and the developmentally handicapped: A guidebook for health care professionals*. Lewiston, NY: E. Mellen Press.

Sexually inappropriate behaviour

Griffiths, D. (2002). Sexual aggression. In W. I. Gardner (Ed.), *Aggression and other disruptive behavioral challenges: Biomedical and psychosocial assessment and treatment* (pp. 325-397). Kingston, NY: NADD.

Griffiths, D., Quinsey, V. L., & Hingsburger, D. (1989). *Changing inappropriate sexual behavior*. Baltimore: Paul H. Brookes.

Haaven, J., Little, R., Petre-Miller, D. (1990). *Treating intellectually disabled sex offenders*. Orwell, VT: Safer Society.

Ward, K. M., Heffern, S. J., Wilcox, D., McElwee, D., Dowrick, P., Brown, T. D., et at. (1992).

Managing inappropriate sexual behavior: Supporting individuals with developmental disabilities in the community. Anchorage, AK: Alaska Specialized Education and Training Services.

Socio-sexual education

Jacobs, R., Samowitz, P., Levy, P. H., Levy, J. M., & Cabrera, G. A. (1992). Young Adult Institute's comprehensive AIDS staff training program. In A. C. Crocker, H. J. Cohen, & T. A. Kastner (Eds.), *HIV infection and developmental disabilities: A resource for service providers* (pp. 161-169). Baltimore: Paul H. Brookes.

Kempton, W. (1988). *Life Horizons I and II.* Santa Barbara, CA: James Stanfield Publishing.

Kempton, W. (1993). *Sexuality and persons with disabilities that hinder learning: A comprehensive guide for teachers and professionals.* Santa Barbara, CA: James Stanfield Publishing.

Watson, S., Griffiths, D., Richards, D., & Fedoroff, P. (2002). Sex education. In D. M. Griffiths, D. Richards, P. Fedoroff, & S. L. Watson (Eds.), *Ethical dilemmas: Sexuality and developmental disabilities* (pp. 175-226). Kingston, NY: NADD.

Socio-sexual resources in ontario

SIECCAN (Sex Information and Education Council of Canada), 850 Coxwell Avenue, East York, ON M4C 5R1

References

Adams, G. L., Tallon, R. J., & Alcorn, D. A. (1982). Attitudes toward the sexuality of mentally retarded and nonretarded persons. *Education and Training of the mentally retarded, 17,* 307-312.

American Psychiatric Association (APA) (1994). *Diagnostic and Statistical Manual of Mental Disorders - Fourth Edition (DSM IV).* Washington, DC: American Psychiatric Association.

Coleman, E. M., & Murphy, W. D. (1980). A survey of sexual attitudes and sex education programs among facilities for the mentally retarded. *Applied Research in Mental Retardation, 1,* 269-276.

Day, K. (1994). Male mentally handicapped sex offenders. *British Journal of Psychiatry, 165,* 630-639.

Doucette, J. (1986). *Violent acts against disabled women.* Toronto, ON: DAWN Canada.

Edgerton, R. (1973). Socio-cultural research considerations. In F. F. de la Cruz, & G. G. La Veck (Eds.), *Human sexuality and the mentally retarded* (pp. 240-249). New York: Brunner/Maze.

Fedoroff, P. (2000). Treatment of paraphilias in people with developmental disaiblities. *Journal on Developmental Disabilities, 7*(1), 50-65.

Fletcher, R., Loschen, E., Stavrakaki, C., & First, M. (2007). *Diagnostic manual – intellectual disability.* Kingston, NY: National Association for the Dually Diagnosed.

Gilby, R., Wolf, L,. & Golberg, B. (1989). Mentally retarded adolescent sex offenders: A survey and pilot study. *Canadian Journal of Psychiatry, 34,* 542-548.

Gordon, S. (1971). Missing in special education: Sex. *Journal of Special Education, 5,* 351-354.

Griffiths, D. (1991). *Myths & mythconceptions. Panel on sexuality and mental retardation – a glance at the present and a view to the future.* Panel discussion at the Annual Meeting of the American Association on Mental Retardation, Washington, DC, May 24-29, 1991.

Griffiths, D. (2002). Sexual aggression. In W. I. Gardner (Ed.), *Aggression and persons with developmental disabilities* (pp. 325-386). Kingston, NY: NADD.

Griffiths, D., & Lunsky, Y. (2000). Changing attitudes towards the nature of socio-sexual assessment and education for persons with developmental disabilities: A twenty-year comparison. *Journal of Developmental Disabilities, 7,* 16-33.

Griffiths, D., Quinsey, V. L., & Hingsburger, D. (1989). *Changing inappropriate sexual behavior.* Baltimore: Paul H Brookes.

Griffiths, D., Richards, D., Watson, S., & Fedoroff, P. (2002). Sexuality and mental health issues. In D. M. Griffihs, C. Stavrakaki, & J. Summers (Eds.), *Dual diagnosis- An introduction to the mental health needs of persons with developmental disabilities* (pp. 419-482). Sudbury, ON: Habilitative Mental Health Resource Network.

Griffiths, D. M., Richards, D., Fedoroff, P., & Watson, S. L. (Eds.). (2002). *Ethical dilemmas: Sexuality and developmental disabilities.* Kingston, NY:

NADD.

Griffiths, D. M., Stavrakaki, C., & Summers, J. (Eds.). (2002). *Dual diagnosis- An introduction to the mental health needs of persons with developmental disabilities.* Sudbury, ON: Habilitative Mental Health Resource Network.

Hingsburger, D., Griffiths, D., & Quinsey, V. (1991). Detecting counterfeit deviance. *The Habilitative Mental Healthcare Newsletter, 10*(9), 51-54.

Johnson, P. R., & Davies, R. (1989). Sexual attitudes of members of staff. *The British Journal of Mental Subnormality, 35,* 17-21.

Johnson, W. (1973). Sex education of the mentally retarded. In F. F. de la Cruz, & G. D. LaVeck (Eds.), *Human sexuality and the mentally retarded* (pp. 57-66). Baltimore: Penguin Books.

Kempton, W. (1975). *Sex education for persons with disabilities that hinder learning.* North Scituate, MA: Duxbury Press.

Kempton, W. (1988). *Life Horizons I and II.* Santa Barbara, CA: James Stanfield Publishing.

Kempton, W. (1993). *Sexuality and persons with disabilities that hinder learning.* Sanata Barbara, CA: James Stanfield.

Lackey, L. B., & Knopp, F. H. (1989). A summary of selected notes from the working sessions of the First National Training Conference on Assessment and Treatment of Intellectually Disabled Juvenile and Adult Sexual Offenders. In F. Knopp (Ed.), *Selected readings: Sexual offenders identified as intellectually disabled.* Orwell, VT: Safer Society Press.

Lunsky, Y., Armstrong, S., & Straiko, A. (1999). *New approaches to the medical care of women with developmental disabilities: The Nisonger Center UAP women's health groups.* Paper presented at American Association on Mental Retardation Annual Meeting. New Orleans, LA.

Mansell, S., & Sobsey, D. (2001). *Counselling people with developmental disabilities who have been sexually abused.* Kingston, NY: NADD.

Mansell, S., & Sobsey, D. (2001). *Alone in a crowd* [Training Video]. Kingston, NY: NADD.

McGillvray, J. A. (1999). Level of knowledge and risk of contracting HIV/AIDS among young adults with mild/moderate intellectual disability. *Journal of Applied Research in Intellectual Disabilities, 12,* 113-126).

Mitchell, L., Doctor, R. M., & Butler, D. C. (1978). Attitudes of caretakers toward the sexual behavior of mentally retarded persons. *American Journal of Mental Deficiency, 83,* 289-296.

Rioux, M. (1996). Reproductive technology: A rights issue. *Entourage,* summer, 5-7.

Rioux, M., & Yarmol, K. (1987). The right to control one's own body: A look at the "Eve" decision. *Entourage,* winter, 28-30.

Roeher Institute. (1988). *Vulnerable.* Toronto, ON: Author.

Rowe, W., & Savage, S. (1987). *Sexuality and the developmentally handicapped: A guidebook for health care professionals.* Lewiston, NY: E. Mellen Press.

Santamour, W., & West, B. (1978). *The mentally retarded offender and corrections.* Washington, DC: U.S. Department of Justice.

Scheerenberger, R. C. (1983). *A history of mental retardation.* Baltimore: Paul. H. Brookes.

Shapiro, S. (1986). Delinquent and disturbed behavior within the field of mental deficiency. In A. V. S. deReuck, & R. Porter (Eds.), *The mentally abnormal offender.* New York: Grune & Stratton.

Sobsey, D. (1993). Sexual abuse of individuals with intellectual disability. In A. Craft (Ed.), *Practice issues in sexuality and intellectual disability* (pp. 93-115). London: Routledge.

Sobsey, D. (1994). *Violence and abuse in the lives of people with disabilities.* Baltimore: Paul H. Brookes.

Sobsey, D., & Doe, T. (1991). Patterns of sexual abuse and assault. *Sexuality and Disability, 9*(3), 243-259.

United Nations. (2006). Convention on the rights of persons with disabilities. Retrieved from http://www.un.org/disabilities/convention/conventionfull.shtml

Wolfensberger, W. (1972). *Normalization.* Toronto, ON: National Institute on Mental Retardation.

47

Developmental Disabilities and Women's Issues: Roles and Relationships

Lillian Burke

What you will learn:

- Roles and relationships of women with developmental disabilities as they relate to:

Social and emotional development	Abuse and violence
Aging	Marriage
Independence/autonomy	Justice
Physical health issues	Parenting
Education, economics, and employment	Cultural issues
Mental health issues	Care provision
Relationships and sexuality	

"There is no homogeneous group of women who are labelled as having intellectual disabilities...they lead diverse and rich lives and also struggle to achieve fulfilment" (Johnson & Traustadottir, 2000, p. 22).

Women and Disability

Feminist literature suggests that the roles and experiences of women have been socially constructed. Centuries-old stories and traditions have continued to impact the value and treatment of women in our modern society (Garland-Thomson, 2001). Early in the women's movement, the focus was on the deconstruction of these beliefs and activism to address the needs and rights of "women." However, the lack of homogeneity in "women" sometimes created confusion about what their actual needs were. This early focus by feminists sometimes interfered with acknowledging or addressing other identities held by women, such as ethnicity or disability (Garland-Thomson, 2001; Johnson & Traustadottir, 2000).

As is the case for women, people with disabilities are measured against socially defined standards that reflect how much they differ from what is considered to be typical or normal (Asch & Fine, 1988; Garland-Thomson, 2001). Social structures have identified both women and those with disabilities in terms of characteristics and behaviours that typically reflect weakness, dependence, and other features that are opposite to those that are socially valued, such as strength and independence. Expectations held by others are based on these beliefs and they often reflect discrimination and oppression. Women with disabilities are "one of the last groups of women to find voices within the feminist literature" (Johnson & Traustadottir, 2000, p. 12).

Women who have developmental disabilities have characteristics that link them to others, both men and women, who have disabilities. Some of these are specific features of their disability, but many are the outcome of social thought. Deegan and Brooks (1985) referred to this as a "double handicap." Mittler (1995) claimed that "there are many examples of the way social systems exclude and put obstacles in the way of people with mental disabilities and their families. This form of discrimination and disadvantage often interacts with other forms of disadvantage related to race, class, and gender" (p. 26). Others may not look for the existing valued characteristics in the woman with a developmental disability, and often she accepts the reflection of herself that society creates.

Changes in philosophy and support practice have occurred within the field of developmental disabilities (Culham & Nind, 2003). These reflect progressive degrees of change since the 1960s, and are seen in the models of care of both the developmental and mental health sectors in Ontario (Burke & Baker, 2009). Lemon and Lemon (2003) suggested that, for those with developmental disabilities, changes parallel the rights achievements of those with physical disabilities, of women, of gays and lesbians, and of racial groups. However, in spite of the changes within policy and systems, the status of individuals, and of women with a developmental disability, has not seen substantive change. "Although policy changes in the last fifty years have had a positive impact in terms of deinstitutionalization and community integration for people with developmental disabilities, it is clear that full social inclusion has not yet occurred" (Salvatori, Trembly, & Tryssenaar, 2003, p. 2).

It is generally acknowledged in our field that a woman who has a developmental disability experiences the same range of practical, physical, emotional, and relationship concerns that other women do. However, she also faces challenges that are unique. We will attempt to understand the woman who has a developmental disability by looking at issues during the developmental period and following her through the many transitions and milestones in her life. We will begin our discussion by telling Kelly's story (Box 1). Kelly is a composite of women seen clinically. Many of the issues that are important to women with disabilities and that are highlighted in this chapter are revealed in her story.

Social and Emotional Development

The developmental experiences of an individual shape her personality, and shape her perception of and reaction to her environment. The effects of social experience on self-concept begin early in life. Harris and Wideman (1988) considered the parents of a child who is born with a disability and how their experiences might impact on the child. Our society does not react positively to the birth of a disabled child. This is emphasized by prenatal testing, which often results in aborting a fetus that is believed to carry a disability (Asch, 1999; Garland-Thomson, 2001). Parents who give birth to a child with a disability may react to the birth with guilt, anger, depression, denial, or their own feelings of failure which may go unresolved (Levitas & Gilson, 1994). These chronic feelings may be projected onto the child, and through time may cause her to respond with negative self-feelings (Downes, 1982).

Although attempts are made to integrate the child into family and community experiences early in her life, the child with a disability often has needs that differ from her siblings. These special challenges impact the child's health and education (Boyle, Decoufle, & Yeargin-Allsopp, 1994). She may require early stimulation, physical therapy, speech therapy, or some other treatment that takes her away from the environment of same-aged playmates (Burke & Gilmour, 1998). The child may engage in activities that are chosen for her because they reflect her cognitive level (Castles, 1996) rather than her chronological age. This may cause others to treat her as younger than she is, perceive deficits that are not there, and encourage her to perform at the level of activity chosen for her, rather than at the level of

Box 1: Kelly

Kelly is a 30 year old woman who has a mild developmental disability. She is attractive, can read and write, and enjoys conversing, music, dancing, and weaving. Kelly has no special health problems but is overweight and is very self-conscious about this. She lived in her family's home until one year ago when her mother died. Kelly has one sister who lives in England with whom she keeps in touch by e-mail. She sees her father once a month and looks forward to his visits. However, he tends to correct her and tell her how fat she is, so she is always unhappy at the end of the visits.

When Kelly was a child, she started school in a class for children with disabilities. Her mother always told her she did not have as many problems as the other children and that when she grew up she could have a job and do whatever other people do. Kelly's mom fought hard to have her integrated into a regular classroom. Kelly was glad she could learn much of what her classmates did. Some children made fun of her but there were girls in her class who were nice to her. When Kelly went to high school, the girls included her less. They had part-time jobs, and went on dates and to parties. Kelly was never asked to go to parties or to go on a date. Her sister shared magazines with her and went shopping with her on weekends. Her mother invited her to the theatre or to women's groups she was attending and tried to include her in social events. Kelly knew her mom and dad sometimes argued about this. She used to hear her dad say, "Kelly wasn't invited. We can't always take her everywhere."

Kelly's sister went to university after high school. Kelly had hoped to find a job, but everywhere she went to apply, they told her they didn't need help. She finally was accepted in a sheltered workshop but got frustrated because they gave her boring jobs and she got little pay. In the end, she quit the workshop and stayed home with her mom to cook and clean and garden. Kelly's sister got married after university and moved to England. Kelly really missed her. She had no friends her own age.

Two years ago, Kelly's mom got sick. She told Kelly she would find a place for Kelly to live. She wasn't going to get well and she didn't think things would work out for Kelly if she and her dad were to live together when she was gone. Kelly was very sad but tried not to show it. When her mom died, Kelly moved to a group home.

Kelly likes her new home. There are two men and one other woman living at her residence. The men work, play sports, and go out with their girlfriends, so Kelly only sees them at mealtimes and on the weekends. The other woman has cerebral palsy and is very nice, but can't talk and has problems using her hands, so she and Kelly watch TV together, and Kelly helps her do things she can't do.

Kelly's staff recently referred her to a therapist because they thought she might be psychotic. They heard her talking to herself at night and found she'd built a "friend" in her room out of a pillow, some towels, and some clothes. The clinician said Kelly wasn't psychotic, but she was lonely and needed someone to talk to. She said there was no reason for her not to have her "friend" – if they took that away, she'd have no-one to talk to, hug, or care about. She suggested Kelly get counselling and that the staff try to find places where Kelly could meet people with some interests similar to her own. She suggested classes, women's groups, and library clubs. If she were eventually to make some real friends, she would have someone with whom to share information and intimacy, and might no longer need the friend she had constructed.

her capability. This may also affect her development of age-appropriate social skills — skills that are learned in large part through interacting with peers. Opportunities to develop friendships and engage in social experiences may be limited if the child is segregated from peers or is encouraged to participate in activities with children of a lower age.

Parents want very much to help their children. Mothers have been noted to try to compensate for their children's difficulties in all areas, including social development (Levitas & Gilson, 1994). The mother may choose more of the child's activities than she would for a child without a disability and become more involved in performing the activity. She may choose playmates and may intervene when problems emerge, rather than letting the child fend for herself. If the child has communication difficulties, she may both communicate and interpret communications for her. She may label the child's feelings and discourage expression of negative feelings because she wants her to be happy (Burke & Gilmour, 1998). Consequently, many of the child's activities and responses become mediated, leading to dependency on the care provider (Levitas & Gilson, 1994), and affecting many other aspects of the person such as the development of personality, the ability to self-regulate, the autonomy of the individual, and self-perception. As the child gets older, other people, including professionals and service providers, may continue to foster dependency by continuing to mediate experiences.

When a girl starts school, her awareness of differences and her social skills difficulties may cause her to withdraw (Levitas & Gilson, 1994). Cuskelly and deJong (1996) found that mothers of children with developmental disabilities expressed concern that their children had difficulty making friends. They also found that girls with Down syndrome showed lower self-rated scores on Peer Acceptance than boys. Sukhodolsky and Butter (2007) found that poor social relationships during childhood relate to later social difficulties, and may be improved through social skills training. These authors recommended that social skills training in children with a developmental disability should reflect the child's level of ability, age, or any specific social difficulties she has. Interventions should include instruction, role play, and feedback.

During childhood, family is the most important source of companionship for a girl with a developmental disability. During adolescence and into young adulthood, however, the nature of her relationship with her family and with her peers changes (Bebco, Wainwright, Brian, Coolbear, Landry, & Vallance, 2006). Mokhtari (2008) pointed out the difference between peer acceptance and friendship, indicating that friendship involves mutuality. Those with developmental disabilities have fewer friends and experience a greater degree of social isolation than their nondisabled peers. During adolescence, friendships increase in importance. Nondisabled teens may be dating, learning to drive, taking part-time jobs, and going to parties. The adolescent with a developmental disability is very often not included in the social activities of her classmates and differences between them are emphasized, leading to

problems of self-esteem and withdrawal. For the teenage girl, appearance and popularity are very important and are emphasized in a wide variety of ways, including the media. Castles (1996) suggested that a girl with a disability engages in social comparison, feels stigmatized, and may escape into fantasy. The young woman with a developmental disability may also observe her peers engaging in more independent activities and may want the same opportunities, and so autonomy becomes an issue her family must address (Levitas & Gilson, 1994).

Independence/Autonomy

At the end of the school years, most friends and siblings leave home to go to college or university, marry, or work. The woman with a developmental disability may have hoped for increased independence in her life, but she may find job opportunities are poor, and her opportunities for more independent living do not parallel those of her siblings and peers (Gilson & Levitas, 1987). In spite of a strong desire to be independent, the constraints put on the individuals with developmental disabilities over time and the resulting socialized dependency make it difficult for them to achieve what they want.

As a consequence, this period of life sometimes becomes a time of family conflict. The family may experience ambivalence, wanting the adult child to achieve and be happy, but they may also see her as vulnerable and want to continue to protect her. Part of this desire to protect comes from actual needs the woman has, either physical or cognitive. Another part, however, comes from longstanding social attitudes that view a person with a developmental disability as being childlike and in need of instruction and corrections. Meyes (cited in Jurkowski & Amado, 1993) suggested that young women are often encouraged or granted the "right to remain in continuing adolescence with little growth or progress" (p. 135). A woman who has a developmental disability often receives contradictory messages. She may be told she is like everyone else, and she should dress and act in adult and "ladylike" ways. At the same time, she may be told that she is unlikely to marry or to have babies or do many of the other things she has assumed will happen when she is an adult (Burke & Gilmour, 1998). She may be encouraged to make choices, and may well have difficulties with coping and problem solving in the absence of a mediating other (Levitas & Gilson, 1994). When she does make choices, these are often not respected, or others strongly attempt to influence her (Knowlton, Turnbull, Backus, & Turnbull, 1988). She may be told where to live, who her roommates will be, and how to spend her money. She may also be expected to engage in activities that are not of her choosing. Jurkowski & Amado (1993) noted that this is often perpetuated by the service system: "dependence… remains essential to the survival of the consumer — dependence on staff, rules, paid services and system-defined boundaries" (p. 135).

The dependency observed in a woman with a developmental disability may appear, at times, to be adaptive. However, it causes her to be vulnerable, not only with regard to safety, but also in terms of self-worth. Most of us develop a strong sense of self. This allows us to be more confident and more resilient when we encounter problems or when we are evaluated in a negative way. The woman with a developmental disability does not develop this core sense of self to the same degree. She is aware of negative perceptions of herself by others (Reiss & Benson, 1984), of differences between herself and others, and of difficulties she has with some activities and behaviours. If she does not feel a personal sense of worth, and if she is aware of not meeting perceived social standards, there may be a further reduction to her self-esteem. Zetlin and Turner (1988) studied self-concept (the mental image or perception that one has of oneself) in adults with a developmental disability and found social conformity was important. Women with disabilities knew they did not always do things as well as others. They also knew they were dependent on care providers to do some things they would like to have done on their own. Benson and Ivins (1992) studied self-concept in persons with developmental disabilities and reported that women had lower ratings for self-concept than did men. For women with a developmental disability, then, there appears to be a relationship between her level of dependence on others, her ability to appear competent to others,

and her own self-concept.

Education, Economics and Employment

Employment is an indicator of independence, as it is one of the main ways women show they are contributing in valued ways to their communities and to their society. In more practical terms, employment provides an individual with the ability to purchase needed resources. Yet, as Kristiansen (2000a) noted, "Many women with little or no education, and most people with intellectual disability, are often forced to be content with having any employment at all" (p. 114). Education, then, is often the key to successful employment, especially since schools are becoming one of the main conduits into the work world.

Historically, those with developmental disabilities were placed in institutions at an early age (Burge, Ouellette-Kuntz, Hutchinson, & Box, 2008). Their education and training emphasized skills that could be utilized in those settings. Burge et al. noted that, as early placement in facilities decreased and children stayed home with their families, advocacy for special education placement occurred and special classes were developed for children with developmental disabilities. The acceptance of normalization and inclusion that swept the developed countries of the world in the 1970s led to legislation in Ontario in 1980 mandating education for all children with disabilities. The thrust here was to integrate children with disabilities into mainstream classrooms with academic support where necessary and appropriate. Although many children now participate in integrated programs, Porter (2004) found that as many as 40% remained in segregated classrooms. Burge and associates (2008) noted that, although there is sometimes an improvement in academic skills of those with disabilities through inclusion in mainstream classrooms, there are also benefits beyond academics to be gained in the educational setting, including respect and recognition by others. As well, the increase in social skills, improved behaviour, increased esteem, and development of social networks are also products of educational inclusion (Katz & Mirenda, 2002).

Blalock (1988) studied individuals with developmental disabilities in the United States following their completion of school. She found that 21% of the students who finished school each year were unemployed, 26% were on welfare, and 40% were under-employed. Kosciulek (2004) cited Harrington (1997) as stating students with disabilities who completed secondary school left without "marketable skills" and had not developed a sense of independence. More recently, Butcher and Wilton (2007) interviewed young adults, their families, and employers in Ontario. They noted that young people who wished to work were engaged in transitional activities for lengthy periods following completion of school due to inadequate planning for the transitional period and lack of appropriate employment options. In the United States, it is estimated that about 26% of those with a developmental disability who are supported by community agencies are employed. Of those, most have low wages and work few hours (Hall, Butterworth, Winsor, Gilmore, & Metzel, 2007). Although no similar data are available for Ontario, there is little reason to believe that the overall trend would differ significantly.

Since the 1980s, supported employment has been a model for training individuals for jobs and ensuring they have learned the skills to maintain employment (Beyer & Robinson, 2009). While this model may increase the success of placements, a study comparing day programs and supported employment options in the United States suggested that supported employment "all but stalled" during the first years of the twenty-first century (Rusch & Braddock, 2004). In Canada, a similar trend was seen that may reflect deterrents to work caused by provincial funding program rules (i.e., capping employment income by those receiving financial support) and by the preference of community agencies to support only those individuals who experience fewer difficulties (Stainton et al., 2006). For those with a severe disability and a high need for support, the cost of supported employment substantially exceeds that of special needs programs (Shearn, Beyer, & Felce, 2000).

Women who have developmental disabilities do not have good employment opportunities and, if they do work, they tend to put in long hours for little pay at jobs that are uninteresting or sometimes are contrived. Many are unemployed and live on social assistance, on levels of income that are below the poverty line (Castles, 1996; Marlatt & Day, 1984; Schucherdt, 1991). In a review of the literature addressing employment for those with developmental disabilities in the United Kindgdom, Beyer and Robinson (2009) found that women worked fewer hours, made lower wages, took longer to find work, and were less likely to have a job than men with disabilities. In another study, differences between job placements for men and for women were examined (Levy et al., 1994). The authors found significant differences in employment trends for men and women with developmental disabilities (e.g., more women had food service jobs). Women's jobs were lower paid and had fewer comprehensive benefits. Also, women's job placements lasted for shorter periods. When placements were terminated, women were more often fired than men, and less often had new employment opportunities.

In order to improve the capacity for women with disabilities to work, the structure for both training and support needs to be in place. It is not only important to offer training in vocational skill development, but also to consider the individual's preferences and strengths (Chadsey, 2007). As well, social skills are important for employment success. In Ontario, the province's employment program is called Ontario Works (Forchuk et al., 2007). It offers assistance to individuals in developing or improving job skills, and attempts to offer suitable placements. In addition to the provincially operated program, a 2010 search of the Internet identified a number of other funded programs and employment supports operated by community agencies supporting individuals with disabilities and private employment agencies that assist those with disabilities in developing resumes, learning employment skills, and providing placements with varying levels of support. The programs were noted to vary substantially across counties and regions. Those who are unable to work due to their disability may qualify for funds through the Ontario Disability Support Program (Ministry of Community and Social Services, 2008).

Although the focus of employment has been on

learning skills, improving economic conditions and striving toward more independent living, there is another aspect of employment. Kristiansen (2000a) wrote about the importance of what one young woman with a developmental disability learned from being around other women: how they cared for their homes, what they did in leisure time, their appearance, and day to day aspects of their lives. Kristiansen (2000b) also identified the pride in one's individual experiences, as well as the pride a woman's family takes in her, the people the individual gets to meet, and the positive environment where the woman gets to spend time. The author contended that the financial aspect of work was less important to the women she interviewed than the social one and the manner in which work symbolized the women's growth.

As indicated above, many women with developmental disabilities are unable to attain or maintain employment. While some are supported by families or community agencies, others live in poverty outside of any structured system of support. Some of these women are homeless and rely on their instincts to survive. A program model for providing outreach to such women was described by Bedard, Drummond, Ricciardi, and Husband (2003). Three community agencies in Toronto liaised to offer a drop-in support group. The women who were invited were those who were homeless or lived within the hostel system and who had a developmental disability. Among the aims of the program were to increase esteem, improve socialization, improve knowledge of health, and assist in accessing other services. A positive outcome and ongoing goal was noted to be the development of relationships.

Relationships

A "sense of loneliness may be particularly intense for people with disabilities who too often have experienced rejection, isolation, abuse, economic deprivation and marginalization" (Munro, 2010, p. 5). Many individuals who have a developmental disability are lonely and isolated and have difficulty developing and maintaining relationships (Traustadottir, 1993). Sometimes, families attempt to match women

who have a developmental disability with their own friends, a "paid volunteer", or some other person. These relationships serve a need, but are artificial in the context of traditional friendships. They may not offer the satisfaction and closeness the woman would experience in a naturally developing relationship, or they may lead to misunderstandings regarding the nature of the relationship. Traustadottir (2000) suggested that "recruited" friends reflect the "ideal" in the field of developmental disabilities as opposed to the "classic ideal."

Many young women with a developmental disability attend segregated activities and may make friends among peers. Others attend and participate in community activities, but it is unclear if they develop relationships that can be sustained. Traustadottir (2000) related the general view of friendship as being a relationship between those who have equal status and who share experiences and interests. She suggested that friendships between those with and without a disability do not fit such a definition. A relationship between a woman who has a disability and one who does not is possible, but is complex and presents challenges both parties need to overcome. Friendship between a developmentally disabled female and a nondisabled male is less likely to occur, as it often arouses concern or suspicion (Traustadottir, 1993).

Sexuality

Development of natural friendships occasionally leads to intimate relationships. Wanting an intimate relationship is a characteristic of all humans; those of us in caring and loving relationships experience the desire for physical closeness (Jurkowski & Amado, 1993). Those who have developmental disabilities have the same need to give and receive in this kind of relationship. Some care providers try to provide for the woman's needs by teaching life skills and self-care, but ignore needs of intimacy and development of social networks (Jurkowski & Amado, 1993). Zetlin and Turner (1988) found that girls and women with developmental disabilities speak of heterosexual relationships and have a desire for love, marriage, and dates. Many women express a high need to have a male companion and sometimes tie their whole identity to this issue. This may place them in high risk situations, as the desire for the relationship may supersede their awareness or acknowledgement of a risk (Stromsness, 1993). "For people with intellectual disabilities, there is a difficult balance to be struck between empowering people to claim their sexual rights and protecting them from abuse" (Murphy & O'Callaghan, 2004, p. 1347).

As in the nondisabled population, people with developmental disabilities may experience issues of gender identity. Topics such as sexual orientation, transsexuality, and homosexuality are usually avoided in discussions of persons who have a developmental disability. Asch and Fine (1988) noted there are no data on lesbian experiences for those who have disabilities, but anecdotal information implies that women with disabilities who might like to find a lesbian partner are less likely to do so than a nondisabled woman. This presents yet another area where the woman with a developmental disability may experience discrimination and nonunderstanding.

Parents, care providers, and social support systems may not always accept or acknowledge the sexual needs of the woman with a developmental disability. This may be because she has been thought of as childlike and therefore not a sexual being; it may relate to the caregiver's fear that the other person will take advantage of or abuse her; or it may reflect the care provider's discomfort in dealing with issues of sexuality (Jurkowski & Amado, 1993; Pendler, 1993). Pendler claimed that some care providers try "reducing the needs of persons with developmental disabilities to only biological urges and reducing sex to a simple behaviour that can be programmed away" (p. 227).

Women with a disability tend to be more protected by caregivers when it appears they are entering into an intimate relationship. The caregiver may attempt to maintain control of the woman's activities. There are some logical reasons for this, including the potential for pregnancy in a consensual relationship and the risk of sexually transmitted diseases. As well, women with a developmental disability, like other women, sometimes encounter

violence in a relationship or marriage (Carlson, 1997; Sobsey, 2000). Although many families and community agencies are increasingly attempting to address the sexual needs of women with disabilities, issues remain that relate to personal values, education, and questions of consent.

This is an area of confusion, as it has already been noted that normalization promoted empowerment to make choices (Burke & Baker, 2009). Along with the trend toward independent living, there has been an assumption that people want and are able to make decisions about their own lives, including decisions around sexual activity. However, those with developmental disabilities have not always had access to adequate information and training to make informed choices. Murphy and O'Callaghan (2004) found that those with a developmental disability had less knowledge about sexuality and were at increased risk of abuse than their nondisabled peers. Thus, determining whether a relationship is consensual or abusive may be problematic. The authors recommended continuing sexuality education and improved definitions to determine whether an individual has the capacity to consent to a sexual relationship. Eastgate (2005) used vignettes to highlight areas of concern around sexual health, potentials for abuse and issues of consent, and also encouraged education and support around decision making. Kennedy (2003) suggested that assessment of one's competency to give consent to engage in sexual activity should include neuropsychological testing.

The woman with a developmental disability is vulnerable. The actual risks she faces are the same ones experienced by nondisabled women, although they may be present at a higher rate due to her disability. Segregation, exclusion, and overprotection are not solutions to these problems. The woman with the disability is also able to enter loving relationships and have satisfying sexual experiences. To deny her the same opportunities and experiences that other women have can be as devastating to her as the things her family and care providers fear for her. Pendler (1993) noted the importance of this by claiming, "Often we are so overwhelmed by our own fears and anxieties that we are not even aware of the impact that our attitudes have on the persons with disabilities… They are often victims of both parental and societal attitudes" (p. 231).

Marriage and Spousal Relationships

Munro (2010) reflected on marriage being a milestone in our society. As well, marriage can provide the support and closeness that appears to improve both physical and emotional health. Munro acknowledged the anxieties experienced by the families and supporting professionals of those with developmental disabilities who want to engage in a spousal relationship. He pointed out that, often, when two persons who have a disability marry, they may compensate for their partner's area of weakness. As a result, the couple may be more successful than each person would be independently. In Munro's review of the literature of couple therapy covering 50 years, he found that people with developmental disabilities can, in fact, have happy and satisfying relationships.

Many women with developmental disabilities become involved in marriage or other forms of intimate or spousal relationships. Asch and Fine (1988) indicated that women who have a developmental disability are more likely to be married than their male peers, or than women with other types of disabilities. This may be because of stereotypic characteristics that assume she will be: dependent, loyal, and passive. Sometimes, women with a developmental disability will enter relationships with others who have higher intellectual abilities. Although Munro (2010) noted that these relationships are among the most successful, such couples may be subject to unwanted social curiosity or pity (Asch & Fine, 1988). Edgerton (1994) looked at women with cognitive disabilities who had been married to men who were intellectually unimpaired, and found that the men were dominant in the marriage. The women depended on them to have most of their needs met. He followed seven such women into widowhood and found that, when the husband died, although difficult, the women made the transition to social competency and independence in other ways. He suggested they had skills that they previously had not needed to use.

Spousal relationships of those with a developmental disability are stable and enduring for some, but others experience difficulties and relationships will dissolve. Again, this mirrors broader trends in our society. These couples may benefit from support, either in attempting to maintain the relationship or in being supported through a separation. Munro (2010) referred to the reluctance of professionals to provide counselling to couples with a developmental disability. These therapists may believe that those with disabilities may not be good candidates for counselling. Munro disagreed with this view, seeing instead relationships between people with developmental disabilities as a positive and rewarding experience.

Parenting

Many couples who have developmental disabilities are "admirable" parents (Castles, 1996). Others will need support in their parenting. The need for support does not suggest, however, that they will not be good and caring parents. Research has indicated that level of intelligence does not predict parenting success and that other factors are important, such as economics, the personal history of abuse (Sigurjonsdottir & Traustadottir, 2000), and access to a social network (Campbell, 2008).

It is unclear how many individuals who have a developmental disability become parents. A conservative estimate in the United States suggests there are about 36,500 families where one parent has an intellectual disability (Campbell, 2008). In Canada, it is reported that 10% of cases of substantiated child maltreatment known to authorities involve families in which at least one parent has an intellectual disability, with the primary concern being neglect and inadequate supervision (McConnell, Feldman, Aunos, & Prasad, 2010). The authors noted that court applications occurred more often when parents had an intellectual disability. They also noted that alternative dispute resolution was rarely used in these cases. Indeed, court systems internationally have made the assumption that having a developmental disability precludes a woman from being a good parent and have removed children from their families without "evidence of dysfunction" (Campbell, 2008).

Ontario-based research examined the impact of parenting programs for women with disabilities. It was shown that mothers with a developmental disability could be taught instrumental skills, such as early child-care activities (bathing, bottle washing), increase positive interactions with the child, engage in healthy home care activities (meals, cleaning), problem solving, and child management (Feldman & Case, 1999; Feldman et al., 1992). The Parenting Enhancement Program (PEP) is an example of a positive model of a supportive parenting program. It is available to families in the City of Toronto where there is a parent with a developmental disability (Surrey Place Centre, 2010).

Although instrumental skills and management strategies can be taught, some parents may experience difficulties parenting throughout all of the child's developmental stages. This is also true for nondisabled women. Personal clinical experience has suggested that empathy may not be acquired as readily. The woman may be successful in parenting a small child, but may encounter difficulties with later childhood or adolescence. This might be the case, for example, when the child's cognitive skills surpass her own. The impact would be not only in terms of problem solving and independent thought, but also in social relationships and expectations. In such cases, additional resources need to be found to support the woman, her child or children and, often, the relationship with her partner.

If a woman is a parent, and is in a spousal relationship that does not endure, the woman with a developmental disability may become a single mother. As well, some women who have children are single by choice, or because of other circumstances. The single mother with a developmental disability experiences the same difficulties as do other single mothers, except that she may well have fewer resources.

Aging

The concerns of aging women with developmental disabilities have largely been ignored (Canrinus & Lunsky, 2003) and, in Ontario, neglect of issues associated with aging and developmental disability has been exacerbated by the "multiple service sys-

tems" that fund and administer supports (Salvatori, Tremblay, & Tryssenaar, 2003). Salvatori and associates questioned individuals with developmental disabilities, their families, and their care providers about the challenges of aging. Parents identified concerns about the finances and the ability of government funds to "maintain the lifestyle that they had fought so hard to achieve for them" (p. 6). Individuals with developmental disabilities identified issues of relationships, autonomy, and meaningful activity. Health issues were also identified by those with disabilities, and their families expressed concern not only about the health of their adult child, but also about their own health.

Canrinus and Lunsky (2003) interviewed women with developmental disabilities to determine how they perceived their lives and to identify areas of challenge. The women reported financial struggles: they relied on government pensions, with some additional assistance by family or by working part-time. Their financial concerns meant they often could not do things they would like to do. They required support with tasks of daily living (housework and shopping), provided for many by a paid worker. When asked about their health, some indicated they did not have a healthy diet. All had a physician and most had at least one health concern (e.g., arthritis). As with finances, health interfered with engaging in activities they would like to do. Most had limited contact with family, and had lost significant family members due to age. The number of friends tended to have some relationship to their living situation or their systems of support. Some had more friends than in the past, and some had fewer. Activities they engaged in were primarily agency planned or supported. They "commonly cited the people in their lives...as important contributors to their happiness" (p. 76).

Physical Health Issues

In the nondisabled population, women live longer than men (Brown & Murphy, 1999). However, they also have a higher frequency of chronic health problems than men do. In the 1990s, concerns arose about the lack of research related to women's health and the probability that treatments offered might not be appropriate. Research on high risk diseases has more often been carried out with men than women, partly because of the risks of involving women during their reproductive years (Johnson & Fee, 1994). This suggests that "women's health care must often be based on untested inferences from data collected about men but, because there are important physiological differences between women and men, such inferences cannot always be presumed to be reliable" (Sherwin, 1994, p. 12). As medical research has responded with more women being included, it has been noted that there are differences between the sexes in the presentation of disease. Specific differences have been found, for example, in cardiovascular disease and in reactions to substances (Rieker & Bird, 2004). As well, some diseases may be gender specific, such as breast or ovarian cancer. When women see a physician with a health problem, her complaint may be considered to be psychological, whereas a man is more likely to have his complaint interpreted as physiological (Resources for Rehabilitation, 2000). This may lead to men receiving more extensive testing, and to increase the likelihood that the source of his complaint is identified and addressed.

People with developmental disabilities are living longer than in the past (Brown & Murphy, 1999). However, as with women, there has been a long-standing tendency to ignore the symptoms of health problems in those with developmental disabilities. Research has shown that some health problems are specific to a disability. For example, thyroid disease occurs at a higher rate in those with Down syndrome (Brown & Murphy, 1999).

Lifestyle may also impact the health of a person with a developmental disability. Yamaki (2005) found that people with a developmental disability were less likely to maintain a healthy weight. The author suggests this may be due to less knowledge about risks of not maintaining healthy weight, low income leading to a less healthy diet and fewer opportunities for exercise, and an increase in individual choice offered to the individual with a developmental disability.

The attention paid to both women in general and to women with disabilities in relation to health has been inadequate and is now a focus of international attention (Walsh et al., 2000). Women with developmental disabilities often have challenges that make their care more complicated than for nondisabled women: sensory impairments, communication disorders, mental health problems, difficult behaviours, unhealthy living situations, negative social perceptions, or physical disabilities (Ouellette-Kuntz et al., 2005). Such challenges may interact in many ways. What is certain is that they make health care for women with disabilities, who already have less than adequate access to quality health care, more complex. Ouellette-Kuntz et al. noted that, for persons who have a developmental disability in Canada, "there are important disparities in access to care that are difficult to disentangle from discriminatory values and practice" (Ouellette-Kuntz et al., p. 8).

Women who have a developmental disability may have more difficulty expressing discomfort or concerns than those without disabilities, and their symptoms are often identified through behaviour. She may also have less access to information about her health and inadequate support around health related procedures (Brown & Murphy, 1999; Walsh et al., 2000). Delays in identifying some diseases, such as breast or cervical cancer, may occur due to the women's lack of understanding about the need for screening, the fear of screening procedures or of pain resulting from these, and economic issues (Walsh et al., 2000).

Personal experience suggests that the identification of symptoms through behaviour may cause some care providers to interpret the issue as "behavioural." For example, women who are nonverbal and act upset or distressed on a cyclical basis may be experiencing Pre-Menstrual Syndrome. This may be interpreted by their support staff as being moody or difficult. As well, many women, during their menopausal years, experience incontinence to varying degrees (Brown & Murphy, 1999). A young support staff may not be aware of this and may interpret incontinence in the older woman she supports as some form of behavioural defiance.

It is not only care providers who may misinterpret symptoms of disorders. Medical practitioners may not attend to health issues because some disorders present earlier or in different ways in individuals with some disabilities than they would in the nondisabled population. Down syndrome, for example, leads to a high prevalence of Alzheimer-like dementia, beginning as early as 35 years of age (Rasmussen & Sobsey, 1994). Women with Down syndrome experience menopause about 10 years earlier than their non-disabled peers (Schupf et al., 1997). Those who have otitis media and have not been able to describe their symptoms, and therefore not had treatment, may be more subject to hearing loss (Connolly, 1998). Those with neuromuscular difficulties who have developmental disabilities very often experience earlier physical effects of aging (Connolly, 1998). Many people who have a developmental disability have taken medication for much of their lives and some of these have long-term effects. For example, a link has been made between long-term use of Dilantin and osteoporosis (Connolly, 1998).

Wilkinson and Cerreto (2008) expressed concern about the ability of women with developmental disabilities to make informed decisions regarding their health care. Based on their review of the literature, they suggested that women with a developmental disability should receive specific attention regarding some key health issues: menstrual disorders, contraception, cervical screening, breast cancer screening, and osteoporosis.

Mental Health Issues

Women with developmental disabilities experience the same range of emotional risks and difficulties as other women (Taggart, McMillan, & Lawson, 2009). However, for many years, the mental health needs of people with disabilities have not been adequately addressed. The fact that such people experience clinical and personality disorders was ignored for a long time, in spite of their actual increased risk of developing these disorders as compared to the general population (Crews, Bonaventure, & Rowe, 1994). When recognized, mental health concerns were often falsely considered as symptoms of the developmental disability (Downes, 1982). Symptom presentation frequently resulted in the use of medications and/or behaviour programs that did not address the real needs of the person. Although symptoms are often expressed and recog-

nized in terms of behaviour, they arise from one or a combination of factors in addition to a psychiatric diagnosis. These other factors include neurological impairment, developmental and family issues, social disadvantages, medical conditions, communication problems, environmental conditions, crisis situations, and low self-esteem (Burke & Gilmour, 1998; Regional Support Associates, 2008).

The majority of people who have a developmental disability can respond to a variety of types of treatments to alleviate their symptoms. Historically, behavioural therapy and psychopharmacology were the primary interventions offered. Issues such as bereavement or sexual assault were often ignored, as the effects of these could not be programmed away. It was initially believed that people with developmental disabilities could not benefit from cognitive therapies (Burke & Gilmour, 1998). Some past treatments were intrusive and reflected the cause of the problem. For example, not long ago (and still in some places), people exhibiting self-injury were restrained. Because the possible relationship between self-injury and sexual assault was ignored, some women, instead of receiving the assistance they needed, were further traumatized (Burke & Bedard, 1994).

Today, the range of treatments available has broadened. Behaviour therapy and pharmacology are still used when appropriate, but women are also increasingly offered individual and group cognitive and cognitive behavioural therapies, symbolic therapies such as play, art, and music, and many other options to address their emotional needs and problems (Burke & Gilmour, 1996). The emphasis on the biopsychosocial model of assessment and treatment in behaviour and psychiatry (Griffiths & Gardner, 2002; Holmes, 2000) has increased the likelihood that a broad range of aspects of the individual's needs will be addressed.

Abuse and Violence

A review of violence toward those with disabilities reflects the power imbalance within our social structures and may include behaviour that is not considered a criminal act, but suggests discrimination toward and some manner of maltreatment of the individual (Ticoll, 1994).

Estimates suggest that 9 out of 10 women who have a developmental disability may be sexually assaulted during their lifetime (Sobsey, 2000). As well, the risk of a woman who has a developmental disability being sexually assaulted is 4 to 10 times greater than for other women. Although both men and women may be victims of abuse, the frequency is higher for women with developmental disability, as is the case in the nondisabled population (Burke, Bedard, Ludwig, & Corrigan-Kent, 1998). The effects of abuse are sometimes severe and chronic, and can last for many years (Sobsey, 1994). The women may experience physical injury, contract sexually transmitted diseases, become pregnant, or experience emotional trauma (Sobsey, 2000). In the cases reviewed by Sobsey, only 20% of those who had been sexually assaulted received appropriate intervention.

The additional vulnerability of the woman with a disability may stem from the fact that she is dependent on others for care or is in a situation where she is accessible to potential abusers. Privacy during physical care is an issue that is often forgotten in relation to the experience of sexuality and of sexual assault. If a woman has a need for physical personal assistance, care providers may assume touching without consent is acceptable without recognizing the potential impact it may have. The woman may feel violated or embarrassed during procedures. It may also place her at increased risk if she then thinks it is acceptable for anyone to touch her in an intimate way (Jurkowski & Amado, 1993).

Violence against women with developmental disabilities is not limited to sexual assault. Sobsey (2000) reported on 208 cases of actual or attempted homicide. He found that 16.8% of cases were sexually motivated assaults, but 83.2% were related to other motives such as anger, punishment, and finances. His review indicated that the perpetrators of violence against women with disabilities may be intimate partners, care providers, or peers.

When a woman with a developmental disability encounters violence in a relationship, she often has difficulty leaving the scene of the violence. This may be because of personal characteristics such as learned dependency, poor self-concept, a tendency to be compliant, and nonassertiveness. She may also be reluctant to tell others if, over her lifetime, people have not listened to her. She may think it is her fault in some way, and she may not have the well-developed problem-solving skills to decide what she should do. As well, social structures and the difficulties the woman may have in accessing services in the system may mean she has fewer resources to help her find a safe place to go.

Women who have been assaulted and wish to have redress are often re-victimized by the system that supports them. The investigative processes can be emotionally and physically devastating. Women who file a complaint in the legal system must subject themselves to a physical examination as "her body is the scene of the crime" and "physical, empirical evidence must be removed from this scene" (Hanington & Ricciotti, 1997, p. 60). For the woman, this process may resemble the initial assault and the effects may be equally traumatic. Then, because a woman who has a developmental disability is often considered not to be a credible witness in court, the case may be dismissed, further devaluing her.

Justice

"There has been increasing ... recognition of the need for more appropriate responses and services for individuals who come in contact with the criminal justice system and who have an intellectual disability and mental health issues" (Riches, Parmenter, Wiese & Stancliffe, 2005, p. 386).

In the United States, it is estimated that people with an intellectual disability make up 2-10% of those in the prison system (Anno, 1991). A Canadian study looking at inmates in the British Columbia prison system identified 6.5% as having a developmental disability (Hitchen, 1994). In the United Kingdom, 7% of adult prisoners were found to have an intellectual disability and an additional 25% fell in the borderline range of functioning (Talbot, 2008). In the latter study, prior to their arrest, most did not have full time employment or any functional activities to engage in. Less than one-third of those interviewed in the study had received support following their arrest and over one-fifth did not understand the court proceedings.

In Canada, most women who are incarcerated spend their time in provincial institutions. Those most likely to spend time in correctional settings are those who are poor, have received a limited education, are young, and have histories of addictions, abuse and/or mental health disorders (METRAC, 2008). In a press release, the Disabled Women's Network of Ontario (Marshall, 2003) accused the federal correctional system of discriminating again women who have mental and developmental disabilities. It was stated that the assignment of security level is based on disability (e.g., cognitive impairments or mental health concerns), which results in women with disabilities being "often isolated, deprived of clothing, and placed in stripped/barren cells" (p. 29).

Currently in Ontario, there is a Forensic Mental Health System that provides assistance to individuals who have mental health issues and have been arrested (Bettridge & Barbaree, 2004). The goal of the program is rehabilitation. Those who are arrested and have a developmental disability are typically routed through the Forensic Mental Health System. As well, Justice Dual Diagnosis Case Managers are available in some areas of the province to assist individuals who have an intellectual disability and mental health disorder and find themselves in the justice system (Regional Support Associates, 2009).

Cultural Issues

Customs develop within ethnic communities or geographic regions and are passed down over generations, offering members of that culture an identity and sense of belonging. These cultural patterns interact with other factors such as religion, gender, and ability to determine the roles or expectations for the person within his or her culture (Hanson, 1992a; McGoldrick & Giordano, 1996). In Western cultures, values "focus on independence, freedom, assertiveness, equality, self-help, and self-directedness" (Hanson, p. 71). Those who come to North America from areas with different cultural values and traditions may attempt to retain many of their customs and values, as these may constitute integral aspects

of their identities.

The roles of men and women are defined to some extent by their cultural traditions and values. In addition to culturally specific roles, women tend to be defined as nurturers and care providers across almost every culture (Walmsley, 2000). Women may have the desire for, and ability to achieve other values, such as independence, equality, and self-directedness, but their role as nurturer and care provider is still embedded within the cultural mentality. Thus, women often struggle to achieve other goals while they continue to meet their culture's expectation as nurturers and care providers.

Every culture also maintains values regarding persons with disabilities. Some cultures have a fatalistic view of the individual with a disability: they assume there is nothing that can be done for the person (Hanson, 1992b). Other cultures see disability as the fate of the family, a punishment, a blessing, or the presence of spirits inhabiting the person. Traditional family and cultural beliefs inform the degree to which respect and support is given to, and intervention obtained for, a girl or woman with a developmental disability.

Viewing women as nurturers and care providers across cultures often adds to the problems of a woman with a developmental disability. Because she is often the receiver rather than the provider of care, her life experience does not match her expected role. When poor educational and work opportunities for women with disabilities are added to this, the woman often experiences "rolelessness" (Deegan & Brooks, 1985). Boylan (1991) stated that "the woman who has a mental handicap is at enormous risk of being invisible and without a voice" (p. 9).

The Woman Care Provider

There are far more women than men in the role of care provider to people with developmental disabilities (Traustadottir, 1993). These may be mothers, sisters, friends, or women paid to act as caregivers.

Mothers

The literature has long suggested that parents who have a child with a disability may feel guilt and may be extremely tired and stressed. More recently, it has been suggested that families are "stressed and coping as best they can" (Dykens, 2005, p. 360). Comparisons of the viewpoints of mothers and fathers, related to the impact on the family of having a child with a disability, were found in the literature, with results showing little disagreement in a couple's responses (Ainge, 1995; Trute & Hiebert-Murphy, 2002). The latter authors noted that the marital relationship was an important factor in family adjustment and parenting stress. The adjustment to having a child with a disability was studied in the context of hope (Kausar, Jevne, & Sobsey, 2006). Each family's experiences were unique in terms of acceptance, support, attitudes by others, and individual characteristics of the child. However, the authors reported that while parents initially found their role to be challenging, they ultimately found it to be a "positive and strengthening experience" (p. 161).

In the traditional family, mothers provide both physical care and nurturance. Ricci and Hodapp (2003) reported that fathers participate in the childrearing activities of the child with a developmental disability. However, the traditional father's role is less focused on direct care. Greater sharing of roles occurs in the modern family, but women still take on a larger number of household and parenting tasks. This is true not only with young children. In looking at families of adults with a developmental disability, Holmes and Carr (1991) indicated no significant differences were found in the amount of care offered to the person by family members, but mothers more often assumed direct care, while fathers offered more supervision.

Meyer (1986) suggested men and women experience different adaptive responses to having a child with a disability. In families that have children with a developmental disability, normal family patterns are altered. The mother not only may function in the usual care-giving role, but also may be the primary provider for any special needs such as physical care of the disabled person. She must attempt, at the same time, to address the needs of the rest of the family. This mother must sometimes give up desired activities, so that she can provide care to her child. The father may be supportive, but he is rarely the primary

care provider and is more likely to continue in his own activities (Mittler, 1995). Cuskelly (2006) stated that fewer mothers of both children and adults with developmental disabilities were employed compared to mothers of nondisabled children.

If the child has social needs, the mother may try to find other children or adults to act as friends. She may also be the main person with whom the child with disabilities interacts, and may have a strong role as an emotional support. Although most mothers balance these roles well, such a situation may sometimes be very challenging for them personally and for other members of their families (Mittler, 1995).

As families age, many continue to be the primary care providers of their adult children who have a developmental disability. Some reports suggest that aging parents may experience a high level of stress and feel they are not supported. Cuskelly (2006) stated that parents of adult children with a developmental disability experienced social isolation, and were at increased risk for both mental health and physical difficulties. In a Canadian study by Minnes and Woodford (2004), it was noted that all parents perceived some stress related to specific areas of planning, such as planning for long-term accommodation and social/emotional support. Older parents did not appear to experience more stress than parents who were younger. As well, mothers and fathers showed no difference. Some parents did experience depression, which was found to be positively related to maladaptive behaviour exhibited by their child and adverse changes due to age. Depression and use of resources were found to be negatively correlated.

Nemzoff (1992) expressed concern that those who are decision-makers regarding services for people with developmental disabilities may not consider the needs of care providers. She pointed out that mothers act as advocates for services that are often difficult to access and, when they have needed to be strong in an advocacy role, they have often been considered aggressive. This view does not recognize the isolation the mother may experience if she has a high needs child. In some places, progress has been made and mothers have received some assistance with resources to help them cope with specific problems. Still, they continue to fulfill multiple demanding roles, and are still often unable to achieve the ends toward which they are working. Throughout this, the emotional needs of the mother are very often not addressed.

Sisters

The impact of a disabled child on a family appears to be varied. There may be greater competition for resources and attention in families where one of the children has a developmental disability. Siblings may experience emotional difficulties because they receive less attention from parents. As well, the child without the disability may not always understand the needs or problems of the child with a disability. Parents may be overly stressed and have increased demands, and require that the nondisabled child assist with care provision. Siblings may also feel they need to compensate for the limitations of their disabled brother or sister by doing better.

In spite of added difficulties for sisters of people with developmental disabilities, there are also many positive effects. Most report being enriched in some ways. Having a child with a developmental disability can also make the family feel more integrated. The child without the disability may provide real and necessary assistance to the disabled child as well as contributing to social development (Crinic & Leconte, 1986). Many of the roles the sibling takes on may impact positively in their own development in terms of maturity, tolerance, and respect.

Siblings of adults who have developmental disabilities and siblings of those with mental health issues were questioned regarding current and future involvement with their siblings. Substantially more of those who have siblings with a developmental disability expected to take on an active role in their care (Greenberg, Selzter, Orsmond, & Krauss (1999). The authors noted that siblings of those with developmental disabilities were also provided more emotional support in the present. Greater responsibilities for providing care may fall on sisters than on brothers. When the parents are aging or die, the sibling sometimes becomes the primary care provider or care coordinator. Thus, having a sibling with a developmental disability may involve a lifelong commitment that not all are prepared to make. West (2000) wrote about the stunning experience of finding she had a sister who had been institutionalized in childhood. As the sisters came to know and care for one another, West talked of both the positive moments as well as the challenges of becoming her "advocate and protector" (p.48).

Friends and others who give support

In childhood, girls are more likely to accept and be friends with someone who has a disability than are boys. Similarly, in adulthood, women are more likely to develop a friendship with someone who has a disability than are men (Traustadottir, 1993).

One view of gender differences is that women's orientation in relation to others is expressive (Traustadottir, 1993). Women tend to enjoy closeness, and their friendship patterns suggest an emotional attachment to others. Women, in general, are sensitive to the needs of others, and tend to nurture and care for others. By contrast, men's orientation in relation to others is more instrumental. Men do things together, but do not appear to develop the same emotional closeness or, if they do, do not express it in the same ways. Men's relationships tend to be more competitive and less intimate and men have a smaller circle of friends than women do. These gender differences are thought, according to this view, to account for the greater proportion of women who are friends of persons with developmental disabilities as compared to men (Traustadottir, 1993).

As noted earlier, if men do want to engage in a relationship with someone who has a developmental disability, particularly a woman, there may be obstacles. Historically, men and women have been less likely to engage in cross-gender friendships, and much of this may be due to sexual tension. In situations in which a man acts as a friend or care provider to a woman with a disability, it may be more likely that his intentions are misunderstood. When women who are nondisabled enter into a friendship with those who have disabilities, including men, support becomes a component of that relationship (Traustadottir, 1993). It has been observed that the person with a disability typically attempts to give to the relationship by being a good listener and supporter and the person who is nondisabled may offer other types of physical and practical care within the relationship.

The women's movement has encouraged fostering friendships and relationships across many lines. Women tend to value and engage in relationships with other women who are quite different from themselves; this includes nondisabled women and those with developmental disabilities (Hooyman & Gonyea, 1995).

The woman with a disability as care provider

Women who have a developmental disability may also act as care providers. In the sections above, it was noted that such women may be a spouse, mother, or friend. Each of these roles implies some provision of care. As well, many provide some support to aging parents, to siblings, and to others in vocational and volunteer roles. Walmsley (2000) talked to women with developmental disabilities who experienced the role of care provider. She noted that, in these cases, caring was a "central activity in their lives" but that their roles "gave them very limited access to life in the public arena, the world outside close relationships with friends and family" (p. 210).

Women with Developmental Disabilities in Ontario

The profile of the woman with a developmental disability in Ontario shows a great deal of variation. Much of this depends on her support system, her abilities and experiences, and the resources available in her community, along with her ability to access the resources. Women with developmental disabilities in Ontario may live with their families, in boarding homes, in group homes, independently by themselves or with roommates, with spouses and sometimes with children, in correctional facilities, in treatment centres, or on the streets. Most live on a limited income that places them below the poverty line. Many work, although few have competitive jobs. Apart from work, some engage in positive and stimulating activities: they sing in the church choir, exercise at the local gym, go horseback riding, act as volunteers, or take classes in cooking or art. However, others engage in no social or leisure activities. Some have one or two good friends and strong relationships with family members; others have no

friends and feel very isolated and lonely. Some have been physically or sexually abused. Others who have no personal experience of abuse may have witnessed the abuse of others. They also report being discriminated against and harassed, often because of their developmental disability.

Many women with developmental disabilities in Ontario have health problems, and too often, treatment has been delayed. This may be because of the lack of a primary care physician or other health professional. It may also be because the women were unable to articulate symptoms and others did not recognize them. Women may have received little information regarding health issues and, when provided, information may not have been in a form they could understand. Many women with developmental disabilities have mental health problems. Some in this latter group receive treatment, which may include medication, behaviour therapy, cognitive therapy, family therapy, or group therapy. Others have apparent psychological or emotional problems that have never been addressed.

In spite of the ongoing need for resources to meet the needs of women in Ontario who have a developmental disability, there are some resources and services available. Generic, community based agencies increasingly recognize the needs of those with developmental disabilities and are educating themselves so that they can offer services. There are also specialized services, but these are not always available in every county or region, and so all women in Ontario may not have access to equal services.

Summary

Women with developmental disabilities are often devalued due to their status as both women and as persons with disabilities. In addition, many are members of other groups that have been oppressed, such as ethnic women, those with mental health problems, the poor, rural women, older women, and children. Their low status is due to social ideologies and gender inequalities that have historically been practised in Western society (Hanington & Riciotti, 1997). These attitudes may also reflect on their care providers, who are also typically women.

Philosophies of inclusion and normalization were intended to increase the likelihood of persons with disabilities participating in life in their communities. However, beliefs about developmentally disabled persons have been slow to change, and some of the stereotypes have been retained, even by the professionals who work with them. Therefore, the woman with developmental disabilities is still often stigmatized and segregated, does not get due respect or privacy, and is often over-supervised and controlled (Jurkowski & Amado, 1993).

In spite of the obstacles they encounter, many women with disabilities in Ontario are engaged in positive relationships and meaningful activities. While resources are inadequate and often inappropriate, and respect is still often wanting, there are increasingly agencies and systems committed to helping women with developmental disabilities to improve their quality of life and inclusion in community activities, and committed to providing resources that adequately address their needs of safety, education, economy, and health.

For Further Thought and Discussion

1. Why are there more women than men who act as care providers to those who have developmental disabilities?
2. Why are women with developmental disabilities considered to face a double disability?
3. If a man does decide to enter a supportive relationship with a woman who has a developmental disability, what concerns might they have?
4. How well do our societal systems support women with developmental disabilities who have been victims of violence?

More Resources

Information about women with developmental and intellectual disabilities can be obtained through books, journals, supporting agencies, and websites.

Clinical services specific to those with developmental disabilities, are funded within many regions.

As the Internet is available to most people, the most practical way to access appropriate resources is by using the key words "women" and "developmental disabilities" and the issue one wants to research. Some specific sources of information are:

The Ontario Women's Directorate: is a provincial government agency that celebrates the achievement of women, identifies and researches issues of concern to women, develops resource information and offers links to appropriate programs and services. *www.citizenship.gov.on.ca/owd*

The Disabled Women's Network of Ontario (DAWN): examines issues of women's rights and advocates for women with disabilities over many issues in a variety of forums. *dawn.thot.net*

The Ontario Women's Health Network (OWHN): was developed to address issues of research, practice, and policy related to women's health issues and to offer accessible resource information to women. *www.owhn.on.ca*

The ARCH Disability Law Centre: attempts to advance the rights of individuals with disabilities in Ontario. *www.archdisabilitylaw.ca*

The Community Networks of Specialized Care: are four networks within the Province of Ontario, funded by the Ministry of Community and Social Services, and created to ensure that the special needs of those with intellectual disabilities are available and accessible. *www.community-networks.ca*

Community Living Ontario (CLO): is an association of agencies that provide community based supports with the aim of individual growth and community participation. CLO provides leadership to its member organizations, and advocates for those with intellectual disabilities and their families. *www.communitylivingontario.ca*

Surrey Place Centre: provides specialized clinical services to those with developmental disabilities and their families in the City of Toronto. *www.surreyplace.on.ca*

Regional Support Associates: provides clinical services in twelve counties in Southern Ontario. *www.regionalsupport.on.ca*

References

Ainge, D. J. (1995). A comparison of couples' views of caring for their child with intellectual disability. *Australia & New Zealand Journal of Developmental Disabilities, 20*(3), 175-188.

Anno, B. J. (1991). *Prison health care: Guidelines for the management of an adequate delivery system.* Washington, DC: National Institute of Corrections, 125-126.

Asch, A. (1999). Prenatal diagnosis and selective abortion: A challenge to practice and policy. *American Journal of Public Health, 89*(11), 1649-1657.

Asch, A., & Fine, M. (1988). Introduction: Beyond pedestals. In M. Fine, & A. Asch (Eds.), *Women with disabilities: Essays in psychology, culture and politics* (pp. 1-37). Philadelphia: Temple University Press.

Bebco, J. M., Wainwright, J. A., Brian, J. A., Coolbear, J., Landry, R., & Vallance, D. D. (2006). Social competence and peer relations in children with mental retardation: Models of the development of peer relations. *Journal on Developmental Disabilities, OADD 20th Anniversary Issue,* 89-113.

Bedard, C., Drummond, C., Ricciardi, J., & Husband, F. (2003). Community Women's Circle: A partnership program developed to connect and serve homeless, poor and socially marginalized women with developmental disabilities. *Journal on Developmental Disabilities, 10*(1), 55-59.

Benson, B. A., & Ivins, J. (1992). Anger, depression and self-concept in adults with mental retardation. *Journal of Intellectual Disability Research, 36,* 169-175.

Bettridge, S., & Barbaree, H. (2004). *The forensic mental health system in Ontario.* Toronto, ON: Centre for Addiction and Mental Health.

Beyer, S., & Robinson, C. (2009). *A review of the research literature on supported employment: A Report for the cross-Government learning disability employment strategy team.* Welsh Centre for Learning Disabilities, School of Medicine, Cardiff Universtiy, UK.

Blalock, G. (1988). Transitions across the lifespan. In B. L. Ludlow, A. P. Turnbull, & R. Luckasson (Eds.), *Transitions to adult life for people with men-* *tal retardation: Principles and practices* (pp. 3-20). Baltimore: Paul H. Brookes Publishing Company.

Boylan, E. (1991). *Women and disability.* London: Zed Books Ltd.

Boyle, C. A., Decoufle, P., & Yeargin-Allsop, M. (1994). Prevalence and health impact of developmental disabilities in US children. *Pediatrics, 93*(3), 399-403.

Brown, A., & Murphy, L. (1999). *Aging with developmental disabilities: Women's health issues.* A joint publication of The Arc of the United States and the Rehabilitation Research and Training Centre on Aging with Mental Retardation.

Burge, P., Ouellette-Kuntz, H., Hutchinson, N., & Box, H. (2008). A quarter century of inclusive education for children with intellectual disabilities in Ontario: Public perceptions. *Canadian Journal of Educational Administration and Policy, 87*(Dec. 3, 2008), 1-8.

Burke, L., & Baker, K. (2009). *Has the script changed?* Paper presented at the annual conference of Regional Support Associates, October 1, 2009, London, Ontario.

Burke, L., & Bedard, C. (1994). Self-injury considered in association with sexual victimization in individuals with a developmental handicap. *The Canadian Journal of Human Sexuality, 3,* 253-262.

Burke, L., Bedard, C., Ludwig, S., & Corrigan-Kent, P. (1998). Dealing with sexual abuse of adults with a developmental disability who also have impaired communication: Supportive procedures for detection, disclosure and follow-up. *SIECCAN Newsletter, 33,* 79-91.

Burke, L., & Gilmour, I. (1996). Counselling survivors of sexual abuse using a developmental cognitive perspective. *The NADD Newsletter, 13,* 1-3.

Burke, L., & Gilmour, I. (1998). *Challenging behaviour viewed as successful function.* Paper presented at the 9th Annual Conference, Ontario Association on Developmental Disabilities, April 16, 1998, Niagara Falls, ON.

Butcher, S., & Wilton, R. (2007). Stuck in transition? Exploring the spaces of employment training for youth with intellectual disability. *Geoforum, 39* (2), 1079-1092.

Campbell, L. S. (2008, August). *Parents with intel-*

lectual disabilities. Family Trends, Jordan Institute for Families, University of North Caroline at Chapel Hill.

Canrinus, M., & Lunsky, Y. (2003). Successful aging of women with intellectual disabilities: The Toronto experience. *Journal on Developmental Disabilities, 10*(1), 73-78.

Carlson, B. E. (1997). Mental retardation and domestic violence: An ecological approach to intervention. *Social Work, 42,* 79-89.

Castles, E. E. (1996). *We're people first: The social and emotional lives of individuals with mental retardation*. Westport, CT: Praeger.

Chadsey, J. G. (2007). Vocational skills and performance. In J. W. Jacobson, J. A. Julick, & J. Rojahn (Eds.), *Handbook of intellectual and developmental disabilities* (pp. 619-634). New York: Springer.

Connolly, B. H. (1998). General effects of aging on persons with developmental disabilities. *Topics in Geriatric Rehabilitation, 13,* 1-18.

Crews, W. D., Bonaventure, S., & Rowe, F. (1994). Dual diagnosis: Prevalence of psychiatric disorders in a large state residential facility for individuals with mental retardation. *American Journal on Mental Retardation, 98,* 688-731.

Crinic, K. A., & Leconte, J. M. (1986). Understanding sibling needs and influences. In R. R. Fewell, & P. F. Vadasy (Eds.), *Families of handicapped children: Needs and supports across the life span* (pp. 75-98). Austin, TX: Pro-ed.

Culham, A., & Nind, M. (2003). Deconstructing normalisation: Clearing the way for inclusion. *Journal of Intellectual and Developmental Disability, 28*(1), 65-78.

Cuskelly, M. (2006). Parents of adults with an intellectual disability. *Family Matters, 74,* 20-25.

Cuskelly, M., & deJong, I. (1996). Self-concept in children with Down syndrome. *Down Syndrome Research and Practice, 4,* 59-64.

Deegan, M. J., & Brooks, N. A. (1985). *Women and disability: The double handicap*. New Brunswick, NJ: Transaction Books.

Downes, M. (1982). Counseling women with developmental disabilities. *Women and Therapy, 3,* 101-109.

Dykens, E. M. (2005). Happiness, well-being, and character strengths: Outcomes for families and siblings of persons with mental retardation. *Mental Retardation, 43*(5), 360-364.

Eastgate, G. (2005). Sex, consent and intellectual disability. *Australian Family Physician, 34*(3), 163-166.

Edgerton, R. B. (1994). Quality of life issues: Some people know how to be old. In M. Marlick Seltzer, M. Wyngaarden Krauss, & M. P. Janicki (Eds.), *Life course perspective in adulthood and old age* (pp. 53-66). Washington, DC: American Association on Mental Retardation.

Feldman, M. A., & Case, L. (1999). Teaching childcare and safety skills to parents with intellectual disabilities through self-learning. *Journal of Intellectual and Developmental Disability, 24*(1), 27-44.

Feldman, M. A., Case, L., Garrick, M., MacIntyre-Grande, W., Carnwell, J., & Sparks, B. (1992). Teaching child-care skills to mothers with developmental disabilities. *Journal of Applied Behavior Analysis, 25*(1), 205-215.

Forchuk, C., Joplin, L., Schofield, R., Cziernik, R., Gorlick, C., & Turner, K. (2007). Housing, income support and mental health: Points of disconnection. *Health Research Policy and Systems, 5*(14), doi:10.1186/1478-4505-5-14.

Garland-Thomson, R. (2001). Re-shaping; re-thinking; re-defining: Feminist disability studies. Retrieved from http://www.thefreelibrary.com/Re-shaping%2c+Re-thinking%2c+Re-defining%3a+Feminist+Disability+Studies.-a084377500.

Gilson, S. F., & Levitas, A. S. (1987). Psychosocial crises in the lives of mentally retarded people. *Psychiatric Aspects of Mental Retardation Reviews, 6,* 27-31.

Greenberg, J. S., Seltzer, M., Orsmond, G. I., & Kraus, M. W. (1999). Siblings of adults with mental illness or mental retardation: Current involvement and expectation of future caregiving. *Psychiatric Services, 50*(9), 1214-1219.

Griffiths, D. M., & Gardner, W. I. (2002). The integrated biopsychosocial approach to challenging behaviours. In D. M. Griffiths, C. Stavrakaki, & J. Summers (Eds.), *Dual Diagnosis: An introduction to the mental health needs of persons with developmental disabilities* (pp. 81-114). Sudbury, ON:

Habilitative Mental Health Resource Network.

Hall, A. C., Butterworth, J., Winsor, J. Gilmore, D., & Metzel, D. (2007). Pushing the employment agenda: Case study research of high performing States in integrated employment. *Intellectual and Developmental Disabilities, 45*(3), 182-198.

Hanington, P., & Ricciotti, P. (1997). *Volunteer resource manual.* London, ON: Sexual Assault Centre.

Hanson, M. J. (1992a). Families with Anglo-European roots. In E. W. Lynch & M. J. Hanson (Eds.), *Developing cross-cultural competence: A guide for working with young children and their families* (pp. 56-83). Baltimore: Paul H. Brookes Publishing Co.

Hanson, M. J. (1992b). Ethnic, cultural and language diversity in intervention settings. In E. W. Lynch & M. J. Hanson (Eds.), *Developing cross-cultural competence: A guide for working with young children and their families* (pp. 3-18). Baltimore: Paul H. Brookes Publishing Co., Inc.

Harris, A., & Wideman, D. (1988). The construction of gender and disability in early attachment. In M. Fine, & A. Asch (Eds.), *Women with disabilities: Essays in psychology, culture, and politics* (pp. 115-138). Philadelphia: Temple University Press.

Hitchen, D. L. (1994). *Fitness to stand trial and mentally challenged defendants: Evaluation of the forensic process and the Criminal Code of Canada.* Burnaby, B.C.: School of Criminology, Simon Fraser University.

Holmes, J. (2000). Fitting the biopsychosocial jigsaw together. *British Journal of Psychiatry, 177*(2), 93-94.

Holmes, N., & Carr, J. (1991). The pattern of care in families of adults with a mental handicap: A comparison between families of autistic adults and Down syndrome adults. *Journal of Autism & Developmental Disorders, 21*(2), 159-176.

Hooyman, N. R., & Gonyea, J. (1995). *Feminist perspectives on family care: Policies for gender justice.* Thousand Oaks, CA: Sage Publications.

Johnson, T., & Fee, E. (1994). Women's participation in clinical research: From protectionism to access. In A. C. Mastroianni, R. R. Fadden, & D.D. Federman (Eds.), *Women and health research: Ethical and legal issues of including women in clinical stud-*

ies, volume 2, workshop and commissioned papers (pp. 1-10). Washington, DC: National Academy Press.

Johnson, K., & Traustadottir, R. (2000). Finding a place. In R. Traustadottir, & K. Johnson (Eds.), *Women with intellectual disabilities: Finding a place in the world* (pp. 9-23). London: Jessica Kingsley Publishers.

Jurkowski, E., & Amado, A. N. (1993). Affection, love, intimacy and sexual relationship. In A. N. Amado (Ed.), *Friendships and community connections between people with and without developmental disabilities* (pp. 129-151). Baltimore: Paul H. Brooks Publishing Co.

Katz, J., & Mirenda, P. (2002). Including students with developmental disabilities in general education classrooms: Social benefits. *International Journal of Special Education, 17*(2), 25-35.

Kausar, S., Jevne, R. F., & Sobsey, D. (2006). Hope in families of children with developmental disabilities. *Journal on Developmental Disabilities, OADD's 20th Anniversary Issue,* 153-163.

Kennedy, C. H. (2003). Legal and psychological implications in the assessment of sexual consent in the cognitively impaired population. *Assessment, 10*(4), 352-358.

Knowlton, H. E., Turnbull, A. P., Backus, L., & Turnbull III, H. R. (1988). Consent and the "Yes, But..." problem in transition. In B. L. Ludlow, A. P. Turnbull, & R. Luckasson (Eds.), *Transitions to adult life for people with mental retardation: Principles and practices* (pp. 45-66). Baltimore: Paul H. Brookes Publishing Co.

Kosciulek, J. F. (2004). Empowering people with disabilities through vocational rehabilitation counseling. *American Rehabilitation,* Autumn, 2004. *www2.ed.gov/news/newsletters/amrehab/2004/autumn/kosciulek.doc.*

Kristiansen, K. (2000a). Learning from and with women: The story of Jenny. In R. Traustadottir, & K. Johnson (Eds.), *Women with intellectual disabilities: Finding a place in the world* (pp. 106-117). London: Jessica Kingsley Publishers.

Kristiansen, K. (2000b). The social meaning of work: Listening to women's own experiences. In R. Traustadottir, & K. Johnson (Eds.), *Women with intellectual disabilities: Finding a place in the world* (pp. 183-190). London: Jessica Kingsley Publishers.

Lemon, C., & Lemon, J. (2003). Community-based cooperative ventures for adults with intellectual disabilities. *The Canadian Geographer, 47*(4), 414-428.

Levitas, A., & Gilson, S. F. (1994). Psychosocial development of children and adolescents with mild mental retardation. In N. Bouras (Ed.), *Mental health in mental retardation: Recent advances and practices* (pp. 34-45). Cambridge, MA: Cambridge University Press.

Levy, J. M., Botuck, S., Levy, P. H., Kramer, M. E., Murphy, B. S., & Rimmerman, A. (1994). Differences in job placements between men and women with mental retardation. *Disability and Rehabilitation, 16,* 53-57.

Marlatt, N. J., & Day, H. I. (1984). Employment options. In N. J. Marlett, R. Gall, & A. Wight Felske (Eds.), *Dialogue on disabilities: A Canadian perspective, Vol. 1: The service system* (pp. 85-110). Calgary, AB: University of Calgary Press.

Marshall, K. (2003). *Prisons are a failed experiment (especially for women).* Press release, May 14, 2003: Dawn Canada: DisAbled Women's Network of Canada.

McConnell, D., Feldman, M., Aunos, J., & Prasad, N. (2010). *Caregiver cognitive impairment: Secondary analysis of the Canadian Incidence Study of Reported Child Abuse and Neglect (CIS-2003).* University of Alberta Family and Disabilities Studies.

McGoldrick, M., & Giordano, J. (1996). Overview: Ethnicity and family therapy. In M. McGoldrick, J. Giordano, & J. K. Pearce (Eds.), *Ethnicity and family therapy* (2nd ed.) (pp. 1-27). New York: The Guilford Press.

Meyer, D. J. (1986). Fathers of handicapped children. In R. R. Fewell, & P. F. Vadasy (Eds.), *Families of handicapped children: Needs and supports across the life span* (pp. 35-73). Austin, TX: Pro-Ed, Inc.

METRAC (2008). Women in provincial institutions. Toronto, ON: Ontario Women's Justice Network.

Ministry of Community and Social Services (2008). *About social assistance in Ontario.* Retrieved April 12, 2010, from *www.mcss.gov.on.ca/en/mcss/programs/ social/odsp/*

Minnes, P., & Woodford, L. (2004). Well-being in aging parents caring for an adult with a developmental disability. *Journal on Developmental Disabilities, 11*(1), 47-66.

Mittler, H. (1995). *Families speak out: International perspectives on families' experiences of disability.* Cambridge, MA: Brookline Books.

Mokhtari, A. (2008). *Listening to the voices of adolescents with intellectual disabilities: Friendship experiences.* A thesis submitted to School of Rehabilitation Therapy as requirement for Master of Science degree, Queen's University, Kingston, ON.

Munro, J. D. (2010). *Couple therapy for people with intellectual disabilities: A positive treatement model.* Woodstock, ON: Regional Support Associates.

Murphy, G. H., & O'Callaghan, A. (2004). Capacity of adults with intellectual disabilities to consent to sexual relationships. *Psychological Medicine, 34*(7), 1347-1357.

Nemzoff, R. (1992). *Changing perceptions of mothers of children with developmental disabilities, 1960-1992: A critical review.* Wellesley, MA: Wellesley College Centre for Research on Women.

Ouellette-Kuntz, H., Minnes, P., Garcin, N., Martin, C., Lewis, S., & Holden, J. J. A. (2005). Adressing health disparities through promoting equity for individuals with intellectual disability. *Canadian Journal of Public Health, 96*(2), 58-22.

Pendler, B. (1993). Opening pandora's box: A parent's perspective on friendship and sexuality. In A. N. Amado (Ed.), *Friendships and community connections between people with and without developmental disabilities* (pp. 227-240). Baltimore: Paul H. Brookes Publishing Co., Ltd.

Porter, G. L. (2004). Meeting the challenge: Inclusion and diversity in Canadian schools. *Education Canada, 44*(1), 11-13.

Rasmussen, D. E., & Sobsey, D. (1994). Age, adaptive behaviour and Alzheimer Disease in Down syndrome: Cross-sectional and longitudinal analysis. *American Journal on Mental Retardation, 99* (2), 151-165.

Regional Support Associates. (2008). *Advanced training manual, module one: Assessment and diagnosis.* Woodstock, ON: Regional Support Associates.

Regional Support Associates. (2009). *Justice dual*

diagnosis case managers. Retrieved February 28, 2010, from *http://www.regionalsupport.on.ca/news/events.htm*

Reiss, S., & Benson, B. A. (1984). Awareness of negative social conditions among mentally retarded, emotionally disturbed outpatients. *American Journal of Psychiatry, 141*, 88-90.

Resources for Rehabilitation. (2000). *A woman's guide to coping with disability*, (3rd ed.), Lexington, MA: Resources for Rehabilitation.

Ricci, R. A., & Hodapp, R. M. (2003). Fathers of children with Down's syndrome versus other types of intellectual disability: Perceptions, stress and involvement. *Journal of Intellectual Disability Research, 47*(4-5), 273-284.

Riches, V. C., Parmenter, T. R., Wiese, M., & Stancliffe, R. J. (2005). Intellectual disability and mental illness in the NSW criminal justice system. *International Journal of Law and Psychiatry, 29*(5), 386-396.

Rieker, P. P., & Bird, C. E. (2004, August). *Rethinking gender differences in health: The need for an integrative perspective*. Paper presented to the American Sociological Association Meeting, San Francisco, CA.

Rusch, F. R., & Braddock, D. (2004). Adult day programs versus supported employment (1988-2002): Spending and service practices of mental retardation and developmental disabilies state agencies. *Research and Practice for Persons with Severe Disabiities, 29*(4), 237-242.

Salvatori, P., Tremblay, M., & Tryssenaar, J. (2003). Living and aging with a developmental disability: Perspectives of individuals, family members and service providers. *Journal on Developmental Disabilities, 10*(1), 1-19.

Schucherdt, E. (1991). The stigma of disability. In E. Boylan (Ed.), *Women and disability* (pp. 1-17). London: Zed Books, Ltd.

Schupf, N., Zigman, W., Kapell, D., Lee, J. H., Kline, J., & Levin, B. (1997). Early menopause in women with Down's syndrome. *Journal of Intellectual Disability Research, 41*(3), 264-267.

Shearn, J., Beyer, S., & Felce, D. (2000). The cost-effectiveness of supported employment for people with severe intellectual disabilities and high support needs: A pilot study. *Journal of Applied Research in Intellectual Disabilities, 13*(1), 29-37.

Sherwin, S. (1994). Women in clinical studies: A feminist view, vol. 2: Workshop and commissioned papers. In A. C. Mastroianni, R. R. Fadden, & D.D. Federman (Eds.), *Women and Health Research: Ethical and legal issues of including women in clinical studies* (pp. 11-17). Washington, DC: National Academy Press.

Sigurjonsdottir, H. B., & Traustadottir, R. (2000). Motherhood, family and community life. In R. Traustadottir, & K. Johnson (Eds.), *Women with intellectual disabilities: Finding a place in the world* (pp. 253-270). London: Jessica Kingsley Publishers.

Sobsey, D. (1994). *Violence and abuse in the lives of people with disabilities: The end of silent acceptance*. Baltimore: Paul H. Brookes Publishing Company.

Sobsey, D. (2000). Faces of violence against women with developmental disabilities. *Impact, 13*(3), 2,3,25.

Stainton, T., Hole, R., Charles, G., Yodanis, C., Powell, S., Crawford, C., & Wilson, L. (2006). *Non-intellectual supports and intellectual disability: A review of the literature on best practices, alternatives and economic impacts*. Vancouver, BC: Community Living Research Project.

Stromsness, M. M. (1993). Sexually abused women with mental retardation: Hidden victims, absent resources. *Women and Therapy, 14*(3-4), 139-152.

Sudhodolsky, D. G., & Butter, E. M. (2007). Social skills training for children with intellectual disabilities. In J. W. Jacobson, J. A. Julick, & J. Rojahn (Eds.), *Handbook of intellectual and developmental disabilities* (pp. 601-618) New York: Springer.

Surrey Place Centre. (2010). *The Parenting Enhancement Program at Surrey Place Centre*. Program (flyer). Toronto, ON: Surrey Place Centre.

Taggart, L., McMillan, R., & Lawson, A. (2009). Listening to women with intellectual disabilities and mental health problems. *Journal of Intellectual Disabilities, 13*(4), 321-340.

Talbot, J. (2008). *Prisoners' Voices: Experiences of the criminal justice system by by prisoners with learning disabilities and difficulties*. London: Prison Reform Trust.

Ticoll, M. (1994). *Violence and people with disabili-*

ties: A review of the literature. Toronto, ON: Roeher Institute for the National Clearinghouse on Family Violence.

Traustadottir, R. (1993). The gendered context of relationships. In A. N. Amado (Ed.), *Friendships and community connections between people with and without developmental disabilities* (pp. 109-127). Baltimore: Paul H. Brookes Publishing Co.

Traustadottir, R. (2000). Friendship: Love or work? In R. Traustadottir, & K. Johnson (Eds.), *Women with intellectual disabilities: Finding a place in the world* (pp. 118-131). London: Jessica Kingsley Publishers.

Trute, B., & Hiebert-Murphy, D. (2002). Family adjustment to childhood developmental disability: A measure of parent appraisal of family impacts. *Journal of Pediatric Psychology, 27*(3), 271-280.

Walmsley, J. (2000). Caring: A place in the world? In R. Traustadottir, & K. Johnson (Eds.), *Women with intellectual disabilities: Finding a place in the world* (pp. 191-212). London: Jessica Kingsley Publishers.

Walsh, P. N., Heller, T., Schupf, N., van Schrojenstein Lantman-de Valk, H. & Working Group. (2000). *Healthy aging - adults with intellectual disabilities: Women's health issues.* Geneva, Switzerland: World Health Organization.

West, R. (2000). Discovering a sister. In R. Traustadottir, & K. Johnson (Eds.), *Women with intellectual disabilities: Finding a place in the world* (pp. 34 - 51). London: Jessica Kingsley Publishers.

Wilkinson, J. E., & Cerreto, M. C. (2008). Primary care for women with intellectual disabilities. *The Journal of the American Board of Family Medicine, 21*(3), 215-222.

Yamaki, K. (2005). Body weight status among adults with intellectual disability in the community. *Mental Retardation, 43*(1), 1-10.

Zetlin, A. G., & Turner, J. L. (1988). Salient domains in the self-conception of adults with mental retardation. *Mental Retardation, 26*(4), 219-222.

Parenting by Persons with Intellectual Disabilities

Marjorie Aunos and Maurice Feldman

What you will learn:

- Challenges that people with intellectual disabilities have as parents
- Factors that influence parenting by people with intellectual disabilities
- Key elements of best practices in supports and services for families headed by persons with intellectual disabilities

Case Example

Ms. Smith is a 35 year old single mother of four children, aged 6 to 11 years. She has a mild intellectual disability and attended special education classes when she was in school. Three of her children live in foster care, because there were concerns about possible neglect. Ms. Smith's father (the children's grandfather) has custody of the fourth child. Ms. Smith is seen as someone having difficulties implementing discipline strategies with her pre-teen children. Furthermore, Ms. Smith has been described by a parenting capacity assessment as not having the capacity to parent her children due to her cognitive limitations. The assumption of parenting inadequacy is based primarily on her lower intellectual functioning (often in the absence of direct evidence of child maltreatment) and is quite common concerning parents with intellectual disabilities.

Researchers have studied parents with intellectual disabilities for over 50 years. They have looked at their capacity and ability to parent, at assessment, support needs, interventions, and at other variables influencing their parenting abilities and child and family outcomes (McConnell, 2008). Recent disability laws, statutes and conventions (e.g., United Nations, 1989, 2006; WHO, 2004) have begun to recognize the parenting rights of persons with disabilities, and the need to support these families to keep the family together. Despite the equal rights movement and the wealth of research-based knowledge regarding effective services and supports, the child welfare system in most jurisdictions still routinely takes away children of parents with intellectual disability (McConnell, Feldman, Aunos, & Prasad, 2011). This chapter will highlight the overall challenges parents with intellectual disabilities continue to face, present a model for understanding factors that influence parenting by people with intellectual disabilities, and discuss key elements of best practices in supports and services for families headed by persons with intellectual disabilities.

Challenges for Parents with Intellectual Disabilities

People with intellectual disabilities have, by definition, some cognitive limitations. When they become parents, many need specialized training and some need ongoing support to parent effectively. There are many barriers to parents with intellectual disabilities receiving the supports they need. Negative stereotypes and misconceptions continue to abound concerning their parenting capacity. There are general misunderstandings that persons with intellectual disabilities: a) are incapable of providing adequate child care, b) cannot benefit from parent training, and c) will have children who also have disabilities (Aunos & Feldman, 2002; Espe-Sherwindt & Kerlin, 1990).

Too often, disability, child welfare, and other family support professionals — and the systems within which they work — hold such misconceptions or at least act as if they do. For example, they may knowingly or unknowingly show bias in their evaluation and referral processes. They may have little experience supporting families in which the parents have intellectual disabilities or may be too busy to do so. Workers may have limited understanding of how to use mediation services or represent parents with intellectual disabilities in court. They might fail to make use of informal supports and other resources, or they may simply work within a system that does not include needed services for parents with intel-

lectual disabilities (McConnell, Aunos, & Feldman, in press; McConnell et al., 2011). As a consequence, many parents with intellectual disabilities are not provided with the supports and resources they require, and some are not even given an opportunity to parent. Their parenting rights are terminated because of concerns about their capacity to raise children (Feldman & Aunos, 2010; McConnell et al., 2011; McConnell, Llewellyn, & Ferronato, 2003). In fact, parents with intellectual disabilities have been, and continue to be, over-represented in child custody proceedings. We now know that, in many cases, these concerns are unwarranted. They may arise more from the failure of the support system to react in a positive and helpful way than from a demonstrated need to protect children.

Such failure has many important consequences. The unjustifiable severance of family ties raises ethical and legal concerns regarding the rights of individuals. In many cases, there is a negative impact on the children's development (Aunos & Feldman, 2008), especially if children grow up in state care where a stable family home is not provided. The unimaginable grief caused for the parents and the impact of family separation may have profound impact on their mental health (Booth & Booth, 2005; Mayes & Llewellyn, 2009). Although we know of these consequences, only limited services are available to support many parents with intellectual disabilities and, in situations where family separation does occur, only limited support is available to parents following the loss of their child (Tarleton, Ward, & Howarth, 2006).

Factors Influencing Parenting

Research in the area of parenting by persons with intellectual disabilities expanded in the 1980s following the end of involuntary sterilization, the growth of the community living and deinstitutionalization movements (see Chapter 2), and the emerging focus on disability rights. Little was known formally about parents with intellectual disabilities at that time, and it was perceived that many could not parent due to their cognitive deficits. Very rapidly, though, research began to show that parents

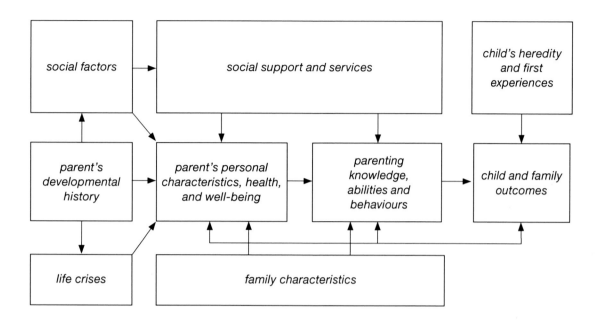

Figure 1. Feldman's parenting interactional model. *(Source: Adapted from Feldman (2002); reproduced with the permission of NADD Press).*

with intellectual disabilities could learn to parent and sustain their learning over time (Aunos, 2000; Feldman, 1994, 1997, 1998; Feldman, Case, & Sparks, 1992; Feldman, Sparks, & Case, 1993/2004). Since then, many authors have argued that parental intellectual functioning is not a valid or sole predictor of a person's parenting abilities (Feldman, 2002; Spencer, 2001).

Parenting models have been proposed to identify the host of variables that could affect parenting abilities and child outcomes. Feldman (2002) proposed a model specifically for families headed by parents with intellectual disabilities. Feldman's model extends parenting models developed by other researchers (Belsky, 1984; Bronfenbrenner, 1979; Sameroff & Chandler, 1975) to parents with intellectual disabilities. In this chapter, these models (including Feldman's) are referred to as "interactional models" because they highlight the complex interactions that occur over time between a wide range of variables within and external to the family that influence parenting and child development. Feldman's model, presented in Figure 1, identifies as variables: social factors, parental developmental

history, personal characteristics, family characteristics, and physical/mental health on parenting abilities. The model includes the importance of informal social supports (e.g., family, friends) and formal services. The arrows connote the hypothesized relationships and influences among the variables. Note that some of these relationships may be reciprocal (each can influence the other at different points in time), but we have only illustrated one key reciprocal relationship — child's development and behaviour on parental health and practices. Box 1 provides the key indicators of these variables.

Feldman's model assumes accumulated risk. That is, given two sets of parents with similar cognitive functioning, the parents who have more impediments (e.g., stigmatized, mental health issues, few supports, history of abuse, poor role models, raising several children, having children with health problems) will not do as well (and their children will be at greater risk for developmental problems) as the parents who have adequate support, no mental ill-health issues, no additional stressors, and caring for one healthy child.

Studies have started to validate part of this model.

Box 1: Key Indicators of Variables in Feldman's Parenting Interactional Model

Social factors
- *Stigmatization (as a person with intellectual disabilities)*
- *Discrimination*

Parent's developmental history
- *Cognitive limitations and deficits in adaptive behaviours*
- *Past abuse*
- *Institutionalization*
- *Parental role models*
- *Past experiences in raising and taking care of children*
- *Age at the birth of the first child.*

Life crises
- *Currently experiencing abuse and violence*
- *Illnesses*
- *Loss of revenue*
- *Loss of a partner or an important person through separation or death*
- *Eviction and homelessness.*

Parent's characteristics
- *Mental health issues, such as depression, anxiety disorder, substance abuse*
- *Physical health issues such as asthma, diabetes, lupus, etc.*
- *High stress levels*
- *Adaptive behaviour, such as capacity to go about everyday life activities and vulnerability to exploitation.*

Parenting knowledge, abilities, and behaviour
- *Basic care needs of children*
- *Safe and healthy home environment*
- *Sensitive, responsive and positive parent-child interactions*
- *Sound judgments (e.g., discipline, limit-setting, supervision)*
- *Positive child behavioural support*
- *Effective problem-solving.*

Larger and more helpful social and service networks are related to a decreased level of stress, more stimulating home environment, and more positive parent-child interactions (Aunos, Feldman, & Goupil, 2008; Feldman, Varghese, Ramsay, & Rajska, 2002). A high level of parenting stress is associated with a more hostile and inconsistent parenting style and increased child problem behaviours (Aunos et al., 2008). This finding is consistent with others showing that parents with intellectual disabilities are at increased risk for high stress and mental health issues (Feldman & Aunos, 2010).

New studies are also bringing forward new information that relates to specific aspects of this model. We now know that mothers with intellectual disabilities are at a higher risk of poor pregnancy or birth outcomes such as pre-eclampsia (high-blood-pressure in the pregnant woman) and low birth-

Social support and services

- *Supportive partner and family*
- *Satisfaction with social network*
- *Type of support and services, and proportion of formal (services) versus informal (family members, neighbors, volunteers, friends)*
- *Involvement of child protection agency*
- *Supports and services needed versus received.*

Family characteristics

- *Family income*
- *Employment status*
- *Quality of the neighbourhood (safety, availability of services, transportation, community activities).*

Children's heredity and first experiences

- *Family history of low I.Q., genetic syndromes, mental illnesses*
- *Prenatal, perinatal, postnatal experiences and conditions that could affect development (e.g., prenatal maternal ingestion of alcohol or drugs, maternal Hepatitis C or HIV/AIDS, birth complications, prematurity, low birth weight, early infections).*

Child and family outcomes

- *Temperament and behaviour (e.g., irritable, behaviour problems)*
- *Developmental level (e.g., delay)*
- *School status (e.g., special education)*
- *Physical and mental health*
- *Family continuance*

weight (McConnell, Mayes, & Llewellyn, 2008a). Factors such as poverty, mental ill-health, parenting stress and lack of adequate services (e.g., prenatal care) are potential risk factors for these poor outcomes (McConnell et al., in press). Furthermore, pregnant women with intellectual disabilities are reporting high levels of anxiety caused, in part, by their fear of losing custody of their children upon birth (McConnell, Mayes, & Llewellyn, 2008b).

Returning to Ms. Smith...

Following allegations of neglect and results from a private parenting capacity assessment, Ms. Smith's four children were placed in foster care by child protection. She was also referred to a specialized organization that works with parents with intellectual disabilities. A team of professionals (psychologist, social worker and parent educator) worked with her. These professionals did an alternative parenting capacity assessment (see section on best-practices) following validated research methods, and identified specific areas of needs. As per Feldman's interactional model of examining supports and impediments, Ms. Smith's cognitive and adaptive functioning did not in themselves negatively impact on her parenting skills. Rather, other issues seemed to impede her parenting. She was socially isolated, had had poor parenting role models as a child, and had various recent stressful events (i.e., separation from her partner, loss of revenue, debts). Further elements of risk included high levels of anxiety related to her parenting role and symptoms related to depression (i.e., extreme fatigue, loss of energy, changes in eating patterns, irritability). In addition, her mother's support seemed to be inhibiting her capacity to resolve problems related to disciplining her children. These impediments may have contributed to Ms. Smith's punitive and inconsistent styles of parenting that increased conflicts with her children and led to their subsequent apprehension. The report concluded that while Ms. Smith had the cognitive capacity to parent effectively, various factors were impeding her ability to do so. Many of these challenges were remediable with appropriate supports and services.

The role of social support networks

More and more, parents with intellectual disabilities have been found to seek appropriate and competence-promoting support — even during their pregnancies — from family, friends, and relatives, and from services (Mayes, McConnell, & Llewellyn, 2008). Support that strengthens social ties may have a positive impact on the parents' well-being (e.g., lower stress levels and depressive symptoms) and on their capacity to advocate for themselves (McConnell, Dalziel, Llewellyn, Laidlaw, & Hindmarsh, 2008; Traustadóttir & Borg Sigurjonsdottir, 2008). The quality of the supports offered and the parent's satisfaction with it are more important than the number of persons and services involved (Feldman et al., 2002). In fact, too large a support network may evoke greater dependency (St-Amand, Goupil, & Aunos, 2010). Thus, not all forms of social support are perceived as beneficial, and supports can either impair or empower parents (Espe-Sherwindt & Kerlin, 1990; Tucker & Johnson, 1989).

The parents' attitude towards supports affects their willingness to accept them. Although most parents with intellectual disabilities recognize that they have learning difficulties, some reject the intellectual disability label. Some parents disguise their disability, and deny that they need help (Feldman, 2002). They are leery of offers of support, and especially distrust child welfare workers. Parents with intellectual disabilities are in a double-bind: the parents fear that an admission of need for assistance may result in their children being taken away by child protection authorities. Conversely, by rejecting offers of support, parents may be perceived as lacking judgment and not understanding how difficult it is to parent (Feldman, 2002). Rapport and trust are essential parts of effective supports. Rapport is well established when worker's attitudes recognize the central role of the parents in their child's life and development (Mayes et al., 2008).

Early life challenges

Children of parents with intellectual disabilities are at risk for developmental delay (especially in the area of language), difficulties in school, and emotional and behaviour problems (Feldman, Case, Towns, & Betel, 1985; Feldman & Walton-Allen, 1997/2002; Gilberg & Geijer-Karlsson, 1983). Developmental delay is seen in children as young as 6 months old, and cognitive development is typically more affected than physical and social development (Feldman et al., 1985; McConnell, Llewellyn, Mayes, Russo, & Honey, 2003). Such developmental problems are also typical of children growing up in poverty but, for children of parents with intellectual disabilities, poverty is not the only reason, as similarly impoverished school-age children raised by parents without intellectual disabilities had higher IQ scores and fewer school and behaviour problems (Feldman & Walton-Allen, 1997/2002). There is some evidence that developmental problems for children of parents with intellectual disabilities continue into adolescence and adulthood. For example, in a study of 30 adult offspring of parents with intellectual disabilities, 50% had learning problems and 23% had emotional or psychiatric problems (Booth & Booth, 1997).

Box 2: Recommendations on How to Adapt Services

Services need to be adapted in view of the specific needs, capacities and limitations of parents with intellectual disabilities. Here are some suggestions:

- *Have a team (or at least one worker) who has expertise in working with these families.*
- *Establish trust and rapport with the family.*
- *Plan for an assessment of the family's needs, and the needs of each family member, including the needs of the parents as individuals.*
- *Identify areas of need — use a systemic, interactional and observational approach (Feldman, 2002).*
- *Provide evidenced-based interventions and other supports in areas identified as needing improvement (e.g., parental and child health, child development, social support, parenting and related skills).*
- *Involve the parents in designing the intervention plan as much as possible.*
- *Establish partnerships and coordinate between various agencies (particularly, Child Protection, if involved).*
- *Objectively monitor progress of the parents in learning new skills, and the child's health and development.*
- *Have the parents identify and enlist others (informal supports) who could help support the intervention plan.*

Source: Adapted from Case & Gang (2003).

New evidence highlights the potential relationship of these negative outcomes in children with high levels of stress during pregnancy (McConnell et al., 2008b), and a high level of parenting stress (Aunos et al., 2008), particularly for parents raising school-age children (Feldman, Léger, & Walton-Allen, 1997) and for women with a paucity of accessible prenatal care (McConnell et al., 2008a). Furthermore, in addition to a genetic predisposition for low intelligence in children of parents with intellectual disability (Reed & Reed, 1965), developmental delays may also be related in part to an impoverished environment. With adapted support, however, the home environment of parents with intellectual disabilities can be become adequate (Feldman et al., 1993/2004; Llewellyn, McConnell, Honey, Mayes, & Russo, 2003; McConnell et al., 2003).

Best Practices in Services: Aiming at Successful Parenting

Assessing parenting skills

Assessing parenting skills has been challenging because of the lack of a universally accepted operational definition of adequate or "good-enough" parenting (Aunos & Feldman, 2002, 2007). In general, it is expected that parents can provide basic child-care, home safety, nutrition, and surveillance to keep their children healthy and safe. Parents are also expected to provide a loving, warm and stimulating environment to foster child development and secure attachment. These parenting skills are further supported by parallel skills such as problem solving, decision making, ability to show success at community living, and social or communication skills. Of course, as noted above, systemic risk and resilience factors also need to be taken into consideration, as poor mental health or lack of adequate resources could have a negative impact on the application of, or ability to learn, these parenting or parallel skills.

Essential components of a comprehensive, competence-based parenting capacity assessment for parents with intellectual disabilities are: a) an examination of impediments and supports in line with Feldman's interaction model (described above and see Figure 1), and b) direct observation of parenting skills, preferably using validated checklists (Aunos & Feldman, 2002; Feldman & Aunos, 2010). Another key element of such assessment is that it be conducted by an open-minded professional who has expertise in working with persons with intellectual disabilities (Feldman & Aunos, 2010). Many parents with intellectual disabilities have been known to be

Box 3: Parent Education Curriculum

PSYCHOEDUCATIONAL COMPONENTS

Parenting skills	Parallel skills
1. Basic Child Care Skills *understanding how the child develops and what skills are acquired at different ages; newborn care; diapering; bathing; supervision; toilet training*	**9. Problem-Solving** *identifying problems; setting priorities; understanding cause of problem; identifying possible solutions; implementing best solution; evaluating outcome; generalization*
2. Child Positive Behaviour Support *clear rules and instructions; limit-setting; reinforcement of appropriate behaviour; corrections for inappropriate behaviour; noncorporal discipline*	**10. Social Skills Training and Communication Skills** *assertiveness; empathy; conversation; asking for help; listening; giving a compliment; responding to criticism; negotiating; apologizing; dealing with persuasion; group pressure; embarrassment*
3. Home Safety *crib; sleep; home; street; playground; park; pool; beach; skating rink; public transport; shopping centre*	**11. Stress/Anger Management** *identifying own emotions and anger triggers; relaxation; removal; self-control; incompatible responses; handling failure; handling stressors; time management*
4. Parent-Child Interactions *attention; listening; supervising; choices; responsivity; engagement; reciprocity; warmth; sensitivity; empathy, play skills,*	
5. Health *treatment of diaper rash, cradle cap, colds, fever, infections, vomiting, teething; taking temperature; using medication; sunscreen; protective clothing*	
6. Emergencies and First Aid *cuts; burns; falls; head injury; poisoning; choking; insect bite; sunburn; heat stroke; frost-bite*	
7. Child Development and Secure Attachment *stimulating home environment and interactions; play; affection; sensitivity; responsiveness; contingent recognition; consistency; reading to child; conversation; asking questions; telling stories; outings*	
8. Nutritional skills *feeding; burping; preparing formula; wholesome foods; menu planning for nutritious and balanced meals; grocery shopping*	

* Based on Aunos & Feldman (2002) and MacLean & Aunos (2010).

PSYCHOSOCIAL COMPONENTS

Parental characteristics / parallel skills	Factors of the environment
12. Empowerment Training *dealing with the "system," workers, other professionals, and bureaucrats; assertiveness; self-advocacy; support groups*	*15. Accessing Community Resources* *daycare/preschool; library; community drop-ins; parent-tot programs; parenting courses; vocational and academic upgrading; counselling services; transit training*
13. Dealing with Your Own Disability or Your Child's Disability *defining disability, identity, emotions, personal experiences, stages of grief and experiences of loss, recognizing strengths, limitations, and rights of people with disabilities, locating resources*	
14. Dealing with Loss of Custody, Adoption, and Death *sharing experiences of having a child placed, grief and loss, coping strategies, benefits of sharing experiences, death, reactions to loss, coping strategies*	

---

defensive or fearful of any type of assessments, especially if they have lost custody of a previous child (Feldman et al., 1993/2004) and are therefore aware of the potential repercussions of such an assessment.

Parent education programs

Several specialized supportive parenting programs have been established for parents with intellectual disabilities (Aunos, 2000; Feldman & Case, 2003; Hur, 1997; Tymchuk, 2006). Evaluation studies and reviews have shown that these programs increase selected parenting skills to levels seen in parents without intellectual disabilities, and that they are of benefit to the children (Feldman, 1994; Feldman & al., 1992; Feldman et al., 1993/2004; Llewellyn et al., 2003; Wade, Llewellyn & Matthews, 2008).

Unfortunately, because few specialized services exist, many of these families are referred to early intervention, family support, public health, and child protection services that often do not have expertise to assist them (Aunos, Pacheco, & Moxness, 2010).

In fact, sometimes these services have negative biases against parents with intellectual disabilities. Services often are fragmented and uncoordinated — as many as six different workers may routinely visit the home! Most community agencies are geared to parents with higher cognitive skills. Important information is often presented in lecture-style "parenting classes," in a short time span, and in a limited number of sessions. The material may be too complex or presented in writing. These approaches are not very effective for most parents with intellectual disabilities (Feldman, 1994; Tymchuk, 1998). As described later, parents with intellectual disabilities do better with concrete instruction of specific skills broken down into small steps, with training carried out in the home or a home-like setting over several sessions (Feldman, 1994, 1998).

As an increasing number of these families are appearing on agency caseloads, a more concerted effort is being made to provide relevant, adapted and long-term supports. Recently, more specialized services and programs for parents with intellectual disabilities and their children are being developed and validated by research (MacLean & Aunos, 2010; Wade et al., 2008). Efforts have begun for broader dissemination of information and training over the internet (e.g., Healthy Start in Australia <healthystart.et.au> (McConnell, Matthews, Llewellyn, Mildon, & Hindmarsh, 2008) and The Association for Successful Parenting <achancetoparent.com>). Nonetheless, there is still a tremendous need to establish new services, and to adapt existing services (see Box 2), to meet the needs of these families so that their children may remain at home in a safe, healthy, and nurturing environment.

Box 3 lists the skills that should be assessed prior to intervention and that could be covered in a parenting program, depending on the age of the child and the family's needs (Aunos & Feldman, 2002, 2008; MacLean & Aunos, 2010). Each parent and family situation is different, so it may not be necessary to address all of these areas every time. Topics that will immediately improve the child's safety, health and development should be covered first. Naturally, as children grow and family's needs adapt and evolve, these elements could be targeted at different times. If the service agency providing services lacks expertise in certain areas, this agency could and should refer to other agencies that do have such expertise. This highlights the importance of partnerships among public agencies and the need for a concerted effort to collaborate among organizations.

Training strategies: Effective programs use concrete, behavioural strategies that have been shown to rapidly increase complex skills in persons with intellectual disabilities (Feldman, 1994). The general procedure involves task analysis and performance-based teaching methods (e.g., audiovisual materials, modelling, role-playing, practice, reinforcement, and error correction). Box 4 presents the specific strategies used to teach child-care skills to parents with intellectual disabilities. More details regarding these strategies can be found in Feldman (1998).

The training can be carried out individually in the home or in a small group (preferably in a home-like setting). Home visits usually occur weekly and last 1-2 hours (of which only a portion focusses on training). The home visit starts with an exchange of pleasantries and updates on events since the last visit. Then the parent educator observes previously learned skills (to check for maintenance), skills to be trained soon (baseline), and/or skills currently being trained. Training time, itself, can vary depending on how long it takes to model and have the parent perform the task; most single task training sessions last about 10 minutes. Following training, the parent and educator often will have a tea or coffee and discuss other issues in the family's life (e.g., difficulties with neighbours, trying to find a job or a day care). The parent educator may offer advice and assistance, or recommend other services. If group instruction is used, it is important to conduct home visits and observations to check that the parent has generalized the skills learned in the group to the home — that she remembers them and uses them in her home life.

Back to Ms. Smith...

Following the results from the parenting capacity assessment, goals and objectives were set with Ms. Smith. Ms. Smith's family physician prescribed anti-depressants to target her symptoms of anxiety and depression. The psychologist from the parenting team worked with her on developing and implementing coping strategies and stress management skills. When Ms. Smith felt she had more energy, she agreed to develop new ties in her community. With the support of the social worker from the parenting team, Ms. Smith identified community support groups and chose to participate to meet other mothers like herself. She distanced herself from her mother, as she saw that her mother was denigrating her in unhelpful ways. Ms. Smith also participated in a parenting group to learn about child development and parenting strategies around discipline, limit settings and the development of positive parent-child interactions. As things got better in Ms. Smith's life, child protection services allowed increased numbers of visitations with her children.

Summary

In brief, we have learned that many factors, instead of or in addition to parental intelligence, may influ-

Box 4: Behavioural Training Components of Effective Parenting Programs

- *Through direct observation, assess how well the parent performs the set child-care skills needed given the child's age.*

- *Use validated child-care checklists that break down skills into smaller steps (e.g., Feldman, 1998; Feldman & Case, 1993; McGaw, 2002).*

- *Teach skills one at a time.*

- *Teach skills in several locations in which the parent will need to learn the skill to promote generalization.*

- *Provide simple, concrete verbal explanations and instructions*

- *Provide a picture book illustrating each step of the skill, along with simple text and an audiotape describing each picture (Feldman, 2004). Try these manuals first on their own as self-learning tools before adding more intensive training.*

- *Model the skill, step-by-step, focusing on the steps that the parent missed in the assessment.*

- *Have the parent practise the skill in real or role-played situations. Role-plays also can be conducted in a game format.*

- *Use verbal, gestural, modelling and physical prompts to guide correct performance as necessary.*

- *Provide immediate praise and feedback for correct performance.*

- *Give corrective feedback. Try to provide four times as much positive feedback as corrective feedback.*

- *Provide tangible rewards contingent on attendance and progress (e.g., parenting coupons exchangeable for small gift items contingent on improvements). Fade the tangible rewards after the parent shows generalization and maintenance of the skill (e.g., over a 3 month period).*

---

ence parenting by parents with intellectual disabilities, There is an over-representation of parents with intellectual disabilities in court proceedings and child protection services (Feldman & Aunos, 2010). The informal support network and competency-enhancing services are very important in developing and empowering parenting abilities for this population. A parent's intellectual disability is not necessarily the main factor affecting their children's development and behaviour (Feldman, McConnell & Aunos, in press).

Despite progressive changes in the recognition of rights of persons with intellectual disabilities, the applicability of these rights to parenting lags behind. The erroneous perception that their low intellectual functioning precludes competent parenting still influences child custody decisions. Indeed, we have known for more than two decades that many factors apart from their cognitive disability may impede their ability to parent adequately and respond to interventions. Ironically, one of these obstacles

is the continuing stigmatization and discrimination of parents with intellectual disability that may lead to a lack of referral to beneficial services that might allow the child to remain or be returned to the home. Many of their children are prematurely removed from their biological parents and spend their childhoods in the foster-care system. The deleterious effects of living in foster care, which often lasts may years and involves living in several homes, often is not considered.

As is the case with non-disabled parents, some parents with intellectual disabilities learn and apply new skills with supports and advice easily, and some do not. For some parents with intellectual disabilities to be successful, specialized and intensive supports may be needed. It has been shown that with appropriate, personalized services and supports, these parents can learn to be effective parents and raise their children in a safe, nurturing and loving home.

To continue to move forward, evidence-based decision-making and practices should be systematized and integrated into formal support services and child protection. More efforts need to insure parents with intellectual disabilities have access to antenatal and prenatal care to increase the chances for positive birth and early developmental outcomes. The interaction model, described in this chapter, should serve as a template for parenting capacity assessments that aim to identify the impact of such things as the parent's past and current experiences, health issues, and poverty on parenting abilities. Families should have access to needed services and supports before the child is permanently removed. Finally, disability services should work closely with child protection services to insure the ongoing protection of the children, as the parents improve their skills.

For Further Thought and Discussion

1. What are the ethical ramifications of allowing or denying the right to parent in persons with intellectual disabilities? How do we balance parenting rights with what is in the best interests of the child?
2. Many studies have documented the need and importance of adequate support in helping parents with intellectual disabilities. This need for support is also described as being, at times, intensive and long-standing. On the other hand, many children are removed from the custody of their parents who have intellectual disabilities. Which solution is the most appropriate: offering extensive support, or placing children into foster care? Which one would be most humane? Which one the most affordable?
3. Parents with intellectual disabilities face many challenges. What are these challenges and how could we offer them support in overcoming them?
4. Countries, and even provinces within Canada, have somewhat different approaches to servicing persons with intellectual disabilities. Based on Ontario's service approach, how could services be adapted to better meet the needs of parents with intellectual disabilities and their children? How do current child welfare laws and practices

impact services and decisions regarding families headed by parents with intellectual disabilities?
5. In looking at Ms. Smith's case, what would be different in the analysis of her strengths or in the way of assessing her parenting skills, if Ms. Smith were a new immigrant to Canada?

More Resources

Books and Book Chapters:

Feldman, M. A. (2002). Parents with intellectual disabilities and their children: Impediments and supports. In D. Griffiths & P. Federoff (Eds.), *Ethical dilemmas: Sexuality and developmental disability* (pp. 255-292). Kingston, NY: NADD Press.

Feldman, M., & Aunos, M. (2010). *Comprehensive competence-based parenting assessment for parents with learning difficulties and their children*. Kingston, NY: NADD Press.

Llewellyn, G., Traustadóttir, R., McConnell, D., & Björg Sigurjónsdóttir, H. (2010). *Parents with intellectual disabilities: Past, present and futures*. Oxford, UK: Wiley-Blackwell.

Reports from Australia:

McConnell, D., Llewellyn, G., & Ferronato, L. (2000). *Parents with a disability and the NSW children's court — Report to the Law Foundation of NSW*. University of Sydney. Contact: David McConnell <david.mcconnell@ualberta.ca>

Reports from Canada:

Aunos, M., Goupil, G., & Feldman, M. (2004). *Les mères présentant une déficience intellectuelle au Québec — Rapport préliminaire concernant 50 mères et leurs enfants*. Centre de Réadaptation de l'Ouest de Montréal. Dépôt légal Bibliothèque Nationale du Canada, Bibliothèque Nationale du Québec. ISBN: 2-9808116-0-2. Contact Marjorie Aunos <maunos.crom@ssss.gouv.qc.ca>

McConnell, D., Feldman, M., Aunos, M., & Prasad, N. (2010). *Child welfare process and outcome, Caregiver cognitive impairment: Secondary analysis of the Canadian Incidence Study of Reported Child Abuse and Neglect (CIS-2003)*. Family and Disability Studies, University of Alberta. ISBN: 978-1-

55195-262-8. Contact: David McConnell <david.mcconnell@ualberta.ca>

Training Manuals:

Feldman, M. (2004). *The Family Game: Enhancing parent-child cooperation and rapport to parents with learning problems.* Contact: M. Feldman, Dept. of Child and Youth Studies, Brock University, St. Catharines, Ontario, Canada L3S 2A1. <mfeldman@brocku.ca>

Feldman, M. A., & Case, L. (1993). *Step by step child care: Teaching aids for parents, child-care workers, and babysitters.* Contact: M. Feldman, Dept. of Child and Youth Studies, Brock University, St. Catharines, Ontario, Canada L3S 2A1. <mfeldman@brocku.ca>

Tymchuk, A. J. (2006). *The health and wellness program: Parenting curriculum for families at risk.* Baltimore: Paul H. Brookes Publishing Co.

Websites:

The Association for Successful Parenting (TASP)
http://www.achancetoparent.com

Healthy Start Australia
http://www.healthystart.net.au/

References

Aunos, M. (2000). Les programmes de formation aux habiletés parentales pour des adultes présentant une déficience intellectuelle. *La revue internationale de l'éducation familiale, 4*(2), 59-75.

Aunos, M., & Feldman, M. A. (2002). Attitudes toward sexuality, sterilisation, and parenting rights of persons with intellectual disabilities. *Journal of Applied Research in Intellectual Disability, 15,* 285-296.

Aunos, M., & Feldman, M. (2007). Assessing parenting capacity in parents with intellectual disabilities. In C. Chamberland, S. Léveillé, & N. Trocmé (Eds.), *Des enfants à protéger, des adultes à aider: Deux univers à rapprocher* (pp. 223-240). Sainte-Foy, QB: Presses de l'université du Québec.

Aunos, M., & Feldman, M. (2008). There's no place like home: The child's right to family. In T. O'Neill &
D. Zinga (Eds.), *Children's rights: Multidisciplinary approaches to participation and protection* (pp. 137-162). Toronto, ON: University of Toronto Press.

Aunos, M., Feldman, M., & Goupil, G. (2008). Mothering with intellectual disabilities: Relationship between social support, health and well-being, parenting and child behaviour outcomes. *Journal of Applied Research in Intellectual Disabilities, 21,* 320-330.

Aunos, M., Pacheco, L., & Moxness, K. (2010). Turning rights into realities in Quebec, Canada. In G. Llewellyn, R. Traustadóttir, D. McConnell, & H. Björg Sigurjónsdóttir (Eds.), *Parents with intellectual disabilities and their children: Living and learning in the community* (pp. 189-204). Oxford, UK: Wiley-Blackwell.

Belsky, J. (1984). The determinants of parenting: A process model. *Child Development, 55,* 83-96.

Booth, T., & Booth, W. (2005). Parents with learning difficulties in the child protection system: Experiences and perspectives. *Journal of Intellectual Disabilities, 9,* 109-129.

Bronfenbrenner, U. (1979). Contexts of child rearing: Problems and prospects. *American Psychologist, 34,* 844-850.

Case, L., & Gang, B. (2003). People with developmental disabilities as parents. In I. Brown & M. Percy (Eds.), *Developmental disabilities in Ontario* (2nd ed.) (pp. 709-724). Toronto, ON: Ontario Association on Developmental Disabilities.

Espe-Scherwindt, M., & Kerlin, S. (1990). Early intervention with parents with mental retardation: Do we empower or impair? *Infants and Young Children, 2,* 21-28.

Feldman, M. A. (1994). Parenting education for parents with intellectual disabilities: A review of outcome studies. *Research in Developmental Disabilities, 15,* 299-332.

Feldman, M. A. (1997). The effectiveness of early intervention for children whose mothers are mentally retarded. In M. J. Guralnick (Ed.), *The effectiveness of early intervention: Direction for second generation research* (pp. 171-191). Baltimore: Paul H. Brookes Publishing Co.

Feldman, M. A. (1998). Preventing child neglect: Child-care training for parents with intellectual disabilities. *Infants & Young Children, 11,* 1-11.

Feldman, M. A. (2002). Parents with intellectual disabilities and their children: Impediments and supports. In D. Griffiths & P. Federoff (Eds.), *Ethical dilemmas: Sexuality and developmental disability* (pp. 255-292). Kingston, NY: NADD Press.

Feldman, M., & Aunos, M. (2010). *Comprehensive competence-based parenting assessment for parents with learning difficulties and their children.* Kingston, NY: NADD Press.

Feldman, M. A., & Case, L. (1993). *Step-by-step child-care: A pictorial manual for parents, child-care workers, and babysitters.* Toronto, ON: Authors.

Feldman, M. A., Case, L., & Sparks, B. (1992). Effectiveness of a child-care training program for parents at-risk for child neglect. *Canadian Journal of Behavioural Science, 24,* 14-28.

Feldman, M. A., Case, L., Towns, F., & Betel, J. (1985). Parent education project I: The development and nurturance of children of mentally handicapped mothers. *American Journal of Mental Deficiency, 90,* 253-258.

Feldman, M. A., Léger, M., & Walton-Allen, N. (1997). Stress in mothers with intellectual disabilities. *Journal of Child and Family Studies, 6,* 471-485.

Feldman, M. A., McConnell, D., & Aunos, M. (in press). Parental cognitive impairment, mental health and child outcomes in a child protection population. *Journal of Mental Health Research in Intellectual Disabilities.*

Feldman, M. A., Varghese, J., Ramsay, J., & Rajska, D. (2002). Relationship between social support, stress and mother-child interactions in mothers with intellectual disabilities. *Journal of Applied Research in Intellectual Disability, 15,* 314-323.

Feldman, M. A., & Walton-Allen, N. (1997/2002). Effects of maternal mental retardation and poverty on intellectual, academic, and behavioral status of school-age children (reprint). In J. Blacher & B. Baker (Eds.), *The best of AAMR: Families and mental retardation: A collection of notable AAMR journal articles across the 20th century* (pp. 235-246). Washington, DC: American Association on Mental Retardation. Originally published in *American Journal on Mental Retardation, 101,* 352-364

(1997).

Gillberg, C., & Geijer-Karlsson, M. (1983). Children born to mentally retarded women: A 1-21 year follow-up study of 41 cases. *Psychological Medicine, 13,* 891-894.

Hur, J. (1997). Review of research on parent training for parents with intellectual disability: Methodological issues. *International Journal of Disability, Development and Education, 44*(2), 147-162.

Llewellyn, G., McConnell, D., Honey, A., Mayes, R., & Russo, D. (2003). Promoting health and home safety for children of parents with intellectual disability: A randomized controlled trial. *Research in Developmental Disabilities, 24*(6), 405-431.

MacLean, K., & Aunos, M. (2010). Addressing the needs of parents with intellectual disabilities: Exploring a parenting pilot project. *Journal on Developmental Disabilities – Special Issue: Falling Through the Cracks, 16*(1) 18-33.

Mayes, R,. & Llewellyn, G. (2009). What happens to parents with intellectual disability following removal of their child in child protection proceedings? *Journal of Intellectual and Developmental Disability, 34,* 92-95.

Mayes, R., McConnell, D., & Llewellyn, G. (2008). Active negotiation: Mothers with intellectual disabilities creating their social support network. *Journal of Applied Research in Intellectual Disabilities, 21,* 341-350.

McConnell, D. (2008). Parents labeled with intellectual disabilities: Position of the IASSID SIRG on parents and parenting with intellectual disabilities. *Journal of Applied Research in Intellectual Disabilities, 21,* 296-307.

McConnell, D., Aunos, M., & Feldman, M. (in press). Parental cognitive imapairment and child maltreatment in Canada. *Child Abuse & Neglect.*

McConnell, D., Dalziel, A., Llewellyn, G., Laidlaw, K., & Hindmarsh, G. (2008). Strengthening the social relationship of mothers with learning difficulties. *British Journal of Learning Disabilities, 37,* 66-75.

McConnell, D., Feldman, M., Aunos, M., & Prasad, N. G. (2011). Child Maltreatment investigations involving parents with cognitive impairments in Canada. *Child Maltreatent, 16*(1), 21-32.

McConnell, D., Llewellyn, G., & Ferronato, L. (2003). Prevalence and outcomes for parents with disabilities and their children in an Australian court sample. *Child Abuse and Neglect, 27,* 235-251.

McConnell, D., Llewellyn, G., Mayes, R., Russo, D., & Honey, A. (2003). Developmental profiles of children born to mothers with intellectual disability. *Journal of Intellectual & Developmental Disability, 28*(2), 122-134.

McConnell, D., Matthews, J., Llewellyn, G., Mildon, R., & Hindmarsh, G. (2008). "Healthy Start": A national strategy for parents with intellectual disabilities and their children. *Journal of Policy and Practice Intellectual Disabilities, 5,* 194-202.

McConnell, D., Mayes, R., & Llewellyn, G. (2008a). Women with intellectual disability at risk of adverse pregnancy and birth outcomes. *Journal of Intellectual Disability Research, 52,* 529-535.

McConnell, D., Mayes, R., & Llewellyn, G. (2008b). Pre-partum distress in women with intellectual disabilities. *Journal of Intellectual and Developmental Disability, 33,* 177-183.

McGaw, S. (2002). Should parenting be taught? *The Psychologist, 15,* 510-513.

Reed, E. W., & Reed, S. C. (1965). *Mental retardation: A family study.* Philadelphia: Saunders.

Sameroff, A. J., & Chandler, M. (1975). Reproductive risk and the continuum of caretaking causality. In F. Horowitz (Ed.), *Review of child development research, vol. 4* (pp. 157-243). Chicago: University of Chicago Press.

Spencer, M. (2001). Proceed with caution: The limitations of current parenting capacity assessments. *Developing Practice,* Winter, 16-24.

St-Amand, K., Goupil, G., & Aunos, M. (2010). La qualité de vie perçue de mères québécoises présentant une déficience intellectuelle. *Journal on Developmental Disabilities, 16(3), 18-27.*

Tarleton, B., Ward, L., & Howarth, J. (2006). *Finding the right support: a review of issues and positive practice to support parents with learning difficulties and their children.* London: The Baring Foundation.

Traustadóttir, R., & Björg Sigurjónsdóttir, H. (2008). The 'Mother' behind the mother: Three generations of Mothers with intellectual disabilities and their family support networks. *Journal of Applied Research in Intellectual Disabilities, 21,* 331-340.

Tucker, M. B., & Johnson, O. (1989). Competence promoting versus competence inhibiting social support for mentally retarded mothers. *Human Organization, 48,* 95-107.

Tymchuk, A. J. (1998). The importance of matching educational interventions to parents needs in child maltreatment: Issues, methods, and recommendations. In J. Lutzker (Ed.), *Handbook of child abuse research and treatment* (pp. 421-448). New York: Plenum Press.

Tymchuk, A. J. (2006). *The health & wellness program: A parenting curriculum for families at risk.* Baltimore: Paul H. Brookes Publishing.

United Nations. (1989). *Convention on the Rights of the Child (CRC).* Retrieved from http://www2.ohchr.org/english/law/crc.htm

United Nations. (2006). *Convention on the rights of persons with disabilities.* Retrieved from http://www.un.org/esa/socdev/enable/rights/convtexte.htm#convtext

Wade, C., Llewellyn, G., & Matthews, J. (2008). Review of parent training interventions for parents with intellectual disability. *Journal of Applied Research in Intellectual Disability, 21,* 351-366.

WHO. (2004). *The Montreal declaration on intellectual disabilities.* Retrieved from http://www.declarationmontreal.com/english/declaration.htm

Aging in People with Developmental Disabilities

Lilian Thorpe and Nancy Jokinen

What you will learn:

- How the increasing life expectancy of people with developmental disabilities has made the study of aging in this population increasingly important to service providers and planners
- How different types of developmental disability may influence the development of aging related health issues
- How the health and social service milieu in Ontario affects older people with developmental disabilities
- Practical suggestions and resources for supporting people with developmental disabilities in Ontario as they age

The study of aging has taken an increasingly prominent position in academic institutions of the developed world as the general population has aged, and as chronic age related conditions have overtaken acute conditions such as communicable diseases as contributors to morbidity and mortality. In response, many universities and colleges now have developed gerontology programs, and knowledge about aging has increased considerably over time. Efforts have also been made to adapt health and social care systems to the needs of an aging population. Medical schools have started training physicians with specialization in geriatric fields and national bodies are continuing to develop standards to ensure consistency across the country. The Royal College of Physicians and Surgeons of Canada approved both geriatric medicine in January 1977 (see Hogan, 2007) and geriatric psychiatry in September 2009 (see also Cole, 1999, and Le Clair & Sadavoy, 1998) as subspecialties of internal medicine and psychiatry, respectively. The College of Family Physicians of Canada approved Care of the Elderly Programs in 1989, which are now offered at 13 universities in Canada (Frank & Seguin, 2009).

Aging is a process influenced by genetics, early life experiences, and the physical and social environments people live in. It remains an inevitable, normal and natural part of life, although advances in science, technology, occupational safety, public health and health care have delayed the onset of many aging related chronic health conditions over the last century (Fogel, 2003). Nonetheless, older people still have to adapt to physical and mental changes, which may limit their functioning in various personal, social and occupational domains, and may eventually decrease their quality of life. These changes do not affect all older people equally, and it is thought that individual variation may even become more pronounced with age, as the differences in genetic predisposition have had longer to interact with differences in the physical and social environment. The rate of decline with aging is also not consistent across domains. For example, changes in motor functioning frequently occur at different rates, and begin at different ages, than changes in sensory abilities or cognition. As a result, some older people are fairly robust physically but cognitively impaired, some are physically frail but cognitively intact, and others have mixed impairments at varying severities in multiple domains.

Older people also experience many life events and transitions, which may pose a challenge to their quality of life (Denton & Kusch, 2006). Interestingly, most seniors cope with transitions such as retirement positively and this may even result in improvements to their mental health (Villamil, Huppert, & Melzer, 2006). Others struggle with transitions. For example, people whose major social relationships and sense of self worth are related to their participation in the workforce may develop social isolation and a lack of meaning in their lives after retirement. Those with poor coping skills may have difficulty following the death of significant others, adapting to illness and declines in physical functioning, or struggle to adjust to a new living situation. Adaptation to life transitions is likely buffered by social support, usually ones that are informal. This includes support from a spouse, adult children, other members of the extended family, and/or from friends and neighbours. The availability of this support is variable, and those with complex needs may require formal services and supports.

In Ontario, health and social policies emphasize community living. In March of 2009, the Ministry of Community and Social Services closed the last remaining institution specifically designed for persons with developmental disabilities. Within the healthcare sector, policies and programs also encourage all older adults to remain living as independently as possible in the community, and to delay entry into a long-term care facility (i.e., nursing homes). Pressure on inpatient, acute care beds in hospitals has resulted in more reliance on outpatient services and home care options. These formal community services are increasingly stretched, however, as the proportion of older people in the population grows. Wait lists for many services are common in different jurisdictions across the province. Families and community supports are and will increasingly continue to be needed to provide high levels of care to older people.

Adults with developmental disabilities who are now in their old age are probably the healthiest of their original birth cohort. They are the healthy survivors, yet they still have increased physical and mental vulnerabilities compared to the general population. Although these are frequently related to the primary cause of the developmental disability, they may also be related to decreased coping skills, reduced communication skills, impoverished life experiences and/or, with age, a diminishing social support network. In Canada and other western countries, older adults with developmental disabilities were born and raised in an era that promoted institutionalization for the provision of care, and had restricted rights and limited opportunities (Parmenter, 2004). Some of those who were institutionalized lost touch with family members, had minimal education, few employment opportunities, and developed little experience interacting with the outside world. Most never married or had children.

The majority of adults with developmental disability worldwide reside with family members (World Health Organization, 2000), who remain the primary source of their support. Increasingly, this is becoming the case in Ontario and other more affluent jurisdictions. Over time, family caregivers also age and become increasingly vulnerable to their own health issues, resulting in challenges to continuing care provision. Health crises in older caregivers may precipitate unplanned and rapid residential moves for the adult with developmental disability, which may result in catastrophic consequences.

Older adults with developmental disability have needs similar to other older adults, such as meaningful relationships and activities, access to (and timely) health care, and adequate housing and transportation (see Bigby, 2004). Unfortunately, the pre-existing physical and mental vulnerabilities described above interact with inadequacies in the ability of the social and health care systems to provide efficient and timely access to necessary resources, resulting in suboptimal, overall quality of life. In terms of health care, difficulty in making an accurate medical diagnosis is a particular problem in older people who have multiple interacting problems, experience polypharmacy (take several medications), have poor communication skills, and have decreased ability to comply with necessary examinations. Behavioural symptoms are often difficult to separate from developmental issues superimposed on a lifetime of restricted social roles and experiences. Further complications are caused by deficiencies in the formal training in developmental disability provided by Canadian medical schools (Lunsky & Bradley, 2001). Physicians providing care generally learn about developmental and intellectual disabilities in a somewhat haphazard way during medical school, and only sporadically from their clinical experiences after graduation. They have less opportunity to develop significant expertise in this area than physicians formerly working in larger institutions dedicated to people with developmental disability. Finally, fee-for-service reimbursement for physicians provides another barrier to good medical care. The time involved for a good assessment of changes associated with aging in a person with developmental disabilities can be quite considerable, yet standard fee codes do not take this increased complexity into account.

This chapter will provide an overview of aging related issues in people with developmental disabilities, with the goal of broadening the reader's understanding of key challenges and potential solutions and, ideally, preparing the reader for further, more in-depth learning.

Epidemiologic and Demographic Issues

There are increasing numbers of older people with developmental disabilities, including those with moderate to severe disabilities, living in the community. For example, an Irish national database report (Kelly, Kelly, & Craig, 2007) noted a growing proportion of persons aged 35+ with moderate, severe, or profound intellectual (developmental) disability receiving or requesting community services — from 29% in 1974 to 48% in 2008. This demographic trend is due to a combination of increased life expectancy in people with developmental disabilities and increasing de-institutionalization, resulting in a greater number of older people with developmental disabilities remaining in the community. The consequence of this is the need for increased education about aging in developmental disability among community service providers, so that the health and quality of life of this vulnerable population can be maximized.

Life expectancy

Overall, the life expectancy of adults with developmental disability has increased over time (Janicki, Dalton, Henderson, & Davidson, 1999). People with Down syndrome have had particular gains in their life expectancy, currently reaching an average life expectancy of almost 60 years (Glasson et al., 2002). Australian cohort studies of children born with Down syndrome show progressive increases in the percentage who survive to the age of 10 years from just over 40% in the cohorts 1948 to 1957, to over 80% in the cohorts 1991 to 1996 (Glasson et al., 2002). Although survival curves still suggest a fairly steep drop-off in the survival of people with Down syndrome at about the age of 60, it appears that an increasingly greater percentage of people will live to that age or beyond as time goes by.

As in the general population, some adults with a developmental disabilities live longer than others, which is likely due to a combination of individual biology (including genetics) and differences in healthcare and living circumstance (World Health Organization, 2000). One likely contributor to increasing life expectancy over time is the improvement in medical care for people with developmental disabilities. For example, improved treatment of congenital heart disease in young children with Down syndrome increases their likelihood of reaching adulthood. Improved availability of effective anticonvulsants may have reduced the likelihood of sudden unexplained death in those with epilepsy, which is common in developmental disability (Nei & Hays, 2010), especially for those with more severe impairment. Also important in later life are improved general health measures such as control of hypertension and treatment of cardiovascular disease or cancer.

Changes in service delivery and social supports may also have improved life expectancy. For example, community support that allows for individualized service delivery in the community, as opposed to support in large, congregate institutional settings, is associated with decreased mortality. One potential reason for this is reduced rates of infection from agents such as the ulcer-causing bacterium, *Helicobacter pylori*, among people living in less crowded settings (Wallace, Webb, & Schluter, 2002). Another reason may be a reduced rate of side effects from psychotropic medications, as ones with adverse side effects tended to be commonly used in institutional settings. Contact with family members and friends may also increase recognition of treatable conditions, as well as decrease the likelihood of hidden abuse. Of course, successful community living requires appropriate supports, and there is some suggestion that people with very high medical and behavioural needs may have increased mortality after discharge to the community unless support is available (Strauss, Shavelle, Baumeister, & Anderson, 1998).

Life expectancy in people with developmental disability is decreased by the severity of the disability, with those affected more severely having the lowest life expectancy (Bittles et al., 2002). This is likely related to underlying health conditions that decrease lifespan, such as severe epilepsy, as well as

to greater predisposition to secondary health conditions, such as infection in people who have mobility challenges or who may be bedbound. There is considerable variation in mortality between different types of developmental disabilities, and there are also differences when comparing different age groups to the underlying population. For example, Tyrer, Smith, and McGrother (2007) reviewed a population of adults with moderate profound intellectual (developmental) disabilities living in the U.K. between 1993 and 2005. They found that both all-cause and disease specific mortality was about three times higher than in the general population, although some age groups had much higher relative mortality than others.

Mortality and healthy survivors

Causes of mortality in older people with developmental disabilities are generally similar to those in the general population, although there are a few differences. Patja, Molsa, and Iivanainen (2001) published a 35-year follow-up study of people with developmental disabilities in a Finnish population. This indicated that the three most common causes of death were cardiovascular disease, respiratory disease, and cancer, very similar to the Finnish national mortality patterns. However, there was less difference between the sexes in this population than in the general population in cause-specific mortality. There also was overall reduced mortality from cancer and some other external causes, such as motor vehicle accidents. The latter makes particular sense, as people with developmental disabilities do not usually drive; they should have fewer deaths due to cancer and obstructive lung disease from smoking; and they should have fewer health problems related to sexually transmitted diseases or disorders related to childbirth.

In general, people who reach older ages are "healthy survivors," and may have been the healthiest of their original birth cohort. Among those with developmental disability, people who survive to older ages are less likely to include those with the most severe, genetic and chromosomal abnormalities, or those with the lowest IQ. Because of the healthy survivor effect, cross-sectional comparisons of data about the physical and mental health of young and older people frequently miss individual, longitudinal aging changes.

General aging changes

People with developmental disabilities reaching older ages can be expected to experience similar physical changes as other older adults in the general population. These include sensory changes (e.g., vision, hearing, and taste), reduced stamina, and the development of one or more of a number of chronic conditions. Studies of older people with developmental disability have confirmed this, although lower rates of cardiovascular risk factors, such as hypertension, hyperlipidaemia, and adult-onset diabetes (Janicki, McCallion, & Dalton, 2002) have been reported. Of particular note in the elderly in general are disorders such as Parkinson's disease, which can decrease mobility and increase falls, cerebrovascular and cardiovascular disease, gastrointestinal disorders (e.g., gastroesophageal reflux disorder, constipation), urological disorders (e.g., benign prostatic hypertrophy, incontinence) and arthritis. These disorders add to the burden of early onset disabilities and can considerably worsen the quality of life of a person, especially if diagnosis is delayed or even missed because of assessment challenges (see later).

Mental health issues

Mental health issues are very common in people with developmental disabilities, and this topic is therefore accorded its own chapter in this book. In summary, however, people with developmental disabilities are more likely to have difficulties with impulse control, impaired attention, poor coping skills, disinhibition and irritability, as well as typical learning challenges and communication problems. These behaviours are somewhat dependent on the condition responsible for the disability, but frequently affect the developmental aging process. For example, adapting to major changes in living situation when a trusted care provider dies or when a person is moved to a long-term care facility is often particularly difficult for someone with a developmental disability. When coupled with poor family and social supports, these transitions can result in a major breakdown in behaviour and functioning, and additional adverse consequences such as overmedication with psychotropic drugs.

Most major mental disorders, including depression and anxiety disorders, generally do not increase with age, contrary to popular misperception (Flint, 1994; Gum, King-Kallimanis, & Kohn, 2009; Patten, Sedmak, & Russell, 2001; Regier et al., 1988; Steffens et al., 2000; Streiner, Cairney, & Veldhuizen, 2006), although specialized populations, such as those in nursing homes, may have very high rates (see, for example, Barca, Engedal, Laks, & Selbaek, 2010). However, the addition of a mental illness such as depression generally has a greater impact on a vulnerable person, as is suggested by increasing hospitalization rates with age for primary medical disorders in older people who have secondary mental disorders (see Figure 2-3 in Health Canada, 2002).

Depressive syndromes (often related to loss and grieving) are more common than major depressive disorder in the general older adult population (Patten et al., 2001), and older people with developmental disabilities are particularly prone to certain losses. Most have never married or had their own families and have relied on parents and siblings for social support. When these parents or siblings die, or become unable to visit because of their own health problems, people with a disability frequently lose almost all their support network in a very short time and may react with pronounced grieving. Grieving may also occur after the loss of an unrelated, trusted care provider or a move into a different residential setting resulting in the loss of daily interaction with long-standing friends (who generally don't have access to a vehicle to visit regularly).

Cognitive changes with age

Normal aging brings with it gradual (and generally subtle) declines in various neuropsychological functions, particularly those affected by speed of processing. Most older people compensate well for these changes, using a lifetime of experience and collected wisdom. However, older adults with developmental disabilities may not have these compensatory skills, and may experience frustration and increased irritability when trying to manage tasks that are now more difficult for them.

A minority of older people have a more marked cognitive and functional deterioration over time, which eventually results in the diagnosis of dementia, although this diagnosis is affected by the particular criteria used (e.g., ICD-10, DSM IV-TR), especially in those with developmental disabilities (Strydom, Livingston, King, & Hassiotis, 2007). In general, the formal diagnosis of dementia requires deterioration that has significantly and adversely affected personal and occupational functioning. This functional dementia criterion tends to be met late in the course of biological brain deterioration in people with developmental disabilities, who tend to have structured, repetitive work and living situations that do not demand much new learning or complex thinking abilities. For example, dementia in a person with Down syndrome might not be diagnosed until the development of a significant medical complication such as a new-onset seizure. (See Menéndez (2005) for a discussion of seizures in Down syndrome.) The clinical diagnosis of dementia in people with developmental disabilities is further complicated by impaired communication skills, low baseline functioning, and concurrent medical, psychological, and social issues. A standard, universally accepted, dementia assessment battery is not available because of a very wide range of baseline intellectual and functional abilities. As a result, there is considerable disagreement in the literature about dementia rates, especially in adults with developmental disabilities who do not have Down syndrome.

Aging Related Issues in Specific Conditions

As mentioned earlier, people with developmental disabilities tend to have greater physical, medical and psychological challenges than those without developmental disability. Although many of these challenges are present at birth, others develop later in life, such as epilepsy, obesity, obstructive sleep apnea, dental problems, hypothyroidism, *Helicobacter pylori* infections, and dementia. These developing health problems may be caused by reduced compliance with (or access to) preventive measures such as exercise,

weight control, periodic health examinations, and dental care. They may also be caused by aspects of medical care, such as side effects of medications for underlying medical and psychiatric conditions. A particularly concerning issue has been the excessive use of psychotropic medications for behavioural problems in developmental disabilities. Guidelines for this difficult area of medical practice have recently been published by Deb et al. (2010).

The underlying cause of an individual's developmental disability is frequently pertinent to the later development of aging related health problems. These causes range from genetic and chromosomal factors, to prenatal insults (e.g., infections, toxins including maternal alcohol abuse, and inadequate nutrition), or early childhood deprivation and childhood brain damage (e.g., accidents, toxins, and encephalitis). Such causes affect life expectancy and lifespan health in a wide variety of ways, although some general comments can be made about most causal conditions (see chapter 13 for details). Some of these conditions merit particular discussion, since they occur commonly in the developmental disability population.

Seizure disorders

Early-life onset of seizure disorders are common in people with developmental disability, especially in those with greater severity of disability, and tend to be related to the underlying cause of the developmental disability. Late-life onset of seizure disorders in developmental disability is less common but, when they occur, are a cause for concern as they tend to be a worrisome symptom of developing health problems, such as advanced dementia, brain tumours and strokes. Seizures can result in a variety of adverse outcomes, including repeated falls and related injuries, which can decrease mobility and increase chronic pain. They may also be related to sudden unexplained death (SUDEP), which is thought to be the cause of death in about 17% of people with epilepsy (Nei & Hays, 2010). Moreover, medications used in the treatment of epilepsy have numerous side effects, including demineralization of bones leading to increased osteoporosis, fractures (often leading to pain) and dental problems. Anticonvulsants also interact with many other medications. Such drug interactions become increasingly problematic in older ages, when medication use tends to be higher in general.

Cerebral palsy

Cerebral palsy is very common in people with intellectual and developmental disabilities, and contributes to decreased mobility and independent functioning. Unfortunately, when people with cerebral palsy reach adulthood, they may experience worsening in the physical and mental functioning (see Haak, Lenski, Hideckier, Li, & Paneth, 2009, and Lifshitz, Merrick, & Morad, 2008). This is possibly related to the high prevalence of multiple health problems such as osteoarthritis, chronic pain, reflux esophagitis, pressure ulcers, constipation, and bladder problems (Ando & Ueda, 2000; Zaffuto-Sforza, 2005).

Down syndrome

People with Down syndrome have increased mortality compared to the general population, although their life expectancy has increased greatly over the last century. Pneumonia is frequently cited as the primary cause of death (Bittles, Bower, Hussain, & Glasson, 2007), although it is thought that dementia is an important underlying cause (Torr, Strydom, Patti, & Jokinen, 2010). Some conditions that are common causes of death in the general population (e.g., cardiovascular disease and solid malignancies) are much less common causes of death in people with Down syndrome (Torr et al., 2010).

Sensory deficits, such as visual and hearing impairments, are very common (but frequently missed) in people with Down syndrome (Evenhuis, Theunissen, Denkers, Verschuure, & Kemme, 2001), and tend to increase with age. These deficits typically affect the person throughout the life span, starting with decreasing effective social interaction and learning in childhood, and impairing occupational functioning in adulthood. Sensory impairment may eventually increase the impact of cognitive deficits in older ages, or even result in premature or inappropriate diagnosis of dementia. Sensory deficits also make the objective assessment of intellectual functioning for the purpose of dementia assessment more challenging.

A significant fraction of people with Down syndrome will eventually develop clinical manifestations of dementia of the Alzheimer's type by old age. This conclusion is based on pathological studies of the brain and also on clinical assessments using standard protocols. However, although most people with Down syndrome who come to autopsy have typical Alzheimer changes in their brains by young adult life, not all people with Down syndrome develop clinical manifestations of Alzheimer's disease (Margallo-Lana et al., 2007; Zigman & Lott, 2007). For example, Holland, Hon, Huppert, Stevens, and Watson (1998) published data suggesting that by the age of 50 to 59 years, 40% of people with Down syndrome have clinically diagnosed Alzheimer's disease. This is much higher than, for example, data from the Canadian Study of Health and Aging (1994), which suggests that overall dementia rates in the general population are 34.5% by the age of 85.

Clinical work and research with adults who have Down syndrome suggests that there are various declines in neuropsychological abilities, general functioning, and behaviour before a formal diagnosis of Alzheimer's disease is made. Executive dysfunction has been reported to be a particularly important pre-diagnosis symptom by some authors (Ball et al., 2006). By midlife, changes such as increased rigidity and decreased adaptation to work and home demands often lead to complaints of stubbornness and other difficult behaviours, and are frequently a cause for mental health referral for people with Down syndrome in their 40s. Early recognition of progressive decline can lead to improved adaptation of work and home schedules to maximize a person's functioning, and to allow for future planning. See Chapter 37 for additional information about dementia.

Older Adults with Developmental Disabilities in Ontario

In Ontario, older adults with developmental disabilities have diverse life experiences. They live in a variety of settings including apartments by themselves, in apartments or homes with other adults, in homes with family members or unrelated adults with and without disabilities, or in long term care

Box 1: Older Adults living in the Community without Formal Developmental Disability Supports

John lived his entire life supported by family and friends in the community despite having a developmental disability. In later life, he had an apartment located in the same building as his older sister. They had a close relationship and helped one another. John fell and broke his hip, requiring surgery and a lengthy recovery. His idiosyncratic behaviours, however, were not well understood or tolerated by staff or patients in the rehabilitation hospital. Exasperated with his behaviour, the hospital staff sought to move him elsewhere. Initially, a dementia care unit was considered although there was not a diagnosis of dementia. Developmental disability services were called upon but could only provide a few hours of support Monday to Friday. John was transferred across town to a long term care facility, making visits by his sister extremely difficult. Eventually John was placed in a psychiatric facility that had a geriatric ward and it was determined that he could not return to live in his apartment.

facilities originally designed for frail older adults (e.g., nursing homes). Ontario no longer has large scale congregate care institutions operating specifically for people with developmental disabilities. Many older-aged adults are also involved in different work, volunteer, leisure or recreation opportunities throughout the week. Some older adults with developmental disabilities and their families have been engaged with formal services over many years, for day and/or residential support. Yet others have managed without formal services over their life-spans, and may only become known in later life to services as they or a member of their family experience difficulties. Sadly, sometimes the outcome of this can have a profound and detrimental impact on the individual (see example in Box 1).

Health and social services and their associated legislation are the responsibility of provincial governments in Canada. Rules and regulations governing program development and service delivery in both sectors change from time to time. It is, therefore, important to keep abreast of changes in order to better support individuals and take advantage of opportunities that might improve services. Overall, there is currently an emphasis on community living and "aging at home" in both health care and social services. However, community services are increasingly challenged in meeting the health care and psychosocial needs (e.g., grief and loss, retirement) as well as in helping to maintain abilities, social relations, and interests of older adults with developmental disabilities.

Service challenges

Across Ontario, developmental disability services that support older people vary in philosophical stance, what services are offered, eligibility criteria, and professional expertise in aging and developmental disabilities. Despite changing demographics, aging and the needs of older adults has not been a priority area. Generally, the sector has tended to focus attention on deinstitutionalization, mental health issues, youth transitioning from the education system, and people in the child welfare system who reach adult status and require lifelong support. Instead of celebrating gains made in relation to increased longevity of people with a developmental disability, the rise in numbers of an older adult population is sometimes viewed as a barrier for younger-aged adults to access services and support. Wait lists for many services exist across jurisdictions and, with an aging population, are likely to continue into the foreseeable future.

There are also several other issues that likely impact a service's ability to meet the needs of older aged adults with developmental disability. Many staff members, for example, have limited knowledge about aging. As well, staff turnover can reduce historical knowledge of the person's abilities. Both these factors can result in a lack of information crucial to the assessment of any physical or cognitive changes that might occur with age. Middle-aged and older adults with developmental disabilities who receive nominal services through an agency may, with age, require additional support hours or differing supports not yet developed. Residential services planned for healthy, younger people may not have staff available during the day, on the assumption that the adults living in the home setting will be engaged in work or day programs. Older people, however, may no longer be able to tolerate or want to continue with established day schedules for work, but it may not be possible for them to stay at home unsupported. Furthermore, older adults living in arrangements with "sleep shift" supervision may experience changes in sleep patterns with age or the onset of disease. It is not always possible to accommodate changes in sleep patterns in "sleep shift" settings. Services are also particularly challenged in situations when the middle-aged or older adult with disability experiences cognitive decline and is diagnosed with dementia (Courtenay, Jokinen, & Strydom, 2010). Compounding these issues, the financial resources available to community agencies limit staffing increases and program development. This possibly leads to inappropriate hospitalization and/or the transfer and institutionalization of an older adult with a developmental disability to a long-term care facility (e.g., nursing home). Nursing homes are designed for frail elderly people, a small minority of older people, and quality of life may be better maintained in community settings (Chaput, 2002).

Work with older families

Staff working in developmental disability services often support older adults. Hence their work likely involves older family members (e.g., parents and/ or siblings) who either live with their relative with a disability or have regular contact with them. Family relationships are an important aspect in the life of an individual aging with developmental disability regardless of living circumstance. Families have potential to provide a fundamental sense of belonging and inclusion, and are often a source of support (both emotional and practical) that is routine oriented. These family members also have historical knowledge (health and social) of the person that is important from a biographical as well as medical perspective. Relationships between older family members and an organization and its service per-

sonnel certainly vary. Sometimes, older parents are viewed as meddlesome and not accepting of current policy and practice. Some middle-aged and older siblings may feel marginalized in their involvement. Nonetheless, building and maintaining positive relations with family is important (Jokinen, 2008).

There has been particular concern about middle-aged and older adults with developmental disability who co-reside with older aged parents. Sometimes, these older families have tenuous links to services and may become socially isolated. The extreme example cited in Box 2 highlights the importance of working with older parents and specifically of making future plans in the event of death or incapacitation.

While this work is a sensitive topic to engage in with individuals and their families, there are several future planning models developed to guide and support staff addressing this issue (see as examples Bigby, 2004, and Heller & Caldwell, 2006).

Health services

Health is another important aspect of life that has an impact on the individual, particularly as a person ages. There are a number of barriers and issues (e.g., reliance on others, knowledge and understanding) to overcome in order for older adults with developmental disabilities to maintain health and have access to timely, appropriate health care in Ontario (Jokinen, 2009). All people, including those with a developmental disability, who require assistance because of an adverse health event or declining health, may have access to a number of different provincially funded services under the Ministry of Health and Long Term Care including:

- In-home care (e.g., nursing, personal support for bathing, physiotherapy, occupational therapy, social work, speech-language therapy, nutritional counselling and medical supplies/ equipment) that helps the person remain living independently in the community.
- Convalescent care that can bridge the gap when a person who was hospitalized requires further recovery time yet does not require acute care and is not quite ready to return home.
- Long-term residential care (i.e., nursing homes) for people who require assistance beyond

supports that can be provided in-home to live independently.

- Respite care may also be available for family caregivers of older adults who have significant needs, for example, as a result of Alzheimer's disease or a stroke.

Generally these health care services are accessed and coordinated through a network of Community Care Access Centres (CCACs) situated across Ontario that act as a central point of access to services in their specific area. CCACs assess the eligibility for service using standardized assessments (i.e., various RAIs — Resident Assessment Instruments). Assessments take into consideration the person's health needs, living circumstance, and availability of services to meet needs. There are, however, limitations to these services. For instance, if a person requires what is determined to be extensive hours of service (e.g., 15+ hrs per week), they are possibly recommended to apply for long term care placement. The formal services offered through CCACs are becoming stretched and wait lists exist in many locales. Furthermore, in the health care sector, familiarity of personnel working in CCACs, acute care, long term care and other health related services with developmental disabilities varies. In many instances, there is a need for further professional training to better meet the needs of this particular population.

Initiatives addressing aging and developmental disability

In 1999, an initiative championed by a southern Ontario organization named Reena, began focussing on aging and developmental disabilities, and building the capacity of both the developmental disability and healthcare sectors to better meet the needs of older adults with developmental disability. The Ontario Partnership on Aging and Developmental Disability (OPADD) was formed with representatives from both sectors. Taking advantage of funding opportunities, an OPADD multi-year project recruited several sites across Ontario to plan and organize local events on aging and developmental disability. A number of local committees, therefore, emerged in different parts of the province and these

continued to focus on efforts to address both local and systemic concerns (Keshen & Stemp, 2004). Furthermore, in 2009, the Ontario Seniors Health Research Transfer Network (SHRTN) supported the establishment of a "Community of Practice" dedicated to aging and developmental disabilities. SHRTN is a network committed to knowledge exchange and development of best practices and learning opportunities. "Communities of Practice" bring together paid and unpaid caregivers, policy makers, and researchers to work collaboratively together. Since its inception the Community of Practice on Aging and Developmental Disability has held a number events. These have included webinars on dementia as it relates to adults with developmental disability and on convalescent care and respite, as well as online panel presentations on adult day programs. The working group plans to continue further events during 2010-2011 and beyond.

Practical Suggestions for Supporting Older Adults with Developmental Disabilities

Most adults with developmental disabilities voice strong wishes to remain living in and maintaining their current situation. Many Canadian seniors have a similar preference. Aging in place requires methodical and anticipatory planning; the physical and social environments of an older adult need to be secured and or adapted as changes occur with age (Bigby, 2004; Janicki, McCallion, & Dalton, 2000). Many developmental disability sector services, however, seem to operate on an individual case basis, which may hamper proactive service planning to adapt to aging and accommodate older adults (Janicki et al., 2002). The following suggestions are offered as a means to become better acquainted with aging as it affects adults with developmental disabilities and to take into consideration when providing support to them:

- *Learn more about aging and specifically about the impact that aging has on adults with developmental disabilities.* Read articles and books on the topic, access credible internet resources, and find people willing to share information. Join local and or provincial committees focussed on aging and developmental disability issues and concerns. In some communities, there are intersectoral committees that are working cooperatively together to support older adults with developmental disabilities. If you are working in a community that does not have such a committee, look for support from one that does. Join the SHRTN "Community of Practice", for instance; it is free and may be a valuable resource.

- *Share what you learn with co-workers, the adults you support and their families, and the organization's management team.* Advocate on behalf of the older adults supported by your agency. In the current era of fiscal restraint, it is often not possible to obtain additional funding and staffing for additional services, and creative solutions are needed to meet challenges brought on by aging. Sometimes there are guidelines available that can be easily adapted for use in your specific locale.

- *Support older adults and their families in making future plans.* How does the person you are supporting and their family envision the future? What activities and relationships are important to them and how might they be continued into the future? Future planning is a particularly critical task for middle-aged and older adults with a disability who receive nominal support from an agency and/or co-reside with older family members. Planning should include advance care directives, substitute decision-making, financial planning, and consideration of how family support might be continued in the future.

- *Promote healthy aging activities (e.g., exercise, diet, social engagement) and monitor the health of older adults.* Use one of the available resources to support the person in keeping a record of their health and medical history, as well as in establishing a baseline record of functional abilities. Become familiar with signs and symptoms of change and seek appropriate referral as needed; know legal or substitute

Box 2: Deaths of a Parent and her Adult Daughter with Down Syndrome

---

In 2007, the news announced that the bodies of an 89 year old woman and her 45 year old daughter who had Down syndrome had been discovered in the family home. They had lived together in the same neighbourhood for decades. The pair had become increasingly isolated over the last few years. A few years before, the mother had withdrawn her daughter from part time involvement with a disability service. The reasons for this were unknown. Sometime prior to finding the bodies, a neighbour reportedly saw the daughter standing outside the home waving at traffic. No one thought to go over to the home and see if everything was okay. After a week of noticing no activity at the home and lights left on all night, police were asked to check on the pair. The police statement indicated the mother died first and the daughter likely succumbed to starvation. A search for relatives found extended family living overseas.

---

decision-makers and advance care plans.

- *Support access to medical services.* Many older adults, including adults with developmental disabilities, need support during medical appointments, at acute care emergency departments, and throughout hospitalization. Family or trusted staff should be available to facilitate care, ensure understanding, and help with follow up. Remember physicians and other specialists have limited time to spend with patients and may not have much information about older adults with developmental disabilities. You can maximize the value of a doctor's visit by briefly and succinctly summarizing previous health conditions, current medication use, and current symptoms, making clear which symptoms are changes from a person's baseline functioning. This information could possibly be sent to the physician prior to the appointment with a copy brought to the interview. Furthermore, this kind of information could also be provided to hospital staff during unavoidable hospitalizations. As well, supplemental information about likes, dislikes and functional abilities could be provided to front-line nursing staff.

- *Assess the home and other environments used by older adults.* Are these environments "age-friendly" and/or can they be easily adapted to accommodate changes with age to prevent moving in later life? For instance, check for stairs that might become a barrier with age, adequate lighting, flooring surfaces, and assistive devices in bathrooms (e.g., grab bars to prevent slips and falls).

- *Review the Edinburgh Principles (Wilkinson & Janicki, 2001) that provide guidelines and recommendations for dementia care.* Small group settings that support an older adult with dementia likely require staff training specific to dementia, home environment modifications to ensure safety (e.g., warning signals on exits and fenced outdoor space to prevent wandering) and declining abilities, and external resources to manage the changes over time.

- *Support moving to a new living arrangement if necessary.* Planned moves are always preferable although not always possible. Moves in later life often disrupt long-standing routines, social relations, and may decrease autonomy. How may these be maintained before, during and after a move? Should a move to a nursing home be required, there are guidelines developed to facilitate the transition and reduce potential iatrogenic risks (Ontario Partnership on Aging and Developmental Disabilities, 2005). (The term iatrogenic, as used here, means risk of harm resulting from the move itself and from the care provided in the nursing home.)

- *Support continued participation in meaningful activities and social relationships important to the person.* Staffing may need to be reconfigured for older people to have shorter workdays, attend seniors' day programs, and possibly retire from the longstanding work/day program involvement. Pre-retirement planning with adults of older ages should consider how long time friendships and connections can be maintained while introducing and trying new activities. Some older adults with developmental disabilities may become involved in adult day programs geared to the general older adult population. Carefully plan inclusion in these programs (e.g., see that it is a positive experience for everyone involved, noting that there may be some resistance on the part of adults with developmental disability attending).

- *Prepare to provide support for grief, death and dying.* Older adults experience the ill health and death of significant others (friends and family) in their life as well as their own decline and death. The importance of rituals surrounding death reflects personal values and beliefs, and grief is an individual experience. Palliative and end of life care are becoming increasingly recognized as areas of work requiring additional training and support.

Summary

The aging of the adult population with developmental disability is a positive outcome of improved health care and supportive community settings, but it poses increased challenges to provision of appropriate health and social services in already resource constrained community programs. Creative solutions involving intersectoral cooperation and coordination will be necessary to support older adults with developmental disabilities to continue to maintain quality of life in community settings and avoid inappropriate transinstitutionalization to more restrictive, long-term care settings.

For Further Thought and Discussion

1. What are the pros and cons of "aging in place" for people with developmental disabilities?
2. Is there a role for long-term, institutional care for older adults with developmental disabilities?
3. How might the excessive use of psychotropic medications for older people with developmental disability be reduced?
4. How might jurisdictional conflicts adversely affect the health of people with developmental disabilities?

More Resources

Developmental Disabilities Division at the University of Waterloo
http://ddd.uwo.ca/resources/aging.html

Rehabilitation Research and Training Center on Aging with Developmental Disabilities, Department of Disability and Human Development, University of Illinois at Chicago
http://www.rrtcadd.org/

Resources on Aging with Intellectual/ Developmental Disabilities Selected Products and Publications
http://www.rrtcadd.org/Resource/Publications/assets/ Short%20Publication%20List%201.08.2010.pdf

Winnserv Inc.'s Library Resources
http://www.winnserv.ca/index.php?categoryID=8

References

Ando, N., & Ueda, S. (2000) Functional deterioration in adults with cerebral palsy. *Clinical Rehabilitation, 14*, 300–306.

Ball, S., Holland, A., Hon, J., Huppert, F., Treppner, P., & Watson, P. (2006). Personality and behaviour changes mark the early stages of Alzheimer's disease in adults with Down's syndrome: findings from a prospective population-based study. *International Journal of Geriatric Psychiatry, 21*(7), 661-673.

Barca, M. L., Engedal, K., Laks, J., & Selbaek, G. (2010). A 12 months follow-up study of depression among nursing-home patients in Norway. *Journal of Affective Disorders, 120*(1-3), 141-148.

Bigby, C. (2004). *Ageing with a lifelong disability: A guide to practice, program and policy issues for human services professionals.* London: Jessica Kingsley.

Bittles, A. H., Bower, C, Hussain, R., & Glasson, E. J. (2007). The four ages of Down syndrome. *European Journal of Public Health, 17*(2), 221-225.

Bittles, A., Petterson, B., Sullivan, S., Hussain, R., Glasson, E., & Montgomery, P. (2002). The influence of intellectual disability on life expectancy. *Journals of Gerontology Series A-Biological Sciences & Medical Sciences, 57A*(7), M470-M472.

Canadian Study of Health and Aging Working Group. (1994). CSHA: Study methods and prevalence of dementia. *Canadian Medical Association Journal, 150,* 899-913

Chaput, J. L. (2002). Adults with Down syndrome and Alzheimer's disease: Comparison of services received in group homes and in special care units. *Journal of Gerontological Social Work, 38*(1/2), 197-211.

Cole, M. G. (1999). Progress in geriatric psychiatry in Canada. *International Psychogeriatrics, 11*(4), 359-362.

Courtenay, K., Jokinen, N. S., & Strydom, A. (2010). Caregiving and adults with intellectual disabilities affected by dementia. *Journal of Policy and Practice in Intellectual Disabilities, 7*(1), 26-33.

Deb, S., Kwok, H., Bertelli, M., Salvador-Carulla, L., Bradley, E., Torr, J., et al. (2009). International guide to prescribing psychotropic medication for the management of problem behaviours in adults with intellectual disabilities. *World Psychiatry, 8*(3), 181-186.

Denton, M., & Kusch, K. (2006). *Well-being throughout the senior years: An issues paper on key events and transitions in later life.* Retrieved from http:// socserv.socsci.mcmaster.ca/sedap/p/sedap165.pdf

Evenhuis, H. M., Theunissen, M., Denkers, I., Verschuure, H., & Kemme, H. (2001). Prevalence of visual and hearing impairment in a Dutch institutionalized population with intellectual disability. *Journal of Intellectual Disability Research, 45*(Pt 5), 457-464.

Flint, A. J. (1994). Epidemiology and comorbidity of anxiety disorders in the elderly. *American Journal of Psychiatry, 151*(5), 640-649.

Fogel, R. W. (2003). Changes in the process of aging during the twentieth century: Findings and procedures of the Early Indicators project. In L. J. Waite (Ed.), *Aging, health, and public policy.* Population and Development Review, *30* (Suppl), 19-47.

Frank, C., & Seguin, R. (2009) Care of the elderly training: Implications for family medicine. *Canadian Family Physician, 55*(5), 510-511.

Glasson, E. J., Sullivan, S. G., Hussain, R., Petterson, B. A., Montgomery, P. D., & Bittles, A. H. (2002). The changing survival profile of people with Down's syndrome: Implications for genetic counselling. *Clinical Genetics, 62*(5), 390-393.

Gum, A. M., King-Kallimanis, B., & Kohn, R. (2009). Prevalence of mood, anxiety, and substance-abuse disorders for older Americans in the national comorbidity survey-replication. *American Journal of Geriatric Psychiatry, 17*(9), 769-781.

Haak, P., Lenski, M., Hidecker, M. J., Li, M., & Paneth, N. (2009). Cerebral palsy and aging. *Developmental Medicine & Child Neurology, 51*(Suppl 4), 16-23.

Health Canada. (2002). A report on mental illnesses in Canada. Ottawa, ON, 2002. Retrieved from http://www.phac-aspc.gc.ca/publicat/miic-mmac/pdf/men_ill_e.pdf

Heller, T., & Caldwell, J. (2006). Supporting aging caregivers and adults with developmental disabilities in future planning. *Mental Retardation, 44*(3), 189-202.

Hogan, D. (2007). History of geriatrics in Canada. Canadian *Bulletin of Medical History, 24*(1), 131-150.

Holland, A., Hon, J., Huppert, F., Stevens, F., & Watson, P. (1998). Population-based study of the prevalence and presentation of dementia in adults with Down's syndrome. *British Journal of Psychiatry, 172*(6), 493-498.

Janicki, M. P., Dalton, A. J., Henderson, C., & Davidson, P. (1999). Mortality and morbidity among older adults with intellectual disability: Health services considerations. *Disability and Rehabilitation, 21*(5/6), 284-294.

Janicki, M. P., McCallion, P., & Dalton, A. J. (2000). Supporting people with dementia in community settings. In M. P. Janicki & A. F. Ansello (Eds.), *Community supports for aging adults with lifelong disabilities* (pp. 387-413). Baltimore: Paul H. Brookes Publishing.

Janicki, M. P., McCallion, P., & Dalton, A. J. (2002). Dementia related care decision-making in group homes for persons with intellectual disability. *Journal of Gerontological Social Work, 38*(1/2), 179-196.

Jokinen, N. (2009). Adults aging with developmental disabilities, perceptions of health. Paper presented at the Northern Health Research Conference, Thunder Bay, ON. Retrieved from http://www.nosm.ca/research/nhrc/general.aspx?id=8174

Jokinen, N. S. M. (2008). Family quality of life in the context of aging and intellectual disability. Ph.D. dissertation, University of Calgary (Canada). Publication No. AAT NR44403.

Kelly, F., Kelly, C., & Craig, S. (2007). *Annual report of the National Intellectual Disability Database Committee 2007* (No. 2009 034X). Dublin, Ireland: Health Research Board.

Keshen, S., & Stemp, S. (2004). Building capacity in communities to support ageing individuals with intellectual disabilities. *Journal of Intellectual Disability Research, 48*(4/5), 426.

Le Clair, J. K., & Sadavoy, J. (1998). Geriatric psychiatry subspecialization in Canada: Past, present, and future. *Canadian Journal of Psychiatry, 43*(7), 681-687.

Lifshitz, H., Merrick, J., & Morad, M. (2008). Health status and ADL functioning of older persons with intellectual disability: Community residence versus residential care centers. *Research in Developmental Disabilities, 29*(4), 301-315.

Lunsky, Y., & Bradley, E. (2001). Developmental disability training in Canadian psychiatry residency programs. *Canadian Journal of Psychiatry, 46*(2), 138-143.

Margallo-Lana, M., Moore, P., Kay, D., Perry, R., Reid, B., Berney, T., et al. (2007). Fifteen-year follow-up of 92 hospitalized adults with Down's syndrome: incidence of cognitive decline, its relationship to age and neuropathology. *Journal of Intellectual Disability Research, 51*(6), 463-477.

Menéndez, M. (2005). Down syndrome, Alzheimer's disease and seizures. *Brain and Development, 27*(4), 246-252.

Nei, M., & Hays, R. (2010). Sudden unexpected death in epilepsy. *Current Neurology and Neuroscience Reports, 10*(4), 319-326.

Ontario Partnership on Aging and Developmental Disabilities. (2005). *Aging with a developmental disability: Transition guide for caregivers.* Toronto, ON: Author. Retrieved from http://www.opadd.on.ca/Documents/transitionguide-final-sept0105_001.pdf

Parmenter, T. R. (2004). Family quality of life: Implications for policy. In A. P. Turnbull, I. Brown, & R. Turnbull (Eds.), *Families and persons with mental retardation and quality of life: International perspectives* (pp. 265-298). Washington D.C.: American Association on Mental Retardation.

Patja, K., Molsa, P., & Iivanainen, M. (2001). Cause-specific mortality of people with intellectual disability in a population-based, 35-year follow-up study. *Journal of Intellectual Disability Research, 45*, 30-40.

Patten, S. B., Sedmak, B., & Russell, M. L. (2001). Major depression: Prevalence, treatment utilization and age in Canada. *Canadian Journal of Clinical Pharmacology, 8*(3), 133-138.

Regier, D. A., Boyd, J. H., Burke, J. D., Jr., Rae, D. S., Myers, J. K., Kramer, M., et al. (1988). One-month prevalence of mental disorders in the United States: Based on five epidemiologic catchment area sites. *Archives of General Psychiatry, 45*(11), 977-986.

Steffens, D. C., Skoog, I., Norton, M. C., Hart, A. D., Tschanz, J. T., Plassman, B. L., et al. (2000). Prevalence of depression and its treatment in an elderly population: The Cache County study. *Archives of General Psychiatry, 57*(6), 601-607.

Strauss, D., Shavelle, R., Baumeister, A., & Anderson, T.W. (1998). Mortality in persons with developmental disabilities after transfer into community care. *American Journal of Mental Retardation, 102*(6), 569-581.

Streiner, D. L., Cairney, J., & Veldhuizen, S. (2006). The epidemiology of psychological problems in the elderly. *Canadian Journal of Psychiatry, 51*(3), 185-191.

Strydom, A., Livingston, G., King, M., & Hassiotis, A. (2007). Prevalence of dementia in intellectual disability using different diagnostic criteria. *British Journal of Psychiatry, 191*, 150-157.

Torr, J., Strydom, A., Patti, P., & Jokinen, N. (2010). Aging in Down syndrome: Morbidity and mortality. *Journal of Policy and Practice in Intellectual Disabilities, 7*(1), 70-81.

Tyrer, F., Smith, L. K., & McGrother, C. W. (2007). Mortality in adults with moderate to profound intellectual disability: A population-based study. *Journal of Intellectual Disability Research, 51*(7), 520-527.

Villamil, E., Huppert, F. A., & Melzer, D. (2006). Low prevalence of depression and anxiety is linked to statutory retirement ages rather than personal work exit: A national survey. *Psychological Medicine, 36*(07), 999-1009.

Wallace, R. A, Webb, P. M., & Schluter, P. J. (2002). Environmental, medical, behavioural and disability factors associated with Helicobacter pylori infection in adults with intellectual disability. *Journal of Intellectual Disability Research, 46*(Pt 1), 51-60.

Wilkinson, H., & Janicki, M. P. (2001). *Edinburgh Principles with accompanying guidelines and recommendations.* Stirling, Scotland: University of Stirling. Retrieved from http://www.iassid.org/iassid_beta_0.1.3/index.php?option=com_content&view=article&id=47&Itemid=171

World Health Organization. (2000). *Ageing and intellectual disabilities - Improving longevity and promoting healthy ageing: Summative report.* Geneva: World Health Organization.

Zaffuto-Sforza, C. D. (2005). Aging with cerebral palsy. *Physical Medicine and Rehabilitation Clinics of North America, 16*(1), 235-249.

Zigman, W., & Lott, I. (2007). Alzheimer's disease in Down syndrome: Neurobiology and risk. *Mental Retardation and Developmental Disabilities Research Reviews, 13*(3), 237-246.

Index

Note: See the OADD website (www.oadd.org) for supplementary information

A

Abnormal behaviours   531, 619-40
Abortion   72, 156, 176, 540-2, 703-5,
Absence seizures   406-7
Abuse
    of children   740, 744, 749, 761, 764, 768-9
    emotional   482, 740, 744, 748, 753, 759, 761, 763
    physical   382. 742, 745-6, 748, 751, 753-4, 756-7, 759
Acculturation   513-14, 516-17, 522, 792, 843-6, 848
Acquired immunodeficiency (AIDS) see Human
    immunodeficiency virus
Adaptive behaviour   11, 48, 309, 358, 424, 686, 792, 906, 912
Adolescence/Adolescent see Brain, Puberty and specific
    syndromes and disorders
Adult
    lifestyles   6,358, 525, 528, 530, 654, 832, 877
    primary care   498, 570, 572, 872
    stem cells   181
Advocacy 121, 854, 799, 899
    groups   35-6, 47, 710, 774, 781, 854
Advocates   117, 121, 321, 535, 539-40, 542, 552, 707, 765,
    773-5, 781, 841, 853, 866, 902
Aggression   139, 237, 249, 251, 253, 286, 311, 314, 318-19,
    363, 366, 602, 615-16, 688, 882-3
Aging   63, 195, 203-5, 288, 289, 292, 527, 530-1, 534, 544,
    566, 894, 903-4, 925
    adults   531, 546, 938
    normal   673-4, 680, 929
    parents   472, 530, 851, 863, 869, 871-2, 899, 901, 906
Agitation   188, 602-3, 608, 610-11, 688
Alcohol see also Fetal alcohol spectrum disorder; Fetal
    alcohol syndrome 100, 174-5, 194, 196, 219, 294, 335,
    357-9, 361-70, 372-6, 379-80, 462, 464, 625, 635
    abuse   55, 216, 229, 358-9, 371-6, 375, 385, 681
    exposure   358, 360, 362, 364, 366-7, 371, 373-4, 376 380
Allele   154, 163, 165
Alternative communication   121, 475-6, 479, 482, 486, 488,
    491, 493-4
Aluminum   75, 182, 221, 223, 640, 678-80, 694
Alzheimer's disease   158, 161, 163, 188, 199-200, 408, 673-94,
    931, 934, 937-9 see also Down syndrome
    diagnosis of 676, 681-2, 687
Amniocentesis   157, 177-9, 196, 269, 288, 294, 701-2
Amygdala see also Limbic system 193-4, 196, 311, 628
Amyloid plaques see also Beta-amyloid 163, 673-5, 691
Amyloid precursor protein (APP)   674-5, 678-9, 683, 691, 693
Anemia   179, 216, 218-9, 221, 226, 241, 275, 281, 361, 575,
    580, 588-9, 698-9, 702
Angelman syndrome   163, 215, 259, 493
Anorexia   256, 578, 580, 588-9, 630-1

Antecedents   45, 447, 452-3
Antibodies   276, 389, 674-5, 702
Anticonvulsant drugs   174, 228, 254, 297, 406-7, 409-11, 413,
    609-10, 688, 930
Antidepressants   219, 221, 568, 603, 605, 608-9, 611-12,
    614-16, 637, 651, 688
Antipsychotics   600, 603-4, 607, 614-17, 637,
    644, 650-1
Anxiety   174, 194, 205, 207, 219, 284, 313, 317, 320, 333-5,
    342-3, 366, 394, 410, 412-13, 460, 462, 516-17, 569, 600-4,
    610-11, 625, 628-9, 637-8, 746, 892-3, 913-14, 938-9
Anxiety disorders   382, 602, 608, 623, 627-9, 631, 641, 651,
    667, 912, 929, 937
Applied behaviour analysis (ABA)   315, 317, 447, 450, 455-6,
    591, 725, 854
Approaches to treatment see also Behavioural, Intervention,
    Medical, Syndromes, and specific disorders, etc.
    educational 369, 636
    family-directed 433, 441-2
    individualized 317, 657, 867
    person-centred 57, 420, 443
    qualitative 138-9
Arched palate, high 271, 342-4
Articulation   296, 299, 476, 502
Asperger disorder/syndrome   56, 256, 329-41, 306, 312, 329,
    331, 337-9, 425, 667, 669
Asphyxia   216, 220, 240, 294, 504
Aspiration   245, 281, 557, 570, 576, 584, 586, 729, 733, 798-9
Assaults, sexual   335, 493, 746, 896-7
Assessment   419 see also Behaviour/Behavioural,
    Communication, Comprehensive, Introduction, Health,
    Nutritional, Psychiatric, Psychological
    approaches 419
    of growth   576, 576-7, 581, 583, 592
    individualized   321, 420-2, 509, 585
    intellectual   50, 547
    methods   420-2
    process   333, 510-11, 515, 520, 652, 781
    team   332, 510-16
Assistive devices   60, 80, 91, 296, 393, 439, 440, 443, 486, 488,
    491-2, 504, 802, 862, 936
Astrocytes   163, 186, 191-2, 197, 201-2
Asylums   25-9, 33-5, 37-40, 769, 829, 848
Atlas   279, 282-3
Atomoxetine   320, 611-12, 624
Attention deficit/hyperactivity disorder (ADHD) see also
    Syndromes, and specific disorders   623-4
Attorney   61, 81-6, 101, 552, 864
Atypical antipsychotics   314, 320, 603, 607-8
Auditory see Hearing

Augmentative & alternative communication (AAC) 475, 477, 479, 480-1, 483, 485, 486-9, 489, 490-1, 492-3
Augmentative communication 49, 122, 299, 318, 482, 488-9, 493, 501, 504
Autism 17, 200-1, 305-28, 336-9, 344, 425-7, 432, 476-7, 494, 642-3, 654-5, 667-9, 854-5, 868-71, 905
    causes of 225, 256, 312
    characteristics of 175, 214, 311-2, 316-17
    diagnosis of 309, 321, 344, 643
    high-functioning 312, 330, 336, 339
    severe 209, 312, 426, 637
    Treatment Network 322, 324-5, 868
Autism spectrum disorder(s) (ASDs) 204, 213, 221 224-5, 286, 306-7, 311, 313, 316, 320-2, 324-7, 329-33, 335-9, 347, 432, 471-2, 663, 670, 724, 738, 854-5, 868-9
Autistic disorder (AD) 248, 259, 306-8, 312-13, 323-5, 327, 330
Autosomal genes 156
Axons 186, 190, 192, 202
Azcue 585-7, 590

B
Babies, healthy 182, 704-5
Barr bodies 154-5
Barrier, blood-brain 196-7
Base triplets (in DNA) 150
Beds 34-5, 38, 391, 449
Behaviour see also Behavioural, Behaviours 456, 494, 519, 620, 637-8
    analysis, applied 315, 317, 447, 450, 455-6, 725, 854
    assessment 49, 319, 348, 368, 446, 449, 451-2
    characteristics 4, 227-9, 236-56, 258
    disorders 17, 236, 264, 285-7, 349, 428-9, 477-8, 504, 622, 667-8, 670, 747
    disturbances 218, 221, 256, 349, 642-3, 645-7, 653, 667, 762
    interventions 136, 253, 287, 319, 349, 324-6, 432, 445-58, 456, 533, 602, 624, 637, 640, 645, 668, 872
    intensive interventions 209, 213, 723, 854-5, 869-70
    management 132, 228, 237, 243, 350, 440, 862, 864
    norms 519, 620, 791
    patterns/profiles see also Syndromes; specific syndromes or disorders 227, 366, 461, 577, 638, 647
    phenotypes (BPs) 246, 257, 291, 355, 366-7, 619, 622, 635-6, 639, 642, 647, 654, 666, 670
    problems see also Problem behaviours 132, 222, 366, 411-2, 428-9, 449, 455, 602, 617, 641, 802, 914
    skills, adaptive 680, 685-6
    sleep problems 286-7
    support, positive 318-19, 448
    techniques 454, 602, 630, 755, 851, 919
    therapists 137, 450, 526, 561, 644-5, 855
    therapy 134, 137, 254, 356, 383, 384, 429, 629, 652, 654, 660, 668, 896, 901
Behaviours see also Challenging, Destructive
    aberrant 456-7, 643, 749
    abnormal see Abnormal behaviours
    aggressive 159, 239, 253, 450, 454, 462, 610, 668, 670, 742, 762
    antisocial 254, 365, 633, 746, 762
    appropriate 319, 451, 454, 820, 916
    autistic 250, 313, 342, 644
    dangerous 616, 653
    difficult 221, 285, 349, 688, 852, 895, 931
    disruptive 130, 316, 366, 448, 647, 662, 819
    inappropriate 447, 755, 762, 874-5, 880, 882, 916
    inappropriate sexual 358, 366, 602, 874, 876-7, 879-81
    maladaptive 249, 253, 291, 319, 370, 424, 632, 866, 899
    normal 620-1, 635
    oppositional 382, 642
    repetitive 313, 320
    self-destructive/self-stimulatory 315, 632-3, 636
    social 219, 877
    suicidal 619, 633-4, 637-8, 704
    typical pain 566, 569
    unacceptable 256, 469
    unusual 306, 308, 323, 601, 603, 645
    violent see Violent behaviour
Beliefs 45, 47, 114, 472, 512-13, 515-16, 519, 540-1, 555, 558, 632-3, 725-6, 761, 834, 854-5, 885-6
Benzodiazepines 606, 610-11, 615, 635
Beta-amyloid 674-6, 679-80, 682-3
Billings ovulation method 704-5, 714
Bipolar disorder 214, 229, 361, 366, 601-2, 609-10, 626-7, 634, 639-40
Birth see also Pregnancy
    asphyxia 295
    complications 176, 913
    defects 63, 177, 217, 223, 236, 288, 367, 371, 375, 430, 698, 868
Birth control 33, 175, 873, 875, 877-8
Blindness 8, 218, 245-6, 250, 279, 698, 725
Body mass index (BMI) 580, 582, 587
Borderline personality disorder 633
Botulinum toxin 297-8, 301-2
Bovine spongiform encephalopathy (BSE) 159-60, 163, 166
Bowel 274-5, 644, 684
Benefits, entitlements, and rights 75
Brain 163, 165-6, 172, 175-7, 185-8, 190-205, 239-41, 255, 294-5, 310-13, 364, 405-8, 609-10, 673-6, 678-80
    adolescent 195
    adult 186, 193-4
    cells 155, 187, 301
    child's 195, 201, 389
    developing 196, 202, 204
    development 176, 195-6, 199, 203, 205, 217-18, 287, 364-5, 377, 381, 698, 762
    function 191, 380, 191, 196, 199, 202, 367, 380, 676
    healthy 187, 201, 675
    injury 55, 188, 196, 208, 216, 220, 223, 262, 532, 611, 619, 624, 634-6, 638, 642
    left, right, male, female 195-6
    regions 194, 620, 676
    structure 185, 194, 196, 367
Brainstem 186, 189, 192, 194, 201, 495, 504-5
Brothers 388, 394, 437, 464, 471, 712-13, 763, 832-3, 835, 854, 864-5, 871, 900
Bulimia nervosa 630-1

C

Canadian Charter of Rights and Freedoms 67, 72-3, 75, 102, 721, 735, 739, 782-3, 854, 876
Canadian Constitution 65-6, 71
Canadian Human Rights Act 65, 67-9, 73
Cancer 157, 281, 287, 291, 388, 635, 704, 928
Capacity 5, 8, 11, 29-30, 34, 45, 49, 80-8, 181, 537-8, 552-8, 560, 644, 909-10, 914-15
  person's 82, 84, 87, 505, 556
Capacity assessment 80-2, 100, 102-3
  alternative parenting 913
  competence-based parenting 915
  current parenting 923
  private parenting 913
Carbamazepine 406, 610, 616
Care
  acute 933-4
  children's 398, 713, 720, 743
  continuity of 653-4
  convalescent 933-4
  direct 420, 899
  individualized 203
  neonatal 260, 705-6
  parental 764, 865
  provision 435, 563, 571, 662, 795, 833, 858, 900, 927
Care facilities 83, 572, 843
  long-term 84, 94-5, 100, 686, 926, 929, 933
Care givers/providers
  of children 745
  primary 221, 348, 553, 557, 616, 664, 686, 689, 726, 865, 899-900
  role of 561
  stress 764, 857
Caregiving 301, 689, 764, 796, 860, 863-6, 870, 904, 937
Carers see Care givers
Carriers (of genetic mutations) 156, 215-16, 280, 341, 348, 354, 713
Case manager 383, 653, 841, 843-4
Case workers 384, 843
Cataracts 236, 246, 279, 685, 706
Causes of developmental disabilities 145, 169, 185, 207, 236, 697, 739 see also Infections, Teratogens
  brain injury 248, 625
  environmental factors 207
  epigenetic factors 145, 207
  genetic factors 207
  maltreatment 752
Cavities, oral 271, 276-7
Celiac disease (CD) 190, 218, 269, 273, 275-6, 285, 291-2, 302, 314, 326, 587-8, 591-2, 685
Cell division (during embryonic and fetal development) see also Meiosis and Mitosis 148, 150-3, 159, 162, 165 170-1
Cells
  daughter 151, 155, 165, 170-1
  diploid 164
  germ 151, 163-4, 170, 180
  nerve 186, 191, 215, 241, 675-6
  non-neural support 186, 202
  somatic 151, 154-5, 164, 180

Central nervous system (CNS) 158, 166, 185, 188-90, 194, 198, 202, 204, 209, 211, 220, 236, 240, 242, 367-8
Cerebral cortex 186, 193-5, 204, 244, 374, 676
Cerebral palsy (CP) 13, 70, 77, 124, 220, 238, 293-304, 425, 529, 585-7, 590-2, 647-9, 706, 931, 937-9
Cerebrospinal fluid (CSF) 185, 187-8, 201-2, 682
Cerebrum 186-7, 193-4
Challenges 45, 47-8, 59, 62-3, 116-17, 329-30, 357-80, 383-4, 441-2, 531, 536, 543-6, 556-8, 709, 856, 894-5
  in adulthood 379-86
  behavioural 334, 857
  inclusive early intervention services 725
  of parenting 401, 910
Challenging behaviours 198, 291, 322, 334, 428, 448, 477, 479, 485, 492, 600-3, 614-16, 644-5, 660, 903-4
  aggressive 573, 670
Challenging families 459-74
  behavioural patterns of 459, 471
  helping 469
Changing perspectives on developmental disabilities 41-52
Changing roles of aging parents 863
Charter 65, 67-8, 73, 75-6, 78-9, 99-101
Charter of Rights and Freedoms 68, 73, 75
Chemicals, environmental 174
Child abuse/neglect 247, 493, 631, 740, 742, 749, 766-9, 922-3
Child and family services 11, 31, 740, 742-4, 748, 768
Child battering 55, 208, 216, 220, 223
Child care
  barriers 737
  centres 723, 727, 730
  private home 727
  service providers 398, 761, 765
  services 735
  training 921
Child development see also Development, Developmental
  health 374, 872, 915
  maltreatment 739-70, 878, 909, 922-3
  psychopathology 457, 668
Child welfare 384, 744, 761, 767-8, 910, 920
  services 740, 742-3, 745, 748, 916
  system 56, 61, 742, 744-5, 768, 910, 932
  workers 749, 764, 914
Childbirth 627, 928
Childhood disintegrative disorder 307, 312, 330
Chorea 163-4, 243
Chorionic villus sampling (CVS) 177-9, 269, 288, 700-2, 714
Chromosomal disorders/syndromes 156
Chromosomes see also Karyotype 287, 291, 353
Creutzfelt-Jacob disease (CJD) 159, 163
Classical lissencephaly (LIS) 244
Clinical dementia 673, 677
Cloning 179-82
Clozapine 607-8
Copy number variations (CNVs) 154-5, 163, 225
Co-ops 813, 818, 823, 825
Cochlea 277, 495-6, 504-5
Cognitive abilities 311-12, 480, 496, 680, 694, 747, 790, 880
Cognitive disabilities 12, 126, 214, 251, 267, 341, 353, 704, 893, 919

Cognitive skills 254, 556, 790
Collaborative team approaches 721, 733-4
Communication
    abilities 121, 496, 498, 500
    aids, voice output 480, 494
    alternative 494, 765
    assessments 488, 648, 478, 504
    competence 490, 493
    complex 480, 486, 493
    deficits 461, 616, 642
    devices 108, 115, 122
    difficulties 329, 477, 494-5, 500, 504, 560, 749, 887
    disabilities 478, 493-4
    disorders 259, 264, 476-7, 493-4, 623, 649, 895
    expressive 126
    facilitated 121, 320
    functional 479, 481
    impairments 314, 476-7, 479, 500, 662, 930
    interventions 477, 494
    methods 480-1, 483, 726
    modes of 481, 483
    non-verbal 329, 518
    partners 477-8, 480-1, 483, 486, 492-3
    picture 272, 453
    professional 778
    profiles 493
    services 494
    skills 41, 272, 481
    styles 518, 520
    systems, personal 491
    written 120, 490
Communicators 478, 480, 482, 503
Community
    activities 47, 467, 851, 891, 902, 913
    agencies 11, 31, 57-8, 60-1, 132, 424, 434, 436, 439, 441, 799-803, 813, 853, 876, 890-2
    building 439, 828
    care 655, 659, 865, 867
    cooperative ventures 828, 906
    environments 9, 754, 826
    experiences 49, 119, 794, 886
    facilities 35, 782
    behaviour therapists 602
    employment 801, 811, 821, 824
    health (centres/care) 504, 708
    homes 833, 837, 839, 841
    inclusion/integration 38, 222, 446, 482, 656, 803, 829, 847-8, 868, 886
    involvement 57, 429, 843-4
    involvement council 827-8
    life/lifestyles 60, 71, 426, 526, 721, 802-3, 839-48, 867, 907
    Networks of Specialized Care 56, 63, 571, 658-60, 663, 902
    nursing 645, 670
    organizations 71, 126, 860
    participation 93, 434, 482, 798, 806, 811, 902
    physicians 319, 322
    placement 31, 602
    practitioners 422, 431, 545, 804, 847
    professionals 310
    programs 37, 252, 350, 725, 737, 798
    psychiatric services 663
    psychiatrist 645, 651
    residences 833, 863, 938
    resources 422, 437, 465, 529, 663, 690, 710
    remote 16, 121
    rural 516, 871
    service organizations 526, 800-2, 804
    service providers 93, 662, 927
    services/supports/resources 37, 56, 58-9, 61-2, 94, 102, 334, 370, 393, 532, 535, 544, 565, 661, 655 835, 852, 791, 799, 801, 803, 807, 828-9, 926, 928
    support personnel, roles 393, 525-34, 540
    Women's Circle 903
    work 802, 826
Competence
    cross-cultural 905
    cultural 510
    individual 48, 832
Complementary & alternative medicine 320-1
Comprehensive assessment 448, 457, 594, 650, 653, 920, 922
Computed tomography see CT
Conception 7, 37, 163, 170-2, 175, 194, 248, 361, 697, 700-1, 719, 734
Conditions, painful 569, 647
Confidentiality 353, 387, 397, 399
Conflict 42, 462, 464, 541-2, 552, 622, 709, 734, 754, 858
Congenital
    heart disease (CHD) 229, 236, 246-7, 258, 270, 273, 285, 287, 928
    hypothyroidism 207, 215, 220, 229-31, 234-5, 259, 280
    rubella syndrome 236, 259
Consent 68, 83, 85-7, 94, 99-102, 347, 542, 551-60, 645, 742-3, 878, 881, 892, 904-6
    obtaining 551, 554, 558
    voluntary 449, 452, 551-3
    withholding 551, 553-5, 557-8
Constipation 250, 257, 275, 278, 296, 314, 555, 555, 562, 571, 576, 588, 624, 647, 929,931
Consultation, multidisciplinary 531-2
Consumers 182, 323, 491, 493, 504, 852, 889
Convulsions see also Seizures, Epilepsy 255-6, 313, 405
Coping 308, 335, 393-4, 398, 413, 461, 466, 468, 472, 512, 645, 689-90, 713, 867, 869-70
    perception-focussed 860
    resources of parents 870
    response 627, 648
Cornelia de Lange syndrome (CdLS) 230-3, 236-7, 259
Cortex 192, 198, 244-5, 326, 502, 674-6
Corticotropin-releasing hormone (CRH) 198
Cortisol 198
Counsel, legal 87-8
Counselling 182, 370, 383-4, 393, 395, 426, 429, 440, 468, 535, 654-5, 873, 875-6, 879-80, 893
    professional 710, 712
    services 30, 383, 439, 880, 917
Couples 88, 179, 332, 335, 463, 471, 531, 704-5, 710-11, 842-4, 881, 893, 903
Court 43-4, 67-8, 71-3, 81-5, 87, 99-101, 743, 763, 897, 910
Creutzfelt-Jacob disease (CJD) 159, 163
Cri du Chat syndrome 213, 237, 259

Crises 460, 462, 534, 538, 540, 556, 570, 645, 650, 652, 654, 661-3, 710, 870
Crisis interventions 449, 653, 767
Computed tomography (CT) 199, 283, 288, 565, 904
Cultural
  background 6, 510-11, 514-16, 520
  differences 511, 517-20, 522, 785
  groups 513, 515, 520, 527, 705, 846, 858
  values 7, 519, 898
Cultures 7, 9, 24, 42-3, 45-6, 49-51, 120-1, 133, 140, 509-11, 513-20, 595, 843, 845-6, 898
  minority 517-18
Current
  services 433, 660
  trends and issues 53-64
Cytoplasm 147, 149, 345

D

Daily living, activities of 20, 89, 93, 95-6, 100-1, 293, 296, 298, 439, 446, 684
Day programs 94, 765, 825, 907, 934, 936
Decisions
  child custody 919
  community-based 55
  person's 86
  responsible 556-7
  right 707, 879
  supported 551, 556, 558
Deinstitutionalization 25, 38-9, 618, 669, 836, 848, 886, 932
Dementia see also Alzheimer's disease 44, 62, 163, 187, 250-1, 285-8, 673-4, 676-7, 680-5, 687-94, 930-1, 933-4, 936-9
  care 690, 936
  causes of 680, 691
  diagnosis of 685, 688, 930, 932
  of the Alzheimer type (DAT) 285-6, 673, 682-7, 691
Dendrites 186, 190, 192, 202
Deoxyribose nucleic acid (DNA) 145-50, 153-4, 157-64, 166-7, 169-71, 178, 181, 222, 242, 289, 312, 344, 352-3, 694, 702
  genes 148
  junk 158-9
  mitochondrial 158, 162, 164-5, 249
  molecules 147-8, 150, 155, 160-1, 164
Depot antipsychotics 608
Depression 242, 256, 334, 382, 394, 410-13, 578-80, 608-11, 627-8, 631-5, 681-2, 685-7, 704, 856, 939
  bipolar 608-10
  major 229, 626-7, 634, 939
  treatment-resistant 603, 609, 611
  treatment 432, 634
Destructive behaviours 455, 457, 633
Development (early, multidisciplinary perspective) 169
Developmental
  assessment (child's) 321
  delays 13, 18, 21-2, 56, 228-9, 344, 387, 390-2, 409, 575-6, 587-8, 719-23, 734, 745, 869-70, 914-15
  history 39, 332, 567-8, 911-12
  level 309, 451, 453, 480, 514
  milestones 169, 176-7, 182-3, 389, 393, 567, 707
  problems 297, 321, 513, 911, 914
Developmental coordination disorder (DCD) 234-5, 238, 259

Developmental disabilities see also Intellectual disabilities
  causes of see Causes of developmental disabilities
  definition of 5-6, 9-11, 22, 41, 110, 572, 659
  diagnosis of 11, 424-6, 441, 515, 707-8
  services 424, 435, 438, 744, 759, 765-6, 932-3
  social meaning of 6, 20
  syndromes and disorders 227
  and women 885-908
Developmental services 56, 58-60, 440-3, 593-5, 655-6, 658-60, 662, 666-7, 824, 835
Developmental service workers (DSWs) 469, 535, 562
Devices see also Assistive devices 122, 408, 479-80, 487, 501, 580, 586, 714
Diabetes 157, 159, 171, 174, 217, 219, 236, 242, 247, 249, 280, 414, 607, 631, 677-8
Diagnosis 419
  of developmental disability 11
  early 244, 273-4, 359, 369, 371, 380, 392
  of FASD in adults 379
  genetic see Genetic, testing for; Syndromes and disorders
  of mental disorders 420, 432, 559, 639, 668
  preimplantation genetic diagnosis 179, 719
  prenatal 352, 701
Diagnostic and statistical manual of mental disorders
  definition of developmental disability 10
Diagnostic overshadowing 565, 601, 618, 643, 645, 670, 856
Diagnostic manual-intellectual disabilities see DM-ID
Diet 162, 173, 217, 237, 248, 277-8, 336, 393, 407-8, 576, 586, 588, 678, 716, 844
Dietary intake 218, 575-7, 584, 587-8
Digestion 189, 257
Dignity 37, 40, 66-7, 70-2, 448, 552, 559, 690, 721, 816, 844
Diploid number 151, 208
Disabilities/Disability
  resources 847
  service organizations 543, 545
  services 115, 436, 440-1, 529-30, 532, 546, 865, 872, 920, 935
  social model of 24, 36, 46, 48-9, 110, 126, 752
  support program 101
  support work 428
  support workers 440, 526
Disability personnel 525-48
  individual 536
  ongoing training of 536-7
  role of 531, 533-5, 537, 539
  work 526, 531-2, 534, 540, 543
Disability professionals 423, 441, 530, 535, 538, 851
Disclosure 333, 394, 397, 399, 402, 413, 552, 709, 746, 748-9, 753, 755, 759-60, 763, 765
Discrimination 10, 46-7, 50, 65-72, 75-7, 113, 124, 182, 222, 395-7, 414, 446, 528, 754, 886
Disease
  autoimmune 174, 588
  cardiovascular 198-9, 517, 577, 677-8, 895, 928-9, 931
  communicable 396-7, 925
  dental/periodontal 278, 285, 570
  prion 160, 167
Disorders see also Genetics; Syndromes; specific disorders
  acute stress 628-9

auditory processing 478, 496, 504, 506
binge-eating 630-1
dominant 165-6, 589
endocrine 570, 629, 697
mood 382, 601, 623, 626, 634, 647, 651
multifactorial 157, 626
neurobehavioural 290
obsessive compulsive 249, 624, 629, 652
panic 608, 629
physical 629-30, 649
post-traumatic stress 199, 203, 262, 602, 629, 762, 767
psychological 621
psychotic 600-1, 623, 625, 651-2
recessive 163, 243, 247-8
respiratory 570, 629
schizoaffective 626
substance-related 623-4
Disturbances, emotional 412, 554, 618, 641-3, 648, 650, 665, 670
Diversity 48, 509-23, 722, 731, 906
of cultural backgrounds 510, 512-13, 515, 520
effects on psychological assessment and intervention 509
DM-ID 431-2, 622, 639, 653, 669
Dolly, the cloned sheep 180
Dominant genes 156
Dopamine 603, 608-9
Down syndrome (DS) 24, 72, 124-5, 153, 177, 210-11, 214-15, 263, 493, 506-7, 546, 700-1, 856-7, 907, 927-8, 930-1, 937-9
Alzheimer's disease/dementia 673-94
health issues 267-93
DR m TAP 595-6
Drugs 100, 154, 173-4, 335, 372-6, 411, 429, 439-40, 541, 594-5, 608-12, 625, 634-5, 680-1, 688
antiseizure 406, 414-15
therapy 228, 258, 392, 406-8, 578, 580
Dual diagnosis 286, 382, 384, 426, 439, 601, 619, 638, 641-2, 656-61, 664, 665-7, 669, 882-4, 904
Dynamic assessment 513-14, 522, 787
Dysphagia 564, 576-8, 580, 583, 586

E
Eardrum 277, 297, 495, 497
Early childhood
education 535, 735-6, 738, 771, 872
educators 299, 719, 724, 726-7, 731, 733-4, 748
inclusion 735-6
intervention 706, 735
programs/services 424, 507, 721-2, 726-7, 729, 734
resource consultants 724, 736
settings 721, 726-7, 733, 736-8
teacher network 722, 735-6
workers 526
Early intervention
effectiveness of 921
for young children 719-38
in Ontario 720-1, 725
practices 735, 738
strategies for parents and therapists 315
worker 323

Early life 325, 697-718
Ears 244, 246, 256, 276-7, 342-3, 349, 495, 497-8, 505
Eating disorders 608, 623-4, 630-1, 746, 762
Edema 255-6, 278, 582-3, 589
Education 76, 771, 789
boards of 778-9
child's 785
continuing 782, 866
formal 537, 543, 545, 678
individual 711
parent 723
plan 412, 734, 787
professional 221
services, special 58, 490, 656, 735, 745, 785
sexual 873
system 323, 348, 773, 857, 932
Education and training 804-6, 808, 827, 883
of disability personnel 525, 535
of young children 721, 736
Educational assistants 412, 486, 782-3
Educators 107, 301, 341, 409, 421, 663, 773, 783, 785, 787, 799-800, 856, 877
Electroencephalogram (EEG) 200, 228, 258, 310, 313, 405, 407
Effects, placebo 431, 613-14, 618
Efferents 188-9, 202
Eggs (ova), fertilized 166, 170
Electrical impulses 191-2, 202, 603
Embryo 148, 155, 157-8, 163, 170, 172-3, 175, 181, 196, 208, 345, 358, 363-4, 705
Embryonic stem cells 181, 364
Emergency
department staff 555
psychiatric services 669-70
Emotional
harm 742-3, 745, 747, 756, 760
responses 644, 650, 653-4, 749, 854
support 392-4, 468, 700-1, 839, 844, 899-900
Emotions (biological basis) see also Amygdala, Limbic system 192-3, 195, 311, 628,
Empirically supported treatments (ESTs) 130
Employees, supported 820-2, 826, 829
Employers 68-9, 306, 323, 413, 469, 536, 540, 713, 791, 801-3, 805, 814, 819-22, 826, 829
Employment see also Work
competitive 90, 807, 811, 825-6
benefits 91
consultation 90
programs 813, 824-5
supported 821, 825
support 88, 90, 99, 102-3, 803, 813-14, 825-7, 890
Enclave 826
Energy requirements 584-8, 592
Entitlements 20, 57, 60-1, 73, 99-100, 535, 633, 710, 740, 776
for individuals 75-104
Environmental assessment 450, 452
Environmental factors and developmental disabilities see Causes of developmental disabilities
Enzyme 156, 159, 163-4, 166, 239, 243, 248-9, 251, 609

Epigenetic mechanisms/processes 145, 155, 160, 162, 170-1, 173, 183, 213, 222, 226
Epigenetics 145-6, 155, 159-60, 162, 183, 225, 637, 640
Epilepsy see also Seizures 44, 217, 244, 255, 261, 313, 405-6, 408, 410-15, 515, 522-3, 564-5, 570, 634-5, 930
   child's 411-2
   idiopathic 406
   syndromes 406
   treatment of 313, 413, 609, 930
   uncontrolled 410, 412-13
Equality 8, 46-7, 67-8, 71, 76, 79, 108, 113, 115, 733, 867, 898
   rights 48, 99. 854
Era(s) 26-7, 804, 926
   post-asylum 26
Estrogen replacement therapy (ERT) 257
Esophagus 190, 237, 258, 274-6, 576, 589
Estrogen replacement therapy (ERT) 257
Ethical
   dilemmas 169, 542, 875, 882-3, 920, 922
   issues of consent in treatment/care 551-60
   objections 181
Ethics 538-40, 545, 551-3, 558-9
Ethnicity 121, 509, 520, 522-3, 639, 885, 906
Etiology 143, 209, 288, 497, 570, 621, 623
   factor(s) 209-11
Eugenics 33, 39, 773, 834
Evaluation 60, 129-42, 224, 253, 264, 283, 325, 401-2, 431, 454-5, 498, 546, 729, 852-3
   diagnostic 198, 204, 642
   and program planning 141-2
   designs 133, 138-9
   of mental retardation 224, 668
   of quality services for people with disabilities 546
   plans 133
   questions 132-3, 136-8
Evidence based medicine (EBM) 612
Evidence-based practice (EBP) 129-31, 140-2, 264, 326, 480, 494, 499, 538, 793, 807
Examination 77, 273, 332, 347, 563, 566-9, 649, 686, 702, 765, 768, 915
Examinee/Examiner 512-14
Exceptional
   children 371, 735-6, 738, 788, 805
   pupils 775-7, 780, 787
   students 12, 440, 775, 777-8, 780-1, 783-4, 787, 840
Expressive language 8, 242, 271, 566, 731
Externalizing behaviours 477, 500
Eyelids 173, 246, 278-9, 407

F

Facial dysmorphology see Syndromes; specific syndromes and disorders 230, 243, 367-8
Facilities, residential 30-1, 904
Factors
   cultural 44, 109, 217, 383, 517-18
   social 10, 212, 519, 601, 637, 911-12
Families 57-62, 320-4, 387-403, 433-8, 461-72, 526-31, 533-5, 710-13, 719-27, 729-35, 789-800, 835-46, 855-60, 863-72, 888-94
   helping 465, 732, 867

   older 871, 933
   poor 7, 929
   single-parent 463 530, 533, 759
   traditional 517, 722, 898-9
   women's role 765, 891
Family
   -directed planning 436
   environments, supportive 527, 839
   history 215, 217, 269, 311, 319, 347, 567-8, 648, 652, 913
   homes 20, 62, 322, 526, 530, 533, 744, 750, 755, 759, 763, 840, 842, 863
   interventions 249, 473
   life and developmental disability 851-72
   physicians 59, 221, 348, 352, 377, 398, 526, 554, 556-7, 561, 570, 625, 660, 700
   -professional partnerships 736, 738
   quality 436, 533, 545-7, 714, 738, 804, 807, 858, 869, 938-9
   resource program 719-20, 724-5, 858, 870
   service 63, 253, 471, 723, 734, 742-4, 768
   support 322, 439, 691, 713, 743
   therapists 468-9, 631
   therapy 335, 339, 429, 469, 471, 624, 637, 901, 906
   well-being 533-4, 792
Fathers 147, 154, 162, 171, 179, 214, 346, 353-4, 515, 749-50, 759, 763, 832, 865-6, 899
FBA (functional behavioural assessment) 319, 449, 451
Feeding 90, 237, 243, 245, 257, 388, 576-7, 584, 586-7, 589, 592, 623, 647, 682, 684
   oral 586
   behaviours 193, 586
   problems 245, 253, 388, 570, 575, 587-8, 590-2, 754
Fertility 183, 285, 413, 704-5, 714, 716
Fetal alcohol spectrum disorder (FASD) see also Alcohol 56, 61, 63, 175, 213, 357-86, 527, 752
   adulthood challenges 379-386
   assessment 382
   in children 357-79
   diagnosis of 357, 365, 368-9, 379-80, 384
Fetal alcohol syndrome (FAS) 196, 359-61, 363-8, 371-7, 379-80, 385, 425, 878
Fetal development 169, 199, 274, 358, 498, 799, 752 see also Fetus, Embryo
Fetal cells 177, 702
Fetus 49, 173, 175-9, 194, 197, 199, 205, 209, 214, 218-20, 236, 244, 269, 288, 357-8, 361-4, 697-703
Field workers 541
Financial assistance 57, 90-1, 97, 350, 382, 690, 839-40
Fistula, tracheoesophageal 273-4, 276
FMR1 gene/protein see also Fragile X syndrome 341-2, 344-7, 351, 354
Focus groups 132, 138
Folic acid/folate 157, 194, 217, 223, 225, 287, 678-9, 681, 684-6, 698-700
Food intake 578-9, 584
Food textures 314, 576, 586-7
Forensic mental health system 898
Formal assessment 421, 423-5, 430, 433
Fragile X syndrome (FXS) 155, 157-8, 160, 163, 171, 208, 215, 221-2, 310, 341-56, 425-6, 857, 870-1

Fragile X tremor ataxia syndrome (FXTAS) 345, 351, 355
Freedom, personal 19, 448
Friendships 122, 333-4, 429, 482, 566, 649, 654, 710, 726, 861, 887-8, 891, 900-1, 905-6, 908
Front line 594-5, 597, 726, 796
   personnel 535-6
   professionals 428, 593-7
   workers 420-1, 532-3, 616
Frontal lobes 192-3, 196, 364
Function
   cognitive 11, 203, 214, 222, 681, 685-6
   communicative 476, 479, 486, 502
   neurobehavioural 222, 288, 635
Functional
   abilities 380, 684, 930, 935-6
   analysis 448, 453, 455, 457
   assessment 134, 319, 384, 451-2, 455, 780-1, 787, 806
   behavioural assessment see FBA
   capacity 576, 578-9, 586-7
   communication training 453, 456, 457, 479
Funding 54-8, 60, 71, 77, 95-6, 487, 490-1, 529-30, 545, 784, 801-2, 813-14, 822, 854-5
   model 784
   special education in Ontario 771
   sources 54, 491-2, 814

G

Gametes 151-2, 163-4, 170
Gamma amino butyric acid (GABA) 191, 200, 610
Ganglia, basal 193-4, 242-3, 254
Gastric emptying, delayed 576, 585
Gastroesophageal reflux disease (GERD) 237, 243, 250, 258, 565, 570, 576, 589
Gastrointestinal problems 250, 273, 314
   575-6, 578, 588
Gastrostomy tube 297, 584-5
Gender identity disorders 623, 630
Gene therapy 180, 183, 353, 429
Generalized anxiety disorder 601-2, 629, 639
Generic services 8, 58, 424, 532, 646, 761, 846
Genes 145-51, 153-8, 160-4, 170-2, 210, 213-15, 221-2, 225-6, 243, 248-50, 287, 311-12, 341, 344-5, 353-4
Genetic(s) 145
   abnormalities 157, 209, 214, 228-9
   inheritance patterns 156
   counselling 179, 228-9, 236-9, 243, 245-6, 249, 251, 349, 353, 527, 700, 703, 710, 713, 938
   counsellors 71, 253, 353, 699-702
   defects 171, 178-80, 704
   preimplantation diagnosis 179, 715, 717
   disabilities/disorders see Syndromes; specific syndromes or disorders
   material 151, 165-6, 180-1, 310, 353-4
   recombination 150-1, 164
   testing 158, 703, 716-17
Genome(s) 154, 157, 159, 163-4, 180, 263, 637
Genomic imprinting 162, 164-5, 169, 171, 259
Genotype 228-9, 236-57, 693
Gestation 172, 175-7, 220, 241, 274, 358-9, 362-4, 701

Gestures 121, 308, 331-2, 453, 476, 479-81, 485, 518, 520, 607, 647, 842
Global memory problems 409
Glucose 187-8, 191, 198, 200
Goals 55-6, 71, 107-8, 114-15, 132, 317-19, 369-70, 452-3, 481-3, 585, 651-2, 731-4, 799-800, 842-3
   individualized 316, 727
   personal 422, 710, 798
Grandparents 336, 437, 461, 856, 865, 870
Gray matter (brain) 186, 193-4, 196, 202
Grey zone 345-6
Grief 429, 460-1, 465, 470-2, 685, 709-10, 713, 917, 929, 932, 936
Group homes 37-8, 61-2, 70, 73, 93, 306, 439, 526, 541, 554, 644, 685-6, 689, 755, 802, 881, 937-8
Groups
   lifestyles of 831
   professional 59, 490
   regional parental 35
   self-advocate 21, 119
   sibling-parent 712
   special interest research 533, 573
   supported 439
   women's 887
Growth 25, 53, 57, 109, 151, 214, 254-5, 269-70, 358-9, 575-7, 581-3, 591-2, 719-20, 772-3, 798. 832, 858, 902
Growth charts 270, 290, 591
Growth retardation 175, 357, 359, 367, 583
Guardian 82-6, 394, 452, 552, 796, 799

H

Hallucinations 600, 625-6, 628, 633, 682, 684
Handicapped children 769, 774, 799, 805, 904, 906
Head circumference 228, 380, 388, 581, 583
Health see also Syndromes 39-40, 94-5, 260-1, 401-2, 549, 555-6, 566, 571-3, 655-63, 665-7, 839, 894-5, 921-3, 925-7, 931-8
   children's 225, 334, 387-8, 886, 915
   guidelines, physical 570
   history, individual 595
   in Down syndrome 267-92
   mental 157, 267, 619, 624
   physical 201, 290, 362, 527, 561-74, 579, 636, 647, 650, 654, 691, 840, 852, 885, 912
   professionals 89, 179, 222-3, 288, 297, 301, 348, 388, 553, 556-7, 596, 645, 653, 699, 861
   promotion 49, 141, 562, 680, 716, 804, 847-9
   and Quality of Life outcomes 338, 376
   record 566-7
Health service providers 398
Health services 17, 20, 438, 527, 933, 938
   mental 56, 661
Health watch Tables 348, 571
Health care
   access 566, 572
   decisions 49, 558, 560
   effective 561-2, 565-6, 570-1, 665, 682, 936
   guidelines 276, 498
   interventions 552, 559
   practitioner 86-7, 369, 563, 571, 662

primary 569, 647, 859
professionals 47, 59, 277, 368, 370, 552, 561, 597, 666, 748, 765, 882, 884
providers 369, 395, 412, 552-5, 558, 561-3, 565, 567-71, 582, 594, 662, 714, 800
sectors 926, 934
services 96, 352, 529, 661, 934
settings 305, 562
systems 60, 321, 370-1, 486, 561, 565, 661, 927
team approach 402
workers 118
women's 895
Healthy
babies 217, 225, 723-4, 737
children 723-4, 737
families 466
lifestyles 699, 839
Hearing 17, 69-70, 87, 90, 126, 188, 195, 199, 201, 218, 424-5, 495-6, 498, 500-1, 504-5
assessment 285, 349, 478, 495-6, 500, 507, 685
disabilities 244
services in schools 494
Hearing loss 229, 258, 277-8, 290, 292, 296-7, 496-9, 501, 504, 507, 685, 896
conductive 239, 277, 349, 496, 498-9
mixed 496, 498
permanent 496, 498
Heart 71-2, 105, 109, 121, 166, 172, 175, 187, 239-40, 252, 255-7, 273-4, 288-9, 293, 367
disease 171, 273, 343, 414
rate 188-9, 240, 568
Height 29, 270, 282, 380, 388, 391, 577, 580, 582-4, 592, 629
velocity 577, 582, 592
Helplessness, learned 554-5, 758, 840
Hemiplegia 238, 295-6, 298
Hemispheres, brain 193-5, 407, 410
HIV see Human immunodeficiency virus
Hippocampus 193-4, 196, 200, 410
Hirshsprung disease 275
Hitting 254, 446-7, 450
Home care 537, 690-1
community-group 450, 743, 852
home environment 254, 297, 912, 915-16
home culture 518
safety 915-16, 922
support services 750
Homeless 749, 753, 891, 903
Hormones 183, 189, 191, 193-4, 201-2, 205, 229, 280, 314
Housing 7, 38, 47, 72, 75-6, 97-100, 102, 108, 439, 532, 663, 751, 753, 844, 904
designated 97-8
projects 97
supportive 61, 78, 93
Hypothalamus-pituitary-adrenal (HPA) axis 196-9, 201
Human Genome Project (HGP) 55, 146, 159, 180, 182, 287
Human immunodeficiency virus (HIV)
78, 179, 197, 218, 387-403, 699-700, 716, 756, 877, 913
in children and effects on families 387-404
diagnosis 394, 397, 399, 401-2

infection 60, 179, 387-92, 394-7, 400-3, 531, 681, 697, 699, 882-3
program staff 398
related symptoms 388
Human rights 8, 19, 41, 47-50, 65-7, 69-72, 108, 739
Board of Inquiry in Ontario 70
Code 738
education 69, 71
framework 48
laws 47, 66-7, 71-2
legal support 76, 101-2
model 45, 47
perspectives 27, 42, 45, 48-9
provisions 48
Tribunal 69-70, 76
Human services 37, 40, 384, 547, 828-9
professionals 545, 937
Humanitarianism 831-2
Hurler syndrome 222, 231, 239, 251, 260
Hygiene, personal 94, 381
Hypothalamus 193-4, 197, 199, 631
Hypothyroidism 208, 218, 220, 236, 242, 278, 280, 681, 685, 856, 930
Hypotonia 229, 240, 242-3, 248-9, 258, 269, 283
Hypoxic-ischemic encephalopathy (HIE) 234-5, 240, 260
Hunter syndrome 213, 215, 238, 251, 259

I

ICD-10 classification of mental and behavioural disorders 670
Ideal body weight 580, 583, 585, 589
Idiocy 26, 43-4, 51, 847
Idiots 4, 20, 23, 25-6, 28-30, 43, 50-1, 291
Isolated lissencephaly sequence (ILS) 244-5
Immune system 198, 201, 218, 388, 620, 628, 679, 697-8
Immunizations 236, 392, 567, 570
Impairments, physical 8, 91, 121, 528, 653
Imprinting, genomic see Development, Genomic, Genetics
Impulsive behaviour 611, 643, 652, 758
In-service training 536, 726
Incapable person 82-7, 109
Incapacity 80-3, 87, 556
Inclusion 47, 50, 54-5, 71, 105-6, 329-30, 336-7, 526, 530, 534, 712, 721-2, 725-6, 733-5, 737-8, 842-5, 889, 902
Inclusive
early intervention services 721
education 68, 528, 721, 736-8, 786-7, 903
programs 723, 725-6
Income 75, 88, 91-2, 97-8, 101, 103, 798, 839, 890
support 88-91, 99-100, 438-9, 814, 904
Independence, legal 796
Individual education plan (IEP) 333, 490, 711, 727, 737, 776, 778-85, 787, 798
Individualized
funding 56-7, 60, 528, 659, 664, 814, 824, 826
in Ontario 828
service goals 135
transition support plans 806
Industrialization 43, 741, 834
Industry, pharmaceutical 599, 614

Infants see Babies, Young children
Infections 176, 188, 197-8, 216, 220-1, 234-6, 247, 276, 278, 280-1, 388, 395-6, 699-700, 704-5, 928
Informal behavioural interventions 453
Informal supports 433-4, 846,869, 910, 913
Information processing
    auditory 498
    sensory 188
Informed consent 86, 112, 269, 552-6, 559, 569-71
Inheritance, genetic 145, 155, 156, 157, 229, 251, 258, 346, 406, 464
Injury, hypoxic ischemic 300-1
Inpatient services 645, 654, 660
Insomnia 313-14, 609, 611, 631, 685
    fatal familial 159, 163
Instability, atlantoaxial 282-3
Institutional
    care 43-4, 434, 528, 621, 648, 740, 936
    child abuse 760
    settings 269, 743, 755, 759, 928
Institutionalization 25-6, 38-9, 119, 533, 743, 771, 773, 878, 912, 933
Institutions 25-6, 29, 32-3, 35, 37-9, 55, 61-2, 123-5, 397, 664, 741-3, 759-60, 771-3, 810-11, 832-4
Intake worker 515
Integration 58, 79, 315, 348, 480, 532, 657, 736, 776, 778, 783, 828-9, 843-6, 848, 859-61
Intellectual disabilities see also Developmental disabilities
    causes and contributing factors 207
    definition of 9
    global 383
    health 692
    history of 42
    mild 31, 515, 541, 909
    severe 286, 527, 643, 668, 802, 829, 907
Intellectual disability psychiatry 639, 667, 669
Intellectual impairment 13, 207, 216, 218, 220, 688
Intelligence 29, 33, 48, 50, 120, 186, 195-6, 256, 311, 380, 382, 392, 410, 513, 772
Intelligence tests 424, 512-13, 772, 780, 875, 878
Intensive behavioural intervention (IBI) 213, 426, 440, 663, 723, 725, 854-5, 869
    program 663
International perspectives 443, 547, 807-8, 906, 939
Intervention(s) 129, 419, 445-9, 453-7, 476, 509
    approaches 228-9, 236-57, 316, 520
    aversive 457
    behavioural 137, 323, 370, 440, 455, 663
    child protection 744
    childhood depression 130
    comprehensive educational 316
    early 18, 45, 56, 177, 182, 315, 322-3, 711, 720-3, 725, 729, 733-4, 779
    early intensive behavioural 314-15, 426
    educational 318, 923
    evaluation of 325
    individualized 720, 722
    neurosurgical 252, 283
    new 131, 288, 429
    nonpharmacological 602, 615-16

pharmaceutical 852
plan 319, 453, 731, 915
process 518, 520, 732-3
programs 371, 729, 731
psychoeducational 370
in school and clinic 787
services 663, 720
strategies 349, 420, 486, 531, 690
techniques 428, 781
Interviews 77, 82, 124, 132, 138, 451, 470, 579, 685-6, 763, 785, 843, 848, 935
Intestines, small 288, 588-9
Intractable epilepsy 405, 432
    co-morbidities of 412
Intraventricular hemorrhage (IVH) 176, 234-5, 241, 260
Introduction to
    assessment, diagnosis, intervention, services 419
    early development 169
    intellectual/developmental disabilities 5
    genetics 145
    nervous systems 185
    services/service systems in Ontario 433-444
Intrusiveness 452-3, 484-5, 602
Iodide 217-18
Iodine deficiency 174, 208, 211, 213, 215, 218, 220, 229-31, 234-6, 280, 698
IQ scores 382, 424, 772
Iron 213-14, 216-18, 430, 432, 588, 624, 640, 678-9, 698
    deficiency 211, 214, 218-19, 698
Ischemic stroke 246
Isolated lissencephaly sequence see ILS
Isotretinoin 174-5, 183

J
Jaw 253, 256, 342-3
Jerking 289, 405, 407
Jobs 67-9, 77-8, 100, 112, 306, 413-14, 535-7, 540-1, 790-1, 810-11, 813-16, 818-24, 843-4, 887, 890
Joints 239, 243, 282, 342-4, 349, 388, 603
Joy 460, 465, 627, 713

K
Karyotype 153, 164, 289
Ketogenic diet 407-8, 415
Key
    concepts for a healthy lifestyle 839
    components of transition services 789-90
    Ontario Ministries 55-7, 439
    Ontario services 433
    services 125, 767
Klinefelter syndrome 156, 164, 212, 214, 233, 241, 260
Knees 278, 282, 344, 685
Kwashiorkor 217

L
Labelling/labels 24-5, 38, 42, 48, 107, 113-14, 116, 117-20, 122-3, 179, 316, 321, 352, 369, 426, 579, 777-8, 782, 815
Labour 92, 169, 175-6, 197, 218, 220
Lafora's disease 249-50, 636
Lamotrigine 406, 609-10

Landlord 96-7, 387
Language 19, 23-4, 26, 42, 44, 106, 108-10, 115-16, 199-201,
  237-8, 330-1, 476-7, 500-3, 509, 511-13
  assessment 477-8, 500
  components of 476-7, 502-3
  and communication disorders 263
  development 299, 301, 348, 350, 477, 493, 511-12, 544,
    705, 738
  difficulties 478, 482, 491, 495, 501-2, 725, 763
  disorders 476-7, 482, 493, 504, 507
  expressive 271, 427, 480, 730, 783
  intervention 272, 478-9
  and learning disabilities 296, 493
  parent training 299
  programs 506, 723. 735
  receptive 272, 479, 512
  sign 121, 228, 237, 318, 476-7, 500, 503, 719, 728-9, 733
  spoken 76, 195, 476, 512
  verbal 728, 730
  skills 11, 93, 271, 332, 684
  training program 350
Laws 8, 24, 40-1, 43-4, 65-73, 75-6, 79-80, 93, 99-100, 551-2,
  558-9, 721-2, 739-40, 774-5
  Canadian and Ontario 630
Lead 223
Learning
  abilities 11, 93, 218, 348, 425
  difficulties 13, 18, 126, 256, 352, 412, 636, 746, 767, 807,
    914, 920-3
  disabilities (LDs) 4, 15, 18, 203-4, 333, 336, 338, 365, 432,
    515, 558-9, 572-3, 598, 653, 667, 670, 778-9, 790, 804-5,
    807
  disorders 623, 777
Legislated rights 111, 113
Legislation 13, 18-20, 43, 71, 73, 551, 658-9, 744, 761, 774,
  777-9, 798, 825, 852-3
Legs 164, 172, 236-8, 250, 252, 255, 257, 278, 289, 294-5, 297,
  631
Lesch-Nyhan syndrome 155, 157, 164, 215, 233, 242, 260
Leukemia 247, 270, 281, 285
  659, 661-2
Life expectancy 26, 246, 249, 258, 270, 273, 336, 563, 673,
  682-3, 927-8, 930-1, 937
Life skills 131, 316, 425, 792-3, 795, 800, 840
Lifespan perspective 329-40
Lifestyles 6, 357-8, 525, 528, 530, 654, 832, 877
  of adults in Ontario 831-50
Limbic system 193-5, 202
Lissencephaly (LIS) 244
Lithium 174, 609-10, 616, 640
Living conditions 35-6, 59, 112, 552, 773
Living skills, daily 381, 384-5, 422, 450, 685, 689, 834, 839
Lobes, brain
  occipital 192-3
  parietal 192-3, 364
Logic models 134, 136-7, 141-2
Long term care 62, 101-3, 486, 655, 716, 723, 737, 931, 933-4
Longevity 288, 683, 694
Low birth weight 201, 220, 256-7, 362, 367, 379, 496, 499,
  697, 714, 716, 913

Lungs 166, 172, 218, 240-1, 255, 274, 297, 576, 584, 586
Lymph 187
Lymphocytes 187, 197-8
Lyonization 154-5, 162, 164, 171

M
Mabry syndrome 231, 237, 243, 260
Magnetic resonance imaging (MRI) 199-200, 205, 244, 289,
  295, 301, 310, 325, 327, 380, 565, 567, 682-3
Major depressive disorder 602, 627, 651, 929
Maltreatment 751, 757, 768
Malaria 216, 697
Malnutrition 60, 208, 211, 213, 217, 223-4, 275, 388, 575-7,
  580, 583, 588-9, 624
Malocclusion 277, 349
Maltreatment 494, 530, 546, 739, 744-5, 747, 749-66, 768-9,
  840, 896
  of children 546, 740, 754, 757, 761, 764, 766, 768
Managers 28-9, 132-3, 136-7, 140, 459, 461-3, 465-6, 468,
  471-2, 525, 532, 540, 645
Mania 44, 603, 610, 612, 627, 652
Marasmus 217
Marriage 112, 333, 338, 540-1, 711, 878-9, 891-3
Masturbation 630, 877, 879
Maternal stress 199
Meals 96, 101, 517, 576-8, 584-5, 587, 841-2, 894
Media 12, 14, 16-17, 71, 335, 797, 853, 856, 888
Mediators 70, 135-7, 468, 748, 855, 871
Medical see also Conditions, Disorders, Syndromes
  care 49, 93, 112, 213, 264, 322, 754, 798, 832, 884, 928, 930
  information 72, 89
  intervention 49, 209, 429, 498, 702
  procedures 554-5
  services 516, 571, 844, 935
  treatment 75, 80, 84, 182, 253, 313, 394, 742, 745
Medication
  administration 95, 594-5, 616
  change 644
  errors 595, 598
  practice 594-7
  support plans 593
Medications see Syndromes; specific conditions, syndromes
  or disorders
  anticonvulsant 313, 406-7, 412, 576, 610
  antipsychotic 600, 603, 608, 635, 645, 651
  effects of 385, 616
  individual receiving 596
  and psychiatric diagnoses 600
Meiosis 145, 150-2, 164-5, 242, 268, 289
Memory 192-5, 201, 204-5, 219, 225, 267, 289, 291, 365, 380,
  392, 407, 410, 681, 686-9
  working 375, 624
Memory problems 389, 410, 610
Mending broken spirits 459-74
Meninges 185-6, 188, 202, 244
Meningitis 176, 188, 197, 202-3, 216, 220, 235, 239, 244, 247,
  260, 294, 499, 505
Mental and behavioural disorders 622
Mental disabilities 4, 12, 14, 51, 68, 70, 88, 493, 500, 560, 721,
  886, 934

definition of 12
Mental disorders 10, 23, 44, 50, 63, 76, 100, 238, 259, 337, 431-2, 619-23, 633-4, 636, 638-9, 689
Mental health 375, 393, 428-9, 554, 638-9, 645-6, 655-6, 659-62, 664-7, 839-40, 870-1, 881-5, 896, 903-4, 929
    good 461, 471
    assessment 646
    disorders 201, 207, 221, 368, 371, 471, 839, 898
    problems 62, 255, 334-6, 358, 361, 363, 365, 376, 382-4, 440, 559, 603, 668, 670, 901
    professionals 258, 319, 621, 646, 661-2
    program 660-1, 663
    sectors 664, 886
    service system 641, 655, 663
    services 56, 64, 427, 440, 601-2, 639, 641, 645-6, 655, 657-8, 661-3, 665-6, 669, 753
    systems 331, 532, 903
    teams 651, 663, 670
    workers 601, 617
Mental ill-health 222-3, 362, 456, 617, 619, 621, 636, 638, 641-72, 913
    treatment of 641, 653, 665
    disorders 221-3
Mental retardation, definition of 10
Mercury 175, 182, 219, 221, 223, 312
Metabolic disorders 164, 179, 310, 647
Metabolic programming 169, 171
Methyl groups 160, 162, 171
Methylphenidate 320, 326, 611
Microglia 186, 192, 197-8, 202
Mild cognitive impairment (MCI) 516, 678, 680-1
Milk 430, 698
    mother's breast 389-90
Miller-Dieker syndrome (MDS) 244-5
Minimum wage 113, 819-20, 822, 825
Ministries see Ontario
Miscarriages 175, 178, 208, 218, 220, 256, 269, 362, 698, 701
Misdiagnoses 321, 347, 652-3, 856-7
Mitochondria 147-8, 158, 164-5, 181, 190
Mitosis 145, 150-1, 155, 165, 170, 289
Mobile work crew 811, 815, 822, 826
Mobility 8, 90, 293, 295, 298-9, 389, 424, 531, 577, 580-1, 587, 684, 929-30
Models 46, 50, 61, 109, 123, 137, 140, 483, 485, 732, 792-3, 855, 890, 910-12, 918-19
    community adjustment 792
    individual pathology 111, 113
    mediator 851-2, 855-6
    mouse 287, 351, 354
    professionally-centred 731-2
    social 8, 24, 36, 46-9, 110, 126
    transition services 807
Modifications, environmental 393, 490
Money 7, 54, 61, 66, 69, 97, 110, 112, 132, 321, 324, 383, 464, 809-10, 817-18
Mood stabilizers 603, 606, 609, 616, 632
Mortality 241, 245, 572, 692-4, 925, 928, 938-9
Mosaicism 153, 155, 165, 268

Mothers 171-3, 218-21, 361-3, 388-90, 699-700, 702, 735, 753, 759, 763, 765, 832-3, 865-6, 869-70, 887-8, 898-901, 906, 921-3
    new 710
    pregnant 219-20, 698
Motor
    disorders 241, 293
    skills 237, 272, 367, 422, 424-5, 447, 578, 586-7, 680
Movement disorders 245, 429, 607-8
Mucopolysaccharide disorders (MPS) disorders 238-40, 239, 251, 259
Multidisciplinary
    assessment 644-5
    perspective 169-84, 207
Muscles 158, 165, 172, 188, 198, 217, 295, 297-8, 353, 589, 607, 684
Mutations 154, 156, 158, 163-5, 200, 214-15, 228, 237, 239, 242-6, 312, 343-7, 352-4, 678, 713
Myotonic dystrophy 156, 158, 165
Myths
    about HIV transmission 391
    about child abuse 753
    about sexuality and disabilities 873

N
Natural speech production 483
Nausea 234, 244, 255, 275, 388, 568, 576-8, 580, 588, 608-10
Neglect 119, 361, 383, 464, 493, 537, 570, 631, 744-5, 747-9, 751-2, 756-7, 759, 766-9, 893-4
    pattern of 742-3
Neonatal encephalopathy (NE) 234-5, 240, 260, 294-5
Nerve cell bodies 186, 189, 202
Nervous systems 185, 357, 620, 676
    autonomic 185, 188-9, 194-5, 255, 628
    central 158, 185, 209, 211, 220, 349, 358, 388, 405
    enteric 185, 188, 190, 204
    peripheral 165, 185-6, 188
    somatic 188
    sympathetic and parasympathetic 189-90
Neural tube defects 157, 175, 177, 179, 210, 217, 219, 221, 225, 698-701
Neurobehavioural assessment of children 431
Neurofibromatosis 210-11, 245-6, 261, 310
Neurogenesis 193-4, 200-1, 204-5
Neurological
    disorders 199, 238, 254, 260-2, 287, 405, 629, 634-5, 638
    impairment 576-8, 586-7, 647, 649, 896
    problems 333, 388-9
    symptoms 240, 283
Neuronal ceroid lipofuscinosis (NCL) 249-50
Neuronal migration disorders 230-1, 233, 235, 244, 261
Neurons 186, 189-93, 195, 197, 202-3, 208, 228, 241, 351, 355, 405, 410, 603, 610, 674-5
Neuropsychological assessment 685-6
Neurotransmitters 185, 190-1, 193, 200-2, 365, 603, 608-9, 676, 688
New challenges 62, 105, 220, 530, 532, 804
Newborns 197, 203, 214-15, 217, 219-21, 224, 234, 236, 240, 247, 249, 280-1, 285, 287, 706
Nobel Prize in physiology 147, 150, 158-9

Non-work alternatives 809, 824, 826
Nondisjunction 152, 165
Noonan syndrome (NS) 231, 246, 261, 737
Norepinephrine 608-9, 612
Normalization 25, 27, 36-8, 107, 380, 534, 547, 773, 828-9, 848-9, 884, 889, 892, 902
Norms 9, 26, 42, 44-7, 176, 511-13, 518, 685, 781, 812
    cultural 511, 518-19
Nucleotides 147-8, 150, 154, 156, 163, 166
Nucleus 146-7, 149, 165, 180-1, 190, 352, 674
Nurse practitioners 561
Nursing care 63, 95-6, 681, 689, 713
Nursing homes 62, 83, 124, 438, 690, 926, 929, 932-3, 936
Nutrition 83-4, 201, 203, 270, 367, 425, 555, 575, 577, 585-7, 590-2, 620, 640, 697, 699
    assessment 391, 575-7, 584, 588, 592
    committee 583, 586, 591
    considerations in children 575
    intervention 401
    status 169, 173, 576, 577, 582-3, 586, 588, 591
    support 575, 586

O

Obesity 219, 226, 230, 248-9, 282, 285-6, 292, 564, 570, 575, 577, 587, 631, 678, 930
Obsessive-compulsive disorder (OCD) 229, 286, 334, 601-2, 608, 630, 652
Obstruction
    intestinal 273-5, 589, 624
    bowel 557 see also Constipation
Occupational
    activity/programs 791, 802, 837, 840
    therapists (OTs) 100, 297-9, 348, 446, 487, 490, 510, 526, 561, 690, 783, 785
Offences 97, 748, 875, 879-80
Older adults 61, 290, 329, 336, 351, 532, 691-2, 824, 847, 926-7, 929, 931-6, 938
Olfactory bulbs 192-3
Ontario child welfare practice 744
Ontario colleges 59, 535-6
Ontario communities 34, 837
Ontario human rights 65, 69-71, 73-4, 76, 101-2, 108, 721
Ontario laws 76, 540
Ontario Ministries see Key Ontario Ministries
Ontario service system 433
Oppositional defiant disorder (ODS) 366, 381-2, 623
Organizations 9-10, 16-17, 44, 69, 71-2, 76, 140, 300-1, 398-400, 434-5, 811, 813-14, 822, 824-6
    professional 9, 323, 425-6, 456, 536, 773
Out-of-home
    care 324, 396, 755, 757, 764
    placement 324, 769, 866, 869
Outbursts, aggressive 139, 343
Over-nutrition 575, 577, 583-4, 588
Ovum/ova 150-2, 155, 162, 164, 166, 170, 179-81, 268, 289, 353, 704

P

Paediatric
    AIDS 389, 396, 401-3
    child health 592
Pain see also Conditions, painful 72, 192, 198, 302, 388, 448-50, 460, 463, 465, 562-3, 569-70, 573, 622, 647-9, 832-3
    disorders 630, 635, 638
Paraphilia 630, 880-1, 883
Parent
    -child interactions 463, 912, 916, 918
    education curriculum 916, 917
    groups 18, 301, 434, 710, 773, 811
    health/self-care 624, 858, 860, 911
    interview 515
    -managed behavioural treatment 432
    perspectives 793, 805
    -professional attitudes/communication 709, 869
    -professional partnerships 736, 853, 867
    programs 872
    psychopathology 364, 366, 376
    stress 857, 869, 871-2, 899, 912-13, 915
    support groups 863
    training 910, 922
Parenting 203, 316, 334-5, 401, 709-10, 741, 763, 857-8, 865, 872-3, 876, 893-4
    abilities 909, 911, 919-20
    capacity assessments 909-10, 918, 920-1
    education 921, 923
    enhancement program (PEP) 894, 907
    knowledge 911-12
    models 911
    by persons with developmental disabilities 909
    programs 894, 907, 918
    rights 910
    skills 439, 707, 914-15, 917, 920
Parents 331-7, 392-5, 397-9, 411-13, 699-703, 705-13, 722-4, 728-33, 772-6, 785-6, 793-803, 851-72, 892-4
    abusive 743-4, 764
    autistic 125
    with developmental disability 909-23
    elderly 62, 530
    new 709-10, 712-13, 860
    older 539, 546, 859-63, 866, 899, 933
    prospective 527, 702
    rights of 754, 879
    roles of 780, 786, 853, 855-6, 866-7
    of adult children 322, 664, 844, 863, 899, 904
    of young children 709, 865
Partial seizures 406-7, 409
Pediatric AIDS 392, 401-2
Pediatricians 294, 297, 332, 348, 352, 440, 510, 706-8, 715
Pediatrics 203, 225, 259-61, 289-90, 325-6, 338-9, 354, 372-3, 375-6, 401, 424, 488, 591-2, 768
Peers 68, 319, 330, 332-5, 350, 412, 482, 596, 643, 649, 721-2, 728, 730-2, 759, 887-8
People-first language 22-3, 115-16, 127
Percutaneous umbilical blood sampling (PUBS) 177-9, 701-2
Perinatal
    care services 361
    programming 169, 171

Perpetrators, alleged 546, 753, 759, 761, 764, 768
Person-directed planning 26, 93, 435-6,443-4 841-2, 848, 853
Personal care 11, 75, 80, 82-6, 89, 95, 101, 384, 392, 552, 753, 783
   assistants 785
Personal Genome Project 146, 166
Personal
   relationships 6, 46, 86, 96, 519
   rights 755, 760
   stories 22, 47, 117
   support worker 562, 573
Personality
   disorders 382, 413, 462, 608, 623, 632-3, 637-8, 641, 896
Perspectives 5, 23-4, 37, 41-2, 45-8, 50, 106, 109, 111, 457, 465, 528, 733-4, 790-1
   parent's 716, 796-9, 906
Pervasive developmental disorders (PDD) 17, 305-6, 312, 323-6, 329-31, 338, 478, 493, 504, 623, 636
   -not otherwise specified (PDD-NOS) 306-7, 312-13
Pharmacological interventions 222, 249, 256, 318, 383-4, 430, 612, 615-17, 706, 755
Phenotype 149, 165-6, 229, 248, 258, 342-3, 364, 368
Phenylalanine 248
Phenylketonuria (PKU) 156, 165, 180, 207, 231, 248, 261, 310, 429, 706
Philosophy 8, 24, 38, 50-1, 182, 321, 434, 490-1, 537-8, 773, 831-2, 834, 846, 848
   professional 539-41
Phobias 601, 629, 652
Phosphate group 147-8, 675
Physical
   care 897, 899
   characteristics 228-9, 232, 236-57, 269, 509
   conditions 36, 622, 634
   disabilities 15, 23, 30, 66-8, 76, 91-2, 176, 222, 296, 395, 439, 482, 494, 532, 541, 582, 634, 714
   examination 294, 310, 563, 565, 567-9, 629, 651, 685, 746, 897
   harm 446, 742, 745
   health 546, 561-74
   health services 440
Pica 218, 623-4, 630, 639-40
Pituitary gland 194, 197-8, 229, 280
Placement 34, 68, 277, 322, 382, 741, 759, 771, 775-83, 787, 793, 870, 890
   educational 781-2, 785-6
   decision 776, 782-3, 866
Placenta 172, 177-8, 180, 294, 362, 364, 369, 700
Planning/Plans
   intervention programs/treatment 317, 651
   process 436-8, 797, 849
   person-directed 436, 442, 842
   strategic 655-7, 767
   team 437-8
Plaques (amyloid) 278, 674-7, 694
Police 335, 541, 711, 750, 759, 761, 763-5, 935
Policies
   and laws affecting 656, 658
   educational 774
   public 37, 43-4, 47, 49, 807, 937

Policy
   history in Ontario 25-40
   makers 21, 54, 99, 136, 222-3, 323, 525-6, 535, 540, 543, 765, 797-8, 800, 804
Polychlorinated biphenyls (PCBs) 219
Polygenic disorders 157
Polymerase chain reaction (PCR) 178, 269, 289, 347
Population assessment 420-1
Positive behavioral interventions and supports (PBIS) 455-457
Positive behaviour support (PBS) 318-19, 448, 455, 916
Positive intervention-family support model 459, 464
Post-asylum society 25-40
Postnatal 216-17, 294
Power of attorney 81, 84-6, 101, 552
   continuing 81-5, 101
Practices
   community of 934-5
   evidence-based 129, 131, 140-2, 264, 326, 480, 494, 499, 538, 793, 807
   family-centred 726, 729, 732-4, 736
   professional 457, 530, 595
   frontline 525-6, 538, 540, 543, 545
Prader-Willi syndrome (PWS) 165, 210, 213, 215, 228, 230-1, 248, 261, 343, 527, 546, 587, 631, 636
Pregnancy 169, 175-6, 178-9, 208, 219-21, 234-6, 357, 361-6, 368-71, 373-6, 379-82, 389-90, 697-705, 715-16, 751-2
   avoidance/prevention 705
   ectopic 176, 702, 704
   healthy 361, 698
   multiple 499, 704
   outcomes 359, 373, 715-16
   termination 352, 369
   unplanned 359, 361-2, 373
Premature birth 176, 241, 704
Premutation see Fragile X syndrome 345-6, 348, 351-2, 354
Prenatal 216-17, 269, 294, 303, 312, 697, 699-703, 705, 713, 715, 886, 913
   alcohol exposure 361, 363, 369, 372-3, 375-7
   and early life issues 697-718
   care 369, 371, 699-700, 716, 752, 913, 920
   detection of developmental disabilities 177
   development 170, 173, 175, 697
   diagnosis 183, 352, 701, 715, 717, 903
Preschool
   autism programs 315
   programs 317, 440, 736, 738
   Speech and Language programs 506, 725
Preterm delivery 219-20, 715
Prevention 146, 169-70, 179, 182, 207, 209, 222-3, 267, 285, 368-9, 400, 415, 609-10, 618, 698, 702-3
   strategies 451-2, 562
Primary care 228, 507, 560-1, 563, 570-1, 669, 865, 908
   of adults 507, 560, 571-3, 670
Prions 158-60, 162, 165-7
Problem behaviours 135-7, 316, 318-19, 323, 428, 446, 448-9, 451-2, 454-7, 597, 600-1, 616, 637, 667, 669
   management of 134, 572, 617, 668, 937
   preventing 449
Problems

alcohol/drug 358, 366
cognitive 214, 412
dental 242, 278, 564, 647, 930
emotional 410-11, 414, 424, 632, 635, 901
interpersonal 336
menstrual 285
personal 632
Process
  decision-making 700, 840, 842
  diagnostic 674, 857
Procreation 242, 773, 797, 874-6, 878
Professional
  assessment of children 394
  development 456, 722
  libraries 421, 429
  staff 844-5
  support roles 562
Professional values of disability personnel 525-48
Professionals 58-61, 221-3, 323-6, 426-8, 461-71, 509-13,
  516-20, 525-6, 537-41, 594-6, 706-11, 723-5, 731-3, 851-9
  educational 26, 723
  family support 910
  front-line 459, 461-2, 465, 468
  frontline 471, 538, 595
  healthcare 252
  key 467, 562
  social services 713
  support 732
  therapeutic service 765
  trained 323, 454, 846, 855
Program
  adaptations 726-7
  elements 136
  evaluation 129, 131-3, 140-2, 793
  improvement 136
  logic models 137, 141-2
  planning 141-2, 727, 733, 737, 782
  recipients 132, 136-8
  staff 136-7, 140
  stakeholders 136-7
  theory, underlying 136
Programming 203-4, 727, 771, 779, 782, 786
  individual 781
Programs
  adult 323
  ameliorative 78
  childcare 722
  child's 775
  community disability 800
  community health care 370
  community recreation 333
  continuing legal education 103
  earliest work 810
  effective individualized 664
  family-centred 729, 731
  family resource 719-20, 724-5
  graduate xii, 520, 537
  home-based 710
  lifestyle 832-3
  model service-education 662

parent-matching 868
parent-tot 917
pre-school 711, 735
segregated 823, 825-6
segregated work 814-16, 826
supported 350
vocational 299, 322, 429, 826
work-related 813-14
Progressive myoclonus epilepsies (PME) 230-1, 249, 261
Property 48, 61, 75, 80-5, 87-8, 100-1, 191, 609, 632, 740
  appointed guardian of 81-2, 84
  guardian of 82-3
  managing 80, 82-3
  personal 80
  person's 80-4, 87, 743
  statutory guardian of 80, 82-3
Protections 20, 67, 96, 108, 111-12, 119, 201, 287, 482, 678,
  721, 739-42, 748, 761, 765-6
Protective behaviours program 769
Protective services 439, 740, 749-50, 753, 759, 761
Psychiatric
  assessment 100, 471, 634, 648, 652-3, 667, 670
  diagnoses 23, 63, 325, 366, 564, 597, 600-1, 652, 896
  disorders 199, 242, 286, 319, 349, 384, 410, 599-600,
    615-16, 621-2, 629-30, 641, 646, 650-4, 670
  facility 80, 83, 87, 100, 932
  intervention 645, 843
  medications 601-3, 609, 613-17
  problems 405, 413, 753, 914
  services 63, 616, 661, 870, 904
  treatment 432, 559, 599, 617, 621, 667
Psychoactive drugs 599, 601
Psychoeducational support groups 872
Psychological/neuropsychological
  assessment 509, 685-6
  services 516, 521
Psychopharmacology 599-618, 617, 655, 896
Psychosocial problems 337, 413-15, 575
  in intractable epilepsy 415
Psychostimulants 606, 611
Psychotherapy 132, 336, 420, 429, 468, 522-3, 531, 535, 629,
  632, 654-5
Psychotropic medications 428-9, 449, 462-3,
  471, 564, 572, 598, 600, 614-15, 617-18,
  644, 652, 667-8, 670, 928
Puberty 164, 195, 205, 242, 246, 285, 577,
  750, 856-7, 877
Public guardian and trustee (PGT) 80-3, 85-8, 99, 101,
  557, 559
Public health nurses 710, 723-4
Punishment 319, 447-8, 457, 617, 760, 897-8

Q
Quality of Life Project 836-7, 839, 848

R
Race 7, 46, 48, 66, 68, 121, 368, 463, 509, 589, 591, 886
Radicals, free 364, 679
Receptors 191, 201-2, 600, 603, 607-8, 610
Recessive genes 156, 878

Recurrence risks 221, 245, 247, 310

Reflex arcs 188-9, 202

Reflexes, tendon 240

Reflux, gastroesophageal (GERD) 274, 564, 583-5, 591-2

Regions 19, 98, 132, 149-50, 154, 156, 158-60, 162-3, 166, 199-200, 345, 365, 528-9, 537-8, 901-2

Registered Social Worker 468-9, 471

Rehabilitation 30, 49, 51, 90, 248, 255, 297, 300-1, 322, 401, 440, 526, 716, 827-8, 906-7

Reinforcement 255, 315-16, 447, 451, 454, 528. 617, 881, 916, 918

Relationships 47, 125, 146-7, 335, 467, 469, 483, 537-9, 552, 619, 621, 632-3, 731-2, 751-2, 885-908

    adult 469

    client-professional 397

    close 463, 632, 901, 932

    excellent working 644

    individual's 760

    interpersonal 465

    intimate 335, 649, 891-2

    supportive 121, 902

Rent 69-70, 96-8, 101, 112

Representation, legal 87

Reproduction 33, 183, 714, 716

Reproductive cloning 180-1

Reproductive health 285, 373

Research and evaluation 129-42

Research and practice 829, 907

Residences 94, 836

Residential

    services 40, 94, 336, 427, 440, 664, 866, 933

    settings 75, 93, 305, 644-5

    support 93, 664, 932

    support staff 686, 690

Resource

    consultants 724-6, 728-33

    information 902

    personnel 711

    teachers 725-7, 729, 733, 736, 782

Resources 62-3, 124-5, 131-3, 176-7, 300-1, 354, 433-5, 490-2, 531-5, 627-8, 661-3, 713-14, 867-9, 899-902, 935-7

    educational 310, 754

    personal 46, 799, 855, 858

    for exceptional children 371

Respite care 322, 350, 440, 470 690, 712, 726, 755, 759, 862, 866, 934

    services 439, 710, 852

Responsibilities 42-3, 108-9, 113-14, 121, 126, 426-7, 434-5, 441, 530, 593-4, 596-7, 663-4, 733-4, 775-9, 796-7

    health-care 352

    public 54, 434, 771

Retirement 336, 824, 926, 932

Rett Disorder/syndrome 60, 200, 204-5, 213, 232-3, 250, 262, 310, 312, 326, 408

Rhesus (Rh) disease 176, 702, 715

Ribonucleic acid (RNA) 147-50, 155, 158-9, 161, 163, 178, 200, 242, 287

    messenger RNA (mRNA) 149-50, 158, 160

    microRNAs (miRNAs) 150, 158, 160, 167

    transfer RNAs (tRNAs) 149-50

Ribosomes 149-50, 165

Rights 42-3, 47, 51, 65-9, 71-4, 75-104, 108-9, 111-14, 124, 126-7, 435, 595, 721, 738-40, 782-3, 841, 875-6, 879, 884, 919, 923

    children's 744, 767, 833, 921

    disabled persons 16, 66, 71, 73, 124, 482, 917

    individual 75, 124, 595, 630, 902, 910

    mentally retarded 739

    in Ontario 65-74

    parental 744

Risk factors 213, 217, 221, 226, 247, 293, 371, 376, 385, 496, 698-9, 752, 754-5, 769

    multiple 213, 295

    potential 221, 294, 301, 913

    strong 210, 268, 677

Risk of miscarriage 178, 269, 701

Risperidone 326, 608, 614-16, 637, 670

Role of diversity in psychological assessment and intervention 509-23

Roles and relationships of women 885

S

Safe medication practice and front line professional practice 593-8

Safety, personal 408-9, 799

Sanfilippo syndrome 251, 262

SBS see Shaken baby syndrome

Schizophrenia 157, 196, 214, 222, 229, 331, 361, 425, 462, 600-1, 603, 623-6, 632, 637-40, 652

School(s) 318, 333-5, 350, 396, 401, 412, 463-5, 490, 771-5, 779-81, 789-92, 794-808, 859-60

    boards 68, 490, 774-85, 787, 854

    high 300, 651, 706, 736, 804, 887

    officials 333, 711

    in Ontario 771-88

    personnel 319, 333-4, 382, 465-6, 469-70, 785-6, 799-800

    professionals 465, 469, 786

    programs 305, 467, 471

    representatives 462, 467-8

    special 68, 773-4, 785

    staff 765, 799

    system 59, 412, 427, 462, 464, 468, 490, 774-5, 781, 799, 803, 860

    -to-work transitions 805

Scrapie 159, 165

Screaming 256, 446-7, 452

Screening 182, 259, 276, 282-3, 292, 309, 325-6, 352, 357, 368-9, 371, 375-6, 568, 624, 706-7

    maternal serum 177, 699-700

SDM (Substitute decision maker) 61, 75, 84, 86-7, 94, 99, 551-3, 556-8

Sectors 38, 47, 49, 58, 60, 72, 120, 660, 932, 934

    adult services 335

    developmental service 120, 660

Seizure disorders 284, 405-7, 409, 576, 643, 752, 930

Seizures see also Epilepsy 122, 228-30, 234, 240-1, 243-5, 249-50, 256, 260-1, 283, 285, 289, 296-7, 313, 405-15, 684

    drug-resistant 406, 408

    epileptic 199, 406, 429

    intractable/uncontrolled 408, 410-11, 413, 415

treatment of 240-1, 653
types 406
Selective serotonin reuptake inhibitors see SSRIs
Self-advocacy 105-28, 492, 794, 801, 917
Self-advocates 13, 21, 71, 106, 108-11, 113-23, 125-6
Self
care skills 568, 682
determination 4, 9, 46, 117, 131, 420, 434, 436, 443-4, 538, 556, 794, 840-1, 847, 849
employment 92, 439, 801-2, 813, 817-18, 825-7
injurious behaviour(s) see also SIB 235, 249, 264, 318, 449, 477, 602, 612, 615-16, 619, 635, 637, 640, 668, 746
reports 361-2, 643
Semantics 5, 322, 476, 502
Sensory sensitivities 332-3, 566
SEP see supported employment program
Serotonin 191, 608-9, 676
Service agencies 56, 93-4, 116, 486, 535, 539, 726, 820, 859, 918
Service
animals 79-80
challenges 665, 932
coordination 132, 322, 659, 662
delivery 222, 301, 490, 538, 658, 663, 724, 733, 786, 793, 848, 853, 856, 859, 867, 928
manager 97-9
models 817, 825
organizations 11, 57, 129, 436, 466-7, 525, 528-9, 534, 536, 803, 836, 839
plans, individual 849, 928
policies 13, 834
providers 62, 68-9, 98-9, 336, 397-9, 435-7, 516-17, 519, 596, 645-6, 663, 748, 759, 824
provision 59, 76, 131, 335, 348, 437, 657, 659, 661, 666, 688, 740, 829, 865, 871
resources 462, 491
system 59, 122, 321, 433-4, 438, 442, 462, 468, 471, 532, 660, 664, 766, 799, 801
adult psychiatric 336
comprehensive community 656, 836, 852
navigate Ontario's developmental disability 440
social 60, 438, 791, 852
workers 519, 801
Services 10-11, 53-64, 78-80, 92-7, 129-34, 419-44, 526-32, 654-64, 774-9, 813-14, 834-6, 851-3, 913-15, 917-20, 932-4
access 76-7, 309, 463, 660, 857, 932
additional 438, 935
adult 796, 801
child protection 744-5, 765-6, 917-20
crisis/reactive health care 665
day 664, 827
dental 91, 844
directors of 536, 543
educational 56, 424
exceptional education-related 92-3
formal 436, 723, 859, 911, 926, 932, 934
full range of 659, 803
funded 56, 58, 933
health-related 486, 662

improving transition 793
integrated 665, 738
introduction to 433-44
monitor 529, 532
new 26, 442, 859, 918
in Ontario 300
out-patient 30, 926
personal assistance 83-5, 100
preschool development 350
private 334, 336
professional 94, 731, 867, 869
public 69, 337
special 11, 57, 91, 99, 103, 438-40, 726, 802, 806, 852
specialist 18, 654, 661
specialist assessment 645
speech-language 504
therapeutic 96-7
vocational 427, 810, 868
Severe disabilities 90, 209, 214, 475, 483, 491, 494, 504, 647, 781-4, 787, 789-90, 802-3, 806-7, 828-9
Severe HIE 240
Sex
chromosomes 152, 153, 163, 170, 215, 242, 353
education 429, 439, 874, 876-8, 883-4
Sexual abuse 47, 199, 389-90, 482, 493-4, 630, 744-6, 748, 754, 756-7, 759-61, 767-9, 879-82, 884, 903
Sexual
behaviour, inappropriate 882-3
behaviour 542, 755, 762, 874, 876-7, 878-9
Sexuality 195, 285, 335, 339, 348, 401, 436, 469, 494, 552, 570, 766, 797, 859, 861, 873-85, 891-2, 920-2
education 873, 877
myths 873-84
SGDs (speech generating devices) 480, 483, 487
Shaken baby syndrome (SBS) 220, 234-5, 251, 262
Sheltered workshops 37, 532, 811-19, 821-2, 824-8, 887
Shyness 342-3, 519
SIB (self-injurious behaviour) 235, 249, 264, 318, 449, 477, 602, 612, 615-16, 619, 635, 637, 640, 644-5, 668
treatment of 615-16
Siblings 245, 299, 342, 394, 397-9, 412, 461, 469-71, 486, 511-12, 712-13, 864-5, 888, 900-1, 929
child's 387, 399, 711
of adults 715, 865, 868, 870, 900, 904
nondisabled 864
younger 864, 869, 872
Side effects 281, 297, 319-21, 407, 428, 564, 568, 576, 597, 603, 607-8, 612-13, 635, 650, 928
potential 602, 609-11
Signals, environmental 161
Single mothers 361, 713, 854, 894
Single nucleotide polymorphisms (SNPs) 154, 680, 683
Single photon emission computed tomography (SPECT) 199-200
Sister chromatids 152, 166, 237
Sisters 306, 388, 394, 437, 469, 471, 712-13, 763, 805, 864, 871, 887, 898, 900, 908
Skills
child-care 919
essential family-work 465

executive functioning 370, 381
functional 490, 644
individual 453, 480-1
professional 543
self-care 681, 684, 794
teaching child-care 904, 918
work-related 272
worker 790
Skin 166, 172-3, 182, 188, 228, 230, 232, 236-7, 245, 248-9, 258, 269, 278, 289, 589
conditions 256, 278, 292
Sleep 194, 239, 286, 289, 292, 313-14, 410-11, 460, 541, 565, 610-11, 620, 627, 631, 916
apnoea 286-7
disorders 253-4, 256, 285-6, 623, 631, 638
disturbances 228, 237, 250-1, 257, 348, 411, 611, 746, 762
problems 253, 286-7, 292, 313, 319, 326, 632
Smith-Lemli-Opitz syndrome (SLOS) 156, 166, 233, 252, 262, 430, 432
Smith-Magenis syndrome (SMS) 233, 253, 262, 637
Social
environments 7, 36, 110, 526-7, 926, 934
experiences 334, 886-7
housing 97, 99-100, 102
inclusion 10-1, 24, 26, 38-9, 55-6, 64, 93-4, 103, 434-5, 443, 659, 666, 814, 853
meaning 5, 7, 19-20, 23, 905
movement 16, 107, 114, 117, 125
role valorization 528, 829
groups 306, 333-4, 336, 338
skills training 130, 370, 429, 630, 888, 907, 916
support 7, 735-6, 801, 833, 843-5, 858, 861-3, 872, 911, 913-15, 921-2, 926, 929
values 530, 723, 834
work 24, 94, 126, 132, 142, 337, 401, 403, 420, 443, 465, 472, 535
workers 33, 100, 297, 299, 392, 395, 440, 469, 472, 561, 575, 748-9, 763
Societal attitudes 110, 749, 754, 764, 893
Society 20, 26-7, 46-7, 49-51, 53-5, 107-11, 113-15, 118-19, 122-4, 369-71, 395, 638-9, 773-4, 809-10, 834
Socio-sexual education 873-5, 877-8, 883
Somatoform disorders 623, 630
Spastic diplegia 293, 295-6
Spastic quadriplegia 295-7, 584, 591
Special education 16-17, 127, 254, 490, 735-8, 748, 771, 773-4, 777-9, 783-8, 804-6, 808, 883
funding 771, 784
grant 784, 787
legislation 779
programs 456, 517, 776-7, 779, 784
Specialized care 56, 63, 561, 571, 658-60, 662-3, 741, 902
Specialized services 93, 348, 352, 440, 527-8, 532, 658, 660, 662, 744, 901
Speech 120-1, 247, 271, 299, 308-9, 317-18, 332-3, 424-5, 439-40, 475-80, 482-3, 490-1, 494-6, 500-5, 724-5
generating devices see SGDs
production 494, 501
therapists 297, 299-300
Speech-language 380, 505

parent training 299
pathologists xvi-xvii, 332, 483, 487, 493, 510, 512, 526, 733
Sperm 150-2, 155, 158, 162, 164, 166, 170-1, 175, 180, 214, 228, 241, 268, 289, 704-5
Spinal cord 172, 180, 185-6, 188-90, 192, 201-2, 204, 217, 244, 282-3, 301, 388-9, 505
Spousal relationships 893-4
SSRIs (Selective serotonin reuptake inhibitors) 320, 336, 608-9, 616, 632
Staff 28-9, 34-5, 94-5, 117-18, 131-3, 136, 140, 452-3, 466-8, 593-5, 721-2, 725-7, 841-3, 876-7, 932-3
development 726, 736
support 655, 842
Stakeholders 136-7, 140, 483
Stature, short 229, 232, 246, 249, 253, 256-7, 269, 343, 589
Statutory guardian 80-2
Stem cells 179-83
Stereotypic behaviour 237, 258, 635-7
Sterilization, nontherapeutic 878
Stigma 391, 393, 395, 397-8, 412, 414, 426, 599, 832, 907
Stomach 188-90, 258, 274, 297, 589, 832
Strategies 222-3, 291, 324, 414, 421, 453-5, 467-8, 479-82, 545, 569-70, 624, 722, 735-6, 819-20, 918
behavioural 319, 531, 644, 852, 918
Strengths, individual 422, 729
Stress 193-9, 347-8, 514, 531-4, 536-7, 620-1, 627-8, 653-4, 678, 711, 794-6, 857-60, 863-4, 869-71, 899
increased 532, 723, 858
Stressors 199, 334, 627-8, 648, 652
environmental 295, 382, 626
Stroke 187, 199-200, 216, 246, 255, 260-2, 273, 283, 294, 408, 634-5, 638, 685, 930, 934
pediatric 235, 246-7, 261
Students 66-8, 92-3, 316-17, 348, 352, 490, 537-9, 771, 774-87, 798-800, 802-3, 806-7, 854-5
bursaries 92
education of 775, 786
rights of 108, 773
Sturge-Weber dyndrome (SWS) 235, 253, 255, 262
Substance abuse 210, 212, 371, 383, 624-6, 628, 638-9, 697, 704, 723, 746-7, 762, 912
Substitute decision maker see also SDM 61, 75, 84, 86, 94, 99, 552-3, 556-7
Successful interventions 255, 324, 327
Successful parenting 915, 921
Suicide 37, 382, 619, 626-7, 631, 633-4, 637-9, 703
risk of 626-7, 634, 640
Supervision 40, 323, 656, 670, 742-3
supervisors 467, 525, 616, 645, 684-5, 725-6, 728, 730-2, 763, 811, 819-20, 826
Support 53-63, 111-14, 116-19, 397-9, 419-22, 526-8, 530-8, 719-25, 793-6, 813-14, 839-46, 852-5, 858-60, 890-4, 935-6
behavioural 285, 455, 655, 912
environmental 796
family-directed 263, 435, 464, 533, 738
formal 526, 859
in-home 350, 862
including work-related 813
individual 22, 654, 657, 812
informal 434, 442, 526, 858

intensive 94, 753, 783
mother's 763, 914
parental 553, 867
personal 61, 94, 429, 933
positive behavior 326, 456, 493
professional 334, 803, 859
specialized 490, 527, 646, 705, 790, 799, 802-3
student 794
and therapy 459-74
Support groups 276, 393, 412, 414, 470, 690, 710, 791, 796, 816, 860, 870, 917
Alzheimer's 690
of caregivers 689, 691
community 918
drop-in 891
mutual 872
of parents 879, 923
post-autism diagnosis 337
social 125
Supports Intensity Scale (SIS) 179, 842, 844, 848-9
Support methods 469, 527
Support networks 436-7, 441, 552, 690, 712, 914, 929
person's 437
social 845, 914, 922, 926
Support personnel 7, 61, 421, 530, 789
frontline 421
persons 79-80, 131, 571, 763, 880
Support plan
individual 481
individualized 842
Support services 75, 82, 84, 97, 398, 426, 498, 538, 793, 857, 868
coordinated 531
formal 866, 920
helpful 361
personal 94-5
provincially-funded 97
school health 95
specialized 436
Support staff 323, 461, 525, 780, 895, 933
Support system, social 653, 892
Support workers 46, 61, 382-3, 540, 552, 685, 796, 819-21, 826, 844, 846
personal 562
residential 686
volunteer 552
work 820
Supported care 434
Supported employment 341, 532, 782, 802, 811, 817-22, 825-9, 851, 862, 890, 903, 907
program (SEP) 812-15, 817-22, 825, 829
Supportive housing providers 97, 99-100, 102
Surgery 237, 253-4, 256, 273, 275, 279, 283, 286, 407-8, 427, 429, 463, 478, 600, 704
Surgical interventions 180, 277, 297, 706
Swallowing 258, 576-8, 586, 590, 685
Synapses 185, 188, 190-1, 195, 200, 202, 355, 603, 608
Synaptic cleft 190, 608, 612
Stereotypic behaviour 231, 233, 235b
Syndromes and disorders 227

Systems
child protection 766, 921
health care service delivery 488

T

Tangles, neurofibrillary 163, 673, 675-7, 679, 691
Taxes 91, 539, 863-4
Teachers 348, 412, 414, 446-7, 454, 477-8, 711, 730, 732-3, 763, 772-4, 779-80, 782-7, 859
Team
collaborative 730, 732-4
interprofessional 487, 510
professional 17, 398, 645, 913
transdisciplinary 727, 731, 734
Teens see also Adolescence 334-5, 627
Teeth 243, 277-8, 502, 566, 624
Telomerase 159
Temporal lobes 192-4, 196, 255, 407, 410, 413
Tenants 65, 96-7
Tension 251, 434, 461-2, 466, 471, 711
Teratogens 157, 169, 173, 175, 208-9, 211, 362
Thalamus 193-4
Therapists 298, 315, 392, 465, 468-71, 483, 516-17, 519, 651, 711, 835, 855-6, 887, 893
Therapy see also Intervention, specific syndromes
biological 320-1
individual 334, 429
non-drug 407-9
supported 130, 141
Thyroid
gland 218, 229, 278, 280, 629
hormones 229, 236, 280
thyroid stimulating hormone (TSH) 229, 236, 280
Tics 254, 333, 429, 431, 648, 652
Tongue 228-9, 269, 271, 276-8, 502
Tourette syndrome 235, 254, 262, 426, 636-7
Toxic threats/toxins 162, 194, 212, 219, 223, 312, 754, 930
Toys 309, 529, 727
Trachea 274, 276
Training
child-care 922
children's friendship 370, 373
in developmental disabilities 804-6, 808
families 472, 871
health care provider 562
individualized 818
ongoing 535-7, 540, 543, 545, 594, 800
professional 60, 537, 668, 934
social skills see Social skills
specialized 59, 297, 801, 815, 910
vocational 439, 772
Traits 145-6, 157, 165, 172, 181, 215-16, 232, 332, 336, 354, 632
autistic 230, 232, 234
Transcription 148-9
Transition 34, 56, 61, 299, 302, 317-18, 428, 460-1, 586, 903, 905, 926, 936-7
to adult life 789-808
planning 322, 350, 776, 780, 792-3, 796-7, 799-800, 802-3, 806-8

Transposons 159
Trauma, physical 751
Traumatic brain injury (TBIs) 196, 199, 234-5, 255, 262, 622, 638, 697
Trazodone 610-11
Treatment see also Behavioural, Intervention, Medical, etc.
    crisis intervention 767
    plan 449-50, 452, 454-5, 553, 558, 566-7, 569, 645, 651, 653-4, 855
Tremor 603, 607, 610
Trisomy 155-6, 212, 215, 268, 282, 287, 590, 691, 700-1, 714
Tuberous sclerosis (TS) 156, 166, 212, 233, 255, 263, 310, 408, 636
Turner syndrome 156, 166, 233, 246, 256, 263
Typical antipsychotics 603, 607-8

U
Ultrasound 177, 179, 269, 700-1
Umbilical cord 172, 176-8, 180, 220, 364, 702
Uniparental disomy 163, 165
United Nations (UN) 47, 50-1, 66, 721, 738-9, 876, 884, 909, 923
Urine 230, 232, 242, 248, 251, 310, 396, 610, 686, 699
Uterus 170, 172, 176, 178, 181, 208, 244, 288, 294, 699-702, 704

V
Vaccines 312
Vagus nerve stimulation 408, 415
Valproate 610, 616
Values
    personal 540, 543, 545, 705, 892, 936
    of disability personnel 525, 530
    professional 540-2
    of social roles 809, 811-13, 817, 828
Variants, copy number 154, 163
Venlafaxine 608-9, 612
Ventricles (brain) 175-6, 186-7, 194, 202, 239, 241, 258
Verbal communication 495, 501, 509, 566, 568, 842
Violent behaviour 118, 494, 626, 632, 720, 723, 751-2, 754, 758, 763, 766, 769, 882, 884, 896-7, 907
Virus(es) 388-91, 395, 678, 680, 700
Vision 19, 48, 90-1, 193, 234, 238, 254, 279, 367, 393, 424-5, 497-8, 505, 564, 570, 685, 706, 726
Vitamins, importance of
Vitamin A 217-8, 698
Vitamin A excess, hazards 174-5, 218
Vitamin B12 217, 284, 670, 681, 684-6
Vitamin D 220-1, 223, 282, 578, 678, 692
Vitamin E 288, 679, 687
In vitro fertilization 157-8, 179, 220, 700, 704
Vocalizations 254, 477, 479-80, 483, 485
Vomiting 234, 244, 252, 275, 314, 412, 563, 568, 576-8, 584-5, 916

W
Weight 65, 173, 187, 270, 282, 289, 362, 364, 380, 382, 568, 570, 576-7, 580-5, 591-2
Western cultures 518-19, 759, 898
White matter (brain) 186, 195, 202, 241, 311, 364

Williams syndrome (WS) 156, 166, 196, 257, 263, 477, 502, 506, 517, 636, 648, 651, 654, 669
Willis, circle of 187, 205, 248, 562, 573
Women/Women's
    health 716, 894, 894-5, 901, 903, 907-8
    roles and relationships 885-908
    societal systems support 902
Work 809 see also Employment
    activities 810-12, 815-16, 819, 822-3, 826
    environment 383, 654, 790, 816, 826
    experiences 793-4, 800, 826
    practical 61, 537-8, 791
    relationships, effective 465
    skills 465, 792, 815, 820
    stations 811, 822, 826
    volunteer 782, 812, 822, 825-6
Worker co-ops 812, 814, 817, 825, 829
Workers
    child-care 526, 921-2
    direct care 573
    front-line 531, 535
    home-care 526, 690
Workplaces 19, 47, 89, 222, 299, 414, 429, 437, 482, 501, 594, 791, 801-3, 819-21, 827-8
Workshops 125, 351, 520, 541, 684, 690, 726, 731, 810-14, 815-16, 818, 822-3
    grandparents' 870
    video-communication 536
World Health Organization 9, 24, 47, 51, 260, 389, 400-1, 403, 515, 523, 528, 547, 566, 591-2, 939

X
X-chromosome 214, 344, 347
    inactivation (Lyonization) 169, 171
X-linked genes 155-6

Y
Young adults see also Adolescent
    transition to adulthood 789
Young children
    early intervention 719-38
    exceptional 735, 737-8
Youth
    and adult clinics 488-9
    services review 142, 766-9
    studies 402, 921

Z
Zygote 162, 165-6, 170

[Created with TExtract / www.Texyz.com]